A GUIDE TO GRADUATE STUDY

Advisory Committee . . .
A GUIDE TO GRADUATE STUDY
Programs Leading to the Ph.D. Degree
Second Edition

Second Edition

A GUIDE TO GRADUATE STUDY

Programs Leading to the Ph.D. Degree

FREDERIC W. NESS, EDITOR

AMERICAN COUNCIL ON EDUCATION • WASHINGTON, D. C.

Printed in the United States of America

FOREWORD

The American Council on Education takes great pleasure in presenting this second edition of *A Guide to Graduate Study: Programs Leading to the Ph.D. Degree.* Its publication represents the successful culmination of the cooperative efforts of two associations concerned with higher education and the preparation of college teachers, the Council and the Association of American Colleges.

The pioneering first edition was conceived by Dean Frederic W. Ness, then Academic Vice President of Dickinson College, and sponsored by the Commission on Professional and Graduate Study of the Association of American Colleges. It was published by the Association in 1957 under a grant from the Ford Foundation, and the Council acted as its distributor.

From the beginning the *Guide* met a long-felt need. It was enthusiastically received both by faculty members deeply concerned with the need for recruiting more well-qualified teachers, and by able young college students desiring more education and wishing to plan for it carefully and well. Indeed, the demand for the *Guide* was much greater than could have been anticipated. Furthermore, under the impetus of the National Defense Education Act, there has been a considerable increase in the past few years, both in the number and variety of Ph.D. programs and in the number of institutions offering them. Hence, a second edition, revised and expanded, emerged as a clear-cut need— both to keep the work in print and to bring these new and important programs to the attention of those seeking them.

The Association of American Colleges and the American Council on Education agreed that the second and future editions of the *Guide* would be prepared and published by the Council. To oversee its preparation, the Council appointed an advisory committee composed of its representatives and those of the Commission on Professional and Graduate Study of the Association. The Council was fortunate indeed in being able to secure the services of Dean Ness as editor of the second edition.

I wish to acknowledge the assistance of the Association of Graduate Schools in the Association of American Universities for its continuing interest in this important work. Grateful acknowledgment should also be made to the Ford

Foundation for its support of the original edition, and to the Woodrow Wilson National Fellowship Foundation for its financial support of the second.

I know that the second edition will be effective in attracting properly prepared individuals into college teaching, and that it will also be useful to all prospective graduate students, whatever their choice of profession may be.

ARTHUR S. ADAMS
President
American Council on Education

August, 1960

PREFACE

The supply of college graduates who continue their formal academic preparation for careers in the learned professions is failing to meet the demands of industry, government, and higher education. Evidence of this fact is found on every hand. Prospective employers of mathematicians and scientists, for example, have resorted to the blandishments of the hucksters in their effort to attract qualified personnel. In the field of college teaching, even our most conservative statisticians are predicting shortages which, within a decade, may well attain critical proportions.

Fortunately the nature of the problem is understood, even though its dimensions may still be in dispute. Efforts to find an adequate solution are mounting. With scarcely an exception, the major governmental and private organizations concerned with higher education and preparation for the professions are giving the problem serious attention. Some of the leading philanthropic foundations are supporting a variety of experiments directed toward its resolution.

As one phase of this nationwide effort the Association of American Colleges, with financial support from the Ford Foundation and with the cooperation of the Association of Graduate Schools in the Association of American Universities, undertook in 1957 the preparation of *A Guide to Graduate Study* for the use of the undergraduate and his faculty adviser. The strong response to the book has made this second edition both possible and necessary.

The *Guide* is designed to serve several ends. First, it is intended to assist the undergraduate in planning, academically and financially, to meet the requirements for graduate study. Second, it attempts to give a realistic view of the educational life of the graduate student. Third, it provides some basis for making a wise selection of a graduate school. Finally, by indicating something of the professional opportunities open to the successful graduate student, it offers the implicit hope of encouraging our better qualified undergraduates to continue their training toward the greatest utilization of their abilities in a life of service to their nation and the world at large.

At the outset it must be said that the *Guide* is not intended to replace the wise and intimate counseling made available by deans, advisers, and faculty members in our undergraduate schools and colleges. From this source has come a large part of the inspiration which provides the learned professions with their younger recruits.

Further, the *Guide* does not pretend to replace the graduate-school catalogue, the ultimate source of detailed and current information to which the student must resort in drawing his final plans. While specific data on such matters as faculty numbers, graduate enrollment, fees, and first-year financial aid are included, these are intended more for the purpose of depicting the institution and its program than of providing current statistical data. Thus, this manual offers a means of making comparisons among schools and, hopefully, of arriving at a more critical understanding of the institutional bulletins.

Much of the material in the introductory essays will be of interest to students considering any type of professional or graduate study. They may be planning to work for one or more among several degrees. Some may stop with the master's; some may qualify for the doctorate in education or in science, and so forth. Nevertheless, because of practical limitations, the detailed information furnished by the *Guide* is restricted to schools offering, and to programs leading to, the Ph.D.—the degree generally regarded as the highest earned degree which an American institution can confer. Limited information about other doctorates will be found in tabular form in Appendix I and, as appropriate, under the institutional entries. Also indicated are the number of master's degrees earned between 1955 and 1959 in each of the fields in which the Ph.D. may be earned.[1]

Within these limitations, then, the first part of *A Guide to Graduate Study* consists of a discussion of the principal matters of concern to the undergraduate in reaching a decision on graduate study, with particular reference to a career in college teaching and research. To assure completeness of coverage the editor has reviewed a variety of secondary sources and has conducted a wide sampling of opinion among deans, faculty members, and undergraduate and graduate students. In addition he has had the benefit of the wise counsel of the Advisory Board established by the American Council on Education, of the Commission on Professional and Graduate Study of the Association of American Colleges, and of the regional representatives of the Woodrow Wilson National Fellowship Foundation.

The second part of the *Guide* is devoted to the graduate schools offering programs leading to the Ph.D. These individual entries do not attempt to give an exhaustive description of the schools or their programs. Rather, they present information useful to the college student in long-range planning for graduate study and in the initial selection of schools and programs. For the most part the information has been supplied by the graduate school deans,

---

[1] Students interested in the master's degree should also refer to Mary Irwin (ed.), *American Universities and Colleges, 1960* (Washington: American Council on Education, 1960), pp. 44-45.

whose generous cooperation has made this project possible. A subject-matter index at the close of this section has been included for quick identification of the institutions offering a Ph.D. in the various fields.

In addition to those whose assistance made the first edition a reality, I should like to mention with gratitude the names of Dr. Arthur Adams of the American Council on Education and the members of the advisory committee whom he designated to guide the production of this revision: Dean William C. DeVane, Yale College, *chairman;* Dean John W. Ashton, Indiana University; Dean Glenn J. Christensen, Lehigh University; Dean J. P. Elder, Harvard University; Provost Robert M. Lumiansky, Tulane University; Dean Thomas C. Pollock, New York University; Dr. Hans Rosenhaupt, Woodrow Wilson National Fellowship Foundation; Dean George Waggoner, University of Kansas; and Mr. F. L. Wormald, Association of American Colleges. I would mention too the tireless labors of my editorial assistant, Elizabeth Quick; and finally, but of primary importance, the generous support of the Woodrow Wilson National Fellowship Foundation, which made this edition possible.

FREDERIC W. NESS
Academic Vice President and Dean
Dickinson College

Carlisle, Pennsylvania
June, 1960

CONTENTS

CONTENTS

PART I

GRADUATE STUDY AND

THE UNDERGRADUATE

Introduction

Experience shows that the undergraduate usually has certain standard questions in his mind when he begins to canvass the possibilities of graduate study. In general these include the following: What is graduate study? For what professions or vocations is a graduate degree desirable? Do I have the personality, ability, and academic background to qualify for graduate study? How can I select the graduate school best suited to my capacities and needs? What can I do to gain admission to the school of my choice? How much will it cost and how can I meet this expense? What can I expect in graduate school? More particularly, what are the requirements for an advanced degree?

In the ensuing pages an attempt is made to suggest answers to these and corollary questions. Although attention will be focused on graduate study leading to the degree of Doctor of Philosophy in the arts and sciences, much of the discussion will be applicable to the master's degree and to other doctoral degrees as well.

1. The Ph.D. in America

The history of graduate education in the United States began virtually with the settlement of America more than three hundred years ago;[1] for graduate instruction was one of the earliest forms of education in this country. Walton C. John divides its development into three periods: (1) from 1642 to 1860, or the period of the supremacy of the master's degree; (2) from 1860 to 1900, or the period of the growth and development of the Ph.D.; and (3) from 1900 to 1934, or the period of the great diversification of degrees on both the master's and the doctor's levels.[2] Since John's study was published in 1934, the question naturally arises whether still another period in this development has not arrived.

The present pattern of study characterizing most of our graduate schools of arts and science developed in this country only about seventy-five years ago in answer to problems which society, and consequently education, were facing at that time. The difficulties besetting our world today, however, are vastly different from those of seventy-five years ago; and from many sides the question is being asked whether our graduate schools have made—or indeed are able to make—the necessary adjustment. Thus, if one were to characterize the current stage in the evolution of the graduate school of arts and science, he might well label it as a period of both dramatic growth and critical reappraisal.

For the most part this reappraisal concerns one of the primary functions of the graduate school—the preparation of college teachers. Here the criticism seems to focus upon certain specific deficiencies. In *The Graduate School Today and Tomorrow*, written by Dean F. W. Strothmann on behalf of "The Committee of Fifteen," a group of outstanding educators, these deficiencies are summed up as follows:

1. Graduate schools, in their efforts to advance the boundaries of knowledge by research, are at present not paying sufficient attention to a function they inherited by a

---

[1] For the history of graduate instruction in America, see especially Isaiah Bowman, *The Graduate School in American Democracy*, Office of Education Bulletin 1939, No. 14 (Washington: Government Printing Office, 1939); Marcia Edwards, *Studies in American Graduate Education* (New York: Carnegie Foundation for the Advancement of Teaching, 1944); Laurence Foster, *The Functions of a Graduate School in a Democratic Society* (New York: Huxley House Publishers, 1936); Byrne J. Horton, *The Graduate School (Its Origin and Administrative Development)* (New York: New York University Bookstore, 1940); Walton C. John, *Graduate Study in the Universities and Colleges in the United States*, Office of Education Bulletin 1934, No. 20 (Washington: Government Printing Office, 1935); Bernard Berelson, "Graduate Education and the Preparation of Teachers," in John W. Gustad (ed.), *Faculty Supply, Demand, and Recruitment: Proceedings of a Regional Conference* (Winchester, Mass.: New England Board of Higher Education, 1959), pp. 74–92. A good short historical sketch may be found in Mary Irwin (ed.), *American Universities and Colleges, 1960* (Washington: American Council on Education, 1960), p. 15.

[2] John, *op. cit.*, p. 59.

3

natural historical process—that of providing effective training for college and high-school teachers;

2. Even the training in research often lacks the vitality necessary to produce humanely-educated men and women capable of providing the moral, intellectual, and political leadership which a free society needs if it is to survive;

3. Since the "tidal wave" of students expected to flood our colleges in the near future will enforce a change of some kind, it is the responsibility of the graduate schools to see to it that this change will not create a chaos in which scholarship and scholarly teaching have become a mere memory;

4. If scholarly teaching is to survive in our colleges—and we believe that non-scholarly teaching simply isn't teaching—it should become the avowed purpose of graduate education to produce more people who are neither mere scholars nor unscholarly teachers, but scholar-teachers.[3]

Just what the result of the current ferment will be cannot, of course, be predicted. The publication of Dr. Bernard Berelson's exhaustive analysis of graduate study in the United States will provide new and significant insights into the field. Since the chief aim of this *Guide* is to help the student to understand and make use of the graduate school as it is at present, however, this passing notice of prospects for the future must suffice.

Another approach to an understanding of graduate study is to look more directly at the Ph.D. degree. For the history of graduate instruction in the United States is, in a very real sense, the history of this degree—which despite the emergence of a variety of other highly respectable doctorates is still the leading degree in the humanities, social sciences, and natural sciences.

The Ph.D. is a European import. The first Americans to wear the purple emblem of its hood had to go to German universities for their training, with Edward Everett, in 1817, charting the way. By mid-century some two hundred and twenty-five Americans had "enjoyed their *Wanderjahre,* many taking the doctorate—successfully undergoing the *Seminar,* the *Doktorarbeit,* and the *examen rigorosum."* In fact, the Ph.D. soon became "the badge of the finished scholar."[4]

At the time of its incorporation into our own educational practice, the Ph.D. was strictly an honorary degree. Begun by Bucknell University in 1852, this usage continued to be popular throughout the nineteenth century. As the use of the Ph.D. as an earned degree increased, its desirability for honorary recognition waned; and when the New York State Board of Regents outlawed it for institutions in that state, the practice was virtually abandoned. The record shows, nevertheless, that the final honorary Ph.D. was awarded as recently as 1938 and that the report blank used by the U.S. Office of Education in assem-

---

[3] New York: Fund for the Advancement of Education, December 1955, pp. 3–4. See also Jacques Barzun, *Graduate Study at Columbia* (New York: Columbia University Press, 1956); E. V. Hollis, *Toward Improving Ph.D. Programs* (Washington: American Council on Education, 1945); John W. Dystra, "The Ph.D. Fetish," *School and Society,* LXXXVI (May 24, 1958), 237–39.
[4] L. A. J. Mercier, *Goals for American Education* (New York: Harper & Bros., 1950), p. 287.

bling its annual statistics on degrees continued to include a place for the honorary Ph.D. until 1946.[5]

The first earned Ph.D.'s at an American institution were conferred on three men by Yale University in the year 1861, and the practice was gradually adopted by the other graduate schools. Even up to World War I, however, the American doctorate was considered inferior to those earned at German universities. With the expansion of our graduate schools at the close of the war and with the ever mounting demand for Ph.D.'s in industry, government, and teaching, the degree has now achieved an indisputable place of distinction among the symbols of academic excellence.[6]

There is difference of opinion among many American educators as to whether the Ph.D. ought to be awarded in recognition merely of a substantial advance along the road to ultimate educational fulfillment; or whether, as in certain European academic systems, it should symbolize arrival at a Parnassian peak of solid accomplishment. Since the latter ordinarily calls for many years of preparation and effort and since the demand in our country for Ph.D.'s vastly exceeds the supply, the former concept is the one which dominates most of the doctoral programs in American colleges and universities.[7] The Ph.D., then, signalizes a high level of preparation rather than a lifetime of significant contribution; but, hopefully, it looks forward, rather than backward, to a career of enlarging usefulness.

This concept is succinctly expressed in the following words of Howard Mumford Jones of Harvard University:

The doctorate is conventionally the mark of the trained scholar, scientist and research worker. . . . For a permanent career in the college or university world, despite constant complaints by deans and presidents that this is so, a Ph.D. in the subject of one's choice is a prerequisite. It is also that mark of mature professional training required for a lifelong career in industrial laboratories, governmental bureaus, some kinds of medical research, international organizations or other professional posts within the gift of government, industry, philanthropic organization, or professional association.[8]

[5] Walter Crosby Eells, "Honorary Ph.D.'s in the 20th Century," *School and Society*, LXXXV (March 2, 1957), 74. See also Leo L. Rockwell, "Whence and Whither the Ph.D.?" *School and Society*, LXXXIV (Sept. 29, 1956), 107–9.

[6] It is interesting to note that, between 1861 and 1958, 37 institutions have been responsible for 78.8 percent of the 157,650 doctorates awarded in the United States. See Walter Crosby Eells, "Doctorates from Leading American Graduate Schools, 1861–1958," *School and Society*, LXXXVIII (Feb. 27, 1960), 93.

[7] O. Meredith Wilson makes a strong plea for realistic modification in the requirements for the Ph.D. in his article "Wisdom Is Better than Strength," *Educational Record*, XLI (January 1960), 25–28.

[8] *A Friendly Guide into the Graduate School*, Bulletin of Birmingham Southern College, Vol. XXIX, No. 4 (Birmingham, Ala.: The College, 1947), p. 14. The emphasis on the Ph.D. in this discussion and in *A Guide to Graduate Study* is not intended in any way to discredit the other doctorates. In many instances, the candidate has a choice of degrees in his field, with no difference in the requirements. In other instances—as frequently with the Ed.D.—the difference rests mainly in the nature of the dissertation requirement.

2. What are the objectives of graduate study?

One of the first questions the prospective graduate student must ask himself is why he should go to the effort, time, and expense to attend graduate school. It is important, therefore, to develop more fully some of the implications of the passage just quoted from Howard Mumford Jones. For graduate study requires substantial sacrifices from the student, and he has an obligation to himself to consider carefully its aims and outcomes.

That there is a tremendous demand for the highly trained specialist needs no iteration. John W. Studebaker, former United States Commissioner of Education, writing in 1939, said: "As never before, human welfare today depends upon the results of research, and upon the steady stream of scholars needed for the increasingly arduous demands of intellectual leadership. That unit of our educational system most directly responsible for stimulating research and for developing scholarly leadership is the graduate schools."[1] Certainly with the passing of World War II and of the Korean conflict, and with the advent of the cold war, whose ending reaches into the unforeseeable future, this challenge to the American graduate school and to the young man or woman of superior intellect is, if anything, even more relevant than in 1939.

The distinguishing characteristic of graduate study in the arts and sciences, as against other types of professional training, is its emphasis on "the acquiring, preserving, and disseminating of advanced knowledge" and particularly on "the advancement of knowledge through research, its evaluation, and application."[2] Regardless of the changes in methodology which may evolve in the present pattern of graduate education—a pattern which has not changed materially in seventy or eighty years[3]—these fundamental objectives are certain to be retained. For the survival of our way of life rests largely upon our maintenance of a strong, viable institution devoted to the extension of our knowledge and to its communication. The graduate school, in the eloquent words of Jacques Barzun, is "the keeper of Scholarship's conscience."[4]

A mere scanning of the fields of study included in the later pages of this manual will offer some idea of the great variety of professional areas in which

[1] In the Foreword to Isaiah Bowman, *The Graduate School in American Democracy*, Office of Education Bulletin 1939, No. 14 (Washington: Government Printing Office, 1939), p. v. Since 1945 the number of graduate schools providing programs leading to the Ph.D. has increased from 96 to the present 174.

[2] Laurence Foster, *The Functions of a Graduate School in a Democratic Society* (New York: Huxley House Publishers, 1936), p. 1.

[3] Howard Mumford Jones, *Education and World Tragedy* (Cambridge, Mass.: Harvard University Press, 1946), pp. 136–37.

[4] Jacques Barzun, *Graduate Study at Columbia* (New York: Columbia University Press, 1956), p. 4.

the Ph.D. is offered.[5] It is possible, however, to generalize to the extent of saying that a majority of the students currently enrolled in our graduate schools of arts and science are in one of the following three groups: (1) those who will teach in college or secondary school; (2) those preparing for work in industrial laboratories, research institutions, government agencies, and business; and (3) those preparing for research careers in college or university departments.[6] Yet the doctorate is not necessarily to be considered a professional degree. For, as averred by the Committee on Policies in Graduate Education of the Association of Graduate Schools, "No degree could be called professional which sets out to nurture individual discovery and which exalts newness in knowledge."[7]

In many vocations the Ph.D. is a *sine qua non;* in others, while not prerequisite, it is of primary importance to professional advancement. It has sometimes been referred to as the "union card," particularly for college teaching; but this is, of course, a much too limited view to deserve serious notice.[8]

Nor is graduate study intended for men only. For more than seventy-five years women have been pursuing academic programs leading to advanced degrees, and the number is advancing rapidly in response to the demands for highly trained women teachers, research workers, and administrators. Currently an estimated 5.6 percent of the male college graduates go on to the Ph.D., in contrast with less than 1 percent of women; but there is ample evidence that the woman student is increasingly looking ahead to a life of service through scholarship.[9]

For the relief of some natural apprehension, it should be pointed out that the attainment of a Ph.D. degree is no bar to marriage. One hundred and seventy-five of the Radcliffe Ph.D.'s who responded to a recent questionnaire (out of some 429 surveyed) are married, with 97 of these currently engaged in some form of professional activity. As might be expected, the largest group of respondents were in college teaching, with the principal fields listed as English, economics, biology, and history.[10] It is worth noting, too, that a considerable percentage of male graduate students are married. While the decrease in the number of veterans has resulted in a decline in number, many candidates for the Ph.D. seem to combine successfully and happily their domestic with their academic responsibilities.

Thus, for men and women; for those of all races, nationalities, creeds;

---

[5] See also Office of Education, *Education for the Professions,* Lloyd E. Blauch (ed.) (Washington: Government Printing Office, 1955). The arrival of the space age has now been confirmed in the awarding, by the University of California at Los Angeles, of the first Ph.D. in space navigation!

[6] Bowman, *op. cit.,* p. 13.

[7] *New York Times* (Nov. 13, 1957), p. 28.

[8] W. W. Brickman, editorial comment, *School and Society,* LXXXIV (Sept. 29, 1956), 111.

[9] In 1958, 964 doctorates were awarded to women. See Research Division, National Education Association, *Teacher Supply and Demand in Universities, Colleges, and Junior Colleges, 1957–58 and 1958–59* (Washington: The Association, June 1959), pp. 21–25.

[10] Committee on Graduate Education for Women, Radcliffe College, *Graduate Education for Women: The Radcliffe Ph.D.* (Cambridge, Mass.: Harvard University Press, 1956). This book is highly recommended to any undergraduate woman contemplating graduate study.

for all who share a love of learning, who have the capacity for high intellectual development, and who believe in a life of service of the highest order—for these the American graduate school provides opportunity for a rewarding membership in the community of scholars.

College teaching as a career

As has been indicated in the previous pages, the three principal functions of the graduate school, in terms of its output, are (1) to train research workers and to carry on basic research; (2) to prepare experts for service in such non-academic fields as business, industry, government, agriculture, and public welfare; and (3) to prepare men and women for careers in college teaching.

Statistically, in relation to the majority of fields of study, the most important of these functions is the preparation of college teachers. It is generally assumed that from 60 to 65 percent of all Ph.D. recipients spend a major portion of their productive careers in college teaching, three-fifths of them in undergraduate programs.[11] In view of these facts, it is appropriate for this *Guide* to give special attention to college teaching as a career.

There is yet another reason for the emphasis—the impending crisis in higher education stemming from vastly increasing enrollments and the failure of teacher recruitment to keep pace. Here again statistics are useful. They provide at least a quantitative measure of the problem. It is estimated that sometime between 1966 and 1971 college enrollments will reach 7 million, or more than double their level in the mid-fifties. If present student-faculty ratios are to be maintained, somewhere between 300,000 and 500,000 new college teachers will have to be added to our present ranks to make up for losses and meet the necessary expansion.[12] The present corps of teachers, variously estimated at between 150,000 and 268,000,[13] will have to be expanded at the rate of some 25,000 a year in the next twelve years to meet the minimum requirements of higher education.[14]

One of the questions which is now receiving the most careful consideration is where these new teachers are to be found. Of equal importance is how the present quality of college teaching can be maintained and even improved, for

---

[11] Rex C. Kidd, "Improving Preservice Education of Undergraduate College Teachers," *Journal of Teacher Education,* III (March 1952), 55; cf. Leo L. Rockwell, "Whence and Whither the Ph.D.?" *School and Society,* LXXXVIII (Sept. 29, 1956), 107–9.

[12] Two useful presentations of this problem have been prepared under the auspices of the Fund for the Advancement of Education: *Teachers for Tomorrow,* Bulletin No. 2 (November 1955) and *Better Utilization of College Teaching Resources* (October 1956).

[13] J. F. Wellemeyer, Jr., "Full-Time Teachers in American Colleges and Universities," *School and Society,* LXXXVIII (June 23, 1956), 220–21. See also Office of Education, *Faculty and Other Professional Staff in Institutions of Higher Education,* Wayne E. Tolliver and Hazel C. Poole (eds.), (Washington: Government Printing Office, September 1959), pp. 1–6.

[14] It is worth noting that Berelson tends to minimize the "critical" shortage of college teachers; see Bernard Berelson, "Graduate Education and the Preparation of Teachers" in John W. Gustad (ed.), *Faculty Supply, Demand, and Recruitment: Proceedings of a Regional Conference* (Winchester, Mass.: New England Board of Higher Education, 1959), pp. 74–92.

there is little likelihood that as much as 40 percent of these needs will be filled by Ph.D.'s. In fact, only one-quarter of the new college teachers employed in 1958–59 had earned doctorates.

The statement was made above that from 60 to 65 percent of the 9,000 annual recipients of the Ph.D. go into college teaching. But statistics can be deceptive; in some fields, for example, relatively few Ph.D.'s are currently entering teaching. The president of a major Midwestern university reported in 1957 that not one of his Ph.D.'s of the previous year in chemistry became a college teacher. And the situation is equally stringent in mathematics and some of the other sciences. It is almost axiomatic, in fact, that a much greater percentage of Ph.D.'s in the humanities and social sciences enter teaching than in the natural sciences.

At the present time an estimated 40 percent of those teaching in colleges and universities have the Ph.D. Furthermore, at the current rate some 134,000 doctorates will be awarded in the next fifteen years (considered by many an overoptimistic figure). Since many of these will enter the other professional areas for which the Ph.D. degree is in high demand, the number of college teachers holding the degree may dip as low as 20 percent.[15]

This naturally raises the question of the future of the Ph.D. degree as the "union card" for the college teacher—a question which cannot be answered definitively in this essay or at this time. College and university policies were surveyed by the Research Division of the National Education Association recently, and the findings are significant:

Appointment to the lowest rank, that of instructor, calls for the doctor's degree in 3.1 percent of the institutions reporting requirements, for the master's degree plus an additional year in 5.4 percent, and for the master's degree in 64.7 percent. . . .

For appointment to a full professorship the doctor's degree is announced policy in 84.4 percent of the institutions reporting requirements, the master's degree plus one year in 9.3 percent, and the master's degree in 5.8 percent.[16]

To what extent the shortage of college teachers will modify these policies can only be conjectured. It would seem logical, however, to expect that the changes will be principally in the lower ranks. The Ph.D. will still hold its place as a prerequisite for appointment to the rank of full professor.

Although past experience does not show any correlation between teaching opportunities and the number of students who elect certain fields of concentration for the Ph.D.—possibly because the information was not readily available—the undergraduate who is thinking of preparing for a career as a college teacher should, among other things, certainly consider carefully the operation

---

[15] Fund for the Advancement of Education, *Better Utilization of College Teaching Resources* (October 1956), p. 4.
[16] *Instructional Staff Practices and Policies in Degree-Granting Institutions, 1953–4,* Bulletin XXXII, No. 4 (Washington: National Education Association, December 1954), p. 166; cf. Lloyd S. Woodburne, *Faculty Personnel Policies in Higher Education* (New York: Harper & Bros., 1950), p. 10.

of the laws of supply and demand in his field. As every college dean knows, his employment problem in certain academic areas is to select the best from many excellent candidates; whereas in other areas he is obliged to employ almost anyone he can get, so great is the shortage. Fortunately or unfortunately, there is no real stability in the situation. Shortages in a field in one year may well turn into surpluses a year or two later.

In 1954–55 Dr. Ray C. Maul of the National Education Association undertook to provide a reliable instrument for measuring trends in the supply and demand for college teaching. The result was a comprehensive study of "how many teaching positions in *what fields* of instruction and in *what types* of institutions are open to candidates at the *various levels* of preparation."[17] This excellent analysis is now published biennially and is strongly recommended to every prospective graduate student and future college teacher. Among other useful data in this study are those concerning the distribution of the current doctoral candidates among the teaching fields, thus providing some measure of the competition which the prospective graduate student can expect. Psychology, with 51.6 percent, leads the field, followed by the biological sciences, with 49 percent, and the physical sciences, with 44.3. Philosophy, with 34.7, and the social sciences, with 33.6, come next. Mathematics, in which there is such a critical need, shows only 20 percent.[18]

Perhaps of more importance here than the number of Ph.D. candidates produced annually are the estimates of the number of teachers needed in the various fields, as projected through 1969–70. Thus, with the permission of the Research Division of the National Education Association, the table on page 12 is reproduced for the benefit of the prospective college teacher.

This, then, is what might be termed the statistical approach to the subject of college teaching. But obviously statistics are not going to induce anyone seriously to consider college teaching as a career. The human side is much more relevant.

Although there is as yet no definitive study of why college teachers become college teachers, some fascinating penetrations have been made into this mysterious area. In addition to the work of Dr. John Gustad at the University of Maryland,[19] Drs. John E. Stecklein and Ruth E. Eckert of the University of Minnesota have succeeded in throwing some light upon the matter.[20] In their preliminary inquiry the reasons most commonly presented by college teachers as influencing their decision to teach were revealed as the following:

[17] Research Division, National Education Association, *Teacher Supply and Demand in Degree-Granting Institutions, 1954–55*, Bulletin XXXIII, No. 4 (Washington: The Association, December 1955), p. 130.

[18] *Teacher Supply and Demand . . . 1957–58 and 1958–59*, p. 14.

[19] Partly reported in "They March to a Different Drummer: Another Look at College Teachers," *Educational Record*, XL (July 1959), 204–11.

[20] Conducted under a research grant from the U.S. Office of Education. The survey at present includes college and university teachers in the State of Minnesota only. See Stecklein and Eckert, "College Faculty Members View Their Jobs," *AAUP Bulletin*, XLV (Winter 1959), 513–28; and "Academic Woman," Association of American Colleges, *Bulletin*, XLV (October 1959), 390–97.

EXTERNAL FACTORS

High school staff member suggested it
College teacher recommended it
College administrator or counselor encouraged me
Parent, friend, or relative favored this choice
Graduate fellowship or assistantship was offered me
College teaching job was offered although I hadn't sought one
G.I. benefits enabled me to take advanced work
Armed forces training led me into field
Husband (wife) was, or planned to be, a college teacher
Just "drifted" into college teaching

INTERNAL FACTORS

Became so interested in subject I wanted to continue its study
Desired to work with college-age students
Wanted a job with security and prestige
Felt I could contribute more to my field by teaching in college
Wanted an opportunity to pursue research activities in my field
Felt I could make the greatest contribution to society in this area
Liked working conditions (flexible schedule, vacations, relative independence, etc.)
Wanted to be a part of the college academic and social life
Desired to emulate a certain college professor
Thought it would offer more intellectual challenge than other careers

While the completed survey will undoubtedly disclose other reasons and indicate the relative importance of those already advanced, this present list would seem to be fairly comprehensive. Furthermore, one cannot help observing that among the internal reasons two seem to predominate: a deep interest in an intellectual life and an abiding desire to be of service to society on the highest level. The following is an interesting summary of reasons, given by Woodrow Wilson fellows,[21] for considering college teaching as a career:

	Percent
Scholarship, dedication to field, pull of subject matter	33.1
Enjoyment of teaching, theories of how to teach, student-oriented	29.8
Have done student teaching	29.1
Usefulness: patriotism, religious and ethical duty, service to mankind	24.5
Self-development, personal satisfaction, and intellectual stimulation	22.4
Influence of college teachers	18.1
Academic-life syndrome, its atmosphere and colleagues	16.6
Teaching as a second or dual choice	7.7
No expressed motivation	6.7

Regardless of what it may have been in the past, college and university teaching is no longer a leisurely, protected, or withdrawn life. The good

[21] *Woodrow Wilson National Fellowship Foundation Report for 1958–1959* (Princeton, N. J.: The Foundation, 1959), p. 69.

ESTIMATED NUMBER OF FULL-TIME UNIVERSITY, COLLEGE, AND JUNIOR COLLEGE
TEACHERS NEEDED, BY FIELD, 1959–60 THROUGH 1969–70

FIELD	Per-cent of Total	ESTIMATED NUMBER OF					
		Full-Time Teachers, 1958–59	New Full-Time Teachers Needed, 1959–60[a]	New Full-Time Teachers Needed, 1960–61[a]	New Full-Time Teachers Needed, 1964–65[a]	New Full-Time Teachers Needed, 1969–70[a]	Total Number of New Full-Time Teachers Needed, 1959–70, Inclusive[a]
Agriculture............	4.4	11,000	1,200	1,250	1,400	1,550	15,250
Biological sciences.....	5.9	14,750	1,600	1,650	1,850	2,100	20,450
Business and commerce	5.2	13,000	1,400	1,450	1,650	1,850	18,050
Education............	7.5	18,750	2,000	2,100	2,400	2,700	26,000
Engineering..........	7.0	17,500	1,900	1,950	2,250	2,500	24,300
English..............	8.3	20,750	2,200	2,350	2,650	2,950	28,800
Fine arts (all)	10.8	27,000	2,900	3,000	3,450	3,850	37,450
Music.............	5.1	12,750	1,350	1,400	1,650	1,850	17,700
Speech and dramatics	2.7	6,750	750	750	850	950	9,350
Others.............	3.0	7,500	800	850	950	1,050	10,400
Foreign languages.....	5.2	13,000	1,400	1,450	1,650	1,850	18,050
Health sciences[b]......	3.7	9,250	1,000	1,050	1,200	1,300	12,850
Home economics......	2.4	6,000	650	650	750	850	8,300
Industrial and voca-tional arts........	2.4	6,000	650	650	750	850	8,300
Library science.......	2.1	5,250	550	600	650	750	7,300
Mathematics.........	4.0	10,000	1,100	1,100	1,300	1,450	13,850
Philosophy...........	1.4	3,500	400	400	450	500	4,850
Physical and health education........	5.3	13,250	1,450	1,500	1,700	1,900	18,400
Physical sciences (all).	8.1	20,250	2,150	2,250	2,600	2,900	28,100
Chemistry..........	3.8	9,500	1,000	1,050	1,200	1,350	13,200
Physics............	2.6	6,500	700	750	850	950	9,000
Others.............	1.7	4,250	450	450	550	600	5,900
Psychology...........	2.5	6,250	650	700	800	900	8,650
Religion..............	1.4	3,500	400	400	450	500	4,850
Social sciences (all)...	10.9	27,250	2,900	3,000	3,450	3,900	37,800
History............	3.4	8,500	900	950	1,050	1,250	11,800
Economics..........	2.5	6,250	650	700	800	900	8,650
Political science.....	1.7	4,250	450	450	550	600	5,900
Sociology..........	1.7	4,250	450	450	550	600	5,900
Others.............	1.6	4,000	450	450	500	550	5,550
Others..............	1.5	3,750	400	400	500	550	5,200
All fields.........	100.0	250,000	26,900	27,900	31,900	35,700	346,800

NOTE: The estimates offered in this table assume that (a) enrollments will increase at a consistent rate, (b) the number of teachers in service will increase at a slower pace, bringing about (c) a steady increase in student-teacher ratio, and (d) the rate of annual replacements will remain constant.
  [a] Presuming no change in the field-by-field distribution of all full-time teachers.
  [b] Excluding dentistry and medicine.
  SOURCE: Research Division, National Education Association, *Teacher Supply and Demand in Universities, Colleges, and Junior Colleges, 1957–58 and 1958–59* (Washington: The Association, June 1959), p. 51.

teacher is constantly "revising and advising." He is in demand as a consultant. He participates actively in community affairs. He has many opportunities for broadening experiences through summer study or work. In short, he leads a more varied existence and has greater opportunity for developing a broad and flexible attitude toward life than is possible for the usual executive in business and industry.

The most serious objection to teaching as a career has to do with salaries. Here is a disadvantage which cannot be glossed over. As compared, for example, with that of the medical doctor, the college teacher's salary is far from satisfactory. It is not, however, at the level of penury. Further, it is on a decided increase, an increase dramatically signalized by the Ford Foundation's grant of $260 million in late 1955 for the specific purpose of improving faculty salaries in private undergraduate colleges.[22]

The most recent figures available at the time of this publication show the following:

The median salary of professors is $9107; one-fourth are at or above $10,755; one-fourth are at or below $7721. The median salary for associate professors is $7332; one-fourth are at or above $8206; one-fourth are at or below $6439. The median for assistant professors is $6231; one-fourth are at or above $6889; one-fourth are at or below $5589. The median for instructors is $5095; one-fourth are at or above $5624; one-fourth are at or below $4599 for nine months of full-time service.[23]

It is important to emphasize that these salaries are for nine, not for twelve, months. Moreover, with so much national attention focused on the problems of encouraging more of our highly qualified men and women to enter college teaching, it seems a safe prediction that the salary status of the profession will continue to make rapid improvement. In fact, one student of the economics of higher education, Professor Seymour Harris of Harvard, predicts a general rise in faculty salaries of 100 percent over the next twelve years.[24]

There is a well-known, but probably apocryphal, story to the effect that when J. Pierpont Morgan was asked if a yacht was expensive, he replied, "Sir, if you have to think about the expense of a yacht then you cannot afford one!" While the problem of employment conditions in college teaching may not be precisely analogous, it is probably fair to assert that if anybody is primarily concerned with the size of salary, with the nature of the tenure program, and with the number and extent of the "fringe benefits," he should not consider college teaching as a career. For teaching is, in the medieval sense of the word, a "vocation"—a calling. And those who enter it should do so with some sense of dedication.[25]

Countless words have been written on the essential qualities of a good college teacher. So idealistic are most of these sketches that they tend to frighten even the experienced teacher, let alone the neophyte. In general, though, it would not seem an overstatement to expect the prospective teacher to possess, to a substantial degree, the following qualities:[26]

1. Emotional control and maturity

2. A strong drive and persistence

3. At least a B average intellectual capacity

[22] The total grant to colleges, medical schools, and hospitals was $400 million.
[23] *Salaries Paid and Salary Practices in Universities, Colleges, and Junior Colleges, 1959–60* (Washington: National Education Association, March 1960), p. 5.
[24] *Woodrow Wilson National Fellowship Foundation Report for 1957–1958* (Princeton, N. J.: The Foundation, 1958), p. 14.
[25] See Robert L. Tyler, "In Lieu of Money: The Rewards of Teaching," *Journal of Higher Education*, XXXI (April 1960), 185–90.
[26] See Theodore C. Blegen and Russell M. Cooper (eds.), *The Preparation of College Teachers* (Washington: American Council on Education, July 1950), p. 62.

4. A deep interest in students and other people
5. A vital enthusiasm for the subjects taught
6. Imagination, inventiveness, and curiosity

In addition to a knowledge of his subject, the teacher should have some aware-ness of the learning process, of the methods and techniques of instruction, of the role of the college teacher, and of the history and function of higher edu-cation in American society.

As with many another art, there is always the question in higher education of whether the good teacher is "born" or "made." Perhaps the answer lies in some-thing of a compromise. Nor is this mere quibbling, for it reflects a diversity of views which have been debated in higher education since at least the time of Plato. A great majority of present college teachers learned to teach by teaching, and in the long run this is the only way to put on the finishing touches. The graduate schools of the past paid, and many of the present pay, little or no attention to specific preparation of their doctoral candidates for classroom duties. This is not to say that teaching experience in some form was not avail-able in graduate school. On the contrary, Kidd's study (1952) discloses that approximately seven out of ten of the college teachers surveyed served as graduate assistants—but generally without any planned supervision. Slightly over four out of ten had some previous high-school teaching.[27]

Good teaching is an art, and often an unconscious one. But it is an art which study, practice, and observation can refine; and since the great majority of can-didates entering college teaching do so with only the most limited experience in the classroom, increasing pressure is being put upon the graduate schools to provide some specific training or orientation for the prospective college teacher.

This discussion has attempted to give a picture of college teaching by pre-senting certain data on supply and demand, by reviewing the reasons for elect-ing—or not electing—a career in teaching, by indicating some of the usual characteristics of the college teacher, and by making some observations on the relevance of graduate study to the practice of college teaching. It has not dis-cussed the relevance of research to teaching, for this is reviewed in the next section. Nor has it assayed to speak, except casually, of the incomparable satis-factions which accrue to the man or woman who spends his or her life in the service of higher education.[28] It would seem appropriate, therefore, to end this

[27] Kidd, op. cit., p. 55.
[28] Throughout this discussion the college teacher is referred to in the masculine. While it is a fact that approximately four out of five college teachers are men, a concerted effort is under way to encourage more women to enter the profession. At present the highest percentage of women teachers is found in teachers colleges, with the next highest in nonpublic colleges, and the smallest in non-public universities. For the division by fields, see Research Division, National Education Association, *Teacher Supply and Demand . . . 1957 58 and 1958 59*, pp. 5 ff. Of interest to prospective women college teachers is the recent study for the Committee on Higher Education of the American Asso-ciation of University Women by Eleanor F. Dolan and Margaret P. Davis, "Antinepotism Rules in American Colleges and Universities: Their Effect on the Faculty Employment of Women," *Educa-tional Record*, XLI (October 1960).

section with a passage from an address by one of America's great teachers, editors, and educational philosophers, Ordway Tead:

Here surely is one of the most obvious instances of a vocation which unites the inner and the outer concern for happy outcomes. Here your personal drive toward unique creativity can coincide with your contribution as a social benefactor because you are helping in the creation of other selves who carry forward the torch after you.

If you enjoy the life of the mind and of ideas, if you like the society of young people and get along with them reasonably well, if you are convinced that it is wise ideas that count and can be shapeful influences in the world—if all these conditions are true for you—teaching can be your dish.

It can be a superb career in which we at once maximize ourselves and transcend ourselves in dedicated service—and all of this in the effort to realize Godlike values in the world through the strivings of more better-educated people whose education we have helped to forward.[29]

The graduate school and research

The preceding pages have made the point that one of the primary functions of the graduate school is the preparation of college teachers. Another important function is training for research. But the distinction between teaching and research is artificial and dangerous, for it is a basic principle in the organization of most doctoral programs that teaching and research are inseparable. Certainly the effective teacher must maintain a lively concern with research, particularly since, in many institutions, his promotion may depend upon it.[30] The outstanding "researcher," however, need not necessarily be immediately involved with teaching. Thus it is that at nearly every major university there are to be found scholars, sometimes called "research fellows," who rarely, if ever, enter the classroom but whose contribution to the academic effort is nevertheless of great significance. Thus, too, the graduate school professor is frequently thought of as a man or woman more interested in research than in teaching. Yet his ardent pursuit of truth and discovery, through his personal or group investigations, may actually constitute the highest form of teaching. By his example he may inspire the students within his purview to a personal dedication which can result not only in their becoming better teachers but in their joining the ranks of discoverers themselves and adding to the storehouse of human knowledge. Therefore, the graduate school, while concerned with the classroom, reaches its fulfillment in the library and laboratory as well.

"Research," in the concise definition offered by Laurence Foster, "may be thought of as any conscious, systematized, investigative effort which has for its

---

[29] "College Teaching as a Spiritual Adventure," one of the James Henry Morgan Lectures on College Teaching delivered at Dickinson College, November 29, 1955. See also *Your Career as a College Teacher* (Ohio College Association, 1959).

[30] See Theodore Caplow and Reece J. McGee, *The Academic Marketplace* (New York: Basic Books, 1958).

purpose the increasing of knowledge, through discovery of tendencies, principles, laws, methodology, or means by which knowledge or methodology may be verified."[31] That the ability to function within this frame of reference is important for the college teacher is almost axiomatic.

Axiomatic also is the assertion that the beginning of wisdom is a love for discipline. Thus the following resolution adopted by the Association of American Universities at its forty-ninth annual conference[32] is worthy of repetition in this context:

The intellectual discipline and the exacting performance called for in the Ph.D. degree program at its best would seem to be more needed today than ever before. A candidate for this degree improves his scholarly capacity through investigations even though the results of his work may not be published. The experience gained in selecting and carrying out a piece of research has inestimable value for the student preparing for an intellectual career, whether as a research scientist, a worker in the social field, or a college teacher.

One of the first institutions in the United States founded primarily for the purpose of offering graduate instruction was Clark University in Massachusetts.[33] An early president, G. Stanley Hall, laid down in 1902 a methodology for research which is fully applicable today:

First, the method must be either invented or adapted to the problem. There are conditions to be controlled; principles of selection must be determined; negative instances rejected; very often machinery must be devised and made. . . .

Second, there must be data collected, experiments made and noted, facts gathered, protocol books filled, instances and experiments multiplied, and the basis of induction made broad and deep. . . . The method must not be too precise and accurate.

The third and main stage is to think it all out; to apply a rigorous philosophic method; to reason logically on the objective facts; to find their unity; to determine what is central and what is unimportant; to relate and determine the place and bearing of all; and find whether the accumulations are mere agglomerations, or have a meaning and value for science.[34]

If on the face of it this seems to be a demanding regimen, then one can only say with Hamlet, "Seems, madam! Nay, it is." Furthermore, the problems of the doctoral research project are in no way less rigorous than, nor essentially different from, those confronting the seasoned scholar.

In the first place, selecting a subject for a research project is difficult and sometimes perilous. It must be in an area that has not previously been thoroughly explored. Then, having found a topic either through his own investigations, or, if a graduate student, through the assistance of his preceptor on the faculty, the scholar must conduct a thorough search to make certain that it has

---

[31] Foster, *loc. cit.*

[32] Held at the University of Pennsylvania, October 20–30, 1948.

[33] See p. 125.

[34] Quoted by Walton C. John, *Graduate Study in the Universities and Colleges in the United States,* Office of Education Bulletin 1934, No. 20 (Washington: Government Printing Office, 1935), p. 39.

not already been adequately covered. This search must include "works in progress," as well as those published; for more than one doctoral candidate has been obliged to discard months of labor and begin anew because some other scholar has "beat him to the draw." Fortunately, in a number of fields there are now annual publications of works either already in print or in progress.

Having selected the topic and made certain of its validity, he must next decide how it should be limited. Even doctoral dissertations sometimes reach a thousand pages in length, but this does not necessarily indicate superior worth. It may mean merely that the student did not properly limit his area of investigation. At the other extreme, a dissertation, regardless of field, may occupy only one page and yet it may well represent a significant contribution to human knowledge.

The next important task of the research scholar is to make a thorough canvass of sources and secondary authorities. He will find the work of other contemporary scholars frequently printed in languages other than his own. In research there is no such thing as a foreign language. In the broadest sense the language of scholarship is universal, and thus the student may have to delve into the language of any area where men have shared his particular scholarly interest. For example, a scientist investigating tropical diseases in which Japanese scholars have done noteworthy work may well have to read their reports in the original. An historian dealing with the history of Jordan would be handicapped if he lacked a knowledge of Arabic and perhaps of Hebrew.

The manner of taking notes is of primary importance, and the scholar or graduate student who has not mastered an efficient system would do well to study one of the many excellent manuals available on the subject of preparing a research paper. One lost reference—and in this the present writer can speak with feeling—may mean many hours of painful search as the thesis is in the final stages of production. Bibliographical information should therefore be scrupulously recorded.[35]

Finally, while doctoral theses are not generally expected to be examples of the finest Attic prose, they are required to show adequate organization and effective presentation. Some dissertations see the light of day in published form. Many are unworthy of such treatment, not because their ideas or discoveries are not significant, but because they are poorly written. Even many works of mature scholars suffer from awkwardness of expression. Although the job of research is difficult, it is not beyond the powers of the usual candidate for the Ph.D. It has many forms of interest and satisfaction, not the least of which is the joy of handling a manuscript and saying, "This is a little thing

---

[35] The writer knows of one instance of a brilliant master's essay that contained many quotations but without a single identification or reference. Fortunately, a team of fellow graduate students lent a hand and, after approximately two weeks, managed to supply the necessary footnotes.

I wrote a few years ago!" And if the reviewers are appreciative, one's delight is complete.[36]

Regardless of its methodologies or its delights, research in higher education is "big business." In 1957–58 colleges and universities received in excess of $534 million from the Federal Government alone for contractual research; and the trend is toward more and more subsidized research as colleges and universities are being called on for assistance in solving the involute problems of our complex civilization.[37]

At one time a distinction may have been drawn between academic and industrial research, with the former leaning primarily toward the fundamental and theoretical and the latter toward the more immediately practical and applicable. But this distinction can no longer be reliably drawn. Another profound change in the concept of research is away from Johnson's "Hermit hoar in solemn cell, Wearing out life's evening gray" to the team of scholars or even to the union of institutions as represented in the Brookhaven Laboratories. For the intricacy of modern research, particularly in the sciences, has made the group approach almost inevitable. Moreover, research has developed a community of interest, as is evidenced by the organization of such groups as the National Research Council, the American Council of Learned Societies, and the like.

Thus, one of the prime functions of the graduate school is to provide basic training and experience in research, a function which has now reached major proportions. And from the standpoint of the graduate student, whether he is working in solitary splendor on a doctoral project, or as one of a "factory" editing the papers of a major historical or literary figure, or as part of a team working on a sponsored scientific project, research can provide one of the major satisfactions of his advanced study as well as representing the culmination of his formal academic training.

[36] I am deeply indebted in this discussion to my colleague Dr. Herbert Wing, Jr., of Dickinson College, who not only taught me how to handle the "card system" in that dim past when I was a college freshman but whose continued interest in research led him to provide a sketch from which these paragraphs have been drawn. See also Preston James, "The Dissertation Requirement," *School and Society*, LXXXIII (March 26, 1960), 147.

[37] See David D. Henry, "New Priorities in Research," *Educational Record*, XLI (April 1960), 148.

3. Who should go to graduate school?

The assumption in the previous chapter was that graduate study and graduate schools have certain definite objectives. It would follow logically, therefore, that no one should undertake graduate training for whom these objectives are not plainly relevant. But determining this relevance and deciding to engage in advanced study are undertakings of such magnitude as to justify some additional comment.

One of the trends of modern American education is to force the student to a vocational choice quite early in his academic life. The future M.D. who has not made his choice before his freshman year in college will find his already long period of training still further protracted. This applies as well to many other professions. In view of the prerequisites for nearly every field of advanced study, it is desirable for the undergraduate to come to a decision as early as possible. Failure to do so does not necessarily render him ineligible for graduate study, but it could result in his having to make up preparatory work he may have missed.

One of the graduate students questioned in the course of this study offered the following advice: "If you have done reasonably good work at the undergraduate level, you have no reason to be afraid of graduate work. If you have an interest in some particular field and want to know more about it, then by all means continue your education. It means putting off many things that may seem important at the time, but in the end the satisfactions you receive in being able to give more both to yourself and to society more than compensate for any inconvenience."

In this advice several important points are made. The first is that graduate study is not limited to the straight A student. Some undergraduates of quite respectable academic ability feel that graduate work is beyond their capabilities, while as a matter of fact many of them could engage in advanced study with success if not with distinction. As Professor Thorndike has expressed it, "There are two golden rules for choosing adults for further education: the rule of ability and the rule of interest."[1] Only the individual, of course, can judge the depth of his interest; but he would be well advised to give the admission committee of the graduate school an opportunity to make the final ruling on his ability.

While something more will be said on the subject of ability in the discussion

[1] Edward Lee Thorndike, "Earned Opportunities," *Journal of Adult Education*, VII (June 1935), 260.

of admission to graduate school, it is relevant to note here that a certain type of ability is desirable for graduate study. Blegen and Cooper define it as "the ability to solve problems." This involves "a healthy respect for facts, for evidence, for principles, for laws; it requires fair evaluation and interpretation of data and the drawing of sound conclusions."[2] It certainly involves more than the ability to memorize, which only too frequently in undergraduate work is all that is needed to earn academic recognition.

Various attempts have been made to study the attitudes and characteristics which make for success or failure in graduate school.[3] Friedenberg and Roth approached the subject from the sociological point of view;[4] Cronbach examined it by administering the Rorschach test to some seventy-five graduate students in education who had passed their preliminary examinations for the doctorate.[5] Without doubt, explorations will continue, but until some definitive answer is reached even the C student should not automatically eliminate himself from the possibility of graduate study. For he may well have unusual abilities which were simply not developed in his undergraduate experience.

A second important consideration in determining who should attend graduate school is interest in a particular subject field or combination of fields.[6] While this interest may ripen and mature through advanced training, it must exist before the inception of graduate study. And this applies to interest in academic work in general as well as in a particular field of specialization.

But interest in the subject and the ability to make a satisfactory average are still not enough, even though the student may have the industry, the thoroughness, and the courage to proceed to a mastery of the field. "To these virtues should be added imagination, discrimination, a capacity to think creatively, and integrity in serving the truth. The unknown quantity for which graduate schools are continually searching is the steady glow associated with true lovers of learning."[7]

From this, one may deduce who should *not* go to graduate school. As every graduate dean is aware, a portion of his students come with no great zest for knowledge. For some, advanced study is merely the line of least resistance. For others it is a retreat from responsibility. In either case the results tend to be

---

[2] Theodore C. Blegen and Russell M. Cooper (eds.), *The Preparation of College Teachers* (Washington: American Council on Education, July 1950), p. 62.

[3] Of particular interest in this connection is Hans Rosenhaupt, *Graduate Students Experience at Columbia University, 1940–1956* (New York: Columbia University Press, 1958).

[4] Edgar Z. Friedenberg and Julius A. Roth, *Self-Perception in the University* (Chicago, Ill.: University of Chicago Press, 1954).

[5] Lee J. Cronbach, "Personality and Intellectual Functioning in Graduate Students," in *Growing Points in Educational Research* (Washington: American Educational Research Association, 1949), pp. 89–95. See also Stuart Conrad Peterson, "The Measurement and Prediction of Scholastic Achievement on the Graduate Level" (Unpublished doctoral dissertation, University of Iowa, 1943).

[6] Research conducted by the National Academy of Sciences—National Research Council suggests that the field of specialization for the doctorate may be a function of the size of the high school graduating class! See L. R. Harmon, in *Science*, CXXX (Nov. 27, 1959), 1473.

[7] Committee on Graduate Education for Women, Radcliffe College, *Graduate Education for Women: The Radcliffe Ph.D.* (Cambridge, Mass.: Harvard University Press, 1956), p. 76.

disillusioning. As a wise man once said, there is a time to learn and a time to live. Some people seem so occupied with the first that they never quite get to the second.

In some areas of endeavor, graduate study is not worth the equivalent of time spent in good, workmanlike participation in a business enterprise. Often the training program provided by a particular industrial organization is the shortest and most satisfactory road to a vocational aim.

There is this to be said, however: the baccalaureate degree is losing—if it has not already lost—its selective significance. Since the annual output of A.B.'s now far exceeds the high-school graduates of fifty years ago, the degree has become almost an accepted minimum for employment above the unskilled level. The M.A., too, has lost much of its earlier distinction, partly because of inconsistency and lack of agreement in its standard. In some phases of industrial or governmental service, the three or four years of sacrifice needed to obtain the Ph.D. are repaid many times in the advancement over those without the degree. Thus for the person with the ability and interest and zest, graduate study may well have material as well as intangible compensations.

In 1940 a survey was taken of 199 Ph.D.'s in which the respondents were asked to indicate the "chief returns realized" from their investment in graduate training. A great majority checked "increased professional skill" (78 percent). The next largest group checked the development of an "enriched philosophy of life" (55 percent), and after this the attainment of a better position (53 percent). Relatively few (25 percent) pointed to a "salary increase for the same work."[8] The availability of other evidence of the salary benefits derived from the advanced degree may suggest that, at least with this group, financial returns were not considered especially important.

This would certainly seem to be borne out in the replies from graduate students who were asked, in the collection of information for this manual, to indicate their reasons for undertaking graduate study. Two of these replies are especially relevant:

The desire to continue in my effort systematically to organize and integrate experience, to relate my acquaintance with my culture and myself; the need to increase my professional skills and my capacity as a person in order that I might make a more worthwhile contribution to my profession and to my community; the motivation to grow as a person so that I might have greater personal fulfillment; to increase professional mobility, status, earning potential, and potential to make a professional contribution.

And this passage, which might well serve as a manifesto for the ideal graduate student:

I have been interested in history and historical problems since secondary school. During my last two years of undergraduate study I realized that only further study and teaching

---

[8] Reported by E. V. Hollis, *Toward Improving Ph.D. Programs* (Washington: American Council on Education, 1945), p. 164.

at the college level would satisfy my own intellectual curiosity and desire to become an effective part of the educational process. I enjoy working among people attempting to understand some of those things which are the bases of our manner of life, thought, expression, and purpose. . . .

Believing in the ultimate perfectibility of man, I feel that the problems which beset us can be solved, for the most part, through thought and understanding. Unless each person is respected as an individual and given the greatest possible opportunity to develop his or her intellectual capacities, this goal can never be approached, much less realized. This to me is a great part of the role of teaching. Beyond this is my desire to contribute some small original bit to the sum of human knowledge in my own area of specialization and interest.

This discussion has offered no criteria for answering the question: Who should go to graduate school? Because of the great variety of motives and objectives, of personalities and abilities, no conclusive answer is possible. But clearly the prospective graduate student should ask himself many questions, not only about graduate study—for graduate study is not an end in itself—but also about the type of life for which graduate study is the entering way.

4. How to prepare for graduate study

Preparation for advanced study in such professional fields as medicine and dentistry is so highly standardized that the student rarely, if ever, is in doubt about the requirements for admission. Since he usually has decided at the outset of his college work what his goal is, he simply elects the "pre-med" or "pre-dent" curriculum and follows its specifications in sequential order. Regardless of which school ultimately accepts him, his prefabricated curriculum will very likely have included all the essentials.[1]

Experience with graduate students in the arts and sciences, on the other hand, shows that they frequently do not develop a definite interest until they are well into their major field. Consequently they often arrive at the point of admission to graduate school with gaps in their major and minor preparation or with deficiencies in foreign languages. The best way to avoid such difficulty, of course, is for the student to reach a decision early in his college years. In the ideal situation this decision would even include the choice of a graduate school. For then a careful study of the catalogue will enable him to chart his undergraduate program so as to include all the prescribed courses in his major and in allied fields.

Part II of this *Guide* is predicated on the assumption that for a majority of prospective graduate students this ideal situation does not prevail. By setting forth the prerequisites for admission, this manual affords a ready means of comparing the requirements of various institutions and departments and enables the student to plan a composite program to qualify him for any one of a number of graduate schools.

It is worth noting here that many undergraduate departments offer dual majors, one for the student whose formal education will end with the baccalaureate, the other for the student who expects to continue into advanced study. If there is any doubt in the student's mind, he should elect the more comprehensive program. Yet there is one caution to be offered here. From the deans, faculty members, and graduate students consulted in the preparation of this manual, an admonition was repeatedly given against too high a degree of undergraduate specialization. Although strong preparation in the major is obviously desirable, the time for intense concentration is in graduate, not undergraduate, school. For example, the chairman of one distinguished graduate department in English customarily disavowed the importance of any particular

---

[1] Nevertheless, the Association of American Medical Colleges sponsors the yearly publication of a manual on admissions requirements to medical schools.

college courses in the major field, stressing instead the necessity of a thorough knowledge of foreign languages. It was the responsibility of the graduate school, he said, to provide the training in the major field. A student majoring in the sciences would do well to obtain a thorough grounding in the humanities and social studies. If he does not receive this in his baccalaureate years, the chances are he never will. One student when asked in the course of the survey what advice he would give the prospective graduate student, answered the question by saying, "Read, read, read, read!"

Even in his major field, the undergraduate would do well to avoid too many of the purely "practical" courses. A broad experience with fundamental courses will afford him the best foundation for his graduate concentration. In psychology, for instance, many graduate schools prefer that the student not have too large a number of undergraduate courses in the field, especially technique courses.[2]

What, then, should the prospective graduate student obtain from his undergraduate preparation? In addition to a firm foundation in his field of interest, he should acquire a grasp of one or more foreign languages to the extent that they can be used as tools in research. Because so much scholarly work is written in other languages, a sound reading knowledge, even if it involves frequent recourse to a dictionary, is fundamental to thorough graduate training. (It is interesting to note in passing that while French and German are still the languages most commonly required, Russian is quite often listed as a substitute for one of them, usually for French. In many fields a good background in Latin can be extremely useful.)

Important as possession of the language tool may be, there is an even more essential academic prerequisite for graduate study, and that is what might be called the proper frame, or habit, of mind. This is characterized by a strong desire, and the accompanying ability, to work independently. One of the principal differences, in fact, between the usual graduate and the usual undergraduate approach to education is the degree of individual initiative required of the student. This is partly, of course, a matter of natural aptitude, as discussed in the preceding chapter, but it may in large measure be developed by appropriate stimuli in the undergraduate program.[3]

Fortunately the move toward greater independence is growing in our better colleges. The increase in the number of seminar courses, independent studies, and honors programs is one of the most encouraging trends in modern higher education. While formerly limited to the upper two years, experiments in independent work are now appearing in the first two years as well. A probable by-product of this tendency is that many more students may acquire an interest in

[2] Bruce V. Moore, "Educational Facilities and Financial Assistance for Graduate Students in Psychology: 1956–7," *American Psychologist*, XI (January 1956), 25.

[3] This is one of the objectives of the new program of undergraduate research awards sponsored by the National Science Foundation.

pursuing graduate study. In addition to the development of a certain habit of mind, properly directed individual projects help evolve skills in research techniques far beyond what is accomplished in the usual college term paper. This is of special importance since one of the major requirements for successful graduate study is a mastery of research techniques.

Nearly every college includes in its freshman orientation program or perhaps in its freshman composition course some minimal training in the use of the library. The prospective graduate student should build on this knowledge so that he becomes thoroughly conversant not only with the general reference works in the field of his special interest but with methods of exploration throughout the highways and byways of secondary materials. This specification is not limited to students in the humanities or social sciences. The vast storehouse of scientific articles is of incalculable value to the research worker in the natural sciences—a value quite equal to that of the test tube and laboratory; and the time for him to acquire a knowledge of, and respect for, the scientific collection in the college library is during his undergraduate years. Toward this end a number of departments have instituted seminars in bibliography and research as required courses for the prospective graduate student or, in many instances, for all majors.

Before passing on to the final point to be raised in this section, some reference should be made to yet another skill which has a bearing upon successful graduate study: the ability to use the typewriter. In many graduate schools and programs written work in longhand is not acceptable, and not infrequently a graduate assistantship may actually hinge upon the ability to type. Thus, while this may seem a lowly concern, at least some minimal mastery of "Mark Twain's folly" seems essential.

But the final, and in some ways most vital, ability which the prospective graduate student should develop by the time he completes college is the ability to use the English language with accuracy, precision, and effectiveness. As with typing, this advice seems almost too obvious to deserve serious mention here; yet unfortunately even many English majors arrive in graduate school with but an uneasy control of the language. Thus to the prospective graduate student, regardless of his field of interest, we might well extend the advice given earlier to "read, read, read" by adding with equal fervor: "Write, write, write!"

5. How to select a graduate school

The selection of a graduate school should be made only after careful investigation and protracted thought. Practical considerations should, and usually do, override any idealizations. For example, a high percentage of the graduate students surveyed in this study reported geographical accessibility and financial advantages as among the compelling reasons for their choice. Nevertheless, there are other important considerations, and it is the purpose of this section to review some of them.

Every graduate student would like to attend the "best" graduate school. But what does this really mean, and how can he be sure? There is no readily available rating of graduate schools or departments,[1] nor is there any organization which specifically accredits graduate schools. In 1933 an attempt was made by a committee of the American Council on Education to list graduate departments in order of merit;[2] and although the attempt was valiant and the methodology reasonably sound, the resultant furor was such as to discourage any further attempt from this source. President Emeritus R. M. Hughes of Iowa State College published privately in 1946 a somewhat less ambitious effort, with data valid through 1941–42. But both these ratings, regardless of their validity at the time, preceded the vast expansion and improvement of graduate instruction since World War II and are now completely out of date.

The absence of any accepted rating does not mean, however, that there is no reliable way of making a selection of graduate schools. As nearly every graduate student can attest, the advice of his undergraduate instructors can be of great assistance—provided that he compensate slightly for a natural tendency toward overenthusiasm! Many colleges provide special advisers—the dean of the college or sometimes a committee on graduate study. In some instances, well-organized programs are maintained, often led by the campus representative of the Woodrow Wilson National Fellowship program.[3]

Even in the absence of such a program, however, there are various sources to which the student can turn for information. The graduate school catalogue is obviously one of the most important. In many of the larger schools the graduate dean issues an annual report, copies of which are available upon request. Certain professional societies regularly publish in their bulletins information about academic requirements and facilties for financial aid. The annual reports

[1] The 1957 Keniston report is still classified as confidential.

[2] *Report of the Committee on Graduate Instruction* (Washington: American Council on Education, 1934). It is interesting to observe that not more than 45 percent of the departments in any subject field were rated as distinguished by the selected group of scholars whose opinions were solicited.

[3] See *The Woodrow Wilson National Fellowships: Past and Present* (Princeton, N. J.: Woodrow Wilson National Fellowship Foundation, n.d.).

of some of the larger foundations often contain information on special grants for graduate programs, by means of which some estimate can be made of the nature and quantity of the school's research activities. For the student who has the initiative to make an exhaustive study, a review of the *New York Times Index* can be rewarding; and as increasing attention is focused on graduate study a wide variety of books and articles is becoming available. Some of these, of recent issue, are included in the selected bibliography appearing on page 55 of this *Guide*.

The graduate schools have their criteria for selecting students. It is equally important for the student to establish his own criteria for selecting a school. High on any list of criteria is the general reputation of the college or university *Reputation* which provides graduate instruction. The fact that no formal rating or accreditation of graduate schools is available in no sense implies that they are all of equal repute. The tendency of the recipients of awards under national fellowship programs to select a certain limited group of graduate schools is presumptive evidence to the contrary, if evidence were needed.

But there are certain cautions to be observed in selection by reputation. In the first place, some of the more popular schools are also the larger schools, and for many students, particularly those from the smaller colleges, the very size may offer distinct disadvantages. Second, the fact that a university has a high reputation does not mean necessarily that each of its graduate departments is equally good. Many of the smaller graduate schools have developed unusually effective programs in particular fields of study. And finally the vagaries of academic life produce many changes, and the outstanding today may be the mediocre tomorrow.

More important by far than the general reputation of the institution at large is the reputation of its present faculty members, particularly those in the department in which the student is mainly interested. Here again, though we are dealing *Faculty* in intangibles, there are certain ways of arriving at an evaluation. For example, in judging a graduate school or department by its faculty—and there is no more important criterion—the prospective student can ascertain the faculty member's productivity from such sources as the president's or the dean's annual report or from listings in such reference works as *American Men of Science, Directory of American Scholars, Who's Who in America,* and the like. In this the reference librarian can be of assistance.

Implicit in the foregoing is the view that the member of a graduate faculty, to a far greater degree than the teacher in an undergraduate college, is to be judged on the quality of his productive research. Thus, it is important to trace his publications and the research projects with which he and his department are associated, as well as the special honors, elections, and awards he has received.

A graduate school is to be judged also by its alumni—the teachers, scholars, *Alumni* research workers, administrators whom it has helped to train. A brilliant student is presumptive evidence of a brilliant teacher, and this may well be applied to the school as a whole. Here, too, the prospective graduate student may find source materials that will help in forming his judgments. For example, as reported in the bibliography to the *Guide,* various professional journals publish annual reviews of research in progress and the University Microfilms in Ann Arbor, Michigan, report on the yearly harvest of doctoral dissertations.[4] The students would do well to review the catalogue of his own college and observe the graduate school origins of faculty degrees. Carrying this type of investigation to its logical conclusion, he would also survey the graduate school origins of various outstanding scholars in his field of interest. This might also include the authors of his favorite textbooks.

The would-be graduate student will want to know something about the students who will be his classmates and perhaps future colleagues. Though this type of information is relatively inaccessible, a study of catalogues, deans' reports, and rosters of fellowship recipients may shed some light. While no brief visit to a campus will enable him to obtain a definitive impression, the prospective graduate student might well attempt to catch the general spirit of the school by talking with some of its students on the scene.

This is the human side of the picture. But there is another side as well. This concerns what lies within the ivy-covered walls—the physical facilities for teaching and research. Thomas Carlyle once said that the true university is a collection of books, and while this is something of an exaggeration, it is an exaggeration of a fundamental truth. The graduate student, regardless of his specific area of concentration, must have a basic interest in the accumulation and preservation of human knowledge—hence his concern with the repository of the best that has been thought and said by the great minds of the past and present.

Judging a library is not to be done lightly. The total number of catalogued volumes is not in itself a definitive criterion. Of greater importance are the breadth and depth of the collection in the student's particular field of interest. Of importance, too, is the number of learned journals in his field and particularly the completeness of back issues. The accessibility of other major libraries is also important. Certain graduate schools and universities have arrangements with other institutions—as for example the "Farmington Plan"—to avoid unnecessary duplications. Arrangements may often be made with nearby public or private libraries for the graduate student to carry on his research using their facilities. Thus, a mere scanning of the card catalogue may result in an underestimate of the library resources available for intensive research.

Of equal importance to the graduate student is the accessibility of library materials. If he is denied ready access to the stacks, he will be at something of

---

[4] See also *Doctoral Dissertations Accepted by American Universities,* compiled for the Association of Research Libraries, Nos. 1–26 (New York: H. W. Wilson Co., 1934–59).

a disadvantage. If he cannot obtain his own cubicle or carrel, he may feel some frustration in the conduct of his work. A few of the more modern libraries provide soundproof areas where one can use the typewriter in taking notes and writing up data. Departments often maintain their own specialized libraries.

Obviously, the library is only one of the facilities of importance to the young scholar and scientist. Laboratories, museums, scientific equipment of all kinds, cooperative arrangements with affiliated educational or industrial institutions— all these are of extreme importance. And here, too, the total plant and equipment may be impressive, but the student should examine closely the facilities which relate to his own field of interest.

In Part II of the *Guide,* which is comprised of exhibits of the individual graduate schools, an attempt has been made to indicate some of the special facilities available in the various graduate schools. But this listing is suggestive, not definitive. The student should consult the institutional bulletins; he should also ask questions at the time he seeks admission, for, with the rapid expansion of university research facilities, even the latest bulletin is apt to be out of date.

It may be well to say here that many graduate schools are more than adequately equipped to serve students who are interested in pursuing work to the master's level but are deficient in resources for the additional work required for the doctorate. Although no rule-of-thumb guide can be offered to meet this situation, it is something which the student should consider.

This same caveat applies to the curriculum. The extent and variety of courses offered in the student's field of interest is obviously of great importance. But graduate schools as well as colleges are sometimes guilty of useless proliferation and consequent overlapping of subject matter. The number and diversity of courses is not nearly so important as the instructor who teaches them. Further, the prospective student would do well to ascertain from the catalogue the percentage of courses which are open exclusively to graduate students as against those which combine graduate and undergraduate instruction. While the common practice in combined courses is for the advanced student to do additional work, the level of instruction cannot help being affected by any marked disparity of preparation among the students in the class. As discussed later, however, the method of conducting the courses is what generally distinguishes the graduate school program from the undergraduate. The instructional methods and philosophies of the teachers in the department are more important than either the variety of courses or the presence of undergraduates.[5]

[5] The newer graduate schools tend to accept combined graduate and undergraduate enrollments as necessary or at least inevitable. The older schools, particularly in the East, frequently exclude undergraduates from all graduate courses. In those schools that have combined classes, the usual pattern is to offer three types of courses: (1) those for advanced undergraduates to which graduate students are admitted for credit; (2) those primarily for graduate students but open to a few highly selected undergraduates; and (3) those exclusively for graduate students—usually seminar courses or courses related to the preparation of the thesis. While there is no standardization here, it may be generally expected that, where combined courses are offered, such courses comprise from one-third to one-half of the graduate student's course work.

What has been said so far in this discussion of selecting a graduate school is admittedly idealistic. Each point is an important desideratum. But the unfortunate fact is that more often than not the graduate student makes his selection on a far less idealistic basis. In the "bidding for brains" which has become much too frequent in the graduate schools (as it has in the undergraduate colleges), the fellowship has become an almost irresistible bait. The student too often cannot bring himself to turn down an award several hundred dollars higher than that of the nearest bidder, even though the school might be less desirable for him. The cost of graduate study in addition to four years of college is one of the strongest deterrents to many an otherwise well-qualified and interested student. Thus, tuition fees and financial aid are of importance in the process of selection, though ideally they should never be decisive.

For the same reason another very common consideration in the selection of a graduate school is its location.[6] Nearness to home, nearness to an area where the student may find employment—or is now employed—are both important to the student of limited means. But there are other aspects in this matter of geographical location which deserve emphasis.

The graduate school in a large urban center has certain advantages not available in the small town. Cultural opportunities are generally greater, with museums, theaters, concerts, and the like in more abundance than would ever be possible in a smaller place. For the student whose background has been rural, or whose undergraduate experience has been on the small college campus, the contrast of attending graduate school in an urban area may have many advantages. Moreover, the city itself may provide a kind of laboratory in many fields of graduate interest. The student of sociology may find a wealth of material for a doctoral project on urban life, or the psychologist invaluable experience in a public hospital or health clinic.

But the urban university also has certain disadvantages. Its very size may make it an undesirable setting for students from more restricted areas. One of the graduate students replying to the survey for this manual asserted that a major reason for his choice of school was "the warm and friendly reception" he received when first visiting the campus. Although such an atmosphere is found at some urban universities, in general it is more characteristic of the small-town campus. The impersonality which often develops at the urban institution tends to increase the apprehension felt by many new graduate students and thus to make their adjustment more difficult. The faster tempo of city living, the higher costs, the frequently less desirable living conditions—these are among the drawbacks found at many of the larger universities located in urban communities.

---

[6] See E. V. Hollis, *Toward Improving Ph.D. Programs* (Washington: American Council on Education, 1945), p. 200. Hollis concluded that, as of 1940, "recruitment for most graduate schools is a state or regional undertaking." Statistics show that, in that year only, ten institutions belonging to the Association of American Universities recruited 50 percent or more of their graduate students from out of the state.

In this matter the prospective graduate student should judge, not only the school, but himself as well.

In the preceding paragraphs, the large city and the large institution have for simplicity been identified, but the identification is not necessarily applicable. Yet what has been said of the relative merits of the large city versus the small applies in general to the large university versus the small. The best advice is for the student to weigh his own characteristics and interests alongside the general characteristics of the institutions he is considering.

Rather than generalize, moreover, he should investigate carefully the character of the campus and the living conditions of the area. Although the situation is fast changing, at many institutions where the undergraduate lives in the most luxurious of dormitories the graduate student must fend for himself, sometimes having to be content with substandard accommodations. Aside from any discomfort, one of the greatest disadvantages of this situation is lack of contact with one's fellow students. To put this positively, one of the great advantages of a graduate school dormitory or center is the opportunity to exchange ideas with fellow students, both in the same and in other fields of interest. This type of cross-fertilization is a useful counteragent to the high degree of specialization characterizing most graduate programs. Here, too, lies one of the advantages of the large over the small institution.

There are many other reasons for the selection of a graduate school—some good, some bad. One male graduate student indicated that he made his choice, in part at least, because of the number of good women's colleges in the vicinity! Another was influenced by the denominational affiliation of the institution. Another had found such satisfaction in his undergraduate experience that he "stayed put" for his graduate study. Still another was influenced by the university's "great tradition of academic freedom and expression."

But there remain two important considerations to be briefly discussed. The first of these is the availability of opportunities to obtain practical experience during graduate study. Before the current shortage of college teachers, many a young Ph.D. found that he was unable to obtain a position because he had had no teaching experience—a nearly perfect example of the classic dilemma. To obviate this, as well as to improve the quality of college teaching, an increasing number of graduate schools are now instituting programs of controlled teaching assistantships. Laboratory and field experience, of course, have a direct transfer value for postdoctoral employment. It should be noted, however, that such work experience tends to protract the period required for the degree—a distinct disadvantage in view of the fact that the average time now spent in attaining the doctorate is six years (though not necessarily continuous years of full-time study).

Finally, a most important consideration in selecting a graduate school is its practices and effectiveness in the placement of its graduates. As one college dean has expressed it, "The graduate student is usually not seeking an education! He is getting ready for a job by putting in the work for an advanced degree. In all fairness, he should know what school is most likely to further these ends."

There is not, of course, any common source where this information is available. The prospective student is certainly within his rights in asking what type of placement service is maintained by the institution and in expecting at least a minimal program. Regardless of his vocational objectives, he can anticipate needing some more or less permanent dossier on file, preferably in the graduate school placement office. Moreover, employers tend, in their search for professional help, to resort more readily to the type of school which maintains efficient and complete employment files. Thus, even though the student may not be able to obtain very specific information on the success of the graduates of a particular school in obtaining employment, he can form some judgment from examining the institution's placement services.

Throughout this discussion of selecting a graduate school, the idea has been implicit that selection is important. It is—but not quite so important as it may sometimes seem. The fact is that with relatively few exceptions most American graduate schools do a competent job. The student who is capable can receive training of as high a quality as he is willing to work for. The individual nature of graduate study makes this particularly true. In general—and especially after the first job—the prospective employer is more interested in whether or not the man has an advanced degree than in the institution from which it was received. Thus, the intending graduate student should choose with care, but if he fails to gain admission to the school of his first or even second choice, he should not be discouraged. The ultimate satisfaction he derives from his career and the contribution he makes to society will be just as great if he has to be content with the school of his third or fourth choice.

6. How to gain admission to graduate school

Within a rather broad range it is safe to say that graduate schools are generous and flexible in their standards of admission. This is not intended to imply an absence of specific requirements. A glance at the admission criteria of two or three of the schools described in the second part of this manual will quickly dispel any such impression. A majority of graduate schools of arts and sciences, are, in fact, highly selective in their admission process, and as applications continue to increase this selectivity will very likely become even more refined.[1]

Before discussing specific criteria of admission, one should draw a distinction, with particular reference to the Ph.D. degree, between admission to the school and admission to candidacy for the degree. In many institutions these represent two entirely different stages. Admission to graduate courses may be relatively easy, even to a program leading to the master's degree; whereas formal candidacy for the doctorate may require the passing of special qualifying examinations, the completion of language requirements, and evidence of a satisfactory level of competence in course work in the field of concentration. Furthermore, there is evidence that departments providing programs leading to the doctorate tend to be more exacting in the process of admission than those offering only the master's degree.[2] Again, in some schools the master's degree is reserved for matriculants who are to be discouraged, or prohibited, from continuing for the doctorate. In this situation admission requirements may be relatively light.

The usual requirements for admission to graduate school are "the bachelor's degree from a recognized college, university, or technical school; an undergraduate record showing competence, if not excellence; other evidence of promise of success as a graduate student; an undergraduate program which serves as a sound general basis for advanced study, including an adequate major."[3]

A review of graduate school catalogues shows that it is sometimes possible to be admitted even without the bachelor's degree. At Johns Hopkins, for example, it is possible for the student to begin work on an advanced degree after only two years of college study.[4] Nevertheless, the bachelor's degree is usually prerequisite for admission to graduate study.

A number of the college students questioned in the preparation of this man-

---

[1] The writer knows of no statistical data that show the percentage of students accepted out of the total number of applicants.

[2] See Marcia Edwards, *Studies in American Graduate Education* (New York: Carnegie Foundation for the Advancement of Teaching, 1944), p. 24.

[3] Walton C. John, *Graduate Study in the Universities and Colleges in the United States*, Office of Education Bulletin 1934, No. 20 (Washington: Government Printing Office, 1935), p. 99.

[4] Most other graduate schools which admit undergraduates from the same institution into graduate courses do not consider them matriculants for advanced degrees.

ual asked about the importance of the particular undergraduate school in gaining admission to graduate study. Perhaps the best answer to this question is to look into history. There was a time, not long ago, when many of the leading graduate schools gave preference to graduates of colleges accredited by the Association of American Universities. Under a grant from the Carnegie Foundation for the Advancement of Teaching, a study was made of the graduate school records of students from the accredited, as against those from the unaccredited, colleges. The results indicated a difference so slight as to fail to justify continuance of the AAU listing.[5]

It is true that a number of universities tend, on the basis of experience, to favor certain undergraduate schools over others. This does not mean that others are not acceptable but only that the records of applicants from the less preferred schools may be more carefully scrutinized. Some colleges do seem to have outstanding success in the number of their graduates who continue for the doctorate, but there is no conclusive evidence that their alumni enjoy preferential treatment either in admission or in the awarding of scholarship or fellowship benefits.[6]

A study of current graduate school catalogues shows that the usual minimum college average expected of the applicant for admission is a B. This is not necessarily a cumulative average for all undergraduate courses. Frequently, it is the average for the work of the junior and senior year or for work in the field of concentration. Some of the schools specify the number of A's, B's, or C's; some reveal different standards in different departments; some, different standards for in-state, as against out-of-state, students. Some are concerned with class standing—upper half, upper quarter, and the like—rather than any set numerical or letter grade or average; others do not spell out any specific requirement but make a statement such as the following: "previous work must be of sufficiently high calibre to meet the minimum requirement, namely a record of marked distinction." Many schools are willing to grant provisional admission to the student below the minimum required average, if in other ways he indicates promise of success in graduate study.

The general assumption is that if the student receives few A's or B's as an undergraduate, he will make few or none in graduate school. This does not mean that an A undergraduate record is required. Such a record might indicate only an unusually facile memory or "excessive intellectual docility." At Rad-

[5] Edwards, op. cit., p. 23. This study also cast doubt on the popular assumption that private universities were more selective than public in their graduate admission programs.

[6] The reader may be interested in looking at the following studies compiled by the Office of Scientific Personnel under the direction of M. H. Trytten: The Baccalaureate Origins of the Science Doctorates Awarded in the United States from 1936 to 1950 Inclusive, Bulletin No. 382 (Washington: National Academy of Sciences—National Research Council, 1955), and Baccalaureate Origins of Doctorates in the Arts, Humanities, and Social Sciences Awarded in the United States: 1936–1950, Bulletin No. 460 (Washington: National Academy of Sciences—National Research Council, 1956). Cf. Robert H. Knapp and Joseph J. Greenbaum, The Younger American Scholar: His Collegiate Origins (Chicago, Ill.: University of Chicago Press, 1953).

cliffe College, for example, the "straight A" applicants are checked carefully for evidence of emotional stability in order to find answers to such questions as: Can they accept a lower grade—their first—without going to pieces? Can they adjust to the fact that competition is keener in graduate school and that not everybody can achieve A's?[7]

In addition to this quality requirement, a great majority of graduate schools or departments expect the applicant to have completed a major in the field, or at least to have taken successfully a specified group of courses in the area of his graduate interest. It is important to note that the student need not necessarily have formally completed a major as such, so long as he demonstrates sufficient competence in the minimum hours or the courses prescribed in the field.

At the risk of repetition, a few additional comments are relevant here on the subject of foreign languages, for a study of the catalogues suggests that language requirements can be rather confusing. In some graduate schools or departments the language requirements must be satisfied by examination on admission. If scores are unsatisfactory, the student may be admitted; but he may suffer the loss of graduate credit if he does not meet the language requirement by a specified date. In some schools the tests are little more than a formality; in others, they are very searching and represent a major hurdle. They usually include, or are composed exclusively of, sight translations, often of passages taken from books or articles in the student's field of interest. In a few instances he may be permitted the aid of a foreign language dictionary. In general the languages required are French and/or German. Recent trends show Russian widely accepted as a second required language, usually as an alternative to French. Other languages, classical or modern, are prescribed in many programs. Some graduate schools, however, permit as an alternative achievement the substitution for the second language of (1) a more thorough knowledge of one language; (2) a series of courses which, in effect, represent a third minor; or (3) some other skill, such as a competence in the use of a mathematical tool or a system of measurements.

Another variable factor in the selection process is the use of letters of reference. While practice varies in the number of letters required, many schools ask for two or three. Here the best advice is for the undergraduate to earn the respect of his senior undergraduate professors, including his departmental chairman, for this man or woman in particular can be of immeasurable help to him in gaining admission to graduate school.

Finally, a number of graduate schools or departments require some form of qualifying examination in the admission process. Since such requirements vary from one school to another, and from one department to another, the student will have to determine for himself the practices of those in which he has an

[7] Committee on Graduate Education for Women, Radcliffe College, *Graduate Education for Women: The Radcliffe Ph.D.* (Cambridge, Mass.: Harvard University Press, 1956), p. 81.

interest. The information in Part II of this manual can be of help. It gives an indication of what examinations are required, although it does not include the dates when scores must be submitted. This information will have to be obtained directly from the school concerned. Some graduate schools ask the applicant to take tests devised and administered by the school itself. If he cannot conveniently come to the campus, he can often make arrangements to take the test at another center, frequently at his own college.

More and more graduate schools are requiring applicants for admission to take certain examinations which have been developed for this purpose by testing agencies operating on a nation-wide basis. Since two such examinations have come to be the most widely used, it may be well to discuss both of them briefly.

One, the Miller Analogies Test (MAT), has been described as a high-level test of scholastic aptitude appropriate for advanced students. It is a fifty-minute test of information and reasoning ability based on verbal analogies. It yields a measure of verbal ability, which has been found to be one of the most important factors contributing to success in graduate study. The MAT, published and controlled by the Psychological Corporation, is available under carefully controlled conditions in testing centers in certain colleges and universities throughout the country. The student who is required to take the MAT by the graduate school to which he is applying may take it at any of these centers and have his score sent to the school (or schools) which he designates. A number of studies have shown that scores on the MAT are positively related to success in graduate study in a variety of fields.

The Graduate Record Examinations (GRE) are offered in the National Program for Graduate School Selection in testing centers throughout the United States and certain foreign countries four times each year—usually in November, January, April, and July. Candidates register in advance with the Educational Testing Service (Princeton, New Jersey, or Los Angeles, California) to take the test at the most convenient center.[8]

Since the GRE offers both an aptitude test and a series of advanced tests, candidates must ascertain from the school of their choice which they should take. The former is a two and one-half hour test of scholastic ability which yields two scores: verbal ability and quantitative (or mathematical) ability. Each of the advanced tests is a three-hour achievement test designed to measure the applicant's comprehension of the materials basic to success in the field of his intended graduate major. A candidate may take any one of the following sixteen advanced tests: biology, chemistry, economics, education, engineering, French, geology, government, history, literature, mathematics, philosophy, physics, psychology, sociology, and Spanish. The GRE are also used by certain

---

[8] In the case of the MAT, the fee is paid directly to the center administering the test, whereas the fee for the GRE must accompany the application.

national and regional agencies in evaluating the qualifications of applicants for graduate fellowships.[9]

One use of the qualifying examinations which deserves special notice is their prescription in cases of doubtful qualifications or provisional admission. Frequently, the recommendation form which the graduate schools request the undergraduate deans or chairmen to fill out asks whether the candidate is recommended with or without a specific qualifying examination. If the candidate gives evidence of not having performed up to his capacity in his undergraduate work, the recommendation usually calls for the examination. Or again, in many graduate schools, if the applicant has not quite achieved the minimum required average or has not completed some of the recommended or required courses, the qualifying examination is specifically requested.[10] At the present time the tests are used more frequently by individual departments than by graduate schools as a whole.

It is important to point out that there is no such thing as a "passing" grade in the qualifying tests, whether the GRE or the MAT. From a survey of graduate school practice, however, it appears that a score below 400 on the GRE Aptitude Test generally results in the student's being discouraged either from admission or from continuing with graduate study. The score on an advanced test must usually be much higher. For example, "one school indicated that a score below 600 in Physics did not warrant financial support, below 500 made admission questionable."[11]

No test has as yet been devised to measure all the multiplicity of qualities with which the graduate schools are concerned. Many institutions "qualify their use of these measures as not the primary criteria but as helpful supplementary information when in doubt on the basis of other criteria."[12]

For the most part, this discussion of admission procedures has been limited to the student who is applying directly from his undergraduate college. A considerable number of students, however, attend one institution for their master's degree and transfer to another for the doctorate—a procedure which has disadvantages as well as advantages. It certainly calls for caution on the part of the student; for, as is evident from information contained in the second part of this manual, a wide variety of practices is followed with students who transfer. Many schools place a strict limitation upon the number of transfer credits they will accept. For the master's degree, it is customary to recognize not more

[9] The material for this discussion was supplied by Dr. Gerald V. Lannholm of the Educational Testing Service.
[10] It is worth noting that these examinations are used by the graduate schools for other purposes as well. For example, the Area Tests of the GRE are at times employed to determine candidacy for the Ph.D. Similarly, these and other tests are frequently utilized for purposes of evaluation and guidance and of establishing admission standards. See Philip R. Harvey, *The Use of the Graduate Record Examinations by Colleges and Universities* (Princeton, N. J.: Educational Testing Service, 1957), p. 21.
[11] *Ibid.*, p. 29.
[12] Bruce V. Moore, "Educational Facilities and Financial Assistance for Graduate Students in Psychology: 1956–7," *American Psychologist*, XI (January 1956), 25.

than six or eight credits; for the doctorate, not more than two years of work done elsewhere. Some institutions will grant no transfer credit if the student cannot satisfy his foreign language requirements at the time of transfer. Because of the diversity of practice, no general advice can be given except for the student to make a careful investigation of requirements before seeking to transfer to another institution.

It is appropriate, in closing this section on admission, to make a few observations on how, where, and when to make application.

Although many schools do not designate a specific deadline for application, one of the greatest mistakes the prospective graduate student can make is to apply too late. Thus, it is highly advisable for the applicant to begin his inquiries in the early fall of his senior year. A few schools specify a period in which the application blank must be requested as well as the final date for its receipt.

It is also important to note that the time for application for admission does not necessarily coincide with the date of application for financial assistance. Ordinarily, the student is not eligible to apply for aid until he has at least initiated the admission process. A large number of graduate schools have agreed on a common date, April 1, for announcing financial awards. No such common date exists, however, for informing successful candidates of their acceptance.

The student may well inquire whether multiple applications are desirable. At the risk of adding to the labor of the admission committees, the best advice seems to call for his making application to three or four different schools, even at the added expense of several application fees. Preferably these should be in what might be considered different categories—perhaps two highly selective schools, one or two less highly selective.

Because of the differing organizational patterns in graduate schools, no uniformity exists as to which office the applicant for admission should address his request. In the larger universities, the application must usually be made either to the graduate school dean or the department head, and the same is true of applications for assistance. For this latter purpose a distinction is sometimes made in the type of assistance; for example, applications for fellowships will go directly to the dean, whereas applications for assistantships will go to the chairman of the department. In the smaller universities, the practice is generally for the application for admission to be made to the graduate school or the admissions office. Individual practices are detailed in the separate entries in Part II of this *Guide*.

7. How to finance graduate study

Perhaps no section of this vade mecum to graduate study is subject to more constant change or in need of more frequent revision than that dealing with the student's financial planning. For this reason a companion volume dealing with financial assistance is published separately as an annual publication under the title *Fellowships in the Arts and Sciences*. Originally conceived by Virginia Bosch Potter, and now edited by Michael E. Schiltz at Loyola University, this useful annual directory bears the same relationship to these introductory essays as do the institutional exhibits which constitute Part II of the *Guide*. The student is urged, therefore, not just to read the following general discussion of financial planning but to study the more detailed information which appears in the directory of fellowships, now in its fourth edition.[1]

Financing graduate study

Experience indicates that one of the obstacles which looms largest in the mind of the undergraduate contemplating graduate study is how he can secure the requisite funds. In many instances the resources which he himself may have acquired for his education have been depleted by his undergraduate preparation. Even where this has not occurred, it is not at all unusual for a young man or woman to begin seriously to question whether he can any longer expect his parents to contribute to his further education, particularly if they do so at some personal sacrifice. As he sees his fellow students accepting positions which will mean financial independence, he cannot but feel a desire for a similar status.

While a majority of undergraduate scholarship awards are based primarily on financial need, a quick survey of governmental and institutional programs for assistance of graduate students suggests that graduate fellowships in general do not recognize financial need as the prime desideratum. In saying this, of course, there is always the danger of overemphasis. Considering the limited resources for higher education at all levels, no one can in good conscience accept an undue share of support. The fact stands, nevertheless, that graduate awards are based primarily on academic accomplishment and scholarly promise.

Another generalization which can be made on the subject of financing graduate study is that, with the right amount of persistence and planning, virtually

---

[1] Washington: Association of American Colleges, published annually. (Distributed by American Council on Education.)

no worthy student need be denied attendance at a graduate school on economic grounds. This is not to say that he will be able to write his own ticket, either as regards the school of his choice or of the type of support; but the resources, and thus the opportunities, for financial assistance have increased tremendously in recent years.

The time was when the first-year graduate student had relatively little available to him in financial support beyond his own resources. This has now changed. Such programs as the Woodrow Wilson National Fellowships and the fellowship provisions of the National Defense Education Act, for example, are especially designed to get the student started in his graduate work. The directory of *Fellowships in the Arts and Sciences* lists some thirty to forty programs, many of them available to the first-year student.

Moreover, as can be seen in the institutional entries in this *Guide,* nearly every graduate school now has some form of aid for which the first-year student is eligible to apply. (These data are, of course, for 1960–61.) Since the annual directory of *Fellowships in the Arts and Sciences* lists only awards made by outside agencies, a student would do well to refer to the periodic surveys of university-controlled or inside fellowships and assistantships published by the U.S. Office of Education under the title *Scholarships and Fellowships Available at Institutions of Higher Education.* In addition, there is an almost unending stream of announcements of fellowships and assistantships flowing from the graduate schools to undergraduate deans and departmental chairmen for the information of the prospective graduate student. Information about assistance for foreign study is to be found in various annual publications of the Institute of International Education and of Unesco.

Types of financial assistance

Although the term "scholarship" is sometimes applied to graduate financial assistance, it has come to be reserved more generally for undergraduate grants. The outright award to a graduate student is more commonly called a fellowship, an award which ranges in amounts from one or two hundred dollars to several thousand. Unless otherwise defined, the fellowship involves no work or services, no *quid pro quo.* As such it is tax free. On the other hand, if it is a "teaching" or "research" fellowship, the recipient can expect that it will have to be reported for income tax purposes.

Another distinction in the fellowship is its source. The fellowship may be derived from the institution's own endowment or current income. Or again, it may be sponsored or controlled by a private foundation, industrial organization, or governmental agency. A comparison of the first and fourth editions of *Fellowships in the Arts and Sciences* will show the interested student both the degree of change and the degree of expansion in these outside awards. Here he will also be able to obtain information concerning the purpose of the awards, the fields in which they are available, qualifications, amount of stipends, addresses, time schedules, and so forth.

The fellowship is by no means the only form of assistance available to the graduate student. In order to provide for their advanced students, as well as to meet some of their own needs in teaching and research, most graduate schools have made available a wide variety of assistantships. These positions may range from that of dormitory proctoring or reading freshman themes to classroom teaching or participation in a complex research project. While they are not infrequently reserved for the more advanced graduate student, they are increasingly available to the first-year student as well. In addition to their financial benefits, these positions frequently provide experience of real value to the student when he comes to seek his first full-time position.

A word of caution is relevant here, however. The amount of time involved in a teaching or research assistantship, although frequently limited by university regulation, cannot but represent a distraction which may well protract the period necessary for achievement of the degree. Thus it might be short-sighted for an individual to add a year or two of graduate study on a subsistence level when he might, by taking advantage of a loan, be available for full-time productive employment that much sooner.

The third major source of financial assistance, then, is the loan, supported either from funds controlled by the institution itself or from private or governmental sources. A relative newcomer in the family of graduate aids, the loan is being increasingly viewed as a desirable means of expanding opportunities for advanced education. Still another reason for the interest in educational loans has been a growing recognition on the part of many educators that broad programs of scholarships and fellowships concentrated in limited areas have seemed to cause certain students in those fields to assume that their training was the responsibility of others. In many cases, the donors of the funds admittedly added to the confusion by competing for good students in much the same way that a manager of a ball club does for a good rookie player. Thus, the rapid acceptance of loans on the undergraduate level is now beginning to find its counterpart in the graduate school. Here, too, the directory of *Fellowships in the Arts and Sciences* provides a good source of information for non-institutional sources of loan funds.

The prospective graduate student should not, of course, limit his thinking to any one of these types of assistance. Rather, he should look to combinations in working out his financial program. The important thing, as recognized more and more by undergraduate as well as graduate advisers, is for him to plan his study in terms of the total program. He may even, as in the almost unique program at Tulane University, be encouraged to think of his undergraduate and graduate years as a financial continuum.

To look at this total planning in more detail, there is almost universal agreement that the first year of graduate study is the best time to have some sort of outright financial support, with no duties in connection with it. This, of course, is the simple fellowship award. Failing to obtain such an award, the first-year student might be well advised to borrow money from one of the growing number of state loan funds or from institutional or commercial sources.

If the results of the first year are successful, the student is now in a position to apply for some form of research or teaching assistantship which may well provide income for the remainder of his period of professional training. The two principal kinds of assistantships, research and teaching, are at once different and the same. What they have in common is the fact that they give a semi-faculty status which is designed to provide regular members of the faculty with assistance from among the better graduate students.

Perhaps the most crucial period in the financing of graduate study is the dissertation year. Too often the student, after completing his formal course work and perhaps exhausting his own financial resources, leaves the graduate school for full-time employment in the thought that he will be able to carry on the research and writing of his doctoral dissertation in his free moments. He then discovers that these free moments are nonexistent. Further, if his dissertation is to represent a truly significant piece of scholarly work, it deserves his undivided attention. For these reasons, foundation officers and graduate school deans are seeking ways of providing assistance to enable more graduate students to devote full time to research at this important stage.

Thus, the student with financial need should plan at the outset not only his first graduate year but his graduate program in its totality.

How to apply

At the risk of stressing the obvious, it should be said that the prerequisite for a successful application for financial assistance is a careful reading of the application forms and of the rules and descriptions of awards which come with them. This, coupled with a scrupulous effort to provide the information requested and to interpret one's background and career intentions in terms of what the award requires, should produce the desired results, provided the candidate's qualifications place him in the upper ranks of those applying.

Perhaps the most serious error which the applicant can make is to overlook the application deadline. A review of various institutional and external fellowship programs indicates that these deadlines are scattered throughout the first semester of an academic year (with a few extending into the spring) for awards which begin in the following September. Obviously, the best advice is to begin early to prepare the application and to ensure that it is filed well in advance of the terminal date.

Although it is not wise to make a number of indiscriminate applications, it would seem equally inadvisable to pin all hopes on one or two. Thus, the prospective graduate student should study carefully the various resources for which he would qualify and apply accordingly.

Almost without exception, applications for graduate assistance must be accompanied by such supporting papers as transcripts and letters of recommendation from the faculty. Since these latter represent a substantial amount of labor on the part of the faculty member, the student should make every effort to ensure that they be held down to a minimum.

It may come as a surprise to some applicants to discover that many application forms are eliminated before the selection process begins because the supporting papers have not arrived to accompany the form. Since the granting agencies seldom check with the college for a missing transcript, the applicant should do whatever is necessary to make certain that his records have actually been sent and that the recommendations have been written in time to meet the deadline.

One of the suggestions under consideration currently is the possibility of some sort of central clearing point for such things as references and transcript forms which could be duplicated and provided to any donor agency. The relief which this could provide the overworked professor is a strong argument for such a development.

Many of the application forms, particularly for foundation awards, call for some statement of purpose or philosophy from the candidate. It need hardly be said that this request should be considered with great care. A perfunctory or poorly written reply deserves the negative response which it will probably receive.

It is difficult to generalize on the date at which the applicant for governmental or foundation awards will know the outcome of his request. There is, however, a tendency for these awards to be made in advance of those granted from the graduate school's own resources. As for these latter, the date of April 1 has been adopted by many universities as the day when the student may expect to learn the fate of his application.

Who should apply

It has already been stated that, while financial need is important, it is not necessarily the primary consideration in the award of assistance to graduate students. Of far greater importance, particularly in view of the competitive nature of graduate awards, is the individual's promise for useful service in the particular field of his interest. This raises another point, however, which deserves at least brief mention—the relative availability of assistance by field and by sex.

A recent survey conducted by the National Science Foundation indicated that there were 47,000 recipients of fellowships or other support in the year 1954. Among the total number of students included in the survey were some 46,000 science and engineering students, nearly half of whom received help. On the other hand, of the 54,500 students in humanities and social sciences, only 25 percent were recipients of financial assistance. Nor does this tell the whole of the story. In that same year the Federal Government spent more than $440 million on research contracts in colleges and universities. Of this sum, 95 percent was devoted to scientific research, which means that substantial sums were available for salaries for graduate assistants in the scientific fields. The amount in the humanities and social sciences was negligible.

It is presumably for these reasons that the largest nongovernment fellowship program—that conducted by the Woodrow Wilson National Fellowship Foundation—has been placing heavy emphasis in its awards on the humanities and social sciences as has the program of the National Defense Education Act. Thus the imbalance is recognized, and an effort is being made to bring about some adjustments. But there is little doubt that in the foreseeable future the sciences will continue to enjoy a lion's share of the facilities for financial aid.

There is also an evident disparity in the ratio of awards to men and women. Although there is no policy of discrimination against women in the granting of financial assistance for completing the doctorate, Dr. Maul in the 1959 edition of *Teacher Supply and Demand* . . . notes that "in actual practice, a male candidate almost always happens to have the most meritorous over-all qualifications."[2] In view of the need to induce more women to enter and complete graduate study, the present situation calls for careful review.

[2] Research Division, National Education Association, *Teacher Supply and Demand in Universities, Colleges, and Junior Colleges, 1957–58 and 1958–59* (Washington: The Association, June 1959), p. 25.

8. What to expect in graduate school

Uncertainty seems to be the greatest problem for the new graduate student. Anxiety, often purely from imaginary sources, plagues him about courses, grades, requirements, the difficulty of the oral examination, the bugaboo of the thesis, and so forth. Other graduate students are not necessarily reliable sources of information. Members of the department are often vague and casual concerning precise problems which worry him. Precision in departmental orientation and the assignment of capable advisers who can and will take the time to help the new student are, perhaps, the best palliatives.

This observation by a graduate student seems a fitting prelude to this final chapter of "Graduate Study and the Undergraduate." Although the previous chapters have considered various aspects of graduate study, from purpose and preparation to admission and financing, they have made little or no effort to describe what the student can expect to experience when he launches upon the arduous, but rewarding, journey toward the doctorate.

Transition from college to graduate school

The transition from college to graduate school is not always easy. The general opinion seems to be that it is easiest if the student enters graduate training immediately upon completion of his baccalaureate. By so doing he presumably brings unabated the skills and knowledge acquired as an undergraduate. A long interruption may require him to re-form successful study habits, to say nothing of renewing his grasp of the fundamentals of his field—this at a time when he should be making the best possible impression upon the professors who will play a vital role in his future. On the other hand, if the period of absence from academic work involves the gaining of practical experience in the area of his interest, this may be of decided benefit in the enrichment of his graduate study.

The student who is entering graduate work at the same institution where he received his undergraduate degree may find the transition relatively painless. A study of graduate-school catalogues shows that many of them offer combined graduate and upper-level undergraduate courses in some, if not all, of the departments. Thus, he may already have completed some of the courses prescribed in the graduate curriculum. Even if he has not, he will undoubtedly have made acquaintance with a substantial number of the professors in his department. For him the transition—at least academically—would be a mere formality.

45

The student who is entering graduate school at an unfamiliar university could help ease the transition by spending a few days on the campus before the close of his undergraduate program. Among other things for him to do on any such visit is to obtain a clear understanding of what will be required of him academically. If he discovers deficiencies in required courses or in languages, he can profitably spend the intervening summer months in an effort to compensate for these arrears.[1] He can also look into housing facilities and perhaps secure accommodations in advance so that he will not have this worry at the time of registration.

Graduate study is, in a sense, the extension of undergraduate work in the direction of specialization and research. The first few days of the graduate student's life, accordingly, have many things in common with the period four years earlier when as a freshman he underwent that first major change in his academic experience. The transition to graduate school is usually not nearly so great as that from secondary school to college. Many familiar procedures recur. The student will be required to register, to fill out a bewildering variety of forms, and, of course, to pay his fees or at least make arrangements for their payment. If he has not already submitted scores on a qualifying examination, he may be asked to take some local or national aptitude or achievement tests for guidance purposes.[2]

After a relatively brief time, however, he will begin to perceive that the differences are far more significant than the similarities. One of the things he will discover at the outset is that, while American colleges and universities are usually conscientious in providing adequate accommodations for their undergraduates, especially freshmen, a majority of them do relatively little for the graduate student. The situation is improving; but still a large percentage of graduate students must make their own arrangements for rooms, meals, laundry, and other personal services.

Social life in graduate school

Another contrast which the student will quickly discover is that he has left behind the expansive social life he enjoyed as an undergraduate. Even if he remains at the institution of his baccalaureate years and continues to eat at his social fraternity house, he will find that he has little in common with his brothers. His graduate study will leave him scant time for leisure, and his interests will become so highly specialized that he will tend to seek the company of others with the same concerns.

This is not to say that graduate school provides no opportunity for social life.

[1] One graduate student, probably speaking from experience, strongly advised straightening out all such difficulties in advance. They become considerably more complicated, he said, after admission.
[2] At some graduate schools these tests are given later in the first semester.

At Cornell University, to take one example, there are some twenty-five graduate clubs which include social events in their programs, but for the most part these clubs are organized along departmental lines and are devoted to the advancement of their members' professional interests. Tulane University sponsors more than one hundred extracurricular activities and organizations for the graduate student, administering them under the direction of a dean of students. The University of Virginia provides a Graduate Students' Center, and at Yale University it has been the practice for many years to hold regular departmental teas, cocktail parties, and picnics, supplemented by occasional afternoon teas in the graduate lounges. Harvard maintains a Graduate Student Council to organize a recreational program and even boasts of a Society of Harvard Dames for wives of graduate students. But though these examples could be multiplied, the important fact is that the new graduate student who has just emerged from the extracurricular whirl of the typical undergraduate campus will find his social activities in graduate school almost ascetic by comparison. What is lacking in breadth, however, is compensated for in depth. He will find that his contacts with professors and fellow students will be characterized by an intellectual excitement and verve lacking in all but a precious few of his undergraduate experiences.

Counseling and guidance

Another striking contrast is the freedom which the student enjoys in the pursuit of his own academic interests. Whereas a majority of undergraduate colleges maintain fairly extensive counseling facilities, the graduate student will find a minimum of guidance. In one of the larger Eastern universities, for example, it is reliably reported that to see certain of the faculty members, a student must make an appointment a month or two in advance. In 1943 Walter A. Jessup, then president of the Carnegie Foundation for the Advancement of Teaching, wrote: "Despite all our talk of the comradeship of scholars, our graduate students in general encounter far greater difficulty in achieving and maintaining fruitful personal relations with the staff than students in medicine or law."[3] This rather serious indictment calls for some additional comments.

Graduate schools have traditionally avoided excessive paternalism. The student is presumed to have ability, initiative, and maturity. He should not need the amount of guidance that he needed as an undergraduate. If he does—and this is not necessarily to his discredit—he should consider the desirability of attending one of the smaller graduate schools where more individual attention is often available. Certain deans, particularly of graduate schools in the larger metropolitan areas, however, are coming to realize that more guidance may be

[3] In the Introduction to Marcia Edwards, *Studies in American Graduate Education* (New York: Carnegie Foundation for the Advancement of Teaching, 1944), p. xii.

desirable. Columbia University, for example, has established the office of graduate student adviser and published a *Graduate Student Guide* to assist in the
orientation of the incoming student. An increasing number of graduate schools
provide some form of service for psychological and vocational counseling, even
though this service is usually university-wide rather than exclusively planned
for the graduate school or schools. A rather common pattern is for the department to have a graduate adviser who represents the graduate school in every
academic aspect of advising the student on his program; alternatively, in some
institutions the student is placed at the time of registration under the direction
of a committee to arrange his program of studies, conduct his examinations,
and so forth. In many schools this adviser or committee does not come into
operation until the student enters on the doctoral project, and then the adviser
may well be a faculty member of the student's own choosing. A few institutions
hold periodic meetings in the departments among graduate students and faculty
for discussion of topics connected with special fields of interest.

There is, in short, evidence to support the view that, while the guidance of
graduate students will probably never equal that of undergraduates in the better
colleges, the traditional laissez faire concept is being somewhat modified. But
the observation of Friedenberg and Roth is still valid: "The business of the
graduate faculty member is research. . . . Student-teacher relationships tend to
be more formal and less supportive . . . ; [the teachers] are most effective with
those students who need less to be nurtured."[4]

Residence, attendance, and grades

Before we look in detail at the curricular requirements for the doctorate,
there are several subjects which deserve at least brief attention: residence requirements, class attendance, and grading systems.

The minimum time the graduate student must spend in completing the requirements for the master's degree is one year, or in some instances two years.
For the doctorate it is usually three years beyond the baccalaureate. The student who completes his Ph.D. degree in the minimum period, however, is the
exception rather than the rule. The average time is said to be six years, though
this may not necessarily be a period of uninterrupted study. Many students take
a break in their work after completing the formal course requirements and
before undertaking the dissertation. Frequently this is for financial reasons or
through a desire to gain practical experience in the field before the completion
of formal training. Although relatively few graduate schools have announced
a maximum limit on the time allowed for completing the degree, there is a

[4] Edgar Z. Friedenberg and Julius A. Roth, *Self-Perception in the University* (Chicago, Ill.:
University of Chicago Press, 1954), p. 3.

marked trend now to set a terminal date, usually eight to ten years after the inception of graduate study. Too great an interruption in graduate study or too long a delay in submitting the dissertation may result in the invalidation of all previous credit for course work.[5]

A few other observations on residence requirements: a substantial number of graduate schools offer courses in the evenings and in summer sessions. Although a master's degree may be obtained through such part-time study, the doctorate ordinarily requires at least some period of full-time residence in a regular term or year. It does not, however, necessarily require residence for the period when the student is preparing his dissertation. Some schools specify merely that he maintain matriculation for the degree by the payment of a minimal fee; others require the fee only for the year in which the candidate expects to receive the degree.

In the matter of class attendance there is little that can be said beyond the fact that relatively few graduate schools publish specific regulations. In general the graduate student is on his own, with the privilege of appearing for class or not; but his attendance is, if anything, more regular than that of the usual undergraduate. A number of his courses—particularly the seminars—may meet at irregular intervals, with the student devoting the intervening time to working on assigned projects, but when the class convenes he is present because it is in his best interests to be there.

While no standard grading system is used among graduate schools, there is a tendency to draw not quite so fine a line as in undergraduate study. For example, many schools limit themselves to two, or at the most three, rating levels: failing or passing, or possibly passing with distinction. Others employ the conventional letter grade, often with the specification that a grade of less than B is not accepted for credit in the major field. Under this system it is common for a minimum grade of C to be required for work in courses taken in minor or related fields. This practice seems most common in schools where graduate and undergraduate students attend the same classes.

It is as difficult to generalize on the sources of grades as on the grading systems used in graduate schools. A rather common pattern of graduate instruction is to require more papers and reports and fewer tests and examinations. Thus, the final grade may represent an evaluation of two or three reports and only one—a terminal—examination. As for the minimum satisfactory grade, many of the school catalogues specify a minimum level of performance based on the particular grading system in force. Several institutions reportedly employ no standard system, eschewing completely the use of grades and credits in connection with advanced degrees. Here, as in many other schools, the stu-

---

[5] Sir Hugh Stott Taylor, president of the Woodrow Wilson National Fellowship Foundation, has strongly urged that the time required for the doctorate be limited to three and one-half years; see *New York Times* (Aug. 7, 1958), p. 23.

dent may be asked to withdraw if he does not appear to be profiting from his graduate study. A study conducted in 1944, however, concluded that there are relatively few failures in course, and that most graduate students make grades in courses high enough to be "satisfactory" under the standards of the institution they are attending.[6]

The curriculum

The student is usually required to complete a minimum of two years of formal course work leading to the Ph.D. degree, at the end of which he may be expected to take a written or oral comprehensive examination. If he completes this successfully, he then begins work on his thesis. On submission of the completed thesis, he often is required to defend his work in a second oral examination. This three- or four-stage procedure is subject to so many variations that each of these stages needs to be discussed separately.[7]

A review of current catalogues shows that the course requirements for the doctorate usually consume from two to three years, with the full-time student ordinarily carrying four courses per term or semester. The program of study revolves around the major field. In some graduate schools, particularly among the older schools, the student may not elect any courses outside his major department; if he does he will receive no credit for them toward his degree. In many of the newer institutions, however, he is required to elect one, or at times two, minors in fields related to his major.[8] Usually this minor is limited to about one-quarter to one-third of his total course load, though in a few schools it may reach as high as one-half.

In a recent article, Harold Taylor, president of Sarah Lawrence College, complained that the traditional Ph.D. program is so highly specialized that it nullifies the likelihood of the candidate's becoming "flexible and imaginative about using the content of his specialized knowledge in many different ways."[9] There are many indications, however, that the conventional one-sided approach is being modified in the social sciences and humanities, and in some instances in the natural sciences as well. Interdepartmental doctorates are springing up in a number of graduate schools, and even where these do not exist formally, the student is often encouraged to elect related courses in other departments or divisions of the university. In some instances, he may even be permitted to register for certain undergraduate courses, though not for credit. The fact remains that

[6] Marcia Edwards, *op. cit.,* pp. 6–8.
[7] By its very nature, graduate study resists standardization in quantitative requirements. Nevertheless, a committee of the American Association of University Professors in 1918 laid down a detailed set of ground rules which are observed even at the present time; see *AAUP Bulletin,* V (January-February 1919), 12–18.
[8] In a few graduate schools a third minor may be substituted for one of the required foreign languages.
[9] "Graduate Preparation of Teachers of General Education—A Controversy," *College and University Bulletin,* IX (March 15, 1957), 4.

graduate study generally continues to have as its primary aim the training of specialists, and the curriculum is designed accordingly.

While it is customary for the departments to prescribe certain courses, the student, particularly in the larger schools, may have a wide latitude of choice among the areas of specialization within the department. Though his degree, for example, is in history, he may well specialize in Roman history, European history since 1789, American history before 1865, colonial America, or even Latin America since 1822, and so forth. In some of the scientific and technological fields, the number of departmental specializations reaches almost astronomical heights.

The curricular pattern often includes a distinction between the courses the student takes in his first year of graduate study and those of the second and succeeding years. On this pattern he will usually take the required basic courses in the first year; and here he may expect to find the larger lecture sections, frequently with advanced undergraduate students present. In the second year he will begin his more highly specialized courses and laboratories, and here his program will consist largely of small seminar classes.

The seminar—which is probably the most characteristic graduate course— may be described as a group of highly competitive young specialists, each working on his own research problem and each concerned as much with the methods of research as with the results of a particular project. In the seminar there is not so much "instruction" as there is "induction." A premium is placed on ability to conduct independent investigations and to report on them effectively. An assigned textbook may be used, but the student is expected to read widely in the field and to go beyond the basic materials of the course. As in graduate work in general, what he is expected to know bears only a limited relationship to any assigned text or formal lectures by the instructor.

Examinations and candidacy

In some graduate schools the student is required, at the end of his first year, to take a series of qualifying examinations, usually in a limited group of subjects chosen from the entire field of the major. If his performance is on too low a level, he is advised not to continue his graduate study. In some instances he may be permitted to salvage something from his investment by completion of the requirements for the master's degree.

A substantial number of graduate schools require some form of comprehensive examination at the end of the second year, or when the student has completed his formal course requirements. These may be written or oral or both, and may include the minor as well as the major fields of study. Failure to pass them does not necessarily mean withdrawal, although the school frequently places a limit on the number of times a student may attempt the examinations. Generally, it is desirable for him to "stand for" his orals as early as possible. Delay does not necessarily mean more thorough preparation, and it almost always entails the growth of a greater mental hazard. The number of students who fail is relatively small. Furthermore, the examinations have great value in forcing the candidate to review and organize his knowledge early in his work. When the examination is oral, the examining committee is usually drawn from the student's department, though it may include members of other related departments or fields; and the length of the oral is usually from one to three hours. Written examinations tend to be longer and may cover a period of days.

In many graduate schools the student is not officially a candidate for the degree until he has completed his course work and successfully passed the qualifying comprehensive examinations. By this time he must also have completed his foreign language requirements and have received approval of the subject for his thesis.

A second oral examination often precedes final approval of the thesis. This may be limited to a defense of the thesis itself or it may include questions on other aspects of the student's doctoral study. In a few schools it is combined with the comprehensive oral examination, but these seem to be in the minority. The examination may be public, which is the pattern in many European universities, but generally it is restricted to members of the department.[10] Quite often this oral defense of the thesis is a mere formality and takes the form of a friendly scholarly colloquy between the student and the faculty members of his department on the problems encountered in his investigation and the significance of his findings.

The doctoral thesis

Blegen and Cooper credit the doctoral thesis with the following distinctive educational benefits:

1. It provides training in the organization and correlation of significant facts and ideas;

2. It gives the student a broad experience in writing as an example of a type of communication essential to effective college teaching;

3. It represents a unique experience in independent investigation under the mastery of the student himself without arbitrary limitations of time.[11]

It is widely regarded by graduate school faculties as the most valuable phase

---

[10] Only four of the institutions included in this manual indicate in their bulletins that the oral defense of the thesis is open to the university public.

[11] Theodore C. Blegen, and Russell M. Cooper (eds.), *The Preparation of College Teachers* (Washington: American Council on Education, July 1950), pp. 97–98.

of the doctoral program. Certainly it is capable of giving the student the maximum in personal satisfaction.

The preparation of the thesis or dissertation takes one, two, or sometimes more years. It is an unfortunate fact that many candidates for the Ph.D. degree complete the requirements except the writing of the dissertation and then stop. The reasons for their delinquency are many and varied. Sometimes they have the misfortune to select a topic which yields no results or which, before the completion of the investigation, is found to have been covered by someone else. Sometimes they are impelled by such a desire for perfection that they become lost in a maze of their own devising. Most often, however, they accept some form of full-time employment and before they know it are too deeply involved in the daily routine of work and home to find time for research. Dean Barzun has aptly named these unfortunate individuals "Rip Van Winkle degree candidates."[12] The time limit now imposed by many graduate schools on the submission of the thesis is intended partly as a "spur to prick the sides" of their intent.

Work on the thesis is usually supervised by one member of the graduate faculty, which makes even more important the candidate's completing it in a relatively short time. Faculty members retire, die, or accept other positions. The loss of a supervisor may well mean that the student has to find an entirely new project, with the consequent loss of much valuable time and effort.

The Edwards study revealed that relatively few doctoral theses are rejected, although they may be returned several times for revision. Eventually most of them are approved.[13] Although the procedures for judging them vary considerably from school to school, the usual practice involves a reading committee, frequently including members from departments other than the one in which the work was completed.

At one time graduate schools commonly required the thesis to be published.[14] The rising costs of printing and the general recognition that many theses offer a very limited contribution to the sum of man's knowledge have led to a substantial modification of this practice. Of the institutions included in this manual some fifteen, if one may judge from the absence of a specific statement in the catalogue, have no publication requirements whatsoever. In one instance, in fact, the student is expressly forbidden to publish without first obtaining permission of the graduate school. A more common practice, however, is to require the student to submit, along with two finished copies of his manuscript, an abstract of one to three thousand words. This may be printed and distributed

---

[12] Jacques Barzun, *Graduate Study at Columbia* (New York: Columbia University Press, 1956), p. 5.

[13] Edwards, *op. cit.*, p. 47.

[14] In 1939–40, sixty-eight graduate schools had some requirement relating to publication, twenty-five of these requiring only an abstract. See *Doctoral Dissertations Accepted by American Universities*, compiled for the Association of Research Libraries, No. 7 (New York: H. W. Wilson Co., 1940), Table 1, p. ix.

by the university (usually at the student's expense), or it may be included in the annual publication of *Dissertation Abstracts*.[15] Many science departments require that an article containing the essence of the student's research be accepted for publication in a learned journal. And a substantial percentage of graduate schools require the candidate to subsidize the publication of his thesis on microfilm or microcards, usually after a specified period in which he is encouraged to seek publication through a commercial or university press.[16]

The road to the Ph.D. degree is a difficult one, with some pitfalls and many hardships. Its professional compensations, as suggested in the earlier sections of this essay, are many; for most graduate students, the sacrifices are well worthwhile. There are, moreover, rich rewards along the way. In the words of that wise and genial teacher and scholar, Howard Mumford Jones, the principal compensations for the hardships of graduate life are:

1. The sense that one's energies are focused upon an adult way of life—the problem of professional preparation.

2. Associating on terms approaching intellectual equality with specialists in the field of the student's choice.

3. A growing awareness . . . of his own proficiency as a young expert in the field.

4. A final glory of graduate work is the sense of being one with a company of learned men the world over, men who are concerned for the advancement of knowledge without reference to class, race, religion, nationality, or language.[17]

If this *Guide to Graduate Study* succeeds in encouraging just a few young men and women, who otherwise might not have done so, to think of themselves in the light of these satisfactions, it will have more than justified the effort involved in its composition.

[15] Ann Arbor, Mich.: University Microfilms.
[16] For a more detailed discussion of the research process, see p. 15 of this manual.
[17] *A Friendly Guide into the Graduate School*, Bulletin of Birmingham Southern College, Vol. XXIX, No. 4 (Birmingham, Ala.: The College, 1947), p. 22.

Selective bibliography

History of graduate study

Barzun, Jacques. *Graduate Study at Columbia.* New York: Columbia University Press, 1956.

Brickman, William W. "The M.A. and the Ph.D.," *School and Society,* LXVI (Aug. 20, 1947), 169–74.

Edwards, Marcia. *Studies in American Graduate Education.* New York: Carnegie Foundation for the Advancement of Teaching, 1944.

Eells, Walter Crosby. "Doctorates from Leading American Graduate Schools, 1861–1958," *School and Society,* LXXXVIII (Feb. 27, 1960), 93–94.

———. "Leading American Graduate Schools, 1948–58," *Liberal Education,* The Bulletin of the Association of American Colleges, XLVI (March 1960), 16–20.

Hollis, Ernest V. "Graduate Schools," in *Encyclopedia of Educational Research: A Project of the American Educational Research Association,* pp. 510–19. Rev. ed. New York: Macmillan Co., 1950.

Horton, Byrne J. *The Graduate School, Its Origin and Administrative Development.* New York: New York University Bookstore, 1940.

Rosenhaupt, Hans. *Graduate Students Experience at Columbia University, 1940–1956.* New York: Columbia University Press, 1958.

Ryan, Will C. *Studies in Early Graduate Education.* Carnegie Foundation for the Advancement of Teaching, Bulletin No. 30. New York: The Foundation, 1939.

Storr, Richard J. *The Beginnings of Graduate Education in America.* Chicago: University of Chicago Press, 1953.

Objectives of graduate study

GENERAL

Calkins, R. D. "Professional and Graduate Education and the Liberal Arts," in *Proceedings of the Conference on Liberal Arts, 1952,* pp. 48–64. Athens, Ga.: University of Georgia, Division of General Extension, 1952.

Foster, Laurence. *The Functions of a Graduate School in a Democratic Society.* New York: Huxley House Publishers, 1936.

Hollis, Ernest V. *Toward Improving Ph.D. Programs.* Prepared for the Commission on Teacher Education. Washington: American Council on Education, 1945.

Irwin, Mary (ed.). *American Universities and Colleges.* 8th ed. Washington: American Council on Education, 1960.

John, Walton C. *Graduate Study in Universities and Colleges in the United States.* Office of Education Bulletin 1934, No. 20. Washington: Government Printing Office, 1935.

Jones, Howard Mumford. *Education and World Tragedy.* Cambridge, Mass.: Harvard University Press, 1946.

McCutcheon, Roger P. (ed.). *Place of the Graduate School in the Training of College Teachers: A Work-Conference Held in New Orleans, November 15–17, 1951.* New Orleans: Tulane University Bookstore, 1952.

Mooney, Ross L. "Evaluating Graduate Education," *Harvard Educational Review,* XXV (Spring 1955), 85–94.

Office of Education, Department of Health, Education, and Welfare. *Education for the Professions.* Lloyd E. Blauch (ed.). Washington: Government Printing Office, 1955.

Radcliffe College, Committee on Graduate Education for Women. *Graduate Education for Women: The Radcliffe Ph.D.* Cambridge, Mass.: Harvard University Press, 1956.

Rockwell, Leo L. "Whence and Whither the Ph.D.?" *School and Society,* LXXXIV (Sept. 29, 1956), 107–9.

Ryan, Louis A. "Toward a Philosophy of the Graduate School," *Journal of Higher Education,* XVIII (October 1947), 367–72.

Stoke, Harold W. "Future of Graduate Education," *Journal of Higher Education,* XVIII (December 1947), 473–77.

Strothmann, Friedrich W. *The Graduate School*

Today and Tomorrow. New York: Fund for the Advancement of Education, 1955.

Taylor, Lily Ross. "Objectives of the Graduate School," *Journal of Higher Education,* XXIII (January 1952), 18–23.

Zetler, Robert C., and Crouch, W. George. "The Graduate School in General Education," *Journal of Higher Education,* XXI (May 1950), 239–42.

COLLEGE TEACHING AS A CAREER

American Council on Education. "The Council at Work: Summary Report of Survey on Interest and Activity Relating to College Teaching," *Educational Record,* XXXVIII (April 1957), 166–75.

Barzun, Jacques. *The Teacher in America.* Boston: Little, Brown & Co., 1945.

Buxton, Claude E. *College Teaching: A Psychologist's View.* New York: Harcourt, Brace & Co., 1956.

Campbell, Anne L. "Perspectives on the Negro College Teacher's World," *CLA Journal,* I (March 1958), 85–92.

Campbell, James Marshall. "An Evaluation of the Present Status of Teaching in Our Undergraduate Colleges—Impressions of Basic Items Which Affect It," National Catholic Educational Association, *Bulletin,* LIV (August 1957), 113–20.

Caplow, Theodore, and McGee, Reece J. *The Academic Marketplace.* New York: Basic Books, 1958.

College Teaching as a Career. Washington: American Council on Education, 1958.

Cronkhite, Bernice B. *Handbook for College Teachers: An Informal Guide.* Cambridge, Mass.: Harvard University Press, 1950.

Eckert, Ruth E., and Stecklein, John E. "College Faculty Members View Their Jobs," *AAUP Bulletin,* XLV (Winter 1959), 513–528.

———. "Why Teach in College?" *NEA Journal,* XLVII (February 1958), 120.

———. "Academic Woman," Association of American Colleges, *Bulletin,* XLV (October 1959), 390–97.

Eells, Walter Crosby. "Journals Publishing Articles on College Teachers and College Teaching," *AAUP Bulletin,* XLIII (September 1957), 458–60.

Ficken, Clarence E. "Opportunities in College Teaching," *Journal of Higher Education,* XXVII (May 1956), 266–73.

Fontanella, Mario A. "Teacher in the Arts College," *Journal of Higher Education,* XXIII (March 1952), 125–30.

French, Sidney J. *Accent on Teaching: Experiments in General Education.* New York: Harper & Bros., 1954.

Frifield, Don. *Careers in College Teaching.* ("Occupational Brief Series.") Washington: B'nai B'rith Vocational Service Bureau, 1954.

Fund for the Advancement of Education. *Better Utilization of College Teaching Resources.* A Report by the Committee on Utilization of College Teaching Resources. New York: The Fund, 1956.

———. *Teachers for Tomorrow.* Bulletin No. 2. New York: The Fund, 1955.

Hastings, William T. "Strait Is the Gate," *American Scholar,* XXVII (Winter 1957–58), 70–78.

Helm, M. Stanley. "Teaching as an Exciting Career," *Journal of Engineering Education,* XLVIII (November 1957), 111–14.

Iddles, Harold A. "Employment Opportunities in College and University Teaching," *Journal of Chemical Education,* XXVII (August 1950), 422–25.

Justman, Joseph, and Mais, W. H. *College Teaching: Its Practice and Its Potential.* New York: Harper & Bros., 1956.

Maul, Ray C. "College Teaching: Challenge, Opportunity," *Phi Delta Kappan,* XXXVIII (February 1957), 175–80.

National Education Association, Research Division. *Teacher Supply and Demand in Colleges and Universities, 1955–56 and 1956–57.* Washington: The Association, 1957.

Ness, Frederic W. "The Summing Up," in Association of American Colleges, *Bulletin,* XLIV (October 1958), 416–22.

Office of Education, Department of Health, Education, and Welfare. *Faculty and Other Professional Staff in Institutions of Higher Education.* Wayne E. Tolliver and Hazel C. Poole (eds.). Washington: Government Printing Office, 1959.

Ohio College Association. *Your Career as a College Teacher.* The Association, 1959.

President's Commission on Higher Education. *Staffing Higher Education: A Report of the President's Commission on Higher Education.* (*Higher Education for American Democracy,*

Vol. IV.) Washington: Government Printing Office, 1948.

Sharp, D. Louise. *Why Teach?* New York: Henry Holt & Co., 1957.

Tead, Ordway. *College Teaching and College Learning: Plea for Improvement.* New Haven, Conn.: Yale University Press, 1949.

Trabue, Marion R. "Characteristics Desirable in College Teachers," *Journal of Higher Education,* XXV (April 1954), 201–4.

Tyler, Robert L. "In Lieu of Money: The Rewards of Teaching," *Journal of Higher Education,* XXXI (April 1960), 185–90.

PREPARATION FOR COLLEGE TEACHING

Albright, A. D., and Barrows, John E. *Preparing College Teachers.* University of Kentucky and Southern Regional Education Board, 1959.

Anderson, Paul R. "Preparation of the Teacher in General Education," *Journal of General Education,* III (January 1949), 98–106.

Angell, George W., and Laws, L. S. "Training the Potential College Teacher," *Journal of Higher Education,* XXV (March 1954), 153–157.

Barrett, Laurence. "Professors and Professionals: Teacher Training and the Liberal Arts," *Yale Review,* XLVI (March 1957), 402–12.

Beichner, Paul E. "Preparation of College Teachers," in National Catholic Educational Association, *Bulletin,* LIV (August 1957), 142–44.

Bentley, Gerald E. "Graduate School as a Preparation for Teachers," *College English,* XII (March 1951), 330–35.

Berelson, Bernard. "Graduate Education and the Preparation of College Teachers," in John W. Gustad (ed.), *Faculty Supply, Demand, and Recruitment: Proceedings of a Regional Conference,* pp. 74–92. Winchester, Mass.: New England Board of Higher Education, 1959.

Bigelow, Karl W. "Promising Programs for the Preparation of College Faculty," in *Current Issues in Higher Education,* pp. 216–21. Washington: Association for Higher Education, 1955.

Bird, Otto. "Training the College Teacher," in *Proceedings of the National Catholic Educational Association,* pp. 203–7. Washington: The Association, 1951.

Blegen, Theodore C. "Graduate Schools and the Education of College Teachers," *Educational Record,* XXIX (January 1948), 12–25.

Carman, Harry J. "Teachers of Tomorrow," Association of American Colleges, *Bulletin,* XXXV (May 1949), 306–16.

Carnegie Foundation for the Advancement of Teaching. *The Education of College Teachers.* (Reprint of *Fifty-third Annual Report, 1957–58,* pp. 9–26.) New York: The Foundation, 1958.

Colwell, Ernest Cadman. "New Programs for Preparing College Teachers," *Educational Record,* XXXIV (April 1953), 152–53.

Dobbins, Charles G. (ed.). *Expanding Resources for College Teaching: A Report of the Conference on College Teaching Sponsored by the American Council on Education, Washington, D. C., January 19–20, 1956.* Washington: The Council, 1956.

Dunkel, Harold B. "Training College Teachers: A Progress Report from the University of Chicago," *Journal of Higher Education,* XXIX (January 1958), 1–7, 57–58.

Eckert, Ruth E., and Linck, O. F. "College Teachers: Improvement of Preparation," in *Current Issues in Higher Education,* pp. 147–56. Washington: Association for Higher Education, 1956.

Erickson, Clifford E. "What Are the Most Promising Procedures by Which Departments Can Pool Efforts To Improve the Preparation of College Teachers?" in *Current Issues in Higher Education,* pp. 204–8. Washington: Association for Higher Education, 1958.

Figueroa, John J. "Postgraduate Teacher Education: Some Experiments in the United States," *Universities Quarterly,* XIII (November 1958), 74–82.

Hard, Frederick. "Academic Training of College Teachers," *Educational Record,* XXXVII (October 1956), 299–302.

Hostler, Amy. "Preparation of College Teachers," in *Current Issues in Higher Education,* p. 220. Washington: Association for Higher Education, 1958.

James, Preston E. "The Dissertation Requirement," *School and Society,* LXXXVIII (March 26, 1960), 147–48.

Kelley, Frederick J. *Toward Better College Teaching.* Office of Education Bulletin 1950, No. 13. Washington: Government Printing Office, 1950.

McCutcheon, Roger P. (ed.). *Place of the*

Graduate School in the Training of College Teachers: A Work-Conference Held in New Orleans, November 15–17, 1951. New Orleans: Tulane University Bookstore, 1952.

Morse, H. Taylor. "Conference on College Teaching: The Minnesota Centennial Conference on College Teaching," *Journal of Higher Education,* XXIX (June 1958), 293–300.

Ness, Frederic W. *The Role of the College in the Recruitment of Teachers.* Washington: Association of American Colleges, 1958.

Stewart, George W. "Ph.D. Thesis and the College Teacher," *American Journal of Physics,* XVI (November 1948), 421–24.

Strothmann, F. W. "What Changes Will Be Necessary or Desirable in the Preparation of College Teachers?" in *Current Issues in Higher Education,* pp. 182–86. Washington: Association for Higher Education, 1957.

Teacher Education: The Decade Ahead. Report of the DeKalb Conference. Washington: National Education Association, National Commission on Teacher Education and Professional Standards, 1955.

Wilson, O. Meredith. "Wisdom Is Better than Strength," *Educational Record,* XLI (January 1960), 25–28.

OBJECTIVES AND PROGRAMS IN SPECIFIC SUBJECTS

Allen, Jack (ed.). *The Teacher of the Social Studies.* Washington: National Council for the Social Studies, 1952.

Allen, Lillian M. *Present Status of Accredited Music Instruction in American Universities.* Washington: Catholic University of America Press, 1954.

Baker, George P., and Tyack, David B. "Doctoral Programs in Business and Business Administration," in *Faculty Requirements and Standards in Collegiate Schools of Business,* pp. 84–110. New York: American Association of Collegiate Schools of Business, 1956.

Bowen, Howard R. "Graduate Education in Economics," *American Economic Review,* XLIII (September 1953), Supplement, Part 2.

Clark, Kenneth E., and Moore, Bruce V. "Doctoral Programs in Psychology: 1957–1958," *American Psychologist,* XIII (November 1958), 631–33.

Eaton, Thelma. "What Is a Good Library School Teacher?" *Improving College and University Teaching,* II (May 1954), 26–27.

Flemming, William. "Wanted: New Program for the Preparation of College Teachers in Art and Music," *Journal of General Education,* III (January 1949), 107–12.

Folsom, Richard G. (ed.). "Facilities and Opportunities for Graduate Study in Engineering: A Report of the ASEE Graduate Study Commission," *Journal of Engineering Education,* XLVIII (June 1958), 938–74.

Gillis, Robert E. "The Teaching and Learning of Microbiology: The Teacher," *Journal of Dental Education,* XXII (March 1958), 103–6.

Gray, Wellington B. "Historical Status of Graduate Degrees in Art Education," *Journal of Educational Research,* L (January 1957), 339–49.

Kelly, William A. "Preparation of the Instructor in Educational Psychology," *Catholic Educational Review,* LII (February 1954), 102–112.

Mann, William R. "The Training of Prospective Dental Teachers," *Journal of Dental Education,* XX (January 1956), 38–49.

McKeachie, Wilbert J. "Program for Training Teachers of Psychology," *American Psychologist,* VI (April 1951), 119–21.

"Preparation of College FL Teachers," *PMLA,* LXX (September 1955), Supplement, 57–68.

Remak, Henry H. H. "The Training and Supervision of Teaching Assistants in German," *Modern Language Journal,* XLI (May 1957), 212–14.

Ryan, Alvan S. (chairman). "Doctoral Studies in English and Preparation for Teaching," *CEA Critic,* XX (March 1958), 1, 7–12.

Sanders, Jennings B. "Preparation for College History Teaching," *Higher Education,* VII (Sept. 1, 1950), 5–6.

Süsskind, Charles. "On Teaching College Science Teachers To Teach," *American Journal of Physics,* XXV (March 1957), 200–202.

Thorp, Willard. "The Training of College Teachers of American Literature," *College English,* VIII (April 1947), 360–65.

Yalem, Ronald J. "Graduate Training in International Relations," Association of American Colleges, *Bulletin,* XLIV (May 1958), 356–361.

Selection and counseling for graduate study

Foster, J. F. *Commonwealth Universities Yearbook.* London: Association of Universities of the British Commonwealth, 1960. (Distributed in the United States by American Council on Education.)

Friedenberg, Edgar Z., and Roth, Julius A. *Self-Perception in the University: A Study of Successful and Unsuccessful Graduate Students.* Chicago, Ill.: University of Chicago Press, 1954.

Harvey, Philip R. *The Use of the Graduate Record Examinations by Colleges and Universities.* Princeton, N. J.: Educational Testing Service, 1957.

Keyes, H. M. R. (ed.). *International Handbook of Universities.* Paris: International Association of Universities, 1959. (Distributed in the U.S. by American Council on Education.)

Lannholm, Gerald V., and Schrader, W. B. *Predicting Graduate School Success: An Evaluation of the Effectiveness of the Graduate Record Examinations.* Princeton, N. J.: Educational Testing Service, 1951.

Lumiansky, R. M. "A Plan for Identifying and Recruiting Outstanding Students for College Teaching," in *Southern University Conference Proceedings, 1958,* pp. 21–25. Chattanooga, Tenn.: University of Chattanooga, 1958.

Office of Education, Department of Health, Education, and Welfare. *Education for the Professions.* Lloyd E. Blauch (ed.). Washington: Government Printing Office, 1955.

Taylor, Hugh, and Rosenhaupt, Hans. *Woodrow Wilson National Fellowship Foundation, Report for 1958–1959.* Princeton, N. J.: The Foundation, April 1960.

Webb, Sam C. "Differential Prediction of Success in Graduate School," *Journal of Educational Research,* L (September 1956), 45–54.

Financing graduate study

About the Ford Foundation. New York: Ford Foundation, 1958.

Boys, Richard C. "National Woodrow Wilson Fellowship Program," in Office of Education, *Staffing the Nation's Colleges and Universities: Report of a Conference, May 20 and 21, 1957, Washington, D. C.,* pp. 26–29.

Washington: Government Printing Office, 1957.

Davis, W. Kenneth. "AEC Educational Assistance to Engineering Colleges," *Journal of Engineering Education,* XLVIII (December 1957), 193–200.

"Educational Facilities and Financial Assistance for Graduate Students in Psychology," *American Psychologist* (article appears annually).

Feingold, S. Norman. *Scholarships, Fellowships, and Loans.* 3 vols. Boston, Mass.: Bellman Publishing Co., 1955.

"Fellowships for Prospective College Teachers," *Higher Education,* VI (Jan. 15, 1950), 121–122.

Mattingly, Richard C. "Institutional Graduate Fellowship Programs," *Higher Education,* XV (November 1957), 48–53.

———. *Scholarships and Fellowships, A Selected Bibliography.* Office of Education Bulletin 1957, No. 7. Washington: Government Printing Office, 1957.

McCoy, Pressley C. "The Danforth Teacher Study Grant Program," *Educational Record,* XXXVIII (October 1957), 368–70.

Moore, Bruce V. "Educational Facilities and Financial Assistance for Graduate Students in Psychology, 1959–1960," *American Psychologist,* XIII (December 1958), 741–60.

Quattlebaum, Charles A. *Federal Aid to Students for Higher Education.* 84th Cong., 2d sess., H.R. Committee Print. Washington: Government Printing Office, 1956.

Rice, Wilmer S. *American Foundations and Their Fields.* 7th ed. New York: American Foundations Information Service, 1955.

Schiltz, Michael E. *Fellowships in the Arts and Sciences, 1961–62.* 4th Ed. Washington: Association of American Colleges, 1960. (Distributed by American Council on Education.)

Stickler, William H. "Graduate Fellowships and Assistantships in State Universities and Land-Grant Institutions," *Higher Education,* XIII (March 1957), 124–27.

"Summary of National Defense Education Act of 1958," *Higher Education,* XV (October 1958), 23–32, 39.

Wilkins, Theresa B. (ed.). *Scholarships and Fellowships Available at Institutions of Higher Education.* Office of Education Bulletin 1951, No. 16. Washington: Government Printing Office, 1951.

Woodrow Wilson National Fellowship Foundation. *The Woodrow Wilson National Fellowships, Past and Present: A Handbook of Information.* Princeton, N. J.: The Foundation, n.d.

"Yale's Teaching Fellows Program," *School and Society,* LXXXVI (April 12, 1958), 179.

Guides to additional sources of information

Armsby, Henry M. *et al. Organized Occupational Curriculums: Enrollments and Graduates, 1957.* Washington: Government Printing Office, 1959.

Dissertation Abstracts: Abstracts of Dissertations and Monographs in Microform [formerly *Microfilm Abstracts*], Vol. I to date. Ann Arbor, Mich.: University Microfilms, 1938 to date. [Since 1956, includes material formerly in *Doctoral Dissertations.*]

Doctoral Dissertations Accepted by American Universities. Nos. 1–22. New York: H. W. Wilson Co., 1934–1955.

Education Index: A Cumulative Author and Subject Index to a Selected List of Educational Periodicals, Books and Pamphlets. New York: H. W. Wilson Co., 1932 to date.

Eells, Walter Crosby. *College Teachers and College Teaching.* Atlanta, Ga.: Southern Regional Education Board, 1957.

———. *College Teachers and College Teaching, Supplement.* Atlanta, Ga.: Southern Regional Education Board, 1959.

Mattingly, Richard C. *Scholarships and Fellowships, a Selected Bibliography.* Office of Education Bulletin 1957, No. 7. Washington: Government Printing Office, 1957.

Office of Education, Department of Health, Education, and Welfare. *Education for the Professions.* Blauch, Lloyd E. (ed.). Washington: Government Printing Office, 1955.

PART II

THE GRADUATE SCHOOLS

OFFERING PROGRAMS

LEADING TO THE PH.D.

Notes on the Text

Information for this section of the *Guide* was obtained from questionnaires which were filled in by responsible officials of the participating institutions. Because of the great variety in the nature of the institutions and their programs, the following notes are offered to assist in interpreting the data:

Arrangement of Material: Institutions are arranged alphabetically by most significant term. An Institutional Index is provided to give further guidance. Where several administrative units within an institution offer programs leading to the Ph.D., these are treated seriatim, with the arts and sciences division usually listed first.

Abbreviations: See Appendix II for list of abbreviations used in this section.

Admission Requirements: The general requirements of the graduate division for *admission to graduate study* and *admission to candidacy for the Ph.D.* are given under this heading. Additional departmental prerequisites are given for each field of study as appropriate.

Financial Assistance: The forms of assistance described are reportedly available to new, or first-year students. No information was requested on types of aid which are available *only* to second- and third-year students, or on the many kinds of financial aid available from sources outside of the universities and colleges themselves.

Courses in the Methodology of Teaching: Where such courses, or other programs designed to assist the graduate student in becoming an effective college teacher, are offered, this information is given in italic type at the beginning of the section entitled "Fields of Study for the Ph.D."

Fields of Study for the Ph.D.: Programs are listed alphabetically for each institution (and are also indexed at the back of this volume). Where several areas of concentration are available within a field, these are specified. The administrative unit may be assumed to be the department, as identified with the field of study, unless otherwise specified. Combined programs are those which provide for the student's working under the aegis of two or more departments or divisions. Prerequisites for graduate study and for Ph.D. candidacy are given *only* if these are in addition to, or departures from, the general requirements of the graduate division for each status. In this connection, it is important to note that many institutions provide opportunities to make up deficiencies after admission.

Other Doctoral Programs: If an institution offers programs leading to doctoral degrees other than the Ph.D., this fact is noted in the exhibit and the degrees are also listed in a table of Doctoral Degrees Awarded by American Universities and Colleges which is presented in Appendix I.

Summer and Evening Courses: Where such courses (applicable to the Ph.D.) are offered, this is indicated. It should be noted, however, that there are usually many fewer such courses than are available during the day and in the regular academic year.

Special Educational Facilities: An attempt has been made to include only those which appear to be distinctive or to give an impression of the scope of such facilities. Many others are, of course, provided in each institution.

Adelphi College

GARDEN CITY, LONG ISLAND, NEW YORK

Division of Graduate Studies

Adelphi initiated graduate instruction in 1948 and awarded its first Ph.D. in 1952. The college uses "institute" approach to related subject-matter fields. Institute of Health, Education and Welfare offers Ph.D. programs in clinical, school, and experimental psychology, as well as master's degree programs in psychiatric nursing, psychology, social work, sociology, speech and hearing, and teacher education. Institute of Science and Mathematics offers Ph.D. programs in chemistry and mathematics, and master's degree programs in applied science, chemistry, biology, mathematics, and physics. Adelphi is privately controlled and nonsectarian. Both men and women are admitted.

No residence facilities are provided for graduate students, but rooms and apartments are available in community.

Special facilities include: the Associated Clinics (mental health center, psychological service center, speech and hearing center, and reading and study center); library of approximately 95,000 volumes, including well-developed library collections in the social sciences, the natural sciences, and mathematics.

Residence requirement for Ph.D.: 3 years of study beyond bachelor's degree. In chemistry, full-time residence at Adelphi is required during final 2 years; in mathematics, 1 full year or 30 credit hours; in psychology, 3 years of full-time study. Evening courses available in all fields except psychology.

ADMISSION REQUIREMENTS

For graduate study: bachelor's degree; high scholastic record; promise of successful professional development. For candidacy for Ph.D.: qualifying examinations; fulfillment of language requirement.

Apply to Director, Division of Graduate Studies, before March 15.

FEES AND FIRST-YEAR AID

Application fee $10. Tuition $960 per academic year ($32 per semester hour credit). Laboratory fees in chemistry approximate $80 per year. Room (in community) $450-$500 per year.

Approximate annual cost of board in college dining room $500-$600. Apartments in community available at $100-$150 per month.

First-year aid available: scholarships, $200-$960; teaching fellowships, $800-$1,600; research assistantships, $800-$2,000; grants-in-aid, $200-$960.

Apply to the Director, Division of Graduate Studies, before March 15.

FIELDS OF STUDY FOR THE PH.D.

Courses in general and special methods of teaching are offered, as well as supervised student teaching at the college level.

Chemistry. Analytical, organic, inorganic, and physical chemistry; biochemistry; chemical instrumentation. Ph.D. candidacy prerequisite: reading knowledge of 2: French, German, Russian. 7 professorial staff. Ph.D. program initiated 1959. 18 master's degrees awarded 1955-59. 55 graduate students registered fall 1959. Ph.D. enrollment limited to 10 per year.

Mathematics. Such areas of concentration as: problems of fluid mechanics related to geophysics; development of probability distributions from causal events with applications to statistical physics; theory of groups; hydromagnetic stability in plasma-field interactions; diffraction of electromagnetic waves; or another (subject to approval). Prerequisite for graduate study: equivalent of a major in one of the physical sciences, mathematics, or engineering, including at least 3 semesters of calculus, an elementary course in differential equations, and 2 semesters of physics. Ph.D. candidacy prerequisite: reading knowledge of 2: French, German, Russian. 9 professorial staff. Ph.D. program begun 1959. 91 master's degrees awarded 1955-59. 456 graduate students registered fall 1959. Ph.D. enrollment limited to 12 per year.

Psychology.—Clinical and School. Prerequisites for graduate study: general, developmental, and abnormal psychology; experimental psychology (with laboratory experience); descriptive statistics; tests and measurements; GRE Aptitude Test and Advanced Test in Psychology. Recommended: background in biological and social sciences, mathematics, and literature. Ph.D. candidacy prerequisite: reading knowledge of 1 foreign language. 13 professorial staff. 31 Ph.D.'s awarded 1955-59. 33 graduate students registered fall 1959. Enrollment limited to 12 per year.

Psychology.—Experimental. General and clinical theory, biological and social bases, research and experimental psychology. Prerequisites for graduate study: courses in general, developmental, and abnormal psychology; experimental psychology (with laboratory experience); descriptive statistics; GRE Aptitude Test and Advanced Test in Psychology. Recommended: background in biological and social sciences, mathematics, and literature. Ph.D. candidacy prerequisite: reading knowledge of 1 foreign language. 13 professorial staff. 3 master's degrees awarded 1955-59. 4 graduate students registered fall 1959.

Akron, University of

AKRON, OHIO

The Graduate Division

The university is controlled by the city of Akron and is open to both men and women. Graduate instruction has been offered for many years, and a program leading to the Ph.D. in chemistry was initiated in 1956. First Ph.D. was awarded in 1959.

Rooms in dormitories available for male students; no residence facilities provided for women or married students.

The Institute of Rubber Research and Library of the Division of Rubber Research of the American Chemical Society are located on the campus. The Institute, which has conducted contract research in pure science on campus since 1943, makes available to qualified students its facilities and personnel, and also provides opportunities for student employment.

Residence requirement for Ph.D.: minimum of 48 credits in graduate courses, of which at least 24 must be taken in residence at the University of Akron. 1 calendar year must be spent in full-time resident research. Summer and evening courses available.

ADMISSION REQUIREMENTS

For graduate study: bachelor's degree; background for graduate work; GPA of 2.5 in all work and 2.75 in chemistry; 2 modern foreign languages. Recommended: GRE. For candidacy for Ph.D. degree: 48 graduate course credits of satisfactory work.

Apply to the Registrar at least 1 week prior to registration.

FEES AND FIRST-YEAR AID

No application fee. Tuition $25 per credit hour for residents of Akron; $27 for nonresidents. Room (in dormitories) for men $300 a year. Approximate annual cost of board in college dining room $600.

First-year aid available: 3 fellowships, $1,700; 5 research assistantships, $3,300-$3,600. Qualified students may be employed by the Institute of Rubber Research on part- or full-time basis and can often use their research work as the foundation for thesis or dissertation.

Apply to the head of the Chemistry Department prior to April 15.

FIELDS OF STUDY FOR THE PH.D.

Chemistry. Polymer chemistry. Professorial staff: 8 full-time, 3 part-time. Ph.D. program initiated 1956. 54 master's degrees and 5 Ph.D.'s awarded 1955-59. 137 graduate students registered fall 1959.

Alabama, University of

UNIVERSITY, ALABAMA

The Graduate School

Graduate instruction has been offered at the University of Alabama since shortly after 1831. The Graduate School was organized in 1924, and the first Ph.D. was awarded in 1952. The Ed.D. degree is also conferred. University is publicly controlled by the state. Both men and women are admitted.

Single graduate students may live in university domitories; 640 university-owned apartments available for married students (graduate fellowship and scholarship holders are given preference).

Residence requirement for Ph.D.: minimum of 3 years beyond bachelor's degree, of which either the second or third year and a minimum of 18 hours of graduate work must be taken in continuous residence at the University of Alabama. Summer courses available and a few evening courses are also offered.

ADMISSION REQUIREMENTS

For graduate study: bachelor's degree; overall GPA of 1.5 (C+) and B average in major field; recommendations; Academic Aptitude Tests. Recommended: GRE. For candidacy for Ph.D.: 2 foreign languages or 1 language and an acceptable field of knowledge outside major or minor fields; preliminary examinations; completion of substantial portion of course work.

Apply to Graduate Dean at least 6 weeks before date of desired entry.

FEES AND FIRST-YEAR AID

No application fee. Tuition for state residents $210 per academic year; others $560. Room (in dormitory) for men $96-$318; for women $186-$354 per year. Approximate annual cost of board in college dining room $370. Apartments $23-$50 per month.

First-year aid available: 25 scholarships, $1,000 plus remission of out-of-state tuition; 20 teaching fellowships, $2,225-$2,500 plus remission of out-of-state tuition; variable number of research assistantships, $2,000-$3,000; large number of teaching assistantships, $1,500-$2,050 plus remission of out-of-state tuition. Some departments have additional special fellowships, scholarships, and traineeships.

Apply to Dean of the Graduate School by March 1.

FIELDS OF STUDY FOR THE PH.D.

Anatomy. Neuroanatomy, histology, embryology. Prerequisites for graduate study: major in biological sciences; GRE or Medical College Admission Test. Ph.D. candidacy prerequisite: 2 foreign languages. 10 professorial staff. 3 master's degrees awarded 1955-59. 6 graduate students registered fall 1959. Total enrollment limited to 12.

Biochemistry. General biochemistry. Offered by Department of Biochemistry, Medical Center. Prerequisites for graduate study: major in chemistry; 1 year biology; French or German; GRE. Recommended: 1 year of physical chemistry. Ph.D. candidacy prerequisites: M.S. in biochemistry; French and German. 5 professorial staff. 6 master's degrees and 5 Ph.D.'s awarded 1955-59. 11 graduate students registered fall 1959.

Biology. Animal ecology; cytology; entomology; genetics; ichthyology; protozoology; vertebrate taxonomy; plant ecology, morphology, or physiology. Prerequisite for graduate study: minimum of 20 semester hours of biology. Recommended: courses in chemistry, geology, mathematics, or physics (at least 2 of these); 12 hours in botany and in zoology. Ph.D. candidacy prerequisite: 2 foreign languages (usually French and German). 9 professorial staff. 15 master's degrees and 5 Ph.D.'s awarded 1955-59. 25 graduate students registered fall 1959.

Business Administration. Accounting, economics, finance, management, marketing, business statistics. Offered by School of Commerce and Business Administration. Prerequisite for graduate study: major in commerce or business administration or equivalent. Ph.D. candidacy prerequisites: 1 foreign language; business statistics. 36 professorial staff. 130 master's degrees and 19 Ph.D.'s awarded 1955-59. 98 graduate students registered fall 1959.

Chemistry. Analytical, inorganic, organic, physical chemistry. Offered by School of Chemistry. Prerequisites for graduate study: fundamental courses in general, organic, analytical, and physical chemistry; physics; mathematics through calculus. Ph.D. candidacy prerequisite: French and German. 21 professorial staff. 21 master's degrees and 12 Ph.D.'s awarded 1955-59. 16 graduate students registered fall 1959.

Education. Secondary or elementary education, school administration, educational psychology, and counseling and guidance. Offered by Department of Education. Prerequisite for graduate study: approved curriculum for teachers of elementary or secondary education. Recommended: 1 year of teaching experience. Ph.D. candidacy prerequisites: counseling tests; 3 years of teaching experience; 2 foreign languages or 1 foreign language and either statistics or study in some appropriate field of learning. 33 professorial staff. 861 master's degrees and 23 Ph.D.'s awarded 1955-59. 222 graduate students registered fall 1959. Ed.D. also awarded (no language requirement).

English. Old and Middle English; Renaissance, modern English, or American literature. Ph.D. candidacy prerequisite: 2 foreign languages (usually French and German). 17 professorial staff. 39 master's degrees awarded 1955-59. 17 graduate students registered fall 1959.

History. Colonial and United States to 1860; United States since 1860; history of the South; Latin American (to 1810 or since 1810); European (1485-1715 or 1715-1850); European history since 1850; England and the British Empire

(1066-1714 or since 1714). Prerequisite for graduate study: major in history or equivalent. Ph.D. candidacy prerequisite: 2 foreign languages. 11 professorial staff. 40 master's degrees and 4 Ph.D.'s awarded 1955-59. 35 graduate students registered fall 1959.

Mathematics. Analysis and topology. Prerequisite for graduate study: 30 semester hours in mathematics. Ph.D. candidacy prerequisites: 2 foreign languages selected from German, French, Italian, or Russian. 13 professorial staff. Ph.D. program begun 1958. 23 master's degrees awarded 1955-59. 23 graduate students registered fall 1959. Total Ph.D. enrollment limited to 10.

Microbiology. Medical and dental microbiology, virology, immunology, microbial metabolism. Prerequisites for graduate study: adequate preparation in mathematics, physics, chemistry, and biology (including bacteriology); French and/or German; GRE, MCAT, or DCAT. 7 professorial staff. Ph.D. program begun 1958. 2 master's degrees awarded 1955-59. 2 graduate students registered fall 1959.

Pharmacology. Prerequisite for graduate study: major in chemistry; GRE or Medical Aptitude Test. Recommended: personal interview. Ph.D. candidacy prerequisites: French and German. 4 professorial staff. 2 master's degrees and 2 Ph.D.'s awarded 1955-59. 1 graduate student registered fall 1959.

Physics. Magnetic resonance, microwaves, atomic and nuclear physics, theoretical physics, radio astronomy, or infrared spectroscopy. Prerequisites for graduate study: major in physics or equivalent; minor in mathematics; 1 intermediate course in each main field of physics; comprehensive background in general physics; standard test in physics. Ph.D. candidacy prerequisite: 2 foreign languages. 10 professorial staff. 19 master's degrees and 6 Ph.D.'s awarded 1955-59. 19 graduate students registered fall 1959.

Physiology. Prerequisites for graduate study: courses in biology, chemistry, physics, mathematics; GRE. Recommended: physical chemistry; nuclear physics; mathematics through calculus. Ph.D. candidacy prerequisite: 2 foreign languages. 7 professorial staff. 2 master's degrees and 1 Ph.D. awarded 1955-59. 3 graduate students registered fall 1959.

Political Science. American or comparative government, international relations, public administration, political theory. At least 1 outside related minor field with a minimum of 12 semester hours, selected with approval of the graduate committee of the department. Prerequisites for graduate study: major in political science or minimum of 18 semester hours in political science, including basic courses in American and comparative government and in international relations. Recommended: work in other social sciences and elementary statistical methods. Ph.D. candidacy prerequisites: master's degree in political science; 2 foreign languages or 1 language and statistics. 10 professorial staff. 16 master's degrees and 2 Ph.D.'s awarded 1955-59. 18 graduate students registered fall 1959.

Psychology. General experimental, clinical. Prerequisites for graduate study: major in psychology; MAT. 10 professorial staff. 20 master's degrees awarded 1955-59. 21 graduate students registered fall 1959. Total enrollment limited to 30.

Romance Languages. French and Spanish (1 as a major and the other as a minor). In French: Renaissance and classical literature, modern drama and novel, French stylistics. In Spanish: philology and medieval period, Spanish Renaissance, Golden Age, Generation of '98, modern novel, and drama of Spanish America. Prerequisite for graduate study: major in French or Spanish. Ph.D. candidacy prerequisite: reading knowledge of German and third Romance language; residence in country which employs language of major interest. 9 professorial staff. Ph.D. program begun 1960. 22 master's degrees awarded 1955-59. 10 graduate students registered fall 1959.

Alaska, University of

COLLEGE, ALASKA

The Graduate Council

Graduate study has been offered since 1950, with the first Ph.D. being awarded in 1955. The program, administered by the Coordinator of Graduate Study under the direction of the Graduate Council and Dean of Faculty, is planned to make maximum use of the unique geographical and climatological advantages of the university. Institution is a university and land-grant college publicly controlled by the state. Both men and women are admitted.

Rooms in undergraduate dormitories available for single graduate students; 2 1-bedroom apartments for married students.

Research facilities of Geophysical Institute and resources of the Arctic Research Laboratory at Point Barrow available for graduate research. Library contains approximately 48,000 volumes and 700 current periodicals.

Residence requirement for Ph.D.: minimum of 3 years of which at least 1 year must be spent in residence at the University of Alaska.

ADMISSION REQUIREMENTS

For graduate study: bachelor's degree; B average in major field; letters of recommendation; GRE Aptitude and Advanced Tests. For candidacy for Ph.D.: B average in all graduate work; examination in 2 foreign languages; comprehensive qualifying examination in major and minor fields.

Apply to Coordinator of Graduate Study before March 15.

FEES AND FIRST-YEAR AID

No application fee. No tuition for state residents; $200 a year for others (waived for assistants working quarter-time or more). Special fees approximate $88 annually. Room (in dormitory) $100-$125 per year. Approximate annual cost of board in college dining room $664. Apartments $97 per month.

First-year aid available: teaching fellowships, $1,000-$3,250 (for ⅛ to ½ time per academic year); research assistantships, $125-$825 per month (such assistants normally work for a calendar year on part- or full-time basis while completing thesis).

Apply to head of department not later than March 15.

FIELDS OF STUDY FOR THE PH.D.

Geophysics. Upper atmosphere physics (photoelectric, photographic, and spectrographic observations of aurora, study of ozone); radio physics (ionospheric physics and arctic radio wave propagation); solar-terrestrial relations (magnetic disturbances, ionospheric storms, earth potential disturbances, and solar radio waves); theoretical geophysics (studies involving above subjects); earth sciences (physical properties of ice; permafrost and glaciers). Prerequisite for graduate study: major in physics, geophysics, mathematics, or electrical engineering. 10 profes-

sorial staff. 3 master's degrees and 4 Ph.D.'s awarded 1955-59. 19 graduate students registered fall 1959. Registration limited to 25.

Alfred University

ALFRED, NEW YORK

The Graduate School

The Graduate School was established in 1947 and has jurisdiction over the master's degree programs in the College of Liberal Arts and the master's and Ph.D. programs in the College of Ceramics. The College of Ceramics was founded in 1900 and became a unit of the State University of New York in 1948. The first Ph.D. was awarded in ceramics in 1958. Cooperative doctoral programs in education have been established with Syracuse University and the University of Buffalo; students pursue studies at Alfred for the Ed.D. degrees conferred by Syracuse and Buffalo Universities. Alfred is privately controlled and nonsectarian. Both men and women are admitted.

No residence facilities for graduate students are provided by the university.

Special facilities include: College of Ceramics library of approximately 12,600 volumes; exceptional facilities in space and equipment for study in field of ceramics.

Residence requirement for Ph.D.: minimum of 3 academic years beyond bachelor's degree, at least 2 of which must be taken in residence at Alfred. Summer courses available.

ADMISSION REQUIREMENTS

For graduate study: bachelor's degree; above-average academic record. For candidacy for Ph.D.: completion of 35 hours of course work with satisfactory grades; reading and writing knowledge of 2 modern foreign languages (French, German, and Russian recommended, and choice must be approved by student's advisory committee); comprehensive examination in ceramics and related sciences; approval of thesis subject by advisory committee and chairmen of Departments of Ceramic Engineering and Technology, Glass Technology, Physical Science, and Research.

Apply to Director of Admissions, Alfred University, by July 1.

FEES AND FIRST-YEAR AID

Application fee $5. Tuition $500 per semester. Special fees approximate $150 annually. Room and board in community average $750 per academic year. Apartments available at about $40 per month.

FIELDS OF STUDY FOR THE PH.D.

Ceramics. Solid-state chemistry or physics, ceramics, materials, earth sciences. Offered by the State University of New York College of Ceramics at Alfred University. Recommended for graduate study: preparation in field of ceramics. Ph.D. candidacy prerequisites: 3 hours of advanced calculus and differential equations. 16 professorial staff. Ph.D. program begun 1955. 24 master's degrees and 3 Ph.D.'s awarded 1955-59. 26 graduate students registered fall 1959.

American University

WASHINGTON, D. C.

The Graduate School

The Graduate School was chartered in 1893 and has offered instruction since 1914. First Ph.D. was awarded in 1916; Ed.D. degree is also conferred. University is privately controlled and is related to the Methodist Church. Both men and women are admitted.

No residence facilities are provided for graduate students.

Library contains approximately 165,000 volumes. Washington environment offers unusual facilities in terms of experts, libraries, and practitioners, especially in social sciences.

Residence requirement for Ph.D.: 72 semester hours of graduate work of which 30 must be taken in residence at the university; maximum of 36 graduate credits may be transferred from other institutions toward the Ph.D. or Ed.D. (6 toward the master's degree).

ADMISSION REQUIREMENTS

For graduate study: bachelor's degree; superior academic record. For doctoral admission:

master's degree or 30 hours of acceptable graduate work. For candidacy for Ph.D.: completion of 12 hours of course work at the university above master's degree; better than B average in course work; promise of success. Recommended: GRE.

Apply to Office of Admissions, American University, 1901 F Street, N.W., Washington 6, D. C., as early as possible.

FEES AND FIRST-YEAR AID

Application fee $10. Tuition $22 per semester hour ($660 for 30 hours). Special fees approximate $10-$15 annually. Board in college dining room costs $195 per semester (5-day week); $250 per semester (7-day week).

First-year aid available: scholarships, half-tuition to $2,500; graduate assistantships, $800 plus full tuition for 15-20 hours per week.

Apply to Committee on Scholarships, Graduate School, 1901 F Street, N.W., Washington 6, D. C., by March 1.

FIELDS OF STUDY FOR THE PH.D.

Area Studies.—Foreign. Western Europe, Eastern Europe and U.S.S.R., Middle East and North Africa, South and Southeast Asia, Far East, Latin America. Offered by Schools of International Service and Government and Public Administration and by Departments of Economics, History, Education, Philosophy and Religion, and Sociology and Anthropology. 163 graduate students registered fall 1959 (including those registered in International Relations and Organization).

Business Administration. Business management and economics, accounting, finance, industrial management and relations, marketing, real estate and insurance, transportation. Offered by School of Business Administration. 24 professorial staff. 111 master's degrees awarded 1955-59. 298 graduate students registered fall 1959.

Economics and Economic History. Economic theory; money, credit, banking; public finance; international economics; economic geography; agricultural, industrial, and business economics; labor policies. 15 professorial staff. 1 master's degree awarded in economic history 1955-59; 94 master's degrees and 25 Ph.D.'s in general economics. 139 graduate students registered fall 1959.

History. General history of Europe, United States, Far East, Latin America, and other areas;

historiography and methods of research. 13 professorial staff. 32 master's degrees and 9 Ph.D.'s awarded 1955-59. 97 graduate students registered fall 1959.

International Relations and Organization. International organization and administration; international law; theories of international relations; United States diplomacy; international relations of U.S.S.R., Eastern Europe, Far East, Latin America, and other areas; the United Nations. Offered by the School of International Service. 23 professorial staff. 68 master's degrees and 31 Ph.D.'s awarded 1955-59. 163 graduate students registered fall 1959 (including those registered in Foreign Area Studies).

Mathematics. Foundations and algebra; analysis, geometry, and topology; numerical analysis and computer systems. Offered by Department of Mathematics and Statistics. 12 professorial staff. 1 master's degree and 2 Ph.D.'s awarded 1955-59. 125 graduate students registered fall 1959 (including those registered in Statistics).

Political Science.—Government. Political theory, governmental processes, public law, political dynamics, comparative government and politics, state and metropolitan studies, public administration. Offered by School of Government and Public Administration. 39 professorial staff. 21 master's degrees and 9 Ph.D.'s awarded 1955-59. 236 graduate students registered fall 1959 (including those registered in Public Administration).

Political Science. — Public Administration. National, state, and municipal government; organization and management; public personnel administration; record and archives administration; budgetary administration and fiscal policy; police, traffic, and safety. Offered by School of Government and Public Administration. 39 professorial staff. 107 master's degrees and 19 Ph.D.'s awarded 1955-59. 236 graduate students registered fall 1959 (including those registered in Government).

Psychology. Social, experimental, personnel, developmental, and counseling psychology; personality; measurement techniques; history and systems of psychology. 9 professorial staff. 19 master's degrees and 15 Ph.D.'s awarded 1955-59. 111 graduate students registered fall 1959.

Sociology. Sociological theory, social research, social organization, population and society, anthropology. Offered by Department of Sociology and Anthropology. 11 professorial staff. 6 master's degrees and 8 Ph.D.'s awarded 1955-59. 34 graduate students registered fall 1959.

Statistics. Theory of probability and statistics, applied probability and statistics. Offered by Department of Mathematics and Statistics. 12 professorial staff. 9 master's degrees and 2 Ph.D.'s awarded 1955-59. 125 graduate students registered fall 1959 (including those registered in Mathematics).

Arizona, University of

TUCSON, ARIZONA

The Graduate College

Graduate instruction has been offered since 1898, and the first Ph.D. was awarded in 1922. The Graduate College, which administers all advanced degree programs, was established in 1934. In addition to the Ph.D., the Ed.D. and the A.Mus.D. are awarded. Institution is publicly controlled by the state. Both men and women are admitted.

Rooms in university dormitories occasionally available for graduate men; limited number of apartments for married veteran students. Most graduate students live in privately-owned rooms and apartments.

Special facilities include: library of approximately 305,000 volumes; numerical analysis laboratory, including a number of IBM and GE computers and complete card-handling equipment; Triga training and research nuclear reactor; medium and high resolution Philips electron microscopes; radiocarbon laboratory; 6 agricultural research centers.

Residence requirement for Ph.D.: 6 semesters of full-time graduate study, of which at least 2 must be spent in residence at the University of Arizona.

ADMISSION REQUIREMENTS

For graduate study: bachelor's degree; above-average academic record; major in field of chosen graduate study; qualifying examinations. Recommended: previous work in foreign languages; GRE. For candidacy for Ph.D.: completion of 2 years of graduate work; comprehensive examinations in major and minor fields; proficiency examinations in French and German (or approved substitute).

Apply to Dean of the Graduate College or to Admissions Office at any time.

FEES AND FIRST-YEAR AID

No application fee. Registration fee (for all students) $182; additional tuition of $500 for nonresidents of Arizona. Room (in dormitory) for men $196-$256 per year; for women $204-$256. Approximate annual cost of board in college dining room $475. Apartments $28-$35 per month.

First-year aid available: nonresident tuition scholarships; teaching and research assistantships, $600-$2,500.

Apply to head of major department, preferably by March 1; late applications will be considered if vacancies are available.

FIELDS OF STUDY FOR THE PH.D.

Agricultural Biochemistry and Nutrition. Lipid, cholesterol, and protein research; vitamin research; tissue culture studies of inflammatory diseases; utilization of agricultural products; poultry, large animal, and human nutrition; plant biochemistry (fatty acid synthesis). Offered by Department of Agricultural Biochemistry. Prerequisites for graduate study: major in chemistry, biology, or agriculture; courses in general, quantitative, organic and physical chemistry. Recommended: zoology; bacteriology; biochemistry. 15 professorial staff. Ph.D. program begun 1955. 7 master's degrees and 6 Ph.D.'s awarded 1955-59. 18 graduate students registered fall 1959.

Agricultural Chemistry and Soils. Soil chemistry, physics, microbiology, fertility, classification, conservation, or hydrology. Prerequisites for graduate study: major in agricultural chemistry or agriculture; chemistry through quantitative analysis and organic; mathematics through analytical geometry; beginning physics; botany through elementary plant physiology. Recommended: calculus; physical chemistry; modern physics. 13 professorial staff. 15 master's degrees and 2 Ph.D.'s awarded 1955-59. 17 graduate students registered fall 1959.

Agronomy. Crop physiology and plant breeding. Prerequisite for graduate study: major in agronomy, botany, or related plant science. Recommended: basic courses in plant physiology, general botany, genetics, chemistry, physics, and

mathematics. 10 professorial staff. Ph.D. program begun 1955. 11 master's degrees and 2 Ph.D.'s awarded 1955-59. 5 graduate students registered fall 1959.

Anthropology. Archaeology; cultural, physical anthropology; linguistics (with special emphasis on the Southwest). Prerequisite for graduate study: major in anthropology. 8 professorial staff. 25 master's degrees and 14 Ph.D.'s awarded 1955-59. 41 graduate students registered fall 1959.

Bacteriology. Microbiology (bacteriology, mycology, virology, rickettsiae, microbial physiology). Prerequisites for graduate study: major in bacteriology with chemistry minor. 7 professorial staff. Ph.D. program begun 1959. 3 master's degrees awarded 1955-59. 14 graduate students registered fall 1959.

Botany. Physiology, taxonomy, genetics, and anatomy. Prerequisite for graduate study: major in the general field of biology and chemistry. 7 professorial staff. 7 master's degrees and 2 Ph.D.'s awarded 1955-59. 16 graduate students registered fall 1959.

Chemistry. Analytical chemistry; biochemistry; biophysical, organic, inorganic, physical chemistry. Prerequisites for graduate study: 4 years of chemistry, including physical chemistry; calculus; 1 year of physics; German. 14 professorial staff. 20 master's degrees awarded 1955-59. 47 graduate students registered fall 1959.

Economics. Economic theory and history of thought, labor economics, economics of money and banking, public utilities, public finance, statistics. Prerequisite for graduate study: major in economics. Recommended: competence in mathematics, statistics, and accounting; reading knowledge of 1 foreign language. 14 professorial staff. Ph.D. program begun 1960. 5 master's degrees awarded 1955-59. 6 graduate students registered fall 1959.

Education. School administration; guidance; educational psychology; elementary, special, or general education. Prerequisites for graduate study: 3 units of psychology and at least 12 units of education; GRE Aptitude Test; MAT. 28 professorial staff. 361 master's degrees and 3 Ph.D.'s awarded 1955-59. 110 graduate students registered fall 1959. Ed.D. degree also awarded in this field.

Engineering.—Aerospace. Aerospacedynamics, aerodynamics, design, aeroplasticity, instrumentation and automatic controls, propulsion and combustion. Offered by Department of Mechanical Engineering. Prerequisite for graduate study: major in aeronautical engineering or equivalent. 16 professorial staff. Ph.D. program begun 1959. 14 graduate students registered fall 1959.

Engineering.—Civil. Structures, hydraulics, sanitary engineering, soil mechanics, materials, highway and transportation, urban planning and development. Prerequisite for graduate study: major in civil engineering preferred, but applicants with degrees in other physical sciences and engineering fields encouraged to apply. 13 professorial staff. Ph.D. program begun 1959. 3 master's degrees awarded 1955-59. 16 graduate students registered fall 1959.

Engineering. — Electrical. Network theory, electronics, servomechanisms, electromagnetics, power, computers. Prerequisite for graduate study: major in electrical engineering. 18 professorial staff. Ph.D. program begun 1956. 51 master's degrees and 2 Ph.D.'s awarded 1955-59. 85 graduate students registered fall 1959.

Engineering.—Mechanical. Theoretical and applied mechanics, materials, thermodynamics, heat transfer, design, automation and instrumentation, propulsion and combustion. Prerequisite for graduate study: major in mechanical engineering or equivalent. 16 professorial staff. Ph.D. program begun 1959. 7 master's degrees awarded 1955-59. 14 graduate students registered fall 1959.

Engineering Mechanics. Solid or fluid mechanics, vibrations. Offered by Department of Civil Engineering. Prerequisite for graduate study: major in civil, mechanical, or aeronautical engineering, or in engineering mechanics preferred, but applicants with degrees in other physical science fields encouraged to apply. 14 professorial staff. Program begun 1959. 11 graduate students registered fall 1959.

Entomology. Insect taxonomy, physiology, morphology, biology, toxicology; apiculture; biological control; economic entomology. Prerequisites for graduate study: major in entomology or zoology or in appropriate related field with at least 1 course in entomology; broad group of foundation courses in biological and physical sciences. 9 professorial staff. Ph.D. program begun 1955. 10 master's degrees awarded 1955-59. 6 graduate students registered fall 1959.

Geology. Mining geology, petroleum geology, ground water geology, engineering geology, structural geology, stratigraphy, geomorphology, sedimentation, mineralogy, petrography and petrology, geochemistry, geophysics, vertebrate and invertebrate paleontology. Prerequisites for graduate study: 40 units in geology, including 27 upper division; general and analytical chemistry; engineering drawing and descriptive geometry; algebra and plane trigonometry; general physics. 13 professorial staff. 43 master's degrees and 18 Ph.D.'s awarded 1955-59. 90 graduate students registered fall 1959.

History. Latin America, United States, history of the West. Prerequisite for graduate study: major in history; 1 allied field. 10 professorial staff. Ph.D. program begun 1960. 16 master's degrees awarded 1955-59. 31 graduate students registered fall 1959.

Horticulture. Plant physiology, genetics, breeding, ecology, or climatology (with particular reference to fruit, vegetable, and landscape plant materials); specific phases of physiology, including flowering, fruiting, nutrition, and water relations. Prerequisites for graduate study: knowledge of botany, plant physiology, chemistry, physics, genetics, soil science, and mathematics (including statistics). 9 professorial staff. Ph.D. program begun 1955. 9 master's degrees awarded 1955-59. 5 graduate students registered fall 1959.

Mathematics. Prerequisite for graduate study: strong major in mathematics. 18 professorial staff. Ph.D. program begun 1959. 20 master's degrees awarded 1955-59. 45 graduate students registered fall 1959.

Metallurgy. Mineral dressing; extractive or physical metallurgy. Offered by Department of Mining and Metallurgical Engineering. Prerequisite for graduate study: major in metallurgy, metallurgical engineering, chemistry, or physics. 4 professorial staff. Ph.D. program begun 1959. 9 master's degrees awarded 1955-59. 16 graduate students registered fall 1959.

Meteorology. Physical and dynamical meteorology, cloud physics, radar meteorology. Prerequisites for graduate study: mathematics through differential equations; 4 semesters of general physics. 7 professorial staff. Program begun 1957. 9 graduate students registered fall 1959.

Pharmacy. Pharmaceutical chemistry, pharmacology, pharmacognosy. Prerequisite for graduate study: major in pharmacy with 5-year undergraduate curriculum. 6 professorial staff. Ph.D. program begun 1959. 4 master's degrees

awarded 1955-59. 3 graduate students registered fall 1959.

Physics. Solid-state, high-energy physics; theory; spectroscopy; biophysics; cosmic rays. Prerequisite for graduate study: major in physics with supporting work in mathematics. 13 professorial staff. Ph.D. program begun 1959. 5 master's degrees awarded 1955-59. 31 graduate students registered fall 1959.

Plant Breeding. Genetics and breeding of agronomic crops. Prerequisite for graduate study: major in biological sciences or agriculture (including preparation in botany, chemistry, and genetics). Recommended: previous work in mathematics, physics, statistics, plant pathology and physiology. 6 professorial staff. Ph.D. program begun 1957. 2 graduate students registered fall 1959.

Plant Pathology. Diseases of deciduous fruits, citrus and subtropicals, vegetable crops, field and forage crops, or ornamentals; virus diseases; forest pathology; mycology. Prerequisite for graduate study: major in plant pathology, botany, horticulture, agronomy, plant breeding, or entomology. 4 professorial staff. 7 master's degrees awarded 1955-59. 5 graduate students registered fall 1959.

Psychology. Experimental-physiological, clinical, social. Offered by Departments of Philosophy and Psychology. Prerequisite for graduate study: major in psychology, including 1 year of laboratory science and 1 term of statistics. 10 professorial staff. Ph.D. program begun 1957. 14 master's degrees and 1 Ph.D. awarded 1955-59. 30 graduate students registered fall 1959.

Range Management. Noxious plant control, plant-water relations, range ecology or economics. Offered by Department of Watershed Management. Prerequisite for graduate study: major in botany, agriculture, or related biological science. 4 professorial staff. Ph.D. program begun 1955. 12 master's degrees and 2 Ph.D.'s awarded 1955-59. 10 graduate students registered fall 1959.

Spanish. Spanish American or Spanish literature. Offered by Department of Romance Languages. Prerequisite for graduate study: major in Spanish. Recommended: proficiency in German; knowledge of Latin and another Romance language. Ph.D. candidacy prerequisites: Latin and 1 other Romance language in addition to French and German. 11 professorial staff. Ph.D. program begun 1960. 4 master's degrees awarded

1955-59. 13 graduate students registered fall 1959.

Wildlife Management. Wildlife or fisheries management; limnology. Offered by Department of Zoology. Prerequisite for graduate study: major in wildlife management, zoology, biology, or related biological science. 3 professorial staff. Ph.D. program begun 1957. 7 master's degrees awarded 1955-59. 4 graduate students registered fall 1959.

Zoology. Cellular and comparative physiology, vertebrate physiology, invertebrate or radiation zoology, cytology, ecology, embryology, endocrinology, herpetology, histology, ichthyology, mammalogy, ornithology, parasitology, protozoology, vertebrate morphology. Prerequisites for graduate study: major in zoology, including general zoology or biology; 1 semester each of comparative anatomy or embryology, physiology, and genetics or evolution; 1 year each of organic chemistry and physics. Recommended: proficiency in calculus. 13 professorial staff. Ph.D. program begun 1957. 8 master's degrees awarded 1955-59. 25 graduate students registered fall 1959.

Arkansas, University of

FAYETTEVILLE, ARKANSAS

The Graduate School

Graduate work at the master's level has been offered since 1886. The Graduate School was established in 1927. Doctoral programs were inaugurated in 1950, and the first Ph.D. awarded in 1953. A program leading to the Ed.D. degree is also offered through the College of Education. University is publicly controlled by the state. Both men and women are admitted.

Single graduate students live in fraternity and sorority houses, cooperative houses, private homes, and off-campus apartments; married students in university-owned and privately-owned housing.

Special facilities include: library of approximately 385,000 volumes; fine arts center; nuclear science laboratories; linear positive ion accelerator; high vacuum and ion ballistic laboratory; magnetic mass spectrometer; electron microscope; IBM 650 computer. Affiliation with Oak

Ridge Institute of Nuclear Studies provides additional opportunities for research.

Residence requirement for Ph.D.: 3 years beyond bachelor's degree; 1 year of last 2 must be in residence on campus.

ADMISSION REQUIREMENTS

For graduate study: bachelor's degree; satisfactory academic record (evaluation made by Graduate Dean's office and department concerned). GRE and other advisory examinations required in certain special cases. For candidacy for Ph.D.: completion of all but last year of residency; certified reading knowledge of German and French (another language or a research tool may be substituted for 1 language in some departments); candidacy examination; recommendation by department.

Apply to Director of Admissions, Registrar's Office, at any time.

FEES AND FIRST-YEAR AID

No application fee. Fees for state residents $200 per academic year; tuition and fees for others $470. Room (in dormitory) $120-$225 per year. Approximate annual cost of board in college dining room $370. Apartments $65 per month.

First-year aid available: scholarships, $200-$600; teaching fellowships, $750-$2,000; other fellowships, $2,000; research assistantships, $800-$2,000.

Apply to Dean, Graduate School, by April 1.

FIELDS OF STUDY FOR THE PH.D.

Anatomy. Hematology, low temperature biology, neurocytology. Prerequisite for graduate study: major in zoology or equivalent. Recommended: general physics and chemistry; organic chemistry; algebra; French; German. 6 professorial staff. Program initiated 1960. Registration limited to 4 graduate students.

Biochemistry. Nutrition, enzymology, protein chemistry, microbial metabolism. Prerequisites for graduate study: major in chemistry or biology. Biology majors must have had general, organic, and physical chemistry; qualitative and quantitative analysis. Recommended: GRE. 4 professorial staff. 13 master's degrees and 2 Ph.D.'s awarded 1955-59. 12 graduate students registered fall 1959.

Botany and Bacteriology. Microbiology, mycology, physiology (plant), morphology, bacteriology. Prerequisite for graduate study: major in botany or bacteriology. 6 professorial staff. Ph.D. program begun 1959. 6 master's degrees awarded 1955-59.

Business Administration. Accounting, finance, management, marketing. Offered by the Graduate School through the College of Business Administration. Ph.D. candidacy prerequisites: M.B.A. or equivalent; 1 language and 1 research tool. 24 professorial staff. Ph.D. program begun 1959. 70 master's degrees awarded 1955-59. 53 graduate students registered fall 1959.

Chemistry. Analytical, inorganic, organic, nuclear, physical chemistry; biochemistry. Prerequisite for graduate study: 40 semester hours in chemistry (including 8 in general, 8 in analytical, 10 in organic, 8 in physical, 3 in structural); 2 additional advanced courses in chemistry of at least 2 hours credit; elementary physics; mathematics through differential and integral calculus; reading knowledge of scientific German. 14 professorial staff. 41 master's degrees and 18 Ph.D.'s awarded 1955-59. 45 graduate students registered fall 1959.

Comparative Literature. 4 concentrations are required of each student: world literature; literatures of 2 linguistic areas; a period or genre. Offered by Departments of Classics, English, French, German, and Spanish. Prerequisites for graduate study: preparation in literatures of 2 linguistic areas; good reading and comprehension knowledge of at least 1 foreign language. 14 professorial staff. Ph.D. program begun 1958. 2 master's degrees awarded 1955-59. 11 graduate students registered fall 1959.

Economics. Economics, accounting, finance, management, marketing. Minor fields in agricultural economics or a social science, or another field related to student's objective. Offered by the Graduate School through the College of Business Administration. Ph.D. candidacy prerequisites: M.A. in economics or business administration, plus work in economic theory and 3 other fields; 1 language and 2 research tools. 24 professorial staff. 2 master's degrees and 4 Ph.D.'s awarded 1955-59. 17 graduate students registered fall 1959.

Engineering. Agricultural, chemical, civil, electrical, industrial, or mechanical engineering; engineering mechanics. An integrated program of graduate courses in engineering and science to which all engineering departments may contribute. Prerequisite for Ph.D. candidacy: Russian or German (French by special permission). 34 professorial staff. Ph.D. program begun 1958. 56 master's degrees awarded 1955-59. 33 graduate students registered fall 1959.

English. Renaissance; 17th or 18th century; Romantic, Victorian, or contemporary period; American literature; Shakespeare. Prerequisite for graduate study: major or minor in English or equivalent. Recommended: GRE; reading knowledge of French and German. 10 professorial staff. 96 master's degrees and 8 Ph.D.'s awarded 1955-59. 66 graduate students registered fall 1959.

Pharmacology. Pharmacology of autonomic drugs, cardiovascular drugs; chemotherapy; action of drugs on enzyme systems; neuropharmacology. Prerequisites for graduate study: chemistry; biology; physics; biochemistry; physiology. Recommended: physical chemistry; advanced organic chemistry; zoology. Ph.D. candidacy prerequisite: master's degree in pharmacology or related field. 3 professorial staff. 2 master's degrees and 1 Ph.D. awarded 1955-59. 2 graduate students registered fall 1959.

Philosophy. History of philosophy, ethics and social philosophy, logic and philosophy of science. Prerequisite for graduate study: major in philosophy. 3 professorial staff. 8 master's degrees awarded 1955-59. 1 graduate student registered fall 1959.

Physics. Isotope shifts and fine structure studies in atomic spectra, optical polarization studies by electron impact, spectroscopic studies with ion beams, low energy nuclear physics, X-ray diffraction by liquid surfaces, high speed gas dynamics, atomic and nuclear theory. Prerequisites for graduate study: 8 to 10 hours of general physics; 1 course in mechanics; 1 in electricity and magnetism; 1 in any other approved field of physics; differential and integral calculus; differential equations. 5 professorial staff. Ph.D. program begun 1959. 10 master's degrees awarded 1955-59. 16 graduate students registered fall 1959.

Psychology. General, experimental, clinical. Prerequisite for graduate study: 18 semester hours of psychology, including statistics; general and experimental psychology; approval of departmental graduate committee. Recommended: MAT; GRE Aptitude and Advanced Tests. Ph.D. candidacy prerequisite: reading knowledge of 1 modern foreign language. 9 professorial staff. Ph.D. program begun 1959. 14 master's degrees awarded 1955-59. 17 graduate students

registered fall 1959. New enrollment limited to about 15.

Zoology. Developmental, environmental, regulatory, or systematic zoology; genetics. Prerequisites for graduate study: 18 hours in zoology, or biology plus zoology (including general biology); comparative morphology; taxonomy; embryology; genetics; physiology; GRE. Recommended: German and/or French; minimum of 1 year each in chemistry, mathematics, and physics; statistics. 9 professorial staff. Ph.D. program begun 1959. 35 master's degrees awarded 1955-59. 14 graduate students registered fall 1959.

Auburn University

AUBURN, ALABAMA

The Graduate School

The Graduate School was formally organized in 1921, although graduate instruction had been offered since 1870. First Ph.D. was awarded in 1955. The Ed.D. degree is also conferred. Institution is publicly controlled by the state. Both men and women are admitted.

University operates dormitories and apartments for single and married students.

Special facilities include: complete laboratory equipment for nutrition studies, including equipment to conduct labeled element studies; equipment for radioisotope studies; agricultural experiment station; engineering experiment station; animal disease laboratory; cooperative wildlife research unit; fisheries laboratory; nematology laboratory; seed physiology laboratory; weed-control laboratory; tillage machinery laboratory; library of more than 260,000 volumes, including special collection of engineering periodicals.

Residence requirement for Ph.D.: 3 academic years or equivalent beyond bachelor's degree, of which at least 1 year (preferably the last) must be spent in residence on campus. Summer courses available.

ADMISSION REQUIREMENTS

For graduate study: bachelor's degree; letters of recommendation. For candidacy for Ph.D.: preliminary examination and GRE.

Apply to the Dean of The Graduate School 3 weeks before registration.

FEES AND FIRST-YEAR AID

No application fee or tuition. Special fees approximate $240 annually. Room (in dormitory) for men $159 a year (2 to a room); for women $189 (2 to a room). Approximate annual cost of board in college dining room: men $336; women $306. Apartments $60 per month (for 1-bedroom apartment); $67.50 (for 2-bedroom apartment).

Teaching fellowships, graduate assistantships, research fellowships, and research assistantships available in many departments. Stipends range from $900-$2,880.

Apply to head of department not later than February 15.

FIELDS OF STUDY FOR THE PH.D.

Agronomy and Soils. Soil fertility, chemistry, morphology, genesis, and classification; crop management; plant breeding. Prerequisites for graduate study: chemistry; physics; biology; mathematics. 15 professorial staff. Ph.D. program initiated 1959. 15 master's degrees awarded 1955-59. 11 graduate students registered fall 1959.

Animal Sciences.—Animal Husbandry and Nutrition. Nutrition, physiology of reproduction, animal breeding. Prerequisites for graduate study: fundamental science courses. 10 professorial staff. 6 master's degrees and 7 Ph.D.'s awarded 1955-59. 4 graduate students registered fall 1959.

Animal Sciences.—Poultry Husbandry. Pathology, nutrition. Offered in cooperation with Department of Animal Husbandry and Nutrition or Department of Zoology-Entomology. Prerequisites for graduate study: fundamental science courses. 6 professorial staff, plus staff in other 2 departments. 10 master's degrees awarded 1955-59. 7 graduate students registered fall 1959.

Botany and Plant Pathology. Ecology of seed- and soil-borne plant pathogenes, epiphytology of plant pathogenes. Prerequisites for graduate study: botany; chemistry; mathematics; physics; zoology. 10 professorial staff. Ph.D. program initiated 1956. 10 master's degrees awarded 1955-59. 8 graduate students registered fall 1959.

Chemistry. Physical, organic, inorganic chemistry; biochemistry. Prerequisites for graduate study: general, analytical, organic, and physical chemistry; college physics; mathematics through calculus. 17 professorial staff. 17 master's degrees awarded 1955-59. 13 graduate students registered fall 1959.

Engineering.—Agricultural. Power and ma-chinery, soil and water management. Interdisciplinary program offered by Departments of Agricultural Engineering, Civil Engineering, Mechanical Engineering, Mathematics, and Physics. Prerequisites for graduate study: training in basic sciences and engineering; for soil and water option, training in agronomy and soils and in botany and plant pathology. Ph.D. program initiated 1959. 4 master's degrees awarded 1955-59. 6 graduate students registered fall 1959.

Entomology. Offered by Department of Zoology-Entomology. Prerequisites for graduate study: chemistry; physics; biology; and mathematics. 25 professorial staff. 14 master's degrees and 4 Ph.D.'s awarded 1955-59. 12 graduate students registered fall 1959.

Fisheries Management. Offered by Department of Zoology-Entomology. Prerequisites for graduate study: chemistry; biology; physics; mathematics. 25 professorial staff. 11 master's degrees and 2 Ph.D.'s awarded 1955-59. 8 graduate students registered fall 1959.

Game Management. Offered by Department of Zoology-Entomology. Prerequisites for graduate study: chemistry; physics; biology; mathematics. 25 professorial staff. 5 master's degrees and 2 Ph.D.'s awarded 1955-59. 3 graduate students registered fall 1959.

Mathematics. Applied mathematics, algebra, analysis, numerical analysis and computing, topology. Prerequisites for graduate study: 30 quarter hours of mathematics beyond freshman level. 24 professorial staff. 28 master's degrees and 6 Ph.D.'s awarded 1955-59. 48 graduate students registered fall 1959.

Zoology. Offered by Department of Zoology-Entomology. Prerequisites for graduate study: chemistry; physics; biology; mathematics. 25 professorial staff. 4 master's degrees and 1 Ph.D. awarded 1955-59. 4 graduate students registered fall 1959.

Baylor University

WACO, TEXAS

The Graduate School

University consists of ten schools and colleges located in Waco, Dallas, and Houston. It has offered graduate instruction since 1894, and the

Graduate School was formally organized in 1947. First Ph.D. was awarded in 1954. At present Ph.D. programs are offered at the Waco campus, the College of Medicine in Houston, and the Graduate Research Institute in Dallas. The Ed.D. degree is also awarded. All branches are responsible to the Dean of the Graduate School with reference to their graduate work. University is privately controlled and is related to the Baptist Church. Both men and women are admitted.

On Waco campus, rooms in dormitories for graduate students are available when requested. One floor in new men's dormitory reserved for male graduate students. Dormitory for married students also provided.

Residence requirement for Ph.D.: 3 full years beyond bachelor's degree; minimum of 2 consecutive semesters (after first year of graduate study) must be spent in residence on campus. Summer courses and a few evening courses available.

ADMISSION REQUIREMENTS

For graduate study: bachelor's degree; 3.0 GPA in major field and 2.7 GPA in total undergraduate record; adequate preparation in field of proposed graduate study. Recommended: GRE. For candidacy for Ph.D.: reading knowledge of 2 foreign languages (usually French and German, although another language may be substituted for 1 of these if approved by Graduate Council); completion of 60 semester hours of graduate work; preliminary examinations in major and minor fields; approval of Dean of the Graduate School.

Apply to Dean of the Graduate School well in advance of beginning of semester of entry.

FEES AND FIRST-YEAR AID

Application fee $25. Tuition $16.50 per semester hour. Room (in dormitory, Waco campus only) for men $162 per year; for women $224. Approximate annual cost of board in college dining room $330. Apartments $202.50 per semester (average).

First-year aid available: all departments have at least 1 graduate assistantship; many have more. Stipend is usually $100 per month with remission of tuition for 10 semester hours per semester.

Apply to chairman of appropriate department or to Dean of the Graduate School well in advance of fall semester.

FIELDS OF STUDY FOR THE PH.D.

Anatomy. Cancer biology, neuroendocrinology, radiobiology, tissue transplantation, histochemistry, electron microscopy. Offered by Department of Anatomy, College of Medicine, Houston. Prerequisites for graduate study: bachelor's or M.D. degree; 2 years of chemistry; 1 year each biology, physics, mathematics. Recommended: GRE; Medical College Admissions Test. 9 professorial staff. 4 master's degrees and 1 Ph.D. awarded 1955-59. 15 graduate students registered fall 1959.

Biochemistry. Lipids as related to cardiovascular diseases, cancer research, enzyme studies. Offered by Department of Biochemistry, College of Medicine, Houston. Prerequisites for graduate study: bachelor's or M.D. degree; 2 years of chemistry; 1 year each of biology, physics, mathematics. Recommended: GRE; Medical College Admissions Test. 5 professorial staff. 4 master's degrees and 4 Ph.D.'s awarded 1955-59. 13 graduate students registered fall 1959. New enrollment limited to maximum of 8 or 10.

Chemistry. Analytical-inorganic, organic, or physical chemistry; biochemistry. Offered by Department of Chemistry, Waco campus. Prerequisites for graduate study: major in chemistry; reading knowledge of German, French, or Russian; orientation examinations in general, analytical, organic, and physical chemistry. 9 professorial staff. 14 master's degrees and 11 Ph.D.'s awarded 1955-59. 19 graduate students registered fall 1959.

Chemistry. Biochemistry; organic, analytical, or radiochemistry. Offered by Department of Chemistry, Graduate Research Institute, Dallas. Prerequisite for graduate study: major in chemistry; 2 years of 1 foreign language. 3 professorial staff. 5 master's degrees awarded 1955-59. 10 graduate students registered fall 1959.

Cytology and Pathology. Cytology, electron pathology, ultrastructure, molecular pathology (all with special reference to cells of the blood, bone marrow, hemopoietic organs, and the reticuloendothelial system). Offered by Department of Pathology and Clinical Pathology and Department of Anatomy and Embryology, Graduate Research Institute, Dallas. 6 professorial staff. 1 Ph.D. awarded 1955-59. 1 graduate student registered fall 1959. Total enrollment limited to 6.

English. Nineteenth-century English and American literature; English and American drama; modern poetry. Offered by Department of English, Waco campus. Prerequisite for graduate study: 15 semester hours of work in English. 5 professorial staff. 16 master's degrees awarded 1955-59. 17 graduate students registered fall 1959.

Microbiology. Medical microbiology with special attention given to immunology and blood-group serology. Offered by Department of Microbiology, Graduate Research Institute, Dallas. Prerequisite for graduate study: major in biology or M.D. 3 professorial staff. 1 master's degree and 1 Ph.D. awarded 1955-59. 5 graduate students registered fall 1959.

Microbiology and Immunology. Immunology; bacterial physiology and genetics; experimental studies of pathogenesis; mycology. Offered by Department of Microbiology, College of Medicine, Houston. Program supplemented by specific graduate training program in allergy and immunology (USPHS). Prerequisites for graduate study: bachelor's or M.D. degree; 2 years of chemistry; 1 year each biology, physics, mathematics. Recommended: GRE; Medical College Admissions Test. 8 professorial staff. 6 master's degrees and 2 Ph.D.'s awarded 1955-59. 3 graduate students registered fall 1959. USPHS training program admits not more than 2 fellows each year. A very limited number of other trainees are also admitted.

Pharmacology. Cardiovascular or biochemical pharmacology, neuropharmacology, toxicology, chemotherapy. Offered by Department of Pharmacology, College of Medicine, Houston. Prerequisites for graduate study: bachelor's or M.D. degree; 2 years of chemistry; 1 year each biology, physics, mathematics. Recommended: GRE; Medical College Admissions Test. 4 professorial staff.

Physiology. Cardiovascular or respiratory physiology, nervous systems, endocrinology, biophysics. Offered by Department of Physiology. College of Medicine, Houston, Prerequisites for graduate study: bachelor's or M.D. degree; 2 years of chemistry; 1 year each biology, physics, mathematics. Recommended: GRE; Medical College Admissions Test. 11 professorial staff. 2 master's degrees and 1 Ph.D. awarded 1955-59. 7 graduate students registered fall 1959.

Psychology. General experimental, clinical, industrial psychology. Offered by Department of Psychology, Waco campus. Prerequisites for graduate study: 29 semester hours of preparation in psychology; MAT; GRE. Recommended: several courses in related fields. 14 professorial staff. Ph.D. program initiated 1959. 56 master's degrees awarded 1955-59. 30 graduate students registered fall 1959. Program limited to approximately 30.

Virology and Epidemiology. Role of enteroviruses as agents of human disease; viruses and their mechanisms of action, using tissue-culture methods; cytochemical and electron microscopic techniques; use of attenuated polioviruses as live virus vaccines; immunology and epidemiology of poliomyelitis, ECHO, and Coxsackie virus diseases; viral genetics; viruses and cancer. Offered by Department of Virology and Epidemiology, College of Medicine, Houston. Prerequisites for graduate study: bachelor's or M.D. degree; 2 years of chemistry; 1 year each of biology, physics, mathematics. Recommended: GRE; Medical College Admissions Test. 4 professorial staff. Ph.D. program initiated 1959. 1 graduate student registered fall 1959.

Boston College

CHESTNUT HILL 67, MASSACHUSETTS

Graduate School of Arts and Sciences

The Graduate School was not organized until 1925, although graduate instruction had been offered since 1913. The first Ph.D. was awarded in 1932. In 1936 it was decided to discontinue doctoral programs, but the Graduate School continued to award the master's degree. Doctoral programs were reestablished in 1953 with an enlarged faculty and greatly expanded laboratory and library facilities. At present the Ph.D. is awarded in four departments: Economics, Education, History, and Chemistry. The Department of Education offers a program leading to the Ed.D. degree. The college is privately controlled and is conducted by the Jesuit Fathers of the Roman Catholic Church. Emphasis is placed on the liberal arts tradition in education. Both men and women are admitted.

Room (in dormitory) and board available for single men. No residence facilities provided for women or for married graduate students.

Doctoral candidates are expected to take most of course work at Boston College; minimum of 1 year in full-time residence is required.

ADMISSION REQUIREMENTS

For graduate study: bachelor's degree; outstanding collegiate record; 2 languages (preferably French and German); GRE. Recommended: general background in scholastic philosophy. For candidacy for Ph.D.: 60 course hours beyond bachelor's degree; 36-48 hours beyond master's degree; comprehensive examination in 3 fields. Recommended: completion of thesis as part of the master's program.

Apply to the Dean of the Graduate School by March 1 for fall semester; by December 1 for spring semester.

FEES AND FIRST-YEAR AID

No application fee. Tuition $720 a year (24 credits at $30 per credit). Special fees: registration $10; laboratory $60 a year. Annual cost of room and board (for men only) $850. Apartments in community available at $90 and up per month.

First-year aid available: limited number of scholarships, $500-$1,000; 20 teaching fellowships, $1,500-$2,100; 35 assistantships, $1,500; 10 research assistantships, $1,600-$2,400. The above fellowships and assistantships available in doctoral departments only; additional assistantships and scholarships are available in master's programs.

Apply to Dean of Graduate School by March 15.

FIELDS OF STUDY FOR THE PH.D.

Chemistry. Organic, physical. Prerequisite for graduate study: adequate mathematical and collegiate chemistry background or master's degree in chemistry. Recommended: good background in liberal arts and physical sciences. Ph.D. candidacy prerequisite: demonstrated ability in research. 9 professorial staff. Ph.D. program begun 1959. 44 master's degrees awarded 1955-59. 19 graduate students registered fall 1959.

Economics. Economic theory and its history, statistics, monetary economics, economic history, international economics, public policy, labor economics. Prerequisite for graduate study: minimum of 18 upper division hours in economics or master's degree. Recommended: general history of country in which economy is studied. 14 professorial staff. 55 master's degrees and 3 Ph.D.'s awarded 1955-59. 65 graduate students registered fall 1959.

Education. History and philosophy of education, educational psychology and measurement, guidance and measurement, educational administration and supervision, curriculum and instruction. Prerequisite for graduate study: outstanding collegiate record or master's degree in education. Recommended: liberal arts background. 12 professorial staff. 475 master's degrees and 2 Ph.D.'s awarded 1955-59. 168 graduate students registered fall 1959. Ed.D. degree also awarded in this field.

History. American, modern European, medieval. Prerequisites for graduate study: minimum of 18 hours in upper division history or master's degree; qualifying examination in Latin for medieval history. 10 professorial staff. 81 master's degrees and 3 Ph.D.'s awarded 1955-59. 72 graduate students registered fall 1959.

Boston University

BOSTON 15, MASSACHUSETTS

The Graduate School

Graduate instruction has been offered since 1871, and the first Ph.D. was awarded in 1877. The Graduate School, which is essentially a Graduate School of Arts and Sciences, was established in 1874 and awards the A.M. and the Ph.D. degrees only. The School of Theology confers the Th.D., the School of Education the Ed.D., and the School of Fine and Applied Arts the A.Mus.D. University is privately controlled and nonsectarian, although it was founded under the auspices of the Methodist Church. Both men and women are admitted.

Rooms in university dormitories available for single graduate students; 1- and 2-room apartments for married students.

Special facilities include: African Studies program; human relations center; microcirculation laboratory. Library contains approximately 530,000 volumes.

Residence requirement for Ph.D.: 48 semester hours beyond master's degree, of which a minimum of 18 semester hours must be completed in 2 consecutive semesters on campus. 6 graduate credits may be transferred from other institutions toward A.M. degree; 18 credits may be transferred toward Ph.D.

ADMISSION REQUIREMENTS

For graduate study: bachelor's degree; GRE or MAT; proficiency in 1 foreign language. For candidacy for Ph.D.: satisfaction of departmental language requirement; master's degree in chosen field; qualifying examination.

Apply to Secretary of Admissions, Boston University Graduate School, 725 Commonwealth Avenue, Boston 15, Massachusetts, by August 1 for fall semester; by January 15 for spring term.

FEES AND FIRST-YEAR AID

Application fee $10. Tuition $1,150 per academic year. Special fees approximate $15-$25 annually. Room (in dormitory) and board $850 per year. Apartments $65-$75 per month.

First-year aid available: 2 scholarships (amounts individually determined); 65 teaching fellowships, $1,200-$1,800 plus tuition; research fellowships, up to $2,500; 60 teaching assistantships, full tuition.

Apply to Dean, Boston University Graduate School, 725 Commonwealth Avenue, Boston 15, Massachusetts, by February 20.

FIELDS OF STUDY FOR THE PH.D.

Programs designed to increase the effectiveness of the candidate as a college teacher include: predoctoral internship programs in biology and history; colloquium in the teaching of English; directed study in the teaching of philosophy; seminar in higher education.

Anatomy. Neurology, histology, embryology, gross anatomy. Prerequisites for graduate study: background in biology, physics, or chemistry; premedical program; course in vertebrate morphology. 7 professorial staff. 1 master's degree and 10 Ph.D.'s awarded 1955-59.

Biochemistry. Biochemistry of cancer, enzymes, nucleic acids, steroids, immunochemistry, blood groups, intermediate metabolism, human genetics. Graduate study prerequisites: chemistry (organic, inorganic, physical); quantitative analysis; calculus; analytical geometry; anatomy; biochemistry; vertebrate morphology. 7 professorial staff. 6 master's degrees and 5 Ph.D.'s awarded 1955-59. 14 graduate students registered fall 1959.

Biology. Peripheral vascular system, cytology and growth, endocrinology, entomology, parasitology, ornithology, botany, microbiology, experimental or aquatic biology, ichthyology, cyto-

genetics, cellular or applied physiology, biochemistry, genetics. Prerequisites for graduate study: 26 semester hours beyond elementary biology; 6 hours each of general chemistry and physics. Recommended: applied electronics; statistics. 25 professorial staff. 75 master's degrees and 24 Ph.D.'s awarded 1955-59. 40 graduate students registered fall 1959. Total graduate registration limited to 60-80.

Chemistry. Analytical, inorganic, organic, physical. Prerequisite for graduate study: major in chemistry. 8 professorial staff. 7 master's degrees and 21 Ph.D.'s awarded 1955-59. 25 graduate students registered fall 1959. Total enrollment limited to 35.

Church History. History of Christian institutions or Christian biography; the Church in the Roman world, in the Middle Ages, in the Reformation, in the modern world, in America, or in the East. Offered by School of Theology. Ph.D. candidacy prerequisite: S.T.B. or equivalent. 3 professorial staff. 3 master's degrees and 5 Ph.D.'s awarded 1955-59. 12 graduate students registered fall 1959.

Economics. Economic theory and its history, economic history or statistics, labor, monetary theory and policy, international economics, corporation finance, public control of industry. Prerequisite for graduate study: background in economics. 12 professorial staff. 14 master's degrees and 2 Ph.D.'s awarded 1955-59. 14 graduate students registered fall 1959. Total enrollment limited to 20-25.

Ecumenics, Missions, and World Religions. Offered by School of Theology. Prerequisite for graduate study: experience in interdenominational or missionary work. Ph.D. candidacy prerequisite: S.T.B. or equivalent. 4 professorial staff. Ph.D. program begun 1957. 2 master's degrees awarded 1955-59. 5 graduate students registered fall 1959.

English Language and Literature. American or English literature. Recommended for graduate study: knowledge of French and German. 19 professorial staff. 91 master's degrees and 17 Ph.D.'s awarded 1955-59. 66 graduate students registered fall 1959.

Fine Arts. Classical, Early Christian, or medieval art; Renaissance art of Italy; Baroque, modern, American, or French art. Prerequisites for graduate study: knowledge of European history; 12 hours of art history. 4 professorial staff. 31

master's degrees and 1 Ph.D. awarded 1955-59. 14 graduate students registered fall 1959.

Geography. Physical, regional, systematic. 4 professorial staff. Ph.D. program begun 1955. 12 master's degrees awarded 1955-59. 15 graduate students registered fall 1959.

Geology. Mineralogy and crystallography, petrology and petrography, geomorphology and meteorology, areal or economic geology, historical geology and paleontology, tectonics. Prerequisites for graduate study: 1 year each of physics, mathematics, and chemistry. 4 professorial staff. 26 master's degrees and 7 Ph.D.'s awarded 1955-59. 11 graduate students registered fall 1959.

German. German literature and linguistics. Prerequisites for graduate study: reading knowledge of German; written French examination. 4 professorial staff. 10 master's degrees and 3 Ph.D.'s awarded 1955-59. 12 graduate students registered fall 1959.

Government. American government and politics, state and municipal government, comparative government, international relations and organization, political theory, public administration and public policy, government and politics of Africa. 10 professorial staff. 69 master's degrees and 4 Ph.D.'s awarded 1955-59. 41 graduate students registered fall 1959.

History. European, Far East, Near East, English, French, Ancient, Middle Ages, or American history; African studies. Offered by Department of History and Government. 14 professorial staff. 128 master's degrees and 14 Ph.D.'s awarded 1955-59. 74 graduate students registered fall 1959.

Mathematics. Numerical analysis, applied mathematics, mathematical statistics, measure theory, algebra. Prerequisite for graduate study: 36 hours of mathematics. 5 professorial staff. 18 master's degrees and 3 Ph.D.'s awarded 1955-59. 25 graduate students registered fall 1959.

Microbiology. Prerequisites for graduate study: quantitative analysis and general bacteriology; premedical program; vertebrate morphology. Recommended: bacteriology; immunology; parasitology. 4 professorial staff. 4 master's degrees and 2 Ph.D.'s awarded 1955-59. 2 graduate students registered fall 1959.

Music. Musicology, music education. Prerequisites for graduate study: general aptitude tests; tests in music history, theory, and performance. 10 professorial staff. 27 master's degrees and 12

Ph.D.'s awarded 1955-59. 18 graduate students registered fall 1959.

New Testament. The Gospels, Acts, Paul's letters, Hebrews, general Epistles and Revelations; introductory work in canon and text. Offered by School of Theology. Prerequisites for graduate study: introduction to New Testament, Old Testament, and Synoptic Gospels. Ph.D. candidacy prerequisites: S.T.B. or equivalent in New Testament; Greek and Hebrew. 5 professorial staff. Ph.D. program begun 1957. 2 master's degrees awarded 1955-59. 7 graduate students registered fall 1959.

Old Testament. Old Testament, introduction and canon; history of Israel, including archaeology; religion of Israel; Old Testament languages (Hebrew and Aramaic). Offered by School of Theology. Ph.D. candidacy prerequisite: S.T.B. or equivalent. 2 professorial staff. Ph.D. program begun 1957. 2 master's degrees awarded 1955-59. 5 graduate students registered fall 1959.

Pathology. Prerequisites for graduate study: premedical program; course in vertebrate morphology. Ph.D. candidacy prerequisites: M.D., D.V.M., or good standing in medical or veterinary school; general pathology. 4 professorial staff.

Pharmacology. General or behavioral pharmacology, chemotherapy, metabolic actions and metabolism of drugs, autonomic nervous system, carcinogenesis, inductive enzymes, biometrics. Prerequisites for graduate study: premedical program; course in vertebrate morphology. 10 professorial staff. 3 master's degrees and 3 Ph.D.'s awarded 1955-59. 2 graduate students registered fall 1959.

Philosophy. Metaphysics, social philosophy, philosophy of religion. Prerequisite for graduate study: 12 hours of philosophy. 12 professorial staff. 18 master's degrees and 12 Ph.D.'s awarded 1955-59. 39 graduate students registered fall 1959.

Philosophy of Education. Combined program offered by Departments of Philosophy and Education. Ph.D. candidacy prerequisite: 1 year of teaching experience or internship under direction of Philosophy of Education committee. 13 professorial staff. Ph.D. program begun 1956. 7 graduate students registered fall 1959.

Physics. Experimental and theoretical physics; low-energy nuclear or theoretical plasma physics; statistical or molecular quantum mechanics; nuclear magnetic resonance; irreversible thermodynamics; theoretical optics and communication theory; foundations of quantum theory; elementary particles; radio and meteor astronomy, philosophy of science. Prerequisites for graduate study: major in physics, including at least 7 semester courses beyond general physics; mathematics through 1 year of advanced calculus. 10 professorial staff. 28 master's degrees and 5 Ph.D.'s awarded 1955-59. 28 graduate students registered fall 1959.

Physiology. General, cardiovascular, and respiratory physiology; muscle physiology; endocrinology. Prerequisites for graduate study: premedical program; course in vertebrate morphology. Recommended for Ph.D. candidates: histology; comparative anatomy; biostatistics. 5 professorial staff. 8 master's degrees and 8 Ph.D.'s awarded 1955-59. 6 graduate students registered fall 1959.

Psychology. Clinical, counseling, experimental, industrial, or social and personality psychology. Prerequisites for graduate study: experimental and general psychology; elementary statistics. Ph.D. candidacy prerequisite: statistics in psychology. 17 professorial staff. 88 master's degrees and 54 Ph.D.'s awarded 1955-59. 158 graduate students registered fall 1959. New enrollment limited to 50 candidates for M.A., 20 for Ph.D.

Psychology and Pastoral Counseling. Psychology of religion, history of psychology, or pastoral psychology. Offered by School of Theology. Ph.D. candidacy prerequisite: S.T.B. or equivalent. 5 professorial staff. 12 master's degrees and 12 Ph.D.'s awarded 1955-59. 23 graduate students registered fall 1959.

Religious Education. Religious education, religions in higher education. Offered by School of Theology. Ph.D. candidacy prerequisite: S.T.B. or equivalent. 6 professorial staff. 7 master's degrees and 8 Ph.D.'s awarded 1955-59. 12 graduate students registered fall 1959.

Romance Languages and Literature. French, Spanish, Italian (in combination). Prerequisites for graduate study: reading examination in German; basic knowledge of Latin. 9 professorial staff. 20 master's degrees and 3 Ph.D.'s awarded 1955-59. 30 graduate students registered fall 1959.

Social Ethics and Sociology of Religion. Offered by School of Theology. Ph.D. candidacy prerequisites: foundation courses in the social

sciences; broad liberal arts training; S.T.B. or equivalent. 6 professorial staff. 5 master's degrees and 7 Ph.D.'s awarded 1955-59. 14 graduate students registered fall 1959.

Sociology and Anthropology. Cultural anthropology, the community, criminology and social deviation. Ph.D. candidacy prerequisites: master's degree in sociology or anthropology or minimum of 15 semester hours of graduate work in these subjects. 9 professorial staff. 20 master's degrees and 4 Ph.D.'s awarded 1955-59. 18 graduate students registered fall 1959.

Systematic Theology. Offered by School of Theology. Recommended for graduate study: concentration in philosophy. Ph.D. candidacy prerequisite: S.T.B. or equivalent. 4 professorial staff. 9 Ph.D.'s awarded 1955-59. 21 graduate students registered fall 1959.

Brandeis University

WALTHAM 54, MASSACHUSETTS

Graduate School of Arts and Sciences

Graduate School was organized in 1953, and the first Ph.D. was awarded in 1957. Programs are individualized by keeping classes small, by providing apprentice-type training, and by maintaining very close and continuous contact between students and faculty. Degrees are granted on evidence of intellectual growth and development rather than solely on the basis of formal course credits. Institution is privately controlled and nonsectarian, although it was founded under Jewish auspices. Both men and women are admitted.

The D.S.W. is granted by the Florence Heller Graduate School for Advanced Studies in Social Welfare, which is under the aegis, and on the campus, of Brandeis University.

No residence facilities are provided. Special facilities include: Florence Heller School for Advanced Studies in Social Welfare (1959-60); Goldfarb Library (1959) with stack capacity for 750,000 volumes.

Residence requirement for the Ph.D.: 2 academic years, of which at least 1 year must be taken in residence at Brandeis. Summer courses available.

ADMISSION REQUIREMENTS

For graduate study: bachelor's degree; high scholastic qualifications. Recommended: GRE. For candidacy for Ph.D.: reading knowledge of 2 foreign languages (usually French and German); qualifying examinations.

Apply to the Dean of the Graduate School of Arts and Sciences before April 1.

FEES AND FIRST-YEAR AID

Application fee $5. Tuition $1,250 per year. Special health fee $40. Approximate annual cost of board in college dining room $550.

First-year aid available: 75 scholarships, up to $1,250; 50 teaching fellowships, $2,250; 20 other fellowships, $2,400. 10 research assistantships, $2,000.

Apply to the Dean of the Graduate School of Arts and Sciences before March 1.

FIELDS OF STUDY FOR THE PH.D.

No courses specifically in the methodology of teaching are offered, but a special effort is made to see that all Ph.D. candidates have some experience as teaching assistants.

Anthropology. Anthropological linguistics, human variation, primitive religion, modern cultures, middle American civilizations, archeology, the American Indian, African and Caribbean cultures. Prerequisite for graduate study: degree in anthropology or sociology-anthropology is preferred. 8 professorial staff. Ph.D. program begun 1959. 5 graduate students registered fall 1959.

Area Studies.—Mediterranean. The Achaemenian Age, cuneiform records of Anatolia and adjacent areas, the origins of Western culture, Mediterranean developments throughout antiquity, Middle Ages and modern times, the Amarna age of synthesis, history of the ancient Near East, history of Hellenic civilization, language studies (Akkadian, Arabic, Aramaic, Egyptian, Hebrew, Ugaritic, Amharic, Coptic, Ethiopian [Geez], Persian, Turkish). Prerequisite for graduate study: Hebrew; Greek; Latin. 4 professorial staff. Ph.D. program begun 1958. 2 master's degrees and 1 Ph.D. awarded 1955-59. 14 graduate students registered fall 1959.

Area Studies.—Near Eastern and Judaic. Semitic languages and literature (Akkadian, Arabic, Aramaic, Egyptian, Hebrew, Ugaritic), history of ancient Near East, cuneiform studies, Islamic studies, Biblical studies, Jewish history, medieval Jewish philosophy and mysticism. Other fields on approval; reading courses in Amharic, Coptic, Ethiopian (Geez), Persian, and Turkish available on demand. Ph.D. candidacy prerequisite: 2 Semitic languages; 2 modern foreign languages. 5 professorial staff. 19 master's degrees and 6 Ph.D.'s awarded 1955-59. 16 graduate students registered fall 1959.

Biochemistry. Enzyme-catalyzed reactions, immunochemistry, biochemical genetics, radiobiology, malignancy, protein chemistry, chemical embryology, neurochemistry, chemotherapy. Prerequisites for graduate study: courses in biology and chemistry subject to approval by faculty; advanced tests in field. 15 professorial staff. Ph.D. program begun 1957. 1 Ph.D. awarded 1957-59. 15 graduate students registered fall 1959.

Biology. Comparative physiology, cytogenetics, microbial genetics and metabolism, vertebrate physiology, invertebrate zoology. Prerequisite for graduate study: major in biology or close equivalent preferred. 10 professorial staff. Ph.D. program begun 1956. 2 master's degrees awarded 1955-59. 24 graduate students registered fall 1959.

Biophysics. Cellular biology, biochemistry, biology, chemistry, physics, mathematics, physical chemistry (including thermodynamics), an area of biophysics research under study by members of the faculty (photobiology, radiobiology, virus reproduction, muscle contraction, etc.). Offered by Graduate Committee on Biophysics. Prerequisites for graduate study: organic and physical chemistry; atomic and nuclear physics; differential equations; courses in cellular biology. 8 professorial staff. Ph.D. program begun 1958. 2 graduate students registered fall 1959.

Chemistry. Advanced inorganic chemistry, qualitative and advanced organic chemistry, chemical thermodynamics, statistical thermodynamics, chemical kinetics, quantum mechanics. Prerequisites for graduate study: physics; higher mathematics; general-analytical, organic, and physical chemistry. 10 professorial staff. 11 master's degrees awarded 1955-59. 19 graduate students registered fall 1959.

English. Restoration comedy, classic American historians, modern comedy, American drama, history and structure of the English language, fiction, poetry, advanced exposition, the American novel, Victorian and Renaissance literature, criticism. Prerequisites for graduate study: major in English or American literature preferred; reading knowledge of Latin, plus French, German, or Greek. Ph.D. candidacy prerequisites: M.A. in English; distinguished master's examination; reading knowledge of 2: Greek, French, Italian, Latin, German. 12 professorial staff. 25 master's degrees and 1 Ph.D. awarded 1955-59. 35 graduate students registered fall 1959.

History. Reformation and Counter-Reformation, medieval philosophy, political thought, intellectual history of England, America, 12th and 13th centuries, the Renaissance and Reformation in 16th century England, modern European thought, history of philosophy, history of social and political theory, history of religion. Prerequisite for graduate study: degree in history, politics, philosophy or sociology. Recommended: GRE. 8 professorial staff. 15 master's degrees awarded 1955-59. 22 graduate students registered fall 1959.

Mathematics. Foundations of analysis, differential geometry, algebraic geometry, algebraic topology, topological groups, homological algebra, complex analytic manifolds. Prerequisite for graduate study: 1 foreign language. Recommended: GRE. 7 professorial staff. Ph.D. program initiated 1957. 4 master's degrees awarded 1955-59. 12 graduate students registered fall 1959.

Music. Historical analysis of music, problems in history of liturgical chant in Middle Ages, history of 16th century music, notation of music in the Middle Ages, 20th century techniques, counterpoint, history and practice of music criticism, homophonic forms, composition, orchestration. Prerequisites for graduate study: examples of advanced work in musical theory and original work in musical composition; moderate proficiency at piano. For composition applicants: evidence of proficiency in piano or other orchestral instrument with standard solo repertory. Ph.D. candidacy prerequisite: reading knowledge of French, German, and Italian; M.F.A. with distinction. 5 professorial staff. 28 master's degrees awarded 1955-59. 23 graduate students registered fall 1959.

Physics. Mathematical physics, quantum mechanics, thermodynamics and kinetic theory, statistical mechanics, particle physics, quantum theory of solids, nuclear physics, astrophysics, theory of ionized gases. Program normally open only to Ph.D. candidates; reading knowledge of 2 languages (French, German, Russian) required for M.A. 11 professorial staff. Ph.D. program begun 1956. 3 master's degrees awarded 1955-59. 28 graduate students registered fall 1959.

Psychology. Personality theory, aesthetics, social interaction, clinical psychology, experimental and comparative psychology, motivation and emotion, symbolic and cognitive processes, human and animal learning, child psychology, psychoanalytic theory, social psychology, psychotherapy, clinical psychopathology. Prerequisites for graduate study: major in psychology, natural, or social sciences; GRE (Advanced, Aptitude, and Profile Tests); MAT; proficiency (evaluated) in history and systems of psychology, abnormal psychology, elementary experimental methods, physiological psychology. M.A. candidates not accepted. 9 professorial staff. 3 master's degrees and 2 Ph.D.'s awarded 1955-59. 26 graduate students registered fall 1959.

Social Welfare. Social work and policy, contributions of socio-psychological concepts and theory to social welfare, research methods, social administration, process of social welfare planning, public welfare, social aspects of mental health programs, social aspects of medical care, service for the aging in modern society, social work and the law, international social welfare programs, trends in social welfare services. Prerequisites for graduate study: M.A. or M.S.W.; appropriate personal qualifications; successful professional experience. Both Ph.D. and D.S.W. granted. 4 professorial staff plus visiting lecturers and professors. Ph.D. program begun 1959. 17 graduate students registered fall 1959.

Brigham Young University

PROVO, UTAH

The Graduate School

Although graduate instruction has been offered since 1916, work on the doctoral level is relatively new. It is anticipated that the first Ph.D. will be awarded in 1961. At present, Ph.D. programs are offered in several areas and the Ed.D. degree is also awarded. University is privately controlled and is related to the Church of Jesus Christ of

Latter-day Saints. Both men and women are admitted.

Graduate students are accommodated in regular student housing on and off campus; university-owned apartments are maintained for married students.

Residence requirement for Ph.D.: the equivalent of 3 years of full-time study; 2 years (including the last) must usually be spent at Brigham Young. Advisory committee has authority to accept or require up to 2 years of full-time study elsewhere. Summer and evening courses available.

ADMISSION REQUIREMENTS

For graduate study: student must have demonstrated high quality scholarship, capacity for research or creativity, facility in written and oral expression, and appropriate professional objectives. For Ph.D. candidacy: 2 years of graduate study; comprehensive examinations; proficiency in 2 modern foreign languages, 1 of which must be French or German.

Apply to Dean of the Graduate School 2 months before admission is desired.

FEES AND FIRST-YEAR AID

No application fee. Tuition $260 per year. Room (in dormitory) for men, $540 per year; for women $225-$540. Approximate annual cost of board in college dining room $416. Apartments $40-$50 per month.

First-year aid available: 20 scholarships, $260-$2,200; approximately 175 teaching fellowships, $850-$1,700; 20 other fellowships, $500-$1,750; 45 research assistantships, $2,000-$2,800; 20 grants-in-aid, $260.

Apply to Dean of the Graduate School before March 15.

FIELDS OF STUDY FOR THE PH.D.

Chemistry. Analytical-physical chemistry; biochemistry; inorganic, organic, or physical chemistry; basic chemistry minor. Prerequisites for graduate study: departmental entrance examinations in 4 areas of chemistry. Recommended: German and/or French. 18 professorial staff. 25 graduate students registered fall 1959.

Geology. Stratigraphy, sedimentation, paleontology, mineralogy, petrography, economic geology. Prerequisites for graduate study: major in geology; qualifying examinations. 8 professorial

staff. Ph.D. program initiated 1958. 30 master's degrees awarded 1955-59. 15 graduate students registered fall 1959.

History. Western America, United States to 1865, United States since 1865 (in these students may do dissertation research). Ancient, medieval, Europe 1500-1815, Europe 1789 to present, Latin America, Asia (these are supporting fields). Prerequisite for graduate study: major in history or equivalent. 11 professorial staff. Ph.D. program initiated 1958. 24 master's degrees awarded 1955-59. 13 graduate students registered fall 1959.

Human Development and Family Relationships. Child development, marriage and family relationships, marriage counseling. Prerequisite for graduate study: major in human development and family relationships or closely related area, such as psychology or sociology. Ph.D. candidacy prerequisites: advisory evaluative examination. Program is affiliated with the Merrill-Palmer School in Detroit, Michigan, and 1 year of work must be done in residence there. 4 professorial staff. Ph.D. program initiated 1959. 11 master's degrees awarded 1955-59. 19 graduate students registered fall 1959.

Music. Music education, musicology, music theory. Prerequisite for graduate study: Music Department qualifying examination. 18 professorial staff. Ph.D. program initiated 1958. 34 master's degrees awarded 1955-59. 3 graduate students registered fall 1959.

Physics. Quantum mechanics, astrophysics, thermodynamics and statistical mechanics, nuclear physics, acoustics, atomic physics and spectroscopy, solid-state physics. Prerequisite for graduate study: approval of department chairman; placement examinations. Ph.D. candidacy prerequisite: approval of dissertation subject. 13 professorial staff. Ph.D. program initiated 1959. 21 master's degrees awarded 1955-59. 15 graduate students registered fall 1959.

Psychology.—Educational. Conducted by the Department of Educational Research and Services. Prerequisites for graduate study: minor in psychology and elementary or secondary certification; Ohio State Psychological Examination; Strong Vocational Interest Blank; MMPI; Cooperative General Culture Test; GED Correctness and Effectiveness of Expression; interview with department members. 13 professorial staff. Ph.D. program initiated 1960. 30 master's de-

grees awarded 1955-59. 33 graduate students registered fall 1959.

Psychology.—General and Clinical. Experimental, physiological, or comparative psychology; statistical analysis; psychological measurement; individual differences; learning; social psychology; personality; developmental psychology; clinical psychology. Prerequisite for graduate study: 27 quarter hours of core courses in psychology. 6 professorial staff. Ph.D. program initiated 1959. 19 master's degrees awarded 1955-59. 15 graduate students registered fall 1959.

Religion. Bible and modern scripture, history and philosophy of religion. Prerequisites for graduate study: background information in field; entrance examination. 14 professorial staff. Ph.D. program initiated 1959. 29 master's degrees awarded 1955-59. 16 graduate students registered fall 1959.

Sociology. Sociological theory, research methods, social disorganization, demography and ecology, social organization, marriage and the family, social psychology, anthropology. Prerequisite for graduate study: master's degree in sociology; screening examinations in sociological theory, statistics, research methods, and social disorganization. Ph.D. candidacy prerequisites: 2 years of graduate study. 10 professorial staff. Ph.D. program initiated 1958. 4 master's degrees awarded 1955-59. 12 graduate students registered fall 1959.

Brooklyn, Polytechnic Institute of

BROOKLYN 1, NEW YORK

Graduate School of Science and Engineering

Graduate instruction has been offered since 1902, and the first Ph.D. was awarded in 1935. The Graduate School of Science and Engineering was organized in 1936. Although it offers a full-time day program of graduate studies, most of its Ph.D. programs are offered on a part-time basis to scientists and engineers employed by industrial, educational, and governmental institutions located in the greater New York area. The Institute

is privately controlled and nonsectarian. Both men and women are admitted.

Other doctorates conferred by the Institute are: Doctor of Aeronautical Engineering; Doctor of Chemical Engineering; Doctor of Electrical Engineering; and Doctor of Mechanical Engineering.

No residence facilities are provided for graduate students, but single rooms and apartments are available in the vicinity of the Institute.

Unusual research facilities organized under the microwave research institute, polymer research institute, and the areodynamics research laboratory. A graduate research center is under construction at Farmingdale, Long Island, which will provide for broad-spectrum research in several fields.

Residence requirement for doctorate: 1 year of full-time residence or its equivalent in part-time residence; credits may be transferred from other graduate institutions if residence requirement is met. Maximum of 6 units may be transferred for master's degree. Summer and evening courses available.

ADMISSION REQUIREMENTS

For graduate study: bachelor's degree in appropriate field; specific preparation for graduate work in field of interest. Recommended: GRE (required for foreign students); professional experience beyond bachelor's degree. For candidacy for the Ph.D.: qualifying examinations (both written and oral); completion of required courses with merit grades; language examination in German, French, or Russian.

Apply to Director of Admissions at any time.

FEES AND FIRST-YEAR AID

Application fee: $5 for part-time studies; $10 for full-time. Tuition $1,200 per year. Laboratory fees approximate $50 per year. Single rooms in community average $300 per academic year. Approximate annual cost of board in college dining room $525. Apartments (in community) $60-$75 per month.

First-year aid available: 50 teaching fellowships, $1,800 plus tuition remission; 70 research assistantships, $3,300-$3,900 (no tuition remission); 25 tuition-plus grants-in-aid. Graduate assistantships providing opportunities on sponsored research projects are available; stipends vary with qualifications of applicant.

Apply to Associate Dean of the Graduate School by February 1.

FIELDS OF STUDY FOR THE PH.D.

Special seminars on the methodology of teaching are held in each department.

Applied Mechanics. Aircraft structures, applied mechanics, and elasticity. Offered by Department of Aeronautical Engineering and Applied Mechanics. Ph.D. candidacy prerequisite: M.S. and collateral professional experience. 15 professorial staff. 19 master's degrees and 21 Ph.D.'s awarded 1955-59. 4 full-time and 60 part-time graduate students registered fall 1959.

Chemistry. Inorganic, organic, physical, and polymer. Prerequisite for graduate study: B.S. in chemistry. 26 professorial staff. 100 master's degrees and 101 Ph.D.'s awarded 1955-59. 117 full-time and 270 part-time graduate students registered fall 1959.

Mathematics. Applied mathematics, analysis, mathematical statistics, mathematical synthesis, and algebra. Ph.D. candidacy prerequisites: M.S. in mathematics. 24 professorial staff. Ph.D. program initiated 1958. 12 master's degrees awarded 1955-59. 2 full-time and 35 part-time graduate students registered fall 1959.

Physics. Physics, X-ray crystallography, solid-state physics, and electrophysics. Ph.D. candidacy prerequisite: M.S. in physics and collateral professional experience. 18 professorial staff. 20 master's degrees and 8 Ph.D.'s awarded 1955-59. 12 full-time and 109 part-time graduate students registered fall 1959.

Brown University

PROVIDENCE 12, RHODE ISLAND

The Graduate School

Graduate instruction was established in 1887, and the first Ph.D. was awarded in 1889. Three years later graduate instruction was opened to women. The Graduate School was founded in 1927 and the programs of instruction have increased greatly since that time. Brown is privately controlled and nonsectarian.

The Graduate Center provides dormitory housing for about 57 graduate men and recreational facilities for all graduate students. No campus housing provided for women or married students.

Special facilities include: library of approximately 906,000 volumes (including Harris collection of American poetry and plays); museum of the American Indian; laboratories for high vacuum electronics, ultrasonics research, nuclear physics, engineering research; computing center; Institute for Research in the Health Sciences; foreign language laboratory. Affiliation with American School of Classics (Athens) and American Academy (Rome) afford additional opportunities for study and research.

Residence requirement for Ph.D.: minimum of 3 years beyond bachelor's degree; at least 1 beyond master's degree must be devoted to full-time study at Brown.

ADMISSION REQUIREMENTS

For graduate study: bachelor's degree or equivalent; scholarship record of distinction (particularly in field of major); 3 letters of recommendation. Recommended: reading knowledge of 2 foreign languages; GRE Aptitude Test. For candidacy for Ph.D.: 1 semester beyond master's degree or equivalent in residence; reading knowledge of 2 foreign languages (usually French, German, or Russian); preliminary examination.

Apply to the Registrar of the Graduate School as early as possible, preferably by April 15.

FEES AND FIRST-YEAR AID

Application fee $5. Tuition $1,250 per academic year. Room (in Graduate Center) for men $300 per academic year. Room (in community) $8-$12 per week. Approximate annual cost of board in college dining room $440-$470.

First-year aid available: 18 tuition scholarships (some include additional aid up to $900); approximately 65 teaching fellowships, $1,800 plus tuition for ¾ of program; 75 other fellowships, $1,000-$2,000 plus tuition; approximately 35 research assistantships, $2,750-$3,250.

Apply to Dean of the Graduate School by February 15.

FIELDS OF STUDY FOR THE PH.D.

While no courses in the methodology of teaching are offered, every candidate is required to serve as a teaching assistant or teaching associate for at least 1 year.

American Civilization. History and culture of America: art, architecture, literature, music, economic and social history, political thought, philosophy, religion, science. Offered by Committee on American Civilization with faculty from Departments of History, English, Music, Economics, Biology, Political Science, American Literature, Philosophy, Art, Bibliography. Prerequisites for graduate study: courses in American history, history of Western Europe, history of philosophy, history and literature of England. 14 professorial staff. 7 master's degrees and 9 Ph.D.'s awarded 1955-59. 15 students registered fall 1959.

Applied Mathematics. Courses in mathematic fundamentals and particular fields of applied mathematics. Emphasis of program is on ability to analyze physical situations by use of mathematical tools. Prerequisites for graduate study: courses in engineering, physics, mathematics. 15 professorial staff. 27 master's degrees and 26 Ph.D.'s awarded 1955-59. 31 graduate students registered fall 1959.

Biology. Physiology, biochemistry, microbiology, developmental biology, cytology, genetics. Prerequisites for graduate study: courses in biology; background in physics, chemistry, and mathematics. 16 professorial staff. 31 master's degrees and 18 Ph.D.'s awarded 1955-59. 46 graduate students registered fall 1959.

Botany. Taxonomy, general morphology, plant physiology, cytogenetics, mycology and plant pathology. Prerequisite for graduate study: major in biological sciences with emphasis on botany. 3 professorial staff. 4 master's degrees awarded 1955-59. 2 graduate students registered fall 1959.

Chemistry. Physical, organic, inorganic. Prerequisites for graduate study: fundamental courses in general, analytical, physical, and organic chemistry; basic courses in physics, mathematics, and biology. 13 professorial staff. 7 master's degrees and 34 Ph.D.'s awarded 1955-59. 55 graduate students registered fall 1959.

Classics. Greek and Latin language and literature, history, archaeology, art. Prerequisite for graduate study: substantial number of courses in Greek and Latin. Ph.D. candidacy prerequisites: examination in sight translation of Latin and Greek in addition to examinations in 2 modern foreign languages. 5 professorial staff. Ph.D. program begun 1959. 13 master's degrees awarded 1955-59. 5 graduate students registered fall 1959.

Economics. Economic theory and its history; monetary theory and institutions; corporations and public control of industry; economic history; labor, mathematical, or international economics; statistics and econometrics; public finance; comparative economic systems. Prerequisite for graduate study: major in economics or other social science; GRE. 10 professorial staff. 11 master's degrees and 4 Ph.D.'s awarded 1955-59. 23 graduate students registered fall 1959.

Egyptology. Fields of Egyptian language and literature. Prerequisite for graduate study: ancient history; elementary knowledge of Greek and 1 Semitic language, preferably Akkadian or Hebrew; competent reading knowledge of French and German. 3 professorial staff. 1 master's degree and 1 Ph.D. awarded 1955-59. 2 graduate students registered fall 1959.

Engineering. Applied mechanics and materials, aerodynamics and thermodynamics, electronics and communications. Prerequisites for graduate study: courses in mechanics of materials and structures, elementary electrical engineering, thermodynamics, fluid mechanics, or hydraulics; courses in engineering on senior-year level; mathematics through elementary differential equations; chemistry; physics; engineering drawing; descriptive geometry; mechanics. 35 professorial staff. 19 master's degrees and 4 Ph.D.'s awarded 1955-59. 47 graduate students registered fall 1959.

English. English language and literature; American literature. Prerequisite for graduate study: concentration in English or American literature. Ph.D. candidacy prerequisite: reading knowledge of Latin in addition to French and German. 22 professorial staff. 31 master's degrees and 19 Ph.D.'s awarded 1955-59. 64 graduate students registered fall 1959.

Geology. Petrology of igneous or metamorphic rocks, geochemistry, paleontology, stratigraphy, sedimentation, and structural geology. Prerequisites for graduate study: major in geology or major in biology, chemistry, mathematics, or physics with main courses in geology. Ph.D. candidacy prerequisite: field experience. 4 professorial staff. Ph.D. program begun 1960. 10 master's degrees awarded 1955-59. 8 graduate students registered fall 1959.

History. American, European, English history; economics; social and intellectual history; history of science. Prerequisite for graduate study: basic training in history with broad study in humanities and social sciences. 12 professorial staff. 7 master's degrees and 6 Ph.D.'s awarded 1955-59. 29 graduate students registered fall 1959.

History of Mathematics. History of the exact sciences in antiquity and the Middle Ages. Prerequisites for graduate study: training in mathematics and astronomy or in classics and history. 2 professorial staff. 1 master's degree and 1 Ph.D. awarded 1955-59. 1 graduate student registered fall 1959.

Mathematics. Analysis, algebra, topology. Prerequisites for graduate study: thorough basic training in mathematics. 10 professorial staff. 13 master's degrees and 9 Ph.D.'s awarded 1955-59. 39 graduate students registered fall 1959.

Modern Languages. French, German, Italian, or Spanish linguistics; Slavic languages. Prerequisites for graduate study: command of major language, spoken and written, and adequate knowledge of its literature; proficiency in reading a third language in addition to French and German. Candidates in Slavic languages will offer a second Slavic language besides major and will be expected to have basic knowledge of Old Church Slavonic as well as understanding of development and structure of modern Russian. Recommended: Latin. 29 professorial staff. 17 master's degrees and 14 Ph.D.'s awarded 1955-59. 33 graduate students registered fall 1959.

Philosophy. Historical, with emphasis on contemporary philosophies. Prerequisite for graduate study: adequate training in philosophy. 9 professorial staff. 18 master's degrees and 6 Ph.D.'s awarded 1955-59. 26 graduate students registered fall 1959.

Physics. Physical acoustics; low-temperature, solid-state, low-energy nuclear, or high-energy physics; high-vacuum electronics; radiofrequency and microwave spectroscopy. Prerequisites for graduate study: major in physics; elements of chemistry; mathematics through calculus and differential equations. 20 professorial staff. 25 master's degrees and 26 Ph.D.'s awarded 1955-59. 65 graduate students registered fall 1959.

Political Science. American government, foreign governments, international politics and organization. Prerequisite for graduate study: major in political science or the social sciences. 5 professorial staff. 10 master's degrees and 4 Ph.D.'s awarded 1955-59. 9 graduate students registered fall 1959.

Psychology. Experimental-sensory, experimental child psychology; learning. Prerequisites for graduate study: major in psychology; at least 1 course each in mathematics, chemistry, physics, and biology; facility in use of statistical methods. Recommended: GRE; MAT. 13 professorial staff. 20 master's degrees and 11 Ph.D.'s awarded 1955-59. 33 graduate students registered fall 1959.

Religious Studies. Prerequisite for graduate study: competence in basic areas of religious studies. 4 professorial staff. 4 master's degrees awarded 1955-59. 5 graduate students registered fall 1959.

Sociology. Prerequisites for graduate study: adequate preparation in general sociology or a related social science field. 8 professorial staff. 13 master's degrees and 2 Ph.D.'s awarded 1955-59. 12 graduate students registered fall 1959.

Bryn Mawr College

BRYN MAWR, PENNSYLVANIA

The Graduate School

First college instruction was offered by Bryn Mawr in 1885 and, from the beginning, graduate students have constituted about 20 per cent of the student body. First Ph.D. was awarded in 1888. The college is privately controlled and nonsectarian, although trustees must be members of the Society of Friends. Undergraduate enrollment limited to women, but since 1931 men have been admitted to graduate study leading to degrees. Since 1958 a few scholarships have been provided for men.

Under a reciprocal plan with the University of Pennsylvania, candidates for higher degrees at one institution may take 1 or 2 courses at the other upon recommendation of the respective graduate deans.

Dormitory facilities for 46 women students; no facilities for men or for married students.

Special facilities include: Marjorie Walter Goodhart Mediaeval Library (incunabula numbering 900 volumes); small but important collections in Departments of Archaeology and History of Art; large mineral collection; laboratory nursery school; Child Study Institute.

Residence requirement for Ph.D.: 2 full years of graduate work at Bryn Mawr; no transfer of graduate credit, although such work is taken into consideration in evaluating candidate's readiness for Ph.D. preliminary examinations. Requirement may be reduced to 1 year for holders of Bryn Mawr bachelor's degree and teaching assistants.

ADMISSION REQUIREMENTS

For graduate study: bachelor's degree in liberal arts; good academic record; major in field of proposed graduate work (in most cases). For candidacy for Ph.D.: 1 year of successful graduate work at Bryn Mawr; examinations in 2 modern foreign languages (usually French and German); preliminary examinations in field of specialization.

Apply to Dean of the Graduate School before the first day of registration each semester.

FEES AND FIRST-YEAR AID

No application fee. Tuition $1,000 (for 8-month academic year). Room (in dormitory) and board $1,000 per academic year.

First-year aid available: 8 scholarships, $1,000; 24 scholarships, $1,600; 10 foreign scholarships; 19 teaching assistantships, $1,400-$1,800 plus part-time tuition; 8 research assistantships, $1,400-$1,800 and part-time tuition; 5 or 6 grants-in-aid (for resident scholars), up to $300. Other assistance includes employment of 9 Wardens of Halls of Residence at $1,400 plus part-time tuition, and 3 or 4 staff assistants at various stipends plus part-time tuition.

For scholarships, apply before March 1 to Dean of the Graduate School; for assistantships to Dean of the Graduate School or to department chairman; for Warden's position to Dean of the College.

FIELDS OF STUDY FOR THE PH.D.

Archaeology. Greek and Roman archaeology (sculpture, architecture, vase painting, numismatics, topography, prehistory), Near Eastern archaeology. Offered by Department of Classical and Near Eastern Archaeology. Prerequisite for graduate study: major in archaeology or 2 years with major in Greek, Latin, or history of art. Recommended: some knowledge of Greek. Ph.D. candidacy prerequisite: reading knowledge of ancient Greek or ancient Near Eastern language. 2 professorial staff. 1 master's degree and 6 Ph.D.'s awarded 1955-59. 6 graduate students registered fall 1959.

Biology. Biochemistry, cytology, embryology, genetics, physiology. Prerequisite for graduate study: major in biology; courses in general and organic chemistry. 5 professorial staff. 8 master's degrees and 1 Ph.D. awarded 1955-59. 12 graduate students registered fall 1959.

Chemistry. Organic, physical. Prerequisites for graduate study: inorganic, organic, analytical and physical chemistry; mathematics; physics. 4 professorial staff plus 1 lecturer. 5 master's degrees and 5 Ph.D.'s awarded 1955-59. 13 graduate students registered fall 1959.

Economics. Economic theory, history of economic thought, industrial organization. Prerequisite for graduate study: economics major or a minor in economics with work in history and political science. Ph.D. candidacy prerequisite: knowledge of statistics and mathematics. 3 professorial staff and 1 lecturer. 7 master's degrees awarded 1955-59. 2 graduate students registered fall 1959.

Education. History and philosophy of education; educational, developmental, and child psychology; guidance; research and measurement. Offered by Department of Education and Child Development. Prerequisite for graduate study: liberal arts subjects and psychology. Ph.D. candidacy prerequisite: working knowledge of statistics. 2 professorial staff plus 2 lecturers. 7 master's degrees awarded 1955-59. 14 graduate students registered fall 1959.

English. English literature from Old and Middle English to present; seminar in philology offered by German Department. Prerequisite for graduate study: English major or equivalent, including critical and historical studies of several periods of English literature and training in at least 1 other humanities field. Ph.D. candidacy prerequisite: Latin for mediaeval period candidates. 9 professorial staff. 14 master's degrees and 1 Ph.D. awarded 1955-59. 18 graduate students registered fall 1959.

Fine Arts. Far Eastern, French 19th century, mediaeval period, Renaissance. Offered by Department of History of Art. Prerequisite for graduate study: preparation in art history. 4 professorial staff. 6 master's degrees and 1 Ph.D. awarded 1955-59. 12 graduate students registered fall 1959.

French. Old French philology and literature, modern French literature. Prerequisites for graduate study: secondary school French; 3 years of college French; advanced French literature;

ability to discuss and report in French; 2 years of secondary school Latin. Ph.D. candidacy prerequisite: German, plus Italian or Spanish. 4 professorial staff. 6 master's degrees and 1 Ph.D. awarded 1955-59. 5 graduate students registered fall 1959.

Geology. Mineralogy-petrology, paleontology-stratigraphy, regional and structural geology. Prerequisites for graduate study: general, physical, and paleontologic-stratigraphic geology; courses in physics, chemistry, biology, and mathematics. 3 professorial staff. 3 master's degrees and 3 Ph.D.'s awarded 1955-59. 13 graduate students registered fall 1959.

German. German literature, philology, Old Norse. Prerequisites for graduate study: 3 years of college German, including advanced German and German literature; Latin. Recommended: Greek for philology candidates. Ph.D. candidacy prerequisite: 1 or more German dialects; French. 3 professorial staff. 5 master's degrees and 3 Ph.D.'s awarded 1955-59. 1 graduate student registered fall 1959.

Greek. Poetry, tragedy, comedy, orators, historians, and other areas. Prerequisite for graduate study: 4 years of college Greek with readings from literature and history; Latin. Ph.D. candidacy prerequisites: German and French; rigorous Greek sight examination. 2 professorial staff. 2 master's degrees and 3 Ph.D.'s awarded 1955-59. 2 graduate students registered fall 1959.

History. American, British, modern European, mediaeval. Prerequisites for graduate study: courses in history, humanities, social sciences; French or German; Latin for mediaevalists. Ph.D. candidacy prerequisite: historiography. 5 professorial staff. 13 master's degrees and 6 Ph.D.'s awarded 1955-59. 7 graduate students registered fall 1959.

Italian. Dante, Provençal, Old Italian, criticism, and other areas. Prerequisite for graduate study: major or minor in Italian with ability to speak, read, and write the language. Prerequisite for Ph.D. candidacy: French and German (Latin may be substituted for one); proficiency in spoken Italian; some work outside department. 1 professor. 1 graduate student registered fall 1959.

Latin. Classical or mediaeval literature, Roman history and religion, classical scholarship, epigraphy paleography. Prerequisite for graduate study: at least 3 years college Latin; some Greek. Ph.D. candidacy prerequisites: sight examinations in French, German, and Latin. Greek sight

examination before final oral. 3 professorial staff. 5 master's degrees and 2 Ph.D.'s awarded 1955-59. 3 graduate students registered fall 1959.

Mathematics. Functional analysis, measure theory. Prerequisite for graduate study: major in mathematics or mathematics and physics. 3 professorial staff. 3 master's degrees awarded 1955-59. 2 graduate students registered fall 1959.

Mediaeval Studies. Mediaeval history, art, philosophy, languages and literatures. Offered by Faculty of Mediaeval Studies (representatives from Departments of English, French, History, History of Art, Italian, Latin, and Philosophy). Prerequisites for graduate study: major in one of the humanities; a modern European language; 2 years of Latin (preferably in college). Ph.D. candidacy prerequisites: graduate work in 2 of the departments; probably 2 modern European languages plus Latin or Icelandic; other requirements undetermined. 7 interdepartmental staff. Ph.D. program begins 1960.

Music. History of music, theory and interpretation of music (mediaeval, Renaissance, baroque, 19th and 20th centuries). Prerequisites for graduate study: 3 years of history and appreciation; 2 years of harmony, counterpoint, and analysis; ability to play, on piano or organ, music of technical difficulty of a Bach figured chorale. 4 professorial staff. Ph.D. program begun 1958. 3 master's degrees awarded 1955-59. 2 graduate students registered fall 1959.

Philosophy. History of philosophy and systematic philosophy; ethics, aesthetics, metaphysics, epistemology, German idealism, 17th century rationalism, and other areas. 6 professorial staff and 1 lecturer. 4 master's degrees and 2 Ph.D.'s awarded 1955-59. 9 graduate students registered fall 1959.

Physics. Classical mechanics, electromagnetic theory, nuclear physics, quantum mechanics, solid-state or chemical physics. Prerequisite for graduate study: degree in physics, mathematics, chemistry, or engineering. For Ph.D. candidacy: mathematics usually required as cognate. 4 professorial staff. 3 master's degrees and 1 Ph.D. awarded 1955-59. 24 graduate students registered fall 1959.

Political Science. Comparative government, constitutional law, world community and law, public administration, Western political thought, Chinese political and social development. 4 professorial staff. 3 master's degrees awarded 1955-59. 6 graduate students registered fall 1959.

Psychology. Sensation and perception, learning and thinking, personality and social psychology, tests and measurements, history of psychology. Prerequisites for graduate study: MAT; psychology or related degree. Ph.D. candidacy prerequisite: test in statistics and experimental design. 5 professorial staff. 7 master's degrees and 3 Ph.D.'s awarded 1955-59. 23 graduate students registered fall 1959.

Russian. Language: Serbo-Croatian; Old Church Slavonic; history of the Russian language. Literature: Pushkin; Lermontov; 18th century critics. Prerequisite for graduate study: ability to speak and read Russian; knowledge of the literature. Ph.D. candidacy prerequisite: an allied field is chosen from any language or literature, European history, or political science. 3 professorial staff. Ph.D. program begun 1959. 4 graduate students registered fall 1959.

Social Work. Social welfare, the social services, research methods (group work, casework, administration and organization, statistics). Emphasis on research. Offered by The Carola Woerishoffer Graduate Department of Social Work and Social Research. Prerequisite for graduate study: social sciences major (with occasional exceptions). Ph.D. candidacy prerequisites: normally completion of work for master's in social work; basic statistics; one language, preferably French. 6 professorial staff plus 4 or 5 lecturers. 77 master's degrees and 3 Ph.D.'s awarded 1955-59. 75 graduate students registered fall 1959.

Sociology and Anthropology. Anthropology: anthropological theory and history (primitive religions, cultural dynamics, ethnography). Sociology: sociological theory, comparative institutions. Prerequisite for graduate study: background in sociology and/or anthropology with a cognate social science. Ph.D. candidacy prerequisites: some work in the other departmental field; those in sociology must have statistics and social research; 1 year of graduate work taken at another approved institution. 4 professorial staff. 4 master's degrees awarded 1955-59. 5 graduate students registered fall 1959.

Spanish. Modern Spanish drama, modern novel, picaresque novel, Cervantes. Prerequisite for graduate study: Spanish major with representative reading in the literature. Ph.D. candidacy prerequisite: an allied field chosen from any other literature, European or Spanish-American history, classical or Romance philology. 3 profes-

sorial staff. 4 master's degrees and 2 Ph.D.'s awarded 1955-59. 4 graduate students registered fall 1959.

Buffalo, University of

BUFFALO 14, NEW YORK

Graduate School of Arts and Sciences

The Graduate School of Arts and Sciences supervises all Ph.D. graduate work offered by the university. It was organized in 1939, although graduate instruction had been offered since 1923 and the first Ph.D. was awarded in 1926. The School of Education offers a program leading to the Ed.D. degree. The Roswell Park Division of the Graduate School is located in the Roswell Park Memorial Institute for the Study of Malignant Diseases; courses and research lead to the Ph.D. at the university. Institution is privately controlled and nonsectarian. Both men and women are admitted.

Rooms for single graduate students available in 6 dormitories; no residence facilities for married students.

Library contains approximately 355,000 volumes, including outstanding collection of the notebooks and published works of James Joyce and extensive collection of modern poetry. Other facilities include: nuclear research center with 1-megawatt reactor, Van de Graaff accelerator, etc.; Carbon Research Institute; psychological clinic; speech clinic; Chronic Disease Research Institute; affiliation with Institute for Study of Malignant Diseases.

Not more than half of total credits between bachelor's degree and Ph.D. may be transferred from other graduate institutions; minimum residence requirement 1 year, additional requirement in some departments. Summer and evening courses available.

ADMISSION REQUIREMENTS

For graduate study: bachelor's degree; C+ average; background in appropriate field of concentration; personal letter outlining aims; letter of recommendation. For candidacy for Ph.D.: approval of proposed program of study; examinations in 2 modern foreign languages (acquisition of a special skill is sometimes permitted in lieu of knowledge of a second foreign language); preliminary examination in major field.

Apply to the Dean of the Graduate School of Arts and Sciences before August 15 for fall term; before January 1 for spring term.

FEES AND FIRST-YEAR AID

Application fee $10. Tuition $1,000 per year. Special fees approximate $15-$25 per year. Room (in dormitory) and board $840 annually.

First-year aid available: approximately 15 scholarships, 1/4 to full tuition; over 100 teaching fellowships, $900-$2,000 plus tuition scholarships; small number of other fellowships, $200-$1,250; small number of research assistantships with a variable stipend on hourly basis.

Apply to department chairman for teaching and research assistantships before March 15 for fall semester; to Dean of Graduate School for other first-year aid.

FIELDS OF STUDY FOR THE PH.D.

Interdepartmental seminar in college teaching offered jointly by the Graduate School and the School of Education. It is devoted to the classroom activities of college teachers (including methods of teaching, evaluation of students, nature of the learning process, and curriculum development) and to the activities and services of college teachers outside the classes.

Anatomy. Human anatomy, vertebrate histology, neuroanatomy, cellular ultrastructure. Prerequisite for graduate study: superior accomplishment in biology and chemistry. 5 professorial staff. 2 master's degrees and 3 Ph.D.'s awarded 1955-59. 4 graduate students registered fall 1959.

Bacteriology and Immunology. Bacteriology, immunochemistry, virology. Prerequisites for graduate study: thorough grounding in biology, chemistry, and physics; minimum of B average in biology and bacteriology courses. Ph.D. candidacy prerequisite: 1 calendar year residence. 9 professorial staff. 5 master's degrees and 3 Ph.D.'s awarded 1955-59. 12 graduate students registered fall 1959.

Biochemistry. Isolation, extraction, and metabolism of tissue extractives; intermediary metabolism of carbohydrates and lipids and hydrogen transport mechanisms; interrelationship of amino acids and lipid metabolism. Prerequisites for graduate study: calculus; physical chemistry. 3 professorial staff. 5 master's degrees and 6

Ph.D.'s awarded 1955-59. 5 graduate students registered fall 1959.

Biology.—General. Animal behavior, bacteriology, cellular biology, ecology, embryology, endocrinology, genetics, histology, invertebrate zoology, mycology, plant physiology, radiation biology. Offered by Department of Biology. Prerequisites for graduate study: biology major or equivalent; chemistry through organic; physics; mathematics through calculus; reading knowledge of French or German; GRE. 10 professorial staff. 16 master's degrees and 2 Ph.D.'s awarded 1955-59. 14 graduate students registered fall 1959.

Biology.—Mammalian. Mammalian genetics, cytology, endocrinology, cell physiology, cytochemistry. Offered by Roswell Park Division. Prerequisites for graduate study: biology; inorganic chemistry plus either organic chemistry or biochemistry; physics; B average; reading knowledge of German. 7 professorial staff.

Biophysics.—General. Transport processes, physical chemistry of macromolecules, radiobiology, replication, bio-electric phenomena, crystallography, thermodynamics of biological systems. Offered by Department of Biophysics. Prerequisites for graduate study: 1 year of physics and biology; mathematics through differential equations; organic and physical chemistry. 3 professorial staff. Ph.D. program begun 1959. 4 graduate students registered fall 1959.

Biophysics.—Physics Applications to Biological Problems. Radiation physics, theoretical and experimental methods in biophysics, physical aspects of cell growth. Offered by the Roswell Park Division. Prerequisites for graduate study: general and 3 specialized fields of physics; biology; organic chemistry; calculus; reading knowledge of French, German, or Russian. 1 professor.

Business Administration. Marketing, industrial relations, business organization, accounting, statistics. Prerequisite for graduate study: adequate background in accounting, accounting principles, economic principles, money and banking, financial organization, business law, corporation finance, economic statistics, marketing principles. 16 professorial staff. 3 Ph.D.'s awarded 1955-59. 2 graduate students registered fall 1959.

Chemistry.—Biological Systems. Physical, organic, bio- and immuno-chemistry of biological systems. Offered by the Roswell Park Division. Prerequisites for graduate study: chemistry major, including physical chemistry; differential and integral calculus; B average; reading knowledge of German. 7 professorial staff.

Chemistry.—General. Rates of precipitation reactions, analytical methods for fission elements, neutron activation analysis, coordination compounds, phase studies of boron compounds, cyanoformamidines and oxamidines, cyanogen reactions, trifluoroacetonitrile reactions, organic derivatives of silicon, phosphorus and sulfur, halogenated mercaptans, chemotherapeutic compounds, isotopic exchange reactions, kinetics of inorganic reactions, physical chemistry of the fission process, properties of polyelectrolytes, dielectric properties of polymers, ion-exchange and electrochemical properties of fused salt systems, mechanism of organic reactions. Offered by Department of Chemistry. Prerequisites for graduate study: chemistry major, including physical chemistry; differential and integral calculus; B average; reading knowledge of German. 8 professorial staff. 20 master's degrees and 18 Ph.D.'s awarded 1955-59. 53 graduate students registered fall 1959.

Economics. Economic theory, business cycles, money and banking, public finance and taxation, government control of business, economic development, international economic problems, public utilities, transportation, labor problems, history of economic thought. Prerequisite for graduate study: major in economics. 3 professorial staff. 5 graduate students registered fall 1959.

Engineering Mechanics. Offered by Department of Engineering. Prerequisite for graduate study: master's degree in engineering field of specialty. 20 professorial staff. Ph.D. program begun 1960.

English. Romantic movement, American literature, literary criticism, modern literature, drama. 9 professorial staff. 11 master's degrees and 1 Ph.D. awarded 1955-59. 33 graduate students registered fall 1959.

History and Government. Medieval Europe, Renaissance and Reformation, England since 1688, Latin America, the Colonies and the Revolution (to 1789), international relations, political theory, comparative government, constitutional law, U.S. government, political parties, public administration. Prerequisite for graduate study: major in history. 7 professorial staff. 17 master's degrees awarded 1955-59. 26 graduate students registered fall 1959.

Linguistics. Offered by the Department of Anthropology and Linguistics. Prerequisites for graduate study: knowledge of social science and psychology; competence in 2 foreign languages or in English studies and 1 foreign language. Recommended: work in biology and mathematics. Ph.D. candidacy prerequisite: attendance at 1 summer Linguistic Institute sponsored by Linguistic Society of America. 3 professorial staff. Ph.D. program begun 1957. 2 master's degrees awarded 1955-59. 6 graduate students registered fall 1959.

Mathematics. Algebra, analysis, topology. Prerequisite for graduate study: minimum of 6 semester hours of upperclass courses in algebra, geometry, and analysis. 5 professorial staff. 18 master's degrees and 2 Ph.D.'s awarded 1955-59. 55 graduate students registered fall 1959.

Pharmacology. Renal function, cardiovascular system, synaptic transmission at autonomic ganglia and the neuromuscular junction, smooth muscle, absorption and excretion of anesthetic gases. Offered by Department of Pharmacology. Prerequisite for graduate study: GRE. Recommended: physical chemistry. 4 professorial staff. 2 Ph.D.'s awarded 1955-59. 4 graduate students registered fall 1959.

Pharmacology. Offered by Roswell Park Division. Prerequisites for graduate study: credits in chemistry through physical; physics; calculus; biology beyond general biology; personal interview. 3 professorial staff.

Pharmacy. Chemistry of natural products, including antibiotics, alkaloids, glycosides and steroids; synthesis of medicinals. 8 professorial staff. 4 master's degrees awarded 1955-59. 2 graduate students registered fall 1959.

Philosophy. Logic, theory of knowledge, theory of values, metaphysics, history of philosophy. 5 professorial staff. 5 master's degrees and 4 Ph.D.'s awarded 1955-59. 10 graduate students registered fall 1959.

Physics. Atomic and molecular, theoretical, and nuclear physics; biophysics; mechanical, thermal, optical, and electrical properties of solids. Prerequisite for graduate study: major in physics preferred, but persons with exceptional records and advanced work in physics considered. 5 professorial staff. 5 master's degrees and 11 Ph.D.'s awarded 1955-59. 41 graduate students registered fall 1959.

Physiology. — General. Cardio-pulmonary, neural, renal, and cellular physiology. Offered by Department of Physiology. Prerequisites for graduate study: courses in biology, physics, calculus, and organic and physical chemistry. 7 professorial staff. 3 master's degrees and 4 Ph.D.'s awarded 1955-59. 4 graduate students registered fall 1959.

Physiology of Human Diseases. Fields of physiology related to the understanding and treatment of human diseases. Offered by the Roswell Park Division. Prerequisites for graduate study: physics; chemistry (organic, analytical, and physical); general and mammalian physiology; biochemistry; calculus. 3 professorial staff.

Psychology. Major programs are in general-experimental and clinical and counseling psychology, but concentration may also be in physiological, social, developmental, abnormal, personality, or perception psychology. Prerequisites for graduate study: above-average undergraduate record; B average in psychology courses; MAT; GRE, including Advanced Examination in Psychology. 14 professorial staff. 4 master's degrees and 28 Ph.D.'s awarded 1955-59. 55 graduate students registered fall 1959.

Sociology. Sociological research, medical sociology. Prerequisite for graduate study: knowledge of general sociology, social theory, elementary statistics. 6 professorial staff. 4 master's degrees awarded 1955-59. 23 graduate students registered fall 1959.

California Institute of Technology

PASADENA, CALIFORNIA

The graduate school is not separately organized, although graduate instruction has been offered since 1916 and the first Ph.D. was awarded in 1920. Undergraduate and graduate student body are about of equal size. Emphasis is placed on research. Opportunities for interdisciplinary studies are provided. Institute is privately controlled and nonsectarian. Although women are accepted on the graduate level occasionally, students are predominantly men.

Limited residence facilities provided at present. Beginning fall of 1961, graduate student houses will provide housing for about 165 men; no residence facilities for women or for married students planned.

On-campus facilities include: computing center; 115,000-volume library with special collections on the history of physical sciences and mathematics. Off-campus facilities include: large telescopes on Mount Wilson and Mount Palomar; radio telescopes at Palomar and Bishop; seismological laboratory; jet propulsion laboratory.

Residence requirement for the Ph.D.: 3 years of graduate study; at least 1 in residence on campus. No summer or evening courses, but research programs may continue throughout summer.

ADMISSION REQUIREMENTS

For graduate study: bachelor's degree in science or engineering; high scholastic standing. Recommended: GRE. For candidacy for Ph.D.: reading knowledge of 2 foreign languages (usually French, German, or Russian); satisfaction of course requirements; oral examination in field of study; evidence of research ability.

Apply to the Graduate Office before February 15. Later applications considered if vacancies are available.

FEES AND FIRST-YEAR AID

No application fee. Tuition $1,275 for 3 quarters; no tuition is charged for summer except for final examinations. Room (in graduate student houses to be opened in 1961) approximately $400 per year.

First-year students may apply for any of the following, but these are also open to second- and third-year students: 300 tuition scholarships; 175 teaching fellowships, $1,320-$1,650 (9 months); 70 other fellowships, tuition plus $1,100-$3,000 (9 months); 80 research assistantships, normally from $1,320 (9 months) to $2,500 (12 months).

Apply to the Graduate Office before February 15. Later applications considered if vacancies are available.

FIELDS OF STUDY FOR THE PH.D.

Astronomy. Stellar spectroscopy, composition of the universe, nature and contents of our own galaxy and extragallactic nebulae, stellar evolution, position and identification of radio sources, 21cm hydrogen line study, radio astronomy, origin of the elements. Offered by Division of Physics, Mathematics, and Astronomy. Prerequisite for graduate study: B.S. in physics or advanced training in astronomy. 10 professorial staff. 8 master's degrees and 7 Ph.D.'s awarded 1955-59. 9 graduate students registered fall 1959.

Biology. Animal and plant biochemistry; bioorganic chemistry; experimental embryology; animal, plant, and chemical genetics; immunology; biophysics; mammalian, comparative, and plant physiology; psychobiology; virology. Prerequisite for graduate study: major in biology. 23 professorial staff. 2 master's degrees and 30 Ph.D.'s awarded 1955-59. 23 graduate students registered fall 1959.

Chemistry and Chemical Engineering. Inorganic, analytical, physical, organic, theoretical chemistry; chemical engineering. Prerequisite for graduate study: major in chemistry. 28 professorial staff. 57 master's degrees and 78 Ph.D.'s awarded 1955-59. 95 graduate students registered fall 1959.

Engineering.—Aeronautical. Fluid mechanics, jet propulsion, solid mechanics, applied elasticity, applied aerodynamics, magnetohydrodynamics. Prerequisite for graduate study: major in engineering. 14 professorial staff. 55 engineer's degrees, 103 master's degrees, and 37 Ph.D.'s awarded 1955-59. 89 graduate students registered fall 1959.

Engineering.—Civil and Mechanical—Engineering Science. Environment health; hydraulic, structural, mechanical engineering; physical metallurgy; soil mechanics; jet propulsion; solid, fluid, and thermodynamics; engineering science. Prerequisite for graduate study: major in engineering. 36 professorial staff. 10 engineer's degrees, 178 master's degrees, and 32 Ph.D.'s awarded 1955-59. 92 graduate students registered fall 1959.

Engineering.—Electrical. Communication and information theory, servomechanisms, microwave, physical electronics and field theory, machine computation and engineering analysis, solid-state fundamentals. Prerequisite for graduate study: major in engineering. 13 professorial staff. 171 master's degrees and 17 Ph.D.'s awarded 1955-59. 85 graduate students registered fall 1959.

Geology. Petrology, geophysics, seismology, geochemistry, geochronology, paleoecology, glaciology, sedimentation. Prerequisite for graduate study: major in geology. 20 professorial staff. 57 master's degrees and 23 Ph.D.'s awarded 1955-59. 58 graduate students registered fall 1959.

Mathematics. Group theory, lattice theory, matrix theory, algebraic and analytic theory of numbers, topology, functional analysis, differential equations, asymptotic series, special functions, numerical analysis, applied mathematics. Offered by Division of Physics, Mathematics, and Astronomy. Prerequisite for graduate study: major in mathematics. 14 professorial staff. 7 master's degrees and 11 Ph.D.'s awarded 1955-59. 16 graduate students registered fall 1959.

Physics. Experimental and theoretical research in classical and nuclear physics, high-energy nuclear physics, cosmic rays, precision measurements of gamma and beta rays, elementary particle studies, optical spectra and transition probabilities, cryogenics, problems related to stellar and interstellar matter, cosmology, astrophysics, plasma physics, quantum theory, and nuclear structure. Offered by Division of Mathematics, Physics, and Astronomy. Prerequisite for graduate study: major in physics. 29 professorial staff. 44 master's degrees and 67 Ph.D.'s awarded 1955-59. 128 graduate students registered fall 1959.

California, University of

BERKELEY 4, CALIFORNIA

The University of California has campuses in Berkeley, Davis, La Jolla, Los Angeles, Riverside, Santa Barbara, and San Francisco. The Graduate Division is divided into 2 sections: the Northern Section which has jurisdiction over the graduate programs offered on the Berkeley, Davis, and San Francisco campuses; the Southern Section which has jurisdiction over the graduate programs offered on the Los Angeles, Santa Barbara, Riverside, and La Jolla campuses. In addition to the Ph.D., the Graduate Division confers the Ed.D.; D.Eng.; D.L.S.; D.P.H.; D.S.W.; and J.S.D. degrees. University is publicly controlled by the state. Both men and women are admitted.

Graduate Division, Northern Section

Graduate instruction has been offered since 1881, and the first Ph.D. was awarded in 1885.

Single graduate students live at International House, in privately owned apartments, and in rooms in private homes. Limited facilities in university-owned housing project for married graduate students.

Special facilities include: library of approximately 2,397,000 volumes; Lick Observatory at Mount Hamilton; George Williams Hooper Foundation for Medical Research; School of Dentistry in San Francisco.

Residence requirement for Ph.D.: 3 years beyond bachelor's degree, at least 2 of which must be spent in residence on campus (including 2 semesters after advancement to candidacy). A few summer and evening courses available.

ADMISSION REQUIREMENTS

For graduate study: bachelor's degree; satisfactory scholarship record; adequate preparation for graduate study in proposed field. For candidacy for Ph.D.: completion of substantial portion of course work with better than B average; reading knowledge of French and German or approved substitutes; qualifying examinations; departmental approval.

Apply to Dean of the Graduate Division, Northern Section, Berkeley 4, California, by July 15 for fall term; by December 15 for spring term.

FEES AND FIRST-YEAR AID

Application fee $5. No tuition for state residents; others $500 per academic year. Annual incidental fee of $136 required of all students.

First-year aid available: graduate scholarships, $100-$3,500; teaching assistantship appointments, $2,250 per academic year; fellowships, $100-$3,500; research assistantships, $2,075-$2,465 (for half-time work during 9-month period); grants-in-aid, $25-$1,500.

Apply to Committee on Fellowships and Graduate Scholarships (Graduate Division, Northern Section, Berkeley 4, California) by February 7 for fellowships and graduate scholarships. Information concerning teaching and research assistantships may be obtained from appropriate department.

FIELDS OF STUDY FOR THE PH.D.

Anatomy. Endocrine and nutritional factors regulating growth, metabolism, reproduction, hemopoiesis; histology and cytology of endocrine and related structures; nutritional-hormonal interrelationships; experimental teratology; radiobiology, especially of bone. Offered by Department of Anatomy and Physiology (Berkeley Campus). Prerequisites for graduate study: major (or equivalent) in biological science, including elementary zoology, comparative anatomy, mammalian embryology; inorganic chemistry, including qualitative and preferably quantitative analysis; organic chemistry lectures; 1 year of physics; reading knowledge of French or German. Recommended: organic chemistry (laboratory). 4 professorial staff. 6 master's degrees and 5 Ph.D.'s awarded 1955-59. 9 graduate students registered fall 1959.

Anatomy. Human anatomy (gross and microscopic), neuroanatomy, biology of cell, human embryology and teratology, electron microscopy, endocrinology, hematology, tissue culture, mammalian biology. Offered by Department of Anatomy, School of Medicine (San Francisco Campus). Prerequisite for graduate study: major in biological science. 12 professorial staff. 9 master's degrees and 7 Ph.D.'s awarded 1955-59. 6 graduate students registered fall 1959.

Animal Physiology. Chemical and biological characteristics of hormones, physiology of reproduction, metabolism, physiology of the gastrointestinal tract, environmental physiology, neurohormonal mechanisms. Offered by Departments of Anatomy, Animal Husbandry, Veterinary Science, Zoology, Entomology, Medical Physics, and Experimental Endocrinology (Davis Campus). Prerequisites for graduate study: organic and physical chemistry; histology; zoology; general physiology; physiology of the systems. 48 professorial staff. 10 Ph.D.'s awarded 1955-59. 15 graduate students registered fall 1959.

Anthropology. Specialization permitted in physical or social anthropology or archaeology, but broad base in all fields required. Offered by Department of Anthropology (Berkeley Campus). Recommended for graduate study: summer field work during period of graduate training. 15 professorial staff. 14 master's degrees and 18 Ph.D.'s awarded 1955-59. 50 graduate students registered fall 1959.

Applied Mathematics. Applications involving analysis with emphasis on ordinary and partial differential equations. Offered by Department of Mathematics (Berkeley Campus). 4 Ph.D.'s awarded 1955-59. 42 graduate students registered fall 1959.

Area Studies—Asian. Country or area (East, Southeast, South) of Asia. Interdepartmental program administered by the Group in Asian Studies (Berkeley Campus). Prerequisites for graduate study: major in 1 of the established disciplines; at least 12 units of advanced lecture courses in history or the social sciences of the area selected; at least 20 units of an East Asian language or 12 units of a Southeast or South Asian language. 35 professorial staff. 5 master's degrees and 1 Ph.D. awarded 1955-59. 15 graduate students registered fall 1959.

Art.—History. Oriental, ancient, medieval, Renaissance and baroque, or modern art. Offered by Department of Art (Berkeley Campus). Prerequisite for graduate study: major in history of art (26-30 units of credit). Recommended: preparation in French and German. 6 professorial staff. 10 master's degrees and 5 Ph.D.'s awarded 1955-59. 28 graduate students registered fall 1959.

Astronomy. Theoretical or observational astrophysics, radio-astronomy, orbits, galactic structure, extra-galactic problems. Offered by Berkeley Astronomical Department (Lick Observatory). Recommended for graduate study: upper-division courses in physics, mathematics, and astronomy. 7 professorial staff. 3 master's degrees and 16 Ph.D.'s awarded 1955-59. 22 graduate students registered fall 1959.

Bacteriology. Microbial physiology, metabolism, and genetics; pathogenesis and immunology of infectious diseases (bacterial and viral in origin). Offered by Department of Bacteriology (Berkeley Campus). Recommended for graduate study: training in biology, biochemistry, and bacteriology. 8 professorial staff. 12 master's degrees and 5 Ph.D.'s awarded 1955-59. 30 graduate students registered fall 1959.

Biochemistry. Metabolism of carbohydrates, amino acids, and vitamins; peptide hormones; chemistry of carbohydrates, proteins, and nucleic acids; iron metabolism; catalytic functions of vitamins and coenzymes; bacterial growth factors. Offered by Department of Biochemistry (Berkeley Campus). Prerequisite for graduate study: major in chemistry or biological sciences. Recommended: courses in biological sciences for chemistry majors; chemistry for biological sciences majors. 13 professorial staff. 13 master's degrees and 39 Ph.D.'s awarded 1955-59. 46 graduate students registered fall 1959. New enrollment limited to about 20.

Biochemistry. Intermediate metabolism, biochemistry of disease, nucleic acids. Offered by Department of Biochemistry, School of Medicine (San Francisco Campus). Prerequisites for grad-

uate study: major in biochemistry, chemistry, or biological science; French, German, or Russian. Recommended: courses in physiology, statistics, and genetics. 20 Ph.D.'s awarded 1955-59. 20 graduate students registered fall 1959.

Biochemistry.—Comparative. Chemical activities of living organisms (animals, plants, microorganisms). Interdepartmental program with faculty drawn from Departments of Biochemistry, Bacteriology, Physiology, Food Technology, Chemistry, etc. (Berkeley Campus). A similar program has been offered on San Francisco Campus but is now inactive. Prerequisites for graduate study: courses in 2 fields: integral calculus; organic and physical chemistry; general physics; biology. 35 professorial staff. 18 Ph.D.'s awarded 1955-59. 9 graduate students registered fall 1959.

Biochemistry.—Comparative. Bacterial, plant, or animal biochemistry; enzyme mechanisms. Offered by Departments of Biochemistry, Food Science, Botany, Chemistry, Veterinary Medicine, Bacteriology, and other related departments (Davis Campus). Prerequisite for graduate study: chemical or biological background. 15 professorial staff. 1 Ph.D. awarded 1955-59. 14 graduate students registered fall 1959.

Botany. Vascular plant morphology and anatomy; algology; bryology; mycology; plant cytology or physiology; vascular plant taxonomy, ecology, and geography. Offered by Department of Botany (Berkeley Campus). Prerequisite for graduate study: major in biological or physical science. 11 professorial staff. 36 graduate students registered fall 1959.

Chemistry, Analytical, inorganic, organic, physical, or nuclear chemistry; electrochemistry. Offered by Department of Chemistry (Berkeley Campus). 38 professorial staff. 37 master's degrees and 146 Ph.D.'s awarded 1955-59. 221 graduate students registered fall 1959.

Chemistry. — Agricultural. Pesticides, food technology, soils, and plant nutrition. All departments in College of Agriculture (Berkeley Campus) participate. Prerequisite for graduate study: major in chemistry or equivalent. 20 professorial staff. 5 Ph.D.'s awarded 1955-59. 5 graduate students registered fall 1959.

Chemistry.—Pharmaceutical. Organic, physical, or analytical chemistry; biochemistry. Offered by Department of Pharmaceutical Chemistry (San Francisco Campus). Prerequisite for graduate study: preparation in physical and biological sciences. Recommended: course in pharmaceutical chemistry. 21 professorial staff. 2 master's degrees and 13 Ph.D.'s awarded 1955-59. 26 graduate students registered fall 1959. Total enrollment limited to about 50.

Classics. Classical archaeology; Greek epigraphy and history, lyric poetry, mythology, or philosophy; Latin epigraphy, paleography, or poetry. Offered by Department of Classics (Berkeley Campus). Prerequisites for graduate study: major in classics, Greek, or Latin. Recommended: reading knowledge of French, German and Italian. Ph.D. candidacy prerequisite: written examinations in Greek and Latin in addition to French and German. 10 professorial staff. 10 master's degrees and 5 Ph.D.'s awarded 1955-59. 16 graduate students registered fall 1959.

Economics. Economic theory, history, or development; business fluctuations; comparative economic systems; history of economic thought; industrial organization; international or mathematical economics; labor economics and industrial relations; monetary theory and policy; quantitative methods in economics; public finance; an approved field offered in another department. Offered by Department of Economics (Berkeley Campus). Prerequisite for graduate study: equivalent of major in economics. Recommended: 1 year of mathematics. Ph.D. candidacy prerequisite: competence in statistics and 2 languages. 41 professorial staff. 80 master's degrees and 74 Ph.D.'s awarded 1955-59. 155 graduate students registered fall 1959.

Economics.—Agricultural. Agricultural marketing, statistics, resource economics, policy; farm management; agriculture in economic development. Offered by Department of Agricultural Economics (Berkeley Campus). 15 professorial staff. 8 master's degrees and 24 Ph.D.'s awarded 1955-59. 50 graduate students registered fall 1959.

Education. Educational administration, psychology, or curriculum; history or philosophy of education; elementary, secondary, adult, or higher education; student personnel and counseling psychology. Offered by Department of Education (Berkeley Campus). 30 professorial staff. 344 master's degrees and 55 Ph.D.'s awarded 1955-59. 775 graduate students registered fall 1959. Ed.D. degree also awarded in the field.

Endocrinology. Offered by Departments of Anatomy, Biochemistry, Physiology, Zoology, Veterinary Sciences, and Animal Husbandry (Berkeley Campus). 26 professorial staff. 1 master's degree and 5 Ph.D.'s awarded 1955-59.

Endocrinology. Interdepartmental program offered at San Francisco Campus.

Engineering.—Chemical. Offered by Department of Chemical Engineering (Berkeley Campus). Prerequisites for graduate study: major in chemical engineering. 10 professorial staff. 25 master's degrees and 10 Ph.D.'s awarded 1955-59. 61 graduate students registered fall 1959.

Engineering.—Civil, Sanitary, Irrigation. Construction, hydraulics, materials, soils, sanitary, or structural engineering; structural mechanics; irrigation. Transportation engineering (professional degrees only: M.Eng., D.Eng.). Offered by Department of Civil Engineering (Berkeley Campus). 44 professorial staff. 143 master's degrees and 13 Ph.D.'s awarded 1955-59. 110 graduate students registered fall 1959.

Engineering.—Electrical. Microwave tubes or propagation, solid-state devices, circuit or information theory, digital computers, energy conversion, nonlinear magnetics, control systems. Offered by Department of Electrical Engineering (Berkeley Campus). 30 professorial staff. 133 master's degrees and 24 Ph.D.'s awarded 1955-59. 142 graduate students registered fall 1959.

Engineering.—Mechanical. Aeronautical sciences, applied mechanics, automatic control, mechanical design, thermal systems. Offered by Department of Mechanical Engineering (Berkeley Campus). 42 professorial staff. 79 master's degrees and 16 Ph.D.'s awarded 1955-59. 83 graduate students registered fall 1959.

Engineering.—Mining. Geological engineering, engineering geoscience, mining. Offered by Department of Mineral Technology (Berkeley Campus). 19 professorial staff. 7 master's degrees and 1 Ph.D. awarded 1955-59. 6 graduate students registered fall 1959.

Engineering.—Petroleum. Offered by Department of Mineral Technology (Berkeley Campus). 19 professorial staff. 5 master's degrees and 1 Ph.D. awarded 1955-59. 10 graduate students registered fall 1959.

Engineering Science. Emphasis in any area of engineering. Offered by Departments of Civil, Electrical, Mechanical, Nuclear, or Industrial Engineering, and Departments of Naval Architecture and Mineral Technology (Berkeley Campus). 152 professorial staff. 81 master's degrees and 4 Ph.D.'s awarded 1955-59. 121 graduate students registered fall 1959.

English. English and American language and literature from 1350 to present with 1 of the following: literature of ancient Greece or Rome; of Italy, France, or Germany; of England before 1950; the English language. Offered by Department of English (Berkeley Campus). Prerequisite for graduate study: major or 18 units of upper-division English. Recommended: preparation in French, German, Latin. 34 professorial staff. 129 master's degrees and 37 Ph.D.'s awarded 1955-59. 244 graduate students registered fall 1959.

Entomology. Agricultural or systematic entomology; apiculture; insect ecology, morphology, or physiology; plant nematology; toxicology. Offered by Department of Entomology and Parasitology (Berkeley and Davis Campuses). Following courses offered on Berkeley Campus only: biological control; insect pathology; insect vectors of plant diseases; parasitology (including medical entomology). Prerequisites for graduate study: courses in general and systematic entomology, and in insect morphology and ecology; 13 units of chemistry, including organic; 26 units of biological sciences other than entomology, including 1 course each in botany, genetics, physiology, zoology; a course in bacteriology, mycology, or protozoology. Recommended: summer field course in entomology. 22 professorial staff on Berkeley Campus; 17 on Davis Campus. 23 master's degrees and 44 Ph.D.'s awarded 1955-59 on Berkeley Campus; 4 master's degrees and 9 Ph.D.'s on Davis Campus. Graduate students registered fall 1959: 79 on Berkeley Campus; 31 on Davis Campus.

Genetics. Population, biochemical, or developmental genetics; microorganisms; cytogenetics (plants and insects); animal or plant breeding; mutation; pseudoalleles; gene conversion. Offered by a Genetics Group made up of faculty from various departments on Berkeley and Davis Campuses. Prerequisite for graduate study: major in plant or animal science, or in genetics. Recommended: reading knowledge of 2 foreign languages, including German; matrix algebra and calculus; organic chemistry and biochemistry. 42 professorial staff. 1 master's degree and 33 Ph.D.'s awarded 1955-59. 53 graduate students registered fall 1959.

Geography. Latin America; historical, physical, or urban geography. Offered by Department of Geography (Berkeley Campus). 8 professorial staff. 15 master's degrees and 14 Ph.D.'s awarded 1955-59. 32 graduate students registered fall 1959.

Geology. Petrology, mineralogy, crystallography, structural geology, stratigraphy, geomorphology, sedimentology, geochemistry, geophysics. Offered by Department of Geology (Berkeley Campus). Prerequisite for graduate study: major in a physical science, engineering, or mathematics. 14 professorial staff. 38 master's degrees and 22 Ph.D.'s awarded 1955-59. 60 graduate students registered fall 1959.

Geophysics. Geology, physics, mathematics. Offered by Department of Geology (Berkeley Campus). Prerequisite for graduate study: major in geophysics, geology, or physics. 3 professorial staff. 8 master's degrees and 8 Ph.D.'s awarded 1955-59. 9 graduate students registered fall 1959.

German. German literature, Germanic linguistics. Offered by Department of German (Berkeley Campus). Prerequisite for graduate study: major in German (24 units). Recommended: reading knowledge of French and Latin (required for Ph.D. candidacy). 10 professorial staff. 21 master's degrees and 17 Ph.D.'s awarded 1955-59. 34 graduate students registered fall 1959.

History. Ancient (Near East, Greece, Rome); medieval Europe; Byzantine and medieval Slavic; early (1400-1789) or late (since 1789) modern Europe; Britain to 1603 or since 1603 (including overseas expansion); American to 1789 or since 1783; Hispanic America to 1825 or since 1763; Far East to 1600 or since 1600; history of science. Offered by Department of History (Berkeley Campus). Prerequisite for graduate study: major in history or equivalent. 37 professorial staff. 155 master's degrees and 46 Ph.D.'s awarded 1955-59. 257 graduate students registered fall 1959.

Linguistics. Descriptive or comparative linguistics. Offered by Department of Linguistics (Berkeley Campus). Prerequisites for graduate study: major in linguistics or in a foreign language; 1 year Latin; if major in a foreign language is not offered, 12 units of French or German are required. Recommended: course in cultural anthropology. 12 professorial staff. 2 master's degrees and 7 Ph.D.'s awarded 1955-59. 21 graduate students registered fall 1959.

Mathematics. Foundations; metamathematics; algebraic topology; functional or numerical analysis; algebraic or differential geometry; universal or homological algebra; analysis; partial or ordinary differential equations; topological or lie groups; number, measure, or operator theory; applied mathematics; complex or real variables; calculus of variations; probability; stochastic processes. Offered by Department of Mathematics (Berkeley Campus). Prerequisite for graduate study: 15 units of mathematics. 42 professorial staff. 72 master's degrees and 40 Ph.D.'s awarded 1955-59. 190 graduate students registered fall 1959.

Metallurgy. Physical or extractive metallurgy, material science. Offered by Department of Mineral Technology (Berkeley Campus). 19 professorial staff. 26 master's degrees and 11 Ph.D.'s awarded 1955-59. 33 graduate students registered fall 1959.

Microbiology. General or technical microbiology, microbial biochemistry, parasitology (animal, plant, insect). Offered by Department of Bacteriology and various other departments (Berkeley Campus). Recommended for graduate study: adequate training in biology, biochemistry, and bacteriology. 28 professorial staff. 2 master's degrees and 5 Ph.D.'s awarded 1955-59. 5 graduate students registered fall 1959.

Microbiology. General or technical microbiology, animal and/or plant parasitological microbiology, microbial metabolism, microbial biochemistry. Offered by Departments of Bacteriology, Food Science, Soils, Enology, Dairy, and Veterinary Medicine (Davis Campus). Prerequisites for graduate study: mathematics through calculus; physics; chemistry, including organic and biochemistry; botany; zoology; bacteriology. Recommended: reading knowledge of French, German, and/or Russian. 16 professorial staff. 2 master's degrees and 7 Ph.D.'s awarded 1955-59. 23 graduate students registered fall 1959. Total enrollment limited to about 25.

Music. Musicology (research). Offered by Department of Music (Berkeley Campus). Prerequisite for graduate study: usually a major in music. 14 professorial staff. 26 master's degrees and 2 Ph.D.'s awarded 1955-59. 37 graduate students registered fall 1959.

Nutrition. Nutrition and biochemistry plus 1 of the following: chemistry; physiology; histology; anatomy. Offered by Departments of Nutrition and Home Economics, Biochemistry, Physiology, Animal Husbandry, Poultry Science, Medicine, and Anatomy (Berkeley Campus), and by Departments of Animal Husbandry, Home Economics, Food Science and Technology, and Veterinary Science (Davis Campus). Prerequi-

sites for graduate study: equivalent of major in nutrition or closely related field, such as biochemistry. 5 professorial staff on Berkeley Campus; 20 on Davis Campus. 10 master's degrees and 10 Ph.D.'s awarded 1955-59 on Berkeley Campus; 1 master's degree and 12 Ph.D.'s on Davis Campus. Graduate students registered fall 1959: 20 on Berkeley Campus; 16 on Davis Campus.

Oriental Languages. Chinese or Japanese language and literature. Offered by Department of Oriental Languages (Berkeley Campus). Prerequisite for graduate study: major in Oriental languages with emphasis on Chinese or Japanese. 8 professorial staff. 5 master's degrees and 5 Ph.D.'s awarded 1955-59. 16 graduate students registered fall 1959.

Paleontology. Invertebrate or vertebrate paleontology, micropaleontology, paleobotany. Offered by Department of Paleontology (Berkeley Campus). Prerequisite for graduate study: major in paleontology or an allied earth or biological science. Recommended: elementary training in mathematics, physical sciences, English composition, earth sciences, and biological science. 8 professorial staff. 28 master's degrees and 7 Ph.D.'s awarded 1955-59. 40 graduate students registered fall 1959. Total enrollment limited to 40.

Parasitology. Medical entomology, helminthology. Offered by Department of Entomology and Parasitology (Berkeley Campus). Prerequisite for graduate study: major in zoological science. Recommended: background in entomology. 2 professors. 2 master's degrees and 6 Ph.D.'s awarded 1955-59. 6 graduate students registered fall 1959.

Pathology.—Comparative. Anatomy, physiology, pathology, microbiology, parasitology, physiological chemistry, and pharmacology (where these sciences relate to disease in animals). This is the area of basic sciences of Veterinary Medicine. Offered by School of Veterinary Medicine (Davis Campus) in cooperation with other departments of the university. Prerequisites for graduate study: biometry; inorganic and organic chemistry; biochemistry; physics; zoology; embryology; histology; anatomy; physiology; general pathology; pathogenic microbiology. Recommended: quantitative chemistry. 56 professorial staff. 5 master's degrees and 12 Ph.D.'s awarded 1955-59. 17 graduate students registered fall 1959.

Pharmacology and Toxicology.—Compara-

tive. Cardiovascular, autonomic nervous, or central nervous system; cellular or biochemical pharmacology. Offered by Department of Pharmacology (Davis and San Francisco Campuses). Prerequisites for graduate study: courses in organic and analytical chemistry, biochemistry, physics, anatomy, and mammalian physiology. 8 professorial staff. 7 master's degrees and 6 Ph.D.'s awarded 1955-59. 11 graduate students registered fall 1959.

Philosophy. Theory of knowledge or of value; metaphysics; philosophy of science, language, or history; logic; ethics; aesthetics; social or political philosophy. Offered by Department of Philosophy (Berkeley Campus). Prerequisites for graduate study: major in philosophy; 1 semester of symbolic logic; 1 year of history of philosophy; at least 6 upper-division courses, including ethics and theory of knowledge. 16 professorial staff. 11 master's degrees and 16 Ph.D.'s awarded 1955-59. 85 graduate students registered fall 1959.

Physics. Offered by Department of Physics (Berkeley Campus). Prerequisites for graduate study: substantial part of physics major; ETS physics examination. Recommended: French, German, or Russian; as much mathematics as possible. 45 professorial staff. 106 master's degrees and 147 Ph.D.'s awarded 1955-59. 325 graduate students registered fall 1959.

Physiological Optics. Anatomy, physics, physiology, psychology of vision. Offered by Departments of Optometry, Physics, Physiology, Psychology, and Ophthalmology (Berkeley Campus). Prerequisite for graduate study: major in anatomy, optometry, physics, physiology, psychology, or zoology, or an M.D. with residency in ophthalmology. 8 professorial staff. 2 master's degrees and 5 Ph.D.'s awarded 1955-59. 3 graduate students registered fall 1959.

Physiology. Offered by Department of Physiology (Berkeley Campus). 5 professorial staff. 5 master's degrees and 30 Ph.D.'s awarded 1955-59. 40 graduate students registered fall 1959.

Physiology. Vision, neurophysiology, endocrinology, metabolism, cardiac or renal function, respiration, electrolyte metabolism. Offered by Department of Physiology, School of Medicine (San Francisco Campus). Prerequisite for graduate study: courses in inorganic and organic chemistry, physics, zoology. Recommended: French; German; calculus; analytical and physical chemistry. 8 professorial staff. Ph.D. program begun 1958. 1 master's degree and 2 Ph.D.'s awarded 1955-59. 9 graduate students registered fall 1959.

Plant Pathology. Diseases caused by viruses, bacteria, and fungi; antibiotics and chemicals in disease control; biological control; root diseases; diseases of forest trees, ornamentals, or field, orchard, and vegetable crops; genetics; taxonomy; physiology of plant pathogens; nature of viruses, mode of infection, serology. Offered by Department of Plant Pathology (Berkeley Campus). Recommended for graduate study: French or Russian; German. 11 professorial staff. 8 master's degrees and 11 Ph.D.'s awarded 1955-59. 28 graduate students registered fall 1959. Total enrollment limited to about 30.

Plant Pathology. Plant pathology or virology, mycology. Offered by Department of Plant Pathology (Davis Campus). Prerequisite for graduate study: major in botany, plant science, or closely allied field. Recommended: a foreign language. 14 professorial staff. 4 master's degrees and 14 Ph.D.'s awarded 1955-59. 32 graduate students registered fall 1959.

Plant Physiology. Programs individually planned with no specific areas. Offered by Departments of Botany, Chemistry, Food Technology, Forestry, Physiology, Biochemistry, Plant Pathology, and Soils and Plant Nutrition, and the Forest and Range Experiment Station (Berkeley Campus). Prerequisite for graduate study: major in biological or physical science. 22 professorial staff. 1 master's degree and 5 Ph.D.'s awarded 1955-59. 15 graduate students registered fall 1959.

Plant Physiology. Physiological problems in areas of participating departments. Offered by Departments of Agronomy, Botany, Food Technology, Irrigation Landscape Horticulture, Plant Biochemistry, Pomology, Soils and Plant Nutrition, Vegetable Crops, Viticulture (Davis Campus). Recommended for graduate study: French and German. 57 professorial staff. 2 master's degrees and 25 Ph.D.'s awarded 1955-59. 32 graduate students registered fall 1959.

Political Science. American government (state, local, and national); political theory; international law and relations; comparative government; public law and jurisprudence; political parties, pressure groups, and public opinion; public administration and public policy; area specialization (including Western Europe, U.S.S.R. and Eastern Europe, Near and Middle

East, South Asia, Far East and Southeast Asia, Latin America, Africa). Offered by Department of Political Science (Berkeley Campus). Prerequisite for graduate study: major in political science or equivalent. Recommended: GRE. 30 professorial staff. 132 master's degrees and 37 Ph.D.'s awarded 1955-59. 207 graduate students registered fall 1959.

Psychology. Clinical, comparative, developmental, differential, experimental, social, industrial, or physiological psychology; personality. Offered by Department of Psychology (Berkeley Campus). Prerequisites for graduate study: major in psychology or equivalent; MAT; ETS Psychology Examination. 33 professorial staff. 9 master's degrees and 54 Ph.D.'s awarded 1955-59. 161 graduate students registered fall 1959.

Romance Languages and Literatures.—French. Emphasis is on French literature with minors in Italian or Spanish literature or in Romance philology. Offered by Department of French (Berkeley Campus). Prerequisite for graduate study: major in French or equivalent. Ph.D. candidacy prerequisites: reading knowledge of French, German, Latin, Italian, and Spanish. 11 professorial staff. 32 master's degrees and 14 Ph.D.'s awarded 1955-59. 87 graduate students registered fall 1959.

Romance Languages and Literatures.—Italian. Emphasis on Italian literature or philology with minors in French and Spanish. Offered by Department of Italian (Berkeley Campus). Prerequisite for graduate study: background in Italian. Recommended: reading knowledge of Spanish, Latin, French, and German (required for Ph.D. candidacy). 5 professorial staff. 5 master's degrees and 2 Ph.D.'s awarded 1955-59. 16 graduate students registered fall 1959.

Romance Languages and Literatures.—Spanish. Emphasis on Spanish and Spanish-American literature with minors in French and Italian. Offered by Departments of French, Italian, and Spanish and Portuguese (Berkeley Campus). Prerequisite for graduate study: major in Spanish and Portuguese or equivalent. Recommended: reading knowledge of French, German, Italian, and Latin (required for Ph.D. candidacy). 12 professorial staff.

Sanskrit. Offered by Department of Classics (Berkeley Campus). 1 professor. 2 Ph.D.'s awarded 1955-59.

Scandinavian Languages and Literatures. Danish, Norwegian, Swedish, or Old Icelandic language and literature. Offered by Department of Scandinavian Languages and Literatures (Berkeley Campus). Prerequisite for graduate study: major in Scandinavian languages and literatures or equivalent. Recommended: knowledge of Scandinavian history and general linguistics. Ph.D. candidacy prerequisites: reading knowledge of French, German, and Gothic. 5 professorial staff. Ph.D. program begun 1957. 4 master's degrees and 2 Ph.D.'s awarded 1955-59. 8 graduate students registered fall 1959.

Slavic Languages and Literatures. Literature or linguistics in Czech, Polish, Russian, and Serbo-Croatian. Offered by Department of Slavic Languages and Literatures (Berkeley Campus). Prerequisites for graduate study: major in Slavic languages and literatures or equivalent; at least 1 survey course of Russian literature and 1 of Slavic literatures; at least 20 semester hours in language of specialization. Recommended: reading knowledge of a second modern Slavic language and of French or German (required for Ph.D. candidacy). 6 professorial staff. 9 master's degrees and 7 Ph.D.'s awarded 1955-59. 19 graduate students registered fall 1959.

Sociology and Social Institutions. Advanced methodology; collective behavior and mass communication; comparative study of non-Western societies; deviance; family; history of sociology; organizations and institutions; political sociology; population; race and ethnic relations; small groups and personal interaction; socialization and personality; social change or stratification; sociological theory; sociology of culture, religion, or work; urban sociology and ecology. Offered by Department of Sociology and Social Institutions (Berkeley Campus). Prerequisites for graduate study: major in sociology or equivalent; basic course in statistics. 16 professorial staff. 39 master's degrees and 17 Ph.D.'s awarded 1955-59. 106 graduate students registered fall 1959.

Soil Science. Soil physics, chemistry, microbiology, biochemistry, or morphology; plant nutrition. Offered by Department of Soils and Plant Nutrition (Berkeley Campus). Prerequisite for graduate study: major in soil science or in physics, chemistry, or other related field. Recommended: courses in chemistry, physics, mathematics (analytical geometry and calculus); botany, bacteriology, or geology; specific soil science courses. 15 professorial staff. 8 master's degrees and 14 Ph.D.'s awarded 1955-59. 23 graduate students registered fall 1959.

Soil Science. Soil morphology, chemistry, physics, microbiology, fertility; plant nutrition. Offered by Departments of Soils and Plant Nutrition, Irrigation, Pomology, Agronomy, Vegetable Crops, and Viticulture (Davis Campus). Prerequisite for graduate study: courses in chemistry, physics, plant science, mathematics, geology, soil science, and bacteriology. 22 professorial staff. 2 master's degrees and 3 Ph.D.'s awarded 1955-59. 28 graduate students registered fall 1959.

Zoology. Vertebrate or invertebrate zoology, physiochemical biology, cytology, embryology, genetics, protozoology, comparative endocrinology and pathology, animal behavior, histochemistry. Offered by Department of Zoology (Berkeley Campus). Prerequisite for graduate study: major in zoology. 22 professorial staff. 53 master's degrees and 41 Ph.D.'s awarded 1955-59. 116 graduate students registered fall 1959. Total enrollment limited to about 115.

Zoology. Animal behavior, comparative anatomy or physiology, ecology, vertebrate embryology, limnology, microanatomy, parasitology, protozoology, systematic zoology and evolution, vertebrate zoology, wildlife. Offered by Department of Zoology (Davis Campus). Prerequisite for graduate study: major in zoology or in a biological science. 8 professorial staff. Ph.D. program established 1959. 6 master's degrees and 3 Ph.D.'s awarded 1955-59. 26 graduate students registered fall 1959.

Graduate Division, Southern Section

In 1936 authority was granted to give work leading to the Ph.D. at Los Angeles campus. The first Ph.D. was awarded in 1938.

Single graduate students may live in university residence halls; married students who are veterans may live in university-owned housing units.

Special facilities include: extensive library facilities on all campuses; Scripps Institution of Oceanography; Citrus Experiment Station.

Residence requirement for Ph.D.: 3 years beyond bachelor's degree, at least 2 of which must be spent in residence on campus (including 2 semesters after advancement to candidacy). Summer and evening courses available.

ADMISSION REQUIREMENTS

These are the same as for the Northern Division.

Apply to Admissions Section, Office of the Dean of the Graduate Division, Southern Section, Los Angeles 24, California, by August 1 for fall term; by January 1 for spring term.

FEES AND FIRST-YEAR AID

Application fee $5. No tuition for state residents; others $500 per academic year. Annual incidental fee of $136 required of all students. Room (in dormitory) and board $780 per academic year. Furnished apartments (for veterans only) $38 per month.

First-year aid available: 7 scholarships, $1,600 each; variable number of teaching fellowships, $2,000 per 10-month year; variable number of other scholarships carrying stipends of variable amounts; variable number of research assistantships, remuneration $2.12 per hour.

For scholarships, apply to Dean of the Graduate Division, Southern Section, Los Angeles 24, California, by February 7. For information on teaching and research assistantships, apply to chairmen of appropriate departments by March 1.

FIELDS OF STUDY FOR THE PH.D.

Anatomy. Physical or biological sciences, medical illustration, paramedical subjects. Offered by Department of Anatomy, School of Medicine (Los Angeles Campus). Prerequisites for graduate study: major in physical or biological science or premedical curriculum; introductory courses in zoology and vertebrate embryology; 1 year each of chemistry and physics. Recommended: comparative anatomy; microscopic technique; elementary statistics; philosophy of science; scientific German and French. 14 professorial staff. 3 master's degrees and 5 Ph.D.'s awarded 1955-59. 15 graduate students registered fall 1959.

Anthropology. Anthropology, sociology, or a combination. Offered by Department of Anthropology and Sociology (Los Angeles Campus). Prerequisites for graduate study: major in anthropology or sociology or equivalent; orientation examinations for preparing plan of study. 25 professorial staff. 22 master's degrees and 7 Ph.D.'s awarded 1955-59. 59 graduate students registered fall 1959.

Art History. Primitive and preclassical, classical, medieval, Renaissance, baroque, modern, American, or Oriental art; theory of art; art of the 18th and 19th centuries. Offered by Department of Art (Los Angeles Campus). 34 professorial staff. Program begun 1955.

Biological Chemistry. Biochemistry, organic chemistry, chemical principles. Offered by Department of Chemistry (Los Angeles Campus). Prerequisites for graduate study: major in biological chemistry, chemistry, or a life science; courses in general and physical chemistry, quantitative analysis, and elementary biological chemistry; at least 2 semester hours of physical chemistry laboratory; organic chemistry; algebra; trigonometry; differential and integral calculus; reading knowledge of German; preliminary examinations. Recommended: other higher science courses and statistics. 29 professorial staff. 6 master's degrees and 11 Ph.D.'s awarded 1955-59. 11 graduate students registered fall 1959.

Biophysics. Mathematics, chemistry, physics, biology. Offered by Department of Biophysics, School of Medicine (Los Angeles Campus). Prerequisites for graduate study: major in biophysics or equivalent. 7 professorial staff. 1 Ph.D. awarded 1955-59. 9 graduate students registered fall 1959.

Biostatistics. Biostatistics; mathematical statistics; biomedical field such as biology, infectious diseases, medicine, microbiology, pharmacology, physiology, psychology, public health, or zoology. Offered by Department of Public Health (Los Angeles Campus). Prerequisite for graduate study: completion of specific courses or qualifying by examination. 16 professorial staff. Program begun 1959.

Botanical Science. Classical botanical field of anatomy, morphology, and taxonomy; plant physiology or pathology; medical mycology; virology; genetics and evolution. Offered by Department of Botany (Los Angeles Campus). Prerequisite for graduate study: major in botany or plant science. 14 professorial staff. 9 master's degrees and 15 Ph.D.'s awarded 1955-59. 38 graduate students registered fall 1959.

Business Administration. Business statistics, operations analysis, and data processing; accounting; finance; production management; transportation and traffic management; personnel management and industrial relations; marketing; real estate and urban land economics; management theory and policy; insurance. Offered by Department of Business Administration (Los Angeles Campus). Prerequisites for graduate study: major in business administration or equiv-

alent; ETS Admission Test. 54 professorial staff. 243 master's degrees and 3 Ph.D.'s awarded 1955-59. 358 graduate students registered fall 1959.

Chemistry. Analytical, biological, inorganic, organic, or physical chemistry. Offered by Department of Chemistry (Los Angeles, La Jolla, and Riverside Campuses). Prerequisites for graduate study: scientific background; orientation examination. 29 professorial staff. 17 master's degrees and 79 Ph.D.'s awarded 1955-59. 113 graduate students registered fall 1959.

Economics. Economic theory or development; history of economic thought; economics institutions; regional, labor, or international economics; public finance; money and banking; econometrics; government and industry. Offered by Department of Economics (Los Angeles Campus). Prerequisites for graduate study: 1 semester course each in accounting, statistics, American economic history, European economic history. 20 professorial staff. 37 master's degrees and 12 Ph.D.'s awarded 1955-59. 68 graduate students registered fall 1959.

Engineering. Aerodynamics, biotechnology, ceramics, chemical unit operations and processes, communications, electronics, fluid or soil mechanics, heat or mass transfer, mechanics, production methods and management, properties of materials, radiation, nuclear processes, petroleum production, physical metallurgy, sanitation, servo-mechanisms, structures, systems engineering, thermodynamics. Offered by Department of Engineering (Los Angeles Campus). Prerequisites for graduate study: major in engineering or equivalent; GRE Advanced Test for foreign students. 75 professorial staff. 333 master's degrees and 29 Ph.D.'s awarded 1955-59. 854 graduate students registered fall 1959.

English. Medieval, American, or contemporary literature; Renaissance; 17th and 18th centuries; Romantic and Victorian periods; literary criticism; bibliography; history of the language; structural linguistics. Offered by Department of English (Los Angeles Campus). Prerequisites for graduate study: major in English; reading test in 1 modern foreign language. 47 professorial staff. 96 master's degrees and 23 Ph.D.'s awarded 1955-59. 190 graduate students registered fall 1959.

French. Medieval, Renaissance and baroque, classicism and enlightenment, modern. Offered by Department of French (Los Angeles Campus). Prerequisite for graduate study: preparation in French. Ph.D. candidacy prerequisites: reading knowledge of German, Latin and either Italian or Spanish. 16 professorial staff. Ph.D. program begun 1957. 24 master's degrees awarded 1955-59. 46 graduate students registered fall 1959.

Geochemistry. Physical and chemical oceanography; submarine geology; biological oceanography, including marine biochemistry, microbiology, botany, and vertebrates and invertebrates. Offered by Scripps Institution of Oceanography (La Jolla Campus). Prerequisites for graduate study: major in chemistry, geology, mathematics, physics, or equivalent; 1 year of biological sciences. 29 professorial staff. Program begun 1958.

Geography. History of geography; systematic physical and cultural geography; historical, economic, and political geography; cartography; regional geography. Offered by Department of Geography (Los Angeles Campus). Prerequisites for graduate study: major in geography, including about 30 semester hours of upper-division geography distributed mainly among regional or systematic courses. Entrance examinations may be required. 19 professorial staff. 21 master's degrees and 6 Ph.D.'s awarded 1955-59. 39 graduate students registered fall 1959.

Geology. Physical or theoretical geology; mineralogy and petrology or mineral deposits; paleontology and stratigraphy, geophysics. Offered by Department of Geology (Los Angeles and La Jolla Campuses). Prerequisite for graduate study: general preliminary examination. 17 professorial staff. 85 master's degrees and 13 Ph.D.'s awarded 1955-59. 73 graduate students registered fall 1959.

Germanic Languages. German literature, philology, and linguistics; Germanic folklore; Scandinavian literature and philology (1 major and 1 minor to be selected). Offered by Department of Germanic Languages (Los Angeles Campus). Prerequisites for graduate study: major in German or equivalent; knowledge of German language and literature. Placement examination sometimes required. Ph.D. candidacy prerequisites: reading examination in French and a modern Scandinavian language. 16 professorial staff. 5 master's degrees and 6 Ph.D.'s awarded 1955-59. 9 graduate students registered fall 1959.

Hispanic Languages and Literature. Spanish or Spanish-American literature. Offered by Department of Spanish (Los Angeles Campus).

Prerequisite for graduate study: major in appropriate field. Ph.D. candidacy prerequisites: knowledge of 2 areas of literature; reading knowledge of Latin, French, and 1 other modern foreign language; qualifying examinations in Spanish and Portuguese. 17 professorial staff. 10 Ph.D.'s awarded 1955-59. 3 graduate students registered fall 1959.

History. Greek, Roman, early and later Middle Ages, Near or Far East, Europe, England, British Empire, United States, American West, Hispanic America, history of science. Offered by Department of History (Los Angeles Campus). Prerequisite for graduate study: major in history. 34 professorial staff. 32 master's degrees and 25 Ph.D.'s awarded 1955-59. 155 graduate students registered fall 1959.

Horticultural Science. Plant biochemistry; chemical and physical basis of morphogenesis and development; genetics and plant breeding; soil-plant relationships. Offered by Department of Horticultural Science (Los Angeles Campus). Prerequisite for graduate study: major in an agriculture, life, natural, or physical science. 9 professorial staff. 31 master's degrees and 15 Ph.D.'s awarded 1955-59. 40 graduate students registered fall 1959.

Infectious Diseases. Medical bacteriology, mycology, parasitology and tropic diseases, virology, immunochemistry, microbiological cytology. Offered by Department of Infectious Diseases, School of Medicine (Los Angeles Campus). Prerequisite for graduate study: major in a related field. 14 professorial staff. 5 master's degrees and 5 Ph.D.'s awarded 1955-59. 13 graduate students registered fall 1959.

Marine Biology. Algology, biophysics, genetics, microbiology, vertebrate and invertebrate zoology, comparative biochemistry or physiology of marine animals and plants, evolution and population dynamics. Offered by Department of Marine Biology (La Jolla Campus). Prerequisites for graduate study: major in 1 of the biological sciences or equivalent; courses in English, mathematics, and physics; at least 12 units of chemistry, including organic (biochemistry and physical chemistry recommended); 20 units of biology, including basic zoology and botany. 29 professorial staff. 1 master's degree awarded 1955-59. 12 graduate students registered fall 1959.

Mathematics. Applied mathematics; functional, numerical, or algebra analysis; geometry;

statistics; Riemann surfaces; topology. Offered by Department of Mathematics (Los Angeles Campus). Prerequisite for graduate study: 24 units of upper-division mathematics. 39 professorial staff. 56 master's degrees and 36 Ph.D.'s awarded 1955-59. 191 graduate students registered fall 1959.

Medical Physics (Radiology). Radiation physics, biology, or chemistry. Offered by Department of Radiology, School of Medicine (Los Angeles Campus). Prerequisites for graduate study: preliminary test in physical, chemical, and biological foundations of medical physics and radiological sciences. 14 professorial staff. Program begun 1959.

Meteorology. Dynamic meteorology: fundamental hydrodynamics, theory of atmospheric waves, turbulence theory, numerical weather prediction. Synoptic meteorology: empirical analysis of atmospheric structures from local to planetary scale, cloud physics and atmospheric electricity, atmospheric radiation and optics, upper-atmospheric physics and photochemistry. Offered by Department of Meteorology (Los Angeles Campus). Prerequisite for graduate study: major in meteorology or related discipline. 11 professorial staff. 23 master's degrees and 7 Ph.D.'s awarded 1955-59. 21 graduate students registered fall 1959.

Microbiology. Agricultural bacteriology, bacteriology, biochemistry, cryptogamic botany, marine or fresh-water microbiology, mycology, phytoplankton, zoology and zooplankton. Offered by Department of Microbiology (Los Angeles Campus). Prerequisites for graduate study: major in bacteriology, biochemistry, botany, microbiology, or zoology; courses in general and organic chemistry, biochemistry, quantitative analysis; 1 year of physics; background in mathematics; 1 semester each of bacteriology, botany, and zoology; work in 2 fields (selected from bacteriology, biochemistry, cytology, histology, mycology, zoology, fresh water and marine microbiology). 8 professorial staff. 17 master's degrees and 17 Ph.D.'s awarded 1955-59. 29 graduate students registered fall 1959.

Music. Harmony, counterpoint, score reading, history and literature of music, formal analysis and identification of styles, solo performance. Offered by Department of Music (Los Angeles Campus). Prerequisite for gradate study: placement examinations. 22 professorial staff. 32 master's degrees and 8 Ph.D.'s awarded 1955-59. 83 graduate students registered fall 1959.

Oceanography. Physical or chemical oceanography; submarine geology; biological oceanography, including marine biochemistry, microbiology, botany, vertebrates, and invertebrates. Offered by Department of Oceanography (La Jolla Campus). Prerequisites for graduate study: major or equivalent in chemistry, geology, mathematics, physics; 1 year of biological sciences. 29 professorial staff. 20 master's degrees and 26 Ph.D.'s awarded 1955-59. 29 graduate students registered fall 1959.

Pharmacology. Pharmacology, toxicology, experimental therapeutics. Offered by Department of Pharmacology, School of Medicine (Los Angeles Campus). Prerequisites for graduate study: major in a biological or physical science (or premedical curriculum, including 6 units of mathematics, 8 of physics, 16 of chemistry, 8 of zoology, 8 of mammalian physiology, and 10 of biochemistry). 7 professorial staff. Ph.D. program begun 1958. 4 master's degrees awarded 1955-59. 6 graduate students registered fall 1959.

Philosophy. Logic, history of philosophy, theory of value, metaphysics. Offered by Department of Philosophy (Los Angeles Campus). 11 professorial staff. 4 master's degrees and 4 Ph.D.'s awarded 1955-59. 54 graduate students registered fall 1959.

Physics. Electronics; optics and spectroscopy; acoustics and electronics; chemical, nuclear, or atmospheric physics. Offered by Department of Physics (Los Angeles and La Jolla Campuses). 26 professorial staff. 31 master's degrees and 41 Ph.D.'s awarded 1955-59. 153 graduate students registered fall 1959.

Physiological Chemistry. Physiochemistry and biochemistry. Offered by Department of Physiological Chemistry, School of Medicine (Los Angeles Campus). Prerequisites for graduate study: major in agriculture, biochemistry, botany, chemistry, microbiology, physical-biological science, or zoology; courses in general and physical chemistry and quantitative analysis with at least 2 additional units of laboratory; organic chemistry; analytic geometry and calculus; general physics; biology. Recommended: advanced quantitative analysis; qualitative organic analysis; general biochemistry; statistics; general zoology. 10 professorial staff. 2 master's degrees and 5 Ph.D.'s awarded 1955-59. 12 graduate students registered fall 1959.

Physiology. Mammalian, cellular, cardiovascular, respiration, gastrointestinal, neurophysiology, endocrinology. Offered by Department of Physiology, School of Medicine (Los Angeles Campus). Prerequisites for graduate study: major in a biological or physical science (or a premedical curriculum, including 6 units of mathematics, 8 of physics, 16 of chemistry, and 12 of zoology); preliminary examinations during first semester. 14 professorial staff. 3 master's degrees and 3 Ph.D.'s awarded 1955-59. 15 graduate students registered fall 1959.

Political Science. Political theory and jurisprudence, international relations and law, politics and legislation, comparative government, public law, public administration and local government. Offered by Department of Political Science (Los Angeles Campus). Prerequisite for graduate study: B.A. in political science or equivalent. Entrance examinations sometimes required. 24 professorial staff. 34 master's degrees and 18 Ph.D.'s awarded 1955-59. 96 graduate students registered fall 1959.

Psychology. Clinical, comparative, counseling, developmental, engineering, experimental, industrial, measurement, physiological, or social psychology. Offered by Department of Psychology (Los Angeles Campus). 52 professorial staff. 73 master's degrees and 79 Ph.D.'s awarded 1955-59. 192 graduate students registered fall 1959.

Public Health. Biostatistics; environmental or occupational health; epidemiology; health administration; public health education. Prerequisites for graduate study: major in public health; specific required courses or qualifying examination. 16 professorial staff. Ph.D. program begun 1958. 2 master's degrees awarded 1955-59. 21 graduate students registered fall 1959.

Romance Languages and Literatures. Literary, philological. Offered by Department of Romance Languages and Literatures (Los Angeles Campus). Prerequisites for graduate study: major in French, Spanish, or Italian; if interest is literary, student must show knowledge of particular literatures and philology of the major field; if interest is philological, he must show specific knowledge of Vulgar Latin, Old French, Old Provençal, Old Italian and Old Spanish, as well as specific acquaintance with French, Italian, Spanish, and Old Provençal literatures with emphasis on the main interest. Ph.D. candidacy prerequisites: Latin; French; German; Italian; Spanish. 37 professorial staff. 7 Ph.D.'s awarded 1955-59. 7 graduate students registered fall 1959.

Sociology. Anthropology, sociology, or combination of both. Offered by Department of Anthropology and Sociology (Los Angeles Campus). Prerequisites for graduate study: major in anthropology or sociology or equivalent; orientation examinations. 25 professorial staff. 11 master's degrees and 3 Ph.D.'s awarded 1955-59. 48 graduate students registered fall 1959.

Speech. Interpretation, public address, speech correction. Offered by Department of English (Los Angeles Campus). Prerequisites for graduate study: major consisting of at least 24 upper-division units in speech, or speech and English, or speech and drama; reading test in 1 modern foreign language; proficiency in public speaking and oral reading. 47 professorial staff. Ph.D. program begun 1958. 8 master's degrees awarded 1955-59. 30 graduate students registered fall 1959.

Zoology. Animal behavior, biophysics, embryology and immuno-biology, comparative physiology, cytology, electron microscopy and ultrastructure, endocrinology, entomology, general physiology, genetics, herpetology, histology, ichthyology, invertebrate zoology, mammalogy, neurophysiology, ornithology, parasitology, physiological ecology, protozoology and protozoan physiology, radiation biology, vertebrate paleontology and morphology, vertebrate physiology. Limited number may arrange to major in zoology at Los Angeles and do research at La Jolla in ichthyology, fishery biology, invertebrate zoology, marine biology, or marine biochemistry. Offered by Department of Zoology (Los Angeles Campus). Prerequisite for graduate study: major in field, with appropriate areas of study. 30 professorial staff. 67 master's degrees and 42 Ph.D.'s awarded 1955-59. 132 graduate students registered fall 1959.

Carnegie Institute of Technology

PITTSBURGH 13, PENNSYLVANIA

The institute was established in 1900, and advanced degree programs were offered as early as 1914. Two separate units offer the Ph.D.: the College of Engineering and Science and the Graduate School of Industrial Administration. The Ph.D. programs of both are described below.

Carnegie is privately controlled and nonsectarian. Both men and women are admitted.

College of Engineering and Science

Founded 1905; first Ph.D. awarded 1920.

Mudge Graduate House provides accommodations for 140 graduate men; Robert E. Doherty Graduate House, a 52-unit apartment building, contains 16 efficiency and 36 1-bedroom apartments for married students.

Special facilities include: Chemical and Petroleum Research Laboratory; Coal Research Laboratory; Metals Research Laboratory; Nuclear Research Center; Computation Center. The Hunt Library, to be occupied late in 1960, will centralize campus collection of more than 155,000 books; special graduate study and research facilities will be available in the new structure.

Residence requirement for Ph.D.: minimum of 2 semesters of full-time graduate work in the second or higher years of graduate program. Evening courses are available.

ADMISSION REQUIREMENTS

For graduate study: completion of 4-year course in subject of specialization; B average or better. Recommended: GRE. For candidacy for Ph.D.: qualifying examination in the appropriate engineering or science program; demonstration of a reading knowledge in 2 foreign languages (in engineering departments, only 1 foreign language may be required).

Apply to the Office of the Dean of Graduate Studies preferably not later than February 1.

FEES AND FIRST-YEAR AID

No application fee. Tuition $1,000 per year. Room (in graduate house) and board approximately $925 per year. Apartments $75-$95 a month.

First-year aid available: full and part-tuition scholarships; fellowships, $1,200-$2,500 plus tuition; research and teaching assistantships, $1,300-$1,600 plus tuition.

Apply to Office of Dean of Graduate Studies or to department of interest preferably not later than February 1.

FIELDS OF STUDY FOR THE PH.D.

Chemistry. Physical and theoretical, organic, inorganic, nuclear. Combined program offered by Departments of Chemistry and Metallurgical Engineering. Prerequisite for graduate study: major in chemistry. 17 professorial staff. 63 master's degrees and 57 Ph.D.'s awarded 1955-59. 118 graduate students registered fall 1959.

Engineering.—Chemical. Transfer processes, thermodynamics, catalysis. Combined program offered by Departments of Chemical Engineering and Metallurgical Engineering. Prerequisite for graduate study: major in chemical engineering. 6 professorial staff. 40 master's degrees and 19 Ph.D.'s awarded 1955-59. 48 graduate students registered fall 1959.

Engineering.—Civil. Solid mechanics and structural engineering; fluid mechanics and hydraulic engineering; soil mechanics and foundation engineering; materials. Prerequisite for graduate study: major in civil engineering. 9 professorial staff. 26 master's degrees and 9 Ph.D.'s awarded 1955-59. 56 graduate students registered fall 1959.

Engineering.—Electrical. Magnetics and magnetic materials, solid-state film, cryogenic and semiconductor electronics, plasma dynamics and magnetohydrodynamics, aerosol transport and corona phenomena, adaptive servomechanisms, data processing and digital switching system synthesis, rotating machines, electromagnetic field boundary-value problems, low-voltage sparkover phenomena and liquid dielectrics, parametric devices. Prerequisite for graduate study: major in electrical engineering, or in physics and mathematics with appropriate minor specialization. 12 professorial staff. 91 master's degrees and 31 Ph.D.'s awarded 1955-59. 87 graduate students registered fall 1959.

Engineering. — Mechanical. Hydrodynamic theory of lubrication, turbulent mixing of fluids, friction and wear, metal forming, thermodynamics of direct conversion devices, cold rolling. Combined program offered by Departments of Mechanical Engineering and Metallurgical Engineering. Prerequisite for graduate study: major in mechanical engineering. 13 professorial staff. 61 master's degrees and 10 Ph.D.'s awarded 1955-59. 87 graduate students registered fall 1959.

Engineering.—Metallurgical. All branches of physical and chemical metallurgy. Combined program offered by Departments of Metallurgical Engineering, Chemistry, Physics, Chemical Engineering, and Mechanical Engineering. Prerequisite for graduate study: major in metallurgical engineering (allowances made for other training). 12 professorial staff. 55 master's degrees and 25 Ph.D.'s awarded 1955-59. 111 graduate students registered fall 1959.

Mathematics. Calculus of variations, ordinary differential equations, partial differential equations, function theory, convex bodies, rational mechanics, elasticity, conformal mapping, abstract analysis, game theory, quality control, mathematical statistics. Prerequisite for graduate study: major in mathematics. Recommended: courses in physics, particularly mechanics; German, French, and (when possible) Russian. 17 professorial staff. 26 master's degrees and 18 Ph.D.'s awarded 1955-59. 42 graduate students registered fall 1959.

Physics. Nuclear and solid-state physics. Combined program offered by Departments of Physics and Metallurgical Engineering. Prerequisite for graduate study: major in physics. 23 professorial staff. 66 master's degrees and 38 Ph.D.'s awarded 1955-59. 110 graduate students registered fall 1959.

Psychology. Experimental or industrial psychology. Combined program offered by Department of Psychology with behavioral science option in Graduate School of Industrial Administration. Prerequisites for graduate study: science background; GRE. 14 professorial staff. 7 master's degrees and 5 Ph.D.'s awarded 1955-59. 11 graduate students registered fall 1959.

Graduate School of Industrial Administration

Founded 1949; first Ph.D. awarded 1956. The school combines work usually found in a graduate school of business with many of the areas usually found in the social sciences and mathematics-statistics. Emphasis is on integrated work in the areas of administration and behavioral sciences, and on newly developing mathematical and quantitative techniques in the analysis of business and organizational behavior. A majority of the faculty of the school drawn from economics, psychology, sociology, mathematics, engineering, statistics, and law; others drawn from the usual fields of business administration. Ph.D. work is offered in close cooperation with related departments on campus, especially psychology and mathematics.

Residence facilities for College of Engineering also available for graduate students in this school.

Special facilities include: large electronic computer; special laboratories for small-group research.

Residence requirement for Ph.D.: minimum 1 year.

ADMISSION REQUIREMENTS

For graduate study: bachelor's degree; excellent undergraduate record with some mathematics; strong scores on GRE Aptitude Test or Admission Test for Graduate Study in Business. For candidacy for Ph.D.: qualifying examinations; general ability tests in 1 foreign language and in mathematics.

Apply to Dean, Graduate School of Industrial Administration, by March 1 of entering year.

FEES AND FIRST-YEAR AID

Fees are the same as for the College of Engineering and Science.

First-year aid available: 10 or 12 financial aid grants to entering men each year. These include: scholarships, $1,000; fellowships, $2,000-$3,500; research assistantships, $2,100-$2,500.

Apply to Dean, Graduate School of Industrial Administration, by March 1 of entering year.

FIELDS OF STUDY FOR THE PH.D.

Doctoral students teach 1 course under close faculty supervision in final year of doctoral program as part of educational program.

Business and Commerce. Administration and the behavioral sciences; business and managerial economics; quantitative methods; functional fields of business (production, marketing, finance); operations research. Offered by the Graduate School of Industrial Administration. Prerequisite for graduate study: no special field required, but most students from mathematics, engineering, physical sciences, social sciences. Recommended: college mathematics through calculus. 29 professorial staff. 140 master's degrees and 7 Ph.D.'s awarded 1955-59. 102 graduate students registered fall 1959. New registration limited to 10 per year in Ph.D. program.

Economics. Managerial economics, mathematical economics, operations research. Offered by Department of Economics in Graduate School of Industrial Administration. Recommended: mathematics through calculus. 22 professorial staff.

18 master's degrees and 3 Ph.D.'s awarded 1955-59. 19 graduate students registered fall 1959. New registration limited to 10 per year in Ph.D. program.

Case Institute of Technology

CLEVELAND 6, OHIO

The Graduate School

Graduate instruction has been offered at Case since 1938, and the first Ph.D. was awarded in 1939. The Graduate School was organized in 1945. Institute is privately controlled and non-sectarian. Both men and women are admitted.

Limited dormitory space available for single graduate students; married students find accommodations in community.

Residence requirement for Ph.D.: 3 years of full-time study or equivalent, with minimum of 1 year in residence at Case.

ADMISSION REQUIREMENTS

For graduate study: bachelor's degree; standing in upper third of graduating class. For candidacy for Ph.D.: reading knowledge of 2 foreign languages, 1 of which must be German or Russian; comprehensive qualifying examinations in field.

Apply to The Graduate School, 10900 Euclid Avenue, Cleveland 6, Ohio, by August 1.

FEES AND FIRST-YEAR AID

No application fee. Tuition $1,400 per academic year. Special fees approximate $35 per year. Room (in dormitory for men only) $240 per year. Meals in college cafeteria cost about $3.75 per day.

First-year aid available: teaching fellowships, $2,000-$2,500 plus tuition; other fellowships, $1,000-$2,500 plus tuition; research assistantships, $1,000-$2,500.

Apply to The Graduate School, 10900 Euclid Avenue, Cleveland 6, Ohio, by March 1.

FIELDS OF STUDY FOR THE PH.D.

Aeronautics. Offered by Department of Mechanical Engineering. 9 professorial staff. 8 master's degrees and 2 Ph.D.'s awarded 1955-59. 6 graduate students registered fall 1959.

Astronomy. Offered by Department of Mathematics and Astronomy. 10 master's degrees and 4 Ph.D.'s awarded 1955-59. 6 graduate students registered fall 1959.

Chemistry. Offered by Departments of Chemistry and Chemical Engineering. 17 professorial staff. 70 master's degrees and 30 Ph.D.'s awarded 1955-59. 40 graduate students registered fall 1959.

Engineering.—Chemical. Offered by Department of Chemistry and Chemical Engineering. 7 professorial staff. 35 master's degrees and 15 Ph.D.'s awarded 1955-59. 12 graduate students registered fall 1959.

Engineering.—Instrumentation. Offered by Department of Mechanical Engineering. 8 professorial staff. 8 master's degrees and 1 Ph.D. awarded 1955-59. 8 graduate students registered fall 1959.

Engineering Mechanics. Offered by Department of Mechanical Engineering. 6 professorial staff. 12 master's degrees and 4 Ph.D.'s awarded 1955-59. 6 graduate students registered fall 1959.

Engineering.—Sanitary. Offered by Department of Civil Engineering. 6 professorial staff. 6 master's degrees and 1 Ph.D. awarded 1955-59. 5 graduate students registered fall 1959.

Engineering.—Structural. Offered by Department of Civil Engineering. 6 professorial staff. 6 master's degrees and 1 Ph.D. awarded 1955-59. 6 graduate students registered fall 1959.

Heat and Power. Offered by Department of Mechanical Engineering. 7 professorial staff. 15 master's degrees and 2 Ph.D.'s awarded 1955-59. 17 graduate students registered fall 1959.

Machine Design. Offered by Department of Mechanical Engineering. 5 professorial staff. 6 master's degrees and 1 Ph.D. awarded 1955-59. 4 graduate students registered fall 1959.

Mathematics. Offered by Department of Mathematics and Astronomy. 8 professorial staff. 28 master's degrees and 12 Ph.D.'s awarded 1955-59. 17 graduate students registered fall 1959.

Metallurgy. Offered by Department of Metallurgical Engineering. 9 professorial staff. 36 master's degrees and 11 Ph.D.'s awarded 1955-59. 21 graduate students registered fall 1959.

Operations Research. Offered by Department of Management Science. 9 professorial staff. Ph.D. program initiated 1955. 12 master's degrees and 3 Ph.D.'s awarded 1955-59. 18 graduate students registered fall 1959.

Physics. 14 professorial staff. 76 master's degrees and 22 Ph.D.'s awarded 1955-59. 22 graduate students registered fall 1959.

Propulsion. Offered by Department of Mechanical Engineering. 7 professorial staff. 12 master's degrees and 2 Ph.D.'s awarded 1955-59. 10 graduate students registered fall 1959.

Catholic University of America

WASHINGTON 17, D. C.

Graduate studies (other than in the Sacred Sciences) were first offered in 1895 in the School of Philosophy and the School of Social Sciences, which today offer Ph.D. degrees together with the Graduate School of Arts and Sciences. Other doctoral degrees offered by the university include: Eng.D. and D.Arch. (School of Engineering and Architecture); S.T.D. (School of Sacred Theology); J.C.D. (School of Canon Law); D.S.W. (School of Social Service). University is privately controlled and is related to the Roman Catholic Church. Both men and women are admitted to all schools except Theology and Canon Law (men only).

Graduate School of Arts and Sciences

Organized 1930.

Dormitory accommodations available for single graduate men; dormitory and apartment facilities for women. No on-campus residence facilities provided for married couples.

Library of approximately 555,000 volumes contains special collections on anthropology, architecture, biology, Arctic botany, Canon and Roman law, Catholic Americana, library science, mathematics, medieval studies, and music. Affiliation with Oak Ridge Institute provides facilities for nuclear research and study.

Residence requirement for Ph.D.: 6 semesters beyond bachelor's degree, of which 4 must be taken in residence at Catholic University. Summer and evening courses available.

ADMISSION REQUIREMENTS

For graduate study: bachelor's degree; B average in all academic work; adequate prepara-

tion in field of proposed study. For candidacy for Ph.D.: satisfaction of language requirements in French and German (additional languages required by certain departments); completion of major portion of course work; written comprehensive examination in major field; recommendation of major department.

Apply to the Registrar at least 1 month prior to date of desired entry.

FEES AND FIRST-YEAR AID

No application fee. Tuition $800 per academic year (students majoring in art, biology, chemistry, music, psychology, and physics required to pay an additional fee of $50). Class dues $2 annually. Room (in dormitory) $300 per academic year for double room. Approximate annual cost of board in college dining room $500.

First-year aid available: 29 tuition scholarships; 24 other scholarships in varying amounts; 17 fellowships for room, board, and tuition; 45 teaching assistantships, tuition plus $900; 6 teaching assistantships, tuition plus $1,250; 3 teaching assistantships, tuition plus $1,600; 6 teaching assistantships, ⅛ to ½ tuition plus $150-$225.

Apply to Chairman, Committee on Scholarships and Fellowships, by February 1. For student loans, apply to the Procurator's Office.

FIELDS OF STUDY FOR THE PH.D.

Anthropology. General anthropology, ethnology. Prerequisite for graduate study: basic introductory courses in anthropology. 4 professorial staff. 4 master's degrees and 3 Ph.D.'s awarded 1955-59. 15 graduate students registered fall 1959.

Biology. Bacteriology, cellular physiology, endocrinology, cytology, plant or insect taxonomy, comparative histology, parasitology, zoology, botany, entomology, physiology. Prerequisites for graduate study: 18 semester hours of undergraduate biology; 1 year each of physics and chemistry. 12 professorial staff. 74 master's degrees and 21 Ph.D.'s awarded 1955-59. 61 graduate students registered fall 1959.

Chemistry. Inorganic, organic, physical, biological, and radiation chemistry. Prerequisites for graduate study: general, organic, analytical, and physical chemistry; German; orientation examination. Recommended: physics; mathematics (including integral calculus). 8 professorial staff. 40 master's degrees and 35 Ph.D.'s awarded

1955-59. 34 graduate students registered fall 1959.

Education. Elementary, secondary, and higher education; administration; supervision; guidance; educational psychology; history; philosophy of education; education of the exceptional child. Prerequisite for graduate study: 12 semester hours of education. 15 professorial staff. 341 master's degrees and 38 Ph.D.'s awarded 1955-59. 182 graduate students registered fall 1959.

English. Literature, literary criticism. Prerequisites for graduate study: ability to write English effectively; Latin test. 12 professorial staff. 106 master's degrees and 10 Ph.D.'s awarded 1955-59. 75 graduate students registered fall 1959.

Greek and Latin. Students major in 1 language and minor in other; ancient history or comparative philology is second required minor. Prerequisites for graduate study: major in Latin; reading knowledge of French or German; qualifying examination. Recommended: knowledge of both Greek and Latin. 8 professorial staff. 60 master's degrees and 5 Ph.D.'s awarded 1955-59. 26 graduate students registered fall 1959.

History. Ancient, Byzantine, medieval, modern European, English, American, American Church, and Ibero-American history. Prerequisites for graduate study: 18 semester hours of history and 12 of social science and philosophy; reading knowledge of French or German. Recommended for Ph.D. candidates in American history: courses in government, international law, constitutional law. 9 professorial staff. 120 master's degrees and 25 Ph.D.'s awarded 1955-59. 65 graduate students registered fall 1959.

Mathematics. Prerequisites for graduate study: higher algebra; calculus; physics. Recommended: reading knowledge of French and German. 12 professorial staff. 32 master's degrees and 17 Ph.D.'s awarded 1955-59. 82 graduate students registered fall 1959.

Modern Languages and Literatures. Celtic, comparative philology, general Romance philology and literature, French, German, Italian, and Spanish. Prerequisite for graduate study: major or 24 semester hours of college work in 1 language, including advanced courses. Ph.D. candidacy prerequisites: knowledge of 3 modern foreign languages (1 major and 2 minors); Latin. 12 professorial staff. 42 master's degrees and 10 Ph.D.'s awarded 1955-59. 47 graduate students registered fall 1959.

Music. Musicology. Prerequisite for graduate study: major in music. 14 professorial staff. 107 master's degrees and 5 Ph.D.'s awarded 1955-59. 94 graduate students registered fall 1959.

Physics. Electronics, nuclear or solid-state physics, quantum mechanics, thermodynamics. Prerequisites for graduate study: courses in physics, mathematics (through calculus), general chemistry; qualifying examinations in elementary physics. 11 professorial staff. 42 master's degrees and 38 Ph.D.'s awarded 1955-59. 102 graduate students registered fall 1959.

Psychology. Clinical, counseling, experimental-physiological, and school psychology. Offered by Department of Psychology and Psychiatry. Prerequisites for graduate study: 2 semesters of general psychology; 1 semester of science (with laboratory); 1 semester of statistics; 2 semesters of philosophy; 1 semester of college algebra; 1 semester of experimental psychology; MAT or CAVD; Doppelt Mathematical Reasoning Test; MMPI; Strong Terman Concept Mastery Test. Recommended: science background. 24 professorial staff. 46 master's degrees and 29 Ph.D.'s awarded 1955-59. 84 graduate students registered fall 1959.

Religious Education. Sacred doctrine, Biblical studies. Prerequisites for graduate study: course in sacred doctrine; 12 semester hours in philosophy; reading knowledge of Latin. 6 professorial staff. 46 master's degrees and 3 Ph.D.'s awarded 1955-59. 27 graduate students registered fall 1959.

Semitic and Egyptian Languages and Literatures. Arabic, Akkadian, Aramaic, Hebrew, Coptic, and Syriac. Prerequisites for graduate study: basic courses in languages selected. 4 professorial staff. 3 master's degrees and 1 Ph.D. awarded 1955-59. 10 graduate students registered fall 1959.

School of Social Science

The School of Social Science was formally established in 1937 and now offers Ph.D. programs in 3 areas. Residence facilities are the same as for graduate students in the School of Arts and Sciences.

ADMISSION REQUIREMENTS

See "Admission Requirements" for the Graduate School of Arts and Sciences.

Tuition $800 per academic year. For other information, *see* "Fees and First-Year Aid" for the Graduate School of Arts and Sciences.

FIELDS OF STUDY FOR THE PH.D.

Economics. Economic theory, economic history, finance, international economics, labor and industrial relations, statistics. Prerequisite for graduate study: 24 semester hours in social sciences, including 15 in economics. 7 professorial staff. 28 master's degrees and 6 Ph.D.'s awarded 1955-59. 22 graduate students registered fall 1959.

Politics. Political theory, government, international law and relations. Prerequisite for graduate study: 21 semester hours in social sciences, including 12 in politics. 5 professorial staff. 21 master's degrees and 1 Ph.D. awarded 1955-59. 17 graduate students registered fall 1959.

Sociology. History and method, marriage and family relationships, social organization, social problems and trends, Catholic social thought. Prerequisite for graduate study: 30 semester hours in social sciences, including 15 in sociology. 8 professorial staff. 73 master's degrees and 14 Ph.D.'s awarded 1955-59. 45 graduate students registered fall 1959.

School of Philosophy

Graduate instruction in philosophy has been offered since 1889. In its present form, the School of Philosophy was established in 1936. Residence facilities are the same as for students registered in the Graduate School of Arts and Sciences.

ADMISSION REQUIREMENTS

See "Admission Requirements" for the Graduate School of Arts and Sciences.

FEES AND FIRST-YEAR AID

Tuition $800 per academic year. For other information, *see* "Fees and First-Year Aid" for the Graduate School of Arts and Sciences.

FIELDS OF STUDY FOR THE PH.D.

Philosophy. Logic, deductive and inductive; methodology; cosmology and philosophy of science; psychology, philosophical and empirical; epistemology; ethics, general, social, and special; metaphysics, general and special; theodicy and philosophy of religion; social and political philosophy; philosophy of history; Thomistic studies; history of philosophy, ancient, patristic, Oriental, medieval (including Christian), Arabic, Jewish, Renaissance, modern, and contemporary. Prerequisite for graduate study: adequate preparation in all fields of scholastic philosophy. For candidacy for Ph.D.: Latin (in addition to French and German); Greek for special studies. 12 professorial staff. 91 master's degrees, 5 Ph.L.'s, and 29 Ph.D.'s awarded 1955-59. 61 graduate students registered fall 1959.

Chicago, University of

CHICAGO 37, ILLINOIS

The University of Chicago includes the following divisions: The College; the 4 divisions (Biological Sciences, Humanities, Physical Sciences, and Social Sciences); the 6 professional schools (Graduate School of Business, Divinity School, Law School, Graduate Library School, School of Medicine, School of Social Service Administration); and University College (which includes the Center for Adult Education). Graduate degrees have been awarded since the establishment of the university in 1892. At present, Ph.D. programs are offered through the 4 divisions and through 4 of the 6 professional schools: Graduate School of Business, Divinity School, Graduate Library School, and School of Social Service Administration. The Ph.D. programs of the School of Medicine are included in those reported for the Division of Biological Sciences. The Law School awards the J.S.D. and the D.Comp.L. University is privately controlled and nonsectarian. Both men and women are admitted.

Residence halls for graduate and undergraduate students are maintained on the university quadrangles; limited facilities are available for the housing of married students. International House, with accommodations for over 500 residents (men and women), is designed to provide living quarters for qualified students from abroad and for American students.

Special facilities include: library of approximately 2,045,000 volumes; several hospitals and clinics; cancer research laboratory; Food Research Institute; Meat Institute Foundation; Oriental Institute; observatories at Williams Bay, Wisconsin, and Fort Davis, Texas; map library; Institute for the Study of Metals; Fermi Institute for Nuclear Studies; 450-Mev synchrocyclotron; low-temperature laboratory; affiliation with Argonne National Laboratory; Economics Research Center; Social Welfare Center; Midwest Administration Center (education); Population Research and Training Center; Chicago Community Inventory; National Opinion Research Center; orthogenic school; centers for counseling, family study, and industrial relations.

Residence requirement for Ph.D.: minimum of 3 years beyond bachelor's degree, of which at least a full program of study for 3 quarters must be taken in residence at the University of Chicago. Summer courses and a few evening courses available in some departments. Graduate School of Business offers Downtown Program, an evening program of graduate study which is identical in content with the campus program leading to M.B.A. degree. Course requirements for Ph.D. may be met in part through courses in this program.

Division of Biological Sciences

Established in 1930 during a general reorganization of the university. Ph.D. programs of the School of Medicine are included with those offered by this division.

ADMISSION REQUIREMENTS

For graduate study: bachelor's degree; undergraduate record of good quality; recommendation from 2 college faculty members who are acquainted with student's character and ability. Aptitude test and a general education test may be required in some cases. For candidacy for Ph.D.: completion with satisfactory grades of substantial portion of course work; reading knowledge of at least 1 modern foreign language at high level of accomplishment (most departments require this competence in more than 1 foreign language); preliminary examinations; recommendation by department and approval of Dean of Students.

Apply to Office of Admissions, University of Chicago, as early as possible but at least 3 months before date of desired admission.

FEES AND FIRST-YEAR AID

Application fee $10. Tuition $1,050 per academic year. General service fee $60. Room (in dormitory) $255-$360 per academic year of 3 quarters. Board in college dining room averages $525 per year. Apartments $60-$115 a month.

First-year aid available: fellowships may be awarded to properly qualified students on nomination by departments.

Apply to Office of Admissions, Committee on Fellowships and Scholarships, Administration Building, Room 304, on or before February 15.

FIELDS OF STUDY FOR THE PH.D.

Special opportunities for studying the problems of higher education and teaching are provided to a limited number of qualified candidates.

Anatomy. Experimental histology, neuroanatomy, or embryology; histochemistry; electron microscopy. Prerequisite for graduate study: approximately the premedical requirements. Ph.D. candidacy prerequisite: 2 modern foreign languages. 10 professorial staff. 3 master's degrees and 9 Ph.D.'s awarded 1955-59. 9 graduate students registered fall 1959.

Biochemistry. Biochemistry of viruses, mechanisms of biological oxidations, protein synthesis, biosynthesis of fatty acids and antibodies. Prerequisite for graduate study: concentration in physical and/or biological sciences. Ph.D. candidacy prerequisites: German and French. 15 professorial staff. 9 master's degrees and 21 Ph.D.'s awarded 1955-59. 31 graduate students registered fall 1959.

Biology.—Mathematical. Physico-mathematical and mathematical studies in biology. Prerequisites for graduate study: major in biology or physical sciences; knowledge of calculus, some differential equations; basic knowledge of physics and biology. 2 professors. 2 Ph.D.'s awarded 1955-59. 6 graduate students registered fall 1959.

Biophysics. Cell ultrastructure, replicative mechanisms in microorganisms and tissue-culture cells, radiation effects (high-energy, ultraviolet, visible), structure and stability of nucleic acids, physical chemistry of proteins of muscle, mitotic spindle. Prerequisite for graduate study: preparation in physics or chemistry. Ph.D. candidacy prerequisites: German and either French or Russian. 6 professorial staff. 7 Ph.D.'s awarded

1955-59. 6 graduate students registered fall 1959.

Biopsychology. Biopsychology, general or social psychology, personality and psychopathology. Prerequisites for graduate study: at least 3 courses in psychology; 1 in introductory statistics; 2 in mathematics; 2 in biological science (including 1 laboratory course); 2 in social science other than psychology. Recommended: GRE Verbal, Quantitative, and Advanced Tests. Prerequisite for Ph.D. candidacy: 2 languages (usually French and German). 18 professorial staff. 13 master's degrees and 73 Ph.D.'s awarded 1955-59. 110 graduate students registered fall 1959.

Botany. Anatomy, morphology, plant physiology and biochemistry, ecology and plant geography, cytology, genetics and cytogenetics, algology and mycology. Ph.D. candidacy prerequisite: 1 language, usually German. 8 professorial staff. 7 master's degrees and 10 Ph.D.'s awarded 1955-59. 26 graduate students registered fall 1959.

Medicine. Medicine, neurology, dermatology. Prerequisite for graduate study: M.D. degree. Ph.D. candidacy prerequisites: German and French. 58 professorial staff.

Microbiology. Genetics and physiology of microorganisms, including viruses, bacteria, and fungi; general bacteriology; medical microbiology; immunology, including effective immunity to disease; parasitology. Prerequisite for graduate study: courses in microbiology, chemistry, biology, or biochemistry. Ph.D. candidacy prerequisites: German and French. 8 professorial staff. 13 master's degrees and 15 Ph.D.'s awarded 1955-59. 21 graduate students registered fall 1959.

Pathology. Immunopathology, nutrition, renal vascular diseases, endocrine pathology, neoplasia, granulomas, electron microscopy. Prerequisite for graduate study. M.D. degree or candidacy for same. 11 professorial staff. 6 master's degrees awarded 1955-59. 15 graduate students registered fall 1959.

Pharmacology. Drug metabolism and chemotherapy; radiobiology; toxicology; drug penetration and action in central nervous system; cardiovascular drugs; anticancer drugs; antibiotics, food toxicology; and growth; neuropharmacology. Prerequisites for graduate study: broad scientific foundation; courses in chemistry, physics, mathematics (including calculus), zoology, botany, comparative anatomy of vertebrates. Ph.D. candidacy prerequisites: French, German.

7 professorial staff. 6 master's degrees and 21 Ph.D.'s awarded 1955-59. 12 graduate students registered fall 1959.

Physiology. Biochemistry of growth; respiratory physiology; neural mechanisms of learning and sensory perception; molecular changes during activation of nerve fibers; physiological genetics of microorganisms and mechanism of synthesis of vitamins by microorganisms; role of stress in pathogenesis. Prerequisites for graduate study: preparation in biology, mathematics, and physics; general, analytical, physical, and organic chemistry; GRE. Ph.D. candidacy prerequisites: German and 1 other foreign language. 8 professorial staff. 12 master's degrees and 14 Ph.D.'s awarded 1955-59. 16 graduate students registered fall 1959.

Surgery. Experimental and clinical surgery. Prerequisite for graduate study: M.D. degree. 45 professorial staff. 4 master's degrees and 3 Ph.D.'s awarded 1955-59. 6 graduate students registered fall 1959.

Zoology. General, human, and medical genetics; compartive physiology; experimental cell physiology, speciation, and behavior; ecology and population studies; developmental biology; embryology; cytology; endocrinology. Ph.D. candidacy prerequisites: 2 modern foreign languages (usually French and German). 10 professorial staff. 6 master's degrees and 24 Ph.D.'s awarded 1955-59. 38 graduate students registered fall 1959.

Division of the Humanities

Established in 1930 as part of a general reorganization of the university. In addition to the Ph.D. programs described below, the division participates in an interuniversity Ph.D. program in Italian offered in cooperation with Cornell, Indiana, Northwestern, Michigan, Pennsylvania, Syracuse, and Tulane universities.

ADMISSION REQUIREMENTS

Requirements are essentially the same as those for the Division of Biological Sciences, except that the candidates for the Ph.D. degree must demonstrate reading knowledge of French and German, or of either French or German and a second language chosen with the approval of the student's department or committee.

Apply to Office of Admissions, University of Chicago, as early as possible.

FEES AND FIRST-YEAR AID

Fees are the same as those described for the Division of Biological Sciences.

First-year aid available: about 45 scholarships, ⅓ to full tuition; about 30 fellowships, $1,200-$2,000. Loan funds available for tuition and other expenses.

Apply to Office of Admissions, Committee on Fellowships and Scholarships, Administration Building, Room 304, on or before February 15.

FIELDS OF STUDY FOR THE PH.D.

Most departments offer special courses in the teaching of their subjects at different levels, including supervised apprentice teaching.

Art History. Ancient, medieval, Renaissance, Baroque, modern or Far Eastern art; history of prints. Offered by Department of Art. Prerequisite for graduate study: 6 survey courses (or equivalent) in history of art. 7 professorial staff. 13 master's degrees and 9 Ph.D.'s awarded 1955-59. 26 graduate students registered fall 1959.

Classical Languages and Literatures. Greek and Latin languages or literatures, ancient philosophy or history, Greek and Roman art and archaeology. Prerequisites for graduate study: work in various areas of classical civilization; qualifying examinations in Greek and Latin languages, literatures, and history. Recommended: Italian. 8 professorial staff. 10 master's degrees and 8 Ph. D.'s awarded 1955-59. 20 graduate students registered fall 1959.

Comparative Literature. Combination of English and 1 foreign literature, or of 2 or more foreign literatures. Concentration may be in a particular genre or period. Language areas: English, French, German, classical Greek, Italian, Latin (classical and medieval), Russian, Scandinavian, Spanish. Combined program offered by interdepartmental and interdivisional Committee on Comparative Studies in Literature. Prerequisites for graduate study: reading ability in French and German sufficient for advanced study; competence in languages used in field of concentration; examination in such languages and literatures; training in methods and techniques of literary history and in methods of analysis and criticism. 2 master's degrees and 2 Ph.D.'s awarded 1955-59. 3 graduate students registered fall 1959.

English Language and Literature. Prerequisite for graduate study: major in field. 17 professorial staff. 192 master's degrees and 51 Ph.D.'s awarded 1955-59. 117 graduate students registered fall 1959.

Germanic Languages and Literatures. Older (beginning to 1600) or modern (1600 to present) German literature; older or modern Scandinavian literature; German or Scandinavian philology. Prerequisites for graduate study: major in German or Scandinavian; work in history and culture of German or Scandinavian area. Recommended: French or Latin. 10 professorial staff. 27 master's degrees and 4 Ph.D.'s awarded 1955-59. 21 graduate students registered fall 1959.

History of Culture. Culture of various geographic areas and historical periods involving either the ideas and movement which coexisted in a period or area or theories and methods applied in different areas or periods. Combined program conducted by interdepartmental and interdivisional Committee on History of Culture. Prerequisites for graduate study: reading knowledge of French or German and any other foreign languages necessary to field of specialization, or willingness to acquire such knowledge. 8 professorial staff. 4 master's degrees and 5 Ph.D.'s awarded 1955-59. 10 graduate students registered fall 1959.

Linguistics. General linguistics, Indo-European linguistics, Indic philology, Slavic languages and literatures. Prerequisites for graduate study: adequate preparation in field; solid preparation in at least 1 major family of languages. 9 professorial staff. 4 master's degrees and 3 Ph.D.'s awarded 1955-59. 18 graduate students registered fall 1959.

Music. Music history or theory, style criticism. Prerequisites for graduate study performance on major instrument and piano; competence in sight-singing and ear training; at least 3 years of music theory and 1 of music history; reading knowledge of French or German; examination in music. Recommended: courses in composition. 5 professorial staff. 7 master's degrees and 5 Ph.D.'s awarded 1955-59. 8 graduate students registered fall 1959.

Oriental Languages and Civilizations. Arabic and Islam, archaeology, Assyriology, Chinese culture, Egyptology, Hebrew and Old Testament, Hellenistic or Japanese culture. Recommended for graduate study: French and German; classical or Oriental languages; previous work in field. 25 professorial staff. 7 master's degrees and 14 Ph.D.'s awarded 1955-59. 28 graduate students registered fall 1959.

Philosophy.—Analysis of Ideas and Study of Methods. Program is concerned with the philosophic implications and foundations of other disciplines. Candidate's program is approximately ½ philosophy and ½ chosen from a field of humanistic, scientific, or social scientific study. Combined program conducted by interdepartmental and interdivisional Committee on the Analysis of Ideas and Study of Methods. Prerequisite for graduate study: training in philosophy. 10 professorial staff. 2 master's degrees awarded 1955-59. 5 graduate students registered fall 1959.

Philosophy.—General. Ethics, aesthetics, political philosophy, epistemology, logic, philosophy of science, metaphysics. Recommended for graduate study: GRE. 12 professorial staff. 37 master's degrees and 19 Ph.D.'s awarded 1955-59. 61 graduate students registered fall 1959.

Religion. Biblical literature (emphasis on New Testament); early Christian literature (including New Testament); Biblical languages (Biblical and Hellenistic Greek); religion and thought; historical and cultural backgrounds; history of the Bible and of Biblical interpretation; New Testament textual studies; archaeology and Bible. Offered by Department of New Testament and Early Christian Literature. Prerequisite for graduate study: work in humanities and in physical and social sciences. Recommended: Latin and Greek. Recommended for Ph.D. candidacy: B.D. or M.A. in religion. 8 professorial staff. 6 Ph.D.'s awarded 1955-59. 14 graduate students registered fall 1959.

Romance Languages and Literatures. 3 fields are selected by student with his adviser, 2 of which may be closely related, the third in a different area. Prerequisites for graduate study: knowledge of French, Spanish, or a combination; placement test in language of major field. Recommended: 1 Romance language in addition to major; reading knowledge of German; some knowledge of Latin. 11 professorial staff. 23 master's degrees and 7 Ph.D.'s awarded 1955-59. 45 graduate students registered fall 1959.

Slavic Languages and Literatures. See program on *Linguistics.*

Division of Physical Sciences

Established in 1930 during a general reorganization of the university.

ADMISSION REQUIREMENTS

These are essentially the same as the requirements for the Division of Biological Sciences, except that candidates for the Ph.D. must demonstrate a reading knowledge of 2 foreign languages designated by his major department.

Apply to Office of Admissions, University of Chicago, at any time.

FEES AND FIRST-YEAR AID

Fees are the same as those described for the Division of Biological Sciences.

First-year aid available: Scholarships (up to full tuition) available in all departments; teaching assistantships ($1,800 plus tuition) in physics and chemistry only; a few other fellowships (tuition and stipend of up to $3,000). Research assistantships (with stipends of up to $320 per month) sometimes available.

Apply to Office of Admissions, University of Chicago, or to head of appropriate department by February 15.

FIELDS OF STUDY FOR THE PH.D.

Astronomy and Astrophysics. Prerequisite for graduate study: major in physics, mathematics, or astronomy. 9 professorial staff. 5 Ph.D.'s awarded 1955-59. 8 graduate students registered fall 1959.

Chemistry. Inorganic, organic, or physical chemistry; chemical physics. Prerequisite for graduate study: placement test after admission. 26 professorial staff. 90 master's degrees and 65 Ph.D.'s awarded 1955-59. 124 graduate students registered fall 1959.

Geography. This department has been transferred to the Social Sciences Division. Information on degrees earned (1955-59) and students registered (fall 1959) are included in description of geography course offered by Social Sciences Division.

Geology. All phases of geology and paleontology. 10 professorial staff. 15 master's degrees and 23 Ph.D.'s awarded 1955-59. 31 graduate students registered fall 1959.

Mathematics. All phases of mathematics except applied. 17 professorial staff. 67 master's degrees and 46 Ph.D.'s awarded 1955-59. 124 graduate students registered fall 1959.

Meteorology. Problems of the atmosphere. Prerequisite for graduate study: major in meteorology or equivalent. 8 professorial staff. 20 master's degrees and 5 Ph.D.'s awarded 1955-59. 42 graduate students registered fall 1959.

Physics. Atomic, molecular, chemical, nuclear, solid-state, experimental, or theoretical physics; spectroscopy. Prerequisite for graduate study: major in physics or equivalent. Recommended: GRE Aptitude and Advanced Tests in Physics. 35 professorial staff. 123 master's degrees and 43 Ph.D.'s awarded 1955-59. 149 graduate students registered fall 1959.

Statistics. 8 professorial staff. 2 master's degrees and 3 Ph.D.'s awarded 1955-59. 23 graduate students registered fall 1959.

Division of the Social Sciences

Established in 1930 during a general reorganization of the university.

ADMISSION REQUIREMENTS

Requirements are essentially the same as for the Division of Biological Sciences, except that candidates for the Ph.D. degree must present the equivalent of work required for a master's degree and must secure approval of dissertation proposal and program of research.

Apply to Office of Admissions, University of Chicago, 1 full quarter before admission is desired.

FEES AND FIRST-YEAR AID

Fees are essentially the same as those described for the Division of Biological Sciences.

First-year aid available: scholarships ranging in value from $140 (for 1 course) to $1,050 (for full tuition); fellowships, $160-$5,000.

Apply to Office of Admissions, Committee on Fellowships and Scholarships, Administration Building, Room 304, on or before February 15.

FIELDS OF STUDY FOR THE PH.D.

Anthropology. Archaeology, ethnology, linguistics, physical or social anthropology. Recommended for graduate study: 2 or more years of French or German. Ph.D. candidacy prerequisites: examination in French or German; statis-

tics. 12 professorial staff. 64 master's degrees and 39 Ph.D.'s awarded 1955-59. 62 graduate students registered fall 1959.

Economics. Price theory, monetary theory and banking, economic history, statistics and econometrics, history of economic thought, agricultural economics, public finance, international economic relations, labor economics and industrial relations, economics of consumption, industrial organization. Prerequisite for graduate study: GRE. Recommended: elements of price and monetary theory; rudiments of differential calculus. Ph.D. candidacy prerequisites: 2 foreign languages or 1 foreign language and competence in a program of mathematics. 27 professorial staff. 73 master's degrees and 63 Ph.D.'s awarded 1955-59. 107 graduate students registered fall 1959.

Education. Preschool and elementary, secondary, general, higher, or adult education; school and social order; quantitative inquiry; educational administration and supervision; educational psychology; philosophy of education; curriculum and methods. Prerequisite for graduate study: basic sequence in education. 37 professorial staff. 371 master's degrees and 80 Ph.D.'s awarded 1955-59. 160 graduate students registered fall 1959.

Geography. Bio- and physical geography; economic geography, including location theory, transportation, and resources management; cultural geography, including political and historical geography; urban geography; cartography and statistics, including special work in quantitative methods. Areas of concentration include the Far East, U.S.S.R., Africa, and Latin America. Recommended for graduate study: foreign languages. 10 professorial staff. 22 master's degrees and 16 Ph.D.'s awarded 1955-59. 37 graduate students registered fall 1959. New enrollment limited to 20.

History. Ancient Oriental and Greek; Roman; medieval Europe 375-1122 or 1095-1450; Renaissance and Reformation 1350-1648; Europe, 1648-1815 or since 1815; Russia; England 1485-1714 or since 1688; modern India; Far East, prior to 1200 or since 1200; United States, 1603-1865 or since 1850. Other special fields to be arranged. 26 professorial staff. 112 master's degrees and 47 Ph.D.'s awarded 1955-59. 177 graduate students registered fall 1959.

Human Development. Psychological development of the individual, social organizations which influence the individual and through which he relates to others, biological bases of behavior. Interdisciplinary program conducted by Committee on Human Development. Prerequisite for graduate study: fundamental knowledge in areas mentioned above. Ph.D. candidacy prerequisite: 2 advanced courses in statistics. 66 master's degrees and 44 Ph.D.'s awarded 1955-59. 91 graduate students registered fall 1959.

Political Science. Political theory, international law and diplomacy, public law or administration, comparative government, parties and politics. Prerequisite for graduate study: major in political science. Recommended: languages; GRE. 19 professorial staff. 133 master's degrees and 70 Ph.D.'s awarded 1955-59. 110 graduate students registered fall 1959.

Social Thought. Intellectual and moral foundations of society; interpretations of historical change; interaction of society, ethics, and culture. Student's work may be in both the humanities and social sciences. Interdisciplinary program offered by Committee on Social Thought. 9 professorial staff. 1 master's degree and 7 Ph.D.'s awarded 1955-59. 39 graduate students registered fall 1959.

Sociology. Sociology, social organization; social psychology and communication; urbanism; population and human ecology; theory and methods. Recommended for graduate study: French or German. 22 professorial staff. 50 master's degrees and 43 Ph.D.'s awarded 1955-59. 100 graduate students registered fall 1959.

Graduate School of Business

Established in 1898 as an undergraduate school.

Graduate instruction in business subjects has been offered at Chicago for many years, and the first Ph.D. was awarded in 1922. The Graduate School of Business maintains close relationship with Departments of Economics, Statistics, Psychology, Sociology, Anthropology, and Mathematics, and conducts an evening program of graduate study in management which is distinct from the Center for Adult Education.

ADMISSION REQUIREMENTS

These are essentially the same as the requirements for the Division of Biological Sciences,

except that all applicants are required to take the Admission Test for Graduate Study in Business and obtain the approval of the Committee on Enrollment for Doctoral Study.

Apply to Director of Doctoral Programs, Graduate School of Business, at any time.

FEES AND FIRST-YEAR AID

Fees are generally the same as those for the Division of Biological Sciences, except that tuition is $1,080 per academic year.

First-year aid available: 13 scholarships, $510-$1,080 plus fees; 20 fellowships, $1,500-$3,600; 16 research assistantships, $2-$2.50 per hour.

Apply to Director of Doctoral Programs, Graduate School of Business, by February 15.

FIELDS OF STUDY FOR THE PH.D.

Business. Accounting, behavorial sciences, business economics, business finance, institution management, marketing, personnel management and industrial relations, production, public policy and business law, mathematical methods and computers, and statistics. Ph.D. candidacy prerequisites: examination in 1 modern foreign language; approval of dissertation proposal; examinations in candidate's discipline and fields of concentration. 60 professorial staff. 1,135 master's degrees and 27 Ph.D.'s awarded 1955-59. 1,264 graduate students registered fall 1959.

Divinity School

At the time the University of Chicago was incorporated in 1892, the Baptist Union Theological Seminary became the Divinity School of the University of Chicago. Since that time its faculty and student body have represented all the major denominations in America. The Ph.D. degree has been awarded by the Divinity School since 1904.

ADMISSION REQUIREMENTS

For graduate study: bachelor's degree; undergraduate record of good quality; recommendation from 2 college faculty members who are acquainted with student's character and ability; University of Chicago Entrance Tests or GRE. Recommended: pretheological studies in courses with recommendation of American Association of Theological Schools. For candidacy for Ph.D.:

completion with satisfactory grades of substantial portion of course work; reading knowledge of French and German (candidates in the field of religion and personality are required to pass examination in only 1 of these); comprehensive qualifying examinations of 5 major sequences, representing basic material in 7 fields of inquiry, with minimum grade of B; field examination (written and oral); approval of research problem and permission to work in field selected for specialization.

Apply to Director of Admissions, University of Chicago, or to Dean of Students, Divinity School, preferably by February 1 or at least 8 months prior to date of proposed entry.

FEES AND FIRST-YEAR AID

Application fee $10. Tuition $1,050 for 3 quarters. General service fee $20 per quarter. Room (in dormitory) for men $255-$360 for three quarters; for women $279-$354. Contract for meals with room approximately $900 for three quarters; meals may be purchased separately in cafeteria or coffee shop at an average cost of $3.50 per day. Furnished apartments $67.50-$90 per month; unfurnished $55-$85.

First-year aid available: approximately 150 scholarships, $50-$720; 9 fellowships, $1,500.

Apply to Dean of Students, Divinity School of the University of Chicago, at least 9 months prior to date of proposed entry; later applications considered if vacancies are available.

FIELDS OF STUDY FOR THE PH.D.

Bible. Languages, history, introduction, history of Bible and Biblical study, themes of the Bible, Old or New Testament. Recommended for graduate study: Syriac, Akkadian, ancient, and Near East history. Ph.D. candidacy prerequisites: the Biblical languages (Hebrew, Greek, Aramaic) and French and German. 5 professorial staff. 5 master's degrees and 9 Ph.D.'s awarded 1955-59. 24 graduate students registered fall 1959.

Ethics and Society. Perspectives, data, and problems involved in understanding interaction of church and society; social institutions; social and political life; theological ethics; social science methods; sociology of the church. Recommended for graduate study: wide reading in sociology, anthropology, and psychology. 4 professorial staff. 5 master's degrees and 3 Ph.D.'s awarded 1955-59. 10 students registered fall 1959.

History of Christianity. Early, Middle Ages, Reformation, or modern period; American church history; English Puritanism; ecumenical movement. 6 professorial staff. 7 master's degrees and 5 Ph.D.'s awarded 1955-59. 15 graduate students registered fall 1959.

History of Religions. Primitive religions, Buddhism, Hinduism, Mohammedanism, religious phenomena or experience. 4 professorial staff. 1 master's degree and 4 Ph.D.'s awarded 1955-59. 10 graduate students registered fall 1959.

Religion and Art. Relation of faith to culture or of theology to the humanities, lyric and epic narrative, serious drama and prose fiction, literary criticism, literary periods, visual arts. 3 professorial staff. 8 master's degrees awarded 1955-59. 20 graduate students registered fall 1959.

Religion and Personality. Knowledge and methods in the sciences of man, interrelation of religion and the sciences of man, methods of study of religion and personality, dynamics of religious work with individuals and groups, religious education, pastoral care. 5 professorial staff. 16 master's degrees and 4 Ph.D.'s awarded 1955-59. 35 graduate students registered fall 1959.

Theology and Philosophy of Religion. Constructive (systematic) theology; history of theology; philosophy of religion. 5 professorial staff. 14 master's degrees and 20 Ph.D.'s awarded 1955-59. 30 graduate students registered fall 1959.

Graduate Library School

The Graduate Library School was established in 1926 and formally opened in 1928. The first Ph.D. was conferred in 1930. Special facilities include a collection of approximately 5,000 current books for children and young people in the Center for Children's Books at the university library.

ADMISSION REQUIREMENTS

The admission requirements are generally the same as those for the Division of Biological Sciences, except that reading knowledge of 2 foreign languages must be demonstrated.

Apply to Dean of Students, Graduate Library School, at least 6 weeks in advance of date of desired admission.

Tuition $960 per academic year. Other fees are essentially the same as those given for the Division of Biological Sciences.

First-year aid available: tuition scholarships to qualified students in both M.A. and Ph.D. programs; fellowships normally awarded to students in doctoral programs only. Extensive tuition and emergency loan funds available.

FIELDS OF STUDY FOR THE PH.D.

Librarianship. All phases of librarianship, with special concentrations in public libraries, college and university libraries, library work with children and young people (both in public libraries and in school libraries), bibliography and reference, bibliographical history, technical processes, and reading and other media of communication. Courses in particular areas of special librarianship are arranged with appropriate schools and divisions of the university. Prerequisites for graduate study: general education and entrance examinations (administered by the University of Chicago) or GRE Area Tests. 13 professorial staff. 81 master's degrees and 16 Ph.D.'s awarded 1955-59. 57 graduate students registered fall 1959.

School of Social Service Administration

Founded in 1908 as an independent school, The Chicago School of Civics and Philanthropy; became integral part of the university in 1920. First Ph.D. degree awarded 1924. No joint programs leading to the Ph.D. are offered, but students are required to take a considerable amount of work (a minimum of 1 quarter) in other parts of the university.

The Social Welfare Center, which is under construction, consists of an assembly of social agencies on or near the campus which will work jointly with the school in education and research. The school has a research center where research in social case work is in progress.

ADMISSION REQUIREMENTS

For graduate study: bachelor's degree (preferably with a major in social sciences or humanities); undergraduate record of good quality; recommendation from 2 college faculty members

who are acquainted with student's character and ability. For candidacy for Ph.D.: master's degree in social work with good academic record; period of successful work practice; motivation and capacity for scholarship; personality and personal characteristics suitable for professional practice; 3 quarters of course work; examination in 3 major fields of study; examination in 1 foreign language; approval of dissertation problem.

Apply to the Dean or the Director of Admissions of the School of Social Service Administration, preferably soon after January but not later than June 1.

FEES AND FIRST-YEAR AID

Fees are approximately the same as those given for the Division of Biological Sciences.

First-year aid available: up to 15 scholarships, ½ tuition to $4,740; 2 teaching fellowships, $6,000.

Apply to Dean of Students, School of Social Service Administration, by May 1 if possible.

FIELDS OF STUDY FOR THE PH.D.

Several courses in the methodology of teaching are offered; one on the Dynamics of Learning deals with learning theories, problems of learning, and course structuring. The school has a career teacher training program in which 1 or 2 advanced students, appointed as teaching fellows, work closely with senior professor in student's field of interest in preparation for career in teaching in a school of social work.

Social Work. Social treatment, research, administration. 11 professorial staff. 360 master's degrees and 16 Ph.D.'s awarded 1955-59. 220 graduate students registered fall 1959.

Cincinnati, University of

CINCINNATI 21, OHIO

Graduate School of Arts and Sciences

Graduate instruction has been offered since 1877, with first Ph.D. being awarded in 1892. The Graduate School was organized in 1906. University is publicly controlled by the city of Cincinnati. Both men and women are admitted.

The university also offers the D.Sc. in certain

areas, the Doctor of Industrial Medicine, and the Ed.D. A joint graduate program has been established between the University of Cincinnati and Hebrew Union College in the areas of the classics, history, Bible, and philosophy. Graduate students may register for courses at either institution, but fees are paid exclusively to the institution from which degree is being sought.

Single graduate students are housed in dormitories, fraternity houses, and in private residences; no facilities for married students are owned by the university.

Residence requirements for the Ph.D.: last 3 years of study must be in full-time residence at the university; not more than 60 graduate credits may be transferred.

ADMISSION REQUIREMENTS

Bachelor's degree; specific preparation in field of study; GRE in certain areas.

Apply to the Dean of the Graduate School before July 1.

FEES AND FIRST-YEAR AID

No application fee. Tuition for residents of Cincinnati $450 a year; others $675. Room (in dormitory) $288 per year. Board in college dining room $12 per week and up.

First-year aid available: scholarships, $400-$600; teaching fellowships, $1,500-$1,700; for other fellowships, $500-$3,000; research assistantships, $2,400-$3,600; graduate assistantships, $1,700.

Apply to Dean of the Graduate School before March 1.

FIELDS OF STUDY FOR THE PH.D.

Anatomy. Gross anatomy, histology, neuroanatomy, hematology, endocrinology, embryology, cancer, radiation biology, histochemistry. Prerequisites for graduate study: consultation with head of department; GRE or Medical Admission Test. 8 professorial staff. 1 master's degree awarded 1955-59. 5 graduate students registered fall 1959.

Applied Science. Any branch of engineering, physical sciences, or chemistry. Offered by the Departments of Physics, Chemistry, and Engineering. 2 professorial staff. 17 master's degrees and 18 Ph.D.'s awarded 1955-59. 14 graduate students registered fall 1959.

Astronomy.—Dynamical. A prerequisite for graduate study: strong mathematics background. 2 professorial staff plus others from Department of Mathematics. Ph.D. program begun 1959. 5 graduate students registered fall 1959.

Biological Chemistry. Prerequisites for graduate study: major in chemistry, including general, organic, and physical chemistry; physics. 11 professorial staff. 1 Ph.D. awarded 1955-59.

Biological Sciences. Bacteriology, botany, zoology. Offered by respective departments. Prerequisite for graduate study: major in chosen field; some chemistry background. 12 professorial staff. 10 master's degrees and 5 Ph.D.'s awarded 1955-59. 39 graduate students registered fall 1959.

Chemistry. Inorganic, analytical, organic, physical, theoretical. Prerequisites for graduate study: fundamental principles of general, inorganic, analytical, organic, and physical chemistry. Recommended: reading knowledge of French and German. 12 professorial staff. 21 master's degrees and 12 Ph.D.'s awarded 1955-59. 75 graduate students registered fall 1959.

Classics. Greek, Latin, ancient history, archaeology. Prerequisite for graduate study: working knowledge of Greek and Latin. 6 professorial staff. 7 master's degrees and 3 Ph.D.'s awarded 1955-59. 16 graduate students registered fall 1959.

Economics. Economic theory, international economics, labor. Prerequisites for graduate study: 1 year of principles of economics, money and banking; any 2 other economics courses. 4 professorial staff. 12 master's degrees and 3 Ph.D.'s awarded 1955-59. 16 graduate students registered fall 1959.

Engineering.—Chemical and Metallurgical. Prerequisites for graduate study: bachelor's degree in chosen area. 9 professorial staff. 14 master's degrees and 7 Ph.D.'s awarded 1955-59. 20 graduate students registered fall 1959.

English. All important periods and topics of English-American literary and theatrical history. 6 professorial staff. 11 master's degrees and 2 Ph.D.'s awarded 1955-59. 29 graduate students registered fall 1959.

Geology. Petrology, paleontology, stratigraphy, glacial geology, structural geology, sedimentology. Prerequisites for graduate study. 1 year each of physics, chemistry, calculus, or statistics; summer field course in geology or equivalent before admission or early in program; GRE.

Recommended: biology, particularly for paleontology. 7 professorial staff. 16 master's degrees and 4 Ph.D.'s awarded 1955-59. 18 graduate students registered fall 1959.

German. Germanic philology, German literature from earliest times to the 20th century. Prerequisites for graduate study: course in classical period; knowledge of history of German literature; minimum of 18 units beyond elementary German. 3 professorial staff; 5 master's degrees and 5 Ph.D.'s awarded 1955-59. 7 graduate students registered fall 1959.

Mathematics. Algebra, analysis, geometry, applied mathematics and mechanics, logic, and foundations. 12 professorial staff. 10 master's degrees and 8 Ph.D.'s awarded 1955-59. 42 graduate students registered fall 1959.

Microbiology. Medical microbiology with special emphasis on host-parasite relationships, bacterial nutrition and metabolism, immunology, cytology. Prerequisites for graduate study: general biology; comparative anatomy and embryology; physics; qualitative, quantitative and organic chemistry; mathematics through trigonometry; major in biology or chemistry. Recommended: working knowledge of statistical methods. 5 professorial staff. 1 master's degree and 2 Ph.D.'s awarded 1955-59. 1 graduate student registered fall 1959.

Pathology. Experimental and comparative pathology. Prerequisites for graduate study: gross and microscopic anatomy, comparative anatomy. Recommended: qualitative and quantitative analytic chemistry; organic chemistry; physiology; embryology. 12 professorial staff. 1 graduate student registered fall 1959.

Pharmacology. Pharmacology of nerve and muscle, autonomic nervous system, heart and circulation, ion transport, and drug metabolism. Prerequisites for graduate study: biology and chemistry. 5 professorial staff. 2 master's degrees and 2 Ph.D.'s awarded 1955-59. 4 graduate students registered fall 1959.

Philosophy. History of philosophy, logic, semantics, ethics, aesthetics, philosophy of religion. 7 professorial staff. 1 master's degree and 1 Ph.D. awarded 1955-59. 8 graduate students registered fall 1959.

Physics. Classical mechanics, modern physics, biophysics. Prerequisite for graduate study: degree in physics, engineering, mathematics, astronomy, or chemistry. 11 professorial staff. 9 master's degrees and 4 Ph.D.'s awarded 1955-59. 47 graduate students registered fall 1959.

Physiology. Prerequisite for graduate study: degree in biology or chemistry, or M.D. 2 professorial staff. 4 Ph.D.'s awarded 1955-59. 3 graduate students registered fall 1959.

Political Science. Public law, comparative government, public administration, international organization and politics. Prerequisite for graduate study: American government or equivalent. 4 professorial staff. 6 master's degrees and 3 Ph.D.'s awarded 1955-59. 7 graduate students registered fall 1959.

Psychology. Theoretical-experimental, clinical, and counseling psychology. Prerequisite for graduate study: basic courses in measurement, experimental method, and theoretical psychology totaling 20 credits minimum; GRE or MAT. 10 professorial staff. 10 master's degrees and 5 Ph.D.s awarded 1955-59. 46 graduate students registered fall 1959.

Romance Languages. French: Renaissance to contemporary literature and philology. Spanish: literature from 1100; Spanish-American literature; philology. 7 professorial staff. 7 master's degrees and 1 Ph.D. awarded 1955-59. 11 graduate students registered fall 1959.

Tanning Research. Courses in the various fields of science related to tanning (chemistry, chemical engineering, biology, biological chemistry, mathematics, microbiology, and physics). Prerequisite for graduate study: either a chemistry or chemical engineering degree. 3 professorial staff. 5 master's degrees awarded 1955-59. 4 graduate students registered fall 1959.

Claremont College

CLAREMONT, CALIFORNIA

Claremont Graduate School

Claremont Graduate School is the common graduate institution of the Associated Colleges at Claremont. It has 30 full-time faculty members on Claremont College appointment and, in addition, many members of the undergraduate colleges participate in graduate teaching, tutorials, research, and dissertation direction. It was organized in 1928 and the first Ph.D. was awarded in

1937. Institution is privately controlled and non-sectarian. Both men and women are admitted.

Graduate School is a member of the Intercollegiate Program of Graduate Studies, together with the other associated colleges, Occidental College, University of Redlands, Whittier College. Purpose is to offer interdisciplinary seminars in the humanities and social sciences for students preparing to become junior and senior college teachers.

Rooms (with kitchen privileges) in Graduate School's residence buildings available for single students; 1- and 2-bedroom apartments for married students.

Special facilities include affiliation with Rancho Santa Ana Botanic Garden and Western Personnel Institute. The Honnold Library of the Associated Colleges contains approximately 60,000 volumes, with several special collections.

Residence requirement for the Ph.D.: 3 years of graduate study, 2 of which must be taken in residence at Claremont. Residence requirement in education waived under certain circumstances. Summer and evening courses available.

ADMISSION REQUIREMENTS

For graduate study: bachelor's degree; satisfactory undergraduate record; strong background in liberal arts and sciences; reading knowledge of 2 foreign languages (usually French and German); GRE or MAT. For candidacy for Ph.D.: written and oral qualifying examinations.

Apply to Director of Student Personnel Services by March 1.

FEES AND FIRST-YEAR AID

Application fee $5. Tuition $700 per year. Rooms (with kitchen privileges) in residence buildings $360 per year. Apartments $63-$80 per month.

First-year aid available: 40 fellowships, $700-$2,000. Apply to Director of Student Personnel Services by March 1.

FIELDS OF STUDY FOR THE PH.D.

A seminar is offered on higher education in America which emphasizes teaching methodology as well as the history and philosophies of American higher education. Teaching internships are arranged in the Claremont undergraduate colleges and neighboring institutions under faculty supervision.

Botany. Systematic botany, genetics, plant breeding, morphology, ecology, mycology, anatomy. Prerequisites for graduate study: fundamental courses in botany; general genetics; general chemistry; general zoology. Recommended: physics and statistics. 7 professorial staff. 9 master's degrees and 5 Ph.D.'s awarded 1955-59. 11 graduate students registered fall 1959.

Economics. Economic theory, industrial organization, finance, labor, economic development, international economics, statistics, mathematics. Prerequisites for graduate study: 30 units in economics; mathematics and statistics may be substituted for one foreign language; GRE. 17 professorial staff. 7 master's degrees and 1 Ph.D. awarded 1955-59. 34 graduate students registered fall 1959.

Education. Social or psychological foundations of education; curriculum and instruction; educational administration; elementary, secondary, or junior college education; collegiate student personnel work. Counseling and guidance included in psychological foundations of education. Education programs are offered in conjunction with Department of Psychology. Recommended for graduate study: minimum of 2 years' teaching experience; master's degree; statistics and research design. 12 professorial staff. 155 master's degrees and 9 Ph.D.'s awarded 1955-59. 294 graduate students registered fall 1959.

English and American Languages and Literatures. Medieval, Renaissance, neo-classical, 19th century British, American to 1900, contemporary. Prerequisites for graduate study: major in English; GRE. 17 professorial staff. Ph.D. program begun 1955. 20 master's degrees and 1 Ph.D. awarded 1955-59. 36 graduate students registered fall 1959.

History. American (diplomatic, intellectual, political, and social); British; Eastern and South Asia. Combined program offered by Departments of History and Government. Prerequisites for graduate study: major in history; GRE. 12 professorial staff. 31 master's degrees and 5 Ph.D.'s awarded 1955-59. 35 graduate students registered fall 1959.

Political Science.—Government. Political theory, public law, political behavior and institutions, public administration, international relations, comparative government, political development (South Asia and Latin America). Combined program offered by Departments of Government and History. Prerequisites for graduate study: 24 units in government or political science;

GRE. 14 professorial staff. 19 master's degrees and 2 Ph.D.'s awarded 1955-59. 27 graduate students registered fall 1959.

Psychology. General experimental psychology, with emphasis on personality, social, motivation, perception, learning, physiological, or child psychology. Combined program offered by Department of Psychology with education and other social sciences. Prerequisites for graduate study: minimum of 15 units in psychology, including experimental, statistics, and other standard courses; 15 units in physical and biological sciences; MAT and entrance examination. For Ph.D. candidacy, advanced mathematics and statistics may be substituted for 1 foreign language with approval. 8 professorial staff. 19 master's degrees and 11 Ph.D.'s awarded 1955-59. 82 graduate students registered fall 1959.

Religion. Old and New Testament, history of religious thought, theology and philosophy of religion, comparative religion. Prerequisites for graduate study: major in religion, philosophy or related fields; placement examinations. 11 professorial staff. Ph.D. program begun 1959. 12 graduate students registered fall 1959.

Clark University

WORCESTER 10, MASSACHUSETTS

The Graduate School

Clark University was initially established in 1887 as one of America's first institutions dedicated exclusively to graduate study and research. The first Ph.D. was conferred in 1891, although the undergraduate college was not established until 1902. Thus, though a small institution, graduate work has always been a dominant element. University is privately controlled and nonsectarian. Both men and women are admitted.

22 dormitory rooms maintained for graduate men; none for women. A few university-owned apartments available for married students.

Residence requirement for Ph.D.: minimum of 3 years beyond bachelor's degree, of which 1 year of full-time study beyond master's degree (or equivalent in part-time study) must be spent in residence at Clark. Some graduate courses are offered in the Summer School.

ADMISSION REQUIREMENTS

For graduate study: bachelor's degree; high academic standing. Recommended: GRE. For candidacy for Ph.D.: completion of 2 years of graduate work, with at least 1 year of full-time graduate work (or equivalent) in residence; certification in German and French (or completion of substitute program approved by the Graduate Board); preliminary examination and payment of $55 fee; meeting of special departmental requirements.

Apply to the Chairmen of the Graduate Departments. For best consideration application should be filed prior to March 1.

FEES AND FIRST-YEAR AID

No application fee. Tuition $1,050 per year. Special fees include $5 matriculation fee, plus special departmental fees. Annual cost of room (in dormitory) for men $300-$400 per year. Approximate annual cost of board in college dining room $480. Apartments, if available, rent for $60-$90 per month.

First-year aid available: 82 tuition scholarships; variable number of fellowships with stipends ranging from $100-$800 (depending on need of student); teaching fellowships in 3 departments, tuition plus $800; research assistantships in 2 departments.

Apply to Chairmen of Graduate Departments by March 1 for best consideration.

FIELDS OF STUDY FOR THE PH.D.

Chemistry. Coordination (inorganic), physical, or organic chemistry; biochemistry; biophysics; radiochemistry; nuclear chemistry. Prerequisites for graduate study: major in chemistry, including standard course in physical chemistry; usually 1 foreign language; departmental placement examination. Recommended: GRE; courses in differential equations and in German. 7 professorial staff. 14 master's degrees and 17 Ph.D.'s awarded 1955-59. 22 graduate students registered fall 1959.

Economics. Money and banking, labor, marketing, public finance and fiscal policy, government control of industry, international economics, economic theory, history of economic doctrine. 8 professorial staff. 19 master's degrees and 8 Ph.D.'s awarded 1955-59. 13 full-time and 4 part-time graduate students registered fall 1959.

Geography. Urban geography (planning),

political geography, climatology, geomorphology, agrarian geography, economic geography, geography in education. 6 professorial staff. 33 master's degrees and 42 Ph.D.'s awarded 1955-59. 26 graduate students registered fall 1959. Program limited to 30 graduate students.

History and International Relations. American, modern European, and British history; history of international relations, international politics, international organization; minors in international economic policy and political geography. Programs in history and in international relations are separate, but both are administered by the Department of History, Government, and International Relations. Minors in international economic policy and political geography are offered in cooperation with the respective departments. Prerequisites for graduate study: 1 foreign language, preferably French or German. 6 professorial staff. 26 master's degrees and 7 Ph.D.'s awarded 1955-59. 20 full-time and 8 part-time graduate students registered fall 1959. Program usually limited to maximum of 20.

Psychology. General, experimental, clinical, developmental, and social psychology; learning. Recommended for graduate study: major in psychology; GRE; MAT. 20 professorial staff. 29 master's degrees and 28 Ph.D.'s awarded 1955-59. 40 graduate students registered fall 1959. New enrollment limited to 10, total in program to 40.

Clemson College

CLEMSON, SOUTH CAROLINA

Graduate School

The Graduate School was organized in 1945, although graduate instruction has been offered since 1924. First Ph.D. was awarded in 1960. Clemson is a public institution, controlled by the state. Both men and women are admitted.

Rooms in men's domitories and in private homes available for single students; 400 apartments for married students owned by college.

Residence requirement for doctorate: 3 academic years, although as many as 2 years may be waived under certain circumstances. Summer courses toward the Ph.D. available.

ADMISSION REQUIREMENTS

For graduate study: bachelor's degree; strong undergraduate record; approval of department head and the Graduate Dean; GRE Aptitude Test. For candidacy for Ph.D.: reading knowledge of 2 foreign languages; qualifying examinations. Up to 6 semester hours of credit of work toward master's degree may be transferred from other graduate institutions; amount individually determined for candidates for Ph.D.

Application may be made to Dean of the Graduate School at any time.

FEES AND FIRST-YEAR AID

No application fee. Tuition $150 per academic year for graduate students. Special fees (not charged to graduate assistants) approximate $180 annually. Rooms (in dormitory) for men $86 per semester. Approximate annual cost of board in college dining room $360. Apartments $24-$42 per month.

First-year aid available: 30 teaching fellowships, $1,700-$2,000 plus reduced tuition; 30 other fellowships, $600-$3,200; 30 research assistantships, $1,800-$2,000 plus reduced tuition; grants-in-aid, $100-$600.

Apply to Dean of the Graduate School by April 15.

FIELDS OF STUDY FOR THE PH.D.

Agricultural Economics. Agricultural marketing, farm finance, farm management. Offered by Department of Agricultural Economics and Rural Sociology. 16 professorial staff. Ph.D. program initiated 1959. 20 master's degrees awarded 1955-59. 12 graduate students registered fall 1959.

Chemistry. Organic, inorganic, physical. Prerequisites for graduate study: placement tests; German. 15 professorial staff. Ph.D. program initiated 1959. 15 master's degrees awarded 1955-59. 22 graduate students registered fall 1959. Registration limited to about 30.

Entomology. Offered by Entomology and Zoology Department. 8 teaching staff; 2 research staff. Ph.D. program initiated 1956. 26 master's degrees awarded 1955-59. 11 graduate students registered fall 1959.

Plant Pathology. Offered by Botany and Bacteriology Department. 7 teaching staff; 5 research staff. Ph.D. program initiated 1956. 4 master's degrees and 1 Ph.D. awarded 1955-59. 8 graduate students registered fall 1959.

Colorado State University

FORT COLLINS, COLORADO

The Graduate School

Graduate instruction has been offered since about 1920, and the Graduate School was organized in 1940. First Ph.D. awarded 1955. University is publicly controlled by the state. Both men and women are admitted.

Single students are accommodated in modern college dormitories; housing on campus provided for married students.

Special facilities include: library of approximately 200,000 volumes; State Agricultural Experiment Station; Colorado State University Research Foundation; Irrigation and Hydraulics Laboratories; Veterinary Medicine Hospital; plant herbarium; nuclear reactor; Irrigation Institute; and Genetics Institute.

Residence requirement for Ph.D.: 9 quarters beyond bachelor's degree; maximum of 4 quarters may be transferred from other graduate schools. A few summer courses available.

ADMISSION REQUIREMENTS

For graduate study: bachelor's degree; B average in senior year. For candidacy for Ph.D.: reading knowledge of 2 foreign languages (usually French, German, or Russian); preliminary examinations; submission of an approved title for dissertation.

Apply to Dean of the Graduate School 1 month before admission is desired (3 months for foreign students).

FEES AND FIRST-YEAR AID

No application fee. Tuition for state residents $225 a year; others $570. Room (in dormitory) $180-$225 a year. Approximate annual cost of board in college dining room $450. Apartments $35 per month.

First-year aid available: 10 tuition scholarships; 5 fellowships, variable stipend; 50 research assistantships, $2,000-$2,200 (12 months); 40 teaching assistantships, $1,500-$1,800 (9 months).

Apply to head of department by May 1 (preferably earlier).

FIELDS OF STUDY FOR THE PH.D.

Animal Pathology. Offered by the Department of Pathology and Bacteriology. 8 professorial staff. Ph.D. program begun 1955. 8 master's degrees awarded 1955-59. 3 graduate students registered fall 1959.

Bacteriology. Bacterial physiology; food, dairy, and sanitary bacteriology; industrial microbiology; pathogenic bacteriology; immunology; virology. Offered by Department of Pathology and Bacteriology. 6 professorial staff. Ph.D. program begun 1955. 5 master's degrees and 1 Ph.D. awarded 1955-59. 2 graduate students registered fall 1959.

Biochemistry. Offered by the Department of Chemistry. 6 professorial staff. 3 master's degrees awarded 1955-59. 2 graduate students registered fall 1959.

Botany. Plant pathology, ecology, physiology. Offered by the Department of Botany and Plant Pathology. 12 professorial staff. Ph.D. program begun 1959. 15 master's degrees awarded 1955-59. 5 graduate students registered fall 1959.

Chemistry. Inorganic, organic, or physical chemistry; biochemistry. 12 professorial staff. 8 master's degrees and 1 Ph.D. awarded 1955-59. 1 graduate student registered fall 1959.

Engineering.—Civil. Civil or irrigation engineering; hydraulics. 12 professorial staff. 40 master's degrees and 7 Ph.D.'s awarded 1955-59. 20 graduate students registered fall 1959.

Forestry. Fisheries science, watershed management, wildlife management. 15 professorial staff. Ph.D. program begun 1958. 57 master's degrees awarded 1955-59. 6 graduate students registered fall 1959.

Genetics. Animal breeding; animal or plant genetics; poultry genetics. Combined program offered by Departments of Agronomy, Animal Husbandry, Horticulture, Poultry Husbandry, Zoology. 12 professorial staff. Ph.D. program begun 1957. 13 master's degrees awarded 1955-59. 2 graduate students registered fall 1959.

Physics. Magnetic properties of spinels, optical properties of metals, nuclear gamma ray spectroscopy, theoretical physics, elastic properties of crystals. 9 professorial staff. Ph.D. program begun 1955. 8 master's degrees and 1 Ph.D. awarded 1955-59. 4 graduate students registered fall 1959.

Soil Science. Soil chemistry, soil physics, soil microbiology. Offered by Department of Agronomy. 15 professorial staff. Ph.D. program begun

1958. 12 master's degrees awarded 1955-59. 5 graduate students registered fall 1959.

Zoology. Limnology and fresh water biology, acarology, mammalogy, genetics, ornithology, ecology-animal, parasitology, invertebrate zoology. 8 professorial staff. Ph.D. program begun 1956. 10 master's degrees and 2 Ph.D.'s awarded 1955-59. 8 graduate students registered fall 1959.

Colorado, University of

BOULDER, COLORADO

The Graduate School

Graduate work was begun on a small scale in 1892, and the first Ph.D. was awarded in 1895. The present school was organized in 1909 with a separate faculty. In addition to the Ph.D., the university confers the Ed.D., the D.Mus.A., and the D.B.A. Institution is publicly controlled by the state. Both men and women are admitted.

Single graduate students find accommodations in private homes in community; married students in university-owned apartments or quonsets.

Special facilities include: high altitude observatory; isotopes, cancer research, and modern languages laboratories; cyclotron; Institute of Behaviorial Science; library containing approximately 645,000 volumes.

Residence requirement for Ph.D.: 6 semesters beyond bachelor's degree, 4 of which must be spent in residence on campus, and 2 of which must be consecutive in 1 academic year. Summer courses and a few evening courses available.

ADMISSION REQUIREMENTS

For graduate study: bachelor's degree; excellent record in undergraduate courses; recommendations. GRE or qualifying examination required during first semester. For candidacy for Ph.D.: 4 semesters of B– average graduate work; reading knowledge of 2 foreign languages; preliminary examinations; comprehensive examination.

Apply to Office of Admissions at least 1 month prior to date of desired entry.

FEES AND FIRST-YEAR AID

No application fee. Tuition for state residents $74-$232 per year; others $330-$720. Rooms in community average $180-$500 per year. Approximate annual cost of board in college dining room $360. Apartments $65-$95 per month.

First-year aid available: up to 40 tuition and fees scholarships; up to 200 teaching fellowships with stipends up to $2,250; up to 100 other fellowships with stipends of $1,000-$2,400 plus tuition and fees; up to 50 research assistantships with stipends up to $2,250. Grants-in-aid in varying amounts also available.

Apply to Graduate School by March 1.

FIELDS OF STUDY FOR THE PH.D.

Anatomy. Histochemistry, neurophysiology, electron microscopy, tissue culture, cinephotomicrography, embryology. Offered by Department of Anatomy, School of Medicine. Prerequisite for graduate study: major in biology. Recommended: physics and integral calculus; physical chemistry. 6 professorial staff. 3 Ph.D.'s awarded 1955-59. 2 graduate students registered fall 1959. Total enrollment limited to 6.

Anthropology.—General. Archaeology; physical, social, or cultural anthropology. Prerequisites for graduate study: 16 semester hours in anthropology, or 12 semester hours in anthropology and 8 hours in sociology. 5 professorial staff. Ph.D. program begun 1956. 12 master's degrees awarded 1955-59. 10 graduate students registered fall 1959.

Astrogeophysics. Solar physics, solar-terrestrial relations. Prerequisites for graduate study: training in physics and mathematics. Recommended: reading knowledge of French, German, or Russian. 6 professorial staff. Ph.D. program begun 1956. 1 master's degree and 1 Ph.D. awarded 1955-59. 12 graduate students registered fall 1959.

Biochemistry. Metabolism and enzymology of 1-C compounds; active transport and nucleotide and protein synthesis in bacterial protoplasts and membranes; metabolic patterns, growth requirements, and electrolyte balance in cultured mammalian cells; function of coenzymes in photochemical reactions; serum enzymes and porphyrins in cardiac infarction. Prerequisites for graduate study: major in chemistry; courses in qualitative and quantitative analysis; organic, inorganic, and physical chemistry; physics; calculus; general biology. 0 professorial staff. 1 master's degree and 3 Ph.D.'s awarded 1955-59. 3 graduate students registered fall 1959.

Biology. 15 professorial staff. 12 master's de-

grees awarded 1955-59. 11 graduate students registered fall 1959.

Botany. Offered by Department of Biology. 15 professorial staff. 2 master's degrees and 5 Ph.D.'s awarded 1955-59. 10 graduate students registered fall 1959.

Chemistry.—Chemical Physics. Chemistry and physics (cognate). Prerequisites for graduate study: major in chemistry or equivalent; qualifying tests in chemistry. Recommended: French, German, and/or Russian. 19 professorial staff. 25 master's degrees and 48 Ph.D.'s awarded 1955-59. 103 graduate students registered fall 1959.

Economics. Economic theory, history, or development; history of economic thought; regional, labor or international economics; money and banking; public finance; economics of agriculture; industrial organization. Prerequisites for graduate study: 16 hours of economics. 12 professorial staff. 14 master's degrees and 7 Ph.D.'s awarded 1955-59. 40 graduate students registered fall 1959.

Education. School administration; elementary, secondary, teacher, higher education; curriculum and instruction; counseling and student personnel work; social foundations of education; educational psychology and measurement; teaching of various subject fields. 20 professorial staff. 405 master's degrees and 3 Ph.D.'s awarded 1955-59. 88 graduate students registered fall 1959. Ed.D. degree also awarded.

Engineering. — Aeronautical. Aerodynamics, structure, propulsion, guidance. 4 professorial staff. 12 master's degrees awarded 1955-59. 25 graduate students registered fall 1959.

Engineering.—Chemical. Cryogenics; solids fluidization, particularly as applied to oil shale retorting; heat transfer phenomena; coking of low-grade bituminous coals; kinetics as applied to coal and oil shale retorting; wood pulping studies. Prerequisites for graduate study: B.S. in chemical engineering. 6 professorial staff. 18 master's degrees and 4 Ph.D.'s awarded 1955-59. 14 graduate students registered fall 1959.

Engineering.—Civil. Structures, mechanics, transportation, hydraulics. Prerequisite for graduate study: major in civil engineering or related field. 13 professorial staff. 41 master's degrees and 4 Ph.D.'s awarded 1955-59. 56 graduate students registered fall 1959.

Engineering.—Electrical. Microwave or network theory, servomechanisms, antennas, propa-

gation. Ph.D. candidacy prerequisite: M.S. in electrical engineering. 9 professorial staff. 23 master's degrees and 3 Ph.D.'s awarded 1955-59. 15 graduate students registered fall 1959.

Engineering.—Mechanical. Heat and thermodynamics, applied or fluid mechanics. Prerequisite for graduate study: B.S. in mechanical engineering. Recommended: strong background in mathematics. 5 professorial staff. Ph.D. program begun 1958. 31 master's degrees awarded 1955-59. 42 graduate students registered fall 1959.

English. Medieval or American literature, the drama, the novel, the Enlightenment, the Romantics, the Victorians, the Renaissance. Offered by Department of English and Speech. Prerequisite for graduate study: 24 hours of English. 15 professorial staff. 43 master's degrees and 17 Ph.D.'s awarded 1955-59. 61 graduate students registered fall 1959.

French. Linguistics, comparative literature, or French literature. Offered by Department of Modern Languages. Prerequisites for graduate study: excellence in reading, speaking, writing, and auditory comprehension in major language; competence in second language (Spanish, German, Italian, Greek, or Latin) and general knowledge of literature and culture of this nation. Recommended: M.A. in French. 6 professorial staff. 11 master's degrees and 4 Ph.D.'s awarded 1955-59. 20 graduate students registered fall 1959.

Geology. Geology, paleontology, mineralogy-petrology, geochemistry. Prerequisites for graduate study: 36 semester hours of geology; 2 semesters each of chemistry, physics, mathematics. Recommended: calculus; physical chemistry; general biology. 13 professorial staff. 55 master's degrees and 12 Ph.D.'s awarded 1955-59. 67 graduate students registered fall 1959.

German. Linguistics, comparative literature, or German literature. Offered by Department of Modern Languages. Prerequisites for graduate study: excellence in reading, speaking, writing, auditory comprehension in major language; competence in second language (Spanish, French, Italian, Greek, or Latin) and general knowledge of literature and culture of this nation. Recommended: M.A. in German. 5 professorial staff. 10 master's degrees and 1 Ph.D. awarded 1955-59. 16 graduate students registered fall 1959.

History. Ancient, medieval, English, modern European, United States, Latin America, Far East, Russia, Pacific areas. 14 professorial staff. 20

master's degrees and 6 Ph.D.'s awarded 1955-59. 64 graduate students registered fall 1959.

Mathematics. Analysis, algebra, number theory, geometry, applied mathematics. Prerequisites for graduate study: B.A. with 18 semester hours beyond calculus in abstract algebra, analysis, geometry. 15 professorial staff. 5 master's degrees and 7 Ph.D.'s awarded 1955-59. 45 graduate students registered fall 1959.

Microbiology. Bacteriology, virology, mycology, parasitology, immunology. Prerequisites for graduate study: degree in general biology; inorganic, organic chemistry; physics. Recommended: calculus; physical chemistry; genetics; statistics. 5 professorial staff. 3 master's degrees and 8 Ph.D.'s awarded 1955-59. 5 graduate students registered fall 1959. New enrollment limited to 2.

Pathology. Autopsies, surgical or experimental pathology, exfoliative cytology. Prerequisite for graduate study: M.D. or first 2 years of medical curriculum. 6 professorial staff. 4 master's degrees awarded 1955-59. 1 graduate student registered fall 1959.

Pharmacology. Prerequisites for graduate study: 12 hours introductory biology or general zoology; general inorganic chemistry, including 12 hours of qualitative analysis; 15 hours of organic chemistry; 4 hours of physical chemistry; calculus; 12 hours of physics. Recommended: invertebrate and comparative zoology; genetics; advanced physics. 6 professorial staff. 1 master's degree and 2 Ph.D.'s awarded 1955-59. 4 graduate students registered fall 1959.

Pharmacy. Pharmacy, pharmacology, pharmaceutical chemistry, pharmacognosy, microbiology; pharmacy administration. Prerequisite for graduate study: degree in pharmacy. 10 professorial staff. Ph.D. programs in pharmacy administration and microbiology begun 1959; in pharmacognosy, 1960. 11 master's degrees and 4 Ph.D.'s awarded 1955-59. 8 graduate students registered fall 1959.

Philosophy. History of philosophy (classical and modern), social philosophy, epistemology, metaphysics, ethics, logic, aesthetics. Prerequisite for graduate study: 18 hours of philosophy, including 6 in history of philosophy. 10 professorial staff. 4 master's degrees and 1 Ph.D. awarded 1955-59. 12 students registered fall 1959.

Physics. Theoretical, low-temperature, upper-atmosphere, or microwave physics; statistical mechanics; nucleon interaction; solid-state molecular theory; experimental nuclear resonance; nuclear scattering; nuclear spectroscopy; plasmas; lambda interaction. Prerequisite for graduate study: B.S. in physics. 20 professorial staff. 30 master's degrees and 21 Ph.D.'s awarded 1955-59. 125 graduate students registered fall 1959. In the future, total enrollment will be limited to about 100.

Physiology. Cardiovascular or respiratory physiology, neurophysiology, metabolism (tissue). Prerequisites for graduate study: mathematics through calculus; physical chemistry; biology. Recommended: genetics. 6 professorial staff. 1 master's degree and 4 Ph.D.'s awarded 1955-59. 2 graduate students registered fall 1959. Enrollment limited to 4.

Political Science. American or comparative government, politics, international relations, public administration, political theory, public law. Prerequisites for graduate study: at least 16 hours of political science, or 12 of political science and 8 of economics, sociology, or history. 12 professorial staff. 15 master's degrees and 3 Ph.D.'s awarded 1955-59. 36 graduate students registered fall 1959.

Psychology. Clinical, general experimental, social psychology. Prerequisites for graduate study: experimental psychology; statistics. 16 professorial staff. 30 master's degrees and 21 Ph.D.'s awarded 1955-59. 80 graduate students registered fall 1959.

Sociology. Theory; research; juvenile delinquency; criminology; culture; family; industrial or political sociology. Prerequisite for graduate study: 16 hours of sociology, or 12 hours of sociology and 8 of economics, political science, anthropology, or psychology. 4 professorial staff. 17 master's degrees and 5 Ph.D.'s awarded 1955-59. 22 graduate students registered fall 1959.

Spanish. Linguistics, comparative literature, or Spanish literature. Offered by Department of Modern Languages. Prerequisites for graduate study: excellence in reading, speaking, writing, auditory comprehension of major language; competence in a second language (French, German, Italian, Greek, Latin) and general knowledge of literature and culture of this nation. Recommended: M.A. in Spanish. 7 professorial staff. 6 master's degrees and 5 Ph.D.'s awarded 1955-59. 20 graduate students registered fall 1959.

Zoology. Offered by Department of biology. 15 professorial staff. 24 master's degrees and 8 Ph.D.'s awarded 1955-59. 24 graduate students registered fall 1959.

Columbia University

NEW YORK 27, NEW YORK

Graduate Faculties

Among the earliest of American institutions to develop graduate study, Columbia awarded its first Ph.D. in 1875. Five years later, the Faculty of Political Science was formally established. This was followed in 1890 by the Faculty of Philosophy and, in 1892, by the Faculty of Pure Science. These 3 faculties comprise 33 departments, staff 7 regional institutes and programs (Russian, East Asian, European, Near and Middle East, Israeli, East Central European, and International Affairs), and supervise interdisciplinary work under 12 standing committees (administrative medicine, applied mathematics, applied mechanics, biophysics, business, education, geography, industrial engineering, nutrition, parasitology, religion, and social psychology). The university is privately controlled and nonsectarian. Both men and women are admitted.

Other doctoral degrees awarded by Columbia are: J.S.D. (Law School); Med. Sc.D. (College of Physicians and Surgeons); D.L.S. (School of Library Science); D.S.W. (New York School of Social Work); D.P.H. (School of Public Health); Ed.D. (Teachers College); and Eng. Sc.D. (School of Engineering).

Students are primarily under the supervision of a department rather than a faculty or school. Doctoral candidates choose and work with a sponsor. Most of the classes are small (40 or more is unusual) and seminars are kept under 12.

Residence facilities provided for graduate men and women; university-owned apartments for married students. Registry of off-campus accommodations also maintained.

Special facilities include: specialized laboratories; departmental libraries; 2 observatories; biological field station; drama museum; foreign language center; social research bureau; institutes. Library of approximately 2,745,000 volumes contains special collections on religion, eco-nomics, Russia, international law, music, and philosophy. Affiliations maintained with Cold Spring Harbor Biological Laboratory, Woods Hole Marine Biological Laboratory, and Commonwealth Observatory at Mount Stromlo in Australia.

Residence requirement for Ph.D.: minimum of 2 academic years (30 semester hours defined as 1 year), with 1 year in residence at Columbia. Some summer and evening courses available.

ADMISSION REQUIREMENTS

For graduate study: bachelor's degree; B average (higher in some departments); recommendations; satisfaction of departmental requirements (which may include personal interview). For candidacy for Ph.D.: successful completion of 1 year of graduate work at Columbia; reading knowledge of 2 modern foreign languages (usually German and French, but another language or research tool may be substituted if approved by department); fulfillment of departmental requirements for certification; demonstration of ability to undertake research (usually through 1 or more qualifying examinations).

Apply to Graduate Faculties Admissions Officer at least 1 month prior to date for which admission is sought. Address: Office of University Admissions, 322 University Hall, Columbia University, New York 27, New York.

FEES AND FIRST-YEAR AID

Application fee $15. Tuition $40 per point ($1,200 per year for full program). Comprehensive fee $50; medical fee $5 per term. Room (in dormitory) for men $250-$400 per year; for women $285-$450. Approximate annual cost of board in college dining room $500-$550. Rent for 1-bedroom furnished apartments $1,260-$1,620 per year, including utilities.

First-year aid available: approximately 95 scholarships, to $2,000; approximately 125 teaching assistantships, to $1,800 plus tuition; approximately 160 fellowships, to $3,000 (a few traveling grants carry higher stipends); approximately 10 research assistantships, to $2,000; 50 to 100 grants-in-aid, to $200 per term. Student employment available on and off campus with average wages of $1.20 per hour on campus and $1.25 per hour off campus. Long-term low-interest loans also available.

Apply between October 15 and February 1 to

Office of Financial Aid, 322 University Hall, Columbia University, New York 27, New York.

FIELDS OF STUDY FOR THE PH.D.

Students interested in a career in college teaching may take courses in the methodology of teaching through Teachers College of Columbia University.

Administrative Medicine. Offered by Subcommittee of Joint Committee on Graduate Instruction of the School of Public Health and Administrative Medicine. 21 professorial staff. New program; no degree awarded to date.

Anatomy. Endocrinology, experimental embryology, histology and histochemistry, biomechanics, neurology, skeletal growth, cardiovascular tissue, tissue culture, electron microscopy, and ophthalmology. Prerequisites for graduate study: background in biology, chemistry, and physics. 17 professorial staff. 1 master's degree and 2 Ph.D.'s awarded 1955-59. 8 graduate students registered fall 1959.

Anthropology. Physical anthropology, archaeology, ethnology, and linguistics. 14 professorial staff. 42 master's degrees and 37 Ph.D.'s awarded 1955-59. 113 graduate students registered fall 1959.

Applied Mathematics. Pure mathematics; work in fields of application (computation, fluid flow, information theory, operations research). Offered by Subcommittee on Applied Mathematics and administered under Joint Committee on Graduate Instruction. Prerequisites for graduate study: 6 college terms of physical science and mathematics, including calculus through partial derivatives and multiple integrals. 12 professorial staff. 17 master's degrees and 2 Ph.D.'s awarded 1955-59. 14 graduate students registered fall 1959.

Architecture, Planning and Housing. Offered by Standing Subcommittee of Joint Committee on Graduate Instruction. 34 professorial staff. 4 Ph.D.'s awarded 1955-59. 1 graduate student registered fall 1959.

Art History and Archaeology. Ancient, Oriental, primitive, medieval, Renaissance, Baroque or modern art, or art of Americas. Work in related fields within department or outside may be taken as required. Offered by Faculty of Philosophy. Prerequisites for graduate study: 18 credits in history of fine arts or in studies leading to archaeology; French or German; screening examination. Ph.D. candidacy prerequisites: French, Ger-

man, and 1 other language. 15 professorial staff. 40 master's degrees and 8 Ph.D.'s awarded 1955-59. 92 graduate students registered fall 1959.

Astronomy. Offered by Faculty of Pure Science. Prerequisites for graduate study: knowledge of general astronomy; 3 years of college mathematics or equivalent; 2 years of physics; 1 year of chemistry or equivalent. 7 professorial staff. 4 graduate students registered fall 1959.

Biochemistry. Offered by Faculty of Pure Science. Prerequisite for graduate study: basic knowledge of physics, chemistry, biology (preference given to students with advanced courses in chemistry). 31 professorial staff. 2 master's degrees and 21 Ph.D.'s awarded 1955-59. 24 graduate students registered fall 1959.

Biophysics. Program administered by Standing Subcommittee of Joint Committee on Graduate Instruction. Prerequisites for graduate study: at least 45 points in physics, chemistry, biology, and mathematics. 7 professorial staff. 3 Ph.D.'s awarded 1955-59. 6 graduate students registered fall 1959.

Botany. Offered by Faculty of Pure Science. Prerequisites for graduate study: training in biological and physical sciences and mathematics adequate for proposed field of specialization; reading knowledge of French or German. Ph.D. candidacy prerequisites: 1 major and 3 minor fields to be chosen from cytology and cytogenetics, morphology, mycology, microbiology, physiology, physiological chemistry of plants, taxonomy. 12 professorial staff. 28 master's degrees and 18 Ph.D.'s awarded 1955-59. 29 graduate students registered fall 1959.

Business. Offered by Graduate School of Business under Permanent Subcommittee of Joint Committee on Graduate Instruction. 59 professorial staff. 28 Ph.D.'s awarded 1955-59.

Chemistry. Offered by Faculty of Pure Science. Prerequisites for graduate study: courses in general, inorganic, analytical, organic, and physical chemistry with laboratory experience in all categories; 1 year of physics; mathematics through differential and integral calculus. 18 professorial staff. 126 master's degrees and 95 Ph.D.'s awarded 1955-59. 113 graduate students registered fall 1959.

Chemistry.—Industrial. 5 master's degrees awarded 1955-59.

Chinese and Japanese. Offered by Faculty of Philosophy. Prerequisites for graduate study: preparation in 1 of the languages; reading knowledge of French, German, or Russian, or (by exception) a second East Asiatic language. Candidates should plan to spend approximately 3 years in residence at Columbia and, if possible, 1 or 2 years in chosen area to gain facility in the language and acquaintance with the country and its people. 9 professorial staff. 8 master's degrees and 6 Ph.D.'s awarded 1955-59. 13 graduate students registered fall 1959.

Economics. Offered by Faculty of Political Science. Prerequisites for graduate study: balanced course of study, including history and other social sciences, philosophy, modern languages, mathematics, and economics. 31 professorial staff. 156 master's degrees and 90 Ph.D.'s awarded 1955-59. 219 graduate students registered fall 1959.

Education. Offered by Teachers College. 2 master's degrees and 231 Ph.D.'s awarded 1955-59. Ed.D. degree also awarded.

Engineering.—Chemical. Offered by Faculty of Pure Science. 10 professorial staff. 10 Ph.D.'s awarded 1955-59. 17 graduate students registered fall 1959.

Engineering.—Civil (and Engineering Mechanics). Offered by Faculty of Pure Science. 22 professorial staff. 1 master's degree and 16 Ph.D.'s awarded 1955-59. 23 graduate students registered fall 1959.

Engineering.—Electrical. Offered by Faculty of Pure Science. 17 professorial staff. 3 Ph.D.'s awarded 1955-59. 21 graduate students registered fall 1959.

Engineering.—Industrial. Offered by Standing Subcommittee of Joint Committee on Graduate Instruction. 9 Ph.D.'s awarded 1955-59. 24 graduate students registered fall 1959.

Engineering.—Mechanical. Offered by Faculty of Pure Science. 13 professorial staff. 9 Ph.D.'s awarded 1955-59. 21 graduate students registered fall 1959.

Engineering.—Mining, Metallurgical, and Mineral. Offered by Faculty of Pure Science. 10 professorial staff. 5 Ph.D.'s awarded 1955-59. 8 graduate students registered fall 1959.

English and Comparative Literature. English and American literature, comparative literature. English and classics, comparative literature and classics, medieval, Renaissance, 16th century, 17th century, 18th century, Romantic movement, Victorian literature, English literature from 1885 to present, American literature to 1870, American literature from 1870 to present. Comparative literature interpreted as literature of at least 1 European culture studied in relation to English or American literature. Offered by Faculty of Philosophy. Ph.D. candidacy prerequisites: French, German, and Latin. 31 professorial staff. 419 master's degrees and 137 Ph.D.'s awarded 1955-59. 621 graduate students registered fall 1959. New enrollment limited to 125 full-time students.

French and Romance Philology. Offered by Faculty of Philosophy. Prerequisites for graduate study: skill in reading, writing, and speaking French; general knowledge of French literature. Recommended: training in German and Latin; preparation in another Romance language. Ph.D. candidacy prerequisites: German and Latin; for Romance philology, 2 Romance languages plus French. 16 professorial staff. 75 master's degrees and 52 Ph.D.'s awarded 1955-59. 143 graduate students registered fall 1959.

Geography. Offered by Subcommittee on Geography under Joint Committee on Graduate Instruction. Recommended for graduate study: economic and general history; reading knowledge of 1 modern language; economics; sociology; botany; statistics; general geology; geography. 11 professorial staff. 10 master's degrees and 3 Ph.D.'s awarded 1955-59. 21 graduate students registered fall 1959.

Geology. Economic or structural geology, geochemistry, geomorphology, geophysics, invertebrate paleontology, mineralogy, petrology, stratigraphy. Offered by Faculty of Pure Science. Prerequisites for graduate study: geological sciences; mathematics; physics; chemistry; biology; GRE Advanced Test in Geology; sight identification test of common rocks, minerals, and fossils; general geology test. Ph.D. candidacy prerequisites: apprenticeship to be served in laboratory or field research. 20 professorial staff. 70 master's degrees and 82 Ph.D.'s awarded 1955-59. 91 graduate students registered fall 1959.

Germanic Languages. Offered by Faculty of Philosophy. Prerequisites for graduate study: qualifying tests on student's ability to read, write, and speak German and knowledge of major works of Lessing, Goethe, and Schiller. For candidacy for Ph.D.: M.A. or equivalent; reading knowledge of French and either Dutch or a Scandinavian language; for philology candidates, a knowledge of Greek and Latin. 7 professorial staff. 16 master's degrees and 8 Ph.D.'s awarded 1955-59. 32 students registered fall 1959.

Greek and Latin. Greek or Latin (major in 1, minor in other). Offered by Faculty of Philosophy. Prerequisite for graduate study: tests on grammar, syntax, sight translation, and composition of either Greek or Latin. Recommended: French or German. 9 professorial staff. 27 master's degrees and 7 Ph.D.'s awarded 1955-59. 26 graduate students registered fall 1959.

History. Ancient, medieval, American, Latin American, East Asiatic, Jewish, or Byzantine history; modern history of Eastern or Western Europe; history of European thought; or history of Great Britain and the British Empire. Offered by Faculty of Political Science. 41 professorial staff. 395 master's degrees and 128 Ph.D.'s awarded 1955-59. 577 graduate students registered fall 1959.

Italian. Offered by Faculty of Philosophy. Prerequisites for graduate study: effective knowledge of English and Italian; acquaintance with Italian literature. Recommended: Latin, German, and another Romance language. Ph.D. candidacy prerequisite: reading knowledge of Latin, French, and German. 7 professorial staff. 10 master's degrees and 6 Ph.D.'s awarded 1955-59. 14 graduate students registered fall 1959.

Linguistics. General linguistics, phonetics, Indo-European comparative linguistics, Hamito-Semitic, Malayo-Polynesian, Uralic, Altaic. Offered by Faculty of Philosophy. Prerequisites for graduate study: French or German; qualifying examination. Recommended for Ph.D. candidacy: Russian. 15 professorial staff. 16 master's degrees and 6 Ph.D.'s awarded 1955-59. 25 graduate students registered fall 1959.

Mathematical Statistics. Offered by Faculty of Political Science. Prerequisite for graduate study: knowledge of matrix algebra. 9 professorial staff. 30 master's degrees and 8 Ph.D.'s awarded 1955-59. 53 graduate students registered fall 1959.

Mathematics. Offered by Faculty of Pure Science. Prerequisites for graduate study: advanced calculus plus the equivalent of such courses as differential equations, complex variables, number theory, modern algebra. Recommended: reading knowledge of French and German. 13 professorial staff. 56 master's degrees and 10 Ph.D.'s awarded 1955-59. 72 graduate students registered fall 1959.

Microbiology. Offered by Faculty of Pure Science. Prerequisites for graduate study: background in biology, physics, and chemistry equal to university's requirements for admission to study of medicine; qualitative analysis; calculus. 12 professorial staff. 5 Ph.D.'s awarded 1955-59. 5 graduate students registered fall 1959.

Music. Musicology. Offered by Faculty of Philosophy. Prerequisites for graduate study: musical theory and history of music; composition students must have reading knowledge of French or German. Ph.D. candidacy prerequisites: reading knowledge of French, German, Italian, Latin. 10 professorial staff. 50 master's degrees and 2 Ph.D.'s awarded 1955-59. 48 graduate students registered fall 1959.

Near and Middle East Languages. Semitic, Turkish, Indo-Iranian, Caucasian. Offered by Faculty of Philosophy. Prerequisites for graduate study: reading knowledge of 2: French, German, Russian, Hungarian; possibly any Near and Middle East language. 8 professorial staff. 12 master's degrees and 4 Ph.D.'s awarded 1955-59. 14 graduate students registered fall 1959.

Parasitology. Offered by Standing Subcommittee of the Joint Committee on Graduate Instruction. Given in School of Public Health and Administrative Medicine. 4 professorial staff. 1 Ph.D. awarded 1955-59. 1 graduate student registered fall 1959.

Pathology. Offered by Faculty of Pure Science. Prerequisite for graduate study: M.D. degree or equivalent. 5 professorial staff. 2 graduate students registered fall 1959.

Pharmacology. Anatomy, biochemistry, microbiology, pathology, physiology, public health, physical chemistry, pharmacology. Offered by Faculty of Pure Science. Prerequisites for graduate study: physics, chemistry, and biology equal to university's requirements for admission to study of medicine. 6 professorial staff. 3 Ph.D.'s awarded 1955-59. 2 graduate students registered fall 1959.

Philosophy. Esthetics, ethics, logic, metaphysics. Offered by Faculty of Philosophy. 20 professorial staff. 51 master's degrees and 49 Ph.D.'s awarded 1955-59. 190 graduate students registered fall 1959.

Physics. Offered by Faculty of Pure Science. Prerequisites for graduate study: 3 years of physics with laboratory work; working knowledge of ordinary differential equations. 24 professorial staff. 125 master's degrees and 85 Ph.D.'s awarded 1955-59. 215 graduate students registered fall 1959.

Physiology. Anatomy, biochemistry, physiology. Offered by Faculty of Pure Science. Prerequisites for graduate study: background in physics, organic and physical chemistry, differential and integral calculus; course in comparative anatomy. Ph.D. candidacy prerequisite: teaching experience. 12 professorial staff. 4 Ph.D.'s awarded 1955-59. 6 graduate students registered fall 1959.

Political Science.—Public Law and Government. American or foreign political institutions, political theory and jurisprudence, comparative legal systems, Roman law. Offered by Faculty of Political Science. Prerequisite for graduate study: 1 foreign language. Prerequisite for Ph.D. candidacy: reading knowledge of 2 approved foreign languages (mathematics may sometimes be substituted for 1 language). 33 professorial staff. 288 master's degrees and 69 Ph.D.'s awarded 1955-59. 381 graduate students registered fall 1959.

Psychology. Offered by Faculty of Pure Science. Prerequisites for graduate study: fundamental mathematics; 1 year of 2 (chemistry, physics, biology or 1 course in each of general psychology, elementary statistics, experimental psychology); GRE Aptitude and Advanced Test. Recommended: French and German. 12 professorial staff. 107 master's degrees and 35 Ph.D.'s awarded 1955-59. 77 graduate students registered fall 1959.

Psychology.—Social. Offered by Standing Subcommittee of Joint Committee on Graduate Instruction. Program open to Ph.D. candidates only. Prerequisites: master's degree in psychology, sociology, anthropology, social psychology, or group development; GRE; knowledge of 2 foreign languages (usually selected from French, German, or Russian). Recommended: mathematics. 9 professorial staff. 3 Ph.D.'s awarded 1955-59. 29 graduate students registered fall 1959.

Religion. History or literature of religion, philosophy of religion and ethics, religion and society. Offered by Standing Subcommittee of Joint Committee on Graduate Instruction. Prerequisites for graduate study: at least 1 course in natural sciences; basic courses in history, literature, and philosophy; reading knowledge of French or German. Ph.D. candidacy prerequisite: reading knowledge of Greek and Hebrew. 24 professorial staff. 33 master's degrees and 45 Ph.D.'s awarded 1955-59. 56 graduate students registered fall 1959.

Slavic Languages. Russian, Polish, Czech, Slovac, Serbo-Croatian, or Bulgarian literatures or linguistics. Offered by Faculty of Philosophy. Ph.D. candidacy prerequisites: 1 additional Slavic language for literature candidates; 2 additional Slavic languages for philology candidates; reading knowledge of French and German (and of Latin or Greek if needed). 10 professorial staff. 30 master's degrees and 6 Ph.D.'s awarded 1955-59. 46 graduate students registered fall 1959.

Sociology. Political, historical, or urban-rural sociology; history of sociology; systematic sociological theory; advanced methodology; family intermarriage; formal organization; occupations and professions; public opinion or communication; social change; stratification; religious institutions. Offered by Faculty of Political Science. Recommended for graduate study: 15 hours in sociology, including statistics, research methods and theory. 18 professorial staff. 46 master's degrees and 60 Ph.D.'s awarded 1955-59. 131 graduate students registered fall 1959.

Spanish and Portuguese. History of Spanish language; classical literature (Middle Ages, Renaissance, and the Golden Age); modern literature of 18th, 19th, and 20th centuries; Portuguese; Spanish America. Offered by Faculty of Philosophy. Prerequisite for graduate study: tests of reading, writing, and speaking knowledge of Spanish and of general knowledge of literature and civilization. Ph.D. candidacy prerequisites: reading knowledge of French, German, and Latin. 6 professorial staff. 36 master's degrees and 14 Ph.D.'s awarded 1955-59. 52 graduate students registered fall 1959.

Uralic and Altaic Languages. Uralic: comparative Uralic philology, Hungarian or Finnish language and literature. Altaic: comparative Altaic philology (Turkic, Mongolian, Manchu-Tungus, Korean), Turkish language and cultural history. Offered by Faculty of Philosophy. Prerequisite for graduate study: 1 Uralic or Altaic language. 5 professorial staff. 1 Ph.D. awarded 1955-59. 2 graduate students registered fall 1959.

Zoology. Offered by Faculty of Pure Science. Prerequisites for graduate study: courses in biology, embryology, histology, genetics, chemistry through organic, physics; French, German, or Russian. Recommended: botany; physiology; calculus. 14 professorial staff. 53 master's degrees and 33 Ph.D.'s awarded 1955-59. 64 graduate students registered fall 1959.

Connecticut, University of

STORRS, CONNECTICUT

The Graduate School

Graduate instruction has been offered since 1918 at the University of Connecticut. The Graduate School was organized in 1939 and the first Ph.D. conferred in 1949. Institution is publicly controlled by the state. Both men and women are admitted.

Rooms (in college dormitory) for single graduate students; no residence facilities for married students.

Special facilities include: Institute of Cellular Biology; Institute of Labor Management; Institute of Public Service; Institute of Gerontology. Work in agricultural sciences is facilitated through Storrs Agricultural Experiment Station. Affiliations with state and local hospitals provide additional facilities for work in clinical psychology and speech pathology. The university is also affiliated with the Marine Historical Association, Inc., and the Frank C. Munson Institute of American Maritime History. Library contains approximately 256,000 volumes.

Residence requirement for Ph.D.: 3 years beyond bachelor's degree, at least 1 of which (second or third year) must be in residence on campus. Summer and evening courses are offered in some fields.

ADMISSION REQUIREMENTS

For graduate study: bachelor's degree; cumulative quality point ratio of 26 or higher in the undergraduate record or a B average in last 2 years of undergraduate work. Recommended: GRE; MAT. For candidacy for Ph.D.: high scholastic standing in undergraduate and graduate work; competence in 2 foreign languages or 2 related areas of knowledge, or 1 language and 1 related area; passing of preliminary examinations.

Apply to Dean of the Graduate School several months in advance of date of desired entry.

FEES AND FIRST-YEAR AID

No application fee. University fee $150 per academic year. Books and incidental fees approximate $207 annually. Room (in dormitory) $188 per academic year. Approximate annual cost of board in college dining room $625.

First-year aid available: about 90 teaching assistantships, $147.50 per month; 32 other fellowships, $2,000; several part-time instructorships, $1,560 for 9 months.

Apply to Dean of the Graduate School several months in advance of desired entry.

FIELDS OF STUDY FOR THE PH.D.

Agricultural Economics. Agricultural marketing, production economics. 8 professorial staff. 17 master's degrees and 1 Ph.D. awarded 1955-59. 8 graduate students registered fall 1959.

Animal Nutrition. Animals, poultry. Offered by Departments of Animal Industries and Poultry Science. 4 professorial staff. 8 master's degrees and 3 Ph.D.'s awarded 1955-59. 8 graduate students registered fall 1959.

Animal Pathology. Offered by Department of Animal Diseases. Prerequisite for graduate study: D.V.M. degree. 3 professorial staff. 3 master's degrees and 1 Ph.D. awarded 1955-59. 7 graduate students registered fall 1959.

Bacteriology. Combined program offered by Departments of Bacteriology, Animal Diseases, and Animal Industries. 5 professorial staff. 17 master's degrees and 6 Ph.D.'s awarded 1955-59. 12 graduate students registered fall 1959.

Biochemistry. Offered by Department of Zoology and Entomology. 3 professorial staff. 2 master's degrees and 1 Ph.D. awarded 1955-59. 7 graduate students registered fall 1959.

Botany. Cytology, plant systematics. 5 professorial staff. 3 master's degrees awarded 1955-59. 5 graduate students registered fall 1959.

Chemistry. Analytical, inorganic, organic, and physical chemistry. 13 professorial staff. 31 master's degrees and 26 Ph.D.'s awarded 1955-59. 37 graduate students registered fall 1959.

Education. Administration; evaluation and measurement; guidance; counseling and personnel; supervision and curriculum development; elementary, secondary, or industrial education; foundations of education. 25 professorial staff. 730 master's degrees and 69 Ph.D.'s awarded 1955-59. 337 graduate students registered fall 1959.

Engineering. Applied mechanics, molecular engineering and microwave systems, network theory and feedback control systems, structural engineering, thermodynamics and heat transfer.

Offered by Departments of Civil, Electrical, Mechanical, and Chemical Engineering. 24 professorial staff. Ph.D. program initiated 1956. 141 master's degrees awarded 1955-59. 205 graduate students registered fall 1959.

English. Shakespeare, modern literature, American literature. 15 professorial staff. Ph.D. program initiated 1959. 124 master's degrees awarded 1955-59. 56 graduate students registered fall 1959.

French. Medieval, 18th century, or modern French literature. Offered by Department of Foreign Languages. 3 professorial staff. Ph.D. program initiated 1959. 5 master's degrees awarded 1955-59. 9 graduate students registered fall 1959.

Genetics. Animal, plant. Combined program offered by Departments of Animal Genetics, Botany, and Horticulture. 3 professorial staff. 2 Ph.D.'s awarded 1955-59. 3 graduate students registered fall 1959.

International Relations. Offered by Department of Political Science. 4 professorial staff. Ph.D. program initiated 1959. 17 master's degrees awarded 1955-59. 10 graduate students registered fall 1959.

Pharmaceutical Science. Pharmacy, pharmaceutical chemistry, pharmacognosy, pharmacology. Offered by Department of Pharmacy. 7 professorial staff. 10 master's degrees and 23 Ph.D.'s awarded 1955-59. 15 graduate students registered fall 1959.

Physics. Acoustics; optics; atomic, molecular, and nuclear physics; low temperature or theoretical physics. 8 professorial staff. 28 master's degrees and 8 Ph.D.'s awarded 1955-59. 49 graduate students registered fall 1959.

Plant Nutrition and Soils. Offered by Department of Plant Science. 5 professorial staff. Ph.D. program initiated 1957. 13 master's degrees awarded 1955-59. 12 graduate students registered fall 1959.

Psychology. Child, clinical, general experimental psychology; personality and social psychology. Prerequisite for graduate study: GRE or MAT. 12 professorial staff. 56 master's degrees and 28 Ph.D.'s awarded 1955-59. 60 graduate students registered fall 1959.

Sociology. Rural sociology, social control and deviant behavior, social organization and institutions, social structure and personality. Offered by Departments of Sociology and Rural Sociology.

12 professorial staff. 16 master's degrees and 1 Ph.D. awarded 1955-59. 11 graduate students registered fall 1959.

Spanish. Golden Age and Renaissance, Latin America, medieval Spanish or 19th century Spanish literature. Offered by Department of Foreign Languages. 4 professorial staff. Ph.D. program initiated 1960. 10 graduate students registered fall 1959.

Zoology and Entomology. Developmental biology, entomology, parasitology, physiology, vertebrate zoology. 10 professorial staff. 8 master's degrees and 10 Ph.D.'s awarded 1955-59. 18 graduate students registered fall 1959.

Cornell University

ITHACA, NEW YORK

The Graduate School

Graduate instruction has been offered at Cornell since 1868, the date of founding of the College of Arts and Sciences, and the first Ph.D. was awarded in 1872. The Graduate School was formally organized in 1909. University is privately controlled and nonsectarian. Both men and women are admitted.

Each student accepted as a candidate for an advanced degree selects a special committee from among the faculty in the field of his major and minor work, and develops a program of study. Each special committee supervises the student's study, judges his performance, and recommends him for the appropriate degree.

The Graduate School of Medical Science at the Cornell Medical College offers work toward the Ph.D. under the general administration of the Cornell University Graduate School. Other doctorates conferred by the institution include: Ed.D., J.S.D., D.Sc. in Veterinary Medicine, and A.Mus.D.

155 rooms in dormitories available for single graduate students; 185 apartments for married students.

Special facilities include: New York State Agricultural Experiment Station at Geneva; Cornell Aeronautical Laboratory at Buffalo; centers for social science research, statistics, housing research, and aerial photographic studies;

Newman Laboratory of Nuclear Studies; Wiegand Herbarium. The university library is the 10th largest library system of its kind in the United States, with world-famous special collections in several areas.

Residence requirement for Ph.D.: 3 academic years. A limited amount of graduate credit may be transferred from other institutions. Summer courses available.

ADMISSION REQUIREMENTS

For graduate study: bachelor's degree or equivalent work; adequate preparation in chosen field, as judged by previous scholastic record or other achievements; evidence of ability to do advanced study and research; prerequisites for program selected. For candidacy for Ph.D.: examinations in 2 of 3 languages (French, German, or Russian) or an approved substitute. GRE or MAT required in some departments.

Apply to the Graduate School, 125 Edmund Ezra Day Hall, between October and February 15 for best consideration for the beginning of an academic year.

FEES AND FIRST-YEAR AID

Application fee $10. Tuition $1,200 per year, except that students registering in the Graduate School with major concentration in subjects within the state-supported colleges (Agriculture, Home Economics, Industrial and Labor Relations, and Veterinary Medicine) pay only $300 per year. Special fees approximate $225 per year. Annual cost of room (in dormitory) $300-$600. Board in college dining room $600-$900 per calendar year. Apartments $60-$125 per month.

First-year aid available: 30 scholarships, tuition and fees; 200 teaching assistantships, $1,200-$1,600 plus tuition and fees; 100 fellowships, $1,000-$2,500 plus tuition and fees; 100 research assistantships, $1,000-$3,000.

Apply to the Graduate School, 125 Edmund Ezra Day Hall, before February 15.

FIELDS OF STUDY FOR THE PH.D.

Two series of special seminars are offered annually by distinguished members of the teaching staff for the preparation of college instructors.

Agricultural Economics. Agricultural economics, policy, and economic development; farm management, prices and statistics; marketing and business management; public administration and finance. 26 professorial staff. 65 master's degrees and 25 Ph.D.'s awarded 1956-59. 73 graduate students registered fall 1959.

Agronomy. Soils, field crop production, meteorology. 28 professorial staff. 50 master's degrees and 21 Ph.D.'s awarded 1956-59. 57 graduate students registered fall 1959.

Animal Sciences.—Animal Breeding and Physiology. Animal breeding, physiology, genetics. 9 professorial staff. 10 master's degrees and 9 Ph.D.'s awarded 1956-59. 21 graduate students registered fall 1959.

Animal Sciences.—Animal Husbandry. Animal husbandry, nutrition, breeding; dairy husbandry. 24 professorial staff. 6 master's degrees and 8 Ph.D.'s awarded 1956-59. 18 graduate students registered fall 1959.

Animal Sciences.—Animal Nutrition. 12 professorial staff. 17 master's degrees and 21 Ph.D.'s awarded 1956-59. 28 graduate students registered fall 1959.

Anthropology. 9 professorial staff. Department established 1959 (previously combined with Sociology). 8 master's degrees and 16 Ph.D.'s awarded 1956-59 in the combined fields. 49 graduate students registered in combined fields fall 1959.

Area Studies.—Far Eastern. Chinese literature, Far Eastern studies. 12 professorial staff. 1 graduate student registered fall 1959.

Astronomy and Space Sciences. Astronomy, astrophysics, space sciences (general), magnetohydrodynamics, radiophysics. 15 professorial staff. Ph.D. program begun 1960.

Bacteriology. 13 professorial staff. 7 master's degrees and 6 Ph.D.'s awarded 1956-59. 10 graduate students registered fall 1959.

Biochemistry. 20 professorial staff. 3 master's degrees and 9 Ph.D.'s awarded 1956-59. 25 graduate students registered fall 1959.

Botany.—General. General botany, cytology, paleobotany, phycology, plant morphology and anatomy, plant physiology, plant taxonomy and ecology. 15 professorial staff. 16 master's degrees and 10 Ph.D.'s awarded 1956-59. 23 graduate students registered fall 1959.

Botany.—Plant Breeding. Plant breeding, biometry and statistics, genetics. 24 professorial staff. 11 master's degrees and 16 Ph.D.'s awarded 1956-59. 34 students registered fall 1959.

Botany.—Plant Pathology. Mycology, plant pathology. 30 professorial staff. 16 master's degrees and 17 Ph.D.'s awarded 1956-59. 29 graduate students registered fall 1959.

Business and Public Administration. The administrative process; finance and accounting; supply, production, and distribution; managerial economics and politics. Prerequisite for graduate study: GRE. 26 professorial staff. 5 Ph.D.'s awarded 1956-59. 17 graduate students registered fall 1959.

Chemistry. Inorganic, analytical, organic, physical, theoretical. 21 professorial staff. 15 master's degrees and 49 Ph.D.'s awarded 1956-59. 113 graduate students registered fall 1959.

Child Development and Family Relationships. 13 professorial staff. 23 master's degrees and 9 Ph.D.'s awarded 1956-59. 27 graduate students registered fall 1959.

City and Regional Planning. City planning, regional planning. Ph.D. candidacy prerequisite: M.A. in regional planning or equivalent. 6 professorial staff. 29 master's degrees and 3 Ph.D.'s awarded 1956-59. 27 graduate students registered fall 1959.

Classics. Latin; medieval, and Renaissance Latin literature; ancient history; comparative Indo-European linguistics; Greek; classical archeology; classical rhetoric in original or translation; ancient thought. 5 professorial staff. 5 master's degrees and 3 Ph.D.'s awarded 1956-59. 11 graduate students registered fall 1959.

Comparative Literature. Prerequisite for graduate study: reading knowledge of Latin or Greek. 17 professorial staff. Ph.D. program begun 1959. 4 graduate students registered fall 1959.

Conservation. Fishery biology; forest conservation; natural resources conservation; oceanography; vertebrate zoology (including herpetology, ichthyology, mammalogy, and ornithology); wildlife management. 15 professorial staff. 14 master's degrees and 15 Ph.D.'s awarded 1956-59. 44 graduate students registered fall 1959.

Dairy Science. Dairy science, dairy chemistry. 11 professorial staff. 8 master's degrees and 2 Ph.D.'s awarded 1956-59. 11 graduate students registered fall 1959.

Economics. Econometrics and economic statistics; economic history; economic theory and its history; industrial organizations and control; in-

ternational economics and the economics of development; labor economics; monetary, financial, and fiscal economics. Prerequisite for graduate study: GRE Aptitude and Advanced Tests. 14 professorial staff. 3 master's degrees and 7 Ph.D.'s awarded 1956-59. 37 graduate students registered fall 1959.

Education and Rural Education. Agricultural education; education; educational administration and supervision; educational psychology and measurement; elementary education; extension and adult education; guidance and personnel administration; history and theory of education; development of human resources; nature, science, and conservation education; secondary education and curriculum; home economics education. 37 professorial staff. 184 master's degrees and 41 Ph.D.'s awarded 1956-59. 169 graduate students registered fall 1959.

Engineering.—Aeronautical. Aeronautical engineering, aerodynamics. 5 professorial staff. 9 Ph.D.'s awarded 1956-59. 14 graduate students registered fall 1959.

Engineering.—Agricultural. Agricultural engineering, farm electrification, farm structures, power and machinery, soil and water engineering. 13 professorial staff. 14 master's degrees and 5 Ph.D.'s awarded 1956-59. 16 graduate students registered fall 1959.

Engineering.—Chemical. Chemical engineering, nuclear process engineering, chemical processes and process control, materials engineering, biochemical engineering. 11 professorial staff. 9 master's degrees and 6 Ph.D.'s awarded 1956-59. 26 graduate students registered fall 1959.

Engineering.—Civil. Drawing and cartography, geodetic and photogrammetric engineering, hydraulic engineering, hydraulics, construction engineering and administration, sanitary engineering, sanitary sciences, structural engineering, soils engineering, transportation engineering, aerial photographic studies. 18 professorial staff. 47 master's degrees and 7 Ph.D.'s awarded 1956-59. 46 graduate students registered fall 1959.

Engineering.—Electrical. Electrical engineering (general); communication, power, control systems, or illuminating engineering. 30 professorial staff. 38 master's degrees and 10 Ph.D.'s awarded 1956-59. 86 graduate students registered fall 1959.

Engineering.—Mechanical. Administrative engineering, engineering drawing, industrial engineering, machine design, materials processing, applied industrial statistics, operations research, thermal processes, thermal power, thermal environment. 37 professorial staff. 43 master's degrees and 7 Ph.D.'s awarded 1956-59. 73 graduate students registered fall 1959.

Engineering Mechanics and Materials. Mechanics, fluid mechanics, materials of engineering. 14 professorial staff. 7 master's degrees and 2 Ph.D.'s awarded 1956-59. 18 graduate students registered fall 1959.

Engineering.—Metallurgical. General metallurgical engineering; extractive, physical metallurgy. 6 professorial staff. 4 master's degrees awarded 1956-59. 5 graduate students registered fall 1959.

Engineering Physics. 15 professorial staff. 9 master's degrees and 9 Ph.D.'s awarded 1956-59. 35 graduate students registered fall 1959.

English Language and Literature. Medieval literature; Old and Middle English; the English Renaissance to 1660; the Restoration and the 18th century; 19th century and after; American literature; English poetry; dramatic literature; prose fiction; folk literature; creative writing; bibliography. 29 professorial staff. 39 master's degrees and 10 Ph.D.'s awarded 1956-59. 70 graduate students registered fall 1959.

Entomology and Limnology. Apiculture; insect ecology; economic entomology; insect morphology, pathology, biochemistry, taxonomy, or physiology; insecticide chemistry; medical entomology; parasitology; limnology; entomology; insect toxicology. 42 professorial staff. 21 master's degrees and 23 Ph.D.'s awarded 1956-59. 68 graduate students registered fall 1959.

Floriculture and Ornamental Horticulture. 9 professorial staff. 7 master's degrees and 5 Ph.D.'s awarded 1956-59. 12 graduate students registered fall 1959.

Food and Nutrition. Food and nutrition, food, nutrition, general home economics. 14 professorial staff. 25 master's degrees and 2 Ph.D.'s awarded 1956-59. 27 graduate students registered fall 1959.

Food Science and Technology. 22 professorial staff. 2 graduate students registered fall 1959.

Geology and Geography. Economic geology, geography, geomorphology, mineralogy and petrology, paleontology and stratigraphy, structural geology and sedimentation. Prerequisite for graduate study: GRE. 7 professorial staff. 10 master's degrees and 5 Ph.D.'s awarded 1956-59. 17 graduate students registered fall 1959.

German. Literature, linguistics. 6 professorial staff. 1 master's degree and 2 Ph.D.'s awarded 1956-59. 12 graduate students registered fall 1959.

History. American, ancient, modern Chinese, or English history; European history since 1789; history of science; medieval, early modern European, Slavic, or Southeast Asian history. Prerequisite for graduate study: GRE. 12 professorial staff. 23 master's degrees and 9 Ph.D.'s awarded 1956-59. 52 graduate students registered fall 1959.

Home Economics Education. Home economics education, general home economics. 5 professorial staff. 17 master's degrees and 3 Ph.D.'s awarded 1956-59. 22 graduate students registered fall 1959.

Hotel Administration. Hotel administration, hotel accounting. Prerequisite for graduate study: degree from school of hotel administration. 10 professorial staff. 5 master's degrees awarded 1956-59. 1 graduate student registered fall 1959.

Household Economics and Management. 8 professorial staff. 14 master's degrees and 5 Ph.D.'s awarded 1956-59. 13 graduate students registered fall 1959.

Housing and Design. 7 professorial staff. 3 master's degrees and 3 Ph.D.'s awarded 1956-59. 6 graduate students registered fall 1959.

Industrial and Labor Relations. Collective bargaining, labor law, and labor movements; economic and social statistics; human resources and administration; labor economics and income security; industrial and labor relations problems; and international and comparative labor relations. Prerequisite for graduate study: GRE. 38 professorial staff. 60 master's degrees and 9 Ph.D.'s awarded 1956-59. 65 graduate students registered fall 1959.

Linguistics.—General. 14 professorial staff. 2 master's degrees and 5 Ph.D.'s awarded 1956-59. 24 graduate students registered fall 1959.

Mathematics. Algebra, analysis, geometry, applied mathematics, mathematics. 23 professorial staff. 8 master's degrees and 11 Ph.D.'s awarded 1956-59. 25 graduate students registered fall 1959.

Music. Musical composition, musicology, theory of music. Prerequisite for graduate study: GRE. 8 professorial staff. 3 master's degrees and 2 Ph.D.'s awarded 1956-59. 8 graduate students registered fall 1959.

Philosophy. Aesthetics, epistemology, ethics, history of philosophy, logic, metaphysics, philosophy, philosophy of religion, philosophy of science, political philosophy. 11 professorial staff. 1 master's degree and 2 Ph.D.'s awarded 1956-59. 20 graduate students registered fall 1959.

Physics. Physics; experimental or theoretical physics; biophysics. 38 professorial staff. 17 master's degrees and 40 Ph.D.'s awarded 1956-59. 124 graduate students registered fall 1959.

Political Science.—Government. American government and institutions, comparative government, constitutional law, international law and organization, international relations, the political process, political theory, public administration. 10 professorial staff. 8 master's degrees and 10 Ph.D.'s awarded 1956-59. 37 graduate students registered fall 1959.

Pomology. 19 professorial staff. 7 master's degrees and 1 Ph.D. awarded 1956-59. 10 graduate students registered fall 1959.

Psychology. Clinical or comparative psychology; differential psychology and psychological tests; experimental psychology; experimental psychopathology; general psychology; history of psychology and systematic psychology; industrial psychology; personality and social psychology; physiological psychology. Prerequisites for graduate study: MAT; GRE Aptitude and Advanced Tests. 13 professorial staff. 5 master's degrees and 11 Ph.D.'s awarded 1956-59. 28 graduate students registered fall 1959.

Romance Studies. French, Italian, Romance, or Spanish linguistics; French, Italian, or Spanish literature. 8 professorial staff. 7 master's degrees and 2 Ph.D.'s awarded 1956-59. 10 graduate students registered fall 1959.

Russian. Russian literature; Slavic linguistics. 3 professorial staff. 2 Ph.D.'s awarded 1956-59. 1 graduate student registered fall 1959.

Seed Technology. 7 professorial staff.

Sociology.—General. Sociology, social psychology, cultural anthropology, statistics. 12 professorial staff. Department established 1959 (previously combined with Anthropology). 8 master's degrees and 16 Ph.D.'s awarded 1956-59 in the combined fields. 49 graduate students registered in combined fields fall 1959.

Sociology.—Rural. Rural sociology, organiza-

tion methods and community development, methods in social research. 14 professorial staff. 33 master's degrees and 15 Ph.D.'s awarded 1956-59. 28 graduate students registered fall 1959.

Speech and Drama. Rhetoric and public address: principles of public address, classical and medieval rhetoric; dramatic production: drama and the theater, dramatic production, playwriting; speech pathology and phonetics: speech and phonetics. Prerequisite for graduate study: GRE. 9 professorial staff. 10 master's degrees and 4 Ph.D.'s awarded 1956-59. 20 graduate students registered fall 1959.

Statistics. 7 professorial staff. 2 master's degrees and 1 Ph.D. awarded 1956-59. 6 graduate students registered fall 1959.

Vegetable Crops. 20 professorial staff. 16 master's degrees and 9 Ph.D.'s awarded 1956-59. 24 graduate students registered fall 1959.

Veterinary Medicine. Veterinary anatomy; animal physiology; pathogenic bacteriology; parasitology; radiation biology; veterinary obstetrics and diseases of the reproductive organs; veterinary virology, pharmacology, medicine, or surgery. Prerequisite for graduate study: D.V.M. in the clinical fields. 35 professorial staff. 17 master's degrees and 8 Ph.D.'s awarded 1956-59. 29 graduate students registered fall 1959.

Zoology. Biogeochemistry, comparative anatomy, comparative and cellular physiology, comparative neurology, ecology, endocrinology, histology and embryology, invertebrate zoology. Prerequisite for graduate study: GRE. 9 professorial staff. 5 master's degrees and 11 Ph.D.'s awarded 1956-59. 19 graduate students registered fall 1959.

Delaware, University of

NEWARK, DELAWARE

School of Graduate Studies

The School of Graduate Studies was organized in 1950, although graduate instruction had been offered since 1925 and the first Ph.D. was awarded in 1947. It is one of 22 schools affiliated with the Westinghouse Graduate Study Program in Engineering and the Physical Sciences. Institution is publicly controlled by the state. Both men and women are admitted.

No dormitory facilities are provided for graduate students; rooms available in community. 1- and 2-bedroom unfurnished apartments for married students on campus; apartments also available in private homes.

Special facilities include: 2 museums devoted to early American culture and history of American science and technology; library which contains almost 250,000 volumes.

Residence requirement for Ph.D.: minimum of 3 years beyond bachelor's degree, of which 1 continuous academic year must be spent in full-time study on campus. On master's level, 8 graduate credits may be transferred, but student must complete 9 hours before such credit is transferred. Summer and evening courses available.

Apply to Dean of the School of Graduate Studies 1 month prior to registration.

ADMISSION REQUIREMENTS

For graduate study: bachelors degree; B average in major for last 2 years of undergraduate work and overall average of B. Recommended: GRE. For candidacy for Ph.D.: reading knowledge in 2 of 3 languages (French, German, or Russian); qualifying examination in some departments; 1 academic year of work.

Apply to Dean of the School of Graduate Studies 1 month prior to registration.

FEES AND FIRST-YEAR AID

Application fee $5. Tuition $13 per credit hour for state residents and full-time out-of-state students; $26 for part-time out-of-state students. Room (in private homes) $8-$10 per week. Annual cost of board in college dining room $410 (7 days). Apartment rentals: $78 (1 bedroom); $90 (2 bedroom) per month.

First-year aid available: teaching fellowships, $1,800-$2,200; other fellowships $1,800-$2,400 (waiver of tuition and fees); research assistantships, $1,800-$2,400.

Apply to department head no later than March 1.

FIELDS OF STUDY FOR THE PH.D.

Applied Sciences. Interdepartmental program in engineering (civil, chemical, electrical, and mechanical), metallurgy, physics, and mathematics. Prerequisites for graduate study: major in engineering, mathematics, or natural science; mathematics through differential equations. Prerequisites for candidacy for Ph.D.: M.S. degree; qualifying examination; proficiency in mathematics, physical sciences, and elected areas. 30 professorial staff. Ph.D. program initiated 1959. 6 graduate students registered fall 1959.

Behavioral Sciences. Experimental psychology, developmental psychology, human growth and development, social psychology, sociology, education research, reading diagnosis and remedial research. Conducted by Departments of Psychology, Sociology, and Education. Prerequisites for graduate study: 30 hours in behavioral sciences (or in biology, mathematics, or physics); recommendation. 17 professorial staff. Ph.D. program initiated 1959. Approximately 20 master's degrees awarded 1955-59. 5 graduate students registered in Ph.D. program fall 1959; 15 in master's program.

Biological Sciences. Zoology, physiology, botany, bacteriology, marine biology. Conducted by Department of Biological Sciences, School of Arts and Science, and appropriate departments in the School of Agriculture. Prerequisites for graduate study: 30 credits in biological sciences; 1 year of college mathematics; 1 year of college physics; 1 year of inorganic chemistry; 1 course in organic chemistry or equivalent; reading knowledge of 1 language (French, German, or Russian). 12 professorial staff. 16 master's degrees and 3 Ph.D.'s awarded 1955-59. 21 graduate students registered fall 1959.

Chemistry. Analytical, biological, inorganic, polymer, organic, physical, radio-chemistry. Prerequisite for graduate study: major in chemistry or related field, including general chemistry, qualitative analysis, quantitative analysis, organic and physical chemistry. Recommended: German; advanced chemistry courses; physics; calculus. 14 professorial staff. 132 master's degrees and 83 Ph.D.'s awarded 1955-59. 75 full-time graduate students registered fall 1959.

Engineering.—Chemical. General chemical engineering science, applied mathematics, thermodynamics, rate processes, fluid dynamics, chemical kinetics, physical and chemical metallurgy. Prerequisites for graduate study: GPA of 3.0; letters of recommendation; placement tests when undergraduate background is not in chemical engineering. 8 professorial staff. 56 master's degrees and 22 Ph.D.'s awarded 1955-59. 43 full-time graduate students registered fall 1959. Enrollment limited to approximately 45.

History. American, modern European, ancient, English, Russian. 13 professorial staff. Ph.D. program initiated 1960. 18 master's degrees awarded 1955-59. 27 graduate students registered fall 1959.

Denver, University of

DENVER 10, COLORADO

The Graduate College

Graduate study was begun in 1891 and has developed gradually. At present Ph.D. programs are offered in several areas and a program leading to the Ed.D. degree is offered by the School of Education. The university is privately controlled and nonsectarian. Both men and women are admitted.

Rooms in dormitories available for single graduate students; apartments in residence hall for married students.

Library contains approximately 350,000 volumes. High-altitude studies can be pursued at university laboratories on Mount Evans and Echo Lake. Special work is done in infrared and related phenomena. Opportunities for field work and internships at hospitals available for students in psychology and social work.

Residence requirement for Ph. D.: 3 years beyond baccalaureate; 6 quarters in residence on campus. Summer and evening courses available.

ADMISSION REQUIREMENTS

For graduate study: bachelor's degree; high scholastic standing. For candidacy for Ph.D.: master's degree or equivalent; written qualifying examinations; "tool" requirements which are determined by candidate's committee and may include 1 or more foreign languages, statistical methods, library, laboratory, or other research skills.

Apply to Office of Admissions and Records at least 8 weeks in advance of registration.

FEES AND FIRST-YEAR AID

Application fee $10. Tuition $16 per quarter hour for all students. Special fees approximate $150 annually. Room (in dormitory) $85-$115. Approximate annual cost of board in college dining room $750. Monthly rental on apartments in residence halls $88.

A limited number of teaching, research, and clinical fellowships are available for first-year students.

Apply to Dean, Graduate College, before March 15.

FIELDS OF STUDY FOR THE PH.D.

Education and Psychology. Education of exceptional children, counseling and guidance, student personnel services in higher education, educational psychology. Combined program offered by School of Education and Department of Psychology. Prerequisites for graduate study: master's degree in education, or academic master's degree with 20 quarter hours in education and psychology; B average in upper-division and graduate work; personal interview; IER Intelligence Scale; CAVD; GRE Advanced Education Section and Psychology Section. 26 professorial staff. 28 Ph.D.'s awarded 1955-59. 1,442 graduate students registered fall 1959.

Engineering.—Chemical. Mass transfer, fluid mechanics, thermodynamics, reaction kinetics. Prerequisites for graduate study: B.S. in chemical engineering or equivalent B.S. in related field; B average in last 2 years; GRE. Recommended: reading knowledge of 2 appropriate languages. 6 professorial staff. Ph.D. program begun 1960. 5 graduate students registered fall 1959.

English. Creative writing and contemporary literature, American studies, comparative literature and humanities. Prerequisites for graduate study: English major; GRE. 6 professorial staff. 24 master's degrees and 17 Ph.D.'s awarded 1955-59. 30 graduate students registered fall 1959.

History. United States; England and the Atlantic Community; medieval, Renaissance, and Reformation Europe. Prerequisites for graduate study: 2 foreign languages; GRE and CAVD. 22 professorial staff. Ph.D. program begun 1959. 22 master's degrees awarded 1955-59. 42 graduate students registered fall 1959.

Psychology. General experimental psychology, counseling. Program in counseling and guidance offered jointly with School of Education. Prerequisites for graduate study: strong background in basic courses in psychology; GRE Aptitude Test. Recommended: GRE Advanced Psychology Examination. Prerequisites for Ph.D.

candidacy: 1 foreign language; CAVD. 12 professorial staff. 53 master's degrees and 78 Ph.D.'s awarded 1955-59. 68 graduate students registered fall 1959. Limit of 6 to 8 in each program at Ph.D. level.

Speech. Public address, speech pathology, audiology, or communications; area program in speech, theatre, and radio-TV. Prerequisites for graduate study: 2 languages, or 1 language and statistics; GRE; major in speech, English, journalism, or psychology. 7 professorial staff. 51 master's degrees and 34 Ph.D.'s awarded 1955-59. 50 graduate students registered fall 1959.

Theatre. Theatre history, dramatic literature and criticism, playwriting, children's theatre. Prerequisites for graduate study: major in theatre; recommendations by former professors; 2 foreign languages; GRE. 9 professorial staff. 25 master's degrees and 18 Ph.D.'s awarded 1955-59. 27 graduate students registered fall 1959.

Drew University

MADISON, NEW JERSEY

The Graduate School

Drew was established in 1867 as a theological seminary of the Methodist Church. A college of liberal arts was added in 1928. The Graduate School, which was established in 1955, offers a Ph.D. program in theological studies. Both men and women are admitted.

Dormitory accommodations available for single graduate students; a few apartments for married students.

Special facilities include: library of approximately 233,000 volumes; program of annual visiting professorships; student-faculty colloquium (which meets 12 times during the academic year and sets the intellectual life of the school).

Residence requirement for Ph.D.: 3 years of full-time study at Drew; however, in some cases, the possession of a B.D. reduces the residence requirement to 2 years.

ADMISSION REQUIREMENTS

Only students who have been admitted to candidacy for a master's or Ph.D. degree may undertake a program of study in The Graduate School. Applicants must hold a bachelor's degree or equivalent, have a record of high academic achievement, show evidence of character and maturity, and give promise of scholarly and personal leadership. Candidates for a master's degree must show competence in either French or German; for a Ph.D., in French and German and such other languages as may be required for study in the proposed field of concentration. GRE Aptitude Test is sometimes required.

Apply to the Office of the Graduate School by April 1.

FEES AND FIRST-YEAR AID

No application fee. Matriculation fee $10. Tuition $800 per academic year. Special fees approximate $25 annually. Room (in dormitories) $615 per academic year. Approximate annual cost of board in college dining room $415. Apartments rent for $50, $60, and $80 per month.

First-year aid available: 6 or 8 scholarships, $800-$2,000.

Apply to Scholarship Committee (with application for admission) by April 1.

FIELDS OF STUDY FOR THE PH.D.

Theological Studies. Biblical studies, church history and the history of Christian thought, theology, personality and society. 24 professorial staff. Ph.D. program initiated 1955. 18 master's degrees and 26 Ph.D.'s awarded 1955-59. 62 graduate students registered fall 1959.

Dropsie College for Hebrew and Cognate Learning

PHILADELPHIA 32, PENNSYLVANIA

Dropsie College is exclusively a graduate school and was established in 1907 to promote the study of Hebrew and of cognate languages and their respective literatures, and rabbinical learning and literature, without theological affiliation. Emphasis is given to the training of scholars. The first Ph.D. was awarded in 1912. The School of Education, which awards the Ph.D. and Ed.D., was established in 1945. The Middle East Institute, which awards the Ph.D., was founded in 1948. The college is privately controlled and nonsectarian. Both men and women are admitted.

No residence facilities are provided for graduate students.

Residence requirement for the doctorate: minimum of 3 years of graduate study, 2 of which must be spent in residence at Dropsie. Summer courses available.

ADMISSION REQUIREMENTS

For graduate study in the College of Hebrew and Cognate Learning (Interrelated Hebrew and Semitic Studies): nonprofessional bachelor's degree or equivalent; good preliminary knowledge of Hebrew language and its literature or of some cognate language and its literature; knowledge of Latin, Greek, and modern languages sufficient for scholarly investigation. For graduate study in the School of Education: adequate knowledge of the Hebrew language and its grammar, of the Bible, and of modern Hebrew literature and Jewish history; practical experience in Jewish school work; undergraduate instruction in education. For graduate study in the Middle East Institute: adequate preliminary education in the social sciences. Recommended for all candidates for admission: GRE. For candidacy for all degrees: qualifying examinations. Apply to Registrar by April 15.

FEES AND FIRST-YEAR AID

No application fee. Tuition $1,000 per year (tuition scholarships available for all qualified students). Registration and library fee total $150 per year.

First-year aid available: fellowships, $600-$1,000; 1 special research fellowship, $1,800. Grants-in-aid also available.

Apply to President of the college by April 15.

FIELDS OF STUDY FOR THE PH.D.

Interrelated Hebrew and Semitic Studies. Biblical and rabbinic literature, Hebrew language and literature, cognate languages and Islamic studies, history, philosophy, Assyriology, comparative religion. Offered in the College of Hebrew and Cognate Learning. 12 professorial staff (plus visiting professors). 1 master's degree and 28 Ph.D.'s awarded 1955-59. 150 graduate students registered fall 1959. Figures include professorial staff, degrees awarded, and the stu-

dents registered in the *Education* and *Middle East Studies* programs described below.

Education. History and philosophy of education, educational psychology, curriculum and teaching, administration and supervision. Offered in the School of Education. See *Interrelated Hebrew and Semitic Studies* (above) for professorial staff, degrees awarded, and students registered.

Middle East Studies. History, social anthropology, economics, political science, languages and literature. Offered in the Middle East Institute. See *Interrelated Hebrew and Semitic Studies* (above) for professorial staff, degrees awarded, and students registered.

Duke University

DURHAM, NORTH CAROLINA

Graduate School of Arts and Sciences

The Graduate School was formally organized in 1926, and the first Ph.D. was conferred in 1928. The Ed.D. degree is also awarded by the Graduate School of Arts and Sciences; the D.F. by the School of Forestry. University is privately controlled and nonsectarian. Both men and women are admitted.

Rooms in residence halls provided for single graduate men and women; no university-owned residence facilities for married students.

Special facilities include: library of approximately 1,400,000 volumes; marine laboratories; liquid helium bubble chamber; forest reserve of 7,000 acres; Van de Graaff accelerator; microwave and low-temperature facilities; radio-isotope and related equipment; nuclear magnetic resonance; mass spectrometer.

Residence requirement for Ph.D.: 2 years beyond master's degree, of which minimum of 1 year must be taken in residence at Duke. Summer courses available.

ADMISSION REQUIREMENTS

For graduate study: bachelor's degree or equivalent; 3 letters of recommendation; evidence of ability, preparation, and motivation to do graduate work. Recommended: GRE and/or MAT. Ph.D. candidacy prerequisites: satisfactory work in all graduate courses; reading knowledge of French and German; preliminary examinations.

Apply to Dean of the Graduate School by August 10.

FEES AND FIRST-YEAR AID

No application fee. Tuition $975 per academic year. Room (in dormitory) for men $200 per academic year; for women $275. Approximate annual cost of board in college dining room $450-$525.

First-year aid available: approximately 50 scholarships, $975-$2,000; 25 teaching fellowships, $1,000-$2,450; approximately 50 other fellowships, $1,000-$3,000; approximately 40 research assistantships, $1,850-$2,450.

Apply to Dean of the Graduate School by February 15.

FIELDS OF STUDY FOR THE PH.D.

Courses in the methodology of teaching offered in several departments. There is a formal seminar in history and an informal seminar in English.

Anatomy. Gross anatomy, histology, and neuroanatomy. Prerequisites for graduate study: equivalent of a major in zoology or biology with basic training in chemistry and physics; reading knowledge of 1 foreign language; GRE. 7 professorial staff. 3 master's degrees and 6 Ph.D.'s awarded 1955-59. 10 graduate students registered fall 1959. Total enrollment limited to 15.

Biochemistry. Occurrence, isolation, and identification of natural products (nucleic acids, polysaccharides, and lipids); biosynthesis and metabolism of nucleic acids, polysaccharides, proteins, amino acids, and lipids; mechanisms of biological oxidations; occurrence and functional mechanisms of enzymes; mechanism of hormone action; nonendocrine control of metabolism; biochemistry and physiology of micro-organisms and of mammalian cells in tissue culture; physical chemistry of proteins and nucleic acids; metabolism of brain; metabolism of connective tissue; biochemical aspect of aging. Prerequisite for graduate study: B.S. in chemistry or B.S. in biology with minor in chemistry. Recommended: maximum possible amount of undergraduate chemistry. 16 professorial staff. 1 master's degree and 12 Ph.D.'s awarded 1955-59. 21 graduate students registered fall 1959.

Botany. Mycology, cytology, ecology, genetics, morphology, and anatomy of seed plants; morphology and taxonomy of lower groups; physiology and taxonomy of seed plants; microbiology. Prerequisites for graduate study: 12 hours of botany beyond elementary course; related work in chemistry, physics, and zoology. Recommended: German plus French or Russian. 11 professorial staff. 13 master's degrees and 23 Ph.D.'s awarded 1955-59. 31 graduate students registered fall 1959. Enrollment limited to about 35.

Chemistry. Analytical methods, fused-salt systems, tracer studies, light scattering, osmotic pressure, statistical mechanical theories of fluids, nuclear magnetic resonance, polymer solutions, reaction kinetics, mechanism and stereochemistry of organic reactions, polarography of organic compounds, organic compounds related to natural products, possible medicinal and fungicidal compounds, organophosphorus compounds, structure and spectra, chemistry of tobacco smoke, fluorination of organic compounds. Prerequisite for graduate study: major in chemistry. Recommended: 3 years of chemistry; physical chemistry; mathematics through integral calculus; 3 semesters of physics; reading knowledge of German and either French or Russian. 15 professorial staff. 30 master's degrees and 41 Ph.D.'s awarded 1955-59. 50 graduate students registered fall 1959. Total enrollment limited to 50-55.

Economics. Economic theory; economic and demographic development; economic history or systems; history of economic thought; industrial and organizational, labor, mathematical, or econometrical economics; international trade; money and banking; public finance; statistics and national income. Prerequisites for graduate study: minimum of 4 courses in economics, including economic theory; money, banking, and statistics; GRE (Quantitative, Verbal Economics). Recommended: mathematics; 2 modern languages; MAT; basic work in psychology, philosophy, and social sciences other than economics; international trade; economic history; skill in composition. 13 professorial staff. 25 master's degrees and 14 Ph.D.'s awarded 1955-59. 34 graduate students registered fall 1959. Enrollment limited to 50.

Engineering—Electrical. Analog computation, dielectric and magnetic materials, superconducting circuitry, electronics, microwaves, energy conversion and control, high voltage phenomena. Prerequisites for graduate study: 12 semester hours in electrical engineering; differential equations; electric and magnetic field theory; theory of networks. Recommended: 1 course in modern physics; GRE Aptitude and Engineering Tests; 1 foreign language. 6 professorial staff. 1 master's degree awarded 1955-59. 23 graduate students registered fall 1959.

Engineering.—Mechanical. Thermodynamics, systems engineering, mathematics, and physics. Prerequisite for graduate study: differential equations. Recommended: 1 language. 4 professorial staff. Program begun 1958. 6 graduate students registered fall 1959. New registration limited to about 10.

English. English language and literature, American literature since 1800. Prerequisites for graduate study: major (18 hours) in English and American literature; 1 foreign language. 15 professorial staff. 61 master's degrees and 26 Ph.D.'s awarded 1955-59. 80 graduate students registered fall 1959.

History. Western European, American, Latin-American, Russian, or military history; Great Britain and the Commonwealth; American foreign relations; the Far East in the modern period. Prerequisites for graduate study: 18 semester hours in history, of which 6 must be in American history if major is in that field; 1 foreign language. 15 professorial staff. 40 master's degrees and 32 Ph.D.'s awarded 1955-59. 78 graduate students registered fall 1959. Total enrollment limited to about 80.

Mathematics. Algebra and number theory, analysis, applied mathematics, logic, numerical analysis, topology. Minor is required in some other department, usually physics. Prerequisites for graduate study: 24 semester hours of mathematics, including at least 6 semester hours beyond calculus. Recommended: knowledge of French, German, or Russian. 12 professorial staff. 14 master's degrees and 12 Ph.D.'s awarded 1955-59. 30 graduate students registered fall 1959.

Microbiology. Medical bacteriology, mycology, virology, microbial genetics, microbial physiology, biochemistry. Prerequisite for graduate study: major in biology or equivalent; chemistry through organic; some knowledge of French and German. Recommended: mathematics through calculus; college physics. 6 professorial staff. 7 Ph.D.'s awarded 1955-59. 9 graduate students registered fall 1959.

Philosophy. History of philosophy, logic, philosophy of science, epistemology, metaphysics, philosophical analysis, ethics, aesthetics, political philosophy, philosophy of law. Prerequisite for graduate study: GRE or MAT. Ph.D. candidacy prerequisites: 12 units in philosophy; 6 units in minor field. 7 master's degrees and 7 Ph.D.'s awarded 1955-59. 21 graduate students registered fall 1959.

Physics. Flame or ultraviolet spectroscopy; microwave and radiofrequency spectroscopy; low-temperature, nuclear, particle, or theoretical nuclear physics. Prerequisite for graduate study: major in physics or equivalent. 9 professorial staff. 13 master's degrees and 39 Ph.D.'s awarded 1955-59. 54 graduate students registered fall 1959.

Physiology. Prerequisites for graduate study: 1 year of biology; 2 years chemistry; 1 year physics; 1 year mathematics. Recommended: reading knowledge of French or German; 2 years of physics; calculus; cellular physiology. 7 professorial staff. 2 master's degrees and 3 Ph.D.'s awarded 1955-59. 3 graduate students registered fall 1959.

Political Science. American government and constitutional law, comparative government (European, Far Eastern, or commonwealth institutions), political theory, American state and local government, international law and organization, public administration. Prerequisite for graduate study: 12 semester hours in political science, including some work in American government. Recommended: reading knowledge of French and German. 7 professorial staff. 24 master's degrees and 22 Ph.D.'s awarded 1955-59. 32 graduate students registered fall 1959. Total enrollment limited to approximately 35.

Psychology. Experimental-biological, clinical, social psychology. Prerequisite for graduate study: minimum of 4 courses in the area. Recommended: background in foreign languages; GRE (Verbal and Quantitative); MAT. 22 professorial staff. 3 master's degrees and 26 Ph.D.'s awarded 1955-59. 55 graduate students registered fall 1959. Total enrollment limited to approximately 18.

Religion. Biblical or historical studies, systematic and contemporary studies. Ph.D. candidacy prerequisite: B.D. degree. 15 professorial staff. 2 master's degrees and 32 Ph.D.'s awarded 1955-59. 45 graduate students registered fall

1959. New registration limited to approximately 15.

Romance Languages. French and Spanish languages and literatures. Prerequisite for graduate study: 24 semester hours in major language and no less than 12 in minor language. Recommended: GRE Verbal and Achievement Test in major language. 11 professorial staff. 21 master's degrees and 1 Ph.D. awarded 1955-59. 13 graduate students registered fall 1959. Total enrollment limited to approximately 25.

Sociology. Theory; methods and statistics; complex social systems; social psychology, organization, and institutions; anthropology. Offered by Department of Sociology and Anthropology. Prerequisites for graduate study: 12 semester hours of sociology. Recommended: previous work in statistics and methods of research; 1 foreign language. 9 professorial staff. 6 master's degrees and 13 Ph.D.'s awarded 1955-59. 12 graduate students registered fall 1959.

Zoology. Biophysics; cellular, developmental, or marine biology; ecology; physiology (comparative and cellular). Prerequisites for graduate study: major in biology; 3 years of college French, German, or Russian. Recommended: chemistry through organic; mathematics through calculus; 1 year of physics; 2 years of college work in each of 2 foreign languages. 17 professorial staff. 20 master's degrees and 21 Ph.D.'s awarded 1955-59. 47 graduate students registered fall 1959. Total enrollment limited to approximately 50.

Duquesne University

PITTSBURGH 19, PENNSYLVANIA

The Graduate School

The Graduate School was organized as a separate unit in 1911; first Ph.D. was awarded in 1954. The university is privately controlled and related to the Roman Catholic Church. Both men and women are admitted.

Limited dormitory space available for both men and women, but cannot be assured to graduate students. No residence facilities provided for married graduate students.

Residence requirement for the Ph.D.: 2 semesters in full-time attendance. Work done at other institutions may be transferred, but each case is considered on its own merits. Summer and evening courses available.

ADMISSION REQUIREMENTS

For graduate study: bachelor's degree; high scholastic standing; qualifying examinations administered by department in major subject. For candidacy for the Ph.D.: comprehensive examinations administered by department in major field; examination in French and German (Russian may be substituted for 1 of these by chemistry students).

Apply to the Dean of the Graduate School by August 15 for fall term; by January 1 for spring term; by June 1 for summer session.

FEES AND FIRST-YEAR AID

No application fee. Tuition $24 per semester hour credit. Special fees approximate $34 annually (laboratory fees additional). Room (in dormitory) for men $150 per year; for women $280. Approximate annual cost of board in college dining room $370 per year.

First-year aid available: 10 teaching fellowships $1,600-$1,900 plus waiver of tuition; 24 research assistantships, $1,600-$2,000 plus waiver of tuition.

Apply to the Dean of the Graduate School before March 1.

FIELDS OF STUDY FOR THE PH.D.

The English Department offers a special seminar for teaching assistants which is specifically devoted to their training and progress in the teaching of college English.

Chemistry. Organic or physical inorganic chemistry; biochemistry. Prerequisites for graduate study: 32 semester hours in chemistry; 1 course in college physics; mathematics through calculus. 6 professorial staff. 11 master's degrees and 5 Ph.D.'s awarded 1955-59. 29 graduate students registered fall 1959. New enrollment limited to 10.

English. Medieval and Renaissance English. Prerequisite for graduate study: 24 semester hours of English literature. Ph.D. candidacy prerequisite: for early literary periods, an examination in Latin. 12 professorial staff. Ph.D. program initiated 1960. 15 master's degrees awarded 1955-59. 31 graduate students registered fall 1959.

Philosophy. Systematic philosophy, history of

philosophy, contemporary philosophy. Prerequisite for graduate study: 24 semester hours in philosophy (including logic, history of philosophy, and fundamentals of systematic philosophy). 9 professorial staff. Ph.D. program begun in 1956. 2 master's degrees and 1 Ph.D. awarded 1955-59. 18 graduate students registered fall 1959.

Emory University

ATLANTA 22, GEORGIA

The Graduate School of Arts and Sciences

Graduate instruction at the master's level has been offered since 1919. Doctoral programs were approved in 1945 and the first Ph.D. awarded in 1948. Emphasis is placed on training in education and research, and the school is especially concerned with preparing those students who plan to teach. University is privately controlled and is affiliated with the Methodist Church. Both men and women are admitted.

Rooms in college dormitories available for single graduate students; university-owned apartments for married students.

Residence requirement for Ph.D.: 6 quarters after master's degree or equivalent. As much as 1 year of graduate credit may be transferred from other institutions. A limited number of summer courses available.

ADMISSION REQUIREMENTS

For graduate study: bachelor's degree. For advanced standing: master's degree or equivalent; reading knowledge of 1 foreign language (usually French or German); GRE. For candidacy for Ph.D.: completion of 45 quarter hours of course work beyond master's degree; preliminary doctoral written examination; approval of final plan for study and research; examination in a second language.

Apply to Dean of the Graduate School at least 30 days before date of desired admission.

FEES AND FIRST-YEAR AID

No application fee. Tuition $795 per year. Matriculation fee $5. Room (in dormitory) $200 per year. Approximate annual cost of board in college dining room $600-$700. Monthly rent for apartments $65-$95.

First-year aid available: 50 teaching assistantships, $1,500-$2,300; 44 fellowships, $1,950-$2,500; 20 research assistantships, $1,800-$3,600.

Apply to Dean of the Graduate School before March 1.

FIELDS OF STUDY FOR THE PH.D.

Biology. Cytogenetics, cytology, experimental embryology (vertebrate and invertebrate), genetics, parasitology, plant ecology, protozoology, radiation biology. 9 professorial staff. 17 master's degrees and 11 Ph.D.'s awarded 1955-59. 23 graduate students registered fall 1959.

Chemistry. Analytical, organic, physical. 12 professorial staff. 16 master's degrees and 11 Ph.D.'s awarded 1955-59. 23 graduate students registered fall 1959.

English. 7 professorial staff. 23 master's degrees and 6 Ph.D.'s awarded 1955-59. 13 graduate students registered fall 1959.

Health Sciences.—Basic. Anatomy, bacteriology, biochemistry, pharmacology, physiology. 37 professorial staff. 13 master's degrees and 6 Ph.D.'s awarded 1955-59. 29 graduate students registered fall 1959.

History. Most phases of American history; limited areas of European and English history. 12 professorial staff. 40 master's degrees and 10 Ph.D.'s awarded 1955-59. 23 graduate students registered fall 1959.

Liberal Arts. Seminars on the liberal arts and studies in Western tradition; critical study of systems of knowledge. Offered by the Institute of Liberal Arts. 18 professorial staff. 3 Ph.D.'s awarded 1955-59. 12 graduate students registered fall 1959.

Philosophy. Epistemology and metaphysics, ethics, philosophy of religion, history of philosophy. 5 professorial staff. Ph.D. program initiated 1957. 7 master's degrees and 1 Ph.D. awarded 1955-59. 23 graduate students registered fall 1959.

Political Science. State and local government, public administration, comparative government, international relations. 6 professorial staff. Ph.D. program initiated 1956. 31 master's degrees and 1 Ph.D. awarded 1955-59. 13 graduate students registered fall 1959.

Psychology.—General. 8 professorial staff. 12 master's degrees and 4 Ph.D.'s awarded 1955-59. 19 graduate students registered fall 1959.

Religion. Biblical studies, history of Christianity, systematic theology, religion and culture. Recommended: B.D. degree. 34 professorial staff. Ph.D. program initiated 1958. 14 master's degrees awarded 1955-59. 21 graduate students registered fall 1959.

Sociology. Social theory, methodology, social organization, social disorganization. Students are required to teach the major portion of one undergraduate course under supervision of a faculty member. 7 professorial staff. Ph.D. program initiated 1958. 4 master's degrees awarded 1955-59. 15 graduate students registered fall 1959.

Florida State University

TALLAHASSEE, FLORIDA

The Graduate School

Although graduate instruction had been offered since 1905, the Graduate School was not organized until 1947. The first Ph.D. was awarded in 1952. Graduate enrollment is now about 15 per cent of the total enrollment. The Ph.D. is awarded in 26 fields, and the Ed.D. is awarded in education, music education, and physical education. The Doctor of Music is conferred through the Department of Music. The university is publicly controlled by the state. Both men and women are admitted.

Rooms in graduate residence hall available for single students; 1- and 2-bedroom apartments for married students.

Special facilities include: library of nearly 500,000 volumes and an extensive microfilm collection; 3 MEV Van de Graaff electron accelerator; and 10 MEV Van de Graaff heavy ion accelerator.

Residence requirements for Ph.D.: minimum of 3 years beyond bachelor's degree; at least 2 regular semesters (consecutive) on campus, in each of which at least 6 semester hours of graduate credit must be earned. Summer and evening courses available.

ADMISSION REQUIREMENTS

For graduate study: bachelor's degree; GRE Aptitude Test. For candidacy for Ph.D.: completion of courses and residence except for 1 semester; reading knowledge of 2 modern foreign languages (usually selected from French, German, or Russian); qualifying and comprehensive examinations; approval of prospectus for dissertation by department and Dean.

Apply to the Admissions Office at least 6 weeks prior to registration; foreign students should apply 3 months or more in advance.

FEES AND FIRST-YEAR AID

Application fee $5. No tuition for state residents; nonresidents $350 a year. Special fees approximate $180 annually. Room (in dormitory) $180-$230 a year. Approximate annual cost of board in college dining room $540. Apartments $34.50-$50 per month.

First-year aid available: 150 out-of-state tuition scholarships; 30-35 fellowships, $1,500-$2,000 plus out-of-state tuition; 15 research assistantships, $1,800-$3,600; 220 graduate assistantships, $150-$225 for half-time. Grants-in-aid available in varying amounts.

Apply to head of appropriate department by February 15 for fellowships starting in fall term; in early spring for assistantships.

FIELDS OF STUDY FOR THE PH.D.

Courses in the methodology of teaching available through the Department of Higher Education in the School of Education.

Biology.—Experimental. Genetics, plant physiology, microbiology, cellular physiology, radiation biology, marine biology, experimental embryology. Offered by Department of Biological Sciences. Prerequisites for graduate study: 24 hours beyond basic course in biology; 1 year physics; mathematics through trigonometry; chemistry through organic; genetics or cytology; 1 year physiology; 1 year taxonomy or ecology; 1 year morphology; 1 year of general biology courses; GRE Advanced Test in Biology. Recommended: 1 year biochemistry; mathematics through calculus. 27 professorial staff. Ph.D. program begun 1958. 7 graduate students registered fall 1959.

Botany. Mycology, bryology, plant taxonomy, plant physiology. Prerequisites for graduate study: minimum of 24 hours beyond basic course in biology (with at least half the work in botany) or a major in botany; GRE Advanced Test in Biology. Recommended: chemistry through organic; 1 year college physics; mathematics through trigonometry. 9 professorial staff. 6 master's degrees and 6 Ph.D.'s awarded 1955-59. 8 graduate students registered fall 1959.

Chemistry. Analytical, inorganic, organic, physical chemistry; biochemistry. Prerequisite for graduate study: major in chemistry. 20 professorial staff. 27 master's degrees and 31 Ph.D.'s awarded 1955-59. 63 graduate students registered fall 1959.

Child or Human Development. Combined program offered by Departments of Education, Home Economics, Psychology, Sociology and Social Welfare. Prerequisite for graduate study: acceptance by one of the departments concerned. 5 master's degrees and 14 Ph.D.'s awarded 1955-59. 8 graduate students registered fall 1959.

Criminology and Corrections. Theory, research methods and administration. Offered by School of Social Welfare and Department of Sociology. Prerequisite for graduate study: credits in sociology. Recommended for graduate study: field placement in a correctional setting for 3 to 12 months. 4 participating professorial staff; 6 more available. Ph.D. program begun 1957. 4 master's degrees awarded 1955-59. 10 graduate students registered fall 1959.

Education. School administration and organization; evaluation, measurement, and statistics; guidance for school personnel; history of education; elementary education; early childhood education; secondary education; supervision and curriculum development; adult education; philosophy of education; vocational education; higher education; teacher education; junior college education; English education; mathematics education; science education; social studies education; student personnel services in higher education. Combined program offered by Departments of Administration, Supervision and Curriculum, Audio-Visual Education, Arts Education, Educational Research and Testing, Guidance and Counseling, Health Education, Higher Education, Physical Education and Recreation, Professional Education Subject Fields, and Vocational and Adult Education. Recommended for graduate study: 2 years' experience; TEEP score. Ed.D. also offered in this field; statistics required rather than foreign languages. 88 professorial staff. 772 master's degrees and 40 Ph.D.'s awarded 1955-59. 268 graduate students registered fall 1959.

English. English literature, American literature, language. Prerequisites for graduate study: major in English; 12 semesters in 1 foreign language. 19 professorial staff. 33 master's degrees and 11 Ph.D.'s awarded 1955-59. 43 graduate students registered fall 1959.

Food and Nutrition. Human nutrition; food science and technology. Prerequisites for graduate study: major in food and nutrition, home economics education, or a related field (such as biochemistry or biology). Recommended: quantitative analysis; bacteriology; organic chemistry; biochemistry. 4 professorial staff. 8 master's degrees and 5 Ph.D.'s awarded 1955-59. 10 graduate students registered fall 1959.

Geology. Paleontology, stratigraphy, petrology, geochemistry, geophysics. Prerequisites for Ph.D. candidacy: 2 courses in laboratory analytical techniques (or equivalent); 2 months of graduate field work. 8 professorial staff. Ph.D. program begun 1960. 21 master's degrees awarded 1955-59. 23 graduate students registered fall 1959.

History. United States to 1865, United States since 1865, Europe from 1870 to 1920, Europe since 1920, modern Asia, diplomatic history. Prerequisites for graduate study: usually both a bachelor's and a master's degree. Recommended: 54 semester hours of history, including 30 or 36 hours of graduate credit; a strong minor in one of the social sciences or humanities. 9 professorial staff. Ph.D. program begun 1958. 19 master's degrees awarded 1955-59. 25 graduate students registered fall 1959.

Home and Family Life. Child development, family economics, housing and/or interior design, family relations, marriage and family living (as a participant in the interdivisional doctoral program). Prerequisites for graduate study: major in home economics or a related field; B average for junior and senior years. Recommended: 2 years of 1 language at college level. 8 professorial staff. 12 Ph.D.'s awarded 1955-59. 13 graduate students registered fall 1959.

Humanities.—Interdepartmental Program. A flexible program offered by Departments of English (Comparative Literature), History, Philosophy, Classics, Modern Languages, Music, Speech, and Art. Prerequisites for graduate study: strong major in one of participating departments plus study above introductory level in 1 (preferably 2) related departments; German and/or French. Prerequisite for Ph.D. candidacy: master's degree in one of participating departments. 75 professorial staff from 8 participating departments. Ph.D. program begun 1955. 3 Ph.D.'s awarded 1955-59. 13 graduate students registered fall 1959.

Marriage and Family Living. College teaching,

marriage and/or family counseling, marriage and/or family research, community program. Program offered jointly by Departments of Sociology, Home and Family Life, and Social Welfare. Prerequisites for graduate study: usually a master's degree or equivalent in a relevant discipline. 10 professorial staff. 17 Ph.D.'s awarded 1955-59. 10 graduate students registered fall 1959.

Mathematics. Topology, modern algebra, functional analysis. 16 professorial staff. Ph.D. program begun 1958. 41 master's degrees awarded 1955-59. 47 graduate students registered fall 1959.

Meteorology. Tropical, synoptic, and theoretical meteorology. Prerequisites for graduate study: mathematics through calculus; 1 year of physics. Recommended: differential equations and vector analysis. 8 professorial staff. 41 master's degrees and 5 Ph.D.'s awarded 1955-59. 42 graduate students registered fall 1959.

Music Education. Offered by School of Music. Prerequisite for graduate study: graduate music examination in music theory, music history, and applied music. Prerequisites for Ph.D. candidacy: 1 foreign language or satisfactory credit and test in statistics. The Ed.D. is also awarded in this field. 31 professorial staff. 54 master's degrees and 15 Ph.D.'s awarded 1955-59. 26 graduate students registered fall 1959.

Music Theory. Offered by School of Music. Prerequisites for graduate study: graduate music examination in music theory, music history, and applied music. Ph.D. program begun 1955. 20 master's degrees and 6 Ph.D.'s awarded 1955-59. 12 graduate students registered fall 1959.

Physical Education and Recreation. Prerequisite for graduate study: major in physical education or equivalent. Recommended: 2 years of experience in full-time teaching, supervision, or administration. The Ed.D. is also awarded in this field. 14 professorial staff. Ph.D. program begun 1958. 40 master's degrees awarded 1955-59. 23 graduate students registered fall 1959.

Physics. Theoretical physics (molecular, atomic, nuclear, fundamental particle, astrophysics); experimental physics (beta and gamma ray spectroscopy; nuclear reaction spectroscopy; 14 MEV neutron reaction studies; nuclear magnetic resonance; X-ray; elementary particle and high-energy nuclear physics; negative ion research; 10 MEV tandem Van de Graaff). 23 professorial staff. 10 master's degrees and 4

Ph.D.'s awarded 1955-59. 40 graduate students registered fall 1959. Enrollment limited to about 40.

Physiology. Biophysics, cellular physiology, comparative physiology, endrocrinology, neurophysiology, sensory physiology. Offered by Department of Biological Sciences. Prerequisites for graduate study: minimum of 24 hours beyond basic course in biology (with at least half the work in physiology) or a major in physiology; GRE Advanced Test in Physiology. Recommended: chemistry through organic; 1 year college physics; mathematics through trigonometry. 5 professorial staff. 5 master's degrees and 2 Ph.D.'s awarded 1955-59. 8 graduate students registered fall 1959.

Political Science. American government, public administration, political theory, comparative government, international relations, public law, political behavior. Prerequisite for graduate study: 18 hours graduate work in government. Recommended: GRE Area Tests and Advanced Government. 12 professorial staff. 32 master's degrees and 1 Ph.D. awarded 1955-59.

Psychology. 19 professorial staff. 38 master's degrees and 38 Ph.D.'s awarded 1955-59. 81 graduate students registered fall 1959. New enrollment limited to 10 to 20.

Sociology. Social psychology, social organization, population, and human ecology. Prerequisite for graduate study: major in sociology, including 3 hours in methods of social research and 3 hours in sociological theory. Prerequisites for Ph.D. candidacy: master's degree or 30 hours of sociology beyond bachelor's degree. 10 professorial staff. 6 master's degrees and 3 Ph.D.'s awarded 1955-59. 8 graduate students registered fall 1959.

Spanish. Medieval Spanish language and literature; Romance philology; Cervantes; Golden Age drama, novel, and poetry; 19th and 20th centuries; American Spanish, Spanish, and American literature; epics and ballads. Offered by Department of Modern Languages. Prerequisites for graduate study: major or minor in field; GRE Advanced Test in Spanish. Recommended: working knowledge of Latin, French, and German. Prerequisites for Ph.D. candidacy: 3 months' residence in a Spanish-speaking country. 7 professorial staff. 12 master's degrees and 2 Ph.D.'s awarded 1955-59. 13 graduate students registered fall 1959. Enrollment limited to not more than 25 students.

Speech and Dramatic Arts. Interpretation and theater, public address, speech education. 7 professorial staff. 15 master's degrees and 7 Ph.D.'s awarded 1955-59. 12 graduate students registered fall 1959. Enrollment of graduate students limited to 4 per graduate faculty member.

Zoology. Parasitology, ornithology, ichthyology, mammalogy, invertebrate zoology, genetics. Prerequisites for graduate study: minimum of 24 hours beyond basic course in biology (with at least half the work in zoology) or a major in zoology; GRE Advanced Test in Zoology. Recommended: chemistry through organic; 1 year college physics; mathematics through trigonometry. 12 professorial staff. 10 master's degrees and 4 Ph.D.'s awarded 1955-59. 17 graduate students registered fall 1959.

Florida, University of

GAINESVILLE, FLORIDA

The Graduate School

Graduate education dates from the establishment of the university in 1905. The Graduate School was organized in 1910, and the first Ph.D. was awarded in 1934. Since then more than 500 Ph.D. degrees have been conferred. Programs leading to the Ed.D. are offered by the College of Education. University is publicly controlled by the state. Both men and women are admitted.

Rooms in dormitories available for single graduate students; 86 1- 2-, or 3-bedroom apartment units reserved for married graduate students.

Residence requirement for Ph.D.: 3 years beyond bachelor's degree; 1 year (either second or third) must be spent in full-time residence on campus. Part-time study may be substituted for full-time study on the basis of 30 semester hours in the calendar year or 35 semester hours in 4 successive registrations (either including or excluding summer session registration). Summer courses and a very limited number of evening courses available.

ADMISSION REQUIREMENTS

For graduate study: bachelor's degree; B average during junior and senior years in most branches of the university; GRE Aptitude Test;

recommendations. Recommended: GRE Advanced Test. For candidacy for Ph.D.: B average or better in all graduate work; written and oral qualifying examinations in major and minor subjects; selection of dissertation subject; functional knowledge of French, German, or Russian, or a reading knowledge of 2 languages other than English, of which the first must be French, German, or Russian (in a few departments, mathematical studies may be substituted for a second language).

Apply to Director of Admissions at least 2 months prior to beginning of term.

FEES AND FIRST-YEAR AID

Application fee $5. Tuition for state residents $180 per academic year plus $54 for 8-week summer term; others $430 plus $154 for summer session. Room (in dormitory) $180-$210 per academic year (rates subject to change). Approximate annual cost of board in college dining room $600-$650. 1-bedroom apartments $26.75-$54 per month; 2 bedrooms $29.50-$57; 3 bedrooms $32.50-$60.

First-year aid available: nonresident tuition scholarships, $350 per academic year ($100 per summer session); fellowships, $1,350-$3,600; research assistantships, $3,000-$6,500; grants-in-aid, $2,400-$3,600; postdoctoral fellowship, $6,000; industrial assistantships, $2,400 and up; traineeship grants, $1,800-$2,000; graduate assistantships, $1,700-$2,800.

Apply to heads of major departments by February 15.

FIELDS OF STUDY FOR THE PH.D.

All departments of the College of Arts and Sciences offer courses in the college teaching of their subjects. These are 6-hour courses and include lectures, conferences, participation in departmental administrative activities, and practice teaching under supervision.

Agronomy. Crop production, weed control, genetics, plant breeding. Ph.D. candidacy prerequisite: reading knowledge of German and French or Spanish (study in mathematics may be substituted for 1 language). 14 professorial staff. Ph.D. program begun 1955. 28 master's degrees and 2 Ph.D.'s awarded 1955-59. 7 graduate students registered fall 1959.

Anatomy. Gross anatomy, microscopic anatomy, neuroanatomy, embryology, teratology, electron microscopy, radiation biology, experimental neurology. Prerequisites for graduate study: major in biological sciences; general and organic chemistry; general physics. 6 professorial staff. Ph.D. program begun 1957. 2 graduate students registered fall 1959. New enrollment limited to 3.

Animal Husbandry. Animal nutrition, breeding, and genetics; animal physiology and meats. Offered by Department of Animal Husbandry and Nutrition. Prerequisite for graduate study: basic courses in bacteriology, biology, botany, and chemistry. 15 professorial staff. 28 master's degrees and 10 Ph.D.'s awarded 1955-59. 19 graduate students registered fall 1959. Enrollment limited to 30-35 students.

Area Studies.—Inter-American. History, political science, economics, international relations, sociology, anthropology, geography, geology, Spanish, Portuguese, French, fine arts, music, journalism. Interdepartment program conducted by School of Inter-American Studies. Prerequisite for graduate study: major in an Inter-American area studies field in the liberal arts. 30 professorial staff. 6 master's degrees and 4 Ph.D.'s awarded 1955-59. 12 graduate students registered fall 1959.

Bacteriology. Bacterial growth, nutrition, physiology, pathogenesis, immunology, virology. Combined program offered by Departments of Bacteriology and Microbiology. Prerequisite for graduate study: sound science foundation, including chemistry through organic. 11 professorial staff. Ph.D. program begun 1956. 15 master's degrees awarded 1955-59. 4 graduate students registered fall 1959.

Biochemistry. Physical chemical characterization and biosynthesis of proteins and nucleic acids, nucleotide metabolism, steroid and carotenoid biosynthesis, biological oxidations, immunochemistry. Prerequisites for graduate study: qualitative, organic, and quantitative chemistry, minimum of 1 year of biology and of physics. Recommended: physical chemistry; calculus; physiology; microbiology; German and French. 7 professorial staff. Ph.D. program begun 1957. 2 Ph.D.'s awarded 1957-59. 6 graduate students registered fall 1959.

Biology. Prerequisite for graduate study: major in zoology or biology. Recommended: comparative vertebrate anatomy; embryology; invertebrate and vertebrate zoology; physiology; ecology; genetics; 1 year each of mathematics and physics; 2 years of chemistry, including organic; 1 year of botany or geology. 30 professorial staff. 10 master's degrees and 20 Ph.D.'s awarded 1955-59. 33 graduate students registered fall 1959. Enrollment limited to 33.

Botany. Plant physiology, radiation biology, cytology, ecology. Prerequisites for graduate study: about 24 credit hours in botany and related plant sciences. Recommended: 1 year each of mathematics, chemistry, and physics. 13 professorial staff. Ph.D. program begun 1960. 2 master's degrees awarded 1955-59. 9 graduate students registered fall 1959.

Chemistry. Analytical, fluorine, inorganic, organic, and physical chemistry; biochemistry. Prerequisite for graduate study: major in chemistry. 22 professorial staff. 25 master's degrees and 39 Ph.D.'s awarded 1955-59. 100 graduate students registered fall 1959.

Economics.—Agricultural. Production, land economics; marketing and agricultural policy. Prerequisite for graduate study: equivalent of a major in agricultural economics. Ph.D. candidacy prerequisite: reading knowledge of 2 foreign languages or of 1 language plus study in mathematics. 9 professorial staff. 14 master's degrees and 9 Ph.D.'s awarded 1955-59. 9 graduate students registered fall 1959.

Economics.—General. Economic theory, public finance, money and banking, labor, international trade, and transportation. Prerequisite for graduate study: major in economics or equivalent. 11 professorial staff. 11 master's degrees and 6 Ph.D.'s awarded 1955-59. 31 graduate students registered fall 1959.

Economics and Business Administration. Business finance, insurance, management, marketing, real estate. Combined program offered by Departments of Finance and Insurance, Management and Business Law, Accounting, Marketing, Real Estate, Economics. Prerequisite for graduate study: major in business administration and/or economics. 22 professorial staff. 36 master's degrees and 3 Ph.D.'s awarded 1955-59. 35 graduate students registered fall 1959.

Engineering.—Chemical. Diffusional operations, heat transfer, kinetics and catalysis, process dynamics and control, thermodynamics, radiochemical processes, pulp and paper, fluorinecarbon compounds, fused salt electrochemistry, economics, asphalt technology, fluidization. Prerequisites for graduate study: major in chemical engineering or equivalent; 8-hour examination in chemical engineering during registration week. 12 professorial staff. 19 master's degrees and 5 Ph.D.'s awarded 1955-59. 22 graduate students registered fall 1959.

Engineering.—Electrical. Network theory, control systems, communication theory, microwave tubes, linear and nonlinear circuits, instrumentation. Prerequisites for graduate study: major in electrical engineering or equivalent. 16 professorial staff. 49 master's degrees and 1 Ph.D. awarded 1955-59. 43 graduate students registered fall 1959.

Engineering Mechanics. Theory of elasticity, theory of plasticity, theory of plates and shells, vibration theory, materials properties, advanced dynamics. Prerequisite for graduate study: B.S. in engineering, physics, or mathematics. Recommended: reading knowledge of German or Russian; as much mathematics as possible. 7 professorial staff. Ph.D. program begun 1958. 4 master's degrees awarded 1955-59. 13 graduate students registered fall 1959. Enrollment limited to 3 Ph.D. candidates for each faculty member.

Engineering.—Sanitary. Water supply and waste-water disposal, air pollution, radiation hygiene and hazard control. Prerequisite for graduate study: B.S. in civil, chemical, or mechanical engineering. Recommended: basic courses in bacteriology, sanitary engineering laboratory, sewage treatment, and environmental sanitation. 10 professorial staff. Ph.D. program begun 1955. 11 master's degrees and 1 Ph.D. awarded 1955-59. 15 graduate students registered fall 1959.

Engineering.—Structural. Foundations and harbor structures, reinforced and prestressed concrete, steel structures. Offered by Department of Civil Engineering. Prerequisite for graduate study: B.S. in civil engineering. Recommended: mathematics beyond ordinary differential equations. 9 professorial staff. Ph.D. program begun 1955. 21 master's degrees and 2 Ph.D.'s awarded 1955-59. 12 graduate students registered fall 1959.

English. Medieval literature, the Renaissance, the Restoration and 18th century, 19th century, American literature, English linguistics. Composite minors are offered in American studies, humanities, language arts, comparative literature, and comparative linguistics. Prerequisite for graduate study: major in English or equivalent. Prerequisites for Ph.D. candidacy: M.A. in English, or equivalent; reading knowledge of both French and German and elementary knowledge of Latin or Greek. 26 professorial staff. 55 master's degrees and 28 Ph.D.'s awarded 1955-59. 68 graduate students registered fall 1959.

Entomology. Taxonomy, ecology, applied entomology, medical and veterinary entomology. Prerequisites for graduate study: minimum of 30 hours in the zoological sciences, including 12 hours in entomology. 17 professorial staff. Ph.D. program begun 1958. 12 master's degrees awarded 1955-59. 12 graduate students registered fall 1959. Enrollment limited to approximately 24 students.

Fruit Crops. Citrus fruits, tropical fruits. Prerequisites for graduate study: 20 hours of horticulture and 10 of botany; background in supporting sciences, such as chemistry, soils, entomology, and mathematics. 12 professorial staff. 14 master's degrees and 5 Ph.D.'s awarded 1955-59. 13 graduate students registered fall 1959.

Geography. Regional studies, cultural geography, physical geography, resource use. Prerequisite for graduate study: 24 hours in geography, including cartography and climatology. Prerequisites for Ph.D. candidacy: 2 languages; field problem. 8 professorial staff. Ph.D. program begun 1955. 4 master's degrees and 3 Ph.D.'s awarded 1955-59. 11 graduate students registered fall 1959.

History. United States (middle period, Civil War and Reconstruction, American cultural and intellectual history, history of American political parties); Latin-American (Mexico, the Caribbean area, Brazil, southern South America). Prerequisites for graduate study: at least 18 hours in history. Recommended: reading knowledge of a foreign language pertinent to the proposed field of research. 20 professorial staff. 22 master's degrees and 8 Ph.D.'s awarded 1955-59. 30 graduate students registered fall 1959.

Mathematics. Algebra, analysis, applied mathematics, geometry, statistical mathematics, theory of numbers, topology. Prerequisite for graduate study: major in mathematics. 19 professorial staff. 25 master's degrees and 16 Ph.D.'s awarded 1955-59. 32 graduate students registered fall 1959.

Microbiology. Bacterial growth physiology, virology, parasitology, infectious diseases, immunology. Offered by Department of Microbiology in cooperation with Department of Bacteriology in College of Agriculture. Prerequisites for graduate study: biology; chemistry; physics;

mathematics. Recommended: physical chemistry. 12 professorial staff. Program established 1957. Enrollment limited to 2-4.

Pharmaceutical Chemistry. Synthesis of medicinal products; identification, isolation, and purification of naturally occurring medicinal products; analytical and control procedures employed in pharmaceutical manufacturing. Prerequisite for graduate study: B.S. in pharmacy. Recommended: French and/or German; physical chemistry; advanced organic chemistry. 6 professorial staff. 5 master's degrees and 9 Ph.D.'s awarded 1955-59. 4 graduate students registered fall 1959.

Pharmacognosy. Structure and chemistry of medicinal plants. Offered by Department of Pharmacognosy and Pharmacology. Prerequisite for graduate study: B.S. in pharmacy. 3 professorial staff.

Pharmacology. General pharmacology and bioassays. Offered by Department of Pharmacognosy and Pharmacology. Prerequisites for graduate study: B.S. in pharmacy or in arts and sciences with major in chemistry or biology. 3 professorial staff. 1 master's degree and 3 Ph.D.'s awarded 1955-59. 3 graduate students registered fall 1959.

Pharmacy. Prerequisite for graduate study: B.S. in pharmacy. 3 professorial staff. 5 master's degrees and 18 Ph.D.'s awarded 1955-59. 4 graduate students registered fall 1959.

Physics. Experimental nuclear physics, experimental low-temperature solid-state physics, chemical physics (experimental and theoretical), theoretical solid-state physics, radio astronomy, cosmology. Prerequisites for graduate study: major in physics or equivalent. 17 professorial staff. 27 master's degrees and 7 Ph.D.'s awarded 1955-59. 40 graduate students registered fall 1959.

Physiology. Respiratory physiology, neurophysiology, physiology of muscle, physiology of newborn, endocrinology. Prerequisite for graduate study: outstanding performance in a science major. Recommended: German or Russian and other foreign languages; mathematics; physics; physical chemistry. 3 professorial staff. Program begun 1956. 2 Ph.D.'s awarded 1956-59. 3 graduate students registered fall 1959.

Plant Pathology. Vegetable, citrus, turf grass, and ornamentals diseases; mycology; virus diseases of plants. Prerequisite for graduate study: 20 hours of credit in biological sciences (12 hours

in botany preferred). 15 professorial staff. 8 master's degrees and 4 Ph.D.'s awarded 1955-59. 10 graduate students registered fall 1959. Enrollment limited to 15 students.

Political Science. International relations, public administration, American government and politics (political behavior), comparative government, political theory, public law, international law. Combined program offered by Department of Political Science with School of Inter-American Affairs. Prerequisites for graduate study: major in political science or equivalent; GRE Advanced Test in Government. Recommended: undergraduate work in 2 languages; basic work in history, economics, and sociology; statistics and mathematics. 14 professorial staff. 20 master's degrees and 4 Ph.D.'s awarded 1955-59. 21 graduate students registered fall 1959.

Psychology. General-experimental, clinical, counseling, school, and social psychology. Prerequisite for graduate study: MAT. 16 professorial staff. 11 master's degrees and 12 Ph.D.'s awarded 1955-59. 53 graduate students registered fall 1959. Enrollment limited to about 75 students.

Sociology.—Latin American. Rural-urban sociology, demography, research methods, social theory, Latin-American societies, social institutions. Prerequisites for Ph.D. candidacy: functional knowledge of Spanish or Portuguese and reading knowledge of German or another language. 8 professorial staff. 5 master's degrees and 3 Ph.D.'s awarded 1955-59. 6 graduate students registered fall 1959. Enrollment limited to 12.

Soils. Soil fertility, chemistry, microbiology, physics, genesis, morphology, and classification. Prerequisites for graduate study: B.S. in agriculture; 20 semester hours in soils. 16 professorial staff. 9 master's degrees and 5 Ph.D.'s awarded 1955-59. 10 graduate students registered fall 1959. Enrollment limited to about 15.

Spanish. Offered by Department of Foreign Languages. Degree is awarded in Romance languages with major in Spanish. Prerequisite for graduate study: 30 semester hours of Spanish or the equivalent, including 12 hours of literature and 6 hours of composition. 15 professorial staff. 3 master's degrees awarded 1955-59. 3 graduate students registered fall 1959.

Speech. Audiology, speech therapy, phonetics, rhetoric and public address, theater and interpretation, speech education and voice science.

10 professorial staff. 12 master's degrees and 14 Ph.D.'s awarded 1955-59. 27 graduate students registered fall 1959.

Vegetable Crops. Vegetable crops production and handling and related fields in botany, plant pathology, soils, biochemistry, and agricultural economics. Prerequisite for graduate study: major in horticulture or adequate training in related field. 10 professorial staff. 2 master's degrees and 2 Ph.D.'s awarded 1955-59. 6 graduate students registered fall 1959.

Fordham University

NEW YORK 58, NEW YORK

Fordham is a Roman Catholic university under the auspices of the Society of Jesus. It was founded in 1841 and offered graduate instruction for the first time in 1916. Both men and women are admitted. Ph.D. awarded by both the Graduate School of Arts and Sciences and the School of Education. The latter division also awards the Ed.D.

Graduate School of Arts and Sciences

Founded in 1916; first Ph.D. awarded 1920. Now offers Ph.D. in 11 major fields.

Dormitory facilities for men; rooms also available in private homes near campus.

Special facilities: New York Botanical Garden adjoins campus; facilities maintained at Marine Biological Laboratory at Woods Hole, Massachusetts; special research facilities available for advanced work in proteins and polymers; fully equipped seismic station maintained. Library contains about 383,000 volumes.

Residence requirement for Ph.D.: 2 years beyond master's degree. Some graduate credit may be transferred, amount depending on program being pursued. Summer session; evening courses (4:30-6:10) available.

ADMISSION REQUIREMENTS

For graduate study: bachelor's degree; 2 letters of recommendation; B average; German and French (substitution of another language allowed where subject of research demands it); GRE and MAT recommended. For candidacy for Ph.D.: completion of master's requirement; B+ average or better; approval of department (students selected on basis of record and qualifications for independent work).

Apply to Registrar of Graduate School of Arts and Sciences by August for fall term; by December for spring term.

FEES AND FIRST-YEAR AID

No application fee. Tuition $35 per credit hour for science students; others $30. Special fees total $50-$100 annually. Rooms in dormitory (men only) $350 annually. Students buy own meals at campus center.

First-year aid available: several scholarships, $720-$1,050; several teaching fellowships, $1,500; 92 research assistantships, $1,000-$2,000. Student loans and campus work (in library and offices, etc.) also available.

Application, with full academic record and recommendations, should be sent to Registrar of Graduate School of Arts and Sciences before March 1.

FIELDS OF STUDY FOR THE PH.D.

Students interested in a career of college teaching may request an apprenticeship to a professor; no formal courses in the methodology of teaching are offered in the Graduate School of Arts and Sciences.

Biology.—General. Cytology, botany, insect physiology. Prerequisites for graduate study: general biology; comparative anatomy; histology; embryology; general and organic chemistry; general physics. 8 professorial staff. 88 master's degrees and 34 Ph.D.'s awarded 1955-59. 57 graduate students registered fall 1959. Total enrollment may not exceed 60.

Chemistry. Inorganic, physical chemistry; biochemistry. Prerequisites for graduate study: inorganic 8 credits; analytical 8; organic 8; physical 8; general physics 1 year; mathematics courses, including differential and integral calculus. Prerequisite for candidacy for Ph.D.: special qualifying examination made up by the department. 14 professorial staff. 63 master's degrees and 29 Ph.D.'s awarded 1955-59. 55 graduate students registered fall 1959.

Classics. Medieval Latin, Greek language and literature, Latin paleography. Prerequisites for graduate study: 24 credits in classical languages and literatures; Latin sight translation text. 9 professorial staff. 43 master's degrees and 5 Ph.D.'s awarded 1955-59. 50 graduate students registered fall 1959.

Economics. History and theory, international trade, finance. Offered by Department of Political Philosophy and the Social Sciences. Prerequisite for graduate study: at least 24 credits in the social sciences, 12 of which must be in economics. 7 professorial staff. 32 master's degrees and 12 Ph.D.'s awarded 1955-59. 31 graduate students registered fall 1959.

English. Medieval literature, American literature, English literature of the 18th and 19th centuries. Prerequisites for graduate study: minimum of 24 credits in English language and literature; French and German; Latin where necessary. Recommended: courses in specific authors. 9 professorial staff. 103 master's degrees and 25 Ph.D.'s awarded 1955-59. 145 graduate students registered fall 1959.

French Literature. Offered by Department of Romance Languages and Literatures. Prerequisites for graduate study: 24 credits in languages, 18 of which must be in French and remainder in French, Spanish, Italian, Latin, or German. 7 professorial staff. 40 master's degrees and 11 Ph.D.'s awarded 1955-59. 74 graduate students registered fall 1959.

History. Early Christian, modern European, American. Prerequisite for graduate study: major in history. 10 professorial staff. 92 master's degrees and 25 Ph.D.'s awarded 1955-59. 162 graduate students registered fall 1959.

Philosophy. Ancient, medieval, and modern philosophy. Prerequisite for graduate study: major in philosophy with minimum of 24 credits. Prerequisite for candidacy for Ph.D.: special qualifying test. 10 professorial staff. 55 master's degrees and 34 Ph.D.'s awarded 1955-59. 123 graduate students registered fall 1959.

Physics. Theoretical, nuclear physics; spectroscopy. Prerequisites for graduate study: 24 credits in physics, including mechanics, electricity and magnetism, and optics; mathematics through differential equations; 1 course in general chemistry. 10 professorial staff. 26 master's degrees and 10 Ph.D.'s awarded 1955-59. 35 graduate students registered fall 1959.

Political Science.—American Government and International Relations. Theory, American government, constitutional law, international rela-

tions. Offered by Department of Political Philosophy and the Social Sciences. Prerequisite for graduate study: minimum of 24 credits in social sciences, 12 of which must be in government or in international relations. 5 professorial staff. 23 master's degrees and 13 Ph.D.'s awarded 1955-59. 37 graduate students registered fall 1959.

Psychology. Clinical and experimental. Prerequisites for graduate study: minimum of 18 credits in psychology, including 1 laboratory course in experimental psychology; MAT. Recommended: GRE. 16 professorial staff. 117 master's degrees and 32 Ph.D.'s awarded 1955-59. 151 graduate students registered fall 1959.

Sociology. Theory, sociology of religion; parish sociology. Offered by Department of Political Philosophy and the Social Sciences. Prerequisite for graduate study: minimum of 24 credits in the social sciences, including 12 in sociology. 6 professorial staff. 62 master's degrees and 11 Ph.D.'s awarded 1955-59. 51 graduate students registered fall 1959.

The School of Education

Teachers College founded 1916; merged with Graduate Department of Education to form School of Education 1938. First Ph.D. conferred 1923.

No residence facilities provided for graduate students.

Residence requirement for Ph.D.: 2 year's work beyond master's degree; transfer students not normally considered for admission. Summer session; evening courses (4:15-6:00; 6:15-8:00) available.

ADMISSION REQUIREMENTS

For graduate study: bachelor's degree; 2 letters of recommendation; B+ average; basic courses in education; reading knowledge of 2 modern languages, usually French or German (under certain conditions statistics may be substituted for 1 language); MAT. For candidacy for Ph.D.: master's degree; B+ average; approval of divisional chairman; library research examination; interview with Graduate Advisory Committee. Recommended: teaching experience (3 years or more) at elementary or secondary level.

Apply to Director of Graduate Studies, The

School of Education, 302 Broadway, New York 7, New York.

FEES AND FIRST-YEAR AID

No application fee. Tuition $30 per credit hour.

First-year aid available: 6 full-tuition scholarships; 6 research assistantships, $800 to $1,200 plus full exemption from tuition fees.

Apply to Director of Graduate Studies, The School of Education, 302 Broadway, New York 7, New York, before February 15.

FIELDS OF STUDY FOR THE PH.D.

Education.—Administration, Supervision, and Methods. Administration of secondary and elementary schools, supervision in secondary schools, methods in secondary school subjects. 6 professorial staff. 125 master's degrees and 20 Ph.D.'s awarded 1955-59. 140 graduate students registered fall 1959.

Education.—Elementary. Prerequisites for graduate study: French or German; statistics. 3 professorial staff. 104 master's degrees and 5 Ph.D.'s awarded 1955-59. 96 graduate students registered fall 1959.

Education.—History and Development. History and philosophy of education. Prerequisite for graduate study: substantial background in history or philosophy or both. 2 professorial staff. 30 master's degrees and 8 Ph.D.'s awarded 1955-59. 25 graduate students registered fall 1959.

Educational Psychology, Measurements, and Guidance. Prerequisites for graduate study: German or French; statistics. 11 professorial staff. 172 master's degrees and 44 Ph.D.'s awarded 1955-59. 250 graduate students registered fall 1959.

George Peabody College for Teachers

NASHVILLE 5, TENNESSEE

The Graduate School

Graduate instruction has been offered since 1914, and the first Ph.D. was awarded in 1919. Master's degree programs are under the direction of the Dean of Administration; post-M.A. programs under the Dean of Instruction. Programs leading to the Ed.D. degree are offered in the Departments of Education, Music, Physical Education, Psychology, and History. Through a reciprocal arrangement, the course offerings at Vanderbilt University are available to Peabody students, and professors from Vanderbilt serve on doctoral committees at Peabody. College is privately controlled and nonsectarian. Both men and women are admitted.

Graduate dormitories maintained for single students. Married students may live in new apartment building or in cottages of frame construction (government housing units).

Special facilities include: library of approximately 760,000 volumes with special collections in the academic fields in which the doctorate is awarded; new student center; remodeled art building.

Residence requirement for Ph.D.: 6 quarters beyond master's degree, 3 of which must be in consecutive full-time residence on campus. Summer and evening courses available.

ADMISSION REQUIREMENTS

For graduate study: bachelor's degree; better than C average. For candidacy for Ph.D.: doctoral aptitude examination (MAT and General Cultural Test); letters of recommendation and interview; approval of department; written and oral preliminary examinations; approval of dissertation topic; proficiency in 2 foreign languages.

Apply to Director of Admissions 1 month prior to date of desired entry.

FEES AND FIRST-YEAR AID

No application fee. Tuition $650 per academic year ($12 per quarter hour). Special fees approximate $25 per year. Room (in dormitory) $130-$225 a year. Approximate annual cost of board in college dining room $500. Apartments $50-$75 a month.

A variety of scholarships, fellowships, and loan arrangements are available. These range in value from $300 to $3,000.

Inquiries should be addressed to Chairman, Committee on Scholarships, or to the chairman of appropriate department. Applications with pertinent transcripts and documents should be received by March 1.

FIELDS OF STUDY FOR THE PH.D.

Several courses in the methodology of teaching are offered and there are opportunities for supervised teaching at the college level. Teaching is done with concurrent seminars and projects in preparing curriculum syllabi for future use of students.

Education. Curriculum and teaching, educational administration, social foundations of education, elementary or secondary education, education of exceptional children. 12 professorial staff. 17 Ph.D.'s awarded 1955-59. Ed.D. degree also awarded in this field (no language requirement).

English. 7 professorial staff. 5 Ph.D.'s awarded 1955-59.

History. 4 professorial staff plus 4 others in closely allied social sciences. 9 Ph.D.'s awarded 1955-59. Ed.D. degree also awarded in this field (no language requirement).

Music. Music education, musicology. Prerequisite for graduate study: musical performance when appropriate. 6 professorial staff. 5 Ph.D.'s awarded 1955-59. Ed.D. degree also awarded in this field (no language requirement).

Psychology. Educational psychology and measurement, guidance and counseling, school psychology. Offered by Division of Human Development and Guidance. Prerequisite for Ph.D. candidacy: GRE or equivalent; experience. 10 professorial staff. 15 Ph.D.'s awarded 1955-59. Ed.D. degree also awarded in this field (no language requirement).

George Washington University

WASHINGTON 6, D. C.

The Graduate Council

Graduate instruction has been offered since 1886, and the first Ph.D. was awarded in 1888. The Graduate Council, which offers only the Ph.D., was organized in 1930 to replace the Graduate School, founded in 1893. The Graduate Council program is built upon the liberal arts curricula of Columbian College, which administers the baccalaureate and master's programs in arts and sciences. The Ph.D. program is limited and is restricted to those fields which have unusual research resources available in Washington. Other doctorates conferred by the university include: Ed.D. (School of Education); D.B.A.

(School of Government); J.S.D. (Law School); D.Sc. (School of Engineering). University is privately controlled and nonsectarian. Both men and women are admitted.

Each doctoral student has his own individual consultative committee and research supervisor. His program, set up by the committee, may move freely across administrative lines dividing departments of instruction or fields of study. The department as such does not control the student's program or research project; the student's committee and research supervisor do. No stated number of credits is required; each consultative committee establishes the amount of graduate work a student may be required to take. A written examination on the fields of study assigned, covering a week or more, satisfies the first phase of the discipline, after which the student becomes a Fellow of the Council and works on his research project.

Rooms in residence halls available for single graduate students; no residence facilities provided for married students.

Library of approximately 332,000 volumes contains several important collections, including the internationally known library of the Carnegie Endowment for International Peace, the W. Lloyd Wright collection of Washingtoniana, the Richard Heinzel collection of Germanic philology and literature, the Curt Wachsmuth collection of Greek and Roman literature, archaeology and history, and the Mount Vernon collection on political history, international law, and social sciences.

Residence requirement for Ph.D.: students must be in residence on campus through completion of Council Fellowship examination and during research work. Master's requirements must be done in residence. Summer and evening courses available.

ADMISSION REQUIREMENTS

For graduate study at master's level: bachelor's degree; B average; examination in 1 modern foreign language by end of 15 attempted semester hours. Recommended: GRE. For admission to Ph.D. program administered by Graduate Council: master's degree or 1 year of graduate work in field of interest, 1 of the 2 language examinations required for degree must be taken during the first semester of residence; the second within a year.

Apply to Director of Admissions for all graduate degrees (except Ph.D.) by July 1 for fall term; by January 1 for spring term; by May 1 for summer session. Persons interested in a Ph.D. degree should apply directly to the Dean of the Graduate Council.

FEES AND FIRST-YEAR AID

Application fee $10. Tuition for candidates for master's degree $720 per academic year. Ph.D. tuition divided into 2 units: $800 up to and including written examination and $800 up to and including final oral examination (both units payable at rate of $200 per semester). Special fees (for students enrolled in physical, biological, or medical programs) approximate $50 annually. Room (in dormitory) for men $37.50 and $40 per month in double room; women $40 per double room per person or $42.50 and $45 per single room. Board in cafeteria and community costs approximately $600 per academic year.

First-year aid available: 16 scholarships, $100-$500; 20 teaching fellowships, $750-$3,000; 23 graduate assistantships, $1,215-$1,700.

Apply to Executive Officer of department concerned by April 1.

FIELDS OF STUDY FOR THE PH.D.

American Language and Literature. Fiction, social themes in literature, literary nationalism. Combined program offered by Departments of English and History. 8 master's degrees awarded 1955-59. 16 graduate students registered fall 1959.

Anatomy. Gross anatomy, histology, neuro-ophthalmology, embryology. Combined program offered by Department of Anatomy and related medical science departments. 5 master's degrees and 2 Ph.D.'s awarded 1955-59. 4 graduate students registered fall 1959.

Bacteriology. Antibiotics, bacterial physiology and nutrition, coliform bacteria and antibiosis, immunology, intestinal microbiology, immunology (antigenic analysis), microbiology, virology, determinative bacteriology, immunity in tuberculosis. Combined program offered by Department of Bacteriology and related medical science departments. 24 master's degrees and 16 Ph.D.'s awarded 1955-59. 22 graduate students registered fall 1959.

Biochemistry. Amino-acid metabolism, animal nutrition, ascorbic acid metabolism, biochemical detoxication, carbohydrate metabolism, nutrition

(emphasis on vitamins), pathological chemistry, chemistry and metabolism of protein, lipids, protein biosynthesis, tissue respiration, metabolic relationships of insulin. Combined program offered by Department of Biochemistry and related medical science departments. 28 master's degrees and 11 Ph.D.'s awarded 1955-59. 28 graduate students registered fall 1959.

Biology. Cytology. Combined program offered by Department of Biology and related biological and medical science departments. 13 master's degrees and 2 Ph.D.'s awarded 1955-59. 9 graduate students registered fall 1959.

Botany. Mycology; plant pathology; taxonomy; plant physiology and vascular plants (or microorganisms); plant ecology. Combined program offered by Department of Botany and related biological and medical sciences. 5 master's degrees and 2 Ph.D.'s awarded 1955-59. 9 graduate students registered fall 1959.

Chemistry. Analytical, inorganic, organic chemistry; physical chemistry (kinetics and electrochemistry, physical-solubilities, physical-organic and reaction mechanisms); geochemistry. 7 professorial staff. 11 master's degrees and 2 Ph.D.'s awarded 1955-59. 37 graduate students registered fall 1959.

Economics and Related Social Sciences. History of economic thought, economic theory, economic policy, international economics, international finance, national income, public finance, Soviet economics, transporation, methodology of economics. Combined program offered by Department of Economics and related social sciences departments. 15 master's degrees and 7 Ph.D.'s awarded 1955-59. 38 graduate students registered fall 1959.

English Language and Literature. 16th century drama; 17th century drama; 17th or 18th century literature; history of English drama; 20th century literature. Offered by Department of English. 5 professorial staff. 14 master's degrees and 1 Ph.D. awarded 1955-59. 12 graduate students registered fall 1959.

Geography. Area synthesis. Combined program offered by Department of Geography and related physical sciences departments. Ph.D. program begun 1955. 14 master's degrees awarded 1955-59. 24 graduate students registered fall 1959.

Germanic Languages and Literatures. Middle High German language and literature, early New High German language and literature, Old

High German language and literature, German romanticism, Old Norse language and literature. Combined program offered by Departments of Germanic Languages and Literatures and English Literature. 3 professorial staff (plus English Department). 3 master's degrees and 2 Ph.D.'s awarded 1955-59. 4 graduate students registered fall 1959.

History. European (diplomatic since 1815, Nationalism, Russian and Soviet); history of religion in the United States; the modern Near East; Latin American; United States (diplomatic, social, economic, political). Combined program offered by Department of History and related social sciences departments. 40 master's degrees and 3 Ph.D.'s awarded 1955-59. 54 graduate students registered fall 1959.

International Relations. International economic policies, development of underdeveloped countries, diplomatic history, international politics and organization. Combined program offered by Departments of Economics, History, and Political Science. 23 professorial staff. Ph.D. program begun 1959. 52 master's degrees awarded 1955-59.

Mathematics. Algebra (finite groups); analysis; analysis (functional); analysis (infinite series); mathematical logic. Combined program offered by Departments of Mathematics and Statistics. 4 professorial staff (plus Statistics Department). 4 master's degrees and 1 Ph.D. awarded 1955-59. 36 graduate students registered fall 1959.

Pharmacology. Chemotherapy, medicinal chemistry, drug metabolism. Combined program offered by Department of Pharmacology and related medical sciences departments. 8 master's degrees and 12 Ph.D.'s awarded 1955-59. 16 graduate students registered fall 1959.

Physics. Biophysics; theoretical (quantum mechanics, molecular physics, or aerodynamics); relativity; electron optics; experimental nuclear physics; radioactivity; low-energy nuclear physics. Combined program offered by Departments of Physics and Mathematics. 13 master's degrees and 2 Ph.D.'s awarded 1955-59. 17 graduate students registered fall 1959.

Physiology. Blood pressure studies, neuromuscular studies, cardiovascular shock, cellular physiology, endocrinology, gastrointestinal physiology, electrolyte metabolism, hemodynamics, peripheral circulation. Combined program offered by Department of Physiology and related

medical sciences departments. 15 master's degrees and 9 Ph.D.'s awarded 1955-59. 7 graduate students registered fall 1959.

Political Science. Comparative government and political theory; international politics and organization; international law (war and neutrality or arbitration); international relations, especially American foreign policy; the political process; political controls over administrative agencies; United States (the legislative process or governmental organization and administration). Combined program offered by Department of Political Science and related social sciences departments. 19 master's degrees and 5 Ph.D.'s awarded 1955-59. 31 graduate students registered fall 1959.

Psychiatry. Problems of treatment. Combined program offered by Department of Psychiatry and related medical sciences departments. Prerequisite for graduate study: M.D. degree. Combined program offered by Department of Psychiatry and related medical departments.

Psychology. Counseling and guidance; military counseling and guidance; personnel psychology; psychological measurements; abnormal, social, comparative, or experimental psychology. Combined program offered by Departments of Psychology, Physiology, and Statistics. 75 master's degrees and 13 Ph.D.'s awarded 1955-59. 106 graduate students registered fall 1959.

Romance Languages and Literatures. Romance linguistics, Spanish-American literature, Spanish literature, 17th century literature, French literature since 1880, modern Spanish literature. 5 professorial staff. 6 master's degrees and 1 Ph.D. awarded 1955-59. 28 graduate students registered fall 1959.

Statistics. Theoretical (probability and sampling); applied (econometrics); multivariate analysis; psychometrics; managerial statistics. Combined program offered by Departments of Statistics and Mathematics. 2 professors plus those from Mathematics Department. 6 master's degrees and 6 Ph.D.'s awarded 1955-59. 36 graduate students registered fall 1959.

Zoology. Parasitology (parasitic protozoa); vertebrate (embryology and morphogenesis or ichthyology); insect physiology. Combined program offered by Department of Zoology and related biological and medical sciences departments. 12 master's degrees and 8 Ph.D.'s awarded 1955-59. 7 graduate students registered fall 1959.

Georgetown University

WASHINGTON 7, D. C.

Georgetown University was founded in 1789 and has offered graduate instruction since 1821. At present, Ph.D. programs are offered through the Graduate School of Arts and Sciences and the Schools of Medicine and Dentistry. The J.S.D. and the D.Comp.L. are conferred by the School of Law. University is privately controlled and is conducted by the Fathers of the Society of Jesus, Roman Catholic Church. Only men are admitted to the undergraduate college; both men and women to the graduate and professional schools.

Graduate School of Arts and Sciences

Founded 1821; first Ph.D. awarded 1897.

No residence facilities provided for graduate students.

Special facilities include: library of approximately 375,000 volumes; special laboratory facilities for language students.

Residence requirement for Ph.D.: 4 semesters beyond the master's degree; maximum of 1 quarter of total course work may be transferred from other graduate institutions. Transfer credit granted only after 1 full semester of residence at Georgetown. Summer and evening courses available.

ADMISSION REQUIREMENTS

For graduate study: bachelor's degree; B average; 18-24 hours in field selected for graduate study; 3 letters of recommendation; language competency test. For candidacy for Ph.D.: minimum of 36 hours past master's degree; examinations in 2 foreign languages (usually French and German, but another language may be substituted where it is more relevant to research); comprehensive examination.

Apply to the Registrar, The Graduate School of Arts and Sciences, 37th and O Streets, N.W., Washington 7, D. C., by September 1.

FEES AND FIRST-YEAR AID

Application fee $10. Tuition $720 per academic year. Special fees approximate $40 per academic year.

First-year aid available: 10 tuition scholarships; 50 fellowships, $1,600-$2,400; 10 research assistantships, $1,800-$2,400. Library gives full tuition to about 25 graduate students per year in return for limited number of hours of assistance.

Apply to the Registrar, Graduate School of Arts and Sciences, 37th and O Streets, N.W., Washington 7, D. C., by February 15.

FIELDS OF STUDY FOR THE PH.D.

No courses specifically in the methodology of teaching are offered, but candidates interested in teaching careers do teach elementary college courses under careful supervision of senior faculty.

Area Studies.—Russian. Core program with number of electives which may be slanted toward almost any angle of Russian history, politics, economics, philosophy, or literature. Combined program offered by Departments of Economics, History, and Government, and the Institute of Languages and Linguistics. Prerequisite for graduate study: strong liberal arts or social science background. Program limited to full-time students who intend to seek the Ph.D. 18 professorial staff. Ph.D. program initiated 1959. 8 graduate students registered fall 1959. Program limited to 12 students a year.

Astronomy. Astrophysics, astronomical geodesy, spectroscopy, celestial mechanics, statistical astronomy. Prerequisites for graduate study: courses in astronomy and physics; mathematics through calculus. 6 professorial staff. 3 master's degrees and 2 Ph.D.'s awarded 1955-59. 32 graduate students registered fall 1959.

Chemistry. Biochemistry; inorganic, physical, organic chemistry; radiochemistry. 7 professorial staff. 59 Ph.D.'s awarded 1955-59. 99 graduate students registered fall 1959.

Economics. Economic theory, statistics, modern capitalism, monetary theory and policy, international economics, labor economics, underdeveloped countries, foreign area economics. 10 professorial staff. 18 master's degrees and 10 Ph.D.'s awarded 1955-59. 111 graduate students registered fall 1959.

History. Medieval and Renaissance Europe, modern Europe, United States, Far East, Latin America, Middle East, Russia, East and Southeast Asia, Great Britain and the Commonwealth, the Iberian Peninsula. 19 professorial staff. 75 master's degrees and 32 Ph.D.'s awarded 1955-59. 179 graduate students registered fall 1959.

International Relations. International politics, law, or organization; foreign policy and diplomacy; area orientations in Latin America, Soviet area, Middle East, Far East. Offered by the Department of Government. 14 professorial staff. 69 master's degrees and 9 Ph.D.'s awarded 1955-59. 166 graduate students registered fall 1959.

Philosophy. Ancient, medieval, contemporary, or classical modern philosophy; philosophy and literature; mathematics and philosophy; philosophical anthropology. 11 professorial staff. 7 master's degrees and 9 Ph.D.'s awarded 1955-59. 31 graduate students registered fall 1959.

Physics. Solid-state or nuclear physics, quantum mechanics, spectroscopy, relativity. 7 professorial staff. 3 master's degrees awarded 1955-59. 31 graduate students registered fall 1959.

Political Science. Political theory or methodology; comparative or American government; international relations; area concentrations in Latin America, Soviet area, Middle East, Far East. Offered by Department of Government. 14 professorial staff. 36 master's degrees and 25 Ph.D.'s awarded 1955-59. 81 graduate students registered fall 1959.

School of Medicine and Dentistry

School of Medicine founded 1851; School of Dentistry founded 1901.

Rooms in Medical Center Dormitory available for male students; no residence facilities provided for women or for married students.

Residence requirement for Ph.D.: 3 years, of which no more than 8 semester hours may be transferred from other graduate institutions.

ADMISSION REQUIREMENTS

For graduate study: bachelor's degree for candidates who do not have either M.D. or D.D.S. degree; 1 modern foreign language.

Apply to Registrar, Medical or Dental School, 3900 Reservoir Road, N.W., Washington 7, D. C., at any time.

FEES AND FIRST-YEAR AID

No application fee. Tuition $25 per semester hour. Room (in dormitory) for men $40 per month.

First-year aid available: 6 teaching fellow-

ships, $1,800-$2,400; 6 research assistantships, $1,800-$2,400.

Apply to department head, 3900 Reservoir Road, N.W., Washington 7, D. C., by May 1.

FIELDS OF STUDY FOR THE PH.D.

Anatomy. Gross anatomy, neuroanatomy, histology. 8 professorial staff. 1 Ph.D. awarded 1955-59. 1 graduate student registered fall 1959.

Bacteriology. Immunology, virology, parasitology. Offered by Department of Microbiology. 6 professorial staff. 2 master's degrees and 2 Ph.D.'s awarded 1955-59. 2 graduate students registered fall 1959.

Biochemistry. Neurochemistry, protein metabolism. Prerequisite for graduate study: 16-20 hours chemistry, including physical; calculus. 8 professorial staff. 2 Ph.D.'s awarded 1955-59. 2 graduate students registered fall 1959.

Pathology. General, clinical pathology. 8 professorial staff. 4 master's degrees and 2 Ph.D.'s awarded 1955-59. 3 graduate students registered fall 1959.

Pharmacology. General pharmacology. 5 professorial staff. 7 Ph.D.'s awarded 1955-59. 4 graduate students registered fall 1959.

Physiology. Cardiology, endocrinology. Offered by Department of Physiology and Biophysics. 8 professorial staff. 2 master's degrees and 4 Ph.D.'s awarded 1955-59. 4 graduate students registered fall 1959.

Georgia Institute of Technology

ATLANTA 13, GEORGIA

Graduate Division

Graduate instruction has been offered since 1922. The Graduate Division was organized in 1941, and the first Ph.D. was awarded in 1950. Institute is publicly controlled by the state. Both men and women are admitted.

Limited accommodations in dormitories for single graduate men; some apartments on campus for married students; no residence facilities for women. Housing Office maintains file of currently available off-campus accommodations.

Special facilities include: library of approximately 215,000 volumes; radioisotopes laboratory; computer center; new electrical engineering building with all floors devoted to graduate work and research; research reactor.

Residence requirement for Ph.D.: minimum of 3 years beyond bachelor's degree with at least 3 consecutive quarters taken in residence at the Georgia Institute of Technology.

ADMISSION REQUIREMENTS

For graduate study: bachelor's degree; standing in upper 25% of college graduating class; strong recommendations; appropriate preparation in field of proposed study; indication of creative ability. Recommended: GRE. For candidacy for Ph.D.: completion of substantial portion of course work (normally at least 5 quarters beyond bachelor's degree); knowledge of 2 foreign languages (usually German and French) or 1 language and 1 research tool; comprehensive examinations; approval of research topic.

Apply to Dean of Graduate Division at least 1 month prior to date of desired entry.

FEES AND FIRST-YEAR AID

No application fee. Tuition for state residents $237 per academic year; others $621. Room (in dormitory) for men $210 per year; meals available in Institute cafeteria. Apartments $42.50-$86 per month.

First-year aid available: 479 teaching fellowships, $1,200-$3,000; 41 other fellowships, $250-$8,400; 204 research assistantships, $1,200-1,800; approximately 89 grants-in-aid per quarter, $79-$207.

Apply to Director of school concerned at least 1 month in advance of date of desired entry.

FIELDS OF STUDY FOR THE PH.D.

A teaching seminar is available for students interested in a career in college teaching.

Chemistry. Analytical, inorganic, organic, and physical chemistry. Offered by the School of Chemistry. Prerequisites for graduate study: at least 1 year of German; placement tests. 16 professorial staff. 16 master's degrees and 15 Ph.D.'s awarded 1955-59. 45 graduate students registered fall 1959. Total enrollment limited to 45.

Engineering. — Chemical. Thermodynamics, cryogenics, heat and mass transfer. Offered by School of Chemical Engineering. 10 professorial staff. 33 master's degrees and 10 Ph.D.'s awarded 1955-59. 44 students registered fall 1959.

Engineering.—Civil. Hydraulic, sanitary, soils, and structural engineering; surveying and photogrammetry; transportation engineering. Offered by School of Civil Engineering. Prerequisite for graduate study: usually a degree in civil engineering. 14 professorial staff plus others in related departments. Ph.D. program initiated 1955. 48 master's degrees awarded 1955-59. 29 graduate students registered fall 1959.

Engineering.—Electrical. Communications circuits, network theory, transients in linear systems, servo and control systems, electromagnetic theory, modulation theory, communication theory, machinery, power transmission, oscillators. Offered by School of Electrical Engineering. Prerequisite for graduate study: major in electrical engineering or closely related area. 8 professorial staff. 112 master's degrees and 7 Ph.D.'s awarded 1955-59. 80 graduate students registered fall 1959.

Engineering.—Industrial. Operations research, engineering economy, methods and standards, engineering statistics, quality control and reliability, facilities and organization planning. Offered by School of Industrial Engineering. Prerequisite for graduate study: background in industrial engineering. 12 professorial staff. Ph.D. program initiated 1958. 57 master's degrees awarded 1955-59. 50 graduate students registered fall 1959.

Engineering.—Mechanical. Fluid flow, heat transfer, thermodynamics, and machine design. Offered by School of Mechanical Engineering. Prerequisite for graduate study: major in mechanical engineering. 9 professorial staff. Ph.D. program initiated 1955. 49 master's degrees and 2 Ph.D.'s awarded 1955-59. 50 graduate students registered fall 1959.

Engineering.—Sanitary. Water supply and waste-water disposal, air pollution, radiological health. Offered by School of Civil Engineering. Prerequisite for graduate study: major in engineering. 10 professorial staff plus others in related departments. Ph.D. program initiated 1955. 3 master's degrees awarded 1955-59. 6 graduate students registered fall 1959.

Physics. Experimental programs in microwave spectroscopy, solid-state physics, nuclear decay processes, gaseous electronics and charge exchange, upper-atmosphere research, reactor kinetics and nuclear resonances, theoretical research in transformation theory, beta decay, nuclear reactions, nuclear decay processes, statistical mechanics, quantum statistics, solid-state physics, radio astronomy. Offered by School of Physics. Prerequisite for graduate study: major in physics with mathematics through differential equations. Recommended: a year of mathematics beyond differential equations. 13 professorial staff. Ph.D. program initiated 1955. 13 master's degrees and 3 Ph.D.'s awarded 1955-59. 35 graduate students registered fall 1959.

Georgia, University of

ATHENS, GEORGIA

The Graduate School

Graduate instruction has been offered since 1868, and the Graduate School was organized in 1910. First Ph.D. was awarded in 1941. In addition to the Ph.D., the university awards the Ed.D. Institution is publicly controlled by the state. Both men and women are admitted.

Rooms available in university dormitories for single students; apartments for married students.

Facilities include: well-equipped science center completed in 1960; institute of statistics; computing center; library with approximately 400,000 volumes. The university maintains a marine biology laboratory on Sapelo Island. It is a member of the Oak Ridge Institute of Nuclear Studies, and the facilities of this laboratory are available for research.

Residence requirement for Ph.D.: minimum of 3 years beyond bachelor's degree, of which 1 academic year of 3 consecutive quarters must be taken in residence on campus; only 10 quarter hours of graduate credit may be transferred. Summer courses available.

ADMISSION REQUIREMENTS

For graduate study: bachelor's degree with major in field chosen for graduate study; standing in upper half of class; recommendations from department; GRE Aptitude and Area Tests. For candidacy for Ph.D.: oral and written preliminary examinations in major field; examinations in 2 modern foreign languages (French and German preferred); approval of program of study and research.

Apply to the Graduate Dean at least 20 days, but preferably 6 weeks, before registration date.

FEES AND FIRST-YEAR AID

Deposit of $25 required of new students in fall quarter. Approximate annual tuition $181 for state residents; additional $100 per quarter required of nonresidents. Room (in dormitory) for men $183-$225; for women $225. Meal tickets for college dining room $1.55 per day. Apartments for married students $25-$32 per month (size varies from efficiency to 3-bedroom).

First-year aid available: 40 out-of-state tuition scholarships, $100-$300; 50 teaching fellowships (departmental assistants), $1,000-$2,000; 10 other fellowships, $1,650-$2,500; 45 research assistantships, $1,500-$2,000; 43 graduate assistantships, $1,500.

Apply to Graduate Dean or appropriate department head before February 15 of year preceding tenure.

FIELDS OF STUDY FOR THE PH.D.

Animal Nutrition. Biochemistry, nutrition. Offered by Departments of Animal Husbandry, Dairy Husbandry, and Poultry Husbandry. Prerequisite for graduate study: concentration in major field and in chemistry. 10 professorial staff. Ph.D. program begun 1958. 25 master's degrees awarded 1955-59. 22 graduate students registered fall 1959.

Bacteriology. Bacterio-physiology, bacterio-metabolism, morphology, taxonomy, soils, immunology, foods. 3 professorial staff. Ph.D. program begun 1958. 5 master's degrees awarded 1955-59. 12 graduate students registered fall 1959.

Chemistry. Analytical, physical, or organic chemistry; biochemistry. Prerequisite for graduate study: tests in 4 out of 5 fields (analytical, biological, organic, inorganic, and physical chemistry). 9 professorial staff. Ph.D. program begun 1959. 24 master's degrees awarded 1955-59. 17 graduate students registered fall 1959.

English. American literature, English literature, linguistics. Prerequisites for graduate study: minors in supporting fields. 6 professorial staff. 28 master's degrees and 3 Ph.D.'s awarded 1955-59. 14 graduate students registered fall 1959.

Food Technology and Dairy Manufactures. Food technology, dairy husbandry. Prerequisite for graduate study: major in field and concentration in chemistry. 6 professorial staff. Ph.D. program begun 1958. 24 master's degrees awarded 1955-59. 14 students registered fall 1959.

History. American and modern European history; foreign area studies; international relations. Prerequisite for graduate study: general qualifying examination. 6 professorial staff. 18 master's degrees and 1 Ph.D. awarded 1955-59. 24 graduate students registered fall 1959.

Mathematics. Topology, modern analysis. 6 professorial staff. 6 master's degrees and 4 Ph.D.'s awarded 1955-59. 16 graduate students registered fall 1959.

Physics. Atomic and molecular. 4 professorial staff. Ph.D. program begun 1959. 9 master's degrees awarded 1955-59. 8 graduate students registered fall 1959.

Plant Sciences. Plant taxonomy, plant physiology. Offered by Departments of Agronomy, Botany, Forestry, Horticulture, and Plant Pathology. Prerequisite for graduate study: concentration in plant sciences. 18 professorial staff. 45 master's degrees and 3 Ph.D.'s awarded 1955-59. 36 graduate students registered fall 1959.

Psychology. General theoretical, experimental, physiological, physical, and comparative psychology. Prerequisite for graduate study: MAT. 2 professorial staff. Ph.D. program begun 1956. 11 master's degrees and 1 Ph.D. awarded 1955-59. 14 graduate students registered fall 1959.

Zoology. Parasitology, physiology, ecology. 9 professorial staff. 9 master's degrees and 10 Ph.D.'s awarded 1955-59. 21 graduate students registered fall 1959.

Hahnemann Medical College and Hospital

PHILADELPHIA 2, PENNSYLVANIA

Graduate School of Basic Medical Sciences

Graduate instruction was initiated in 1949 and, in 1950, the Graduate School was founded. First Ph.D. was awarded in 1956. Institution is privately controlled and nonsectarian. Both men and women are admitted.

No residence facilities provided for graduate students.

An AEC-approved course of instruction in radio-isotope methodology is offered. Specialized apparatus for such instruction is available.

Residence requirement for Ph.D.: 6 semesters beyond bachelor's or M.D. degree; maximum of 4 semesters of graduate credit may be transferred from other institutions.

ADMISSION REQUIREMENTS

For graduate study: bachelor's or M.D. degree; high scholastic achievement; reading knowledge of 2 foreign languages (these may be made up after entrance by spending 1 additional semester in residence); GRE. Recommended: undergraduate courses in mathematics, chemistry, and biological sciences.

Apply to chairman, Graduate School Committee, Hahnemann Medical College, 235 North 15th Street, Philadelphia 2, Pennsylvania, by April 30.

FEES AND FIRST-YEAR AID

No application fee. Tuition $500 per academic year. Special fees approximate $60 annually.

First-year aid available: 12 teaching fellowships, waiver of tuition and laboratory fees; 12 other fellowships, $1,500-$2,500 (including waiver of tuition and laboratory fees); variable number of research assistantships, $2,500-$3,200 (including waiver of tuition and laboratory fees).

Apply to chairman, Graduate School Committee, Hahnemann Medical College, 235 North 15th Street, Philadelphia 2, Pennsylvania, by April 30.

FIELDS OF STUDY FOR THE PH.D.

No special courses in the methodology of teaching are offered, but all doctoral candidates participate in the teaching program and are closely observed and aided in improving their teaching methods.

Anatomy. Enervation and de-enervation studies of the heart; coronary circulation in man and animals; cardiac conduction systems; carcinogenesis of thyroid, parathyroid, and thymus; embryonic and tumor transplantation; embryology and histochemistry of developing hypothalmus; endocrinology of the adrenal cortex and pituitary gland; cellular vulnerability to ultraviolet light during metastasis of cells. 10 professorial staff. 4 master's degrees awarded 1955-59. 4 graduate students registered fall 1959.

Bacteriology. Activity and mode of action of antibiotics and other chemotherapeutic agents; induced synthesis of penicillinase and factors affecting penicillinase synthesis; role of phospholipids in microbial metabolism; purine biosynthesis; selection and isolation of auxotrophic mutants of yeast using antifungal antibiotics; role of biotin in microbial metabolism; amino-acid metabolism; alterations in metabolism of cells grown in tissue culture following virus infection; tissue culture metabolism. Offered by Department of Microbiology. Recommended for graduate study: advanced courses in microbiology and biochemistry. 6 professorial staff. 8 master's degrees and 4 Ph.D.'s awarded 1955-59. 8 graduate students registered fall 1959.

Biological Chemistry. Instrumentation; biochemistry of nucleic acids and nucleoproteins; methods of isolation, characterization, and biological significance of proteins; chemistry and biochemistry of porphyrins; biometry; general biophysics; nuclear radiation; radiobiology and physical instrumentation; application of radioactivity to problems in medicine and biology. Recommended for graduate study: physical chemistry; advanced organic chemistry. 10 professorial staff. 2 master's degrees and 3 Ph.D.'s awarded 1955-59. 8 graduate students registered fall 1959.

Pathology. Morphogenesis of atherosclerosis; histochemistry of myocardial infarction; carcinogenesis of plastics; transplantation of human neoplasms to hamsters; carcinogenesis in the cervix with benzpyrene; pseudomonas in septicemia following cardiac surgery; electrophoresis and fluorescence of LE-cell phenomenon. Prerequisite for graduate study: M.D. degree. 14 professorial staff. 1 master's degree awarded 1955-59. 3 graduate students registered fall 1959.

Pharmacology. Biochemistry of neuropharmacology; metabolism of neoplastic tissues; mechanism of cardiac arrhythmias; localization of drugs using radioactive techniques; problems in human pharmacology. Recommended for graduate study: advanced courses in biological and organic chemistry. 6 professorial staff. 3 master's degrees and 4 Ph.D.'s awarded 1955-59. 5 graduate students registered fall 1959.

Physiology. Cardiac dynamics (coronary flow, work, and output); reflex regulation of respiration; gas exchange across pulmonary epithelium; factors influencing the removal and mobilization of lipids; role of lipemia clearing factor in normal and pathologically altered fat metabolism; metabolic studies of human low-density lipoproteins using immunochemical techniques. Recommended for graduate study: advanced courses in

physiology, chemistry, biochemistry. 5 professorial staff. 2 master's degrees awarded 1955-59. 2 graduate students registered fall 1959.

Hartford Seminary Foundation

HARTFORD 5, CONNECTICUT

Council for Advanced Studies

The Hartford Seminary Foundation was chartered in 1913 as an interdenominational university of religion, combining in one administration the Hartford Theological Seminary, the Hartford School of Religious Education, and the Kennedy School of Missions. An Institute of Church and Community was added in 1951. The Council for Advanced Studies was formed in 1952 and is responsible for the academic program for the Foundation's Ph.D. degree, which is offered by the Foundation as a whole, and not by the constituent schools separately. The Ed.R.D. (an advanced professional degree for religious educators) is administered by the Hartford School of Religious Education. The Foundation is controlled by a private corporation. Historically there has been a strong Congregationalist tradition, but there are no denominational requirements for trustees, students, or faculty. Both men and women are admitted.

No formal joint Ph.D. programs have been worked out as yet, but 2 master's degree programs have been established with the state university and close academic liaison has been developed with Trinity College.

Rooms in dormitories available for single men and women; 4 dormitories maintained for married students, and 3 of these are used to house postgraduates.

Special facilities include: The Case Memorial Library of 250,000 volumes; The Bissell Linguistics Laboratory; small teaching anthropological museum; concentration of other libraries and research facilities in the area.

Residence requirement for Ph.D.: minimum of 2 years beyond B.D. or M.A. No graduate credit may be transferred for 2-year minimum residence requirement, although previous graduate work is taken into consideration in determining how much more than 2 years of work at Hartford will be required.

ADMISSION REQUIREMENTS

For graduate study: bachelor's degree with high scholastic standing; B.D. with high scholastic standing; GRE. For candidacy for Ph.D.: master's degree in the intended doctoral field; reading knowledge of at least 2 languages (usually French and German with substitutes sometimes permitted); general examination; definition of subject for thesis. 1 semester course in historical method is required of all persons intending to write theses.

Apply to the Registrar by March 1.

FEES AND FIRST-YEAR AID

Application fee $10. Tuition $485 per academic year. Annual fee for field candidates $10. Semester fee for thesis supervision $25. Room (in dormitory) $200 per academic year. Approximate annual cost of board in college dining room $400 (exclusive of Sundays and vacations). Apartments $650-$920 annually.

First-year aid available: no teaching fellowships in first year; grants-in-aid as required.

Apply to the Registrar by March 1.

FIELDS OF STUDY FOR THE PH.D.

No specific courses in the methodology of teaching offered, but there is informal supervision of the teaching fellows and of graduate students teaching in neighboring institutions.

Missions Disciplines. Area studies, anthropology, linguistics. Combined program offered by the faculties of the Hartford Theological Seminary and the Kennedy School of Missions. Under the "field" program, a period of field research intervenes between the beginning and end of the academic course, and the dissertation is based primarily on the field research. 20 professorial staff. 19 master's degrees and 4 Ph.D.'s awarded 1955-59. 8 candidates registered fall 1959. Total enrollment limited to approximately present size.

Theological Disciplines. Bible, church history, theology, philosophy of religion. Combined program offered by the faculty of the Hartford Theological Seminary and Kennedy School of Missions. 20 professorial staff. 9 master's degrees and 10 Ph.D.'s awarded 1955-59. 7 candidates registered fall 1959. Total enrollment limited to approximately present size.

Harvard University

CAMBRIDGE 38, MASSACHUSETTS

Graduate School of Arts and Sciences

Graduate study has been offered at Harvard since 1872, and the first Ph.D. was conferred in 1873. Graduate School was organized in 1890. At present, membership in faculty of Arts and Sciences totals 503. University is privately controlled and nonsectarian. Only men are admitted to The College and The Graduate School of Arts and Sciences; women receive graduate instruction at Radcliffe College, an affiliated institution (*see* exhibit elsewhere in this volume), and are also admitted to some of the other graduate schools within the university.

Other doctoral degrees awarded by the university include: D.B.A. (Graduate School of Business Administration); Ed.D. (Graduate School of Education); J.S.D. (Law School); Med.Sc.D. (Faculty of Medicine); D.P.A. (Graduate School of Public Administration); D.P.H. and D.Sc. in Hygiene (School of Public Health); and Th.D. (Divinity School). Cross-registration permitted (up to half of student's program) with other graduate schools of Harvard, and with Massachusetts Institute of Technology, Episcopal Theological School, and Fletcher School of Law and Diplomacy.

Four dormitories available for students in the Graduate Schools of Arts and Sciences, Design, Education, and Public Administration; married graduate students have preference in the several apartment buildings owned by university.

Special facilities include library of over 6 million books, separate departmental libraries, laboratories.

Residence requirement for Ph.D.: 2 years full-time residence and study; up to 1 year of graduate work may be done elsewhere (by special permission after student has been enrolled for at least 1 term). Summer courses offered.

ADMISSION REQUIREMENTS

For graduate study: bachelor's degree or the equivalent and undergraduate record of distinction. Language requirements vary with program selected, but students are expected to have had college courses in foreign languages. Normally departments require 1 language before M.A. is taken and 2 languages for the Ph.D. MAT and parts of GRE required or urged by some departments. General or qualifying examination must be taken before student may do independent research on thesis.

Apply to Admissions Office by February 1.

FEES AND FIRST-YEAR AID

Application fee $10. Tuition $1,250 per academic year. Health fee $68. Room (in dormitory) $330-$400 per year. Approximate annual cost of board in college dining room $610. Apartments $80-$100 per month.

First-year aid available: scholarships, $500-$3,000; teaching fellowships $840-$3,240 (amount depends on time involved in teaching). Teaching fellows may also apply for staff tuition scholarships, maximum $800. Research assistantships and grants-in-aid are departmentally controlled.

For scholarships, apply to Admissions Office before February 1; for teaching fellowships and research assistantships, to appropriate departmental office.

FIELDS OF STUDY FOR THE PH.D.

Anthropology. Physical or biological anthropology, ethnology and social anthropology, archaeology and ethnography. *See also* "Social Relations" for other work in anthropology offered by Department of Social Relations. 35 master's degrees and 19 Ph.D.'s awarded 1955-59. 30 graduate students registered fall 1959.

Applied Mathematics. Mathematical techniques, analysis and algebra, statistics, applied mechanics, electromagnetic phenomena, information processing systems. Two programs offered by Division of Engineering and Applied Physics and the Committee on Applied Mathematics. Prerequisite for graduate study: courses in physics, mathematics, and engineering. 57 master's degrees and 22 Ph.D.'s awarded 1955-59. 51 graduate students registered fall 1959.

Applied Physics. Acoustics, solid-state physics, oceanography, meteorology, metallurgy, electronics. Offered by Division of Engineering and Applied Physics. Prerequisite for graduate study: courses in physics, mathematics, and engineering. 92 master's degrees and 57 Ph.D.'s awarded 1955-59. 101 graduate students registered fall 1959.

Architecture. Architecture, landscape architecture, city and regional planning. Offered by Joint Committee between Faculty of Arts and Sciences and Faculty of Design. Degrees awarded in each area. Program open only to Ph.D. candidates; M.A. program administered by School of Design. 3 Ph.D.'s awarded 1955-59. 2 graduate students registered fall 1959.

Astronomy. Astrophysics, the Milky Way and galaxies, radio astronomy, meteor astronomy, the earth's upper atmosphere. Prerequisites for graduate study: 2 years beyond elementary level in mathematics, physics, and astronomy. 23 master's degrees and 16 Ph.D.'s awarded 1955-59. 20 graduate students registered fall 1959.

Biochemistry. Offered by Committee on Biochemistry. *See also* "Medical Sciences" for other work in biochemistry offered by Division of Medical Sciences. Prerequisites for graduate study: basic chemistry; biology; physics; mathematics. Graduate program initiated 1955. 4 master's degrees and 1 Ph.D. awarded 1955-59. 12 graduate students registered fall 1959.

Biology. Prerequisites for graduate study: 1 full course each in zoology, botany, physics, chemistry; 1 half-course each in botany (above elementary), zoology (above elementary), physiology or biochemistry; 3 additional courses in biology or related subjects. 34 master's degrees and 76 Ph.D.'s awarded 1955-59. 62 graduate students registered fall 1959.

Celtic Languages and Literatures. Prerequisites for graduate study: preliminary study of at least 1 Celtic language, or appropriate background for Celtic; knowledge of French, German, or Latin. 1 Ph.D. awarded 1955-59.

Chemical Physics. Offered by Committee with membership from Departments of Chemistry and Physics. Program open only to Ph.D. candidates. Prerequisite: preparation in intermediate physical chemistry, physics, and mathematics. 11 Ph.D.'s awarded 1955-59. 12 graduate students registered fall 1959.

Chemistry. Analytical, biological, inorganic, organic, physical. Prerequisites for graduate study: at least 1 year each of inorganic, organic, physical, and analytical chemistry; 1 year college physics; mathematics through calculus. 102 master's degrees and 99 Ph.D.'s awarded 1955-59. 91 graduate students registered fall 1959.

The Classics. Degrees awarded in: classical philology, classical archaeology, Biblical and Patristic Greek, mediaeval Greek, mediaeval Latin, and classics and philosophy (last 3 open to Ph.D. candidates only). Offered by Department of the Classics. Prerequisites for graduate study:

for classical philology, competence in both Greek and Latin languages and composition; for classical archaeology, good knowledge of either Greek or Latin, elementary knowledge of the other; for Biblical and Patristic Greek, good command of Greek, 2 years of college Latin; for mediaeval Greek, mediaeval Latin, and classics and philosophy, M.A. in classical philology. Recommended: B.A. in classics. 21 master's degrees and 17 Ph.D.'s awarded 1955-59. 35 graduate students registered fall 1959.

Comparative Literature. Classical, mediaeval, Renaissance, modern. Prerequisite for graduate study: secure control in original language of literatures to be studied. Recommended: 1 classical and 2 modern languages. 23 master's degrees and 11 Ph.D.'s awarded 1955-59. 23 graduate students registered fall 1959.

Economics. Economic history, theory, and statistics; business economics. Recommended for graduate study: GRE Aptitude Test. 85 master's degrees and 108 Ph.D.'s awarded 1955-59. 102 graduate students registered fall 1959.

Education. Offered by joint committee between Faculty of Arts and Sciences and Faculty of Education. Program open to Ph.D. candidates only. Prerequisites: evidence of capacity to do independent graduate work and interest in a scholarly career in education (as opposed to professional career of Ed.D.); breadth in philosophy and social science. 4 Ph.D.'s awarded 1955-59. 6 graduate students registered fall 1959.

Engineering. Civil, sanitary, soils, mechanical, electronic. Offered by Division of Engineering and Applied Physics. Prerequisite for graduate study: courses in physics, mathematics, and engineering. 143 master's degrees and 25 Ph.D.'s awarded 1955-59. 57 graduate students registered fall 1959.

English. Ph.D. candidacy prerequisites: M.A. degree (including written examination in English and American literature); satisfactory course record; knowledge of 1 ancient and 1 modern language. 91 master's degrees and 93 Ph.D.'s awarded 1955-59. 146 graduate students registered fall 1959.

Far Eastern Languages. Chinese, Japanese, Korean, Mongolian, Prerequisite for graduate study: special knowledge or aptitude in the field. 4 master's degrees and 1 Ph.D. awarded 1955-59. 11 graduate students registered fall 1959.

Fine Arts. Recommended for graduate study: study of history of art; reading knowledge of

German and either French or Italian. 28 master's degrees and 24 Ph.D.'s awarded 1955-59. 24 graduate students registered fall 1959.

Foreign Area Studies. Administered by joint committees of fields involved. Regional studies in East Asia, Middle East, and Soviet Union lead to M.A. There are, however, a number of Ph.D. programs of combined fields, among them the following: history and Far Eastern languages; anthropology and Middle Eastern studies; economics and Middle Eastern studies; history and Middle Eastern studies; political science and Middle Eastern studies; Near Eastern languages and Middle Eastern studies.

Geology. Geology, geophysics. Offered by Division of Geological Sciences. Prerequisites for graduate study: in geology, minimum of 4 courses in geology plus 3 in two or more related sciences (physics, chemistry, mathematics, biology); in geophysics, minimum of 5 courses in mathematics and physics plus 2 courses in geology. Prerequisites for Ph.D. candidacy: 1 full year of graduate work in geology and related sciences required; M.A. preferred. 45 master's degrees and 39 Ph.D.'s awarded 1955-59. 53 graduate students registered fall 1959.

German. Germanic languages and literatures. Ph.D. programs in history of Germanic literature and thought, history of the German language, and Germanic philology. Prerequisite for graduate study: work in German language and literature approximately equal to requirement for B.A. with honors in German at Harvard. 6 master's degrees and 8 Ph.D.'s awarded 1955-59. 12 graduate students registered fall 1959.

History. 155 master's degrees and 113 Ph.D.'s awarded 1955-59. 160 graduate students registered fall 1959. New enrollment limited to approximately 50.

History of American Civilization. Program conducted by Committee on Higher Degrees in the History of American Civilization (membership from several departments) and is open to Ph.D. candidates only. Prerequisites: general knowledge of European and American history; English or another European literature; and history of philosophy; tests in 2 languages (French, German, Spanish) during first year. 11 Ph.D.'s awarded 1955-59. 16 graduate students registered fall 1959.

History of Science and Learning. Prerequisite for graduate study: major in mathematics or a natural science. Recommended: background in

French and German. 4 master's degrees and 3 Ph.D.'s awarded 1955-59. 10 graduate students registered fall 1959.

Linguistics. For Ph.D. program, emphasis may be on combination of linguistic fields or on geographical area. Prerequisite for graduate study: undergraduate or equivalent training in at least 1 foreign language and literature. Ph.D. candidacy prerequisite: work in 1 linguistic field, either ancient or modern or a combination. 17 master's degrees and 11 Ph.D.'s awarded 1955-59. 13 graduate students registered fall 1959.

Mathematics. Recommended for graduate study: concentration in mathematics or physics. 85 master's degrees and 33 Ph.D.'s awarded 1955-59. 73 graduate students registered fall 1959.

Medical Sciences. Degree programs in anatomy, bacteriology, biochemistry, biophysics, pathology, pharmacology, and physiology. Offered by Division of Medical Sciences. Prerequisite for graduate study: sound training in chemistry, biology, and physics. Biochemistry and biophysics require mathematics also, and biochemistry requires a reading knowledge of German and another modern language. Recommended for pharmacology: courses in mathematics, statistics, physical chemistry. 22 master's degrees and 32 Ph.D.'s awarded 1955-59. 27 graduate students registered fall 1959.

Music. Prerequisites for graduate study: preentrance examinations in harmony and counterpoint, history and literature of music, piano playing, which includes both performance of prepared pieces and sight reading test (exceptions for Harvard and Radcliffe B.A.'s with honors in music). Recommended: reading knowledge of French and German. Ph.D. candidacy prerequisites: M.A. in music (if M.A. was not earned at Harvard, examinations listed above plus written examination in French or German and an interview if possible). 35 master's degrees and 12 Ph.D.'s awarded 1955-59. 19 graduate students registered fall 1959.

Near Eastern Languages and Literatures. Prerequisite for graduate study: equivalent of 2 courses in Hebrew or Arabic. For Ph.D. candidacy: advanced knowledge of 1 Semitic language. 4 master's degrees and 4 Ph.D.'s awarded 1955-59. 4 graduate students registered fall 1959.

Philosophy. Philosophy; philosophy and classics. Latter open to Ph.D. candidates only. Pre-

requisites for graduate study: for philosophy, creditable record in philosophy, broad training in humanities, or training in natural or social sciences; for philosophy and classics, background in both philosophy and classics. 33 master's degrees and 29 Ph.D.'s awarded 1955-59. 60 graduate students registered fall 1959.

Physics. "Pure physics" (nuclear structure, nuclear radiations, nuclear magnetism, elementary particle physics, atomic and molecular physics). Prerequisite for graduate study: good preparation in intermediate physics and in mathematics. Prerequisite for Ph.D. candidacy: at least 2 terms of graduate work with high record; for experimental work, demonstrated promise of skill plus understanding of theoretical physics; for theoretical physics, strong record in mathematical courses plus acquaintance with experimental physics. 121 master's degrees and 66 Ph.D.'s awarded 1955-59. 118 graduate students registered fall 1959.

Political Economy and Government. Offered by Committee on Higher Degrees in Political Economy and Government. 14 master's degrees and 28 Ph.D.'s awarded 1955-59.

Political Science. Political thought and institutions, American constitutional law, national government of the United States, state and local government, comparative modern government (with special attention to Great Britain, France, Germany, or another suitable state), comparative legislation, comparative administration, comparative public law, international relations (special attention to international law, international organization, international politics, American foreign relations, nationalism, imperialism, or other approved topic). Offered by Department of Government. Recommended for graduate study: history; political science; economics; philosophy; sociology. 24 master's degrees and 48 Ph.D.'s awarded 1955-59. 60 graduate students registered fall 1959.

Psychology. Sensation and perception, learning, motivation, physiological psychology, psycho-acoustics, experimental analysis of behavior, history of psychology. Prerequisite for graduate study: GRE Aptitude Test and/or MAT. Recommended: major in psychology or breadth of training in biology, mathematics, physics, philosophy, and social science. 10 master's degrees and 24 Ph.D.'s awarded 1955-59. 19 graduate students registered fall 1959.

Religion.—History and Philosophy. Philosophy of religion, a religion other than Judaism or Christianity, Old Testament and intertestamental Judaism, New Testament and Christian origins, church history, Christian theology, religious ethics, religion and society. Offered by Committee on Higher Degrees in the History and Philosophy of Religion (membership from Faculty of Arts and Sciences and Divinity School). Prerequisites for graduate study: general, broad preparation in philosophy, languages, history, and social sciences; for philosophy of religion, history of philosophy and ability to use Latin texts; for religion other than Judaism or Christianity, knowledge of languages necessary for study of religion chosen; for Old Testament and intertestamental Judaism, 2 years Hebrew; for New Testament and Christian origins, 2 years Greek; for church history, strong record in history, politics, sociology, literature, and language and proficiency in classical languages; for Christian theology, history of philosophy, history of Western religious thought and Latin proficiency; for religious ethics, advanced courses in social science and history of Western philosophy; for religion and society, background in theology equivalent to B.D. or S.T.B. degrees, or considerable advanced work in the social sciences and history. 10 master's degrees and 18 Ph.D.'s awarded 1955-59. 56 graduate students registered fall 1959.

Romance Languages and Literatures. French, Italian, Spanish, Portuguese. For Ph.D., emphasis may be placed on linguistics or on literature. Prerequisite for graduate study: major in at least 1 Romance language and its literature. 27 master's degrees and 20 Ph.D.'s awarded 1955-59. 19 graduate students registered fall 1959.

Sanskrit and Indian Studies. Prerequisite for graduate study: work in some area of Indian studies, either history or literature. Recommended: French or German. 2 master's degrees and 3 Ph.D.'s awarded 1955-59. 3 graduate students registered fall 1959.

Slavic Languages and Literatures. Russian, Polish, Czech, Serbo-Croatian, Bulgarian. For Ph.D., emphasis may be placed on literature or language. Prerequisite for graduate study: adequate knowledge of 1 Slavic language. 24 master's degrees and 14 Ph.D.'s awarded 1955-59. 34 graduate students registered fall 1959.

Social Relations. Degrees awarded in sociology, social anthropology, social psychology, clinical psychology. Prerequisites for graduate study: general, background in psychological and social sciences; MAT; GRE Aptitude Test and Advanced Test in any field; for sociology and social anthropology, background in scientific study of human social behavior; for social psychology and clinical psychology, background in general psychology, including a course in biology and a half-course in physiological psychology. 35 master's degrees and 85 Ph.D.'s awarded 1955-59. 87 graduate students registered fall 1959.

Statistics. Theory of statistics, applied statistics. Prerequisites for graduate study: good mathematical background, including analytic geometry, differential and integral calculus. Ph.D. program initiated 1957. 1 master's degree and 1 Ph.D. awarded 1955-59. 15 graduate students registered fall 1959.

Hawaii, University of

HONOLULU, HAWAII

The Graduate School

Graduate instruction has been offered by the university through its Graduate Division since 1910 and the first Ph.D. was awarded in 1933. The Graduate School was organized in 1950. The university is publicly controlled by the state. Both men and women are admitted.

No residence facilities for graduate students are provided.

Proximity to Hawaii Marine Laboratory, U.S. Bureau of Commercial Fisheries, Honolulu Biological Laboratory, and Bishop Museum provides additional facilties for research. University Graduate School Faculty is supplemented by Affiliate Graduate Faculty, composed of senior scientists in closely associated private and governmental research institutes and laboratories.

Residence requirements for Ph.D.: 6 semesters, 3 of which must be taken at the University of Hawaii. Summer courses available in some fields.

ADMISSION REQUIREMENTS

For graduate study: bachelor's degree; high GPA. For candidacy for Ph.D.: 2 foreign languages (as determined by faculty committee); qualifying examinations.

Apply to Dean of the Graduate School at any time.

FEES AND FIRST-YEAR AID

No application fee. Tuition $180 a year. Approximate annual cost of board in college dining room $500-$600.

First-year aid available: 26 scholarships, $2,000-$2,500; 40 teaching fellowships, $2,000 (half-time); 40 research assistantships, $2,300 (half-time).

Write to the Dean of the Graduate School for information as to the time application should be made for the particular type of aid desired.

FIELDS OF STUDY FOR THE PH.D.

Botany. Marine botany, plant physiology. Prerequisite for graduate study: 18 semester hours of appropriate work, including cryptograms, physiology, taxonomy, anatomy, and morphology. Recommended: bacteriology and chemistry. 11 professorial staff. 8 master's degrees and 1 Ph.D. awarded 1955-59. 9 graduate students registered fall 1959.

Chemistry and Biochemistry. Inorganic, analytical, organic, biological, or physical chemistry. Offered by Department of Chemistry. Prerequisites for graduate study: general and organic chemistry; qualitative analysis; quantitative analysis; physical chemistry. 15 professorial staff. 11 master's degrees and 4 Ph.D.'s awarded 1955-59. 42 graduate students registered fall 1959.

Entomology. Taxonomy, ecology, biological control, toxicology. Offered by Department of Zoology and Entomology. Prerequisites for graduate study: general zoology; general entomology; economic entomology; insect morphology; systematic entomology. Recommended: organic and inorganic chemistry; physics; algebra; botany; genetics. 13 professorial staff. 2 master's degrees awarded 1955-59. 10 graduate students registered fall 1959.

Genetics. Offered by the Graduate Field of Genetics. Prerequisites for graduate study: genetics; botany; chemistry; entomology; mathematics; and zoology. 5 professorial staff. 1 Ph.D. awarded 1955-59. 9 graduate students registered fall 1959.

Psychology. General, social, developmental, experimental, and applied industrial psychology. Prerequisites for graduate study: 26 semester hours of psychology, including general or experi-

mental psychology, or history of psychology; GRE. Recommended: algebra; general zoology. 12 professorial staff. Ph.D. program initiated 1958. 22 master's degrees awarded 1955-59. 25 graduate students registered fall 1959.

Soil Science. Soil physics, tropical soil genesis, classification, soil management, weathering of soils, fundamental physical and chemical properties of soils. Prerequisites for graduate study: 18 semester hours in soil science and related fields; 2 years of college chemistry. 6 professorial staff. 10 master's degrees awarded 1955-59. 14 graduate students registered fall 1959.

Zoology. Marine aspects. Offered by Department of Zoology and Entomology. Prerequisite for graduate study: 18 semester hours in field, including comparative anatomy, embryology, general physiology. Recommended: 2 years of chemistry; 1 year of physics; courses in algebra and botany. 12 professorial staff. 3 master's degrees and 4 Ph.D.'s awarded 1955-59. 30 graduate students registered fall 1959.

Hebrew Union College—Jewish Institute of Religion

CINCINNATI 20, OHIO

The Graduate School

In conjunction with the rabbinic training program, the college has offered graduate instruction since 1875. The Graduate School was formally organized in 1947, and the first Ph.D. conferred in 1951. The D.H.L. is also awarded. Institution is privately controlled. Both men and women are admitted.

A joint program has been established with the University of Cincinnati, under which graduate students may register in either institution for courses in the areas of classics, history, Bible, and philosophy. Fees are paid exclusively to the institution in which degree is being sought.

Rooms in dormitories available for single graduate students.

Residence requirements for Ph.D.: 2 years; up to 32 hours of graduate credit may be transferred from other institutions.

ADMISSION REQUIREMENTS

Bachelor's degree; specific preparation for-

graduate work in field. For candidacy for Ph.D.:
2 foreign languages other than Hebrew (usually
German and French); candidacy examination.

Apply to the Chairman, Committee on Graduate Study, between September 1 and March 1.

FEES AND FIRST-YEAR AID

No application fee. Tuition $500 per year.
Dormitory fee (including room and board) $900
per year.

First-year aid available: resident Interfaith
Fellowships with stipend of $3,000 for married
students and $2,400 for single students.

Apply to the Chairman, Committee on Graduate Study, before February 1.

FIELDS OF STUDY FOR THE PH.D.

Hebraic and Cognate Studies. Bible, Jewish
history, rabbinics, Hebrew literature, Semitic and
non-Semitic Oriental languages and literatures,
Jewish religious thought and education. Student
elects 1 major and 2 minors from above areas.
Prerequisites: bachelor's degree (usually B.D.)
for Interfaith Fellows; M.A. in Hebrew Letters
for rabbinical graduate students. Additional language courses sometimes required for a specific
field chosen by candidate. 16 professorial staff.
7 Ph.D.'s awarded 1955-59. 22 graduate students registered fall 1959.

Houston, University of

HOUSTON 4, TEXAS

The Graduate School

Graduate work was first offered in 1939. Doctoral programs were added gradually beginning
in 1945. The Graduate School was organized and
the first Ph.D. conferred in 1953. Ed.D. degree is
also awarded (through the College of Education).
Although privately administered and financed,
university receives some financial support from
the state. Both men and women are admitted.

Room in dormitories available for single graduate students; no residence facilities provided for
married students.

Library contains approximately 205,000 volumes and has special collections on the history of
architecture, art, the Far East, Texas, geology,
and law.

Residence requirement for Ph.D.: 4 semesters
of graduate study beyond master's degree or
equivalent, of which 1 year must be spent in continuous residence on campus. Up to 60 credit
hours of graduate work may be transferred from
other institutions.

ADMISSION REQUIREMENTS

For graduate study: bachelor's degree; 2.5
GPA; major in selected field. For candidacy for
Ph.D.: B average in all graduate work; approval
of faculty; qualifying examinations; reading examination in 2 foreign languages.

Apply to Dean of the Graduate School by
September 1 for fall term; by January 15 for
spring term; by May 20 for first summer term;
by July 10 for second summer term.

FEES AND FIRST-YEAR AID

Application fee $5. Tuition approximately
$675 per year. Registration fee $6. Room (in dormitory) approximately $120 per semester; cafeteria available.

First-year aid available: 6 scholarships, $250-
$1,312; 68 teaching assistantships, $600-$2,000;
23 other fellowships, $1,000-$5,300; 35 research
assistantships, $400-$2,400.

Apply to department chairman before April 1.

FIELDS OF STUDY FOR THE PH.D.

Biology. Microbiology and physiology. Prerequisite for graduate study: master's degree in a
natural science or completion of 24 hours of
graduate work. 7 professorial staff. Ph.D. program initiated 1960. 14 master's degrees awarded
1955-59. 17 graduate students registered fall
1959.

Chemistry. Inorganic, organic, physical, and
analytical chemistry. Prerequisite for graduate
study: satisfactory completion of diagnostic examinations in basic fields of chemistry. 6 professorial staff. Ph.D. program initiated 1960. 13
master's degrees awarded 1955-59. 26 graduate
students registered fall 1959.

Economics. Economics, business administration, and a related field. Offered by Department
of Economics and Finance. Prerequisite for graduate study: 18 semester hours of economics.
Ph.D. candidacy prerequisites: reading knowledge of French and German; proficiency in 2 of
3 tool subjects (accounting, statistics, or mathematics). 5 professorial staff. Ph.D. program

initiated 1959. 12 master's degrees awarded 1955-59. 25 graduate students registered fall 1959.

Engineering. — Chemical. Prerequisite for graduate study: M.S. in the field or 24 hours of graduate work. 7 professorial staff. Ph.D. program initiated 1959. 5 master's degrees awarded 1955-59. 26 graduate students registered fall 1959.

Psychology. Business and industrial, clinical, counseling, educational, and general psychology. 14 professorial staff. 36 master's degrees and 38 Ph.D.'s awarded 1955-59. 83 graduate students registered fall 1959.

Howard University

WASHINGTON 1, D. C.

The Graduate School

Howard has been offering graduate instruction at the master's level since 1919, and the Graduate School was organized in 1934. Doctoral programs have been established in recent years with the first Ph.D. being awarded in 1958. University is privately controlled and nonsectarian. Both men and women are admitted.

Rooms in dormitories available for single graduate students; no special residence facilities provided for married students.

Library contains approximately 354,000 volumes. Location in Washington, D. C., affords access to many facilities of the various departments of the Federal Government.

Residence requirement for Ph.D.: 6 semesters of full-time residence in graduate study or equivalent; 4 semesters must be spent in residence at Howard and 2 must be consecutive. Summer courses available. School day extends from 8 a.m. to 8 p.m.

ADMISSION REQUIREMENTS

For graduate study: bachelor's degree; recommendation of major department. For candidacy for Ph.D.: qualifying examination; examinations in 2 foreign languages (preferably French and German); GRE; junior comprehensive examination in English; recommendation of major department; approval of Graduate Council.

Apply to Director of Admissions at any time,

but preferably at least 6 weeks before date of desired entry.

FEES AND FIRST-YEAR AID

No application fee. Matriculation fee $10. Tuition $225 per academic year ($7.50 per semester hour). Special fees approximate $38.50. Room (in dormitory) $270 a year for single room; $216 for double room. Approximate annual cost of board in college dining room $400.

First-year aid available: approximately 17 scholarships, tuition and fees up to $247.50; approximately 15 teaching fellowships, $2,100; approximately 14 other fellowships, $663-$1,800; approximately 50 research assistantships, $650-$1,750; 2 grants-in-aid, $2,300.

Apply to head of major department or Dean of the Graduate School by April 1.

FIELDS OF STUDY FOR THE PH.D.

Informal instruction in teaching provided for most teaching fellows.

Chemistry. Analytical, inorganic, physical, and organic chemistry; biochemistry. Prerequisite for graduate study: 3 years of chemistry. 10 professorial staff. Ph.D. program initiated 1955. 21 master's degrees and 5 Ph.D.'s awarded 1955-59. 54 graduate students registered fall 1959.

Physics. Biophysics; experimental or theoretical physics. Prerequisites for graduate study: physical mechanics; electricity and magnetism; acoustics; heat and thermodynamics; optics; atomic physics. 8 professorial staff. Ph.D. program initiated 1959. 23 master's degrees awarded 1955-59. 29 graduate students registered fall 1959.

Physiology. Heart, circulation, and kidney endocrinology. Offered by Department of Physiology in the College of Medicine. Prerequisites for graduate study: bachelor's degree or M.D. degree; 2 years of research; minor in 1 of the medical or allied basic sciences. Recommended: master's degree. 8 professorial staff. Ph.D. program initiated 1959. 3 master's degrees awarded 1955-59. 5 graduate students registered fall 1959. New registration limited to 3.

Zoology. Cytology, endocrinology, experimental embryology, genetics (insects), physiology of parasites, protozoology. 9 professorial staff. Ph.D. program initiated 1959. 21 master's degrees awarded 1955-59. 23 graduate students registered fall 1959. New registration limited to 5.

Idaho, University of

MOSCOW, IDAHO

The Graduate School

Graduate instruction has been offered since 1897, and the Graduate School was organized in 1925. No Ph.D.'s have been awarded to date, but programs leading to this degree were established in a number of fields in 1959, as well as a program leading to the Ed.D. degree which is offered by the College of Education. Institution is a land-grant university, controlled by the state. Both men and women are admitted.

Rooms in dormitories available for single graduate students; room and board may also be obtained in community. University maintains a number of apartment units for married students (limited to couples with 1 child); other apartments available in community.

Special facilities include: 7,000-acre experimental forest located near the campus; a radio-isotopes laboratory; library containing approximately 200,000 volumes.

Residence requirement for Ph.D.: 2 years of study beyond master's degree, at least 2 semesters of which must be spent in full-time study in continuous residence on campus. 10 graduate credits may be transferred towards master's degree; amount transferrable toward doctorate individually determined. Summer courses available.

ADMISSION REQUIREMENTS

For graduate study: bachelor's degree; acceptable academic record; 1 foreign language in some fields (or deficiency status). Recommended: letters of recommendation. For candidacy for Ph.D.: reading knowledge of 2 foreign languages approved by student's committee; preliminary examinations in major and minor fields; A or B grades in most of required course work.

Apply to Registrar by August 15 for fall term; by January 1 for spring term.

FEES AND FIRST-YEAR AID

Application fee $5 for out-of-state students; none for state residents. No tuition for graduate students. Special fees approximate $120 annually. Room (in dormitory) $255 for 2 semesters. Board in college dining room $450 for 2 semesters. Apartments $72.50 per month.

First-year aid available: tuition scholarships for all graduate students; teaching fellowships in many divisions, $1,500 for 9 months; some industrial fellowships, $1,500-$2,000; research assistantships in many divisions, $1,500 for 9 months or $2,100 for 12 months. Students may also be employed on research projects at salaries of $1,500 and up.

Apply to the Dean of the Graduate School by April 1.

FIELDS OF STUDY FOR THE PH.D.

Several courses in the methodology of teaching are offered by the College of Education and may be elected by Ph.D. candidates who have necessary prerequisites.

Agricultural Chemistry. Biological chemistry, food technology, soil chemistry. 5 professorial staff. Ph.D. program initiated 1959. 4 master's degrees awarded 1955-59. 4 graduate students registered fall 1959. Enrollment limited to 10 students.

Botany. Systematic botany, ecology, plant physiology, anatomy, mycology. Offered by Department of Biological Sciences. 6 professorial staff. Ph.D. program initiated 1959. 3 master's degrees awarded 1955-59. 2 graduate students registered fall 1959. Enrollment limited to 6.

Chemistry. Physical, organic, inorganic. Offered by Department of Physical Sciences. 9 professorial staff. Ph.D. program initiated 1959. 11 master's degrees awarded 1955-59. 12 graduate students registered fall 1959.

Education.—Administration. Offered by the College of Education. 6 professorial staff. Ph.D. program initiated 1959. 284 master's degrees awarded 1955-59. 25 graduate students registered fall 1959 (about 300 in summer session). New registration limited to 3 or 4 students per year.

Entomology. Systematic, forest, or economic entomology; insect physiology or ecology. 5 professorial staff. Ph.D. program initiated 1959. 3 master's degrees awarded 1955-59. 3 graduate students registered fall 1959. Enrollment limited to 4.

Forestry. Forest, range, fisheries, or wildlife management. 13 professorial staff. Ph.D. program initiated 1959. 48 master's degrees awarded 1955-59. 21 graduate students registered fall 1959. Registration limited to 10.

History. American history (primarily western). Offered by Department of Social Sciences.

4 professorial staff. Ph.D. program initiated 1959. 5 master's degrees awarded 1955-59. 7 graduate students registered fall 1959. Enrollment limited to 10.

Mathematics. Applied mathematics, mathematical statistics. 7 professorial staff. Ph.D. program initiated 1959. 5 master's degrees awarded 1955-59. 17 graduate students registered fall 1959. Enrollment limited to 20.

Political Science. Public administration, state and local government, international relations. 5 professorial staff. Ph.D. program initiated 1959. 4 master's degrees awarded 1955-59. 3 graduate students registered fall 1959. Enrollment limited to 10.

Zoology. Herpetology, mammalogy, ornithology, parasitology. Offered by Department of Biological Sciences. 4 professorial staff. Ph.D. program initiated 1959. 5 master's degrees awarded 1955-59. 5 graduate students registered fall 1959. Enrollment limited to 6.

Illinois Institute of Technology

CHICAGO 16, ILLINOIS

The Graduate School

The institute was established in 1940 by a merger of Armour Institute of Technology (founded 1892) and Lewis Institute (founded 1896). The Graduate School had been established 3 years earlier, and first Ph.D. was awarded in 1939. Institute is privately controlled and nonsectarian. Both men and women are admitted.

Rooms in dormitories available for single graduate students; apartments of varying sizes for married students.

Special facilities include: A.C. network calculator; x-ray diffraction unit; 1.75-MEV electrostatic generator for acceleration of hydrogen and helium ions; IBM 650 digital computer and auxiliary equipment. Armour Research Foundation, an affiliated institution, has 50-KW nuclear reactor and a Univac 1105 and auxiliary equipment. A liaison committee may arrange for certain training and research with Argonne National Laboratories for particular doctoral candidates.

Residence requirement for Ph.D.: usually 3 years beyond bachelor's degree, of which a minimum of 1 year must be spent in residence at Illinois Institute of Technology. Limited number of summer and evening courses may be used in doctoral programs.

ADMISSION REQUIREMENTS

For graduate study: bachelor's degree; B average; major in field of specialization; transcripts of academic work; letters of recommendation. No tests are required routinely for admission, but GRE and other examinations may be required in special cases. For candidacy for Ph.D.: reading knowledge of 2 foreign languages (student may petition to substitute another tool of research for 1 language); removal of all entrance deficiencies; completion of 32 semester hours credit (or master's degree) in field; qualifying comprehensive examination.

Apply to Office of Admissions, Illinois Institute of Technology, at any time.

FEES AND FIRST-YEAR AID

No application fee. Tuition approximately $32 per semester credit hour with a minimum of $475 (except for evening students for whom there is no minimum) and a maximum of $950 per academic year. Room (in dormitory) $310 per academic year. Approximate annual cost of board in college dining room $440. Apartments $67.50-$180 per month.

First-year aid available: 10 tuition scholarships; 60 teaching fellowships, $1,800-$2,025 plus tuition; 25 other fellowships, $1,500-$3,000 plus tuition; 50 research assistantships, $2,350-$2,575; 6 grants-in-aid, $2,350-$2,575.

Apply to Admissions Office, The Graduate School, before March 1.

FIELDS OF STUDY FOR THE PH.D.

Architecture. Structural approach to architecture. 5 professorial staff. 22 master's degrees awarded 1955-59. 16 graduate students registered fall 1959.

Bacteriology. Amino-acid metabolism in yeasts, effect of freezing on bacterial viability. Offered by Department of Biology. Prerequisites for graduate study: botany or zoology; quantitative analysis; 2 semesters of organic chemistry; college physics; mathematics through integral calculus. 4 professorial staff. 9 master's degrees and 4 Ph.D.'s awarded 1955-59. 6 graduate students registered fall 1959.

Biochemistry. Enzymology (active transport and nucleic acid metabolism). Offered by Department of Biology. 4 professorial staff. 5 master's degrees and 3 Ph.D.'s awarded 1955-59. 26 graduate students registered fall 1959.

Biology. 4 professorial staff. 20 graduate students registered fall 1959.

Business and Economics. Economics, management. 9 professorial staff. 13 master's degrees and 3 Ph.D.'s awarded 1955-59. 86 graduate students registered fall 1959.

Chemistry. Physical, organic, inorganic. Prerequisite for graduate study: minimum of 1 year training (including laboratory) in general, analytical, organic, and physical chemistry. 15 professorial staff. 11 master's degrees and 33 Ph.D.'s awarded 1955-59. 78 graduate students registered fall 1959.

City and Regional Planning. 2 professorial staff. 8 master's degrees and 1 Ph.D. awarded 1955-59. 15 graduate students registered fall 1959.

Engineering. — Chemical. Reactor design, process dynamics, back-mixing in equipment, mass transfer in dispersal systems, bubble and drop phenomena, equations of state, application of computer techniques to chemical engineering calculations, heat transfer to gases at low pressure, drying. 6 professorial staff. 48 master's degrees and 15 Ph.D.'s awarded 1955-59. 77 graduate students registered fall 1959.

Engineering.—Civil. Structural, sanitary engineering. 7 professorial staff. 31 master's degrees and 4 Ph.D.'s awarded 1955-59. 90 graduate students registered fall 1959.

Engineering.—Electrical. Energy conversion and utilization, electronics and communication. 8 professorial staff. 95 master's degrees and 10 Ph.D.'s awarded 1955-59. 157 graduate students registered fall 1959.

Engineering.—Gas. Offered by Institute of Gas Technology (affiliated department). Prerequisite for graduate study: major in gas technology, or major in physical science or engineering with minor in gas technology. 5 professorial staff. 1 master's degree awarded 1955-59. 6 graduate students registered fall 1959.

Engineering.—Industrial. Engineering economics, industrial statistics, computers and data processing, operations research, automation and manufacturing methods. 3 professorial staff. 20 master's degrees and 3 Ph.D.'s awarded 1955-59. 43 graduate students registered fall 1959.

Engineering.—Mechanical. Aircraft and missile propulsion, heat transfer, dynamics of machinery and vibrations, gas dynamics. 9 professorial staff. 86 master's degrees and 11 Ph.D.'s awarded 1955-59. 159 graduate students registered fall 1959.

Engineering.—Metallurgical. Physical metallurgy. 5 professorial staff. 16 master's degrees and 6 Ph.D.'s awarded 1955-59. 31 graduate students registered fall 1959.

Mathematics. 12 professorial staff. 16 master's degrees and 11 Ph.D.'s awarded 1955-59. 60 graduate students registered fall 1959.

Mechanics. Dynamics, experimental stress analysis, fluid or solid mechanics. 7 professorial staff. 13 master's degrees and 15 Ph.D.'s awarded 1955-59. 38 graduate students registered fall 1959.

Physics. Solid-state, nuclear, theoretical physics. 8 professorial staff. 26 master's degrees and 23 Ph.D.'s awarded 1955-59. 85 graduate students registered fall 1959.

Physiology. Cellular physiology, study of active transport, carbohydrate metabolism in protozoa. Offered by Department of Biology. 4 professorial staff. 2 graduate students registered fall 1959.

Psychology. Offered by Department of Psychology and Education. 7 professorial staff. 18 master's degrees and 19 Ph.D.'s awarded 1955-59. 50 graduate students registered fall 1959.

Illinois, University of

URBANA, ILLINOIS

The university was founded in 1867. Advanced degree programs were offered as early as 1874, and the first Ph.D. was conferred in 1903. At present, Ph.D. programs are offered through the Graduate College at Urbana and the Graduate College Division at the Chicago Professional Colleges. These are described below. Other doctoral degrees conferred include: Ed.D., D.Mus.Ed., J.S.D., D.B.A., and D.Mus.A. University is publicly controlled by the state. Both men and women are admitted.

The Graduate College

Founded 1908.

Residence halls available for single graduate students; apartments for married students.

Special facilities include: library of over 3,200,000 volumes; special laboratories (digital computer, electron microscope, radiocarbon, ultracentrifuge, etc.); physical environment unit; Illinois Historical Survey.

Residence requirement for Ph.D.: 3 years of full-time study beyond baccalaureate, 2 of which must be taken in residence at the university. Summer and a few evening courses available.

ADMISSION REQUIREMENTS

For graduate study: scholastic average of at least 3.5 (A being 5) computed on basis of last 60 hours of work completed; approval of major department (which may require a higher average). Recommended: proficiency in at least 1 foreign language. For candidacy for Ph.D.: reading proficiency in 2 modern foreign languages (selected from French, German, or Russian); preliminary examination.

Apply to the Office of Admissions and Records, Graduate Division, University of Illinois, Urbana, Illinois, at least 6 weeks prior to date of desired registration.

FEES AND FIRST-YEAR AID

No application fee. Tuition for state residents $150 per academic year; others $500. Special fees approximate $50 annually. Room (in residence hall) $456 for double room for 12 months. Board in college dining hall averages $474 per academic year. Apartments $47-$120 per month.

First-year aid available: 50 teaching fellowships, $2,000 per academic year; 200 other fellowships, at least $1,500 per academic year; 2,000 teaching or research assistantships, $1,900 per academic year for half-time; 425 tuition and fee waivers which carry no stipend.

Apply to Graduate College, Urbana, Illinois, or to major department by February 15.

FIELDS OF STUDY FOR THE PH.D.

Accountancy Prerequisites for graduate study: 20 hours of work in accountancy: at least 1 course in economics and 1 in finance. 19 professorial staff. 61 master's degrees and 26 Ph.D.'s awarded 1955-59. 57 graduate students registered fall 1959.

Agricultural Economics. Farm management, marketing, land economics, rural sociology, prices and statistics, agricultural finance. Prerequisites for graduate study: major in agriculture; 12 hours of agricultural economics and economics; at least 8 hours in accountancy, business law, or social science. 20 professorial staff. 68 master's degrees and 29 Ph.D.'s awarded 1955-59. 48 graduate students registered fall 1959.

Agronomy. Soil fertility, plant genetics, soil morphology, genesis and classification, soil chemistry, crop production, plant chemistry, crop physiology, forage crops, pasture management, biometry, soil physics, soil management, cytogenetics, physical edaphology, soil biology, weed control. Prerequisites for graduate study: proficiency in crop and soil areas; supporting sciences. 34 professorial staff. 80 master's degrees and 40 Ph.D.'s awarded 1955-59. 72 graduate students registered fall 1959.

Animal Science. Population and immunogenetics; physiology of reproduction, including endocrinology; animal nutrition; nutritional biochemistry; meats technology. Prerequisite for graduate study: courses in biological and physical sciences and mathematics. 24 professorial staff. 47 master's degrees and 53 Ph.D.'s awarded 1955-59. 47 graduate students registered fall 1959.

Anthropology. American Indian, India, Southeast Asia, archaeology, ethnology, contemporary culture change. Recommended for graduate study: major in anthropology or social science. 7 professorial staff. Ph.D. program begun 1958. 4 master's degrees awarded 1955-59. 9 graduate students registered fall 1959.

Astronomy. Cosmology, galactic structure, radio-astronomy. Prerequisite for graduate study: major in astronomy, mathematics, physics, electrical engineering, or engineering physics. Recommended (required for Ph.D. candidacy): 1-year course in descriptive astronomy. 5 professorial staff. Ph.D. program begun in 1958. 3 master's degrees awarded 1955-59. 4 graduate students registered fall 1959.

Biophysics. Special interdisciplinary programs are available for students who wish to major in biophysics and biophysical chemistry (molecular biology). Recommended for graduate study: background in one of the physical or biological sciences; mathematics through calculus. Program begun 1957. 1 master's degree and 3 Ph.D.'s awarded 1955-59. 3 graduate students registered fall 1959.

Botany. Genetics, morphology, taxonomy, ecology and physiology (corn genetics, physiological genetics, cellular physiology, paleobotany, mycology, and phycology). Prerequisite for graduate study: basic knowledge in specific fields of concentration listed above. Recommended: organic chemistry and biochemistry. 14 professorial staff. 26 master's degrees and 20 Ph.D.'s awarded 1955-59. 30 graduate students registered fall 1959.

Business. Concentration in economic theory, management, and marketing required, plus two additional areas. Interdepartmental program. Prerequisite for graduate study: basic work in accountancy, economics, management, and marketing. 15 Ph.D.'s awarded 1955-59. 30 graduate students registered in fall of 1959.

Chemistry and Chemical Engineering. Analytical chemistry; biochemistry; chemical engineering; inorganic, organic, and physical chemistry. Prerequisites for graduate study: calculus; physics; chemistry courses, including a year of physical chemistry. 50 professorial staff. 186 master's degrees and 287 Ph.D.'s awarded 1955-59. 335 graduate students registered fall 1959.

Classics. Greek and Latin languages and literatures; if 1 language is the major, the other must be the sole minor or 1 of 2 minors. Prerequisite for graduate study: at least 2 years of college Latin (beyond 4 years in high school) or 3 years college Greek. Recommended: at least 2 years of a modern foreign language, preferably French or German. 6 professorial staff. 10 master's degrees and 5 Ph.D.'s awarded 1955-59. 7 graduate students registered fall 1959.

Communications. Concentration in public opinion and attitude formation, communications policies and structures, advertising, interpersonal communication, psycholinguistics, linguistics, experimental phonetics. An interdepartmental program. Prerequisite for graduate study: major in the social sciences. 22 Ph.D. degrees awarded 1955-59. 33 graduate students registered fall 1959.

Dairy Science. Bacteriology, microbiology, biochemistry, genetics, nutrition, physiology. Prerequisites for graduate study: major in dairy science or in any of above-named areas of concentration. 11 professorial staff. 31 master's de-

grees and 13 Ph.D.'s awarded 1955-59. 20 graduate students registered fall 1959.

Economics. Economic theory, history of economic thought, public finance and taxation, monetary theory, international economics, labor economics, transportation, economic statistics, econometrics, quantitative economic analysis. Prerequisites for graduate study: 27 hours of work in social science, 15 of which must have been in economics (including a course in principles and a course in statistics). 30 professorial staff. 57 master's degrees and 37 Ph.D.'s awarded 1955-59. 84 graduate students registered fall 1959.

Education. Agricultural education, child development, curriculum, educational psychology, guidance and counseling, home economics education, industrial education, measurement and evaluation, school administration and supervision, school psychology (offered in cooperation with Department of Psychology), social foundations of education, social psychology and its application to education, special education of exceptional children, statistical and research methods, teaching (elementary or secondary), teacher education, and teacher personnel problems. 78 professorial staff. 70 master's degrees and 43 Ph.D.'s awarded 1955-59. 522 graduate students registered fall 1959. The Ed.D. degree is also awarded in this area.

Engineering.—Aeronautical. Aeronautical engineering and astronautics; aerodynamics (subsonic, supersonic, hypersonic, magneto-aerodynamics, aerodynamic heating); propulsion (air-breathing reaction engines, chemical rockets, electrical propulsion systems); structures (theory of structures at normal and elevated temperatures, aeroelasticity, aeroviscoelasticity); vehicle dynamics (performance, control, and stability of airplanes, missiles, and space vehicles). Prerequisite for graduate study: previous study in engineering, the physical sciences, or mathematics. 7 professorial staff. 30 master's degrees and 6 Ph.D.'s awarded 1955-59. 22 graduate students registered fall 1959.

Engineering.—Ceramic Engineering and Ceramics. Refractories and high temperature materials; porcelain enamels; glass; whitewares; structural clay products; electrical, solid-state, and nuclear ceramics and materials. Prerequisites for graduate study: for ceramic engineering, an undergraduate degree in engineering; for ceramics, an engineering or scientific major. 7 professorial staff. 29 master's degrees and 12 Ph.D.'s awarded 1955-59. 15 graduate students registered fall 1959.

Engineering.—Civil and Sanitary. Structural engineering (including structural dynamics), soil mechanics and foundation engineering, hydraulic engineering, highway engineering, traffic engineering, transportation, surveying and photogrammetry, sanitary engineering. 38 professorial staff. 381 master's degrees and 39 Ph.D.'s awarded 1955-59. 234 graduate students registered fall 1959.

Engineering.—Electrical. Electronics, power, communication, physical electronics, servomechanisms, circuits. Prerequisite for graduate study: B.S. in electrical engineering, physics, or other areas of engineering. 57 professorial staff. 253 master's degrees and 67 Ph.D.'s awarded 1955-59. 219 graduate students registered fall 1959.

Engineering.—Mechanical. Thermodynamics, gas dynamics, heat transfer, machine design, production. Prerequisite for graduate study: solid background in higher mathematics (through differential equations, advanced calculus, and complex variables). 29 professorial staff. 114 master's degrees and 15 Ph.D.'s awarded 1955-59. 107 graduate students registered fall 1959.

Engineering.—Metallurgical. Point defects and diffusion, phase transformations, plastic deformation and annealing, theory of alloying, corrosion, point defects in metals, alloying behavior of transition elements, martensite transformations, tempering of steel, malleabilizing of cast iron, cathodic protection, hydrogen embrittlement, recovery and recrystallization, precipitation and dislocation interactions in interstitial solid solutions, theoretical and experimental studies of dislocation motion, lattice defects and corrosion, precipitation, ordering. Prerequisites for graduate study: B.S. in metallurgy, physics, or chemistry; some preparation in thermodynamics, physics of metals, X-ray, and diffraction. Recommended: advanced calculus; differential equations. 15 professorial staff. 33 master's degrees and 13 Ph.D.'s awarded 1955-59. 36 graduate students registered fall 1959.

Engineering.—Mining. Rock mechanics, coal carburization, petroleum engineering. Prerequisite for graduate study: B.S. in engineering or geology. Recommended. basic courses in mining engineering. 6 professorial staff. 8 master's degrees awarded 1955-59. 9 graduate students registered fall 1959.

English. English and American literature and language. Prerequisites for graduate study: equivalent of 2 years of French, German, or Russian; departmental qualifying examination. 40 professorial staff. 113 master's degrees and 46 Ph.D.'s awarded 1955-59. 178 graduate students registered fall 1959.

Entomology. Insect morphology, physiology, taxonomy, bionomics, or control. Prerequisites for graduate study: 1 year each of general zoology, general botany, general chemistry, or the equivalents. Recommended: fundamentals of physical and biological science; mathematics. 8 professorial staff. 28 master's degrees and 28 Ph.D.'s awarded 1955-59. 37 graduate students registered fall 1959.

Finance. Central banking history and policy, corporation finance, corporation history, investment, insurance, urban land utilization. Prerequisites for graduate study: at least 27 hours in social sciences, 15 of which must have been in economics (including 1 course in principles of economics and 1 in statistics). 9 professorial staff. Ph.D. program begun 1959. 6 master's degrees awarded 1955-59. 12 graduate students registered fall 1959.

Food Technology and Dairy Technology. Dairy technology, food chemistry of fats and oils, food microbiology, food processing. Prerequisite for graduate study: adequate training in chemistry, bacteriology, chemical engineering, horticulture, or other recognized fields of biological, physical, agricultural, or engineering science. 11 professorial staff. 28 master's degrees and 38 Ph.D.'s awarded 1955-59. 41 graduate students registered fall 1959.

French. Any period of French literature may be designated as a specific area of concentration. Prerequisite for graduate study: major in French or equivalent. Recommended: Latin; other Romance languages and literatures; English literature. 7 professorial staff. 28 master's degrees and 9 Ph.D.'s awarded 1955-59. 34 graduate students registered fall 1959.

Geography. Climatology; economic geography; cartography; land utilization; conservation of resources; regional, political, historical, or educational geography. Prerequisite for graduate study: work in climatology, cartography, field methods, cultural geography, regional geography Recommended: physical or biological science; social science; statistics; work in written and oral expression. 9 professorial staff. 26 master's degrees and 10 Ph.D.'s awarded 1955-59. 37 graduate students registered fall 1959.

Geology. Stratigraphy, paleontology, micropaleontology, petrography, mineralogy, clay mineralogy, engineering geology, ore deposits, sedimentary petrology, groundwater geology, glacial geology. Prerequisites for graduate study: physical geology; historical geology; mineralogy; geomorphology; structural geology; paleontology; stratigraphy; summer field course; chemistry; physics; mathematics. 14 professorial staff. 96 master's degrees and 50 Ph.D.'s awarded 1955-59. 86 graduate students registered fall 1959.

German. Germanic philology and linguistics, older German literature, modern German literature. Prerequisite for graduate study: ability to follow lectures in German. Recommended: reading knowledge of French and some fluency in Latin; general background in German and European history, philosophy, art. 8 professorial staff. 14 master's degrees and 10 Ph.D.'s awarded 1955-59. 20 graduate students registered fall 1959.

History. Virtually all fields of European, American, and Latin-American history. Prerequisite for graduate study: departmental tests in 3 major fields in history. 19 professorial staff. 77 master's degrees and 38 Ph.D.'s awarded 1955-59. 92 graduate students registered fall 1959.

Home Economics. Foods and nutrition. Prerequisite for graduate study: major in home economics or allied field. 19 professorial staff. Ph.D. program begun 1959. 33 master's degrees awarded 1955-59. 27 graduate students registered fall 1959.

Horticulture. Genetics, physiology, mineral nutrition, plant-soil relationships, ecology, anatomy, morphology. Prerequisite for graduate study: 20 hours of work in horticulture or allied subjects. Recommended: fundamental science courses. 14 professorial staff. 20 master's degrees and 10 Ph.D.'s awarded 1955-59. 18 graduate students registered fall 1959.

Library Science. All aspects and types of librarianship are covered: library administration, cataloging and classification, bibliography, history of printing, history of libraries, documentation, communications, adult education. Prerequisites for graduate study: a major and at least 1 minor in any recognized subject discipline; good general educational background; at least 1 modern foreign language. Recommended: additional languages. Prerequisites for Ph.D. candidacy: master's degree in library science; experience. 12 professorial staff. 323 master's degrees and 10 Ph.D.'s awarded 1955-59. 110 graduate students registered fall 1959.

Mathematics and Statistics. Analysis (including complex variables, real variables, partial differential equations, functional analysis); algebra (including groups, group representations, homological algebra); geometry; topology; applied mathematics (including numerical analysis, digital computer, hydrodynamics); statistics; number theory; mathematical logic. Prerequisite for graduate study: 4 semester courses beyond calculus. 54 professorial staff. 133 master's degrees and 53 Ph.D.'s awarded 1955-59. 160 graduate students registered fall 1959.

Mechanics.—Theoretical and Applied. Mechanics of deformable solids, mechanics of fluids, dynamics of rigid bodies, vibration of deformable solids. Prerequisites for graduate study: courses in mechanics as required for B.S. degree in any of the curricula in engineering. 25 professorial staff. 48 master's degrees and 16 Ph.D.'s awarded 1955-59. 48 graduate students registered fall 1959.

Microbiology. Prerequisite for graduate study: chemistry through organic. Recommended: calculus; 1 year of physics. 8 professorial staff. 16 master's degrees and 19 Ph.D.'s awarded 1955-59. 39 graduate students registered fall 1959.

Musicology. Musicology, theory of music. Prerequisite for graduate study: qualifying examination in the history and theory of music. Recommended: knowledge of Latin. 4 professorial staff. 6 master's degrees and 2 Ph.D.'s awarded 1955-59. 16 graduate students registered fall 1959.

Philosophy. History of philosophy; theory of knowledge, including logic and philosophy of science; theory of value, including ethics and aesthetics; philosophy of religion. Prerequisite for graduate study: courses in logic, ethics, and history of philosophy. 31 professorial staff. 21 master's degrees and 9 Ph.D.'s awarded 1955-59. 30 graduate students registered fall 1959.

Physical Education. Health education, physical education, recreation. Prerequisites for graduate study: 30 hours in physical education or related fields; 18 hours in science; 16 hours in education; a course in statistics or measurement. 9 professorial staff. 145 master's degrees and 14

Ph.D.'s awarded 1955-59. 65 graduate students registered fall 1959.

Physics. Cryogenics; high-energy physics; magnetic resonance; nuclear physics; physics of crystals, metals, and semiconductors; quantum theory; physics of electrodes. Prerequisite for graduate study: 20 semester hours beyond general physics, including mechanics and electricity. 45 professorial staff. 191 master's degrees and 81 Ph.D.'s awarded 1955-59. 225 graduate students registered fall 1959.

Physiology. Cellular physiology; comparative physiology; mammalian physiology, including neurophysiology and endrocrinology; human physiological anatomy; bioclimatology; radio biology. Recommended for graduate study: 1 semester each of calculus, vertebrate embryology, organic chemistry, and physical chemistry; 2 semesters of physics. 13 professorial staff. 50 master's degrees and 26 Ph.D.'s awarded 1955-59. 35 graduate students registered fall 1959.

Plant Pathology. Diseases of field crops, forest and shade trees, fruit crops, ornamentals, vegetable and canning crops, plant virology, nematology, fungicides, antibiotics, physiology of fungi, and biochemistry of plant diseases. Prerequisites for graduate study: chemistry through organic; bacteriology; entomology; genetics; 1 course in statistical methods. 11 professorial staff. 18 master's degrees and 22 Ph.D.'s awarded 1955-59. 15 graduate students registered fall 1959.

Political Science. American government and politics, comparative government and politics, international law and relations, public administration, political theory, and jurisprudence. Prerequisites for graduate study: minimum of 12 hours in political science and 8 in economics, finance, sociology, or history. 18 professorial staff. 49 master's degrees and 21 Ph.D.'s awarded 1955-59. 41 graduate students registered fall 1959.

Psychology. Experimental (including physiological), measurement, personality, social, applied experimental, industrial, clinical and counseling, or school psychology. (Offered by Department of Psychology in cooperation with College of Education.) Prerequisites for graduate study: 12 hours in psychology, including course in statistics and experimental; GRE. Recommended: mathematics; laboratory science; good background in social, biological, and physical science. 40 professorial staff. 45 master's degrees

and 73 Ph.D.'s awarded 1955-59. 106 graduate students registered fall 1959.

Sociology. Social organization, sociological theory, industrial sociology, criminology. 13 professorial staff. 30 master's degrees and 16 Ph.D.'s awarded 1955-59. 38 graduate students registered fall 1959.

Spanish, Italian, and Portuguese. Prerequisite for graduate study: major in field of concentration. 10 professorial staff. 34 master's degrees and 15 Ph.D.'s awarded 1955-59. 37 graduate students registered fall 1959.

Speech and Theatre, Speech Disorders, and Audiology. Rhetoric and public address, oral interpretation of literature, theatre, speech science and phonetics, speech disorders, audiology, speech education. Prerequisite for graduate study: 16 hours of speech. 24 professorial staff. 70 master's degrees and 48 Ph.D.'s awarded 1955-59. 55 graduate students registered fall 1959.

Veterinary Medical Science. Anatomy, microbiology, parasitology, pathology, physiology, and pharmacology. Prerequisites for graduate study: D.V.M. or B.S.; 5 semester hours of physics or mathematics; 14 hours of chemistry; 15 hours of biological science. 17 professorial staff. 18 master's degrees and 4 Ph.D.'s awarded 1955-59. 27 graduate students registered fall 1959.

Zoology. Vertebrate zoology; invertebrate zoology; embryology and basic knowledge of cells and tissues; ecology, natural history, and taxonomy; genetics, phylogeny, and evolution. Prerequisite for graduate study: major in zoology or equivalent. Recommended: 2 semesters of physics, chemistry, and mathematics (2 of the 3). 19 professorial staff. 43 master's degrees and 43 Ph.D.'s awarded 1955-59. 74 graduate students registered fall 1959.

Graduate College Division of the Chicago Professional Colleges

Graduate instruction in the basic sciences related to medicine, dentistry, and pharmacy is offered by the University of Illinois through its Professional Colleges in Chicago. The Division was established in 1924 and it first awarded the Ph.D. in 1927.

Graduate students may live in university dormitories or in private housing (rooms and apartments) recommended and approved by Dean of Students.

Residence requirement for Ph.D.: 3 years, 2 of which must be spent in residence at the university. Summer courses available.

ADMISSION REQUIREMENTS

For graduate study: bachelor's degree; 3.5 average ("A" being 5) for all undergraduate work; approval of major department; GRE; 1 year of college physics; 1 year of biological science; general, qualitative, quantitative, and organic chemistry; proficiency in 1 foreign language (usually French or German). Recommended: some knowledge of a second foreign language. For candidacy for Ph.D.: reading examinations in French and German; completion of requirements for minor; preliminary examinations.

Apply to Graduate College, University of Illinois, 1853 West Polk Street, Chicago 12, Illinois, by August 1.

FEES AND FIRST-YEAR AID

No application fee. Tuition for state residents $150 per academic year; others $500. Special fees approximate $33 annually. Room (in dormitory) and board for academic year $920.

First-year aid available: fellowships, $1,500-$1,800; research assistantships, $950-$1,900.

Apply to Graduate College, University of Illinois, 1853 West Polk Street, Chicago 12, Illinois, by February 15.

FIELDS OF STUDY FOR THE PH.D.

Anatomy.—Human. Embryology, fetal circulation, cancer, endocrinology. Recommended for graduate study: mammalian physiology; biochemistry; histology. 10 professorial staff. 9 master's degrees and 7 Ph.D.'s awarded 1955-59. 13 graduate students registered fall 1959.

Biochemistry. All areas. Offered by Department of Biological Chemistry. Recommended for graduate study: physical chemistry. 15 professorial staff. 12 master's degrees and 6 Ph.D.'s awarded 1955-59. 33 graduate students registered fall 1959.

Chemistry.—Pharmaceutical. Application of chemistry and chemical synthesis to drug activity. Offered by Department of Chemistry. Prerequisite for graduate study: B.S. in pharmacy or

equivalent. 7 professorial staff. 7 master's degrees and 4 Ph.D.'s awarded 1955-59.

Microbiology. Virology, medical microbiology, immunology, tissue culture; metabolism of viruses, antigenic analysis of viruses, dental bacteriology, mycological pathogens. Prerequisite for graduate study: general microbiology. 10 professorial staff. 10 master's degrees and 6 Ph.D.'s awarded 1955-59. 16 graduate students registered fall 1959.

Pathology.—Human. Tumors, cancer, kidney diseases. Prerequisite for graduate study: 2 years of medical curriculum or, preferably, M.D. degree. 14 professorial staff. 4 master's degrees and 1 Ph.D. awarded 1955-59. 2 graduate students registered fall 1959.

Pharmacology. Clinical structure and pharmacological action of drugs, toxicity of drugs, neuropharmacology, renal pharmacology. Offered by Department of Pharmacology and Toxicology. Prerequisites for graduate study: general physiology and biochemistry. 9 professorial staff. 15 master's degrees and 5 Ph.D.'s awarded 1955-59. 19 graduate students registered fall 1959.

Physiology.—Human. Brain, cardiovascular, or space physiology; endocrines; neurophysiology. 13 professorial staff. 18 master's degrees and 6 Ph.D.'s awarded 1955-59. 19 graduate students registered fall 1959.

Surgery. Carcinogens, anticarcinogens, tumor transplantation, tissue culture. Prerequisite for graduate study: M.D. or current pursuit of medical curriculum. 6 professorial staff. 11 master's degrees awarded 1955-59. 7 graduate students registered fall 1959.

Indiana University

BLOOMINGTON, INDIANA

The Graduate School

Graduate instruction has been offered at Indiana since 1881. The Graduate School was organized in 1904. University is publicly controlled by the state. Both men and women are admitted.

Other doctoral degrees conferred by the university are: D.B.A. (School of Business); Ed.D. (School of Education); D.Mus. and D.Mus.Ed. (School of Music); Doctor of Health and Safety, Doctor of Physical Education, and

Doctor of Recreation (School of Health, Physical Education, and Recreation).

A graduate residence center provides room and board for over 1,000 students; married students are accommodated in university-owned housing units (more than 1,200 available).

Special facilities include: biological station; geologic field station in Montana; extensive wildlife preserves; human relations area files; cyclotron; achroic and anachroic laboratories; audio-visual center; Slavic and East European Institute. Library of over 1,200,000 volumes includes many special collections and archives of folk and primitive music and of languages of the world. Affiliations with Argonne National Laboratories, Midwest Universities Research Association, and Association of Universities for Research in Astronomy provide additional facilities for research.

Residence requirement for Ph.D.: 6 semesters of resident study, of which at least 2 consecutive semesters must be spent on campus. Summer courses available.

ADMISSION REQUIREMENTS

For graduate study: bachelor's degree; high scholastic standing; major or substantial work in field selected. Recommended: 1 foreign language; GRE. For candidacy for Ph.D.: reading knowledge of 2 foreign languages (usually French, German, or Russian, but under certain circumstances another language may be substituted for one of these); qualifying examination; approval of dissertation topic.

Apply to Dean of the Graduate School at least 2 months before admission is desired.

FEES AND FIRST-YEAR AID

No application fee. Tuition for state residents for academic year, $14 per credit hour; others $30.50 per credit hour. Room and board in graduate residence center $705-$715 per academic year. Apartments $45-$92.50 per month.

First-year aid available: 40 fee-remission scholarships; 450 teaching fellowships, $1,000-$2,000; 65 other fellowships, $1,400-$1,800; about 20 research assistantships, $1,500-$2,400; 85 dormitory counselorships; loan funds.

Apply to Dean of Graduate School by February 15 for fellowships; to appropriate department chairman for teaching fellowships and research assistantships.

FIELDS OF STUDY FOR THE PH.D.

Many departments have a seminar on teaching methods. This is usually offered in connection with the teaching assistantships.

Anatomy. Studies on age changes in the body, cytochemistry, electron microscopy, comparative histology. Offered by the Department of Anatomy in the Indianapolis Medical Center. Prerequisite for graduate study: major in chemistry, physics, or biology. Recommended: biophysics; physical chemistry. 6 professorial staff. Program initiated 1959. 1 graduate student registered fall 1959.

Anatomy and Physiology. Anatomy: experimental histology, microcirculation, histopathology, cytology, neuroanatomy, gross anatomy. Physiology: circulation, respiration, temperature regulation, human stress physiology, kidney-water and electrolyte metabolism, general physiology, comparative physiology. Prerequisites for graduate study: 1 basic course in major subject; chemistry through organic; 1 year of physics; 1 year of biology. Recommended: mathematics through calculus. 8 professorial staff. 6 master's degrees and 2 Ph.D.'s awarded 1955-59. 12 graduate students registered fall 1959.

Anthropology. Archaeology, ethnology, anthropological linguistics, physical (bio-anthropology), theory. Recommended for graduate study: major in anthropology. 7 professorial staff. 9 master's degrees and 13 Ph.D.'s awarded 1955-59. 15 graduate students registered fall 1959.

Area Studies.—Latin-American. Spanish-American or Brazilian literature, Spanish or Portuguese language, Latin-American history. Latin-American literature and language and Latin-American history must both be taken, one as a major and one as a minor. Courses in anthropology, geography, and folklore constitute the second minor. Combined program offered by Departments of Spanish and Portuguese, History, Anthropology, Geography, and Folklore. Prerequisites for graduate study: major in Spanish, Portuguese, or history; 13 hours of Spanish above elementary course. Ph.D. candidacy prerequisite: reading examination in 3 foreign languages. 7 professorial staff. 1 master's degree awarded 1955-59. 2 graduate students registered fall 1959.

Astronomy. Astronomy, physics, mathematics.

Recommended for graduate study: chemistry; geology. 4 professorial staff. 8 master's degrees and 6 Ph.D.'s awarded 1955-59. 17 graduate students registered fall 1959.

Bacteriology.—General. Prerequisite for graduate study: major in bacteriology or (with deficiency at the graduate level) in biology, chemistry, or other areas of science. 6 professorial staff. 15 master's degrees and 6 Ph.D.'s awarded 1955-59. 21 graduate students registered fall 1959.

Biochemistry. Enzymes, proteins, bacteriophages, plant pigments, protozoa, hemoglobin, protease inhibitors, intermediary metabolism of carbohydrates and fatty acids, dental biochemistry, neurochemistry. Combined program offered by Departments of Chemistry, Zoology, Botany, Bacteriology, and Anatomy and Physiology (on the Bloomington campus), and by the Department of Biochemistry in the Medical School at Indianapolis. Prerequisite for graduate study: major in chemistry or one of the biological sciences; basic courses in organic and physical chemistry; physics; mathematics through calculus; 1 foreign language. 22 professorial staff. Program initiated 1959. 19 graduate students registered fall 1959.

Botany. Plant physiology, plant morphology and anatomy, paleobotany, mycology, biosystematics, cytology, cytogenetics, phycology, plant biochemistry. 8 professorial staff. 14 master's degrees and 13 Ph.D.'s awarded 1955-59. 36 graduate students registered fall 1959.

Chemistry. Analytical, biological, inorganic, organic, physical. Prerequisites for graduate study: major in chemistry, including 2 semesters of physical; physics; mathematics through integral calculus; German, French, or Russian; placement examination. 20 professorial staff. 33 master's degrees and 57 Ph.D.'s awarded 1955-59. 85 graduate students registered fall 1959.

Classics. Greek literature or history, Latin literature, Roman history, comparative literature or linguistics or philosophy. Prerequisite for graduate study: major in classics or equivalent; reading knowledge of Greek and Latin plus French or German. Recommended: study of ancient history; reading knowledge of second modern language. 9 professorial staff. Ph.D. program initiated 1960. 6 master's degrees awarded 1955-59. 1 graduate student registered fall 1959.

Comparative Literature. 19th and 20th century European literature, Renaissance literature, comparative drama, American-European literary relations, Renaissance studies, literature and criticism, Christian classics, Asian-Western literary relations. Prerequisite for graduate study: good knowledge of 1 foreign language. Recommended: knowledge of second foreign language. 20 professorial staff. 14 master's degrees and 7 Ph.D.'s awarded 1955-59. 26 graduate students registered fall 1959.

Economics—Economics and Business. Economics, offered by the Department of Economics, includes: economic theory and history of economic thought (required); economic history; comparative economic systems or economic development; international economics; labor economics; money and banking; public finance; statistics; social control and economics of industry. Economics and Business, offered by Department of Economics and School of Business, includes: economic theory and history of economic thought; 1 other economics field; 2 business fields. Prerequisites for graduate study: 30 hours of social science and business courses, including basic courses in accounting, economic history, statistics, money and banking, and intermediate economic theory. Recommended: modern languages; mathematics. 16 professorial staff. 51 master's degrees and 22 Ph.D.'s awarded 1955-59. 56 graduate students registered fall 1959.

Education. School administration; business, adult, elementary, secondary, higher, or vocational education; history and theory of education; guidance; educational psychology; audiovisual communications. Offered by Graduate Division of the School of Education. 68 professorial staff. 10 master's degrees and 26 Ph.D.'s awarded 1955-59. 42 graduate students registered fall 1959. Ed.D. degree also awarded in this field.

English. English and American literature. 38 professorial staff. 71 master's degrees and 29 Ph.D.'s awarded 1955-59. 139 graduate students registered fall 1959.

Folklore. American folklore, the folktale, ballad and folksong, ethnomusicology, American Indian folklore. An interdepartmental program offered by the Department of Folklore in cooperation with other departments. Prerequisite for graduate study: broad background in humanities or social sciences. Recommended: fluency in 1 or more foreign languages. 11 professorial staff. 6

master's degrees and 5 Ph.D.'s awarded 1955-59. 17 graduate students registered fall 1959.

French. French literature (all periods), language, applied French linguistics. Offered by Department of French and Italian. Prerequisites for graduate study: 25 semester hours of French beyond first-year courses; Latin or another Romance language. Ph.D. candidacy prerequisite: 2 other languages. 15 professorial staff. 18 master's degrees and 8 Ph.D.'s awarded 1955-59. 28 graduate students registered fall 1959.

Geography. Climatology, Eastern Europe and the U.S.S.R., humid tropics. 9 professorial staff. 19 master's degrees and 6 Ph.D.'s awarded 1955-59. 15 graduate students registered fall 1959.

Geology. Areal, economic, glacial, petroleum, or structural geology; clay mineralogy; mineralogy; geochemistry; geomorphology; geophysics; invertebrate paleontology; petrology; sedimentation; stratigraphy. Prerequisites for graduate study: 1 year of chemistry; 1 year of physics; mathematics through integral calculus; 30 semester hours of geology. Recommended: additional physics, mathematics, and chemistry; 1 year of zoology. 10 professorial staff. 70 master's degrees and 16 Ph.D.'s awarded 1955-59. 44 graduate students registered fall 1959.

German. Language, literature, linguistics. Prerequisite for graduate study: major in German; reading knowledge of French. 8 professorial staff. 15 master's degrees and 5 Ph.D.'s awarded 1955-59. 19 graduate students registered fall 1959.

History. Ancient, medieval, Renaissance and Reformation, early modern European, recent European, East Central European, Russian, English, early American, Latin-American, later American, Far Eastern history. Prerequisite for graduate study: 25 semester hours in history. Recommended: related work in collateral fields such as economics, government, languages. 18 professorial staff. 83 master's degrees and 31 Ph.D.'s awarded 1955-59. 76 graduate students registered fall 1959.

Linguistics. General, descriptive, comparative linguistics. Offered by Committee on Linguistics. Recommended for graduate study: French and German; some acquaintance with 2 or 3 other languages; 20 credit hours of anthropology or linguistics or major in foreign or classical language. 12 professorial staff. 25 master's degrees and 10 Ph.D.'s awarded 1955-59. 34 graduate students registered fall 1959.

Mathematics and Mechanics. Mechanics:

analytic dynamics, elasticity, fluid mechanics, plasticity, relativity, statistical mechanics. Mathematics: algebra, analysis, differential equations, foundations, geometry, probability, statistics, topology. Offered by Graduate Institute for Mathematics and Mechanics. 16 professorial staff. 35 master's degrees and 16 Ph.D.'s awarded 1955-59. 67 graduate students registered fall 1959.

Microbiology. Parasitology, bacteriology, virology, immunology, microbial physiology, microbial genetics, immunochemistry, medical mycology. Prerequisites for graduate study: courses in physics, chemistry, mathematics, biology; French or German. Recommended: calculus; physical chemistry; genetics; biochemistry; bacteriology; mycology. 6 professorial staff. 1 Ph.D. awarded 1955-59. 2 graduate students registered fall 1959.

Microbiology.—General. Combined program offered on Bloomington campus by Departments of Bacteriology, Botany, and Zoology. Prerequisite for graduate study: major in bacteriology, general biology, chemistry, or other physical science. Recommended: French and German. 10 professorial staff. Program established 1960.

Music. Theory, education, musicology. Offered by the School of Music. Prerequisite for graduate study: music major; 40 hours of liberal arts subjects. 25 professorial staff. 5 master's degrees and 33 Ph.D.'s awarded 1955-59. 27 graduate students registered fall 1959. D.Mus. and D.Mus.Ed. also awarded.

Optics.—Physiological. Offered by the Division of Optometry and the Graduate Program in Physiological Optics. Prerequisite for graduate study: 5-year curriculum in optometry, including 60 semester hours of liberal arts credits. Recommended: calculus. 6 professorial staff. Ph.D. program initiated 1955. 10 master's degrees awarded 1955-59. 6 graduate students registered fall 1959.

Pharmacology and Toxicology. Mechanism of action and metabolism of drugs, neuropharmacology, forensic and medical toxicology. Offered by Department of Pharmacology, School of Medicine, and Indiana Toxicology Laboratory. Recommended for graduate study: courses in chemistry, biology, and mathematics. 6 professorial staff. Program initiated 1960.

Philosophy. History of philosophy; logic; ethics; philosophy of art, science, history, or culture; metaphysics. Prerequisite for graduate study: major or strong minor in philosophy. 6

professorial staff. 15 master's degrees and 4 Ph.D.'s awarded 1955-59. 23 graduate students registered fall 1959.

Physics. Experimental nuclear, theoretical physics. 11 professorial staff. 28 master's degrees and 23 Ph.D.'s awarded 1955-59. 56 graduate students registered fall 1959.

Physiology. Circulatory, environmental, or renal physiology; shock; digestion; neurophysiology; endocrinology. Offered by Department of Physiology, Indiana University Medical Center. Prerequisites for graduate study: biology; either developmental anatomy or comparative anatomy and embryology; chemistry (general, organic, physical; qualitative and quantitative analysis); mathematics (basic courses extended through differential and integral calculus); 1 year college physics. 8 professorial staff. Program initiated 1959. 2 graduate students registered fall 1959.

Political Science.—Government. Normative and empirical political theory; international politics, law, organization and administration; American government, politics, and political behavior; public administration and public law; comparative government and politics (including special programs in Soviet and East European politics, Asian studies). Prerequisite for graduate study: major in political science, government, or politics. Recommended: 2 languages (German, French, or Russian); undergraduate minor or equivalent in an allied social science. 23 professorial staff. 80 master's degrees and 21 Ph.D.'s awarded 1955-59. 70 graduate students registered fall 1959.

Psychology. Program designed to provide broad foundation in experimental and theoretical bases of psychology, special competence for research, and thorough background in 1 or more of following: learning; perception; vision; audition; physiological psychology; quantitative theory; clinical psychology. Prerequisite for graduate study: 20 hours' work in psychology, including thorough study of general psychology, laboratory work, and 1 course in statistics; MAT; GRE. 22 professorial staff. 12 master's degrees and 32 Ph.D.'s awarded 1955-59. 54 graduate students registered fall 1959.

Science.—History and Logic. Exploration of the conceptual development of scientific ideas, as well as their internal logical structure. The place of scientific thinking within the more comprehensive context of history of western thought examined via techniques of historical and logical analysis. Prerequisite for graduate study: background in liberal arts or sciences; fluency in 1 foreign language. Recommended: mathematics and science; some Latin and Greek; some history and philosophy. 6 professorial staff. Program initiated 1960.

Slavic Languages and Literatures. Russian literature, Slavic linguistics. Prerequisite for graduate study: general acquaintance with 19th and 20th century Russian literature; knowledge of Russian language adequate for graduate study. Recommended: reading knowledge of French and German; broad background in liberal arts. Ph.D. candidacy prerequisite: for Russian literature, reading knowledge of second Slavic language; for Slavic linguistics, reading knowledge of second and third Slavic language. 9 professorial staff. Ph.D. program initiated 1959. 30 master's degrees awarded 1955-59. 49 graduate students registered fall 1959.

Sociology. Social organization, disorganization, or psychology; history and theories; methods and statistics. 13 professorial staff. 18 master's degrees and 8 Ph.D.'s awarded 1955-59. 35 graduate students registered fall 1959.

Spanish and Portuguese. Spanish or Portuguese languages; Spanish-American, Portuguese, Brazilian literature. Prerequisite for graduate study: minimum of 25 semester hours in Spanish above elementary course; French or German as first minor. Recommended: courses in comparative literature, English, folklore, Greek, history, Italian, Latin, or linguistics. Ph.D. candidacy prerequisite: knowledge of Latin. 8 professorial staff. 15 master's degrees and 3 Ph.D.'s awarded 1955-59. 20 graduate students registered fall 1959.

Speech and Dramatic Arts. Public address and rhetoric, theatre and drama, speech pathology, audiology, and experimental phonetics. Offered by Department of Speech and Theatre. 17 professorial staff. 54 master's degrees and 6 Ph.D.'s awarded 1955-59. 58 graduate students registered fall 1959.

Zoology. Experimental embryology, endocrinology, genetics, biochemistry, ecology, limnology, evolution, experimental morphogenesis of invertebrates. Prerequisite for graduate study: major in zoology. Recommended: French and German. 11 professorial staff. 30 master's degrees and 27 Ph.D.'s awarded 1955-59. 46 graduate students registered fall 1959.

Iowa, State University of

IOWA CITY, IOWA

The Graduate College

Graduate instruction has been offered at the State University of Iowa since 1855. The Graduate School was organized in 1900 and conferred the first Ph.D. in that year. All graduate degrees are granted by and under supervision of The Graduate College, regardless of the school or college in which instruction is received. University is publicly controlled by the state. Both men and women are admitted.

Single graduate students find accommodations in dormitories and in private homes; married students in university-owned and off-campus housing.

Special facilities include: Writer's Workshop for original writing in novel and poetry; Natural History Museum; 5 hospitals; Child Welfare Research Station; Bureau of Educational Research; Institute of Agricultural Medicine; Institute of Hydraulic Research; Bureau of Labor and Management; Institute of Public Affairs; Institute of Gerontology; Social Service Unit; Television Center; 2 theaters; Computer Center; Iowa Lakeside Laboratory; Radiation Research Laboratory; Cosmic Ray Laboratory; State Historical Society; Iowa and United States Geological Surveys; State Bacteriological (hygienic) Laboratory; Bureau of Audio-Visual Instruction. Library contains approximately 1,000,000 volumes.

Residence requirement for Ph.D.: minimum of 2 years (but usually 3 are required), of which 1 must be spent in residence on campus. Summer courses available.

ADMISSION REQUIREMENTS

For graduate study: bachelor's degree; satisfactory academic record (2.0 GPA or better); recommendations. For candidacy for Ph.D.: approval of plan of study; satisfaction of research tool requirements in 2 fields; comprehensive examination.

Apply to Office of the Registrar well in advance of registration.

FEES AND FIRST-YEAR AID

No application fee. Tuition and fees $280 per academic year. Single room (in dormitory) $390 a year; multiple room $300. Approximate annual cost of board in college dining room $520. University-owned apartments $62.50 per month.

First-year aid available: scholarships up to amount of tuition and fees; fellowships, $530-$2,400; teaching assistantships, $1,800-$2,400 (depending on teaching load); research assistantships, $1,800-$2,400 (varying with departmental recommendations and number of hours).

Apply to Graduate College or chairman of appropriate department by March 1 (some awards made later if circumstances warrant).

FIELDS OF STUDY FOR THE PH.D.

Courses in the methodology of teaching are offered by some departments and by the College of Education.

Accounting. Accounting, economics, finance, statistics. Recommended for graduate study: courses in business required for the B.B.A. 5 professorial staff. 5 master's degrees awarded 1955-59. 7 graduate students registered fall 1959.

American Civilization. Major emphasis on American literature and history; other work in social sciences and humanities. Combined program offered by Departments of English and History. 20 professorial staff. 5 master's degrees and 2 Ph.D.'s awarded 1955-59. 20 graduate students registered fall 1959.

Anatomy. Endocrinology, experimental diabetes and eye pathology, neuroanatomy, neurophysiology, neurological bases of behavior, teratology. Prerequisites for graduate study: courses in biology, chemistry, physics, and mathematics; adequate communications skills. Recommended: psychology; philosophy; German and another modern language. 8 professorial staff. 3 master's degrees and 6 Ph.D.'s awarded 1955-59. 9 graduate students registered fall 1959.

Art.—History and Theory. Theory and history of art within the major divisions (ancient, medieval, Italian or Northern Renaissance, baroque, 19th century, modern, Oriental, primitive). The concentration may be stylistic, iconographic, cultural, or anthropological. Prerequisites for graduate study: basic courses in history of art and studio art; review of studio work. Recommended: French and German; humanities and philosophy. Ph.D. candidacy prerequisites: 2 foreign languages, usually French and German; completion of requirements for M.F.A. 17 professorial staff. 134 master's degrees and 16 Ph.D.'s awarded

1955-59. 100 graduate students registered fall 1959.

Bacteriology. General bacteriology, immunology, physiology, virology. Minors in biology, chemistry, physics, mathematics. Prerequisites for graduate study: basic skills; 1 foreign language. Recommended: courses in chemistry, mathematics, physics, and biology. 7 professorial staff. 7 master's degrees and 8 Ph.D.'s awarded 1955-59. 13 graduate students registered fall 1959. Total enrollment limited to 21.

Biochemistry. Amino-acid metabolism, chemistry of polysaccharides, clinical or physical biochemistry, hormones and steroids, mechanism of enzyme action, lipids, nucleic acids and synthetic polyphosphates, proteins. Prerequisites for graduate study: major in chemistry; mathematics through calculus; physics and zoology; ACS tests in biochemistry and organic and physical chemistry. Ph.D. candidacy prerequisites: reading knowledge of French and German (statistics may be substituted for 1). 8 professorial staff. 6 master's degrees and 15 Ph.D.'s awarded 1955-59. 11 graduate students registered fall 1959.

Botany. Plant anatomy, morphology, physiology, or taxonomy; mycology. Prerequisites for graduate study: 16 semester hours of botany; 1 year each of mathematics, chemistry, and a foreign language (preferably German). Recommended: organic chemistry; calculus; other foreign languages. 9 professorial staff. 17 master's degrees and 16 Ph.D.'s awarded 1955-59. 17 graduate students registered fall 1959. Total enrollment limited to 22.

Business (General) and Economics. Business finance; business and economic statistics; insurance; money, banking, and fluctuation; regulated enterprise. Offered by Department of General Business. Prerequisites for graduate study: major in business administration and economics. 12 professorial staff. 15 master's degrees and 2 Ph.D.'s awarded 1955-59. 11 graduate students registered fall 1959.

Chemistry. Analytical, inorganic, organic, and physical. Prerequisites for graduate study: general, organic, and qualitative organic chemistry; qualitative, quantitative, and instrumental analysis; physics; mathematics through integral calculus; German or French; English and humanities. Recommended: differential equations; advanced calculus. 15 professorial staff. 46 master's degrees and 62 Ph.D.'s awarded 1955-59. 82 graduate students registered fall 1959.

Child Development and Guidance. Minor in general psychology with concentration on personality theory. Prerequisites for graduate study: GRE; MAT; ACE Psychological Examination or Ohio State Psychological Examination. Recommended: major in psychology, sociology, or elementary education; 9-12 hours of mathematics and elementary statistics. Ph.D. candidacy prerequisites: M.A. with research problem or thesis; 9-12 hours of statistics and experimental design beyond elementary statistics. 19 professorial staff. 14 master's degrees awarded 1955-59. 12 graduate students registered fall 1959.

Child Psychology. Prerequisite for graduate study: GRE, MAT, ACE Psychological Examination or Ohio State Psychological Examination. Recommended: major or minor in psychology; 9-12 hours of mathematics and elementary statistics. Ph.D. candidacy prerequisite: M.A. with research problem or thesis. 19 professorial staff. 10 master's degrees and 14 Ph.D.'s awarded 1955-59. 7 graduate students registered fall 1959.

Child Somatology. Developmental physiology, physical anthropology. Prerequisites for graduate study: major in biological sciences; GRE, MAT, ACE Psychological Examination or Ohio State Psychological Examination. Recommended: 9-12 hours of mathematics; elementary statistics. Ph.D. candidacy prerequisite: M.A. with research problem or thesis. 19 professorial staff. Ph.D. program initiated 1959. 1 Ph.D. awarded 1959.

Child Welfare (Parent-Family Life Education). Child development, family relations. Prerequisites for graduate study: major in education, psychology, home economics, or nursing; GRE, MAT, ACE Psychological Examination or Ohio State Psychological Examination. Recommended: 9 hours of mathematics; elementary statistics. Ph.D. candidacy prerequisite: M.A. with research problem or thesis. 19 professorial staff. 2 master's degrees and 3 Ph.D.'s awarded 1955-59. 1 graduate student registered fall 1959.

Classical Studies. Greek or Latin language, Greek or Roman literature, Greek history and culture, Roman history and literature. Offered by Department of Classics in cooperation with Departments of Classics at Universities of Minnesota and Wisconsin. Prerequisites for graduate study: major in Greek or Latin; reading knowledge of Latin. Recommended: GRE; reading knowledge of Greek, German, or French. Ph.D. candidacy prerequisite: reading knowledge of German or French. 6 professorial staff at Iowa,

Ph.D. program initiated 1960. 8 master's degrees awarded 1955-59. 5 graduate students registered fall 1959.

Economics. Economic microtheory and macro-theory, international economics, public finance and fiscal policy. Prerequisite for graduate study: major in economics. Recommended: courses in mathematics. Ph.D. candidacy prerequisite: M.A. in economics with thesis. 6 professorial staff. 12 master's degrees and 6 Ph.D.'s awarded 1955-59. 26 graduate students registered fall 1959.

Education.—Administration. General administration, the superintendency, assistant superintendency, supervision, the principalship. Offered by College of Education. Prerequisite for graduate study: teaching certificate. Recommended: teaching experience. Ph.D. candidacy prerequisites: master's degree; experience in administration. 7 professorial staff. 120 master's degrees and 2 Ph.D.'s awarded 1955-59. 12 graduate students registered fall 1959.

Education.—Comparative. History or philosophy of education, comparative education. Offered by College of Education. Prerequisite for graduate study: teaching certificate. Recommended: teaching experience. 1 professor. Program discontinued in 1954 and resumed in 1959.

Education.—Elementary. Instructional and curricular problems of the major elementary school subject fields with emphasis on actual materials and classroom practices. Minors in problems of supervision, evaluation of instruction, development of research interests, and teacher preparation. Offered by College of Education. 6 professorial staff.

Education.—Guidance and Counseling. Secondary school counseling, college student personnel work, rehabilitation counseling. Offered by College of Education. Prerequisites for graduate study: MAT during first semester; for secondary school counseling, valid teaching certificate. Recommended: teaching experience. Ph.D. candidacy prerequisite: successful work experience in proposed field of specialization; M.A. with thesis. 3 professorial staff. 65 master's degrees and 7 Ph.D.'s awarded 1955-59. 44 graduate students registered fall 1959.

Education.—Psychology. Offered by College of Education. Prerequisite for graduate study: teaching certificate for elementary or secondary school. Ph.D. candidacy prerequisites: advanced statistics; reading knowledge of 1 foreign language. 3 professorial staff. 15 master's degrees and 30 Ph.D.'s awarded 1955-59.

Education.—Science. Combined major in 2 areas of science and 1 or 2 areas of education. Offered by College of Education and various science departments. Prerequisites for graduate study: strong background in science; teaching experience. Recommended: mathematics through calculus. Recommended for Ph.D. candidacy: master's degree in a scientific area. Ph.D. program initiated 1958. 7 master's degrees awarded 1955-59. 29 graduate students registered fall 1959.

Education.—Secondary Administration and Curriculum. Secondary curriculum or supervision, guidance and counseling, educational psychology and measurement, school administration. Offered by College of Education. Prerequisites for graduate study: valid teaching certificate; 2 years of teaching experience. Recommended: educational psychology and philosophy. Ph.D. candidacy prerequisites: master's degree with preparation in school administration and supervision. 3 professorial staff. 130 master's degrees and 11 Ph.D.'s awarded 1955-59. 31 graduate students registered fall 1959.

Education.—Social Studies. Major in education plus work in 2 of following areas: history; political science; geography; sociology or anthropology; economics. Offered by Colleges of Education and Liberal Arts. Recommended for graduate study: GRE; major in social studies or a social science. 61 professorial staff. 13 master's degrees and 3 Ph.D.'s awarded 1955-59. 12 graduate students registered fall 1959.

Education.—Special. Education of the mentally retarded or physically handicapped. Offered by the College of Education. Prerequisite for graduate study: teaching certificate for elementary or secondary school, except in case of 2-year school psychology program. Ph.D. candidacy prerequisites: statistics; 1 foreign language. 4 professorial staff. 55 master's degrees and 3 Ph.D.'s awarded 1955-59.

Education.—Statistical Measurements. Statistical methods, educational measurement or psychology, guidance and counseling, elementary and secondary curriculum. Offered by College of Education. Prerequisite for graduate study: mathematics through differential and integral calculus. Recommended: major in mathematics. 9 professorial staff. 2 master's degrees and 6 Ph.D.'s awarded 1955-59. 3 graduate students registered fall 1959.

Education.—Tests and Measurements. Educational psychology, mathematical and applied statistics, educational and psychological measurement. Offered by College of Education. Prerequisites for graduate study: major in education, psychology, or mathematics; 1 year of teaching or professional experience. Recommended: 2 years of mathematics. Ph.D. candidacy prerequisites: 2 foreign languages or 1 language plus statistical methods. 4 professorial staff. 10 master's degrees and 4 Ph.D.'s awarded 1955-59. 1 graduate student registered fall 1959.

Engineering.—Chemical. Gaseous diffusion and separation processes, flow of gases and vapors in barriers, separation in liquid phase systems. Prerequisite for graduate study: B.S. in chemical engineering. Recommended: master's degree; statistics; computer knowledge. Ph.D. candidacy prerequisites: 2 foreign languages, preferably German and Russian. 4 professorial staff. 15 master's degrees and 2 Ph.D.'s awarded 1955-59. 8 graduate students registered fall 1959.

Engineering.—Civil. Prerequisite for graduate study: major in civil engineering. Recommended: GRE. Ph.D. candidacy prerequisites: French and/or German (statistics may be substituted for 1); master's degree or 30 hours beyond B.S. 5 professorial staff. 13 master's degrees and 1 Ph.D. awarded 1955-59. 10 graduate students registered fall 1959.

Engineering.—Electrical. Electronics. Prerequisite for graduate study: major in electrical engineering. 6 professorial staff. 18 master's degrees and 6 Ph.D.'s awarded 1955-59. 24 graduate students registered fall 1959.

Engineering.—Hydraulic. Mechanics of fluids and solids, hydraulic engineering. Offered by Department of Mechanics and Hydraulics. Prerequisites for graduate study: B.S. in engineering. Ph.D. candidacy prerequisites: M.S. in engineering. 11 professorial staff. 50 master's degrees and 8 Ph.D.'s awarded 1955-59. 37 graduate students registered fall 1959.

Engineering.—Industrial and Management. Work measurement, man-machine system analysis and design, human factors in design, microeconomic analysis. Ph.D. candidacy prerequisites: M.S. in engineering with thesis; German and statistics; 2 years of practical experience in the field. 23 professorial staff. 11 master's degrees and 4 Ph.D.'s awarded 1955-59. 32 graduate students registered fall 1959.

Engineering.—Mechanical. Thermodynamics, heat transfer, systems design, vibrations, dynamics of machines (fluid and solid). Ph.D. candidacy prerequisites: M.S. in engineering with thesis; German and a second language or statistics. 26 professorial staff. 12 master's degrees and 2 Ph.D.'s awarded 1955-59. 40 graduate students registered fall 1959.

Engineering.—Sanitary. Sanitary engineering and sanitary chemistry, chemistry, fluid mechanics, bacteriology. Cooperative program offered by Department of Civil Engineering and Department of Hygiene and Preventive Medicine. Prerequisite for graduate study: major in civil or related field of engineering. 5 professorial staff. 8 master's degrees and 3 Ph.D.'s awarded 1955-59. 10 graduate students registered fall 1959.

English Language and Literature. English literature or language, creative writing. Prerequisite for graduate study in creative writing: submission of samples of writing. 24 professorial staff. 146 master's degrees and 41 Ph.D.'s awarded 1955-59. 218 graduate students registered fall 1959.

Geography. Recommended for graduate study: college algebra; statistics. Ph.D. candidacy prerequisites: advanced statistics; 1 foreign language or 1 course beyond integral calculus. 5 professorial staff. 12 master's degrees and 5 Ph.D.'s awarded 1955-59. 20 graduate students registered fall 1959.

Geology. General geology, paleontology-stratigraphy. Prerequisites for graduate study: 30 semester hours of geology; physical and biological sciences; mathematics. Recommended: mathematics through calculus; 1 foreign language; GRE or civil service rating. 6 professorial staff. 48 master's degrees and 9 Ph.D.'s awarded 1955-59. 41 graduate students registered fall 1959. Total enrollment limited to approximately 40.

German. Literature or language (linguistics). Prerequisites for graduate study: major in German; 8 hours of another foreign language. Recommended: GRE. 5 professorial staff. 5 master's degrees and 7 Ph.D.'s awarded 1955-59. 9 graduate students registered fall 1959.

History. Ancient and medieval (especially Western Europe); early modern Europe (especially Reformation); Europe since 1815 (especially England, France, Germany, Russia); British Empire; Latin America; Far East (especially modern China); America (especially colonial, middle period [1840-1877], recent

[1877 on], the West, and intellectual). 11 professorial staff. 57 master's degrees and 12 Ph.D.'s awarded 1955-59. 60 graduate students registered fall 1959.

Hospital Administration. Administration concepts and techniques, such as clinic management, prepayment health insurance plans, and rehabilitation programs; research in hospital and health teaching and administration, related to specific problems within the institution; social concepts and practices in health care from a socio-economic view; place of the hospital in medical health. Cooperative program offered by Graduate College and Department of Hospital Administration of the College of Medicine. Prerequisites for graduate study: broad background in business administration, social sciences, humanities, and biological sciences; personal interview. Recommended: Admission Test for Graduate Study in Business (ETS). Ph.D. candidacy prerequisite: master's degree in hospital administration. 3 professorial staff. 53 master's degrees and 4 Ph.D.'s awarded 1955-59. 40 graduate students registered fall 1959.

Hygiene and Preventive Medicine. Industrial hygiene (with physical sciences contributing); entomology and parasitology (with biological sciences contributing); teaching of hygiene and preventive medicine (with social sciences contributing). Recommended for graduate study: major in biological sciences. 7 professorial staff. 5 master's degrees and 2 Ph.D.'s awarded 1955-59. 4 graduate students registered fall 1959.

Labor and Management. Management theory, production or personnel management, labor economics and labor relations, labor legislation. Prerequisites for graduate study: principles of economics and of accounting; labor economics; management theory; business law; finance; marketing; statistics; algebra. 4 professorial staff. 24 master's degrees and 13 Ph.D.'s awarded 1955-59. 20 graduate students registered fall 1959.

Marketing. General marketing, retailing, sales management, marketing research, geography and economics. 4 professorial staff. 10 master's degrees and 7 Ph.D.'s awarded 1955-59. 15 graduate students registered fall 1959.

Mass Communications. Social significance and economics of mass communications, principles and theories of communication (all required); 3 of the following: advertising; semantics; management; public relations; media dis-

tribution; problems and theories of esthetics and production in mass media; electronics; acoustics. Offered by School of Journalism. Recommended for graduate study: major in mass communications; commercial experience. Ph.D. candidacy prerequisites: 1 foreign language; test of proficiency in research methods in mass communications. 11 professorial staff. 2 master's degrees and 14 Ph.D.'s awarded 1955-59. 6 graduate students registered fall 1959.

Mathematics. Pure and applied mathematics, mathematical statistics, teaching of mathematics. Prerequisite for graduate study: major in mathematics or equivalent. Recommended: GRE. Ph.D. candidacy prerequisite: 2 foreign languages. 12 professorial staff. 78 master's degrees and 7 Ph.D.'s awarded 1955-59. 68 graduate students registered fall 1959.

Music. Composition, theory, musicology, music education, music literature and performance. Prerequisite for graduate study: major in music. Ph.D. candidacy prerequisites: 2 foreign languages or, for music education, 1 language plus statistics. 21 professorial staff. 88 master's degrees and 33 Ph.D.'s awarded 1955-59. 95 graduate students registered fall 1959.

Nutrition. Nutrient requirements, metabolism of nutrients, nutrition in diseased states. Offered by Department of Internal Medicine. Prerequisite for graduate study: courses in quantitative analysis, biochemistry, human physiology and nutrition, food preparation. Recommended: nutrition internship. 24 professorial staff. 56 master's degrees and 1 Ph.D. awarded 1955-59. 30 graduate students registered fall 1959.

Office Management and Business Education. Offered by Department of Office Management and Business Education, College of Business Administration. Prerequisite for graduate study: major in business education, including economics and business administration. Ph.D. candidacy prerequisites: 2 research tools selected from logic, accounting, statistics, or economic theory. 3 professorial staff. 13 master's degrees and 9 Ph.D.'s awarded 1955-59. 10 graduate students registered fall 1959.

Pharmacology. Offered by Department of Pharmacology, College of Medicine. Prerequisites for graduate study: major in science, including general zoology, physics, mathematics, and organic and inorganic chemistry; good liberal arts background. Recommended: mathematics through calculus; qualitative organic chemistry.

5 professorial staff. 15 master's degrees and 7 Ph.D.'s awarded 1955-59. 12 graduate students registered fall 1959. New enrollment limited to 10.

Pharmacy. Pharmacy, pharmaceutical chemistry, pharmacognosy, hospital pharmacy. Prerequisite for graduate study: B.S. in pharmacy. 9 professorial staff. 31 master's degrees and 14 Ph.D.'s awarded 1955-59. 28 graduate students registered fall 1959.

Philosophy. History of philosophy, metaphysics, philosophy of science, ethics, logic. Prerequisite for graduate study: major or strong minor in philosophy. Recommended: background in physical sciences, mathematics, history, and psychology. 4 professorial staff. 8 master's degrees and 5 Ph.D.'s awarded 1955-59. 12 graduate students registered fall 1959.

Physical Education for Men. Administration of physical education, adapted physical education, research, hygiene, physiology of exercise, anatomy and kinesiology, mechanics of motor activities, curriculum in physical education, methodology. Prerequisite for graduate study: major in physical education. Recommended: courses in physics, chemistry, and mathematics. Ph.D. candidacy prerequisites: reading proficiency in German; elementary statistics. 9 professorial staff. 87 master's degrees and 22 Ph.D.'s awarded 1955-59. 36 graduate students registered fall 1959.

Physical Education for Women. Teaching of physical education for public schools or college, recreation, measurement and research. 6 professorial staff. 34 master's degrees and 27 Ph.D.'s awarded 1955-59. 20 graduate students registered fall 1959.

Physics and Astronomy. Cosmic rays, space science, low-energy or theoretical nuclear physics, quantum mechanics, field theory. Prerequisite for graduate study: major in physics. 12 professorial staff. 32 master's degrees and 14 Ph.D.'s awarded 1955-59. 45 graduate students registered fall 1959.

Physiology. Neuromuscular, gastro-intestinal, cardiovascular, environmental, or cellular physiology; biophysics. Prerequisite for graduate study: science major. 10 professorial staff. 15 master's degrees and 23 Ph.D.'s awarded 1955-59. 28 graduate students registered fall 1959.

Political Science. American government, public law or administration, political theory, foreign governments, international relations. 11

professorial staff. 40 master's degrees and 11 Ph.D.'s awarded 1955-59. 41 graduate students registered fall 1959.

Psychology. General experimental, personality and social, clinical, or guidance and counseling psychology. Prerequisites for graduate study: 21 hours of psychology; strong background in mathematics and biology; 1 foreign language; GRE. 20 professorial staff. 57 master's degrees and 39 Ph.D.'s awarded 1955-59. 57 graduate students registered fall 1959. New enrollment limited to 25.

Religion. Biblical studies; church history; historical, contemporary, or philosophical theology; religion in America. Offered by School of Religion. Prerequisites for graduate study: GRE; examination in religion. Ph.D. candidacy prerequisite: reading knowledge of at least 2 foreign languages selected from Hebrew, Greek, Latin, German, French. 5 professorial staff. 5 master's degrees and 5 Ph.D.'s awarded 1955-59. 26 graduate students registered fall 1959.

Romance Languages. Spanish, French, or Italian language and literature. Prerequisite for graduate study: major in chosen field. 10 professorial staff. 71 master's degrees and 5 Ph.D.'s awarded 1955-59. 37 graduate students registered fall 1959.

Sociology. Social psychology, population and community, social institutions, urban community studies. Offered by Department of Sociology-Anthropology. Prerequisites for graduate study: 1 year each of statistics and theory; 1 semester each of research methods and social psychology; 18 additional hours of sociology. Recommended: GRE or MAT. 12 professorial staff. 47 master's degrees and 13 Ph.D.'s awarded 1955-59. 47 graduate students registered fall 1959.

Speech and Dramatic Art. Rhetoric and public address; dramatic theory, criticism, and literature; history of theater; original plays; history and criticism of radio, television, and film; quantitative and experimental studies in public address, theater, radio, television, and film. Recommended for graduate study: GRE. 17 professorial staff. 40 master's degrees and 98 Ph.D.'s awarded 1955-59. 100 graduate students registered fall 1959.

Speech Pathology and Audiology.—Speech and Hearing Science. Speech pathology, audiology, speech science (experimental phonetics), hearing science. Offered by Department of Speech Pathology and Audiology. Prerequisite for graduate study: prescribed courses in speech pathology, psychology, and related fields. Recommended: GRE. 8 professorial staff. 66 master's degrees and 13 Ph.D.'s awarded 1955-59. 46 graduate students registered fall 1959.

Zoology. Protozoology; ecology; experimental embryology; insect, nerve, or general physiology; endocrinology; parasitology, genetics; entomology, field biology; histology; cytology; electron microscopy. Prerequisites for graduate study: general and invertebrate zoology, comparative anatomy, embryology, general physiology, genetics, chemistry, physics. Recommended: mathematics through calculus; organic chemistry; French and German. 11 professorial staff. 29 master's degrees and 38 Ph.D.'s awarded 1955-59. 37 graduate students registered fall 1959. New enrollment limited to 10 per year.

Iowa State University of Science and Technology

AMES, IOWA

Graduate College

Graduate instruction has been available since 1877. Graduate College was organized in 1913 and first Ph.D. awarded in 1916. The university is publicly controlled by the state. Both men and women are admitted.

Rooms in dormitories available for single students; 1,000 units in temporary and permanent structures for married students.

Facilities include library of almost 500,000 volumes with serial publications in basic and applied fields of physical and biological sciences.

Residence requirement for Ph.D.: minimum of 3 years beyond bachelor's degree, of which at least half must be taken in residence on campus. Summer courses available.

ADMISSION REQUIREMENTS

For graduate study: bachelor's degree; standing in upper half of class; GRE. For candidacy for Ph.D.: reading knowledge of 2 foreign languages; preliminary examinations in major and minor fields.

Apply to the Registrar or Dean of Graduate College at least 1 month before opening of quarter in which admission is desired.

FEES AND FIRST-YEAR AID

No application fee. Tuition $252 per year. Rooms (in dormitories) $210-$315 per year. Approximate annual cost of board in college dining room $405. Apartments $30-$56 a month.

First-year aid available: 80 teaching fellowships, $100-$200 per month; 50 other fellowships, $100-$200 per month; 75 research assistantships, $100-$200 per month.

Apply to head of appropriate department.

FIELDS OF STUDY FOR THE PH.D.

Course on methods of college teaching is offered and supervised training is provided for teaching fellows.

Agronomy. Crop production and breeding; soil physics, fertility, microbiology, morphology, genesis, and management; agricultural climatology. 16 professorial staff. 73 master's degrees and 78 Ph.D.'s awarded 1955-59. 76 graduate students registered fall 1959.

Animal Husbandry. Breeding, nutrition, and reproduction (with the opportunity to specialize in beef cattle, dairy cattle, sheep or swine). 12 professorial staff. 47 master's degrees and 49 Ph.D.'s awarded 1955-59. 58 graduate students registered fall 1959.

Bacteriology. Physiological, systematic, soil, dairy, veterinary, sanitary, food, and household bacteriology. 8 professorial staff. 2 master's degrees and 8 Ph.D.'s awarded 1955-59. 15 graduate students registered fall 1959.

Biochemistry and Biophysics. 10 professorial staff. New program begun 1960 (formerly combined with Chemistry and Physics Departments).

Botany and Plant Pathology. Plant ecology, morphology, mycology, pathology, physiology; systematic and economic botany. 17 professorial staff. 18 master's degrees and 47 Ph.D.'s awarded 1955-59. 38 graduate students registered fall 1959.

Chemistry. Inorganic, analytical, physical, and organic. 36 professorial staff. 116 master's degrees and 142 Ph.D.'s awarded 1955-59. 211 graduate students registered fall 1959.

Dairy and Food Industries. Food technology, dairy bacteriology, and dairy chemistry. Offered by Department of Dairy and Food Industries in cooperation with basic science departments. 5 professorial staff. 8 master's degrees and 3 Ph.D.'s awarded 1955-59. 12 graduate students registered fall 1959.

Economics and Sociology. Agricultural, consumption, and industrial economics; rural sociology. 23 professorial staff. 57 master's degrees and 62 Ph.D.'s awarded 1955-59. 101 graduate students registered fall 1959.

Education.—Home Economics. 3 professorial staff. 37 master's degrees and 4 Ph.D.'s awarded 1955-59. 20 graduate students registered fall 1959.

Education.—Vocational. 6 professorial staff. 99 master's degrees and 17 Ph.D.'s awarded 1955-59. 34 graduate students registered fall 1959.

Engineering.—Agricultural. Work may be taken as a divided major with departments offering work in related fields. 7 professorial staff. 19 master's degrees and 13 Ph.D.'s awarded 1955-59. 24 graduate students registered fall 1959.

Engineering.—Ceramic. Ceramics and ceramic engineering. 3 professorial staff. 1 master's degree and 3 Ph.D.'s awarded 1955-59. 2 graduate students registered fall 1959.

Engineering.—Chemical. 6 professorial staff. 35 master's degrees and 18 Ph.D.'s awarded 1955-59. 38 graduate students registered fall 1959.

Engineering.—Civil. Structural, sanitary, soil, and highway engineering. 8 professorial staff. 85 master's degrees and 13 Ph.D.'s awarded 1955-59. 44 graduate students registered fall 1959.

Engineering.—Electrical. Electrical engineering and medical electronics. 10 professorial staff. 33 master's degrees and 10 Ph.D.'s awarded 1955-59. 48 graduate students registered fall 1959.

Engineering.—Industrial. Engineering valuation. 1 professor. 9 master's degrees and 1 Ph.D. awarded 1955-59. 6 graduate students registered fall 1959.

Engineering.—Mechanical. Work may be taken as a divided major with departments offering work for the Ph.D. in related fields. 3 professorial staff. 13 master's degrees and 3 Ph.D.'s awarded 1955-59. 15 graduate students registered fall 1959.

Engineering.—Metallurgical. Offered by Departments of Chemical Engineering, Chemistry, Mechanical Engineering, and Physics. 6 professorial staff. Ph.D. program begun 1956. 15 master's degrees awarded 1955-59; 8 Ph.D.'s since 1956. 17 graduate students registered fall 1959.

Engineering.—Nuclear. Offered by Engineering Department. 4 professorial staff. Ph.D. program begun 1957. 16 master's degrees awarded 1955-59. 31 graduate students registered fall 1959.

Engineering.—Theoretical and Applied Mechanics. 3 professorial staff. 12 master's degrees and 12 Ph.D.'s awarded 1955-59. 10 graduate students registered fall 1959.

Forestry. Work may be taken in silviculture or wood technology or as a divided major with departments offering work in related fields. 4 professorial staff. 12 master's degrees and 4 Ph.D.'s awarded 1955-59. 7 graduate students registered fall 1959.

Genetics. 4 professorial staff. 6 master's degrees and 12 Ph.D.'s awarded 1955-59. 13 graduate students registered fall 1959.

Geology. Work may be taken as a divided major with departments offering work in related fields. 3 professorial staff. 24 master's degrees and 3 Ph.D.'s awarded 1955-59. 16 graduate students registered fall 1959.

Home Economics.—Food and Nutrition. 6 professorial staff. 18 master's degrees and 6 Ph.D.'s awarded 1955-59. 16 graduate students registered fall 1959.

Home Economics.—Household Equipment. Work may be taken as a divided major with departments offering work in related fields. 2 professorial staff. 3 master's degrees and 2 Ph.D.'s awarded 1955-59. 5 graduate students registered fall 1959.

Home Economics.—Institution Management. Work may be taken as a divided major with departments offering work in related fields. 1 professor. 6 master's degrees and 2 Ph.D.'s awarded 1955-59. 5 graduate students registered fall 1959.

Horticulture. Fruit, vegetable, and nursery crops; floriculture. 2 professorial staff. 6 master's degrees and 3 Ph.D.'s awarded 1955-59. 6 graduate students registered fall 1959.

Mathematics. Mathematics and applied mathematics. 11 professorial staff. 32 master's degrees and 16 Ph.D.'s awarded 1955-59. 43 graduate students registered fall 1959.

Physics. 21 professorial staff. 40 master's degrees and 33 Ph.D.'s awarded 1955-59. 75 graduate students registered fall 1959.

Poultry Husbandry. Nutrition, breeding, physiology, and poultry products technology. 4 professorial staff. 2 master's degrees and 6 Ph.D.'s awarded 1955-59. 10 graduate students registered fall 1959.

Statistics. 7 professorial staff. 23 master's degrees and 13 Ph.D.'s awarded 1955-59. 33 graduate students registered fall 1959.

Veterinary Medicine.—Anatomy. Microscopic and gross anatomy. 1 professor. 3 master's degrees and 2 Ph.D.'s awarded 1955-59. 2 graduate students registered fall 1959.

Veterinary Medicine.—Hygiene. Veterinary bacteriology. 5 professorial staff. 2 master's degrees and 2 Ph.D.'s awarded 1955-59. 7 graduate students registered fall 1959.

Veterinary Medicine.—Pathology. 5 professorial staff. 6 master's degrees and 1 Ph.D. awarded 1955-59. 12 graduate students registered fall 1959.

Veterinary Medicine.—Physiology and Pharmacology. 3 professorial staff. 2 Ph.D.'s awarded 1955-59. 4 graduate students registered fall 1959.

Zoology and Entomology. Morphology, ecology, apiculture, taxonomy, embryology, parasitology, physiology, protozoology, entomology, wildlife management, and fishery management. 15 professorial staff. 57 master's degrees and 49 Ph.D.'s awarded 1955-59. 50 graduate students registered fall 1959.

Jefferson Medical College of Philadelphia

PHILADELPHIA 7, PENNSYLVANIA

Graduate Studies in the Medical Sciences

The Graduate School was organized in 1948, and the first Ph.D. was awarded in 1951. College is privately controlled and nonsectarian. Both men and women are admitted.

A joint program of graduate studies is also offered in association with The Pennsylvania State University. Students in this program may be candidates for degrees with major concentration in a medical science at the Jefferson Medical College or candidates for degrees with major concentration in a basic science at The Pennsylvania State University.

No residence facilities are provided for graduate students.

Residence requirement for Ph.D.: minimum of 3 years of graduate study, of which at least 2 must be taken in residence at Jefferson Medical College.

ADMISSION REQUIREMENTS

For graduate study: bachelor's, master's, or M.D. degree; particular proficiency or aptitude in field of proposed study; qualifying examinations in some departments. Candidates for the Ph.D. must demonstrate reading knowledge of French and German and pass a preliminary examination before taking final examination for the degree.

Apply to the Secretary of the Board for the Regulation of Graduate Studies in the Medical Sciences at any time.

FEES AND FIRST-YEAR AID

No application fee. Tuition $500 per year. Special fees approximate $60 per year.

First-year aid available: 6 teaching fellowships, $2,900; 20 research assistantships, $1,800-$3,500.

Apply to the Secretary of the Board for the Regulation of Graduate Studies in the Medical Sciences at any time.

FIELDS OF STUDY FOR THE PH.D.

Anatomy. Gross anatomy, cytology, anthropology, histology, embryology, neuroanatomy, endocrinology, histochemistry. 12 professorial staff.

Biochemistry. 7 professorial staff. 1 Ph.D. awarded 1955-59. 2 graduate students registered fall 1959.

Microbiology. 7 professorial staff. 2 master's degrees and 2 Ph.D.'s awarded 1955-59. 6 graduate students registered fall 1959.

Pathology. Experimental pathology. Prerequisite for graduate study: M.D. 6 professorial staff.

Pharmacology. Neuropharmacology, muscle pharmacology, toxicology of pesticides, drug metabolism, pharmacology of antimitotic agents. Prerequisite for graduate study: equivalent of degree in chemistry or biology with chemistry minor. Recommended: French and German. 7 professorial staff. 3 master's degrees and 9 Ph.D.'s awarded 1955-59. 14 graduate students registered fall 1959.

Physiology. Mammalian physiology, physiology of gastrointestinal tract (experimental gastroenterology), endocrine and cardiovascular physiology. 10 professorial staff. 3 master's degrees and 5 Ph.D.'s awarded 1955-59. 10 graduate students registered fall 1959.

Johns Hopkins University

BALTIMORE 18, MARYLAND

Established in 1876, Johns Hopkins was the first institution of higher education in the United States to emphasize university methods as contrasted with collegiate. There is considerable variety in the course offerings and the degree requirements of the departments, but all programs are oriented toward the doctoral degree with emphasis on productive scholarship and research. Some departments offer an intermediate master's degree as well as the doctorate; others prefer not to accept students who desire only the master's. The university is privately controlled and nonsectarian. Both men and women are admitted.

Graduate programs leading to the Ph.D. are administered by the Faculty of Philosophy, the School of Engineering, some preclinical departments of the School of Medicine, and by the School of Advanced International Studies in Washington, D.C. In addition, the School of Engineering gives the D.Eng., and the School of Hygiene gives the D.P.H. and the D.Sc. in Hygiene.

Competent students admitted at any level of preparation; grades and formal credit requirements are de-emphasized.

Residence requirement for Ph.D.: at least 1 year of full-time study must be spent in residence at Johns Hopkins. Summer and evening courses available, but degree cannot be earned in this way.

Graduate Programs in Baltimore

Rooms and housekeeping apartments available for graduate students in university-operated apartment house.

Special facilities include: library of approximately 1,162,300 volumes, with special collections in economic classics, modern German drama, French drama, linguistics, architectural classics, orientalia, Swiss history, early Maryland items, history of medicine, and Lanier manuscripts; archaeological museum; 2 Van de Graaff generators; mass spectrometer; ultracentrifuges; wide-range computing calorimeter; range of au-tomatic spectrophotometric equipment; high-voltage X-ray; Institute for Cooperative Research; field work in oceanography through Chesapeake Bay Institute; research in micronutrients; geology field camp. Operations Research Office offers instruction for doctoral candidates with Department of Industrial Engineering. Other opportunities for research result from affiliation with Brookhaven National Laboratory.

ADMISSION REQUIREMENTS

For graduate study: fitness for advanced study in chosen field is individually determined, although most students have bachelor's degree. Recommended: GRE. Before receiving Ph.D. degree, students are required to show competence in 2 foreign languages and take comprehensive examinations in the field.

Apply to Director of Admissions, preferably in the first term of the senior year in college. Applications received later in the year will be considered if financial assistance is not required.

FEES AND FIRST-YEAR AID

No application fee. Tuition $1,200 per academic year ($1,450 beginning 1961-62). Room (in university-operated apartment house) $55 per month; apartments $70-$90. Meals available only in cafeteria on cash basis.

Full-time fellowships are available to first-year students, many carrying cash stipends. The number of awards changes from year to year as vacancies occur within the departments. Some departments offer part-time employment on contract research.

Applications should be sent to Director of Admissions by March 1 with application for admission.

FIELDS OF STUDY FOR THE PH.D.

Most departments offer teaching opportunities and some require teaching experience for the doctor's degree. All teaching fellows are directed and supervised through departmental organizations.

Anatomy. Gross, microscopic, or comparative anatomy; neuroanatomy; histochemistry; physical anthropology. Offered by Department of Anatomy, School of Medicine. Prerequisites for graduate study: good background in fundamentals of biology, chemistry, and physics, at least equivalent to medical school requirements. Recommended: ability to read French and German.

8 professorial staff. Program begun 1958. 1 graduate student registered fall 1959.

Art. Any area from Early Christian through modern art. Prerequisites for graduate study: A.B. with excellent academic record; French or German. 3 professorial staff. 3 master's degrees and 2 Ph.D.'s awarded 1955-59. 5 graduate students registered fall 1959. New enrollment limited to 3-5.

Biochemistry. Programs offered in the Departments of Biology, Chemistry, and Physiological Chemistry in the School of Medicine, and also in the School of Hygiene and Public Health.

Biology. Growth and development, cytogenetics, genetics and evolution, physiology and biochemistry. Prerequisites for graduate study: fundamentals of biology; inorganic and organic chemistry; physics. Recommended: calculus; statistics; analytical and physical chemistry; geology (paleontology). 23 professorial staff. 3 master's degrees and 34 Ph.D.'s awarded 1955-59. 60 graduate students registered fall 1959. New enrollment limited to approximately 10.

Biophysics. Molecular biology, virus synthesis, protein structure, electron microscopy, photobiology, nerve and muscle biophysics. Prerequisites for graduate study: general biology and 1 additional subject in biology; inorganic and organic chemistry; general physics and 2 other courses in physics; differential and integral calculus; French, German, or Russian. Recommended: physical chemistry; additional mathematics, second language. 6 professorial staff. 4 Ph.D.'s awarded 1955-59. 12 graduate students registered fall 1959. New enrollment limited to 4 or 5.

Chemistry. General training in all major branches. Special training in synthetic organic chemistry, natural products, organic biochemistry, mechanisms of reactions, reaction kinetics, catalysis, crystallography, molecular structure, nuclear chemistry, structural inorganic chemistry, colloid chemistry, electrochemistry, calorimetry, thermodynamic measurements, spectroscopy, theoretical chemistry. Prerequisite for graduate study: adequate knowledge of chemistry, physics, and mathematics. Recommended: reading knowledge of French and German. 12 professorial staff. 38 master's degrees and 25 Ph.D.'s awarded 1955-59. 56 graduate students registered fall 1959. Total enrollment limited to about 60.

Chemistry.—Physiological. Enzymatic oxidations and phosphorylations: biochemistry of mitochondria; enzymatic processes and cellular metabolism; lipid metabolism and hormonal control; passage of substances across biological barriers and *in vivo* metabolic activities; reaction mechanisms, catalysis, and enzyme models; chemistry of porphyrins; cytochrome oxidase; biosynthesis of cholesterol; reaction mechanisms; physical chemistry of proteins; action of vitamin D; biological oxidations; enzymatic phosphate transfer reactions; protein synthesis; neurochemistry and lipid metabolism; cytochrome reductases. Offered by Department of Physiological Chemistry, School of Medicine. Prerequisites for graduate study: inorganic, organic, analytical, and physical chemistry; general biology; physics and calculus. Ph.D. candidacy prerequisites: ability to read scientific publications in German and 1 other modern foreign language; preliminary and cumulative examinations; acceptance of dissertation. 12 professorial staff. 4 Ph.D.'s awarded 1955-59. 10 graduate students registered fall 1959. New enrollment limited to 5.

Classics. Greek and Latin languages, literatures, and epigraphy; ancient history and classical archaeology. Prerequisite for graduate study: 3 years each of Latin and Greek. 4 professorial staff. 6 master's degrees and 6 Ph.D.'s awarded 1955-59. 9 graduate students registered fall 1959. Total enrollment limited to 14.

Comparative Literature. Interdepartmental programs with English, Romance Languages, and Oriental Seminary.

Crystallography. Interdepartment program with Chemistry, Geology, and Physics.

Education. History and philosophy of education; educational psychology; guidance; administration (particularly theory); secondary or teacher education. Prerequisites for graduate study: basic knowledge of 1 or more fields related to education, such as history, philosophy, psychology, political science. 7 professorial staff. 8 master's degrees and 9 Ph.D.'s awarded 1955-59. 14 graduate students registered fall 1959. Doctoral enrollment limited to 12-15.

Engineering.—Chemical. Reaction kinetics and reactor dynamics, transport processes, rheology, laminar flame theory and experiment, fluid/particle systems. Prerequisite for graduate study: outstanding record in physical sciences or engineering. For doctoral candidacy: 2 foreign languages; qualifying examination. Recommended: NSF Examination or GRE. 6 professorial staff. 11 master's degrees and 8 doctorates

awarded 1955-59. 18 graduate students registered fall 1959.

Engineering.—Electrical. Signal analysis and synthesis, information theory, network synthesis, control systems, applied solid-state physics, magnetic resonance, microwaves, curriculum in systems engineering. Prerequisite for graduate study: outstanding record in the physical sciences or engineering. For doctoral candidacy: qualifying examination; 2 foreign languages. 7 professorial staff. 27 master's degrees and 22 doctorates awarded 1955-59. 54 graduate students registered fall 1959.

Engineering. — Industrial. Operations research, human engineering, industrial statistics. Prerequisites for graduate study: B.S. in engineering, science, or mathematics; B average or better; letters of reference. Recommended: GRE. For doctoral candidacy: 2 foreign languages; comprehensive preliminary oral examination. 5 professorial staff. 10 master's degrees and 4 doctorates awarded 1955-59. 29 graduate students registered fall 1959. Total enrollment limited to 25-30.

Engineering.—Mechanics. Fluid, solid, continuum, or geophysical mechanics; plasma dynamics; material sciences. Offered by Department of Mechanics. Prerequisite for graduate study: major in engineering or science. Recommended: GRE. For doctoral candidacy: 2 foreign languages; comprehensive examination. 15 professorial staff. Department of Mechanics was formed in June 1960 by combining Departments of Aeronautics, Civil Engineering, and Mechanical Engineering. The following figures represent combined data for these departments. 41 master's degrees and 24 doctorates awarded 1955-59. 66 graduate students registered fall 1959.

Engineering.—Sanitary. Water quality or supply, waste-water disposal, water resources conservation and development. Offered by Department of Sanitary Engineering and Water Resources. Prerequisites for graduate study: major in engineering, physical sciences, or biology; high scholastic attainment; letter of reference. Recommended: personal interview. For doctoral candidacy: approximately 2 years of academic study at graduate level. 4 professorial staff. 40 master's degrees and 7 doctorates awarded 1955-59. 23 graduate students registered fall 1959. Total enrollment limited to about 23.

English. — Comparative Literature. Linguistics; literature of the Middle Ages or of the 16th, 17th, or 18th centuries; Romantic, Victorian, or American literature. Prerequisites for graduate study: liberal arts background; 1 or 2 languages (Greek, Latin, French, Italian, German, Spanish). Recommended: GRE. 7 professorial staff. 8 master's degrees and 23 Ph.D.'s awarded 1955-59. 32 graduate students registered fall 1959. Total enrollment limited to about 35.

Geography. Physical, plant, or human geography. Prerequisites for graduate study: good background in physical or social sciences; 1 foreign language. Recommended: basic sciences and mathematics. 4 professorial staff. 3 master's degrees and 7 Ph.D.'s awarded 1955-59. 8 graduate students registered fall 1959.

Geology. Petrology, geochemistry, structural geology, sedimentation, paleontology, research scholar training. Prerequisites for graduate study: biology; chemistry; physics; mathematics; B average or better; French and German; GRE. 8 professorial staff. 3 master's degrees and 20 Ph.D.'s awarded 1955-59. 23 graduate students registered fall 1959. Total enrollment limited to 25.

German. Old and Middle High German, Renaissance and Baroque, Age of Goethe, 19th century or modern literature; Anglo-German or American-German literary relations; Germanic philology. Combined program with Departments of History, Philosophy, Classics, and Romance Languages and Literatures. Prerequisites for graduate study: knowledge of spoken and written German; acquaintance with historical and literary background. 4 professorial staff. 10 master's degrees and 2 Ph.D.'s awarded 1955-59. 17 graduate students registered fall 1959. Total enrollment limited to approximately 20.

History. American intellectual history; economic history; Renaissance Italy; England and France in the Middle Ages; Southern or modern American history; modern Germany and diplomatic history of modern Europe; Chinese and Inner Asian history; England in the 18th, 19th, and 20th centuries; foreign relations of the United States. Recommended for graduate study: good reading knowledge of French and German. 10 professorial staff. 14 master's degrees and 22 Ph.D.'s awarded 1955-59. 45 graduate students registered fall 1959. Total enrollment limited to 45.

*History of Medicine.—*All aspects of the history of medicine. Offered by the Institute of the History of Medicine, School of Medicine. Prerequisites for graduate study: training in medical or kindred sciences; preferably M.D. degree; reading knowledge of 2 languages (French, German, Latin). Ph.D. candidacy prerequisites: French, German, and Latin; departmental examinations. 2 professors. 1 Ph.D. awarded 1955-59.

International Relations. Interdepartmental programs in the Social Sciences Group of the Faculty of Philosophy.

Mathematics. Analysis, especially differential equations; functional analysis and operator theory; algebraic geometry; abstract algebra; lie group theory; group representations; differential geometry; algebraic topology or numbers; applied mathematics. Prerequisites for graduate study: advanced calculus, including infinite series; differential equations; vector analysis and a few courses beyond this level. Recommended: thorough background in physical sciences; reading knowledge of French and German; complex variables, basic analysis or introduction to modern algebra. 14 professorial staff. 6 master's degrees and 3 Ph.D.'s awarded 1955-59. 27 graduate students registered fall 1959.

Meteorology and Astrophysics. Combined program with Chemistry, Geology, and Physics.

Microbiology. Bacteriology, virology, immunology, cellular chemistry. Offered by Department of Microbiology, School of Medicine. Prerequisites for graduate study: elementary courses in biology; chemistry, including organic; physics; reading knowledge of 2 foreign languages; qualifying examination; at least 2 years full-time study in the department. 10 professorial staff. Program begun 1959. 2 graduate students registered fall 1959. Total enrollment limited to about 20.

Oceanography. Physical, chemical, and biological oceanography, dynamics of circulation, turbulence and diffusion, interaction of ocean and atmosphere, physiology and biochemistry of phytoplankton growth, primary production, zooplankton growth. Prerequisite for graduate study: background in sciences or engineering, including mathematics, physics, chemistry, biology, and geology. 5 professorial staff. 6 master's degrees and 2 Ph.D.'s awarded 1955-59. 8 graduate students registered fall 1959. Total enrollment limited to 20.

Oriental Studies. History and literatures of the ancient Orient, the Bible, Jewish and Islamic studies, Semitic philology. Offered by Oriental Seminary. Prerequisite for graduate study: some French and German. 6 professorial staff. 15 mas-

ter's degrees and 21 Ph.D.'s awarded 1955-59. 28 graduate students registered fall 1959. New enrollment limited to approximately 10.

Philosophy. History of philosophy, metaphysics, and theory of knowledge; logic and philosophy of science; ethics; aesthetics; philosophy of history. Interdepartmental programs in history of ideas or of science and philosophy of education. Prerequisites for graduate study: strong undergraduate record; previous acquaintance with some of the chief topics and problems of philosophy. Ph.D. candidacy prerequisite: reading knowledge of French and German. 6 professorial staff. 11 master's degrees and 6 Ph.D.'s awarded 1955-59. 32 graduate students registered fall 1959. New enrollment limited to approximately 8.

Physics. Atomic and molecular physics with specialties such as plasma physics, spectroscopy, solid-state and low-temperature physics, infrared, X-rays, nuclear physics, high-energy physics, theoretical physics, thermodynamic and statistical mechanics, field theory and elementary particle theory. Prerequisites for graduate study: good background in physics, chemistry and mathematics. Recommended: knowledge of French or German. 15 professorial staff. 10 master's degrees and 44 Ph.D.'s awarded 1955-59. 123 graduate students registered fall 1959. Total full-time enrollment limited to 80.

Physiology. Neurophysiology (especially physiology of central nervous system), neuroendocrinology, transport mechanism and properties of cell membranes. Offered by Department of Physiology, School of Medicine. Prerequisites for graduate study: mathematics through calculus; at least 3 years of biology; general, physical, and organic chemistry; physics; reading knowledge of 2 foreign languages. 7 professorial staff. 4 Ph.D.'s awarded 1955-59.

Political Economy—Economics. Monetary, price, and income theory; development, growth, and fluctuations; labor economics; economic history; statistics, mathematical economics, econometrics; public finances; methodology; international economics; history of economic theory. Prerequisites for graduate study: background of liberal arts, including fundamentals of economics; elementary statistics; differential calculus; 1 foreign language, 11 professorial staff. 10 master's degrees and 17 Ph.D.'s awarded 1955-59. 33 graduate students registered fall 1959. New enrollment limited to 12.

Political Science. Politics, public administration, theoretical and legal structure of political organization, constitutional law and development, international law and relations, comparative government. Prerequisites for graduate study: broad background of basic work in political science; 2 foreign languages. 6 professorial staff. 11 master's degrees and 9 Ph.D.'s awarded 1955-59. 26 graduate students registered fall 1959. Total enrollment limited to 30.

Psychology. Human engineering, learning, perception, personality and abnormal psychology; physiological and comparative psychology; psychometrics and social psychology. Prerequisite for graduate study: reading knowledge of French, German or Russian. Recommended: background in biological and physical sciences and in mathematics; GRE and MAT. 7 professorial staff. 11 master's degrees and 12 Ph.D.'s awarded 1955-59. 20 graduate students registered fall 1959. New enrollment limited to 5.

Romance Languages. French, Hispanic, and Italian languages and literature; Romance philology. Prerequisite for graduate study: good background in at least 1 of the 3 major fields. 9 professorial staff. 15 master's degrees and 1 Ph.D. awarded 1955-59. 31 graduate students registered fall 1959. New enrollment limited to 20.

Social Relations. Social organization, mathematical sociology. Recommended for graduate study: GRE. Ph.D. candidacy prerequisites: 2 foreign languages; written examination. 4 professorial staff. Program begun 1959.

School of Advanced International Studies

The School is located in Washington, D.C. It was founded in 1944 to provide thorough training for a limited number of young men and women who are seeking careers of international service with the government, with private business, or with private research or educational institutions. First Ph.D. was awarded in 1949.

No residence facilities are provided.

Residence requirement for Ph.D. is the same as for the university as a whole.

ADMISSION REQUIREMENTS

For graduate study: bachelor's degree with adequate preparation in the social sciences; satisfactory academic record; faculty references; interview; reading knowledge of at least 1 modern foreign language; course in the principles of economics. Recommended: work in history and political science, including 19th-century European history, American diplomatic history, and basic economics. For candidacy for Ph.D.: 1 full year of residence work completed with distinction; acceptance of a plan for doctoral research which can be carried out effectively either in Washington or through foreign study and travel.

Apply to Registrar, School of Advanced International Studies, 1906 Florida Avenue, N.W., Washington 9, D. C., at least 30 days prior to registration.

FEES AND FIRST-YEAR AID

Application fee $10. Tuition $1,200 per academic year ($1,450 beginning 1961-62).

School's total fellowship budget approximates $30,000. Fellowships range from partial tuition to full-expense fellowships of $2,500.

Apply to the Registrar, School of Advanced International Studies, 1906 Florida Avenue, N.W., Washington 9, D. C., by March 1.

FIELDS OF STUDY FOR THE PH.D.

Africa Studies. Political, economic, and social trends, particularly south of the Sahara. 4 of the following: international relations and organization; European or American diplomacy and diplomatic history; international economics; international and public law. 1 professor. Ph.D. program begun 1958. 12 master's degrees awarded 1955-59. 14 graduate students registered fall 1959. Total enrollment limited to approximately 20.

Asian Studies. Far East and Southeast Asia: background courses; political, economic, and social studies; area problems of an international nature, such as economic aid, modern strategy, and international politics. 4 of the following: international relations and organization; European or American diplomacy and diplomatic history; international economics; international and public law. 3 professorial staff. 33 master's degrees awarded 1955-59. 12 graduate students registered fall 1959. Total enrollment limited to approximately 20.

Europe. Contemporary developments in Western Europe and/or study of the Soviet State and its institutions. 4 of the following: international relations and organization; European or

American diplomacy and diplomatic history; international economics; international and public law. 2 professors. 63 master's degrees and 1 Ph.D. awarded 1955-59. 39 graduate students registered fall 1959.

Middle East Studies. Geographical, historical, economic, and cultural background of the area as well as its current problems. 4 of the following: international relations and organization; European or American diplomacy and diplomatic history; international economics; international law and public law. 2 professors. 22 master's degrees and 3 Ph.D.'s awarded 1955-59. 14 graduate students registered fall 1959. Total enrollment limited to approximately 20.

Kansas City, University of

KANSAS CITY 10, MISSOURI

The university is a young institution which has been offering college work only since 1933. First graduate instruction was offered in 1939, and the first Ph.D. was awarded in 1957. At present, programs leading to the Ph.D. are offered only in the Schools of Education and Pharmacy. A new program leading to the D. Mus. will be initiated 1960 by the Conservatory of Music. Institution is privately controlled and nonsectarian. Both men and women are admitted.

School of Education

Founded 1953 (after operating as a department 1933-53); first Ph.D. awarded 1957.

Rooms in dormitories available for all students; apartments in community for married students.

Residence requirement for Ph.D.: 3 years beyond bachelor's degree, 2 semesters of which must be spent in residence on campus. Summer and evening courses available.

ADMISSION REQUIREMENTS

For graduate study: bachelor's degree; evidence of high scholastic attainment; entrance test; GRE; approval by Dean of the School of Education and major professors. For candidacy

for Ph.D.: completion of most course work; comprehensive examination; acceptance of thesis proposal or dissertation plan; proficiency in 2 of 3 research skills selected from statistical analysis and experimental design, documentary research, and 1 foreign language; faculty acceptance of plan of work.

Apply to the Office of Admissions before August 15.

FEES AND FIRST-YEAR AID

No application fee. Tuition $22 per credit hour. Special fees approximate $25 annually. Room (in dormitory) $270 per school year. Approximate annual cost of board in college dining room $550 per school year. Teaching fellowships available, stipend $1,800.

Apply to the Dean of the School of Education before August 15.

FIELDS OF STUDY FOR THE PH.D.

Education. Administration and community leadership, general education (common learnings, core curriculum, and general college education), personnel guidance and human development, curriculum and instruction. 13 professorial staff. 187 master's degrees and 7 Ph.D.'s awarded 1955-59. 114 graduate students registered fall 1959.

Education.—General. Humanities, physical sciences, and social sciences. Offered by the School of Education and the College of Arts and Sciences. 30 professorial staff. Ph.D. program begun 1956. 114 graduate students registered fall 1959.

School of Pharmacy

Founded 1943. Programs leading to the Ph.D. offered for the first time in 1960.

Facilities for housing graduate students are the same as for the School of Education.

Residence requirement for Ph.D.: 3 years beyond bachelor's degree, 4 semesters of which must be taken in residence on campus.

ADMISSION REQUIREMENTS

These are generally the same as for the School of Education except that German and French (or an approved language substitute) are required for candidacy for Ph.D.

Apply to the Office of Admissions before August 15.

FEES AND FIRST-YEAR AID

Fees are the same as for the School of Education. Application for first-year aid should be made to the Dean of the School of Pharmacy by August 15.

FIELDS OF STUDY FOR THE PH.D.

Pharmaceutical Chemistry. Synthesis of organic medicinal products. 2 professorial faculty plus associates in related fields. Ph.D. program begun 1960. 2 master's degrees awarded 1955-59. 4 graduate students registered fall 1959.

Pharmacology. 2 professorial faculty plus associates in related fields. Ph.D. program begun 1960. 5 master's degrees awarded 1955-59. 3 graduate students registered fall 1959.

Pharmacy. Manufacturing, physical, and chemical pharmacy. 2 professorial staff plus associates in related fields. Ph.D. program begun 1960. 2 master's degrees awarded 1955-59. 3 graduate students registered fall 1959.

Kansas State University of Agriculture and Applied Science

MANHATTAN, KANSAS

The Graduate School

Although graduate instruction was offered as early as 1868 and master's degrees awarded by 1871, it was not until 1886 that a standing committee on graduate work was created. The present graduate school was organized in 1919, and the first Ph.D. was awarded in 1933. Institution is publicly controlled by the state. Both men and women are admitted.

Room and board in college dormitories available for men; for women only during summer session. Single rooms and some apartments available in community. University operates 456 permanent dormitory apartments for married students.

Library contains approximately 230,000 cataloged volumes and receives 4,000 serial publications.

Residence requirement for Ph.D.: 3 years

beyond bachelor's degree, with minimum of 1 year in residence on campus. Summer courses available.

ADMISSION REQUIREMENTS

For graduate study: bachelor's degree; B average in last 2 years; specific preparation for graduate study in selected field; recommendations. For candidacy for Ph.D.: completion of substantial portion of course work; reading knowledge of 2 modern foreign languages (usually French and German, although Russian or other approved language may be substituted in certain cases); preliminary examinations in major and minor fields.

Apply to the Dean of the Graduate School at least 1 month before admission is desired.

FEES AND FIRST-YEAR AID

No application fee. Tuition for state residents and staff members $208 a year; others $308. Approximate cost of room in community for men $220; for women $240. Approximate annual cost of board in college dining room $440. 1-bedroom apartments $62.50 per month; 2-bedroom $67.50.

First-year aid available: teaching fellowships and research assistantships, $1,485-$2,280.

Apply to Dean of Graduate School before April 1.

FIELDS OF STUDY FOR THE PH.D.

Two seminars on the skills basic to the processes of communicating knowledge to university students are offered. Each carries 2 hours of graduate credit and one seminar is offered each semester.

Agricultural Economics. Marketing, farm organization, agricultural credit, conservation, land economics, prices, taxation, agricultural policy, agricultural industries, general agricultural economics. Offered by Department of Economics and Sociology. Prerequisites for graduate study: economics plus mathematics or statistics. 23 professorial staff. Ph.D. program begun 1958. 55 master's degrees awarded 1955-59. 24 graduate students registered fall 1959.

Agronomy. Crop production, physiology, and ecology; pasture improvement; plant breeding; weed control; plant genetics; soil chemistry, fertility, physics, and management; irrigation; soil classification; wind erosion. Prerequisite for graduate study: B.S. in agriculture, biological science, or physical science. 21 professorial staff. 48 master's degrees and 15 Ph.D.'s awarded 1955-59. 28 graduate students registered fall 1959.

Animal Breeding. Population genetics (in rodents, dairy cattle, poultry, swine, sheep, and beef cattle); reproductive physiology in these same species. Prerequisites for graduate study: algebra; physics or another physical science or advanced mathematics; general and organic chemistry; botany; zoology. Recommended: advanced mathematics; quantitative analysis; genetics; 6 hours of livestock production or management courses. 8 professorial staff. Ph.D. program begun 1956. 17 master's degrees and 3 Ph.D.'s awarded 1955-59. 3 graduate students registered fall 1959.

Animal Nutrition. Nutrition, biochemistry, physiology, bacteriology, endocrinology, anatomy, mathematics. Offered by Departments of Animal Husbandry, Dairy Husbandry, Poultry Husbandry, Chemistry, and Physiology. Prerequisites for graduate study: B.S. in one of above departments, including 6 units of animal production courses; bacteriology; zoology; histology or cytology; algebra; trigonometry; physics; general, quantitative, qualitative, and organic chemistry. 27 professorial staff. 30 master's degrees and 10 Ph.D.'s awarded 1955-59. 22 graduate students registered fall 1959.

Applied Mechanics. Stress analysis (strength of materials and theory of elasticity), dynamics, vibrations, applied mathematics. 9 professorial staff. 65 master's degrees and 2 Ph.D.'s awarded 1955-59. 17 graduate students registered fall 1959.

Bacteriology. Dairy, food, general, sanitary, and soil bacteriology; bacteriology of poultry diseases; physiology of micro-organisms; virology; microbial genetics. Prerequisites for graduate study: 15 semester hours of chemistry, including organic; 10 of biology, excluding bacteriology; 13 of bacteriology; 1 year of college physics. Recommended: genetics; biochemistry; mathematics through calculus. 9 professorial staff. 14 master's degrees and 16 Ph.D.'s awarded 1955-59. 17 graduate students registered fall 1959.

Botany. Plant pathology, physiology, taxonomy, ecology, anatomy, cytology, and nematology; cytogenetics. Offered by Department of Botany and Plant Pathology. Prerequisite for graduate study: degree in biological or agricul-

tural sciences. 14 professorial staff. 11 master's degrees and 9 Ph.D.'s awarded 1955-59. 14 graduate students registered fall 1959.

Chemical Engineering. Heat transfer, fluid mechanics, fluidization, mass transfer, phase equilibria, chemurgy of farm crops. 6 professorial staff. Ph.D. program begun 1959. 18 master's degrees awarded 1955-59. 12 graduate students registered fall 1959.

Chemistry. Analytical chemistry; biochemistry; inorganic, organic, or physical chemistry. Prerequisite for graduate study: reading knowledge of German; written qualifying examinations in four fields. 25 professorial staff. 27 master's degrees and 38 Ph.D.'s awarded 1955-59. 66 graduate students registered fall 1959.

Electronics. Switching circuits, networks theory, electromagnetic waves, information theory, servomechanisms, analog computation, pulse techniques, noise and modulation theory, digital techniques, power systems. Offered by Department of Electrical Engineering. 9 professorial staff. Ph.D. program begun 1959. 17 master's degrees awarded 1955-59. 18 graduate students registered fall 1959.

Entomology. Insect physiology, toxicology, behavior, growth, development, ecology, taxonomy; host-plant resistance to insects; apiculture; attacks of insects on stored grain, fruits, and vegetables, shade trees, field crops, man, and animals. Prerequisites for graduate study: 9 semester hours of entomology; 8 each of animal and plant science; 10 of chemistry and/or physics; 1 course in bacteriology; college mathematics. Recommended: report writing; modern language; statistics; biochemistry. 8 professorial staff. 27 master's degrees and 21 Ph.D.'s awarded 1955-59. 32 graduate students registered fall 1959.

Foods and Nutrition. Chemical, histological, bacteriologic, and organoleptic qualities of foods; human nutrition. 8 professorial staff. 15 master's degrees and 2 Ph.D.'s awarded 1955-59. 10 graduate students registered fall 1959.

Genetics. An interdepartmental program of broad scope in both basic and applied research. Offered by Departments of Agronomy, Animal Husbandry, Bacteriology, Botany, Dairy Husbandry, Horticulture, Poultry Husbandry, and Statistics. Prerequisites for graduate study: general and organic chemistry; general botany and zoology; 6 units advanced biological science; college algebra; trigonometry; elementary genetics. 10 professorial staff. 4 master's degrees and

8 Ph.D.'s awarded 1955-59. 12 graduate students registered fall 1959.

Horticulture. Floriculture, olericulture, ornamental horticulture, pomology. 7 professorial staff. Ph.D. program begun 1960. 19 master's degrees awarded 1955-59. 10 graduate students registered fall 1959.

Mechanical Engineering. Heat transfer, thermodynamics, gas dynamics, automatic controls, machine design, instrumentation. 9 professorial staff. Ph.D. program begun 1956. 23 master's degrees awarded 1955-59. 31 graduate students registered fall 1959.

Milling Industry. Cereal chemistry, flour milling technology, feed technology. Offered by Department of Flour and Feed Milling Industries. Prerequisites for graduate study: B.S. in physical or biological sciences, engineering, or agriculture; courses in mathematics, chemistry, and physics. 11 professorial staff. 8 master's degrees and 3 Ph.D.'s awarded 1955-59. 6 graduate students registered fall 1959.

Parasitology. Offered by the Department of Zoology. Prerequisite for graduate study: 19 hours advanced zoology. Recommended: statistics; biochemistry; entomology; bacteriology. 2 professorial staff. 7 master's degrees and 7 Ph.D.'s awarded 1955-59. 7 graduate students registered fall 1959.

Physics. Solid-state, molecular, nuclear, or theoretical physics; gaseous electronics. Prerequisite for graduate study: physics major with adequate mathematical background. 17 professorial staff. 29 master's degrees and 4 Ph.D.'s awarded 1955-59. 31 graduate students registered fall 1959.

Psychology. General-experimental, industrial, and counseling psychology. Prerequisites for graduate study: 18 units of psychology or equivalent, including experimental psychology, history of psychology, and statistics; GRE or MAT. 10 professorial staff. Ph.D. program begun 1957. 22 master's degrees awarded 1955-59. 13 graduate students registered fall 1959.

Veterinary Medicine. Veterinary pathology and physiology. Offered by Departments of Pathology and Physiology. Prerequisite for graduate study: D.V.M. Ph.D. program begun 1959. 34 master's degrees awarded 1955-59. 10 graduate students registered fall 1959.

Zoology. Embryology, endocrinology. Prerequisite for graduate study: 19 hours of advanced zoology. Recommended: biochemistry; botany; entomology; bacteriology. 9 professorial staff. Ph.D. program begun 1959. 12 master's degrees awarded 1955-59. 10 graduate students registered fall 1959.

Kansas, University of

LAWRENCE, KANSAS

The Graduate School

Established in 1896, the Graduate School conferred its first Ph.D. degree in that year. A program leading to the Ed.D. degree is also offered. University is publicly controlled by the state. Both men and women are admitted.

Most graduate students live in private homes, although some men students are assigned rooms in dormitories. 240 apartments available for married students.

Established at the university are: the Geological Survey; museums of natural history and of art; bureaus of child research and business research; a governmental research center; an engineering research center. University is also affiliated with Argonne National Laboratory, Los Alamos Scientific Laboratory, Menninger Clinic, Kansas School for the Deaf, and the Linda Hall Library in Kansas City. Library contains approximately 820,000 volumes, with special collections in European history, modern English literature, history of botany, and ornithology.

Residence requirement for Ph.D.: 3 years beyond bachelor's degree, of which 1 year must be taken in residence at the University of Kansas. Summer courses offered in many fields; evening courses in education and engineering only.

ADMISSION REQUIREMENTS

For graduate study: bachelor's degree; B average; specific preparation for graduate study in proposed field. Recommended: GRE and MAT. Reading knowledge of 2 of 3 languages (French, German, or Russian) required for degree.

Apply to the Dean of the Graduate School at least 3 weeks before admission is desired.

FEES AND FIRST-YEAR AID

No application fee. Tuition for residents of Kansas $208 per year; others $308. Usually no other fees are required. Room and board in community for single students averages $850-$1,050 per year. Furnished apartments for married students available at $60-$85 per month.

First-year aid available: about 40 scholarships, $740-$840; about 400 teaching fellowships, $1,800-$2,100 (half-time); about 40 other fellowships, $940-$1,240; about 300 research assistantships, $1,800-$2,000 (half-time); about 35 departmental fellowships, $700-$2,500.

Apply to the Dean of the Graduate School before March 1.

FIELDS OF STUDY FOR THE PH.D.

No specific courses in the methodology of teaching are offered, but several departments supervise their teaching assistants and assistant instructors and offer concrete suggestions on successful teaching.

Anatomy. Gross anatomy, neurology, endocrinology. Prerequisites for graduate study: course in gross anatomy; the courses in biology, chemistry, and physics that are normally required for admission to medical school. 7 professorial staff. 5 master's degrees and 8 Ph.D.'s awarded 1955-59. 17 graduate students registered fall 1959.

Bacteriology. Immunology, bacterial chemistry, bacterial genetics, virology. Prerequisite for graduate study: 26 units in biological sciences, including core work required for major in bacteriology. 6 professorial staff. 18 master's degrees and 11 Ph.D.'s awarded 1955-59. 19 graduate students registered fall 1959.

Biochemistry. Prerequisites for graduate study: organic and inorganic chemistry; qualitative and quantitative analysis; introductory course in biological chemistry. 4 professorial staff. 2 master's degrees and 6 Ph.D.'s awarded 1955-59. 6 graduate students registered fall 1959.

Botany. Mycology, paleobotany, taxonomy, cytology, phycology. Prerequisite for graduate study: 25 units in biological sciences, including 15 in botany. 7 professorial staff. 10 master's degrees and 6 Ph.D.'s awarded 1955-59. 17 graduate students registered fall 1959.

Chemistry. Organic, analytical, inorganic, physical, and high-temperature chemistry; radiochemistry. (A program of pharmaceutical chemistry is offered in collaboration with the Department of Pharmaceutical Chemistry in the School of Pharmacy.) Prerequisites for graduate study: mathematics at least through calculus; inorganic,

organic, analytical, and physical chemistry. 15 professorial staff. 18 master's degrees and 41 Ph.D.'s awarded 1955-59. 110 graduate students registered fall 1959.

Economics. History of economic thought, money and banking, monetary theory, economic theory, labor economics, public finance. Prerequisites for graduate study: 20 units in economics; related courses in political science, history, and sociology. 9 professorial staff. 18 master's degrees and 10 Ph.D.'s awarded 1955-59. 29 graduate students registered fall 1959.

Education. Administration, evaluation, counseling and guidance, curriculum. (Department also collaborates with Department of Psychology in offering a program in counseling psychology.) 29 professorial staff. 377 master's degrees and 7 Ph.D.'s awarded 1955-59. 263 graduate students registered fall 1959.

Engineering.—Chemical. Prerequisites for graduate study: undergraduate chemical engineering program. 5 professorial staff. 18 master's degrees and 4 Ph.D.'s awarded 1955-59. 19 graduate students registered fall 1959.

Engineering. — Electrical. Servomechanisms, analog and digital computers, fields and waves, antennas, circuit theory. 8 professorial staff. 20 master's degrees awarded 1955-59. 55 graduate students registered fall 1959.

English. 18th and 19th century literature, Shakespeare, contemporary poetry, American literature. Prerequisite for graduate study: 24 units in English. 24 professorial staff. 24 master's degrees and 9 Ph.D.'s awarded 1955-59. 82 graduate students registered fall 1959.

Entomology. Basic aspects of entomology, including systematics; morphology; ecology; insect behavior; acarology. Prerequisite for graduate study: 30 units in biological sciences, including a beginning course in entomology. 7 professorial staff. 7 master's degrees and 11 Ph.D.'s awarded 1955-59. 23 graduate students registered fall 1959.

French. 17th, 19th, and 20th century literatures; literature of the Renaissance. Offered by Department of Romance Languages and Literatures. Prerequisite for graduate study: minimum 26 units in French. 5 professorial staff. 9 master's degrees and 3 Ph.D.'s awarded 1955-59. 13 graduate students registered fall 1959.

Geography. Cartography, map planning, vegetation mapping, regional geography. Prerequisites for graduate study: social sciences; basic geography courses. 6 professorial staff. 5 master's degrees and 1 Ph.D. awarded 1955-59. 21 graduate students registered fall 1959.

Geology. Stratigraphic paleontology, geophysics, geochemistry, ground-water geology. Prerequisite for graduate study: courses in mathematics, chemistry, physics, and principal areas of geological study. 13 professorial staff. 71 master's degrees and 9 Ph.D.'s awarded 1955-59. 73 graduate students registered fall 1959.

German. 18th, 19th and 20th century German literature. Offered by Department of Germanic and Slavic Languages and Literatures. Prerequisite for graduate study: 24 hours college credit in German, including minimum of 8 semester hours upper-class credit. 7 professorial staff. Ph.D. program begun 1959. 4 master's degrees awarded 1955-59. 17 graduate students registered fall 1959.

History. American, Far Eastern, Russian, modern European. Prerequisite for graduate study: minimum of 20 semester hours of credit in history. 14 professorial staff. 23 master's degrees and 5 Ph.D.'s awarded 1955-59. 33 graduate students registered fall 1959.

Mathematics. Analysis, topology, algebra. Prerequisite for graduate study: major in mathematics. 19 professorial staff. 34 master's degrees and 12 Ph.D.'s awarded 1955-59. 127 graduate students registered fall 1959.

Medical Microbiology. Viral and rickettsial infections, immunochemistry. Prerequisite for graduate study: courses as needed for admission to medical school, including introductory course in bacteriology or microbiology. 6 professorial staff. 4 master's degrees and 2 Ph.D.'s awarded 1955-59. 9 graduate students registered fall 1959.

Medical Pharmacology. Pharmacodynamics, toxicology. Prerequisites for graduate study: mathematics through trigonometry; 25 semester credits in chemistry; 10 in physics. 9 professorial staff. 1 Ph.D. awarded 1955-59. 3 graduate students registered fall 1959.

Music Education. Music in society, psychological foundations of music. Prerequisite for graduate study: basic program in music education or equivalent. 6 professorial staff. 55 master's degrees and 5 Ph.D.'s awarded 1955-59. 34 graduate students registered fall 1959.

Physics. Solid-state, nuclear, low-temperature, and theoretical physics. Prerequisites for graduate study: minimum of 22 semester hours of physics; working knowledge of calculus. 15 pro-

fessorial staff. 18 master's degrees and 17 Ph.D.'s awarded 1955-59. 51 graduate students registered fall 1959.

Physiology. Cardiovascular or neuromuscular physiology, biophysical instrumentation. Prerequisites for graduate study: the courses needed for admission to medical school. 6 professorial staff. 3 master's degrees and 3 Ph.D.'s awarded 1955-59. 5 graduate students registered fall 1959.

Political Science. Administration, local government, theory, international affairs, political processes, comparative government. Prerequisites for graduate study: 15 semester hours of political science; work in a related field of social science. 15 professorial staff. 35 master's degrees and 5 Ph.D.'s awarded 1955-59. 55 graduate students registered fall 1959.

Psychology. General experimental, social, child, and clinical. Offered by the Department of Psychology which also cooperates with the Department of Education in offering a program in counseling psychology. Prerequisites for graduate study: 15 semester hours of psychology, including a course in experimental; introductory statistics. 15 professorial staff. 45 master's degrees and 35 Ph.D.'s awarded 1955-59. 90 graduate students registered fall 1959.

Sociology. Family relationships, urban sociology, human ecology, groups and associations, collective behavior. Prerequisite for graduate study: minimum of 25 semester credits of social sciences, including 15 hours of sociology. 10 professorial staff. 13 master's degrees and 2 Ph.D.'s awarded 1955-59. 16 graduate students registered fall 1959.

Spanish. Literatures of the 19th and 20th centuries, the Golden Age, and Latin America. Offered by Department of Romance Languages and Literatures. Prerequisite for graduate study: minimum of 26 semester hours of Spanish. 6 professorial staff. 12 master's degrees and 8 Ph.D.'s awarded 1955-59. 17 graduate students registered fall 1959.

Speech and Drama. General speech, drama, speech pathology, and audiology. Prerequisite for graduate study: minimum of 12 hours of speech and drama. 13 professorial staff. Ph.D. program begun 1960. 20 master's degrees awarded 1955-59. 37 graduate students registered fall 1959.

Zoology. Ecology and natural history, comparative serology, invertebrate paleontology, radiation biology. Prerequisite for graduate study: major in biology. 13 professorial staff. 25 master's degrees and 14 Ph.D.'s awarded 1955-59. 35 graduate students registered fall 1959.

Kentucky, University of

LEXINGTON 29, KENTUCKY

The Graduate School

The Graduate School was not organized until 1912, although graduate instruction had been offered since 1870. First Ph.D. was awarded in 1933. Institution is a land-grant university controlled by the state. Both men and women are admitted.

Other doctorates conferred by the university are: Eng.D. (Department of Metallurgical Engineering) and Ed.D. (College of Education).

Rooms in dormitories available for single graduate students; apartments for married students.

Special facilities include: library of approximately 825,000 volumes; affiliation with Oak Ridge Institute of Nuclear Studies.

Residence requirement for Ph.D.: minimum of 3 years beyond bachelor's degree, of which 2 semesters beyond the master's degree must be spent in residence at the University of Kentucky. Summer and evening courses available.

ADMISSION REQUIREMENTS

For graduate study: bachelor's degree; C+ average; undergraduate background in fields selected; GRE during first semester. For candidacy for Ph.D.: proficiency in 2 foreign languages; preliminary qualifying examinations in most fields.

Apply to Dean of Admissions at least 30 days before admission is desired.

FEES AND FIRST-YEAR AID

No application fee. Tuition for state residents $162 a year; others $362. Room (in dormitory) and board for men $255-$275 a year (2 meals, 6 days a week); for women $295. Efficiency apartments $69-$73 a month; 1 bedroom $82-$86.

First-year aid available: 25 scholarships, $600-$750; large number of teaching fellowships, vari-able stipends; 6 other scholarships, $1,800-$2,400; large number of research assistantships, variable stipends.

Apply by March 1 to Dean of Graduate School for scholarships; to departments for assistantships.

FIELDS OF STUDY FOR THE PH.D.

Agricultural Economics. Production economics; agricultural policy, statistics, marketing, and finance; general agricultural economics. Recommended for graduate study: mathematics courses; at least 1 statistics course; philosophy or logic; sociology. 17 professorial staff. 31 master's degrees and 3 Ph.D.'s awarded 1955-59. 19 graduate students registered fall 1959. Enrollment limited to 30-35 candidates.

Animal Husbandry. Beef cattle, sheep, swine, meats, animal nutrition, animal breeding. 10 professorial staff. Ph.D. program begun 1956. 66 master's degrees awarded 1955-59. 39 graduate students registered fall 1959.

Biology. Anatomy and physiology, botany, cytogenetics and evolution, plant pathology, zoology. Offered by the Departments of Anatomy and Physiology, Botany, Agronomy (plant pathology section), and Zoology. Entomology and Pharmacy Departments are advisory only. Prerequisites for graduate study: general botany; elementary physiology; zoology; comparative anatomy. 18 professorial staff. Ph.D. program begun 1959. 5 master's degrees awarded 1955-59. 6 graduate students registered fall 1959.

Chemistry. Inorganic, analytical, organic, physical. Prerequisites for graduate study: about 40 semester hours of chemistry; mathematics through integral calculus; 1 year of physics; 2 years of German. 16 professorial staff. 27 master's degrees and 18 Ph.D.'s awarded 1955-59. 37 graduate students registered fall 1959.

Dairy Science. Dairy nutrition, breeding, technology. 8 professorial staff. Ph.D. program begun 1956. 17 master's degrees and 1 Ph.D. awarded 1956-60. 11 graduate students registered fall 1959.

Diplomacy and International Economics. World politics and organization, foreign policy, international commerce and economics. Offered by Patterson School of Diplomacy and International Economics. Prerequisite for graduate study: major in economics, history, or political science preferred. 8 professorial staff. Ph.D.

program begun 1959. 18 graduate students registered fall 1959. New enrollment limited to 12.

Economics. Economic theory, money and banking, private finance, public finance, mathematical economics, labor economics and industrial relations, statistics, accounting, management, marketing. Offered by Economics Department of College of Commerce. Recommended for graduate study: statistics; accounting; economic history; money and banking; intermediate economic theory. 17 professorial staff. 4 master's degrees and 2 Ph.D.'s awarded 1955-59. 17 graduate students registered fall 1959.

Education.—General. Administration, supervision, curriculum, instruction, agricultural education, home economics education. 38 professorial staff plus arts and sciences staff. 772 master's degrees and 7 Ph.D.'s awarded 1955-59. 456 graduate students registered fall 1959. New enrollment limited to 250 (400 in summer).

Education and Psychology. Guidance and counseling, education, psychology. Offered by College of Education in cooperation with Psychology Department. 36 professorial staff. Ph.D. program begun 1959. 12 master's degrees awarded 1955-59. 140 graduate students registered fall 1959.

English. Major in English and American literature; minors in linguistics and folklore. 25 professorial staff. 38 master's degrees and 12 Ph.D.'s awarded 1955-59. 62 graduate students registered fall 1959.

History. American, British, Russian, ancient, modern European, Far Eastern, social and intellectual history. 17 professorial staff. 22 master's degrees and 11 Ph.D.'s awarded 1955-59. 35 graduate students registered fall 1959.

Mathematics. Analysis, applied mathematics. Offered by Department of Mathematics and Astronomy. Prerequisite for graduate study: 18 hours of upper-division mathematics beyond calculus. 9 professorial staff. 16 master's degrees and 6 Ph.D.'s awarded 1955-59. 31 graduate students registered fall 1959.

Microbiology. Morphology and physiology of micro-organisms, immunology and serology, public health bacteriology. Prerequisites for graduate study: mathematics; chemistry; biology, including microbiology; qualifying examinations. 6 professorial staff. 13 master's degrees and 6 Ph.D.'s awarded 1955-59. 17 graduate students registered fall 1959.

Physics. General or theoretical physics, astrophysics, low-energy nuclear or high-energy nuclear physics, optics and spectroscopy, solid-state physics. 12 professorial staff. 9 master's degrees and 1 Ph.D. awarded 1955-59. 30 graduate students registered fall 1959.

Political Science.—General. Public law, political parties and public opinion, public administration, political theory, comparative government, international law and diplomacy, state and local government. 7 professorial staff. 16 master's degrees and 2 Ph.D.'s awarded 1955-59. 18 graduate students registered fall 1959.

Psychology. Clinical, experimental, or social-personality psychology; speech pathology; counseling psychology. Prerequisite for graduate study: 1 year of college mathematics. 13 professorial staff. 39 master's degrees and 34 Ph.D.'s awarded 1955-59. 84 graduate students registered fall 1959. New enrollment limited to 15-20 per year.

Sociology and Rural Sociology. Rural sociology, demography and population study, medical sociology, the community, social psychology, criminology and delinquency, marriage and family. (Other subject areas, such as social theory, research methodology, social stratification, and social and cultural structure and change, are considered core areas and required of all students, but some specialization in these and allied fields may be arranged.) Offered by Departments of Sociology and Rural Sociology and with collaboration of Department of Behavioral Science (College of Medicine). Recommended for graduate study: minimum of 3 sociology courses; anthropology; economics; political science; psychology; mathematics; statistics. 15 professorial staff. 7 master's degrees and 7 Ph.D.'s awarded 1955-59. 10 graduate students registered fall 1959.

Lehigh University

BETHLEHEM, PENNSYLVANIA

The Graduate School

Graduate instruction was begun at Lehigh in 1866 and, in 1883, two doctoral degrees were conferred. Instruction at the doctoral level was then dropped for a number of years, but was reestablished in 1936. Ph.D. programs are now offered in several areas and the Ed.D. degree is also conferred. University is privately controlled and nonsectarian. Only men are admitted to the undergraduate college; both men and women to the Graduate School.

A limited number of graduate men may live in upper-class residence halls; no residence facilities provided for women or for married students. Rooms and apartments are available in community.

Special facilities include: million-pound universal testing machine in engineering laboratory; extensive Amsler equipment for studies of cyclic loading; fatigue laboratory in psychology; exceptional laboratory facilities in electrical and metallurgical engineering. Library contains approximately 375,000 volumes.

Residence requirement for Ph.D.: 3 years beyond bachelor's degree, of which a minimum of 1 full year of graduate study and research must be taken in residence at Lehigh.

ADMISSION REQUIREMENTS

For graduate study: bachelor's degree; B— overall average or better in major field; evidence of readiness and motivation to pursue graduate courses and research successfully; recommendations. Recommended: GRE Aptitude and Advanced Tests. For candidacy for Ph.D.: completion of substantial portion of course work; satisfaction of language requirements; qualifying examinations; approval of Executive Committee of the Graduate Faculty.

Apply to Office of Admission by March 1.

FEES AND FIRST-YEAR AID

No application fee. Tuition $800 per academic year. Room (in residence hall) for men $220 per academic year. Average cost of room in community $250-$300 annually. On contract, board in college dining room (men only) costs $500 annually; a la carte (men and women) $600 and up. Apartments $60-$125 per month.

First-year aid available: scholarships, tuition up to $800 maximum; teaching fellowships, $1,750 plus tuition; other fellowships, $1,000-$1,500 plus tuition; research assistantships, $175-$250 per month. Grants in aid available in varying amounts. Loans of up to $1,000 per year ($5,000 total) may be obtained.

Apply to Office of Admission by March 1.

FIELDS OF STUDY FOR THE PH.D.

Biology. Biology, microbiology. Prerequisite for graduate study: major in biology with adequate preparation in physics and in analytical and organic chemistry. 7 professorial staff. 11 master's degrees and 4 Ph.D.'s awarded 1955-59. 22 graduate students registered fall 1959.

Chemistry. Analytical, inorganic, organic, physical, or surface chemistry; reaction kinetics; synthesis of medicinal agents; rheology; chelation. Prerequisites for graduate study: 1 year each of general, analytical, organic, and physical chemistry; thorough grounding in physics; mathematics through calculus. 12 professorial staff. 54 master's degrees and 24 Ph.D.'s awarded 1955-59. 52 graduate students registered fall 1959.

Engineering. — Chemical. Unit operations, thermodynamics, and kinetics. Prerequisite for graduate study: major in chemical engineering. Ph.D. candidacy prerequisite: 1 language. 4 professorial staff. 6 master's degrees and 2 Ph.D.'s awarded 1955-59. 38 graduate students registered fall 1959.

Engineering.—Civil. Structural engineering (with collateral work available in hydraulics); sanitary engineering; soil or engineering mechanics; mathematics and other related fields; soil engineering. Prerequisite for graduate study: major in civil engineering. Recommended: familiarity with allied fields (such as soil mechanics) if structural engineering is major. 12 professorial staff. 71 master's degrees and 12 Ph.D.'s awarded 1955-59. 56 graduate students registered fall 1959. Total enrollment limited to approximately 62.

Engineering.—Electrical. Power systems, electronics. Prerequisites for graduate study: B.S. in electrical engineering; background in physics and mathematics. 6 professorial staff. 28 master's degrees and 3 Ph.D.'s awarded 1955-59. 41 graduate students registered fall 1959.

Engineering.—Mechanical. Design, dynamics of machinery, heat transfer, thermal stresses. Prerequisite for graduate study: major in mechanical engineering. 7 professorial staff. 59 master's degrees and 4 Ph.D.'s awarded 1955-59. 62 graduate students registered fall 1959.

Engineering.—Metallurgical. Mechanical or welding metallurgy, magnetics, induction heating, solid-state physics. Prerequisite for graduate study: major in metallurgy. 5 professorial staff. 20 master's degrees and 16 Ph.D.'s awarded

1955-59. 32 graduate students registered fall 1959.

English. English literature: medieval; Chaucer; Renaissance; Shakespeare; 19th century. American literature: Emerson; Hawthorne; Whitman; Melville; 20th century. Prerequisite for graduate study: major in English or equivalent. 15 professorial staff. 21 master's degrees and 3 Ph.D.'s awarded 1955-59. 27 graduate students registered fall 1959.

Geology. Structural, marine, or economic geology; stratigraphy; sedimentation; geochemistry or sediments; petrology. Prerequisites for graduate study: major in geology, chemistry, biology, or physics; 1 year each of calculus, chemistry, physics. Recommended: summer geology camp or field experience in geology. 5 professorial staff. 18 master's degrees and 4 Ph.D.'s awarded 1955-59. 17 graduate students registered fall 1959. Total enrollment limited to 20-25.

History. American, American Colonial, and English history. Offered by Department of History and Government. Prerequisite for graduate study: degree in history or in allied field with at least 12 semester hours of history. 9 professorial staff. 15 master's degrees and 2 Ph.D.'s awarded 1955-59. 40 graduate students registered fall 1959.

Mathematics. Analysis, algebra, geometry. Offered by Department of Mathematics and Astronomy. Prerequisite for graduate study: major in mathematics with minimum of 12 semester hours of work, including a year of calculus. 12 professorial staff. 18 master's degrees and 4 Ph.D.'s awarded 1955-59. 20 graduate students registered fall 1959.

Physics. Elementary particle theory, general theory of relativity, nonequilibrium statistical mechanics, transient fluid dynamics, elastic and plastic deformation of metals, thermal conductivity, ferromagnetic behavior of materials. Prerequisite for graduate study: major in physics. 10 professorial staff. 37 master's degrees and 19 Ph.D.'s awarded 1955-59. 40 graduate students registered fall 1959.

Psychology. Physiological psychology, especially evaluative studies in work and fatigue; sensory psychology (auditory); learning; clinical psychology (at M.S. level). Prerequisite for graduate study: preferably a major in psychology, but physics, mathematics, and biology are acceptable; GRE Aptitude and Advanced Tests. Recommended: MAT. 7 professorial staff. Ph.D.

program begun 1957. 15 master's degrees awarded 1955-59. 20 graduate students registered fall 1959.

Louisiana State University and Agricultural and Mechanical College

BATON ROUGE 3, LOUISIANA

The Graduate School

Graduate instruction was offered at Louisiana State as early as 1869. The Graduate School was organized in 1931, and the first Ph.D. was awarded in 1935. The Ed.D. degree is also conferred. University is publicly controlled by the state. Both men and women are admitted.

Special sections in dormitories maintained for single graduate students; 296 unfurnished apartments for married students.

Special facilities include: Coastal Studies Institute; summer institutes for teachers of mathematics, science, and foreign languages; library of approximately 805,000 volumes. Residence requirement for Ph.D.: 3 years of graduate study beyond bachelor's degree; 1 full academic year of continuous residence beyond the master's degree must be spent on campus. Summer and evening courses available.

ADMISSION REQUIREMENTS

For graduate study: bachelor's degree; B— average; departmental acceptance for specific field of study. For candidacy for Ph.D.: completion of prescribed courses; B average in graduate work; reading proficiency in French and German; comprehensive general examination.

Apply to Dean of the Graduate School at any time.

FEES AND FIRST-YEAR AID

No application fee. Tuition for state residents $50 a year (general university fee); nonresident fee $100. Special fees approximate $70 per year. Room (in dormitory) for men $180-$234 per year; for women $297. Approximate annual cost of board in college cafeterias $280-$380. Apartments $35-$75 per month (including utilities).

First-year aid available: 13 scholarships,

$270-$3,000; 187 teaching fellowships, $500-$3,340; 146 L.S.U. research assistantships, $500-$4,000; 53 industrial research assistantships, $1,500-$3,600; 193 miscellaneous types of aid, $405-$2,400; 52 honorary fellowships (Mathematics Institute), $3,650-$5,376; 59 other honorary fellowships, $450-$3,000.

Apply to head of department at least 6 months prior to registration.

FIELDS OF STUDY FOR THE PH.D.

Agricultural Chemistry and Biochemistry. Plant biochemistry, animal biochemistry, nutrition. Prerequisite for graduate study: background in chemistry. Ph.D. candidacy prerequisite: mathematics through calculus. 5 professorial staff. 55 master's degrees and 25 Ph.D.'s awarded 1955-59. 8 graduate students registered fall 1959.

Agricultural Economics. Farm management, marketing, land economics, agricultural finance, prices and statistics, agricultural policy. Minors must be taken in 2 other disciplines. Prerequisites for graduate study: 6 semester hours of economic principles; 3 of accounting; 3 of elementary statistics; 6 of applied courses. Recommended: farm experience. 9 professorial staff. 27 master's degrees and 5 Ph.D.'s awarded 1955-59. 18 graduate students registered fall 1959.

Agronomy. Crops and social science. Combined program conducted by Departments of Agronomy and Horticulture. Prerequisite for graduate study: major in agronomy. Recommended: 1 year of experience in agronomy under practical conditions or with a research agency. 7 professorial staff. 32 master's degrees and 12 Ph.D.'s awarded 1955-59. 20 graduate students registered fall 1959.

Anatomy. Human anatomy, histology, embryology, neuroanatomy, electron microscopy of tissues and cells, cytology, comparative anatomy, and embryology of vegetables. Offered by Department of Anatomy in Medical School. Prerequisite for graduate study: major in biology. Recommended: laboratory experience in biology, chemistry, and physics. 10 professorial staff.

Animal Industry. Animal breeding, nutrition, production; food preservation; meat technology; physiology of reproduction. Recommended for graduate study: science and mathematics background. 9 professorial staff. 24 master's degrees awarded 1955-59. 12 graduate students registered fall 1959.

Animal Science.—Dairy. Nutrition, breeding, physiology, production. Prerequisites for graduate study: major or equivalent in dairy production or manufacturing; entrance test. 7 professorial staff. 15 master's degrees and 4 Ph.D.'s awarded 1955-59. 15 graduate students registered fall 1959.

Animal Science.—Poultry Industry. Nutrition, breeding, production. Combined program conducted by Departments of Poultry Industry, Animal Industry, and Dairying in conjunction with Department of Biochemistry (nutrition) and Department of Zoology (breeding). Prerequisite for graduate study: 18 hours of poultry industry or allied courses. 6 professorial staff. 12 master's degrees and 5 Ph.D.'s awarded 1955-59. 6 graduate students registered fall 1959.

Biochemistry. Comparative biochemistry, metabolism and renal biochemistry, hepatic biochemistry, nutrition of micro-organisms, organic chemistry of the carbohydrates. Offered by Department of Biochemistry in Medical School. Prerequisites for graduate study: B.S. in chemistry or equivalent; courses in biology. 6 professorial staff.

Botany, Bacteriology, and Plant Pathology. Prerequisite for graduate study: basic courses in general botany, plant physiology, bacteriology, plant pathology, general chemistry, and organic chemistry. Recommended: 18 hours of chemistry. 23 master's degrees and 29 Ph.D.'s awarded 1955-59. 11 professorial staff. 40 graduate students registered fall 1959.

Business Administration. Accounting, business communications, corporation finance and investments, foreign trade, insurance and real estate, marketing, money and banking, and statistics. Combined program offered by Departments of Accounting, Finance, and Management and Marketing. (Students major in one of these fields.) Prerequisite for graduate study: 24 semester hours of course work in field of student's major. Recommended: practical teaching and/or business experience. Ph.D. candidacy prerequisite: ability to use accounting and statistics as tools in research. 18 professorial staff. 28 master's degrees and 5 Ph.D.'s awarded 1955-59. 56 graduate students registered in accounting fall 1959; 24 in finance; 56 in management and marketing.

Chemistry. Physical, organic, analytical, or inorganic chemistry; sugar technology or chemical physics. Prerequisites for graduate study: concentration in chemistry, physics, and materials;

written qualifying tests. Recommended: German; advanced courses in major areas of chemistry. 17 professorial staff. 59 graduate students registered fall 1959.

Economics. Economic theory, history of economic thought, transportation, public finance, labor, government regulation of business, money and banking, foreign trade. Prerequisites for graduate study: 24 credit hours in economics and allied subjects; ability to use statistics and accounting. Recommended: GRE. 8 professorial staff. 11 master's degrees and 6 Ph.D.'s awarded 1955-59. 15 graduate students registered fall 1959.

Education.—General. A general course designed to prepare Ph.D. candidates for teacher training positions. Prerequisites for graduate study: lifetime teaching certificate; successful teaching experience. 29 professorial staff. 992 master's degrees and 21 Ph.D.'s awarded 1955-59. 262 graduate students registered fall 1959. The Ed.D. degree is also awarded in this field.

Education.—Vocational Agricultural. Prerequisite for graduate study: 12 hours in basic vocational agricultural education. Recommended: 1 year of successful teaching. 4 professorial staff. 55 master's degrees and 9 Ph.D.'s awarded 1955-59. 18 graduate students registered fall 1959.

Engineering.—Chemical. Heat transfer, distillation, evaporation, thermodynamics, reactor design, mass transfer, materials handling, instrumentation. Prerequisite for graduate study: B.S. in engineering. 6 professorial staff. 13 master's degrees and 5 Ph.D.'s awarded 1955-59. 58 graduate students registered fall 1959.

English. English or American literature or language. 21 professorial staff. 40 master's degrees and 11 Ph.D.'s awarded 1955-59. 43 graduate students registered fall 1959.

Foreign Languages. French, German, or Romance philology. This is an interdepartmental program in linguistics. Prerequisites for graduate study: 24 semester hours in major field; reading knowledge of French, Spanish, German; 2 semesters of Latin; fluent oral-aural proficiency in language of major field. Recommended: Greek and Latin literature; 6 months of travel in country of major language. 16 professorial staff. 26 master's degrees and 1 Ph.D. awarded 1955-59. 29 graduate students registered fall 1959.

Geography. Cultural geography, geomorphology. Offered by Department of Geology and Anthropology. Recommended for graduate study:

travel; wide reading. 5 professorial staff. 10 master's degrees and 10 Ph.D.'s awarded 1955-59. 24 graduate students registered fall 1959.

Geology. Paleontology, petrology, stratigraphy, geomorphology, areal and subsurface geology. Prerequisites for graduate study: undergraduate work in geology; English proficiency test. Recommended: knowledge of French, German, or Russian. 9 professorial staff. 75 master's degrees and 10 Ph.D.'s awarded 1955-59. 72 graduate students registered fall 1959.

Health and Physical Education. Offered by Department of Health and Physical Education. Students desiring to qualify for administrative positions in Louisiana Public Schools are permitted to schedule sufficient courses in Department of Education to permit them to do so. Prerequisite for graduate study: 20 semester hours of credit in health, physical education, recreation, or dance. Recommended: approved teaching certificate; 2 years of teaching experience. 15 professorial staff. 50 master's degrees awarded 1955-59. 27 graduate students registered fall 1959.

History. American history (Colonial, Ante-Bellum South, Civil War and Reconstruction, New South, diplomatic, frontier, intellectual, Louisiana); Latin American. Prerequisite for graduate study: major in history and social sciences. 9 professorial staff. 26 master's degrees and 5 Ph.D.'s awarded 1955-59. 47 graduate students registered fall 1959. Attempt is made to hold overall graduate enrollment to a maximum of 40.

Horticulture. General or ornamental horticulture. Minors may be selected from any field in horticulture, or from related fields such as botany and agronomy. Prerequisites for graduate study: major in horticulture. Recommended: courses in botany, plant physiology, and genetics. 6 professorial staff. 23 master's degrees and 6 Ph.D.'s awarded 1955-59. 21 graduate students registered fall 1959.

Linguistics. Historical, comparative, descriptive linguistics. A Ph.D. program in Romance philology is also offered. Interdepartmental program administered by committee from Departments of English, Speech, and Foreign Languages. (Student registers in 1 department.) Prerequisite for graduate study: major in English, speech, or a foreign language. Recommended: knowledge of Latin or Greek. 13 professorial staff. 6 students registered fall 1959.

Mathematics. Algebra, topology, number theory, topological algebra. Prerequisite for graduate study: undergraduate work in mathematics. Recommended: theory of equations; advanced calculus. 20 professorial staff. 11 master's degrees and 4 Ph.D.'s awarded 1955-59. 94 graduate students registered fall 1959.

Microbiology. Virology, parasitology, immunology, medical bacteriology. Offered by Department of Microbiology in Medical School. 4 professorial staff. 1 master's degree and 1 Ph.D. awarded 1955-59. 1 graduate student registered fall 1959.

Pharmacology. Offered by Department of Pharmacology in Medical School.

Physics. Theoretical physics (nuclear, solid-state, low-temperature, astrophysics). Experimental physics (particle accelerators; neutron spectrometry; nuclear reactions and energy levels; beta-, gamma-, and X-ray spectrometry; cosmic rays and mesons; low-temperature; solid-state; sound; physical electronics). Prerequisite for graduate study: 30 hours of basic courses in physics, including general physics, mechanics, electricity and magnetism (with laboratory), atomic and nuclear physics. Recommended: advanced calculus. 13 professorial staff. 29 master's degrees and 16 Ph.D.'s awarded 1955-59. 51 graduate students registered fall 1959.

Physiology. Physiology of the cardiovascular system and neurophysiology. Offered by Department of Physiology in Medical School. Prerequisites for graduate study: premedical chemistry, biology, and physics; GRE; basic medical course in physiology, medical pharmacology. Recommended: comparative or mammalian anatomy and histology; period of serving as assistant to faculty members. Departments of Physiology, Pharmacology, and Biochemistry. 46 master's degrees and 11 Ph.D.'s awarded 1955-59.

Psychology. Clinical, personnel-industrial, general-experimental psychology. Prerequisite for graduate study: MAT. Recommended: GRE. 13 professorial staff. 31 master's degrees and 20 Ph.D.'s awarded 1955-59. 60 graduate students registered fall 1959. New enrollment limited to 25.

Sociology. Theoretical sociology, methods of social investigation, social structure and community, social change and social movements, social problems and social control, demography, rural sociology, sociology of work, inter-group relations. Recommended for graduate study:

broad training in social sciences and humanities. 10 professorial staff. 17 master's degrees and 14 Ph.D.'s awarded 1955-59. 34 graduate students registered fall 1959.

Speech. Recommended for graduate study: 18 semester hours of credit in speech. 10 professorial staff. 50 master's degrees and 17 Ph.D.'s awarded 1955-59. 48 graduate students registered fall 1959.

Zoology. General zoology, embryology, parasitology, entomology, genetics, vertebrate and invertebrate zoology, physiology. Offered by Department of Zoology, Physiology, and Entomology. Prerequisites for graduate study: major in biology or zoology; GRE either before entrance or during semester. 14 professorial staff. 33 master's degrees and 10 Ph.D.'s awarded 1955-59. 51 graduate students registered fall 1959.

Louisville, University of

LOUISVILLE 8, KENTUCKY

The Graduate School

Graduate instruction has been offered since 1908, and the Graduate School was organized in 1926. First Ph.D. was awarded in 1953. University is an independent institution with municipal support. Both men and women are admitted.

Rooms in dormitories available for single graduate students; no university-owned residence facilities for married students.

Residence requirement for Ph.D.: 3 years beyond baccalaureate, at least 1 of which must be taken in residence at the University of Louisville. Summer and evening courses available.

ADMISSION REQUIREMENTS

For graduate study: bachelor's degree; B average; GRE in some departments. For candidacy for Ph.D.: reading knowledge of 2 modern foreign languages; preliminary qualifying examination.

Apply to the Dean of the Graduate School at any time.

FEES AND FIRST-YEAR AID

No application fee. Tuition for residents of Louisville $22 per semester hour (maximum

$262.50 per semester); others $28 per semester hour (maximum $336 per semester). Room (in dormitory) for men $240 per year ($620 for room and board); room (in dormitory) for women $150 per year. Approximate annual cost of board in college dining room $400.

A few graduate assistantships are available for first-year students. Apply to head of the major department by March 1.

FIELDS OF STUDY FOR THE PH.D.

Anatomy. Gross and microscopic anatomy, cytology, histology, organology, neuroanatomy, embryology. Prerequisite for graduate study: major in biology; physics and chemistry. 9 professorial staff. Ph.D. program begun 1956. 2 master's degrees awarded 1955-59. 1 graduate student registered fall 1959. Total enrollment limited to 5.

Biochemistry. Biochemistry and biophysical chemistry. Offered by Department of Biochemistry of The School of Medicine and The Graduate School. Prerequisites for graduate study: major in chemistry or biology (or combination); physical chemistry; calculus; GRE. 10 professorial staff. Ph.D. program begun 1956. 3 master's degrees awarded 1955-59. 12 graduate students registered fall 1959.

Biology. Algology, ecology, embryology, entomology, fishery biology, herpetology, histology, ichthyology, limnology, ornithology, plant physiology, potamology, plant anatomy, radiation biology, vertebrate anatomy. Offered by Department of Biology and Potamological Institute. Prerequisite for graduate study: entrance examination. 9 professorial staff. Ph.D. program begun 1958. 14 master's degrees awarded 1955-59. 17 graduate students registered fall 1959.

Chemistry. Organic, analytical, or physical chemistry. Prerequisite for graduate study: minimum of 24 units in chemistry; reading knowledge of German. 8 professorial staff. 10 master's degrees and 22 Ph.D.'s awarded 1955-59. 38 graduate students registered fall 1959.

Engineering.—Chemical. General unit operation with emphasis on transfer process. Prerequisite for graduate study: major in chemical engineering (or in chemistry with certain provisions). 7 professorial staff. Ph.D. program begun 1956. 47 master's degrees and 1 Ph.D. awarded 1955-59. 15 graduate students registered fall 1959. New enrollment for Ph.D. candidacy limited to 2 per year.

Microbiology. Bacteriology, mycology, virology, immunology, protozoology, helmintology, entomology. Prerequisites for graduate study: biology; chemistry; physics; GRE in some cases. 6 professorial staff. 2 master's degrees awarded 1955-59. 11 graduate students registered fall 1959.

Pharmacology. Lachesiology, or the fate (absorption, distribution, excretion) of substances in the animal body; metabolism and excretion of drugs by liver and kidney; mechanisms of active transport in liver and kidney; actions of drugs on cell surfaces. Prerequisites for graduate study: major in chemistry or biology; GRE and/or entrance examination in some cases. 6 professorial staff. Ph.D. program begun 1956. 1 master's degree and 1 Ph.D. awarded 1955-59. 1 graduate student registered fall 1959.

Physiology. Cardiovascular, respiratory, electrophysiology, osmotic work. Prerequisites for graduate study: 1 year each of physics and mathematics; 2 years of chemistry. Recommended: additional physics and mathematics; personal conference whenever possible. 4 professorial staff. Ph.D. program begun 1957. 2 master's degrees awarded 1955-59.

Lowell Technological Institute

LOWELL, MASSACHUSETTS

The Graduate School

At the master's level, graduate instruction has been offered at Lowell since 1935. The Graduate School was organized in 1951, and a Ph.D. program in chemistry was initiated in 1958. It is anticipated that the first Ph.D. will be awarded in 1962. Institute is publicly controlled by the state. Both men and women are admitted.

No residence facilities provided for graduate students.

Library of approximately 25,000 volumes contains special collections on textiles, paper, leathers, dyes, and dyeing.

Residence requirement for Ph.D.: 3 years beyond bachelor's degree, with at least 1 year spent at Lowell.

ADMISSION REQUIREMENTS

For graduate study: bachelor's degree in

chemistry or closely allied field; uniformly high scholastic rating; GRE Aptitude Test. For candidacy for Ph.D.: completion of 1 year of graduate study; qualifying examinations; demonstrated reading ability in German and 1 other foreign language; approval of advisory committee and division chairman.

Apply to Director of the Graduate School by June of year of desired entrance.

FEES AND FIRST-YEAR AID

Application fee $10. Tuition for state residents $200 per year; residents of other states $300; noncitizens $550. Special fees approximate $45 annually. Average annual cost of board in college dining room $750.

First-year aid available: 4 to 6 teaching fellowships ranging in value from $1,400-$2,200.

Apply to Director of Graduate School by April 30.

FIELDS OF STUDY FOR THE PH.D.

Chemistry. Organic, physical. Prerequisite for graduate study: diagnostic tests in 4 main areas of chemistry (given during registration). 9 professorial staff. Ph.D. program initiated 1958. 1 master's degree awarded 1955-59. 12 graduate students registered fall 1959.

Loyola University

CHICAGO 11, ILLINOIS

The Graduate School

Graduate instruction has been offered at Loyola since 1918. The Graduate School was constituted as a distinct unit in 1926, and the first Ph.D. was conferred in 1928. The Ed.D. and S.T.D. degrees are also awarded. University is privately controlled and is conducted by the Society of Jesus of the Roman Catholic Church. Both men and women are admitted.

Residence halls maintained for single graduate students; no residence facilities for married students.

Facilities for clinical training and research include: the Lake County Mental Hygiene Clinic; Catholic Charities Guidance Bureau; Cook County Psychopathic Hospital; Chicago State and Loretto Hospitals; and the Loyola Center for Guidance and Psychological Services. There are 6 university libraries which contain approximately 330,000 volumes.

Residence requirement for Ph.D.: 3 years beyond bachelor's degree, with minimum of 1 year of full-time residence at Loyola. Both summer and evening courses available.

ADMISSION REQUIREMENTS

For graduate study: bachelor's degree; overall B average; recommendations. Recommended: GRE. For candidacy for Ph.D.: reading knowledge of 2 foreign languages (usually French, German, or Russian, although sometimes another language may be substituted if connected with dissertation); qualifying comprehensive examinations; completion of ⅔ of course work with satisfactory grades; approval of dissertation outline; recommendation of student's committee.

Apply to the Graduate School, Loyola University, 820 North Michigan Avenue, Chicago 11, Illinois, at least 4 weeks before opening of classes.

FEES AND FIRST-YEAR AID

Application fee $10. Tuition $600 per academic year ($800 for some programs). Laboratory fees approximate $40-$75 annually. Room (in dormitory) $400 per year. Approximate annual cost of board in college dining room $500.

First-year aid available: 50 partial- or full-tuition scholarships; 30 teaching fellowships, $800-$3,000; 10 other fellowships, $1,400-$3,500; 25 research assistantships, $1,100-$3,000. Grants-in-aid available as needed. ½ tuition reduction for all ministers, religious, etc.

Apply to Dean, Graduate School, Loyola University, 820 North Michigan Avenue, Chicago 11, Illinois, before March 1.

FIELDS OF STUDY FOR THE PH.D.

Anatomy. Endocrines, electromiography and regeneration of muscles, experimental embryology, cytology and histochemistry, nervous system and behavior. Prerequisite for graduate study: science major, preference for biology. 5 professorial staff. 10 master's degrees and 3 Ph.D.'s awarded 1955-59. 11 graduate students registered fall 1959.

Biochemistry. Diagnostic separation of plasma proteins and lipoproteins, healing of wounds, cancer metabolism, functions of parathyroid hormone, oral hypoglycemic agents, role of metal ions in biochemical processes, electrophoresis and chromatography in biochemistry. Prerequisites for graduate study: calculus (differential and integral); physical chemistry (with laboratory); B.S. in chemistry. 6 professorial staff. 11 master's degrees and 6 Ph.D.'s awarded 1955-59. 12 graduate students registered fall 1959. New enrollment limited to maximum of 5; total in program to 16.

Chemistry. Organic, physical, analytical, inorganic. Prerequisite for graduate study: B.S. in chemistry. 9 professorial staff. Ph.D. program initiated 1956. 28 master's degrees and 2 Ph.D.'s awarded 1955-59. 39 graduate students registered fall 1959. Total enrollment limited to approximately 40.

Education. Administration, curriculum, guidance, foundations. Prerequisites for graduate study: 2 modern foreign languages. 11 professorial staff. 420 master's degrees and 3 Ph.D.'s awarded 1955-59. 86 graduate students registered fall 1959. The Ed.D. degree is also awarded in this field and 14 were conferred 1955-59.

English. Medieval, Renaissance, 19th-century, or modern literature; literature of the drama. Prerequisites for graduate study: 30 hours of English; GRE Advanced Test in Literature. Recommended: French and German or suitable substitute. 16 professorial staff. 130 master's degrees and 3 Ph.D.'s awarded 1955-59. 60 graduate students registered fall 1959.

History. Modern European, medieval European, Latin American, United States, or Ancient history; studies in the origins of Western civilization and culture (classics and ancient philosophy). The latter is a combined program offered by Department of History in cooperation with the Departments of Classics and Philosophy. Prerequisite for graduate study: major in history. 14 professorial staff. 87 master's degrees and 8 Ph.D.'s awarded 1955-59. 68 graduate students registered fall 1959.

Microbiology. Morphology, taxonomy, diagnostic, virus, tissue culture. Prerequisites for graduate study: science courses; 1-year course in a foreign language of scientific importance. Recommended: 2 years of chemistry; 1 year each of physics, botany or zoology, and mathematics. 4 professorial staff. 10 master's degrees and 2 Ph.D.'s awarded 1955-59. 6 graduate students registered fall 1959. Enrollment limited to 8-10.

Pharmacology. Techniques and theory of neuropharmacology, including areas of central, autonomic and somatic (neuromyal) transmission; relationship of chemical transmitters, enzymes, and membrane phenomena to transmission; techniques and theory of atherosclerosis; role of stress and oxogenous and endogenous sympathins in atherosclerosis; synthesis and testing of barbiturates and wound-healing agents. Offered by Department of Pharmacology and Experimental Therapeutics. Prerequisite for graduate study: courses in biological, chemical, and physical sciences. Recommended: general course in college enzymology. 6 professorial staff. 7 master's degrees and 10 Ph.D.'s awarded 1955-59. 7 graduate students registered fall 1959. New enrollment limited to 8.

Physiology. Cardiovascular physiology, neurophysiology, temperature regulation. Offered by Departments of Physiology, Neuroanatomy, and Pharmacology. Prerequisites for graduate study: background in chemistry and physics or in biology (the former preferred); 1 foreign language (preferably 2). 9 professorial staff. 6 master's degrees and 3 Ph.D.'s awarded 1955-59. 7 graduate students registered fall 1959.

Psychology. General-experimental, clinical-personality, industrial-social, behavioral-experimental. Prerequisites for graduate study: 24 semester hours in psychology, including 6 in experimental psychology; GRE; MAT. 14 professorial staff. Ph.D. program in experimental-behavioral psychology initiated 1959. 46 master's degrees and 28 Ph.D.'s awarded 1955-59. 94 graduate students registered fall 1959. Total enrollment limited to approximately 95.

Sociology. Theory and methods, social organization, social problems, social psychology, social anthropology. 8 professorial staff. Ph.D. program initiated 1959. 15 master's degrees awarded 1955-59. 35 graduate students registered fall 1959.

Maine, University of

ORONO, MAINE

The Graduate Division

Graduate instruction at the master's level has been offered since 1880, and the Graduate Division was organized in 1923. Doctoral programs have been established very recently, the first Ph.D. being awarded in 1960. University is publicly controlled by the state. Both men and women are admitted.

A dormitory section is reserved for male graduate assistants; family-type housing available on campus for married students holding teaching graduate assistantships; limited residence facilities provided for women.

Requirement for Ph.D.: 3 academic years or equivalent, at least 2 of which must be spent in residence on campus. Maximum of 30 semester hours of graduate credit may be transferred from other institutions.

ADMISSION REQUIREMENTS

For graduate study: bachelor's degree; high general scholastic standing. For candidacy for Ph.D.: satisfactory completion of 30 hours of graduate work; approval of department, Graduate Executive Committee, and Graduate Dean; proficiency in 2 foreign languages; comprehensive examination; approval of dissertation subject.

Apply to Dean of Graduate Study at least 6 weeks prior to beginning of semester in which admission is sought.

FEES AND FIRST-YEAR AID

Application deposit of $25 must be paid when admission is approved. Tuition for state residents $400 per year; others $800. Room (in dormitory) and board $650-$700 per year.

First-year aid available: 20 full-tuition scholarships; variable number of teaching fellowships, $1,400-$1,800.

Apply to Graduate Dean for tuition scholarships at any time; to department head for fellowships and assistantships.

FIELDS OF STUDY FOR THE PH.D.

Chemistry. Organic and physical. Prerequisites for graduate study: adequate preparation in chemistry; reading knowledge of German; mathematics through calculus; 1 year of physics. 10 professorial staff. Ph.D. program initiated 1957. 16 master's degrees awarded 1955-59. 23 graduate students registered fall 1959.

History. American. Offered by Department of History and Government. Prerequisite for graduate study: adequate grounding in fundamental courses. Recommended: reading proficiency in 1 foreign language. 12 professorial staff. Ph.D. program initiated 1959. 14 master's degrees awarded 1955-59. 17 graduate students registered fall 1959.

Marquette University

MILWAUKEE 3, WISCONSIN

The Graduate School

Graduate instruction has been offered since 1889, and the Graduate School was organized in 1922. First Ph.D. awarded in 1926. University is privately controlled and is related to the Roman Catholic Church. Both men and women are admitted.

Rooms available in university residence halls, in private homes, and in fraternity and sorority houses for single students; apartments in community near campus for married students.

Residence requirement for Ph.D.: usually 3 years beyond bachelor's degree, of which 1 academic year must be spent in residence on campus. 6 graduate credits may be transferred from other institutions. Summer courses available.

University library has approximately 275,000 volumes. Milwaukee Public Library, which houses about 1 million volumes, located just off campus. Research affiliation maintained with Argonne National Laboratory.

ADMISSION REQUIREMENTS

For graduate study: bachelor's degree; B average; recommendations; MAT; GRE. Special tests which may be required include: Teacher Education Examination Program; Admission Test for Graduate Study in Business; Graduate Nurse Qualifying Examination, Plan A. For candidacy for Ph.D.: completion of most course work; satisfaction of language requirements (French and German in most disciplines).

Apply to Dean of the Graduate School by March 15.

FEES AND FIRST-YEAR AID

No application fee. Tuition $528 per year. Special fees approximate $20 annually. Room (in dormitory) $350 per year. Approximate annual cost of board in community $700.

First-year aid available: scholarships, $400-$600; teaching fellowships, $1,600-$1,800; other fellowships, $1,500-$2,000; research assistantships, $1,600.

Apply to Dean of the Graduate School before March 15.

FIELDS OF STUDY FOR THE PH.D.

Anatomy. Gross anatomy, histology, embryology, neuroanatomy. Prerequisite for graduate study: M.D. degree. 4 professorial staff. Ph.D. program begun 1957.

Biochemistry. Coagulation of blood, conjugation mechanism, enzyme reactions, polysaccharides, isotopes in intermediary metabolism. Prerequisites for graduate study: general, inorganic, organic, and physical chemistry; quantitative analysis; general biology; related electives. 4 professorial staff. Ph.D. program begun 1957.

Biology. Plant and animal anatomy or ecology, animal behavior, cytology, endocrinology, experimental embryology, genetics, mycology, plant physiology, radiation biology, serology. Prerequisite for graduate study: B.S. in biological science. 10 professorial staff. Ph.D. program begun 1957.

Microbiology and Immunology. Bacteriology, virology, parasitology, mycology, immunology, serology. Prerequisites for graduate study: major in biology or chemistry, including general, and organic chemistry and physics; background in mathematics, including statistics and calculus. 3 professorial staff. Ph.D. program begun 1957.

Pathology. Post mortem, pathology, surgical and clinical pathology. Prerequisites for graduate study: for medical pathology, successful completion of 4 years of medicine; for experimental pathology, 2 years of courses in approved medical school or equivalent. 4 professorial staff. Ph.D. program begun 1957.

Pharmacology. Prerequisite for graduate study: 2 years of courses in approved medical school or the equivalent. 4 professorial staff. Ph.D. program begun 1957.

Philosophy. Philosophy of St. Thomas Aquinas provides general norm of evaluation for work of this department. Prerequisites for graduate study: 24 semester hours of philosophy, including logic, metaphysics, ethics; 2 survey courses in history of philosophy. Recommended: reading facility in Latin. 4 professorial staff. Ph.D. program begun 1957.

Physiology. Biophysics, circulation and respiration, renal or endocrine physiology, physiology of growth. Prerequisite for graduate study: major in physiology, including chemistry. Students in field of research of biophysics must show competence in differential and integral calculus, biostatistics, biochemistry, physical chemistry, advanced theoretical and practical physics, and physiology. Recommended: neuroanatomy; biochemistry. 10 professorial staff. Ph.D. program begun 1957.

Maryland, University of

COLLEGE PARK, MARYLAND

Graduate School

Although graduate instruction has been offered at Maryland since about 1900, the Graduate School was not established until 1918. First Ph.D. was awarded in 1920. The Ed.D. degree is also awarded through the Department of Education under the jurisdiction of the Graduate School. The university is publicly controlled by the state. Both men and women are admitted.

Except for a few barracks-type apartments for married students, there are no residence facilities for graduate students. Housing Bureau recommends rooms and apartments in community.

Library of approximately 406,000 volumes contains special collections on agriculture, American history, anesthesia, chemistry, history of medicine and dentistry, U.S. and U.N. documents. Affiliations with many government laboratories and installations provide additional opportunities for study and research.

Residence requirement for Ph.D.: 3 years beyond bachelor's degree; 1 year of residence or equivalent must be spent at the University of Maryland.

ADMISSION REQUIREMENTS

For graduate study: bachelor's degree; B average. For candidacy for Ph.D.: reading knowledge of 2 foreign languages, 1 of which must be either French or German; comprehensive examinations.

Apply to the Graduate School by September 1 for the fall term; by January 1 for spring term; by June 1 for summer admission.

FEES AND FIRST-YEAR AID

No application fee. Matriculation fee of $10 at first registration. Tuition $12 per credit hour ($240 per academic year maximum). Health fee $5 per year. Variable laboratory fees. Room and board in community averages $100-$145 per month; apartments $60-$100.

First-year aid available: 700 teaching fellowships, $180 per month plus fee exemption; 40 other fellowships, $80-$200 per month plus fee exemption; 100 research assistantships, $180 and up.

Apply by March 1 to department heads for teaching or research assistantships; to Graduate School Office for fellowships.

FIELDS OF STUDY FOR THE PH.D.

No formal credit courses in the methodology of college teaching are offered, but many departments have informal noncredit programs of this sort.

Agronomy. Crop breeding; weed control; turf and forage management; grain and tobacco production; soil physics, chemistry, or classification; mineralogy; fertility and microbiology. Supporting work required in botany, chemistry, mathematics, physics, geology, microbiology, engineering, biometrics. Prerequisite for graduate study: B.S. in agriculture. Recommended: chemistry; mathematics; physics; botany. Ph.D. candidacy prerequisite: M.S. in agronomy. 16 professorial staff. 27 master's degrees and 11 Ph.D.'s awarded 1955-59. 25 graduate students registered fall 1959.

American Civilization. Combined program administered by Committee on American Civilization made up of faculty from Departments of English, History, Government and Politics, and Sociology. Prerequisite for graduate study: major in 1 of above fields. 5 professorial staff. 9 master's degrees and 3 Ph.D.'s awarded 1955-59. 13 graduate students registered fall 1959.

Anatomy. Gross and neuroanatomy, histology, microbiology, physiology, biochemistry, pathology. Offered by Department of Anatomy, School of Dentistry, Baltimore. Prerequisites for graduate study: biology major or minor in biology with major in chemistry or physics; GRE. Recommended: chemistry and physics. 3 professorial staff. 1 Ph.D. awarded 1955-59.

Anatomy. Gross, micro-, and neuroanatomy; embryology; genetics; anthropology; physiology; oncology. Recommended for graduate study: background in physics and chemistry. 6 professorial staff. 1 master's degree and 3 Ph.D.'s awarded 1955-59. 5 graduate students registered fall 1959.

Animal Husbandry. Nutrition and physiology, breeding and genetics, livestock management, meats and meat products. Recommended for graduate study: mathematics through calculus; 2 years of college chemistry, including organic. 5 professorial staff. Ph.D. program begun 1957. 7 master's degrees and 1 Ph.D. awarded 1955-59. 12 graduate students registered fall 1959.

Biochemistry. General biochemistry, normal and abnormal cellular metabolism. Offered by Department of Biochemistry, School of Medicine, Baltimore. Prerequisite for graduate study: B.S. in chemistry, biology, or combined program. Recommended: physical chemistry; calculus. 6 professorial staff. 4 master's degrees and 4 Ph.D.'s awarded 1955-59. 7 graduate students registered fall 1959. Total enrollment limited to 9.

Botany. Anatomy, cytology, cytogenetics, plant physiology or pathology, taxonomy, ecology. 14 professorial staff. 22 master's degrees and 20 Ph.D.'s awarded 1955-59. 27 graduate students registered fall 1959. New enrollment limited to 25-30.

Chemistry. Organic, analytical, physical, and inorganic chemistry; biochemistry; molecular structure. Prerequisite for graduate study; major in chemistry. 26 professorial staff. 39 master's degrees and 50 Ph.D.'s awarded 1955-59. 110 graduate students registered fall 1959.

Dairy. Dairy chemistry and technology, cattle nutrition, physiology and breeding. 9 professorial staff. 16 master's degrees and 10 Ph.D.'s awarded 1955-59. 20 graduate students registered fall 1959.

Economics. Economic theory, history and development, or growth and business cycles; history of economic thought; money and banking; international economics; public finance and fiscal policy; comparative economic systems and economic planning; labor and industrial relations; public utilities and social control of business; financial or industrial administration; accounting; transportation; marketing; institutional economics. Offered by Department of Economics. A cooperative program with Department of Business Administration is also offered. Prerequisite for graduate study: 18 hours of economics, including economic statistics. Recommended: 1 foreign language; GRE; mathematics. 20 professorial staff. 10 master's degrees and 5 Ph.D.'s

awarded 1955-59. 45 graduate students registered fall 1959.

Economics.—Agricultural. Agricultural taxation, finance, or policy; production economics; marketing; land economics and resource development; foreign agricultural trade. Prerequisite for graduate study: adequate training in agriculture, economics, statistics. 10 professorial staff. 17 master's degrees and 2 Ph.D.'s awarded 1955-59. 41 graduate students registered fall 1959.

Education. Curriculum and instruction; educational administration and supervision; guidance; elementary, human development, industrial arts, secondary, or vocational-industrial education; history, philosophy, and comparative education. Combined program offered by Departments of Education, Industrial Education, and Human Development Education. Prerequisites for graduate study: MAT; Cooperative English Test; ACE Psychological Examination. Recommended: teacher certification and experience in field. 30 professorial staff. 656 master's degrees and 9 Ph.D.'s awarded 1955-59. 1,010 graduate students registered fall 1959. Ed.D. degree is also awarded in this field.

Engineering. — Aeronautical. Aerodynamics, structures. Prerequisite for graduate study: degree in aeronautical engineering. 3 professorial staff. Ph.D. program begun 1959. 12 master's degrees awarded 1955-59. 40 graduate students registered fall 1959.

Engineering.—Chemical. Fuels, heat transfer, distillation, refrigeration, nuclear phases of chemical engineering. Prerequisite for graduate study: B.S. in chemical engineering or chemistry. 5 professorial staff. 3 master's degrees and 8 Ph.D.'s awarded 1955-59. 15 graduate students registered fall 1959.

Engineering.—Civil. Structural engineering, advanced mechanics, properties of materials. Prerequisite for graduate study: B.S. in civil engineering. 4 professorial staff. Ph.D. program begun 1959. 7 master's degrees awarded 1955-59. 13 graduate students registered fall 1959.

Engineering.—Electrical. Microwave engineering, radio wave propagation, quantum electronics, network synthesis. 6 professorial staff. 47 master's degrees and 4 Ph.D.'s awarded 1955-59. 194 graduate students registered fall 1959.

Engineering.—Mechanical. Mechanics, heat transfer, thermodynamics, fluid mechanics. Prerequisite for graduate study: B.S. in mechanical

or aeronautical engineering. 7 professorial staff. 30 master's degrees and 8 Ph.D.'s awarded 1955-59. 55 graduate students registered fall 1959.

Engineering. — Metallurgical. Diffusion, graphitization, welding, fatigue, physical metallurgy, oxidation. Offered by Department of Chemical Engineering. Prerequisite for graduate study: B.S. in metallurgy, chemistry, or chemical engineering. 3 professorial staff. 2 master's degrees and 3 Ph.D.'s awarded 1955-59. 14 graduate students registered fall 1959.

Engineering.—Nuclear. Design, construction, and operation of high-energy or nuclear irradiation facilities (nuclear reactors, gamma ray facilities, Cobalt 60, high-speed electron facilities); special related operations (uranium and thorium); chemical separations and isotopic separations. Offered by Department of Chemical Engineering. Prerequisite for graduate study: B.S. in engineering, physics, chemistry, or mathematics. Recommended: advanced mathematics and physics. 2 professors. 35 graduate students registered fall 1959.

English. English literature before 1660 or after 1660, American literature, English language. Ph.D. in American Civilization may be taken, with emphasis on American literature. Prerequisite for graduate study: 30 credit hours of English. Recommended: French and German. 20 professorial staff. 21 master's degrees and 7 Ph.D.'s awarded 1955-59. 69 graduate students registered fall 1959.

Entomology. Agricultural or medical entomology; insect biology, taxonomy, morphology, and physiology. Prerequisite for graduate study: major in entomology. Recommended: organic chemistry; 4 years in 2 languages. 8 professorial staff. 16 master's degrees and 12 Ph.D.'s awarded 1955-59. 29 graduate students registered fall 1959.

French—German—Spanish. French, German, Spanish (including Latin-American) literatures. Offered by Department of Foreign Languages and Literatures. Prerequisites for graduate study: 30 hours in field of concentration; speaking ability in chosen language. 15 professorial staff. 13 master's degrees and 6 Ph.D.'s awarded 1955-59. 18 graduate students registered fall 1959.

Geography. Physical, economic, or regional (domestic and foreign) geography. Prerequisites for graduate study: 24 semester hours of geography, including 6 in morphology, map reading, and interpretation; courses in anthropology, economics, introductory or general botany; 12 semester hours of a foreign language. 13 professorial staff. 6 master's degrees and 7 Ph.D.'s awarded 1955-59. 35 graduate students registered fall 1959.

History. American: Colonial, the middle period, recent, or intellectual history. European: Greek and Roman, modern, intellectual, or Russian history; England and the British Empire. Asian: Chinese, Middle Eastern history. Prerequisite for graduate study: at least the equivalent of a minor in history. Recommended: supplementary work in political science, economics, sociology or philosophy. 17 professorial staff. 45 master's degrees and 2 Ph.D.'s awarded 1955-59. 81 graduate students registered fall 1959.

Horticulture. Pomology, olericulture, floriculture, ornamental horticulture, horticultural processing. 9 professorial staff. 17 master's degrees and 11 Ph.D.'s awarded 1955-59. 23 graduate students registered fall 1959.

Mathematics. Analysis, algebra, number theory, topology, geometry, functional analysis, applied mathematics, statistics. Offered by Department of Mathematics through Institute for Fluid Dynamics and Applied Mathematics. Prerequisite for graduate study: 12-18 hours of mathematics beyond calculus, including advanced calculus. Recommended: 1 foreign language; courses in physics or other science. 24 professorial staff. 23 master's degrees and 14 Ph.D.'s awarded 1955-59. 116 graduate students registered fall 1959.

Microbiology. Prerequisites for graduate study: chemistry through organic; 8 hours of physics; 6 of mathematics. 5 professorial staff. 20 master's degrees and 15 Ph.D.'s awarded 1955-59. 60 graduate students registered fall 1959.

Microbiology. Dental or pharmaceutical microbiology. Offered by Department of Microbiology, Schools of Dentistry and Pharmacy, Baltimore. 15 professorial staff. 4 master's degrees and 2 Ph.D.'s awarded 1955-59. 9 graduate students registered fall 1959.

Microbiology. Offered by Department of Microbiology, School of Medicine, Baltimore. Open to students who have completed 2 years of M.D. curriculum. 5 professorial staff. 7 graduate students registered fall 1959.

Pharmaceutical Chemistry. Organic pharmaceutical chemistry. Minor work usually in phar-

macology, physical chemistry, biochemistry, pharmacy. Offered by Department of Pharmaceutical Chemistry, School of Pharmacy, Baltimore. Prerequisite for graduate study: B.S. in pharmacy or chemistry. 2 professors. 3 master's degrees and 5 Ph.D.'s awarded 1955-59. 9 graduate students registered fall 1959.

Pharmacology. Action of chemical compounds on living systems. Cooperative program offered by School of Medicine, Baltimore. Prerequisite for graduate study: chemistry or biology major. Recommended: M.D. degree. 4 professorial staff. 2 master's degrees and 8 Ph.D.'s awarded 1955-59. 3 graduate students registered fall 1959. New enrollment limited to 2 or 3.

Pharmacology. Bioassays, drug combinations, drug absorption, reduction of toxicities. Offered by Department of Pharmacology, School of Pharmacy, Baltimore. Recommended for graduate study: B.S. in pharmacy; French; German; calculus. 1 professor. 5 master's degrees and 3 Ph.D.'s awarded 1955-59. 1 graduate student registered fall 1959.

Pharmacy. Stabilization of drugs, kinetic studies of degradation, physical pharmacy problems; manufacturing pharmacy, formulation of pharmaceutical dosage forms, emulsion technology, rheology of pharmaceutical systems. Offered by Department of Pharmacy, School of Pharmacy, Baltimore. Prerequisite for graduate study: B.S. in pharmacy. Recommended: French; German; calculus. 4 professorial staff. 17 master's degrees and 7 Ph.D.'s awarded 1955-59. 10 graduate students registered fall 1959.

Philosophy. Philosophy of science, aesthetics, logic, ethics, metaphysics and epistemology, history of philosophy. Prerequisite for graduate study: equivalent of major in philosophy. 5 professorial staff. Ph.D. program begun 1958. 8 master's degrees awarded 1955-59. 8 graduate students registered fall 1959.

Physical Education, Recreation, and Health. Prerequisite for graduate study: 16 credit hours in area of specialization. Recommended: background in 1 or more of mathematics, physics, chemistry, zoology, psychology, history, sociology, art, drama, music, dance. 9 professorial staff. 32 master's degrees and 3 Ph.D.'s awarded 1955-59. 85 graduate students registered fall 1959.

Physics. Astrophysics, cosmic rays, elementary particles; field theory; fluid dynamics; gaseous electronics; microwave and radio frequency spectroscopy; relativity; high-energy, molecular, plasma, or solid-state physics. Prerequisite for graduate study: strong major in physics or equivalent. Recommended: GRE. 40 professorial staff. 43 master's degrees and 47 Ph.D.'s awarded 1955-59. 140 graduate students registered fall 1959.

Physiology. Central nervous system, muscle, endocrines, kidney and body fluids. Offered by Department of Physiology, School of Medicine, Baltimore. Prerequisites for graduate study: biology; chemistry; physics; mathematics. Recommended: GRE. 4 professorial staff. 1 master's degree and 2 Ph.D.'s awarded 1955-59. 1 graduate student registered January 1960.

Physiology. Central nervous system, muscle, endocrines, kidney and body fluids. Offered by Department of Physiology, School of Dentistry, and Pharmacy, Baltimore. Prerequisites for graduate study: biology; chemistry; physics; mathematics. Recommended: GRE. 2 professors.

Political Science.—Government and Politics. International affairs; comparative or state and local government; public law, policy, or administration; political theory. Offered by Department of Government and Politics. Prerequisite for graduate study: 18 semester hours in political science. 9 professorial staff. 44 master's degrees and 6 Ph.D.'s awarded 1955-59. 73 graduate students registered fall 1959.

Poultry Husbandry. Genetics, physiology, nutrition, products technology as related to poultry husbandry. Prerequisite for graduate study: B.S. in agriculture or the biological sciences. Recommended: background in biological chemistry, mathematics, or statistics. 8 professorial staff. 7 master's degrees and 11 Ph.D.'s awarded 1955-59. 11 graduate students registered fall 1959.

Psychology. Experimental, social, industrial, quantitative, or mental health psychology. Prerequisites for graduate study: background in laboratory sciences, statistics, and experimental psychology; MAT; GRE. Recommended: mathematics; physiology. 11 professorial staff. 16 master's degrees and 31 Ph.D.'s awarded 1955-59. 41 graduate students registered fall 1959. Total enrollment limited to about 40.

Sociology. Community anthropology; criminology; rural, urban, or industrial sociology; mental health; the family; social theory or psychology; research methods. Prerequisites for graduate study: 24 hours of sociology or 12 semester hours of sociology and 12 hours of work in economics, political science, or psychology; courses in principles of sociology, social theory, and statistics. 10 professorial staff. 32 master's degrees and 4 Ph.D.'s awarded 1955-59. 48 graduate students registered fall 1959.

Toxicology. Toxicology (analytical), pharmacology. Offered by Department of Legal Medicine. Prerequisites for graduate study: chemistry major with courses in general, organic, analytical (qualitative and quantitative), and physical chemistry; physics, biology, organic qualitative analysis. 3 professorial staff. 1 master's degree and 1 Ph.D. awarded 1955-59. 2 graduate students registered fall 1959.

Zoology. Acarology, animal behavior, cytology, ecology, embryology, parasitology, physiology, systematics, fisheries. Recommended for graduate study: 2 foreign languages; 1 year of physics; 2 of chemistry; 1 of mathematics. 11 professorial staff. 18 master's degrees and 17 Ph.D.'s awarded 1955-59. 41 graduate students registered fall 1959. Total enrollment limited to 55.

Massachusetts College of Pharmacy

BOSTON 15, MASSACHUSETTS

The Graduate Division

Graduate instruction has been offered since 1896. In 1939 the graduate curriculum was placed under the direction of the Graduate Council. First Ph.D. was awarded in 1950. Institution is privately controlled and nonsectarian. Both men and women are admitted.

No residence facilities provided.

Residence requirements for Ph.D.: 3 academic years beyond bachelor's degree, of which at least 2 must be spent in residence at Massachusetts College of Pharmacy.

ADMISSION REQUIREMENTS

For graduate study: B.S. in pharmacy; reading knowledge of German. Recommended: advanced mathematics. For candidacy for Ph.D.: reading knowledge of French and German; qualifying examination.

Apply to the Graduate Council before June 1.

FEES AND FIRST-YEAR AID

No application fee. Tuition $15 per credit hour.

First-year aid available: scholarships, $300; teaching fellowships, $1,500; other fellowships, $1,200-$1,800; research assistantships, $1,500.

Apply to Dean of the College before June 1.

FIELDS OF STUDY FOR THE PH.D.

Pharmaceutical Science. Pharmacy, pharmacognosy, pharmaceutical chemistry, and pharmacology. Offered by the Departments of Pharmacy, Chemistry, and Biological Science. 21 professorial staff. 46 master's degrees and 3 Ph.D.'s awarded 1955-59. 20 graduate students registered fall 1959. Enrollment in program limited to 25.

Massachusetts Institute of Technology

CAMBRIDGE 39, MASSACHUSETTS

The Graduate School

Graduate instruction has been offered since 1886, with the first Ph.D. being awarded in 1907. The Graduate School was organized in 1925. Ph.D. and D.Sc. are awarded by all divisions interchangeably, according to wish of student and faculty. The institute is privately controlled and nonsectarian. Both men and women are admitted, but students are predominantly men.

The Graduate Houses accommodate about 400 men. No residence facilities are provided for women or married students.

Residence requirement for a doctorate: at least 2 years.

ADMISSION REQUIREMENTS

Mathematics 2 years; physics 2 years; chemistry 1 year; at least 6 semester courses in cultural subjects. GRE recommended.

Apply to Director of Admissions before February 15.

FEES AND FIRST-YEAR AID

No application fee. Tuition $1,500 per academic year. Room (in dormitory) for men $370 a year. Approximate annual cost of board in college dining room $610.

Scholarships, teaching fellowships, some other fellowships, and research assistantships are available to first-year students.

Apply to Director of Admissions before February 15.

FIELDS OF STUDY FOR THE PH.D.

Aeronautics and Astronautics. Aeronautical and astronautical engineering, vehicle design and operation, aerodynamics and gas dynamics, space mechanics, structures, aero-elasticity, propulsion, instrumentation. 35 professorial staff. 174 master's degrees and 15 Ph.D.'s awarded 1955-59. 186 graduate students registered fall 1959.

Architecture. 15 professorial staff. 104 master's degrees awarded 1955-59. 34 graduate students registered fall 1959.

Biology. Analytical biology, biochemistry, biophysics, general physiology, microbiology. 17 professorial staff. 12 master's degrees and 22 Ph.D.'s awarded 1955-59. 61 graduate students registered fall 1959.

Chemistry. Analytical, inorganic and nuclear, organic, and physical chemistry. 36 professorial staff. 15 master's degrees and 176 Ph.D.'s awarded 1955-59. 203 graduate students registered fall 1959.

City Planning. Offered by Department of City and Regional Planning. 7 professorial staff. Ph.D. program authorized for 1960. 53 master's degrees awarded 1955-59. 43 graduate students registered fall 1959.

Economics and Social Sciences. Economics and engineering (or science), industrial economics, industrial relations, political science. 38 professorial staff. 10 master's degrees and 51 Ph.D.'s awarded 1955-59. 113 graduate students registered fall 1959.

Engineering.—Chemical. Applied chemistry, engineering operations, fuel engineering. 24 professorial staff. 412 master's degrees and 59 doctorates awarded 1955-59. 165 graduate students registered fall 1959.

Engineering.—Civil. Civil engineering: hydromechanics and hydraulic engineering; photogrammetric, including data engineering; soil, structural, and transportation engineering. Sanitary engineering. Building engineering and construction: construction management; materials of construction. Offered by Department of Civil and Sanitary Engineering. 29 professorial staff. 297 master's degrees and 37 doctorates awarded 1955-59. 139 students registered fall 1959.

Engineering. — Electrical. Communication, computation, control, electrical science and engineering, electronics, energy processing, molecular engineering. 72 professorial staff. 619 master's degrees and 74 Ph.D.'s awarded 1955-59. 449 graduate students registered fall 1959.

Engineering.—Mechanical. Applied mechanics, design and control, fluid mechanics, heat engineering, materials, power and propulsion, textile technology, thermodynamics. 60 professorial staff. 296 master's degrees and 67 doctorates awarded 1955-59. 234 graduate students registered fall 1959.

Engineering.—Nuclear. Nuclear engineering, fission technology, thermonuclear processes. 10 professorial staff. Ph.D. program initiated 1957. 33 master's degrees and 7 doctorates awarded 1955-59. 109 graduate students registered fall 1959.

Food Technology. Food bacteriology, food engineering, food processing, food technology, industrial microbiology, nutritional biochemistry, radiation preservation, rheology of foods, biochemical engineering. 7 professorial staff. 28 master's degrees and 18 doctorates awarded 1955-59. 47 graduate students registered fall 1959.

Geology and Geophysics. Classical or theoretical geology, geochemistry, geophysics. 19 professorial staff. 21 master's degrees and 28 Ph.D.'s awarded 1955-59. 66 graduate students registered fall 1959.

Industrial Management. 44 professorial staff. Ph.D. program authorized for 1960. 347 master's degrees awarded 1955-59. 177 graduate students registered fall 1959.

Mathematics. 36 professorial staff. 45 master's degrees and 36 Ph.D.'s awarded 1955-59. 131 graduate students registered fall 1959.

Metallurgy. Ceramics, materials engineering, metallurgy, mineral engineering. 28 professorial staff. 117 master's degrees and 94 doctorates awarded 1955-59. 165 graduate students registered fall 1959.

Meteorology. 11 professorial staff. 45 master's degrees and 16 doctorates awarded 1955-59. 48 graduate students registered fall 1959.

Naval Architecture and Marine Engineering. Marine engineering, naval architecture. 10 professorial staff. 104 master's degrees awarded 1955-59. 109 graduate students registered fall 1959.

Physics. 57 professorial staff. 54 master's degrees and 139 doctorates awarded 1955-59. 233 graduate students registered fall 1959.

Massachusetts, University of

AMHERST, MASSACHUSETTS

The Graduate School

The Graduate School was organized in 1897, although graduate instruction had been offered since 1876. First Ph.D. was awarded in 1902. University is publicly controlled by the state. Both men and women are admitted.

A new cooperative Ph.D. program has been established with Amherst, Smith, and Mount Holyoke Colleges. Programs have been organized in biology and chemistry to date. Students may do thesis and research with members of the faculty of the 3 colleges if they have been elected to membership on the University of Massachusetts Graduate Faculty. Degree is awarded by the University of Massachusetts.

No dormitory facilities provided for single graduate students; apartments available for married students.

Residence requirement for the Ph.D.: minimum of 3 years beyond bachelor's degree, of which 1 academic year of full-time graduate work must be taken in residence at the University of Massachusetts. For the cooperative Ph.D. degree, "residence" is defined as the institution where the thesis work is being done. Summer and evening courses available.

ADMISSION REQUIREMENTS

For graduate study: bachelor's degree; standing in upper half of graduating class; 2 letters of recommendation; acceptance by the department and the Graduate School; MAT and GRE. For candidacy for Ph.D.: reading knowledge of 2 foreign languages not in the same linguistic group; preliminary comprehensive examinations in major and minor fields.

Apply to Dean of the Graduate School before June 1.

FEES AND FIRST-YEAR AID

No application fee. Tuition for state residents $200 a year; others $300. Special fees approximate $22 annually. Room (in dormitory) $265 a year. Approximate annual cost of board in college dining room $600. Apartments $60-$90 a month.

First-year aid available: 21 teaching fellowships, $1,800 plus remission of tuition and fees; 44 other fellowships, $1,800 plus remission of tuition and fees; approximately 30 research assistantships with varying stipends.

Apply to Dean of the Graduate School before March 1.

FIELDS OF STUDY FOR THE PH.D.

Agronomy. Soil chemistry and utilization, turf management and culture, statistics in agronomy. 8 professorial staff. 6 master's degrees and 1 Ph.D. awarded 1955-59. 7 graduate students registered fall 1959.

Animal Science. Animal nutrition and genetics; meat processing; beef, sheep, dairy cattle, horse, and swine production; histology of domestic animals; fertility and fecundity. Offered by the Department of Dairy and Animal Science. 10 professorial staff. Ph.D. program begun 1959. 3 master's degrees awarded 1955-59. 3 graduate students registered fall 1959.

Bacteriology. Bacterial physiology, cytology, immunology, virology, microbial genetics, antiseptics and disinfectants, sanitary bacteriology, quantitative and qualitative analysis, microbiological fermentations, microbial genetics, antibiotics. Offered by the Department of Bacteriology and Public Health. Prerequisite for graduate study: courses in general chemistry, qualitative and quantitative analysis, organic chemistry, physics, and bacteriology. 7 professorial staff. 27 master's degrees and 4 Ph.D.'s awarded 1955-59. 22 graduate students registered fall 1959.

Botany. Plant physiology, ecology, mycology, morphology, taxonomy, geography, or cytogenetics; the angiosperms; comparative anatomy of green plants. 7 professorial staff. 1 master's degree awarded 1955-59. 4 graduate students registered fall 1959.

Chemistry. Inorganic, organic, physical, analytical, quantum, or heterocyclic chemistry; biochemistry; biocolloids; chemical thermodynamics; gases; kinetics; catalysis. Prerequisite for graduate study: placement examination. 13 professorial staff. 20 master's degrees and 10 Ph.D.'s awarded 1955-59. 27 graduate students registered fall 1959.

Economics. Central banking, mathematical economics, monopoly and public utility problems, collective bargaining, advanced economic theory, taxation, economic fluctuations, monetary policy, economics of consumption, economics of international trade, labor legislation, current economic problems, comparative economic systems. 6 professorial staff. 7 master's degrees and 1 Ph.D. awarded 1955-59. 11 graduate students registered fall 1959.

Entomology and Plant Pathology. Insect embryology, histology, physiology, morphology, and phylogeny; geographical distribution of animals and plants; biological or chemical control of insects; coccidology; medical entomology; arthropod taxonomy; apiculture; pest control; forest pathology; advanced plant pathology; forest and shade tree pathology; insect transmission of plant diseases. 10 professorial staff. 13 master's degrees and 5 Ph.D.'s awarded 1955-59. 13 graduate students registered fall 1959.

Food Sciences. Bacteriology, chemistry, dairy and animal science, food technology, home economics (foods and nutrition). Cooperative program offered by the Departments of Bacteriology, Chemistry, Dairy and Animal Science, and Food Technology, and the School of Home Economics. Program is designed to prepare students for research in various phases of the food sciences. 49 interdepartmental staff. 3 graduate students registered fall 1959.

Food Technology. Thermal processing of foods, food packaging, edible fats and oils, food acceptance—theory and methodology, food colorimetry, fisheries technology, biological and toxicological assay of foods, industrial practices, analysis of food products, food preservation, sensory evaluation methods. Prerequisites for graduate study: basic sciences and food technology. 9 professorial staff. 35 master's degrees and 21 Ph.D.'s awarded 1955-59. 26 graduate students registered fall 1959.

Poultry Science. Avian genetics; advanced poultry genetics, nutrition, and physiology; poultry biology, nutrition, and breeding. 5 professorial staff. Ph.D. program begun 1958. 3 master's degrees awarded 1955-59. 4 graduate students registered fall 1959.

Psychology. Clinical and general experimental psychology, child counseling, industrial psychology, school and social psychology. Prerequisites for graduate study: introductory course and 21 additional credits in psychology, including a course in laboratory experimental psychology or equivalent; 1 course in statistics. 9 professorial staff. 17 master's degrees and 10 Ph.D.'s awarded 1955-59. 57 graduate students registered fall 1959.

Zoology. Physiology, genetics, morphology, invertebrate and vertebrate zoology. 14 professorial staff. Ph.D. program begun 1955. 13 master's degrees awarded 1955-59. 27 graduate students registered fall 1959.

Medical Evangelists, College of

LOMA LINDA, CALIFORNIA

School of Graduate Studies

Graduate instruction has been offered by the college since 1946, and the School of Graduate Studies was organized in 1954. First Ph.D. was awarded 1958. The college is privately controlled and is related to the Seventh-day Adventist Church. Both men and women are admitted.

Rooms in residence halls for single students; apartments available in community for married students.

Residence requirement for Ph.D.: 2 years of study beyond master's degree. These years must be taken in residence at the College of Medical Evangelists unless master's degree has been taken there; then part of the work may be done in absentia by permission.

ADMISSION REQUIREMENTS

For graduate study: undergraduate credits as follows: biology, 10 semester units, chemistry 16, English 6, modern foreign language 6, physics 8, religion 12; GPA of 2.5; M.A. or M.S. degree or equivalent; French and German, or substitution for 1 on approval of the Council on Graduate Studies. For candidacy for Ph.D.: 72 semester hours beyond master's degree; 2 years in residence; outline of thesis and proposed bibliography; comprehensive examinations.

Apply to Dean, School of Graduate Studies, 1 month before beginning of term.

FEES AND FIRST-YEAR AID

Application fee $5. Tuition $22 per semester unit; $14.50 per quarter unit. Special fees approximate $110 annually. Room (in residence halls) for men $20-$30 per month; women $24 and up. Approximate annual cost of board in college dining room $540-$600. Apartments in community $50-$85 per month.

First-year aid available: fellowships with stipends of up to $4,800; grants-in-aid of $1,620-$1,800.

Apply to Dean, School of Graduate Studies at time application for admission is made.

FIELDS OF STUDY FOR THE PH.D.

All graduate students do practice teaching under supervision in department of their major.

Anatomy. 36 hours of didactic instruction must be taken in Department of Anatomy. Student then does research in his area of interest. Prerequisites for graduate study: comparative vertebrate anatomy; vertebrate embryology; physiology; genetics. 6 professorial staff. Ph.D. program initiated 1955. 1 master's degree and 1 Ph.D. awarded 1955-59. 5 graduate students registered fall 1959.

Biochemistry. Prerequisites for graduate study: mathematics, including differential and integral calculus; zoology. 4 professorial staff. Ph.D. program initiated 1955. 14 master's degrees awarded 1955-59. 6 graduate students registered fall 1959.

Pharmacology. 3 professorial staff. Ph.D. program initiated 1955. 1 master's degree awarded 1955-59. 1 graduate student registered fall 1959.

Physiology. Prerequisites for graduate study: differential and integral calculus; physical chemistry. Recommended: major in physics. 4 professorial staff. Ph.D. program initiated 1956. 3 master's degrees awarded 1955-59. 3 graduate students registered fall 1959.

Miami, University of

CORAL GABLES 46, FLORIDA

The Graduate School

The Graduate School, established in 1941, has jurisdiction over all graduate work offered by the university. Doctoral programs are relatively new, and the first Ph.D. degrees are not expected to be conferred until 1961. The first Ed.D. degree will probably be awarded at this time also. University is privately controlled and nonsectarian. Both men and women are admitted.

Rooms in college dormitories available for graduate students; apartments for married students.

Special facilities include: Marine Laboratory; special library and museum collections in biological fields, relating particularly to the tropics and semitropics; Morton Collectanea, dealing with world's sources of food and food elements; new medical research building. Affiliation with Miami Cerebral Palsy Clinic affords unusual facilities for training psychology students in this field. Special rapid courses for reading knowledge of German and Russian planned for 1960.

Residence requirement for Ph.D.: minimum of 3 years beyond bachelor's degree, of which 1 year must be spent in full-time residence at the University of Miami. This requirement cannot be met by summer school or part-time residence only. Maximum of 18 semester hours of graduate credit may be transferred from other institutions. Summer courses available in education, zoology, and chemistry; evening courses only in education.

ADMISSION REQUIREMENTS

For graduate study: bachelor's degree; B average; adequate training in major field (usually at least 18 semester hours); GRE; examinations and/or interviews as required by individual departments. For candidacy for Ph.D.: reading knowledge of 2 foreign languages (French, German, Russian); qualifying examinations; B average in all graduate work; acceptance of dissertation outline.

Apply to Dean of the Graduate School prior to August 15.

FEES AND FIRST-YEAR AID

No application fee. Tuition $35 per credit hour. Matriculation fee $10; optional fees $25. Room (in dormitory) for men $340 per year; for women $340-$420. Approximate annual cost of board in college cafeteria $550. Apartments $72.50-$82.50 per month.

First-year aid available: approximately 80 new teaching fellowships, $1,200-$2,000; 4 new fellowships in special fields, $1,400; variable number of research assistantships, $1,000-$2,200.

Apply to Dean of the Graduate School before March 1. Applications received at other times considered only if vacancies appear.

FIELDS OF STUDY FOR THE PH.D.

Although there are no formal courses in the methodology of college teaching, informal seminars are held for teaching assistants. In psychology a doctoral specialization in the teaching of psychology is offered.

Anatomy. Study directed toward training for teaching and research in basic science departments of medical schools. Offered by Department of Anatomy, School of Medicine. Prerequisites for graduate study: bachelor's degree in biology or chemistry; Medical College Admission Test; basic courses in comparative vertebrate anatomy, embryology, general and organic chemistry, and physics. 3 professorial staff. Ph.D. program begun 1959. 2 master's degrees awarded 1955-59. 3 graduate students registered fall 1959.

Biochemistry. Offered by Department of Biochemistry, School of Medicine. Prerequisites for graduate study: major in chemistry; mathematics through calculus; 2 semesters of biology; 2 semesters physics; reading knowledge of 1 foreign language. Recommended: additional courses in biology and physics. Prerequisite for Ph.D. candidacy: completion, during second year of graduate work, of an apprenticeship, during which student works for a time under each member of the department. 7 professorial staff. Ph.D. program begun 1959. 1 master's degree awarded 1955-59. 8 graduate students registered fall 1959.

Cell Physiology. Interdepartmental program offered by Departments of Zoology, Biochemistry, and Physiology with participants from Departments of Anatomy, Microbiology, Medicine, Botany, and Marine Biology, and the Howard Hughes Medical Institute. Prerequisites for graduate study: bachelor's degree in biology, physics, or chemistry. 4 professorial staff. Program begun 1960.

Chemistry. Organic, inorganic, physical. Prerequisite for graduate study: bachelor's degree in chemistry. 7 professorial staff. Ph.D. program begun 1959. 16 master's degrees awarded 1955-59. 10 graduate students registered fall 1959.

Education. Elementary, secondary education; guidance; curriculum and supervision; administration. A program leading to qualification as school psychologist is offered jointly with the Department of Psychology. Prerequisites for graduate study: major in appropriate field of education; work in a field outside education.

Prerequisites for Ph.D. candidacy: master's degree; 2 years of successful teaching; admissions interview with faculty committee. 9 professorial staff. Ph.D. program begun 1959. 334 master's degrees awarded 1955-59. 459 graduate students registered fall 1959. Ed.D. degree also awarded in this field.

Marine Sciences. Marine biology, fisheries, oceanography. Prerequisite for graduate study: GRE Advanced Test in Biology, Chemistry, or Physics. 13 professorial staff. Ph.D. program begun 1959. 26 master's degrees awarded 1955-59. 31 graduate students registered fall 1959.

Microbiology. Bacteriology, immunology, microbial metabolism, mycology, parasitology, virology. Offered by Department of Microbiology, School of Medicine. Prerequisites for graduate study: general bacteriology; general biology; inorganic and organic chemistry. 6 professorial staff. Ph.D. program begun 1959. 2 master's degrees awarded 1955-59. 14 graduate students registered fall 1959.

Parasitology. Animal, veterinary, and medical parasitology. Combined program sponsored by Departments of Zoology and Microbiology. Prerequisite for graduate study: approximately the same preparation as required for medical school. 2 professorial staff. Program begun 1959.

Pharmacology. Toxicology, and several areas of pharmacology. Offered by Department of Pharmacology, School of Medicine. Prerequisites for graduate study: approximately the requirements for admission to medical school, including 2 full years of biology. 3 professorial staff. Ph.D. program begun 1959. 1 master's degree awarded 1955-59. 3 graduate students registered fall 1959.

Physiology. Cell and cardiovascular physiology. Offered by Department of Physiology, School of Medicine, in cooperation with Departments of Biochemistry and Zoology. Prerequisites for graduate study: approximately the courses for admission to medical school. 3 professorial staff. Program begun 1959. 1 graduate student registered fall 1959.

Psychology. Experimental and theoretical psychology, clinical psychology, teaching of psychology, psychological research. A program leading to qualification as school psychologist is offered jointly with the School of Education. Prerequisites for graduate study: major in psychology, including courses in tests and measurements, statistics, experimental psychology; GRE Advanced Test in Psychology. Prerequisite for Ph.D. candidacy: MAT. 8 professorial staff. Ph.D. program begun 1959. 38 master's degrees awarded 1955-59. 45 graduate students registered fall 1959.

Zoology. Physiology (cellular, comparative, and vertebrate), experimental embryology, parasitology, ecology, limnology, animal populations. Prerequisite for graduate study: zoology or biology major or its equivalent. 7 professorial staff. Ph.D. program begun 1959. 8 master's degrees awarded 1955-59. 18 graduate students registered fall 1959.

Michigan State University

EAST LANSING, MICHIGAN

School for Advanced Graduate Studies

Master's degrees have been awarded at Michigan State since 1864, and the first Ph.D. was awarded in 1925. The School for Advanced Graduate Studies was founded in 1930 and reorganized in 1959. At present the Ph.D. is awarded in a number of fields and the Ed.D. and D.B.A. are also conferred. University is publicly controlled by the state. Both men and women are admitted.

Single graduate students live in Graduate Residence Center which has 422 single rooms and a dining room; married students are eligible for space in the 1,940 1- and 2-bedroom apartments (furnished) on campus.

Special facilities include: library of approximately 720,000 volumes; museum; biological station; electronic computer; art center.

Residence requirement for Ph.D.: 3 quarters beyond the master's degree or its equivalent; amount of graduate credit which may be transferred from other institutions individually determined by guidance committee. Summer and evening courses available.

ADMISSION REQUIREMENTS

For graduate study: bachelor's degree; B average in major courses; satisfaction of departmental prerequisites. For candidacy for Ph.D.: master's degree or equivalent; reading knowledge of 2 foreign languages or of 1 language and completion of an approved program of study; qualifying and comprehensive examinations; departmental approval. Certain departments require MAT, GRE, or other standardized tests.

Apply to Office of Admissions and Scholarships not later than 1 month before beginning of term in which enrollment is desired.

FEES AND FIRST-YEAR AID

No application fee. Tuition for state residents $279 per academic year; others $645-$750 (depending on the fees of the land-grant university in the state from which student comes). Room in dormitory $60 per month (single room); $45 (double room). Approximate annual cost of board in college dining room $500. 1-bedroom apartments $75 per month (including all utilities); 2-bedroom $81.

First-year aid available (sponsored by the university and outside agencies): 15 tuition scholarships; 65 fellowships, $2,200 plus tuition; 300 research assistantships, $1,800-$2,100 (about ½ first year); 450 graduate teaching assistantships, $2,000-$2,200 (about ½ first year).

Apply to Office of Admissions and Scholarships by March 1.

FIELDS OF STUDY FOR THE PH.D.

Seminar programs in the methodology of teaching are offered for graduate assistants.

Anatomy. Cytology, embryology, gross anatomy, hematology, histology, neurology. Prerequisite for graduate study: biological background with at least 1 year each of chemistry and physics. 6 professorial staff. 2 master's degrees awarded 1955-59. 10 graduate students registered fall 1959.

Animal Husbandry. Animal breeding, nutrition, physiology, or production; meats. 18 professorial staff. 24 master's degrees and 16 Ph.D.'s awarded 1955-59. 31 graduate students registered fall 1959.

Art. Art history, practice. Prerequisite for graduate study: 60 quarter credits in appropriate art courses. 22 professorial staff. 61 master's degrees awarded 1955-59. 33 graduate students registered fall 1959.

Biochemistry. Animal metabolism and nutrition; biochemistry of genetics, of microorganisms, or of plants. Cooperative programs offered by Departments of Chemistry and Agricultural Chemistry. Prerequisites for graduate study: basic courses in physics, mathematics, and biology; 1 year each of organic and physical chemistry and quantitative analysis. 13 professorial staff. Program begun 1957. 9 graduate students registered fall 1959.

Botany and Plant Pathology. Anatomy, cytology-cytotaxonomy, ecology, lichenology and bryology, morphology, mycology, pathology, phycology, physiology, phytogeography, taxonomy. Prerequisites for graduate study: major in botany; 1 year each zoology, physics, chemistry, and mathematics; 1 foreign language. 31 professorial staff. 20 master's degrees and 25 Ph.D.'s awarded 1955-59. 45 graduate students registered fall 1959.

Business Administration. Accounting, financial distribution, marketing, personnel or production administration, transportation. 46 professorial staff. 239 master's degrees awarded 1955-59. 41 graduate students registered fall 1959.

Chemistry. Analytical, inorganic, organic, or physical chemistry; biochemistry. Prerequisites for graduate study: 1 year each of physics and calculus, and general, analytical, organic, and physical chemistry; reading knowledge of French or German. 27 professorial staff. 54 master's degrees and 92 Ph.D.'s awarded 1955-59. 140 graduate students registered fall 1959.

Communication Arts. Communication research methods, communication theory and process, mass communications. 9 professorial staff. 2 master's degrees awarded 1955-59. 36 graduate students registered fall 1959.

Comparative Literature. Cooperative program offered by Departments of English and Foreign Languages. 30 professorial staff. Program begun 1960.

Dairy. Breeding; dairy bacteriology, chemistry, plant management, or sanitation; physiology; herd management; nutrition. 22 professorial staff. 21 master's degrees and 12 Ph.D.'s awarded 1955-59. 30 graduate students registered fall 1959.

Economics. Econometrics, economic development, history of economic thought, income and employment theory, industrial organization and public policy, international economics, labor and industrial relations, money and banking, price and value theory, public finance. Prerequisite for graduate study: 30 term credits in social sciences, including 18 in economics. 37 professorial staff. 24 master's degrees and 12 Ph.D.'s awarded 1955-59. 34 graduate students registered fall 1959.

Economics.—Agricultural. Agricultural business management, econometrics, production economics; consumer marketing; farm management; land economics; prices and marketing. Prerequisite for graduate study: background in technical agriculture and economics. 39 professorial staff. 59 master's degrees and 13 Ph.D.'s awarded 1955-59. 48 graduate students registered fall 1959.

Education. Adult and continuing, agricultural, business and distributive, higher, home economics, industrial, physical, or special education; general school administration; guidance and counseling; measurement, evaluation, and research; social-philosophic foundations of education; educational psychology. 114 professorial staff. 1,093 master's degrees and 119 Ph.D.'s awarded 1955-59. 912 graduate students registered fall 1959.

Engineering.—Agricultural. Farm structures, food engineering, power and machinery, processing farm products, rural electrification, soil and water conservation. Prerequisite for graduate study: major in agricultural engineering. 26 professorial staff. 39 master's degrees and 30 Ph.D.'s awarded 1955-59. 33 graduate students registered fall 1959.

Engineering.—Applied Mechanics. Acoustics, turbulent flow, boundary layer studies, elastic constants of crystals, plate bending, propagation of plastic waves, viscoelastic studies. Offered by Department of Applied Mechanics. Prerequisites for graduate study: major in engineering or related curriculum; strong background in mathematics. 7 professorial staff. 16 master's degrees awarded 1955-59. 31 graduate students registered fall 1959.

Engineering.—Chemical. Absorption, computer applications, diffusion, distillation, drying, extraction, heat transfer, industrial works, kinetics, mass transfer, plastics, pulsed columns, water treatment. Prerequisite for graduate study: major in chemical engineering. 6 professorial staff. 12 master's degrees and 2 Ph.D.'s awarded 1955-59. 10 graduate students registered fall 1959.

Engineering.—Civil. Hydraulics, sanitary engineering, soils, structures, transportation. Prerequisite for graduate study: major in civil engineering. 15 professorial staff. 23 master's degrees and 2 Ph.D.'s awarded 1955-59. 26 graduate students registered fall 1959.

Engineering. — Electrical. Electromagnetic fields, electronic circuits and systems, electronic instrumentation, feedback system analysis, theoretical network analysis, nonlinear systems, numerical analysis, switching circuits. Prerequi-

site for graduate study: major in electrical engineering. 13 professorial staff. 33 master's degrees and 3 Ph.D.'s awarded 1955-59. 33 graduate students registered fall 1959.

Engineering.—Mechanical. Machine or automotive design, theoretical and applied thermodynamics, heat transfer, gas dynamics, mechanisms. Prerequisite for graduate study: major in mechanical engineering. 23 professorial staff. 30 master's degrees and 4 Ph.D.'s awarded 1955-59. 24 graduate students registered fall 1959.

Engineering.—Metallurgical. Cast metals, deformation, diffusion, hardenability, nucleation and growth, semiconductor materials. Prerequisite for graduate study: major in metallurgical engineering. 3 professorial staff. 6 master's degrees and 3 Ph.D.'s awarded 1955-59. 1 graduate student registered fall 1959.

English. American, comparative, 17th or 19th century English literature, Restoration and 18th century English literature; Renaissance; contemporary English and American literature; early and medieval English literature. Prerequisite for graduate study: 30 term credits of English and allied subjects. 30 professorial staff. 36 master's degrees and 16 Ph.D.'s awarded 1955-59. 54 graduate students registered fall 1959.

Entomology. Apiculture, applied entomology, taxonomy. Prerequisite for graduate study: background in entomology, technical agriculture, chemistry, biology, and zoology. 12 professorial staff. 13 master's degrees and 4 Ph.D.'s awarded 1955-59. 13 graduate students registered fall 1959.

Farm Crops. Physiology of farm crops; plant genetics and breeding. Prerequisites for graduate study: courses in botany, soil science, plant pathology, chemistry, and statistics. 22 professorial staff. 19 master's degrees and 15 Ph.D.'s awarded 1955-59. 21 graduate students registered fall 1959.

Fisheries and Wildlife. Conservation education; fish or game management; fisheries, pollution, or wildlife biology; limnology. Prerequisite for graduate study: background in zoology and ecology. 9 professorial staff. 24 master's degrees and 8 Ph.D.'s awarded 1955-59. 31 graduate students registered fall 1959.

Forest Products. Wood technology. 10 professorial staff. 19 master's degrees and 4 Ph.D.'s awarded 1955-59. 13 graduate students registered fall 1959.

Forestry. Forest ecology, economics, genetics, influences, management, or soils; mensuration; silviculture; tree nutrition. 14 professorial staff. 36 master's degrees and 12 Ph.D.'s awarded 1955-59. 24 graduate students registered fall 1959.

Genetics. Human, forest, plant, or poultry genetics; biochemistry of genetics; genetics of dental caries. Programs in genetics offered by each of the following departments: Agricultural Chemistry, Zoology, Forestry, Farm Crops, and Poultry Science. 9 professorial staff. 10 master's degrees and 4 Ph.D.'s awarded 1955-59. 15 graduate students registered fall 1959.

Geography. Economic, historical, physical, political, or regional geography; population and settlement; geographic techniques. Prerequisite for graduate study: major or 30 term credits in geography. 7 professorial staff. 5 master's degrees awarded 1955-59. 27 graduate students registered fall 1959.

Geology. Economic or structural geology, geochemistry, geophysics, geomorphology-glaciology, hydrology, mineralogy-crystallography, sedimentation, paleontology-micropaleontology, petrology-petrography, stratigraphy, photogrammetry-aerogeology. 10 professorial staff. 51 master's degrees and 2 Ph.D.'s awarded 1955-59. 44 graduate students registered fall 1959.

History. Early modern European, English, Latin-American, medieval, recent European, Russian, or United States history. Prerequisite for graduate study: 30 term credits in history. 18 professorial staff. 40 master's degrees and 3 Ph.D.'s awarded 1955-59. 51 graduate students registered fall 1959.

Home Economics. Foods, home management, nutrition. Prerequisites for graduate study: 2 years of chemistry; human physiology; sociology; economics. 21 professorial staff. 82 master's degrees and 7 Ph.D.'s awarded 1955-59. 55 graduate students registered fall 1959.

Horticulture. Floriculture, ornamental horticulture, pomology, vegetable production. Recommended for graduate study: background in botany, chemistry, soil science, and farm crops. 38 professorial staff. 64 master's degrees and 48 Ph.D.'s awarded 1955-59. 27 graduate students registered fall 1959.

Mathematics. Algebra, analysis, applied mathematics, geometry, topology. Prerequisite for graduate study: mathematics background, including 1 year beyond calculus. 27 professorial

staff. 34 master's degrees and 14 Ph.D.'s awarded 1955-59. 75 graduate students registered fall 1959.

Microbiology and Public Health. Bacteriology, parasitology, virology. Prerequisites for graduate study: 1 year each mathematics, physics, chemistry. 19 professorial staff. 54 master's degrees and 43 Ph.D.'s awarded 1955-59. 62 graduate students registered fall 1959.

Music. Applied music, composition, music education, musicology, theory. 39 professorial staff. 87 master's degrees and 5 Ph.D.'s awarded 1955-59. 45 graduate students registered fall 1959.

Philosophy. Aesthetics, history of philosophy, political philosophy, logic, metaphysics, philosophy of science, semantics, theory of knowledge, value theory. Prerequisite for graduate study: 20 term credits of philosophy. 6 professorial staff. 10 master's degrees and 3 Ph.D.'s awarded 1955-59. 25 graduate students registered fall 1959.

Physics and Astronomy. Electromagnetic, elementary particle, molecular spectra, or solid-state theory; high-energy, infrared, or solid-state experimental; nuclear physics; ultrasonics. Prerequisite for graduate study: work in fields of mechanics, electricity and magnetism, and optics. 24 professorial staff. 27 master's degrees and 30 Ph.D.'s awarded 1955-59. 63 graduate students registered fall 1959.

Physiology and Pharmacology. Comparative, reproductive, renal, and cardiovascular physiology; endocrinology; radiobiology. Prerequisites for graduate study: 1 year each of physiology, zoology, mathematics, and physics; chemistry through qualitative analysis. Recommended: biochemistry. 10 professorial staff. 10 master's degrees and 10 Ph.D.'s awarded 1955-59. 20 graduate students registered fall 1959.

Political Science. Foreign political systems, international politics, political organizations and behavior, political thought, public administration, public law and judicial behavior, research concepts and methods, state and local government. Prerequisite for graduate study: MAT. 30 professorial staff. 24 master's degrees awarded 1955-59. 54 graduate students registered fall 1959.

Poultry Science. Poultry genetics, management, nutrition, or physiology; poultry and egg processing and marketing. Prerequisites for graduate study: 20 term credits in poultry science; courses in other livestock fields. 9 professorial staff. 11 master's degrees and 7 Ph.D.'s awarded 1955-59. 19 graduate students registered fall 1959.

Psychology. Child and developmental, clinical, counseling, general experimental, industrial, quantitative-theoretical, school, or social and personality psychology. Prerequisites for graduate study: course in experimental psychology; MAT. 33 professorial staff. 59 master's degrees and 46 Ph.D.'s awarded 1955-59. 108 graduate students registered fall 1959.

Sociology and Anthropology. Anthropology, general or rural sociology, social psychology. Prerequisite for graduate study: 15 term credits of sociology. 27 professorial staff. 39 master's degrees and 26 Ph.D.'s awarded 1955-59. 58 graduate students registered fall 1959.

Soil Science. Soil chemistry, fertility, genesis and classification, microbiology, or physics. Prerequisite for graduate study: good background in chemistry, physics, mathematics, geology. 18 professorial staff. 30 master's degrees and 31 Ph.D.'s awarded 1955-59. 27 graduate students registered fall 1959.

Speech. Rhetoric and public address, speech pathology and audiology, theater and interpretation. 24 professorial staff. 63 master's degrees and 49 Ph.D.'s awarded 1955-59.

Statistics. Applied or mathematical statistics. Prerequisite for graduate study: major in mathematics or statistics. 11 professorial staff. 1 master's degree awarded 1955-59. 16 graduate students registered fall 1959.

Television, Radio, and Film. Educational radio and TV. 7 professorial staff. 1 master's degree awarded 1955-59. 12 graduate students registered fall 1959.

Veterinary Pathology. Mammalian, avian, or clinical pathology. Prerequisite for graduate study: background in histology, physiology, biology, and biochemistry. 6 professorial staff. 4 master's degrees and 3 Ph.D.'s awarded 1955-59. 10 graduate students registered fall 1959.

Zoology. Animal behavior, biometrics, comparative anatomy, ecology, embryology, genetics, herpetology, histochemistry, histology, ichthyology, invertebrate zoology, limnology, mammalogy, ornithology, zoogeography. Prerequisites for graduate study: major in zoology; 1 year each mathematics, physics, and chemistry. 9 professorial staff. 30 master's degrees and 11 Ph.D.'s

awarded 1955-59. 37 graduate students registered fall 1959.

Michigan, University of

ANN ARBOR, MICHIGAN

Horace H. Rackham School of Graduate Studies

Graduate instruction was begun at the University of Michigan in 1856, and the first Ph.D. was conferred in 1876. In 1892 a graduate department was organized in connection with the College of Literature, Science, and the Arts. In 1912 this department was separated from the college and organized into a distinct school. In 1935 the Horace H. Rackham and Mary A. Rackham Fund provided a building for the Graduate School, and generous endowment for research and studies in human adjustment. University is publicly controlled by the state. Both men and women are admitted.

In addition to the Ph.D., the university awards the following doctoral degrees: Ed.D., and A.Mus.D. (Graduate School); D.P.H. (School of Public Health); S.J.D. (Law School); Pharm.D. (College of Pharmacy).

Single graduate students live in university residence halls, fraternities and sororities, league houses, co-operatives, and private homes in Ann Arbor; married students in university-owned and privately-owned apartments.

Special facilities include: library of approximately 2,690,000 volumes, including a library of Americana; archaeological, art, and natural history museums; observatories; research facilities specializing in child development; nuclear reactor; lake hydraulic laboratory; automotive and other engineering laboratories. There are also institutes for study in the following areas: science and technology; human adjustment; English language; engineering research; public administration; social research; industrial health; fisheries research; labor and industrial relations; mental health research; medical research; cancer research, and legislative research.

Residence requirement for Ph.D.: 1 year must be spent in full-time graduate study or research on the Ann Arbor Campus. In most of the schools and colleges there is no general course or credit requirement for the doctorate. Length of residence depends largely upon student's previous training. Summer courses available.

ADMISSION REQUIREMENTS

For graduate study: holders of a bachelor's degree may apply. Number of students who can be accepted is limited, and selection is based on quality and scope of academic work completed. For candidacy for Ph.D.: reading knowledge of French and German or approved substitute; completion of major portion of course work; departmental preliminary examinations; recommendation of Advisory Committee or chairman of student's field of specialization.

Apply to Admissions Office, Horace H. Rackham School of Graduate Studies, by August 15 for fall term; by January 1 for spring term; by May 15 for summer session.

FEES AND FIRST-YEAR AID

Application fee $5. Tuition for state residents $280 per academic year; others $750. Room (in dormitory) and board $800 per academic year. University apartments rent for $85, $97, and $112 per month for efficiency, 1- and 2-bedroom apartments respectively.

First-year aid available: approximately 10 tuition scholarships (resident and nonresident); approximately 680 teaching fellowships, $4,400 for equivalent of full-time work; approximately 75 other fellowships, $1,000-$2,400 plus tuition.

For teaching fellowships, apply to appropriate department. Application for other types of assistance should be sent to the Dean, Horace H. Rackham School of Graduate Studies. Applications should be received between November 1 and February 1 in the year previous to that for which application is made.

FIELDS OF STUDY FOR THE PH.D.

The Department of Education offers a course on the college teacher, a college professors' workshop, and a seminar on the community college. A seminar on college teaching is open to teaching fellows in academic departments only.

Anatomy. Gross or microscopial anatomy, embryology, neuroanatomy. Prerequisites for graduate study: 14 semester hours each of zoology and chemistry; 8 of physics; beginning courses in 2 foreign languages. 21 professorial staff. 18 master's degrees and 16 Ph.D.'s awarded 1955-59. 8 graduate students registered fall 1959.

Anthropology. Physical or cultural anthropology, archaeology, linguistics. Combined programs are offered with Departments of Near Eastern Studies, Human Genetics, or Orthodontics. 22 professorial staff. 20 master's degrees and 13 Ph.D.'s awarded 1955-59. 37 graduate students registered fall 1959.

Astronomy. Solar physics, radio-astronomy, astrophysics, galactic structure, stellar spectroscopy, solar system (exclusive of sun). Prerequisites for graduate study: major in mathematics, physics, or astronomy; mathematics through calculus; 1 year each of elementary physics, advanced general astronomy, and practical observational astronomy; placement test. Recommended: differential equations; intermediate-level and modern physics; electricity and magnetism; optics; mechanics. 10 professorial staff. 13 master's degrees and 12 Ph.D.'s awarded 1955-59. 22 graduate students registered fall 1959. Enrollment limited to 30.

Bacteriology. Medical bacteriology, bacterial physiology, genetics, metabolism, immunology, viruses, industrial microbiology, tissue culture. Prerequisites for graduate study: quantitative analysis; organic chemistry; physics; biology. Recommended: German or French; calculus. 15 professorial staff. 105 master's degrees and 35 Ph.D.'s awarded 1955-59. 40 graduate students registered fall 1959.

Biological Chemistry. Genetic variations in protein structure; bacterial viruses and their control of protein synthesis; synthesis, degradation, and transport of amino acids; protein synthesis; nucleotide and coenzyme synthesis; enzymology; glucosamine metabolism; transport of sugars, alkali, and trace metals; fatty aldehyde and acid metabolism; bacterial mutants (most studies employ isotope techniques). Recommended for graduate study: chemistry major; zoology; microbiology; botany or general biology; French and German. 18 professorial staff. 12 master's degrees and 9 Ph.D.'s awarded 1955-59. 32 graduate students registered fall 1959.

Biophysics. Molecular biophysics: relationships between structure and function of biologically significant large molecules. Combined program offered by Departments of Physics, Zoology, Botany, Bacteriology, and Epidemiology. Prerequisites for graduate study: mathematics through calculus; 15 semester hours of physics; 8 of biology. Recommended: organic chemistry. 1 Ph.D. awarded 1955-59. 2 graduate students registered fall 1959.

Botany. Ecology, palynology, morphology, pteridology, plant physiology, anatomy, cytology, phytogeography, forest pathology, genetics, microbiology, mycology, paleobotany, phycology, taxonomy. Prerequisites for graduate study: 1 year each mathematics and physics; organic chemistry; reading knowledge of French, German, or Russian; minimum 20 semester hours of course work in botany. 22 professorial staff. 31 master's degrees and 40 Ph.D.'s awarded 1955-59. 30 graduate students registered fall 1959.

Business Administration. Accounting, finance, industrial relations or management, marketing, statistics, business economics. Offered by School of Business Administration. 45 professorial staff. 1,178 master's degrees and 27 Ph.D.'s awarded 1955-59. 47 graduate students registered fall 1959.

Chemistry. Organic, inorganic, physical, analytical. Prerequisite for graduate study: 25 semester hours in chemistry. 31 professorial staff. 79 master's degrees and 66 Ph.D.'s awarded 1955-59. 111 graduate students registered fall 1959.

Classical Studies. Greek and Roman literature, with minors in classical archaeology, classical linguistics, or papyrology. Prerequisites for graduate study: 16 semester hours of Greek; 32 of Latin or equivalent. 9 professorial staff. 35 master's degrees and 1 Ph.D. awarded 1955-59. 26 graduate students registered fall 1959.

Communication Sciences. Logic and computers, information or automata theory, language automation. Combined program offered by Departments of Mathematics, Electrical Engineering, Philosophy, and Psychology. Prerequisites for graduate study: mathematics through calculus; basic physics; basic circuit theory. Recommended: biology; language. 9 professorial staff. Ph.D. program begun 1957. 4 master's degrees and 1 Ph.D. awarded 1955-59. 12 graduate students registered fall 1959.

Comparative Literature. Programs encompass 2 foreign literatures: French-Spanish, French-German, Russian-German, etc. Studies concerned mainly with generic comparisons. Interdepartmental program. Prerequisites for graduate study: major or sufficient work in a foreign language to do graduate study in it; reading knowledge of a second foreign language. Ph.D. candidacy prerequisite: knowledge of a third foreign language. 14 master's degrees and 6 Ph.D.'s awarded 1955-59. 16 graduate students registered fall 1959.

Conservation. Conservation education, natural resources administration, general conservation. Combined program offered by Departments of Conservation and Botany. 4 professorial staff. 10 master's degrees and 6 Ph.D.'s awarded 1955-59. 17 graduate students registered fall 1959.

Economics. Theory, money and banking, labor, industrial organization and public control, international economics, economic history or development, public finance, quantitative research methods. Prerequisite for graduate study: background in field. Recommended: mathematics through calculus. Ph.D. candidacy prerequisite: 9 hours of graduate mathematics may be substituted for 1 foreign language. 24 professorial staff. 88 master's degrees and 34 Ph.D.'s awarded 1955-59. 79 graduate students registered fall 1959.

Education. Adult, business, elementary, health, higher, industrial arts, physical, secondary, special, or vocational-industrial education; history and philosophy of education; child or curriculum development; educational administration or psychology; guidance and counseling; tests and measurements; teaching of English, Latin, mathematics, music, science, or social studies. Prerequisites for graduate study: 15 hours of work in education; at least 1 introductory course in psychology; MAT. Ph.D. candidacy prerequisite: 2 years of successful teaching experience. 70 professorial staff. 2,359 master's degrees and 137 Ph.D.'s awarded 1955-59. 1,617 graduate students registered fall 1959. The Ed.D. degree is also awarded in this field.

Engineering.—Aeronautical and Astronautical. Gas dynamics, aerodynamics, magnetohydrodynamics, flight structures, aeroelasticity, aerothermodynamics, propulsion, flight dynamics of aircraft and space vehicles, guidance and control. Prerequisites for graduate study: B.S.E. or B.S. in mathematics or physical sciences. 23 professorial staff. 160 master's degrees and 8 Ph.D.'s awarded 1955-59. 89 graduate students registered fall 1959. Total enrollment limited to about 90.

Engineering.—Chemical and Metallurgical. Chemical, metallurgical, and materials engineering; solid-state science. 28 professorial staff. 200 master's degrees and 87 Ph.D.'s awarded 1955-59. 145 graduate students registered fall 1959.

Engineering.—Civil. Structural, hydraulic, soils, highway, or traffic engineering. Prerequisite for graduate study: major in civil engineering or equivalent. 27 professorial staff. 214 master's degrees and 13 Ph.D.'s awarded 1955-59. 71 graduate students registered fall 1959.

Engineering. — Electrical. Communications, computer, electric power, or automatic control engineering; electrical engineering design; electrical measurements and instrumentation; electronics illustration; industrial electronics and control; electromagnetic theory; solid-state electronics. Prerequisite for graduate study: course in electromagnetic field theory. 35 professorial staff. 165 master's degrees and 27 Ph.D.'s awarded 1955-59. 164 graduate students registered fall 1959.

Engineering.—Industrial. 16 professorial staff. 10 master's degrees and 1 Ph.D. awarded 1955-59. 45 graduate students registered fall 1959.

Engineering. — Instrumentation. Measurements, dynamics, probability and information theory, computers, telemetry, data processing, automatic control, nonlinear systems, missile guidance and control. 5 professorial staff. 65 master's degrees and 2 Ph.D.'s awarded 1955-59. 39 graduate students registered fall 1959.

Engineering.—Marine, and Naval Architecture. Prerequisite for graduate study: major in field or equivalent. Recommended: 1 year of practical experience. Ph.D. candidacy prerequisite: master's degree in field or equivalent. 6 professorial staff. 18 master's degrees awarded 1955-59. 12 graduate students registered fall 1959.

Engineering.—Mechanical. Thermodynamics, heat transfer, fluid flow, internal combustion engines, mechanical design, vibration, stress analysis, metal cutting, plastic working of metals. 30 professorial staff. 177 master's degrees and 16 Ph.D.'s awarded 1955-59. 77 graduate students registered fall 1959.

Engineering Mechanics. Dynamics, fluid mechanics, elasticity, plasticity. Prerequisite for graduate study: major in engineering mechanics or equivalent; strong mathematics background. 17 professorial staff. 37 master's degrees and 17 Ph.D.'s awarded 1955-59. 78 graduate students registered fall 1959.

Engineering.—Nuclear. Reactor theory and design, behavior and effects of high-energy radiation, thermonuclear reactions (theory and experiment). Ph.D. candidacy prerequisite: equivalent of a master's degree in nuclear engineering.

12 professorial staff. 108 master's degrees and 6 Ph.D.'s awarded 1955-59. 102 graduate students registered fall 1959.

English Language and Literature. English literature or language, general literature, English and education. Department cooperates with Committee on the Ph.D. in Comparative Literature. 68 professorial staff. 291 master's degrees and 53 Ph.D.'s awarded 1955-59. 288 graduate students registered fall 1959.

Environmental Health. Community air pollution, water resources and stream pollution, food sanitation, radiological health and health physics, public health engineering (practice and administration). Offered by Department of Environmental Health, School of Public Health. Prerequisite for graduate study: background in mathematics and in basic physical, chemical, biochemical, or biological sciences. Recommended: experience in public health or related field. 10 professorial staff. 113 master's degrees and 2 Ph.D.'s awarded 1955-59. 40 graduate students registered fall 1959.

Epidemiologic Science. Epidemiology, immunology, virology, parasitology, bacteriology, microbial biochemistry. Combined program offered by Departments of Epidemiology and Biophysics. Prerequisite for graduate study: biological preparation. Recommended: courses corresponding to those taken in first 2 years of medical school. 13 professorial staff. 2 master's degrees and 7 Ph.D.'s awarded 1955-59. 8 graduate students registered fall 1959. New enrollment limited to 5.

Far Eastern Languages and Literatures. Far Eastern (mainly Chinese and Japanese) languages, literature, and thought. Prerequisites for graduate study: 2 years' work in 1 of the languages offered by the department; reading knowledge of French or German. 10 professorial staff. 2 master's degrees and 1 Ph.D. awarded 1955-59. 6 graduate students registered fall 1959.

Fine Arts. European, American, Latin American, Near Eastern, and Far Eastern art. Offered by Department of History of Art. Prerequisite for graduate study: 3-hour course in ancient, medieval, Renaissance, baroque, and modern art. Ph.D. candidacy prerequisite: M.A. in history of art. 9 professorial staff. 14 master's degrees and 8 Ph.D.'s awarded 1955-59. 20 graduate students registered fall 1959.

Fisheries. Fishery biology, technology, or economics; aquatic physiology; ichthyology; aquiculture; fish management. Prerequisites for graduate study: general and inorganic chemistry; economics; comparative anatomy of vertebrates; geology; general invertebrate zoology; comparative physiology. Recommended: science major; summer employment in field; attendance at a summer biological station or marine laboratory. 11 professorial staff. 16 master's degrees and 11 Ph.D.'s awarded 1955-59. 21 graduate students registered fall 1959.

Forestry. Management, silviculture, economics, forest entomology or pathology, soil and watershed management. Offered by Department of Forestry, School of Natural Resources. Recommended for Ph.D. candidacy: solid basis of successful professional experience. 9 professorial staff. 17 Ph.D.'s awarded 1955-59. 14 graduate students registered fall 1959.

Genetics. Interdepartmental program administered by a committee of faculty members from Departments of Anthropology, Bacteriology, Botany, Human Genetics, Zoology, and Mathematics. Prerequisites for graduate study: 16 hours in biological science, including introductory course in genetics; laboratory courses in inorganic and organic chemistry; 1 year each in physics, mathematics, and French or German. 10 professorial staff. Ph.D. program begun 1957. 1 master's degree awarded 1955-59. 4 graduate students registered fall 1959.

Geography. Far East, Europe, U.S.S.R., Latin America, Anglo-America, Australia and Oceania, Near East and Africa, political, historical, settlement, economic, land use and classification, recreation, field techniques. Combined programs with Departments of Education and Japanese Studies also offered. Prerequisite for graduate study: major in geography or equivalent. 12 professorial staff. 34 master's degrees and 21 Ph.D.'s awarded 1955-59. 27 graduate students registered fall 1959.

Geology. Structural, petroleum, economic (metals and nonmetals), or glacial geology; ground-water geology; geophysics; geochemistry; stratigraphy; sedimentation; invertebrate or vertebrate paleontology; micropaleontology; paleobotany; geomorphology. Students may take additional courses offered by Department of Mineralogy. Prerequisites for graduate study: 20 hours of geology and mineralogy; 1 year each of chemistry, physics, and mathematics. 16 professorial staff. 44 master's degrees and 14 Ph.D.'s awarded 1955-59. 68 graduate students registered fall 1959. Total enrollment limited to 70.

Germanic Languages and Literatures. Linguistics; German, Dutch, and Scandinavian literatures. Combined programs in French and Russian linguistics may be arranged. Prerequisites for graduate study: 8 courses in German; 5 hours senior work in literature. Recommended: course in Shakespeare; introduction to philosophy and to history. 11 professorial staff. 27 master's degrees and 12 Ph.D.'s awarded 1955-59. 30 graduate students registered fall 1959.

History. Greek, Roman, medieval, Italian Renaissance, Reformation, modern Europe, Russian, Eastern Europe and Balkans, Latin America, British, British Commonwealth, Far East, Japan, India, military and naval. Combined program with Departments of Japanese and Russian Studies also offered. Prerequisite for graduate study: preparation in field. Ph.D. candidacy prerequisites: reading knowledge of French and German and of special languages needed for research. 26 professorial staff. 191 master's degrees and 39 Ph.D.'s awarded 1955-59. 157 graduate students registered fall 1959.

Human Genetics. Prerequisites for graduate study: general genetics; embryology; comparative anatomy; inorganic and organic chemistry; introductory physics; minimum of 1 year of mathematics. 6 professorial staff. Ph.D. program begun 1957. 4 master's degrees awarded 1955-59. 8 graduate students registered fall 1959. New enrollment limited to 5-6.

Library Science. Bibliography, history of books and printing, library administration. 7 professorial staff. 381 master's degrees and 16 Ph.D.'s awarded 1955-59. 287 graduate students registered fall 1959.

Linguistics. General linguistics; English, Far Eastern, Near Eastern, Romance, Germanic, Slavic, Latin and Greek, American Indian languages; descriptive linguistics; comparative and historical linguistics; linguistic geography. Cooperative program under administration of Committee on Linguistics. Prerequisite for graduate study: basic courses in linguistics or in the history and structure of a particular language or group of related languages. 24 professorial staff. 107 master's degrees and 11 Ph.D.'s awarded 1955-59. 65 graduate students registered fall 1959.

Mathematics. Actuarial or applied mathematics, history and teaching of mathematics, algebra, analysis, foundation and logic, number theory, statistics and probability, topology. Ph.D. candidacy prerequisites: 2 cognate courses outside mathematics. 50 professorial staff. 250 master's degrees and 48 Ph.D.'s awarded 1955-59. 203 graduate students registered fall 1959.

Meteorology. Atmospheric pollution, cloud and precipitation physics, micrometeorology, polar atmospheres, instrumentation design. Offered by Department of Civil Engineering. Prerequisites for graduate study: mathematics through calculus; 1 year of basic physics. 3 professorial staff. Ph.D. program begun 1957. 17 master's degrees awarded 1955-59. 14 graduate students registered fall 1959.

Mineralogy. Petrography, crystallography, X-ray analysis of crystal structure, crystal optics. Prerequisites for graduate study: 1 year each of mathematics, physics, chemistry, and geology. 4 professorial staff. 7 master's degrees and 8 Ph.D.'s awarded 1955-59. 13 graduate students registered fall 1959.

Music. Musicology, music education. Prerequisites for graduate study: major in music or music literature; tests in basic musicianship; performance ability on instrument or voice. 67 professorial staff. 6 master's degrees and 27 Ph.D.'s awarded 1955-59. 74 graduate students registered fall 1959. A.Mus.D. and Ed.D. degrees are also awarded in this field.

Near Eastern Studies. Ancient, medieval, or modern Near East. Combined program offered by Departments of Near Eastern Studies, Anthropology, Economics, Art, and History. Ph.D. candidacy prerequisites: French or German; 1 year of a Near Eastern language. 18 professorial staff. 16 master's degrees and 6 Ph.D.'s awarded 1955-59. 48 graduate students registered fall 1959.

Pathology. Areas related to diseases. Prerequisite for graduate study: M.D., D.V.M., or D.D.S. 5 professorial staff. 3 master's degrees and 1 Ph.D. awarded 1955-59. 1 graduate student registered fall 1959.

Pharmaceutical Chemistry. Analytical or synthetic pharmaceutical chemistry, product development. Offered through the College of Pharmacy and the Graduate School. Prerequisite for graduate study: major in pharmacy or chemistry. 6 professorial staff. 25 master's degrees and 20 Ph.D.'s awarded 1955-59. 36 graduate students registered fall 1959.

Pharmacology. Neuropharmacology; cardiovascular, autonomic, renal, cellular, or clinical pharmacology; chemical pharmacology (metabolic disposition); toxicology. Prerequisite for graduate study: major in physical, biological, or general science. 10 professorial staff. 2 master's degrees and 11 Ph.D.'s awarded 1955-59. 23 graduate students registered fall 1959.

Philosophy. Prerequisites for graduate study: major in philosophy or equivalent; elementary logic; history of philosophy. 15 professorial staff. 34 master's degrees and 15 Ph.D.'s awarded 1955-59. 48 graduate students registered fall 1959.

Physics. Nuclear, theoretical, infrared, high-energy particle, or solid-state physics; biophysics; magnetic resonance and optical pumping; spectroscopy. Prerequisites for graduate study: 15 hours of intermediate physics; differential equations; 1 year of chemistry. 34 professorial staff. 135 master's degrees and 58 Ph.D.'s awarded 1955-59. 138 graduate students registered fall 1959.

Physiology. Acid-base chemistry and gastro-intestinal physiology; membrane transport of electrolytes; electrocellular physiology; smooth-muscle neurophysiology; kidney, cardiovascular, and neurophysiology; hypertension; metabolism-endocrine; oxygen toxicity. Prerequisites for graduate study: chemistry, including organic; elementary physics; mathematics; biology; departmental interview; French or German. Recommended: physical and electrochemistry; advanced zoology courses. 12 professorial staff. 8 master's degrees and 3 Ph.D.'s awarded 1955-59. 9 graduate students registered fall 1959. Total enrollment limited to 20.

Political Science. Political theory; American government and politics; public administration; foreign and comparative governments and politics; international relations; parties, elections, and political behavior. Prerequisite for graduate study: 18 hours of political science, including 3 hours of American government. Recommended: courses in international relations, comparative government, and political theory. 25 professorial staff. 68 master's degrees and 40 Ph.D.'s awarded 1955-59. 70 graduate students registered fall 1959.

Psychology. Clinical, mathematical, social, educational, industrial, physiological, personality, developmental, learning, motivation, sensory, perception, or engineering psychology. Combined programs with Department of Sociology and the Schools of Education and Social Work also offered. Prerequisites for graduate study: 18 hours of psychology, including 1 course in statistics and 1 in experimental psychology; MAT; Doppelt Mathematical Reasoning Test. Recommended: 1 year of mathematics. 63 professorial staff. 104 master's degrees and 89 Ph.D.'s awarded 1955-59. 192 graduate students registered fall 1959.

Public Health Economics. Medical care. Offered by Bureau of Public Health Economics and Department of Public Health Practice. Ph.D. candidacy prerequisite: M.P.H. or equivalent. 4 professorial staff. 1 Ph.D. awarded 1955-59. 3 graduate students registered fall 1959.

Public Health Statistics. Prerequisites for graduate study: major in statistics or equivalent; background in natural sciences. 6 professorial staff. 2 Ph.D.'s awarded 1955-59. 4 graduate students registered fall 1959.

Romance Languages and Literatures. French, Spanish, or Italian language and literature; Romance linguistics. Combined program offered by Departments of Romance Languages and Literatures, Literature, Comparative Literature, and the interdepartmental linguistics program. Prerequisites for graduate study: concentration in 1 Romance language; at least 1 other Romance language. Recommended: knowledge of Latin; study and/or travel in country of language interest. 22 professorial staff. 57 master's degrees and 25 Ph.D.'s awarded 1955-59. 75 graduate students registered fall 1959.

Slavic Languages and Literatures. Russian language and literature or Russian literature and Slavic linguistics. Prerequisite for graduate study: major in Russian. Recommended: Russian history. 8 professorial staff. Program begun 1958. 5 graduate students registered fall 1959.

Social Psychology. Jointly sponsored and supported by Departments of Psychology and Sociology. Ph.D. candidacy prerequisites: master's degree in psychology or sociology; GRE; MAT. 22 professorial staff. 44 Ph.D.'s awarded 1955-59. 46 graduate students registered fall 1959. New enrollment limited to 15.

Sociology. Population and human ecology, social organization or psychology, social science and social work. Social psychology offered in cooperation with Department of Psychology; social science and social work with School of Social Work. Prerequisites for graduate study: 15 hours of sociology, including 3 hours of statistics. 17 professorial staff. 66 master's degrees

and 15 Ph.D.'s awarded 1955-59. 70 graduate students registered fall 1959. New enrollment limited to 30 candidates for master's degree, 15 for Ph.D.

Speech. Public address, oral interpretation, theater, radio and television, speech science or correction, audiology. Prerequisite for graduate study: 20 hours in speech courses taken in 3 fields of speech. Ph.D. candidacy prerequisite: 20 hours of graduate speech courses distributed between 2 fields of speech. 43 professorial staff. 166 master's degrees and 32 Ph.D.'s awarded 1955-59. 101 graduate students registered fall 1959.

Wildlife Management. Plant and animal ecology; aquatic and terrestrial land management related to agriculture, range, and forestry, ornithology, mammalogy, and fisheries. Combined program offered by Departments of Wildlife Management, Forestry, Conservation, and Fisheries in the School of Natural Resources. Special studies in waterfowl, big game, upland game, fur animals. Prerequisite for graduate study: major in biological sciences. 4 professorial staff. 16 master's degrees and 3 Ph.D.'s awarded 1955-59. 12 graduate students registered fall 1959. Total enrollment limited to 16.

Wood Technology. Wood structure and properties, wood adhesion, wood-moisture relations, machining of wood, wood properties-tree growth relations. Prerequisite for graduate study: strong background in physical sciences and mathematics. Recommended: major in wood technology. Ph.D. candidacy prerequisite: M.S. in wood technology or related field. 4 professorial staff. 10 master's degrees and 2 Ph.D.'s awarded 1955-59. 5 graduate students registered fall 1959.

Zoology. Biometry, cellular and comparative physiology, comparative anatomy, ecology, entomology, experimental cytology and histology, experimental embryology, electron microscopy, endocrinology, general and mammalian genetics, herpetology, ichthyology, immunobiology, invertebrate zoology, limnology and oceanography, malacology, mammalogy, ornithology, parasitology, protozoology, radiobiology, sociobiology, vertebrate natural history. Prerequisites for graduate study: 12 hours of zoology; 4 of botany; 1-year laboratory course in physics; course in mathematics; laboratory course in biochemistry or organic chemistry; 1 year of a foreign language. 41 professorial staff. 96 master's degrees and 63 Ph.D.'s awarded 1955-59. 93 graduate students registered fall 1959.

Middlebury College

MIDDLEBURY, VERMONT

Language Schools

Graduate study has been offered at Middlebury since early in the 19th century. The Doctor of Modern Languages was created in 1930 as a degree for teachers, rather than primarily for research. Resident study for this degree may be done only in the language schools, summer session. An academic year of supervised study in a foreign university is required. The college is privately controlled and nonsectarian. Both men and women are admitted.

Full resident facilities for single students provided during summer session; none during winter. No college-owned facilities for married students.

Special facilities include: resident "language houses" where the foreign language is used exclusively, by formal pledge, at all times; complete language laboratory facilities for practice or research.

Residence requirement for D.M.L.: 30 credits beyond master's degree; 10 credits may be transferred from other graduate institutions.

ADMISSION REQUIREMENTS

For graduate study: B.A. degree with major in foreign language; placement tests on arrival. Recommended: some teaching experience. For candidacy for D.M.L.: master's degree in chosen language. Knowledge of 2 other modern foreign languages in addition to language specialization required for degree.

Apply to Director of the Language Schools by May 1 at latest; much earlier if possible.

FEES AND FIRST-YEAR AID

Registration fee (after acceptance) $50. Room, board, tuition for 7 weeks approximately $375 ($1,200 for full 30 credits).

First-year aid available: small scholarships (up to $100) and work opportunities during the summer session.

Apply to Director of Language Schools by May 1.

FIELDS OF STUDY FOR THE D.M.L.

Courses in methods of teaching modern languages offered, at elementary and secondary levels, with observation of demonstration classes.

French. Language and literature. Offered by French Summer School. 32 professorial staff. 244 master's degrees and 5 D.M.L.'s awarded 1955-59. 310 graduate students registered summer 1959.

German. Language and literature. Offered by German Summer School. 14 professorial staff. 15 master's degrees awarded 1955-59. 112 graduate students registered summer 1959.

Italian. Language and literature. Offered by Italian Summer School. 8 professorial staff. 18 master's degrees and 1 D.M.L. awarded 1955-59. 42 graduate students registered summer 1959.

Russian. Language and literature. Offered by Russian Summer School. 16 professorial staff. 13 master's degrees awarded 1955-59. 99 graduate students registered summer 1959.

Spanish. Language and literature. Offered by Spanish Summer School. 24 professorial staff. 192 master's degrees and 3 D.M.L.'s awarded 1955-59. 166 graduate students registered summer 1959.

Minnesota, University of

MINNEAPOLIS, MINNESOTA

Graduate School

Although the Graduate School was not organized as a separate unit until 1905, the university awarded the master's degree as early as 1880 and its first Ph.D. degree in 1888. University faculty of full and associate members, numbering more than 1,300, include those in the Graduate School and in the several undergraduate and professional colleges. Graduate work crosses the boundaries of the departments, schools, and colleges comprising the university, including the Mayo Foundation at Rochester. University is publicly controlled by the state. Both men and women are admitted.

Graduate students are eligible for residence in university dormitories and in the permanent and temporary housing facilities maintained by the university for married students.

Special facilities include: library of approximately 2 million volumes; natural history museum; radio station; laboratory for research in social relations; social science research center; theater; hospitals; electron microscopes; human genetics institute; biological station; forest; agricultural research institute; linear accelerator; Van de Graaff generator.

Residence requirement for Ph.D.: 3 years beyond bachelor's degree, of which the first 2 years or the last year must be spent in residence at the University of Minnesota. Summer and evening courses available, but there are restrictions as to how credit earned in such courses may be applied toward master's and Ph.D. degrees.

ADMISSION REQUIREMENTS

For graduate study: bachelor's degree; satisfactory scholastic record; satisfactory character and professional qualifications; approval of major department. Recommended: GRE; 1 foreign language. For candidacy for Ph.D.: master's degree; reading knowledge of 2 foreign languages (or of 1 foreign language plus a special research technique or collateral field of knowledge); preliminary examinations.

Apply to Dean, Graduate School, 316 Johnston Hall, University of Minnesota, Minneapolis 14, Minnesota, at least 4 weeks prior to date of desired entry.

FEES AND FIRST-YEAR AID

No application fee. Tuition for state residents $213 per academic year; others $540. Special fees approximate $60 annually. Room and board in university dormitories for men $708-$822 per academic year; for women $687-$828. Apartments $45-$80 per month (unfurnished).

First-year aid available: scholarships and fellowships, $75-$1,800 (depending on department); teaching assistantships, $1,057 ($1/4$ time) to $2,115 ($1/2$ time). For teaching and research assistantships, apply to appropriate department by February 15; for fellowships, apply to department or college or to the Graduate School.

FIELDS OF STUDY FOR THE PH.D.

Classes and seminars in higher education are offered to doctoral candidates in many fields.

Agronomy. Agricultural biochemistry, botany, horticulture, plant pathology or physiology, soils, other biological sciences. Offered by Department of Agronomy and Plant Genetics. Prerequisite for graduate study: preparation in plant sciences. 12 professorial staff. 15 master's degrees and 6

Ph.D.'s awarded 1955-59. 25 graduate students registered fall 1959.

Analytical Chemistry. Offered by Division of Analytical Chemistry, School of Chemistry. Prerequisites for graduate study: inorganic, analytical, organic, and physical chemistry; 1 year each of physics and mathematics. 4 professorial staff. 15 master's degrees and 12 Ph.D.'s awarded 1955-59. 19 graduate students registered fall 1959.

Anatomy. Embryology, gross anatomy, histology, human neuroanatomy, hematology. Prerequisite for graduate study: 9 quarter credits of general zoology. 9 professorial staff. 6 master's degrees and 10 Ph.D.'s awarded 1955-59. 23 graduate students registered fall 1959.

Animal Husbandry. Animal breeding, meats, nutrition, physiology. Prerequisite for graduate study: 24 quarter credits in animal husbandry or closely allied subjects. 12 professorial staff. 32 master's degrees and 20 Ph.D.'s awarded 1955-59. 23 graduate students registered fall 1959.

Anthropology. Archaeology, cultural anthropology, physical anthropology and linguistics, general ethnography. 4 professorial staff. 13 master's degrees awarded 1955-59. 22 graduate students registered fall 1959.

Area Studies.—American. American history, literature, philosophy and fine arts, social sciences, foreign civilization. Combined program offered by Departments of History, English, Philosophy, Art, Music, Anthropology, Economics, Education, Journalism, Political Science. Prerequisites for graduate study: major in a participating department or in American studies; MAT. 30 master's degrees and 24 Ph.D.'s awarded 1955-59. 41 graduate students registered fall 1959.

Art. History and criticism of art. Prerequisite for graduate study: 27 credits in history of art or equivalent. 16 professorial staff. 17 master's degrees and 2 Ph.D.'s awarded 1955-59. 24 graduate students registered fall 1959.

Bacteriology. Prerequisites for graduate study: general, organic, and introductory physical chemistry; qualitative and quantitative analysis; basic physics; mathematics through differential and integral calculus; 1 year botany or zoology; general bacteriology. 16 professorial staff. 19 master's degrees and 20 Ph.D.'s awarded 1955-59. 34 graduate students registered fall 1959.

Biochemistry.—Agricultural. Colloids, proteins, carbohydrates, lipides, enzymes, cereal or dairy chemistry, animal nutrition, plant biochemistry. Prerequisites for graduate study: mathematics through integral calculus; general physics; bacteriology; inorganic and organic chemistry; qualitative and quantitative analysis; general biology (or botany or zoology). Recommended: physical chemistry. 9 professorial staff. 17 master's degrees and 35 Ph.D.'s awarded 1955-59. 42 graduate students registered fall 1959.

Biophysics. Prerequisite for graduate study: preparation in biology, physics, chemistry, and mathematics with major in 1 of these subjects or in biophysics. 12 professorial staff. 3 master's degrees and 1 Ph.D. awarded 1955-59. 4 graduate students registered fall 1959.

Biostatistics. Prerequisites for graduate study: premedical curriculum or the equivalent of a major and a minor which together encompass 2 of the following areas: mathematics; biological, behavioral, or physical sciences. 5 professorial staff. 11 master's degrees and 2 Ph.D.'s awarded 1955-59. 19 graduate students registered fall 1959.

Botany. Prerequisites for graduate study: general biology; at least 17 credits in botany. Credits in related subjects may be substituted with consent of major adviser. 11 professorial staff. 20 master's degrees and 10 Ph.D.'s awarded 1955-59. 24 graduate students registered fall 1959.

Botany.—Agricultural. Offered by Department of Plant Pathology and Botany. Prerequisite for graduate study: general background in basic sciences and mathematics. 13 professorial staff. 3 master's degrees and 3 Ph.D.'s awarded 1955-59. 5 graduate students registered fall 1959.

Business Administration. Accounting; business finance; industrial relations, management, administration, and organization; insurance; marketing; statistics; transportation; European economic history; history of economic thought; international or manpower economics; monetary theory; public finance. Prerequisites for graduate study: 6 credits in economics; courses in at least 5 of first 8 fields of specialization shown above; MAT. 33 professorial staff. 126 master's degrees and 11 Ph.D.'s awarded 1955-59. 123 graduate students registered fall 1959.

Cancer Biology. Cytology and organology, bacteriology, pathology, physiology, genetics. Prerequisite for graduate study: broad background in basic medical sciences. Recommended: M.D. 4 professorial staff.

Chemistry.—Inorganic. Offered by Division of Inorganic Chemistry, School of Chemistry. Prerequisites for graduate study: major in chemistry, including 1 year each of organic and physical chemistry, calculus, and physics; 1 year of German. 9 professorial staff. 8 master's degrees and 8 Ph.D.'s awarded 1955-59. 14 graduate students registered fall 1959.

Chemistry.—Organic. Offered by Division of Organic Chemistry, School of Chemistry. Prerequisites for graduate study: 4 years of chemistry, including 1 year each of organic and physical chemistry; integral calculus; physics; German. 8 professorial staff. 26 master's degrees and 45 Ph.D.'s awarded 1955-59. 58 graduate students registered fall 1959.

Chemistry.—Physical. Offered by Division of Physical Chemistry, School of Chemistry. Prerequisites for graduate study: inorganic, analytical, organic, and physical chemistry; at least 1 year each of physics and mathematics. 14 professorial staff. 8 master's degrees and 25 Ph.D.'s awarded 1955-59. 47 graduate students registered fall 1959.

Chemistry.—Physiological. Prerequisites for graduate study: analytical, organic, and physical chemistry. Recommended: work in a biological science. 16 professorial staff. 5 master's degrees and 12 Ph.D.'s awarded 1955-59. 34 graduate students registered fall 1959.

Child Development and Welfare. Prerequisites for graduate study: at least 12 credits in psychology; 8 in social sciences; 3 in statistics; MAT. 11 professorial staff. 25 master's degrees and 14 Ph.D.'s awarded 1955-59. 21 graduate students registered fall 1959.

Classical Civilization. Inter-university program in cooperation with University of Wisconsin and University of Iowa. Offered by Department of Classics. Prerequisite for graduate study: major in Greek or Latin. 5 professorial staff. Program begun 1958. 1 graduate student registered fall 1959.

Classics. Greek, Latin, Sanskrit. Prerequisite for graduate study: major in Greek or Latin. 5 professorial staff. 2 master's degrees awarded 1955-59. 3 graduate students registered fall 1959.

Comparative Literature. Renaissance, Age of Reason, Romanticism, late 19th century and 20th century, drama, fiction, poetry, and literary criticism. Combined program offered by Departments of Romance Languages, English, Scandinavian

Languages, Classics, and German. Prerequisites for graduate study: major in 1 field of language and literature; special sight-reading examinations in 2 foreign languages. Recommended: a third foreign language. Ph.D. candidacy prerequisite: M.A. in comparative literature or in any field of language and literature. 3 Ph.D.'s awarded 1955-59. 14 graduate students registered fall 1959.

Dairy Husbandry. Dairy production; dairy cattle reproduction and management. Prerequisite for graduate study: background in chemistry, genetics, animal physiology, and mathematics. 6 professorial staff. 35 master's degrees and 24 Ph.D.'s awarded 1955-59. 32 graduate students registered fall 1959.

Dairy Industries. Dairy products, bacteriology. Prerequisites for graduate study: background in bacteriology, chemistry, mathematics, physics, economics, or dairy products. 6 professorial staff. Program begun 1960.

Dermatology. Offered by Department of Internal Medicine. Prerequisites for graduate study: M.D.; 1 year as intern in a hospital or as laboratory assistant in a medical school. Recommended: bacteriology; biochemistry; pathology; pharmacology; physiology. 9 professorial staff. 17 master's degrees and 1 Ph.D. awarded 1955-59. 10 graduate students registered fall 1959.

Economics. Economic theory and analysis, development and area studies, or history; econometrics; accounting; agricultural, international, labor, or monetary economics; history of economic thought; industrial organization; marketing; public finance; statistics. Prerequisites for graduate study: minimum of 9 quarter credits in economics, including principles of economics; MAT. 20 professorial staff. 40 master's degrees and 17 Ph.D.'s awarded 1955-59. 79 graduate students registered fall 1959.

Economics.—Agricultural. Marketing; farm management or finance; economics of agricultural production; agricultural prices or policy; land economics. Prerequisite for graduate study: 18 quarter credits in appropriate courses. 13 professorial staff. 41 master's degrees and 18 Ph.D.'s awarded 1955-59. 62 graduate students registered fall 1959.

Education. Industrial, agricultural, music, art, home economics, or business and distributive education; history and philosophy of education; physical education and health; curriculum and instruction (elementary or secondary). Prereq-

uisites for graduate study: at least 6 quarter credits in psychology; not less than 18 quarter credits in education, including introductory course in elementary or secondary school teaching. Recommended: teaching certificate. 156 professorial staff. 759 master's degrees and 96 Ph.D.'s awarded 1955-59. 351 graduate students registered fall 1959.

Educational Administration. Elementary or secondary school principal, school superintendent. Prerequisites for graduate study: elementary or secondary teaching curriculum; at least 6 quarter hours in psychology. Recommended: teaching experience. 4 professorial staff. 230 master's degrees and 6 Ph.D.'s awarded 1955-59. 72 graduate students registered fall 1959.

Educational Psychology. College or high school guidance and counseling, educational measurement, statistics and research, school psychology, special education, psychology of learning. Prerequisites for graduate study: at least 6 quarter credits in psychology; no less than 18 quarter credits in education, including introductory course in elementary or secondary school teaching; MAT. Recommended: teaching experience. 24 professorial staff. 187 master's degrees and 64 Ph.D.'s awarded 1955-59. 134 graduate students registered fall 1959.

Engineering.—Aeronautical. Prerequisite for graduate study: adequate preparation in mathematics, physics, mechanics, and chemistry. 21 professorial staff. 47 master's degrees and 4 Ph.D.'s awarded 1955-59. 31 graduate students registered fall 1959.

Engineering. — Chemical. Prerequisites for graduate study: B.S. in chemical engineering or equivalent; 1 year of physical chemistry, including laboratory. 11 professorial staff. 58 master's degrees and 22 Ph.D.'s awarded 1955-59. 59 graduate students registered fall 1959.

Engineering.—Civil. Hydraulic, structural, or sanitary engineering; surveying; highway engineering and soils mechanics. Prerequisite for graduate study: B.S. in civil engineering or equivalent. 10 professorial staff. 122 master's degrees and 6 Ph.D.'s awarded 1955-59. 65 graduate students registered fall 1959.

Engineering. — Electrical. Prerequisite for graduate study: B.S. in electrical engineering or equivalent. 23 professorial staff. 61 master's degrees and 21 Ph.D.'s awarded 1955-59. 107 graduate students registered fall 1959.

Engineering.—Mechanical. Industrial laboratories or engineering, machine elements and instrumentation, thermodynamics and heat transfer, power and propulsion, air conditioning and refrigeration, engineering graphics. Prerequisites for graduate study: preparation in chemistry, physics, mathematics, and mechanics; MAT. 25 professorial staff. 81 master's degrees and 18 Ph.D.'s awarded 1955-59. 72 graduate students registered fall 1959.

Engineering.—Metallurgical. Process metallurgy, mineral dressing. Prerequisite for graduate study: preparation in physical sciences and general engineering subjects. 3 professorial staff. 10 master's degrees and 3 Ph.D.'s awarded 1955-59. 6 graduate students registered fall 1959.

Engineering.—Mineral. Mining, petroleum, mine plant, or industrial engineering; rock mechanics; mineral economics or exploration. Prerequisites for graduate study: B.S. in mining or geological petroleum engineering or equivalent. 5 professorial staff. Ph.D. program begun 1958. 7 master's degrees awarded 1955-59. 9 graduate students registered fall 1959.

English. Old English and Middle English, including linguistics; Renaissance; 17th, 18th, 19th, and 20th centuries; American literature. Prerequisite for graduate study: at least 27 quarter credits of English literature (including courses in Chaucer, Shakespeare, and Milton). 25 professorial staff. 92 master's degrees and 38 Ph.D.'s awarded 1955-59. 149 graduate students registered fall 1959.

Entomology. Offered by Departments of Entomology and Economic Zoology. Prerequisite for graduate study: major in a zoological science. Recommended: good background in several basic sciences. Ph.D. candidacy prerequisite: M.S. in entomology. 15 professorial staff. 25 master's degrees and 21 Ph.D.'s awarded 1955-59. 36 graduate students registered fall 1959.

Epidemiology. Offered by School of Public Health. 3 professorial staff. Ph.D. program begun 1958. 2 master's degrees awarded 1955-59. 4 graduate students registered fall 1959.

Fishery and Wildlife Management. Offered by Departments of Entomology and Economic Zoology. Prerequisite for graduate study: major in a zoological science. Recommended: good background in several basic sciences. Prerequisite for graduate study: M.S. in fishery and wildlife management. 15 professorial staff. Ph.D. program begun 1955. 8 master's degrees and 5 Ph.D.'s awarded 1955-59. 5 graduate students registered fall 1959.

Fluid Mechanics. Hydraulics, compressible or turbulent flow, energy or mass transfer, combustion meteorology, acoustics and astrophysics. Cooperative program offered by Physical Science Group. Prerequisite for graduate study: work in a related field such as aeronautical, chemical, civil, or mechanical engineering, or mathematics or physics. 5 graduate students registered fall 1959.

Forestry. Silviculture, measurements, forestry management, forest products engineering. Prerequisite for graduate study: degree in forestry or equivalent. 13 professorial staff. 30 master's degrees and 9 Ph.D.'s awarded 1955-59. 36 graduate students registered fall 1959.

French. Offered by Department of Romance Languages. Prerequisite for graduate study: 27 credits in French or equivalent. Ph.D. candidacy prerequisites: knowledge of Latin; reading knowledge of second Romance language. 6 professorial staff. 10 master's degrees and 3 Ph.D.'s awarded 1955-59. 13 graduate students registered fall 1959.

Geography. Urban geography; geography of Anglo-America, South America, middle America, U.S.S.R., or Europe; geographic thought; urban planning. Prerequisites for graduate study: introductory courses in physical, social, and economic geography; at least 7 courses in systematic and regional geography; minor in a related biological, physical, or social science. 6 professorial staff. 10 master's degrees and 5 Ph.D.'s awarded 1955-59. 18 graduate students registered fall 1959.

Geology. Mineralogy and petrology, paleontology and stratigraphy, economic or structural geology, geomorphology, geochemistry, geophysics. Prerequisites for graduate study: courses in elementary geology and physics, mineralogy, rock study, mathematics through calculus, and general chemistry; GRE. 9 professorial staff. 59 master's degrees and 16 Ph.D.'s awarded 1955-59. 49 graduate students registered fall 1959.

German. Germanic linguistics and philology, literature. Prerequisite for graduate study: 27 credits in German or equivalent. 5 professorial staff. 14 master's degrees and 2 Ph.D.'s awarded 1955-59. 15 graduate students registered fall 1959.

Greek. Offered by Department of Classics. Prerequisite for graduate study: major in Greek. 5 professorial staff. 6 master's degrees awarded 1955-59. 4 graduate students registered fall 1959.

History. Ancient; medieval and Renaissance to 1500; modern European (1500 to present); English; America and its Colonial backgrounds; Latin America; South and East Asia. Prerequisites for graduate study: general survey courses in at least 2 areas, including 1 course in which intensive work was done. 18 professorial staff. 61 master's degrees and 48 Ph.D.'s awarded 1955-59. 94 graduate students registered fall 1959.

Home Economics. Prerequisites for graduate study: credits in social sciences, physical and biological sciences, art and education; adequate training in field of proposed specialization. 20 professorial staff. 29 master's degrees and 1 Ph.D. awarded 1955-59. 25 graduate students registered fall 1959.

Horticulture. Prerequisite for graduate study: work in plant sciences. 8 professorial staff. 9 master's degrees and 9 Ph.D.'s awarded 1955-59. 22 graduate students registered fall 1959.

Hospital Administration. Administration-management, public health, social sciences. Combined program offered by Departments of Business Administration, Anthropology, Economics, Political Science, Psychology, Sociology, and the School of Public Health. Prerequisite for graduate study: prior training and experience in hospital administration. Recommended: course work in elements and principles of accounting. Ph.D. candidacy prerequisite: master's degree in hospital administration. Program begun 1960.

International Relations. Northwest Europe, Russia, East and South Asia, Latin America. Combined program offered by Departments of Political Science, Geography, History, Journalism, and Economics. Prerequisites for graduate study: major in international relations, an area study, or a social science; 1 appropriate foreign language; MAT. 38 master's degrees awarded 1955-59. 18 graduate students registered fall 1959.

Journalism. Theory of communication and public opinion, history of communications, communication agencies as social institutions, international communications and comparative foreign journalism, specialized research methodology. Prerequisite for graduate study: minimum of 15 quarter credits in basic journalism, includ-ing writing and editing. 9 professorial staff. 46 master's degrees and 3 Ph.D.'s awarded 1955-59. 40 graduate students registered fall 1959.

Latin. Offered by Department of Classics. Prerequisite for graduate study: major in Latin. 5 professorial staff. 4 master's degrees awarded 1955-59. 5 graduate students registered fall 1959.

Mathematics. Algebra, analysis, applied mathematics, statistics, geometry, topology. Prerequisite for graduate study: 10 quarter credits in calculus; 14 quarter credits in other mathematics courses (exceptions made in unusual circumstances). 51 professorial staff. 26 master's degrees and 22 Ph.D.'s awarded 1955-59. 142 graduate students registered fall 1959.

Mechanics and Materials. Prerequisite for graduate study: preparation in mathematics, physics, mechanics, and chemistry. 11 professorial staff. 6 master's degrees and 4 Ph.D.'s awarded 1955-59. 16 graduate students registered fall 1959.

Medicine.—Internal. Prerequisites for graduate study: M.D.; 1 year's experience as intern in hospital or assistant in laboratory of a medical school. 100 professorial staff. 126 master's degrees and 11 Ph.D.'s awarded 1955-59. 85 graduate students registered fall 1959.

Metallurgy. Chemical or physical metallurgy, crystalline properties of metals. Prerequisite for graduate study: principles of physical metallurgy, physical chemistry, intermediate general physics; differential and integral calculus. 5 professorial staff. 3 master's degrees and 2 Ph.D.'s awarded 1955-59. 8 graduate students registered fall 1959.

Music. Music history and literature, theory and composition, music education. Prerequisites for graduate study: working knowledge of piano; performing ability in some phase of instrumental or vocal music; 30 quarter credits in history and literature of music, theory and composition, normal piano, or music education; placement tests in music theory and applied music. 13 professorial staff. 43 master's degrees and 2 Ph.D.'s awarded 1955-59. 23 graduate students registered fall 1959.

Neurology. Offered by Department of Psychiatry and Neurology. Prerequisites for graduate study: M.D.; 1 year's experience as intern in hospital or assistant in laboratory of a medical school. Recommended: extensive training in anatomy, pathology, and physiology. 50 professorial staff. 8 master's degrees and 1 Ph.D. awarded 1955-59. 15 graduate students registered fall 1959.

Neurosurgery. Prerequisites for graduate study: M.D.; 1 year's experience as intern in hospital or assistant in laboratory of medical school. 9 professorial staff. 18 master's degrees and 1 Ph.D. awarded 1955-59. 6 graduate students registered fall 1959.

Obstetrics and Gynecology. Prerequisites for graduate study: M.D.; 1 year's experience as intern in hospital or laboratory assistant in medical school. 7 professorial staff. 6 master's degrees awarded 1955-59. 12 graduate students registered fall 1959.

Ophthalmology. Prerequisites for graduate study: M.D.; 1 year's experience as intern in hospital or laboratory assistant in a medical school. 18 professorial staff. 17 master's degrees awarded 1955-59. 15 graduate students registered fall 1959.

Orthopedic Surgery. Prerequisites for graduate study: M.D.; 1 year's experience as intern in hospital or laboratory assistant in a medical school. 12 professorial staff. 21 master's degrees awarded 1955-59. 15 graduate students registered fall 1959.

Otolaryngology. Prerequisites for graduate study: M.D.; 1 year's experience as intern in hospital or laboratory assistant in a medical school. 10 professorial staff. 4 master's degrees awarded 1955-59. 10 graduate students registered fall 1959.

Pathology. Pathologic anatomy; surgical, experimental and comparative, or clinical pathology. Prerequisite for graduate study: equivalent of first 2 years work in medical school. 22 professorial staff. 11 master's degrees and 3 Ph.D.'s awarded 1955-59. 29 graduate students registered fall 1959.

Pediatrics. Prerequisites for graduate study: courses in bacteriology, immunology, pathology, physiology, and physiological chemistry. 28 professorial staff. 14 master's degrees and 2 Ph.D.'s awarded 1955-59. 31 graduate students registered fall 1959.

Pharmaceutical Chemistry. Prerequisite for graduate study: B.S. in pharmacy (consideration given to applicants with training in related fields). 4 professorial staff. 3 master's degrees and 9 Ph.D.'s awarded 1955-59. 19 graduate students registered fall 1959.

Pharmaceutical Technology. Homogeneous or heterogeneous systems, pharmaceutical development. Prerequisite for graduate study: degree in pharmacy (consideration given to applicants with degrees in related fields). 4 professorial staff. Program begun 1958. 1 graduate student registered fall 1959.

Pharmacognosy. Prerequisite for graduate study: degree in pharmacy (consideration given to applicants with degree in related field). 3 professorial staff. 1 Ph.D. awarded 1955-59.

Pharmacology. Prerequisite for graduate study: satisfaction of requirements for admission to medical school. 6 professorial staff. 4 master's degrees and 5 Ph.D.'s awarded 1955-59. 16 graduate students registered fall 1959.

Philosophy. History of philosophy, logic, metaphysics and epistemology, ethics, philosophy of science or religion, aesthetics, social and political philosophy. Prerequisite for graduate study: 18 credits in philosophy. 9 professorial staff. 27 master's degrees and 6 Ph.D.'s awarded 1955-59. 45 graduate students registered fall 1959.

Physical Medicine and Rehabilitation. Prerequisites for graduate study: M.D.; 1 year's experience as intern in hospital or laboratory assistant in a medical school. 9 professorial staff. 3 master's degrees awarded 1955-59. 3 graduate students registered fall 1959.

Physics. Theoretical, atmospheric, nuclear, low-temperature, or solid-state physics; cosmic rays; mass spectroscopy. Prerequisites for graduate study: differential and integral calculus; 2 years of physics; MAT. 26 professorial staff. 48 master's degrees and 26 Ph.D.'s awarded 1955-59. 98 graduate students registered fall 1959.

Physiological Hygiene. 1 professor. Ph.D. program begun 1955. 1 master's degree and 1 Ph.D. awarded 1955-59. 2 graduate students registered fall 1959.

Physiology. Prerequisite for graduate study: general zoology or anatomy; general and organic chemistry; physics. Recommended: physical chemistry. 36 professorial staff. 11 master's degrees and 9 Ph.D.'s awarded 1955-59. 23 graduate students registered fall 1959.

Plant Genetics. Offered by Department of Agronomy and Plant Genetics. Prerequisite for graduate study: credits in plant sciences. 12 professorial staff. 22 master's degrees and 33 Ph.D.'s awarded 1955-59. 27 graduate students registered fall 1959.

Plant Pathology. Offered by Departments of Plant Pathology and Botany. Prerequisite for graduate study: background in basic sciences and mathematics. 13 professorial staff. 35 master's degrees and 32 Ph.D.'s awarded 1955-59. 45 graduate students registered fall 1959.

Political Science. American government and politics, comparative government and politics, theory, international affairs, political behavior. Prerequisites for graduate study: minimum of 27 quarter credits in political science (in exceptional cases some courses in other social sciences may be accepted); MAT. 17 professorial staff. 89 master's degrees and 27 Ph.D.'s awarded 1955-59. 92 graduate students registered fall 1959.

Poultry Husbandry. 6 professorial staff. 8 master's degrees and 2 Ph.D.'s awarded 1955-59. 13 graduate students registered fall 1959.

Psychiatry. Offered by Department of Psychiatry and Neurology. Prerequisites for graduate study: M.D.; 1 year's experience as intern in hospital or laboratory assistant in a medical school. 50 professorial staff. 6 master's degrees awarded 1955-59. 21 graduate students registered fall 1959.

Psychology. Social, experimental-theoretical, clinical, counseling-guidance, industrial, child psychology. Prerequisites for graduate study: 15 quarter credits in psychology; MAT. 35 professorial staff. 104 master's degrees and 87 Ph.D.'s awarded 1955-59. 180 graduate students registered fall 1959.

Radiology. Physics of radiation, radiobiology, radiation therapy, radiographic technique, roentgen diagnosis, nuclear medicine. Prerequisites for graduate study: M.D.; 1 year's experience as hospital intern or laboratory assistant in medical school. Recommended: internal medicine and/or pathology. Ph.D. candidacy prerequisite: M.S. in radiology. 15 professorial staff. 28 master's degrees and 1 Ph.D. awarded 1955-59. 32 graduate students registered fall 1959.

Sanitation. Offered by School of Public Health. Prerequisites for graduate study: B.S. in physical or biological science or in a field of engineering; basic and applied science, including bacteriology. 6 professorial staff. Ph.D. program begun 1958. 3 master's degrees awarded 1955-59. 5 graduate students registered fall 1959.

Social Work. Field work, social services or work practice, human growth and behavior. Prerequisites for graduate study: 39 credits in social sciences, such as sociology, political science, economics, psychology, history or anthropology, including a course in statistics; MAT. Ph.D. candidacy prerequisite: master's degree in social work. 16 professorial staff. 159 master's degrees and 11 Ph.D.'s awarded 1955-59. 71 graduate students registered fall 1959.

Sociology. Social problems and policy; social psychology and processes; social organization and institutions; rural life and welfare; theories of social change and social order; research methods and techniques. Prerequisites for graduate study: 18 quarter credits in sociology; MAT. 14 professorial staff. 26 master's degrees and 27 Ph.D.'s awarded 1955-59. 48 graduate students registered fall 1959.

Soils. Classification, chemistry of soils, fertility, microbiology, physics. Prerequisites for graduate study: good background in chemistry, including quantitative analysis; physics; mathematics through analytic geometry or equivalent. Recommended: calculus. Ph.D. candidacy prerequisite: M.S. in soils. 11 professorial staff. 18 master's degrees and 11 Ph.D.'s awarded 1955-59. 17 graduate students registered fall 1959.

Spanish. Composition, literature. Offered by Department of Romance Languages. Prerequisite for graduate study: 27 credits in Spanish or equivalent. Ph.D. candidacy prerequisites: knowledge of Latin; reading knowledge of second Romance language. 4 professorial staff. 13 master's degrees and 3 Ph.D.'s awarded 1955-59. 10 graduate students registered fall 1959.

Speech Pathology and Audiology. Offered by Department of Speech and Theater Arts. Prerequisite for graduate study: 18 quarter credits in speech. 5 professorial staff. 5 master's degrees and 3 Ph.D.'s awarded 1955-59. 10 graduate students registered fall 1959.

Speech and Theater Arts. Theater, oral interpretive reading, rhetoric, radio and television, voice science, public address. Prerequisites for graduate study: 18 quarter credits in speech; comprehensive entrance examination. 17 professorial staff. 62 master's degrees and 25 Ph.D.'s awarded 1955-59. 45 graduate students registered fall 1959.

Statistics. Interdepartmental program. Prerequisites for graduate study: differential and integral calculus. 26 professorial staff. 18 master's degrees and 6 Ph.D.'s awarded 1955-59. 17 graduate students registered fall 1959.

Surgery. General or plastic surgery, proctology. Prerequisites for graduate study: M.D.; 1 year's experience as hospital intern or laboratory assistant in a medical school. 56 professorial staff. 103 master's degrees and 21 Ph.D.'s awarded 1955-59. 123 graduate students registered fall 1959.

Urology. Offered by Department of Surgery. Prerequisites for graduate study: M.D.; 1 year's experience as hospital intern or laboratory assistant in a medical school. 11 professorial staff. 7 master's degrees and 2 Ph.D.'s awarded 1955-59. 11 graduate students registered fall 1959.

Veterinary Anatomy. Offered by Department of Veterinary Medicine. Prerequisite for graduate study: D.V.M. or equivalent. 3 professorial staff. Ph.D. program begun 1955. 2 Ph.D.'s awarded 1955-59. 2 graduate students registered fall 1959.

Veterinary Bacteriology. Offered by Department of Veterinary Medicine. Prerequisite for graduate study: D.V.M. or equivalent. 5 professorial staff. Ph.D. program begun 1955. 6 master's degrees and 3 Ph.D.'s awarded 1955-59. 6 graduate students registered fall 1959.

Veterinary Medicine. Prerequisite for graduate study: D.V.M. or equivalent. 12 professorial staff. Ph.D. program begun 1955. 5 master's degrees and 19 Ph.D.'s awarded 1955-59. 11 graduate students registered fall 1959.

Veterinary Parasitology. Offered by Department of Veterinary Medicine. Prerequisite for graduate study: D.V.M. or equivalent. 3 professorial staff. Ph.D. program begun 1955. 2 graduate students registered fall 1959.

Veterinary Pathology. Offered by Department of Veterinary Medicine. Prerequisite for graduate study: D.V.M. or equivalent. 4 professorial staff. Ph.D. program begun 1955. 1 Ph.D. awarded 1955-59. 9 graduate students registered fall 1959.

Veterinary Physiology and Pharmacology. Offered by Department of Veterinary Medicine. Prerequisite for graduate study: D.V.M. or equivalent. 4 professorial staff. Ph.D. program begun 1955. 2 Ph.D.'s awarded 1955-59. 2 graduate students registered fall 1959.

Zoology. Prerequisites for graduate study: 1 year of introductory zoology or biology; minimum of 18 quarter credits of advanced work; MAT. 18 professorial staff. 10 master's degrees and 24 Ph.D.'s awarded 1955-59. 42 graduate students registered fall 1959.

Mississippi Southern College

HATTIESBURG, MISSISSIPPI

The Graduate School

Although graduate instruction has been offered since 1947, instruction at the doctoral level is relatively new. Two programs leading to the Ph.D. were established in 1958 and the first doctoral degrees will probably be awarded in 1962. The college is also authorized to award the Ed.D. degree. The institution is publicly controlled by the state. Both men and women are admitted.

Rooms in dormitories available for single graduate students; apartments for married students.

Residence requirement for Ph.D.: 9 quarters of work, of which 3 consecutive quarters must be spent in residence at Mississippi Southern. Summer courses available; also a very few evening courses.

ADMISSION REQUIREMENTS

For graduate study: bachelor's degree; B average in major field and overall distinguished academic record; GRE before admission or during first term; MAT in some cases; English proficiency test. For Ph.D. candidacy: qualifying examinations; reading knowledge examinations in French and German; approval of dissertation subject.

Apply to Director of Admissions 2 weeks before beginning of quarter.

FEES AND FIRST-YEAR AID

No application fee. Tuition $201 per year. Room (in dormitory) $140 per year. Approximate annual cost of board in college dining room $207. Apartments $45-$55 a month.

First-year aid available: scholarships, $800; teaching fellowships, $800-$1,600; other fellowships, $800-$1,600.

Apply to Dean of the Graduate School by March 1.

FIELDS OF STUDY FOR THE PH.D.

Education. School administration, secondary and elementary education, guidance and counseling, educational psychology. Offered by School of Education and Psychology. Recommended: at least 2 years of teaching experience. 19 professorial staff. Ph.D. program initiated 1958. 547 master's degrees awarded 1955-59. 200 graduate students registered fall 1959. Ed.D. degree also awarded in this field.

Psychology. Offered by the School of Education and Psychology. 8 professorial staff. Ph.D. program initiated 1960. 1 master's degree awarded 1955-59. 12 graduate students registered fall 1959.

Mississippi State University of Agriculture and Applied Science

STATE COLLEGE, MISSISSIPPI

The Graduate School

Graduate instruction has been offered since 1885, and the Graduate School was organized in 1936. First Ph.D. was awarded in 1953, and several programs leading to this degree are now offered. University is publicly controlled by the state. Both men and women are admitted.

Rooms in university dormitories available for single graduate students; apartments for married students.

Special facilities include: library of over 200,000 volumes, including highly specialized libraries in chemistry and entomology; computing center; agricultural experiment station with strong research staff; excellent facilities for work in animal, dairy, and poultry husbandry; new facilities for work in physiology, nutrition, and genetics. Several state agencies are located on campus and provide additional opportunities and facilities for research.

Residence requirement for Ph.D.: 3 years beyond bachelor's degree; 1 year (the last) must be spent in residence on campus. A few summer courses are offered.

ADMISSION REQUIREMENTS

For graduate study: bachelor's degree; good academic record; letters of reference. Recommended (required in some departments): GRE prior to admission or during first term. For Ph.D. candidacy: 60 graduate credits of B average work; reading knowledge of 2 modern languages (usually French and German); GRE Aptitude

and Advanced Tests; preliminary oral and written examinations; approval of dissertation topic.

Apply to the Registrar by August 1 for fall semester.

FEES AND FIRST-YEAR AID

No application fee. Tuition for state residents approximately $227.50 a year; others $427.50. Room (in dormitory) $140 per year. Approximate annual cost of board in college dining room $400-$450. Apartments $20 per month and up.

First-year aid available: 30 or more out-of-state tuition scholarships; 2 fellowships, up to $1,200; 60 or more research assistantships, $450-$2,500.

Apply to Dean of Graduate School by March 1 (later applications considered if funds are available).

FIELDS OF STUDY FOR THE PH.D.

Several programs require students to take courses in methodology of teaching. Opportunities for teaching under departmental supervision also provided.

Agronomy. Crops, soils, grassland management, or seed technology. 19 professorial staff. 34 master's degrees and 7 Ph.D.'s awarded 1955-59. 14 graduate students registered fall 1959. Enrollment limited to 20-25.

Animal Sciences. Nutrition, genetics and animal breeding, physiology. Offered by Departments of Animal Husbandry, Poultry Husbandry, and Dairy Husbandry. 6 professorial staff. Ph.D. program initiated 1956. 20 master's degrees awarded 1955-59. 8 graduate students registered fall 1959. Enrollment limited to 10-15.

Economics.—Agricultural. Agricultural marketing and finance. 4 professorial staff. Ph.D. program initiated 1956. 21 master's degrees awarded 1955-59. 5 graduate students registered fall 1959. Enrollment limited to 8 or 10.

Engineering. Mechanical, civil, electrical, and aeronautical engineering. Combined program in general engineering offered by the School of Engineering in cooperation with Departments of Mathematics and Physics. Prerequisites for graduate study: B.S. in engineering; good background in physics and mathematics. 21 professorial staff. Ph.D. program initiated 1956. 29 master's degrees awarded 1955-59. 12 graduate students registered fall 1959.

History. American, modern European, medieval. Combined program offered by Department of History and Government in cooperation with Departments of English, Economics, and Sociology. 7 professorial staff. Ph.D. program initiated 1956. 31 master's degrees awarded 1955-59. 9 graduate students registered fall 1959.

Sociology. Rural sociology, population trends, social stratifications. Offered by Department of Sociology and Rural Life. 7 professorial staff. Ph.D. program initiated 1956. 6 master's degrees awarded 1955-59. 3 graduate students registered fall 1959.

Mississippi, University of

UNIVERSITY, MISSISSIPPI

The Graduate School

The university has offered graduate instruction since 1870, and the Graduate School was organized in 1928. In the 1890's, 3 Ph.D.'s were awarded, but the degree was not conferred again until 1950. At present, Ph.D. programs are offered in several fields and the Ed.D. degree is also conferred. University is publicly controlled by the state. Both men and women are admitted.

Separate dormitory maintained for graduate men; separate dormitory housing, insofar as possible, for women. University-owned apartments available for married students.

New air-conditioned library, with special facilities for graduate study, contains approximately 310,000 volumes.

Residence requirement for Ph.D.: 3 years beyond bachelor's degree, 2 years of which must be spent in residence on campus. A few courses in education are offered during the summer; limited numbers of seminars in the evening.

ADMISSION REQUIREMENTS

For graduate study: bachelor's degree; high scholastic standing; GRE Advanced Tests. For candidacy for Ph.D.: completion of substantial portion of course work; reading knowledge of 2 modern foreign languages (usually French and German); qualifying comprehensive examination in major and minor fields; approval of dissertation topic; recommendation of department.

Apply to the Office of the Graduate School at any time.

FEES AND FIRST-YEAR AID

No application fee. Tuition for state residents $171 per academic year; nonresidents pay an additional fee of $100 per semester. Special fees approximate $50 per year. Room (in dormitory) for men $140 per year; for women $165. Students purchase meals at cafeterias, fraternity and sorority houses, and in community. Apartments $15-$52.50 per month.

First-year aid available: teaching fellowships, $600-$2,400; nonservice fellowships, $1,600.

Apply to Dean of the Graduate School by March 1 for nonservice fellowships; to department concerned for assistantships.

FIELDS OF STUDY FOR THE PH.D.

Chemistry. Analytical, inorganic, organic, pharmaceutical, physical. Prerequisite for graduate study: 42 semester hours of chemistry. 10 professorial staff. Ph.D. program initiated 1957. 14 master's degrees awarded 1955-59. 36 graduate students registered fall 1959.

Education. Educational administration. Prerequisite for graduate study: teaching certificate or evidence of eligibility for such. 12 professorial staff. 291 master's degrees and 3 Ph.D.'s awarded 1955-59. 81 graduate students registered fall 1959. Ed.D. degree also awarded in this field.

English. English or American literature. Prerequisites for graduate study: 30 semester hours of English in specified courses; 1 foreign language. 11 professorial staff. Ph.D. program initiated 1957. 35 master's degrees awarded 1955-59. 36 graduate students registered fall 1959.

History. Ancient, medieval, English, American, or Latin-American history. Prerequisite for graduate study: major in history. 11 professorial staff. Ph.D. program initiated 1959. 18 master's degrees awarded 1955-59. 9 graduate students registered fall 1959.

Medical Science. Anatomy, biochemistry, microbiology, pharmacology, physiology, biophysics, preventive medicine. Program offered on campus of School of Medicine in Jackson; each Ph.D. designated according to area of concentration. 37 professorial staff. 4 master's degrees and 2 Ph.D.'s awarded 1955-59. 21 graduate students registered fall 1959.

Psychology. General experimental psychology, teaching of psychology. Prerequisite for graduate study: major in psychology. 7 professorial staff.

Ph.D. program initiated 1958. 18 master's degrees awarded 1955-59. 13 graduate students registered fall 1959.

Missouri, University of

COLUMBIA, MISSOURI

The Graduate School

The university has offered graduate instruction since 1892, and the first Ph.D. was awarded in 1891. The Graduate School was organized in 1910 and now has jurisdiction over all Ph.D. programs, including those offered at the School of Mines and Metallurgy at Rolla, Missouri. The Ed.D. degree is also conferred by the Graduate School. University is publicly controlled by the state. Both men and women are admitted.

Rooms in residence halls available for single graduate students; 1- and 2-bedroom apartments for married students.

Library of approximately 950,000 volumes includes special collections on agriculture, biology, engineering, geology, journalism, law, medicine, mining and metallurgy, and veterinary medicine. Collection of Western historical manuscripts is outstanding.

Residence requirement for Ph.D.: 3 years beyond bachelor's degree, 1 of which must be spent in residence at the University of Missouri. Summer courses available.

ADMISSION REQUIREMENTS

For graduate study: baccalaureate degree; good academic record. For candidacy for Ph.D.: qualifying examinations; approval of program. Before being admitted to comprehensive examinations, candidate must demonstrate reading knowledge of German and either French or Spanish; a research technique or collateral field may be substituted for 1 language under certain circumstances.

Apply to Director of Admissions at any time.

FEES AND FIRST-YEAR AID

No application fee. No tuition. Special fees approximate $215 annually. Room (in dormitory) $262.40 per academic year. Average annual cost of board in college dining room $380. Apartments $52.50-$62.50 per month.

First-year aid available: 12 to 15 scholarships, $1,000; teaching fellowships, $1,600-$2,400; research assistantships, $1,600-$2,400. 65 grants-in-aid, $215 per year.

Apply by March 1 to Dean of Graduate School for scholarships; to chairman of appropriate department for teaching and research assistantships.

FIELDS OF STUDY FOR THE PH.D.

College of Education offers a course in college teaching. Several departments offer formal courses, seminars, or conferences on the problems of college teaching.

Accounting. Offered by Department of Accounting and Statistics. Prerequisite for graduate study: major in accounting. 11 professorial staff. 33 master's degrees and 1 Ph.D. awarded 1955-59. 12 graduate students registered fall 1959.

American Civilization. Combined program offered by Departments of English, History, Music, Philosophy, and Political Science. Prerequisite for graduate study: major in art, English, political science, history, music, philosophy, or American civilization. 20 professorial staff. Ph.D. program initiated 1955. 1 graduate student registered fall 1959.

Anatomy. Quantitative anatomy, neurophysiology, neuroanatomy, electron microscopy, hermatology. Ph.D. candidacy prerequisite: first year of regular medical curriculum or major in zoology or biology or equivalent. 7 professorial staff. 1 master's degree and 1 Ph.D. awarded 1955-59. 4 graduate students registered fall 1959. Total enrollment limited to 6.

Animal Husbandry. Animal breeding, meat technology, animal nutrition, production, and management. 16 professorial staff. 41 master's degrees and 18 Ph.D.'s awarded 1955-59. 32 graduate students registered fall 1959.

Biochemistry. Mechanisms of enzyme catalyzed reactions, peptide synthesis, amino-acid metabolism, effects of hormones on metabolism, identification of unknown growth factors, germ-free research, comparative biochemistry, metabolism of cells in tissue culture, induced enzyme synthesis, biochemistry of bone. 4 professorial staff. 5 master's degrees and 1 Ph.D. awarded 1955-59. 14 graduate students registered fall 1959.

Botany. Anatomy-morphology, bacteriology-microbiology, ecology, genetics, paleobotany, physiology, systematic botany. Prerequisite for graduate study: major in botany. Prerequisite for Ph.D. candidacy: master's degree in botany. 8 professorial staff. 11 master's degrees and 11 Ph.D.'s awarded 1955-59. 13 graduate students registered fall 1959.

Chemistry. Analytical, inorganic, organic, and physical. 13 professorial staff. 7 master's degrees and 27 Ph.D.'s awarded 1955-59. 44 graduate students registered fall 1959.

Chemistry.—Agricultural. Nutrition, physiological chemistry of domestic animals, spectroscopy, analysis of agricultural products. Prerequisites for graduate study: equivalent of a major in chemistry, including background in biology. 11 professorial staff. 20 master's degrees and 12 Ph.D.'s awarded 1955-59. 23 graduate students registered fall 1959.

Dairy Husbandry. Dairy cattle nutrition and ruminant microbiology, artificial insemination and reproductive physiology, dairy cattle breeding and herd management, dairy microbiology and public health, dairy processing and market milk, environmental physiology, endocrinology and milk secretion. Prerequisite for Ph.D. candidacy: M.S. or M.A. in related field. 7 professorial staff. 50 master's degrees and 14 Ph.D.'s awarded 1955-59. 23 graduate students registered fall 1959.

Economics. Economic theory and its history, labor economics, monetary economics and business fluctuations, international economics, public finance, social control of business, business finance and investments, insurance and real estate, industrial organization and management, marketing, personnel management and labor relations. Offered by Department of Economics and Business. Prerequisite for graduate study: equivalent of a major in economics or business administration. 17 professorial staff. 19 master's degrees and 1 Ph.D. awarded 1955-59. 33 graduate students registered fall 1959.

Economics.—Agricultural. Production economics, farm management, agricultural marketing, land economics, agricultural credit, resource economics, agricultural policy, agricultural prices, econometrics, economic development. Prerequisite for graduate study: 16 semester hours credit in agricultural economics or equivalent. 11 professorial staff. 35 master's degrees and 6 Ph.D.'s awarded 1955-59. 38 graduate students registered fall 1959.

Education. Educational administration; guidance and counseling; elementary, industrial, secondary, agricultural, and special education. Prerequisite for graduate study: Advisory Battery Examination. 26 professorial staff. 779 master's degrees and 8 Ph.D.'s awarded 1955-59. 242 graduate students registered fall 1959. Ed.D. also awarded in this field.

Engineering.—Agricultural. Electric power and processing, soil and water engineering, farm power and machinery, farm structures (including environmental control). Prerequisites for graduate study: major in some branch of engineering or the equivalent. 7 professorial staff. 12 master's degrees and 3 Ph.D.'s awarded 1955-59. 13 graduate students registered fall 1959. New enrollment limited to 12-15.

Engineering. — Ceramic. Physical and/or structural properties of crystalline and crystalline-glass systems, with particular emphasis upon high-temperature stability in such systems. Offered by Department of Ceramic Engineering, Rolla Campus. 2 professorial staff. 2 master's degrees and 2 Ph.D.'s awarded 1955-59. 2 graduate students registered fall 1959.

Engineering.—Chemical. Solvent extraction, flow of fluids, thermodynamics, kinetics, waste disposal, radioisotopes, purification of metals. Offered by Department of Chemical Engineering. 5 professorial staff. 6 master's degrees awarded 1955-59. 6 graduate students registered fall 1959.

Engineering.—Chemical. Protective coatings, including paints, varnishes, lacquer; high polymers; corrosion; nuclear chemistry; vapor-liquid equilibria; applied ultrasonics; chemical engineering process design; organic synthesis; unit operations; diffusion of gases; crystal structure. Offered by Department of Chemical Engineering, Rolla Campus. Prerequisites for graduate study: preparation in field; diagnostic examination. Prerequisite for Ph.D. candidacy: GRE. 14 professorial staff. Ph.D. program begun 1956. 10 master's degrees awarded 1955-59. 17 graduate students registered fall 1959.

Engineering.—Civil. Structural, sanitary engineering. 13 professorial staff. 49 master's degrees and 2 Ph.D.'s awarded 1955-59. 15 graduate students registered fall 1959.

Engineering.—Electrical. Circuit analysis and synthesis, antennas and wave propagation, power systems analysis, solid-state electronics, computers. Prerequisite for graduate study: major in electrical engineering. 8 professorial staff. 33 master's degrees and 1 Ph.D. awarded 1955-59. 12 graduate students registered fall 1959.

Engineering.—Mechanical. Power plants, metallurgical investigations, refrigeration and air conditioning, dynamics of machines. 10 professorial staff. 13 master's degrees awarded 1955-59. 9 graduate students registered fall 1959.

Engineering.—Metallurgical. Physical metallurgy, extractive metallurgy, corrosion, highly precise X-ray diffraction measurements of metals and metal compounds. Offered by Department of Metallurgical Engineering, Rolla Campus. 8 professorial staff. 15 master's degrees and 6 Ph.D.'s awarded 1955-59. 14 graduate students registered fall 1959.

Engineering.—Mining. Explosives and explosive effects; rock mechanics, dynamic and static; mine operation in all its phases; exploration geophysics; mineral economics. Offered by Department of Mining Engineering, Rolla Campus. 6 professorial staff. 7 master's degrees awarded 1955-59. 15 graduate students registered fall 1959.

Engineering Physics. Theoretical, nuclear physics; engineering and spectroscopy. Offered by Department of Engineering Physics, Rolla Campus. Prerequisite for graduate study: mathematics through differential equations. 11 professorial staff. Ph.D. program begun 1960. 15 master's degrees awarded 1955-59. 12 graduate students registered fall 1959.

English. Linguistics; Old English, Middle English, Renaissance, 17th, 18th, or 19th century English, Colonial American, 19th century American, or 20th century English and American literature. 13 professorial staff. 47 master's degrees and 16 Ph.D.'s awarded 1955-59 61 graduate students registered fall 1959.

Entomology. Insect taxonomy, physiology, ecology, toxicology, or morphology; applied entomology. 7 professorial staff. 6 master's degrees and 1 Ph.D. awarded 1955-59. 7 graduate students registered fall 1959.

Field Crops. Genetics, plant breeding, crop production. Prerequisites for graduate study: for genetics, broad background in biological sciences; for plant breeding and crop production, 26 hours of field crops, botany, and soil science. 8 professorial staff. 8 master's degrees awarded 1955-59. 14 graduate students registered fall 1959.

French. French language and literature. Offered by the Department of Romance Languages. 5 professorial staff. 3 master's degrees and 2 Ph.D.'s awarded 1955-59. 11 graduate students registered fall 1959.

Genetics. Genetics of corn, wheat; arabidopsis and certain microorganisms. Combined program offered by Departments of Botany, Animal Husbandry, Field Crops, and Zoology. 7 professorial staff. 2 Ph.D. degrees awarded 1955-59. 6 graduate students registered fall 1959.

Geology. Invertebrate paleontology, micropaleontology, economic geology, stratigraphy, clay mineralogy, petrography and petrology, sedimentology, X-ray crystallography. Offered by Department of Geology. 9 professorial staff. 64 master's degrees and 8 Ph.D.'s awarded 1955-59. 43 graduate students registered fall 1959.

Geology. Economic geology, geochemistry, geomorphology, geophysics, invertebrate macro- and micro-paleontology, mineralogy, petrology, stratigraphy, and structural geology. Offered by Department of Geology, Rolla Campus. 9 professorial staff. 16 master's degrees awarded 1955-59. 19 graduate students registered fall 1959.

History. European: Greece and Rome (700 B.C.-300 A.D.); medieval Europe (300-1300); Renaissance and Reformation (1300-1600); early modern Europe (1555-1789); history of England and the British Empire (1485-1789); history of England and the British Empire (1789 to present); modern Europe (1789-1848), modern Europe (1848-1914). American: American Colonial period and Revolution (to 1787), National Period in United States Constitution through Reconstruction (1787-1877); recent United States (South, West, American Constitutional, American diplomatic, American economic, social and intellectual); Latin America. Prerequisite for graduate study: 25 hours of history or equivalent. 12 professorial staff. 56 master's degrees and 11 Ph.D.'s awarded 1955-59. 49 graduate students registered fall 1959.

Home Economics. Food and nutrition. 16 professorial staff. 20 master's degrees awarded 1955-59. 8 graduate students registered fall 1959.

Horticulture. Nutrition, virology, pathology, physiology, water relationships, antibiotics, genetics. 12 professorial staff. 14 master's degrees and 3 Ph.D.'s awarded 1955-59. 8 graduate students registered fall 1959.

Journalism. Prerequisites for graduate study: 14 hours of basic journalism courses. 25 professorial staff. 82 master's degrees and 6 Ph.D.'s

awarded 1955-59. 65 graduate students registered fall 1959.

Mathematics. Distance geometry, statistics and probability, topological dynamics, algebra, topology, differential equations. 10 professorial staff. 26 master's degrees and 7 Ph.D.'s awarded 1955-59. 43 graduate students registered fall 1959.

Microbiology. Medical bacteriology, bacterial physiology, mycology, virology, immunology, and parasitology. Recommended for graduate study: GRE. Prerequisite for Ph.D. candidacy: master's degree. 4 professorial staff. Ph.D. program begun 1956. 9 master's degrees awarded 1955-59. 13 graduate students registered fall 1959.

Pathology. Experimental pathology. Prerequisite for Ph.D. candidacy: medical degree. 3 professorial staff. New enrollment limited to 2 or 3 students.

Philosophy. Ethics, political philosophy, aesthetics, philosophical sociology, logic and theory of knowledge, presuppositions and methodology of the sciences, metaphysics, history of philosophy. 4 professorial staff. Ph.D. program begun 1959. 1 master's degree awarded 1955-59. 5 graduate students registered fall 1959.

Physics. High-energy nuclear physics, cosmic rays, experimental solid-state, theoretical solid-state, ultrasonics, X-ray and neutron diffraction by solids, liquids and gases, small angle scattering of X-rays. 8 professorial staff. 19 master's degrees and 14 Ph.D.'s awarded 1955-59. 34 graduate students registered fall 1959.

Physiology. Cardiovascular, environmental, and renal physiology. Offered by Department of Physiology and Pharmacology. Prerequisites for graduate study: biology and chemistry. 7 professorial staff. 3 master's degrees and 2 Ph.D.'s awarded 1955-59. 4 graduate students registered fall 1959.

Physiology and Pharmacology. Cardiovascular, environmental, and renal physiology; pharmacology of blood-brain barrier; pharmacology of indigenous plants. Prerequisites for graduate study: biology and chemistry. 7 professorial staff. 2 master's degrees awarded 1955-59. 3 graduate students registered fall 1959.

Political Science. Comparative government, international law and relations, political theory, politics and legislation, public administration, public law. 11 professorial staff. 13 master's degrees and 4 Ph.D.'s awarded 1955-59. 27 graduate students registered fall 1959.

Poultry Husbandry. Breeding, nutrition, poultry products, physiology, management. 7 professorial staff. Ph.D. program begun 1957. 9 master's degrees awarded 1955-59. 8 graduate students registered fall 1959.

Psychology. Experimental, clinical, counseling, social. Prerequisites for graduate study: acceptance by staff; MAT. 15 professorial staff. 31 master's degrees and 17 Ph.D.'s awarded 1955-59. 55 graduate students registered fall 1959. Enrollment limited to 60 students.

Sociology.—General. Social theory, social psychology, collective behavior, social organization and disorganization, demography and population, anthropology. Offered by Department of Sociology and Anthropology. 6 professorial staff. 7 master's degrees and 4 Ph.D.'s awarded 1955-59. 25 graduate students registered fall 1959.

Sociology.—Rural. Population, health, diffusion, community, and marketing. 6 professorial staff. 5 master's degrees and 2 Ph.D.'s awarded 1955-59. 14 graduate students registered fall 1959.

Soils. Soil physics, chemistry, mineralogy, fertility, microbiology, genesis, morphology, conservation, and testing. Prerequisite for graduate study: 32 hours in soils and related subjects. 7 professorial staff. 15 master's degrees and 8 Ph.D.'s awarded 1955-59. 15 graduate students registered fall 1959.

Spanish. Spanish language and literature, Spanish-American literature. Offered by Department of Romance Languages. 5 professorial staff. 8 master's degrees and 1 Ph.D. awarded 1955-59. 9 graduate students registered fall 1959.

Speech and Dramatic Arts. Speech pathology, rhetoric and public address, theater (majority of course work in allied fields with dissertation in area of theater). 7 professorial staff. 27 master's degrees and 9 Ph.D.'s awarded 1955-59. 32 graduate students registered fall 1959.

Zoology. Physiology, both invertebrate and vertebrate; comparative, developmental, general, cellular, physiological ecology; mammalian reproduction; embryology; endocrinology; wildlife ecology and management; fish distribution, management, and ecology; game biology, management, ecology; limnology; ornithology; population biology; genetics. Prerequisite for graduate study: 24 hours of zoology. Prerequisite for Ph.D. candidacy: GRE or MAT. 9 professorial staff. 27 master's degrees and 13 Ph.D.'s awarded 1955-59. 37 graduate students registered fall 1959.

Montana State College

BOZEMAN, MONTANA

The Graduate Division

Graduate instruction has been offered since 1901 and the Graduate School was formally organized in 1948. First Ph.D. was awarded 1956. A program leading to the Ed.D. degree is offered by the Department of Education. College is publicly controlled by the state. Both men and women are admitted.

Rooms in dormitories available for single students; college-owned apartments and houses for married students.

The college has a library of approximately 140,000 volumes. Very rapid growth of research activities on campus has given great impetus to the development of graduate study in recent years.

Residence requirement for Ph.D.: minimum of 3 academic years of full-time graduate study beyond bachelor's degree; 6 quarters, including last 3, must be spent in residence at Montana State College. A few summer courses available.

ADMISSION REQUIREMENTS

For graduate study: bachelor's degree; high scholastic standing; completion of department requirements; GRE. For candidacy for Ph.D.: reading knowledge of 2 foreign languages (usually French, German, Russian); comprehensive examinations.

Apply to Director of Admissions at least 1 quarter before admission is desired.

FEES AND FIRST-YEAR AID

No application fee. No tuition as such, but graduate students who are state residents pay special fees of $80-$83 per quarter; nonresidents pay $170.50 per quarter. Single room (in dormitory) $80 per quarter; double room $65. Board in college dining room $57 per month. Apartments $30-$60 per month.

First-year aid available: approximately 30 fee-exemption scholarships; 39 teaching fellowships, $1,500-$2,700; 42 research assistantships, $1,500-$4,500; several teaching assistantships.

Apply to Dean of the Graduate Division no later than March 15.

FIELDS OF STUDY FOR THE PH.D.

Agricultural Economics. Agricultural marketing, prices, and policy; land economics; farm and ranch management. Prerequisite for graduate study: equivalent of a major in agricultural economics or economics. 9 professorial staff. Ph.D. program begun 1957. 37 master's degrees awarded 1955-59. 21 graduate students registered fall 1959.

Bacteriology. Cellular degradation, soil microbiology, microbial physiology, pathogenic anaerobic bacteriology. Offered by Department of Botany and Bacteriology. Prerequisite for graduate study: major in bacteriology or the equivalent. 9 professorial staff. Ph.D. program begun 1955. 6 master's degrees and 1 Ph.D. awarded 1955-59. 6 graduate students registered fall 1959.

Botany. Plant physiology, ecology, pathology, and taxonomy. Offered by Department of Botany and Bacteriology. Prerequisite for graduate study: major in botany or closely related biological science. 10 professorial staff. Ph.D. program begun 1955. 4 master's degrees awarded 1955-59. 2 graduate students registered fall 1959.

Chemistry. Physical, organic, analytical, and inorganic chemistry; biochemistry. Prerequisite for graduate study: major in chemistry. 17 professorial staff. 13 master's degrees and 5 Ph.D.'s awarded 1955-59. 19 graduate students registered fall 1959.

Engineering.—Chemical. Petroleum processing, manganese chemicals, shale oil processing, catalysis, heat transfer. Offered by Department of Chemical Engineering. Prerequisite for graduate study: major in chemical engineering or chemistry. 4 professorial staff. 21 master's degrees and 7 Ph.D.'s awarded 1955-59.

Engineering.—Electrical. Electronics, servomechanisms. Prerequisite for graduate study: major in electrical engineering (physics is permissible). 7 professorial staff. Ph.D. program begun 1957. 11 master's degrees awarded 1955-59. 22 graduate students registered fall 1959.

Entomology. Population biology, experimental embryology of insects. Prerequisite for graduate study: major in entomology or closely related biological science. 5 professorial staff. Ph.D. program begun 1955. 1 master's degree and 1 Ph.D. awarded 1955-59. 5 graduate students registered fall 1959.

Fish and Wildlife Management. Population biology of fish and game animals (including upland birds). Offered by Department of Zoology and Entomology. Prerequisite for graduate study: major in wildlife management or a closely related biological science. 2 professorial staff. Ph.D. program begun 1955. 20 master's degrees awarded 1955-59. 6 graduate students registered fall 1959.

Genetics. Physiological genetics, cytogenetics, population genetics, microbial genetics, animal genetics (agriculture), plant genetics (agriculture). Offered by the Genetics Committee of the Graduate School. Prerequisites for graduate study: major in a biological or agricultural field; 1 year of college mathematics; courses in introductory genetics and in organic chemistry. 9 professorial staff. Program begun 1960. 3 graduate students registered fall 1959.

Mathematics. Differential equations, applied mathematics, statistics. Prerequisite for graduate study: major in mathematics. 11 professorial staff. Ph.D. program begun 1958. 10 master's degrees awarded 1955-59. 11 graduate students registered fall 1959.

Zoology. Stress physiology, histology, experimental embryology. Offered by Department of Zoology and Entomology. Prerequisites for graduate study: major in zoology or a closely related biological science. 7 professorial staff. Ph.D. program begun 1955. 8 master's degrees awarded 1955-59. 6 graduate students registered fall 1959.

Montana State University

MISSOULA, MONTANA

The Graduate School

The first master's degree was awarded in 1899. A graduate department was organized in 1913 and this became the Graduate School in 1946. Doctoral programs were introduced in 1956 when the School of Education was authorized to confer the Ed.D. Three Ph.D. programs were initiated in 1959. University is publicly controlled by the state. Both men and women are admitted.

Most graduate students find rooms or apartments in the community; a limited number of family-dwelling apartments are operated by the university.

Special facilities include: biological station on Flathead Lake; Montana Cooperative Wildlife Research Unit; forest conservation and experiment station; 22,000-acre forest; research institute on allergies; library of approximately 268,000 volumes. The university has cooperative arrangements with: Rocky Mountain Laboratory of the Public Health Service; The National Bison Range; United States Fish and Wildlife Refuges; United States Forest Service Region No. 1.

Residence requirement for Ph.D.: 3 full academic years of graduate study; at least 5 quarters in residence on campus. Limited number of summer and evening courses available.

ADMISSION REQUIREMENTS

For graduate study: bachelor's degree; superior academic record. For candidacy for Ph.D.: comprehensive examinations; departmental recommendation; completion of minor field work; reading knowledge of 2 foreign languages; proficient use of English.

Apply to Dean of the Graduate School at least 1 month prior to date of expected registration.

FEES AND FIRST-YEAR AID

No application fee. No tuition as such, but state residents pay special fees of $283 annually; others $545.50. Approximate cost of board in college dining room $455 per academic year. Apartments in community rent for $60-$100 per month.

First-year aid available: graduate teaching or research assistantships with stipends of $1,500-$1,800 for 10 to 15 hours service per week, plus remission of major portion of fees.

Apply to Dean of Graduate School by March 15.

FIELDS OF STUDY FOR THE PH.D.

Bacteriology. Immunology, physiology of bacteria, medical and general bacteriology. Offered by Department of Microbiology and Public Health. Prerequisite for graduate study: major in bacteriology, biology, chemistry, or related field. GRE may be required of certain individuals. Recommended: physical chemistry; calculus; 3 courses in bacteriology; 1 or 2 foreign languages. 11 professorial staff. Ph.D. program initiated 1959. 2 master's degrees awarded 1955-59. 8 graduate students registered fall 1959. Enrollment limited to 10 until new facilities become available in 1961.

Geology. Areal geology, geology of metallic and nonmetallic deposits, geochemistry, geomorphology, ground-water geology, mineralogy, clay mineralogy, petrology, vertebrate paleontology, invertebrate paleontology, stratigraphy, sedimentation, structural geology. Prerequisite for graduate study: GRE. Recommended: 1 or 2 foreign languages; a summer field camp. 8 professorial staff. Ph.D. program initiated 1959. 14 master's degrees awarded 1955-59. 22 graduate students registered fall 1959. Enrollment limited to approximately 30.

Zoology. Vertebrate or invertebrate zoology, ecology, ichthyology, ornithology, mammalogy, physiology, parasitology, embryology. Prerequisites for graduate study: major in zoology; 1 year each of botany, chemistry, and physics; GRE. Recommended: 1 or 2 foreign languages; work in invertebrate and comparative vertebrate zoology, physiology, genetics, embryology, histology, and bacteriology. 9 professorial staff. Ph.D. program initiated 1959. 13 master's degrees awarded 1955-59. 9 graduate students registered fall 1959.

Nebraska, University of

LINCOLN 8, NEBRASKA

Graduate College

Graduate instruction was begun in 1886. In 1896 the Graduate School was organized and the first Ph.D. was awarded in the same year. By this action Nebraska became the first public university in America to organize its graduate instruction into a school. The name was changed to the Graduate College in 1909. University is publicly controlled by the state. Both men and women are admitted.

A program leading to the Ed.D. degree is offered by the Teachers College, and is conferred as an advanced professional degree.

Rooms in dormitories available for graduate students. Married students accommodated in university-owned apartments.

Residence requirements for the Ph.D.: 3 years. Up to 6 semester hours of graduate credit may be transferred toward the master's degree; up to 3 semester's work toward the Ph.D. Minimum 1 academic year must be spent in residence on campus. Summer courses available. Courses in education and a few other isolated and irregular courses are offered in the evening.

ADMISSION REQUIREMENTS

For graduate study: bachelor's degree; courses which meet specific requirement in major field. For Ph.D. candidacy: reading knowledge of 2 foreign languages (usually French and German); comprehensive examinations.

Apply to Dean of Graduate College by May 1 for summer session; by July 1 for fall term.

FEES AND FIRST-YEAR AID

Alien applicants are charged $5 which is applied toward tuition if student is admitted and enrolled. Tuition for state residents $240; others $480. Room (in dormitory) $225 a year. Approximate annual cost of board in college dining room $400. Apartments $70-$80 per month.

First-year aid available: 250 teaching assistantships, $1,000-$2,000; 30 nonteaching fellowships, $1,000-$2,000; 50 research assistantships, $1,500-$2,000; 42 tuition fellowships, $180-$420.

Apply to Dean of Graduate College by March 1. GRE scores desirable and, if available, should accompany application.

FIELDS OF STUDY FOR THE PH.D.

Agricultural Economics. Prerequisites for graduate study: 18 semester hours of agricultural subjects, including agricultural economics; 12 of social sciences, including 6 of economics. 9 professorial staff. Ph.D. program begun 1957. 39 master's degrees awarded 1955-59. 24 graduate students registered fall 1959.

Agronomy. Crops, soils. Prerequisites for graduate study: 18 semester hours in agricultural subjects; 12 in biological sciences; 12 in chemistry. 28 professorial staff. 57 master's degrees and 24 Ph.D.'s awarded 1955-59. 55 graduate students registered fall 1959.

Anatomy. Prerequisites for graduate study: bachelor's or master's degree with equivalent of 2 semester's credit in basic medical sciences. 5 professorial staff. Ph.D. program initiated 1956. 3 master's degrees and 1 Ph.D. awarded 1955-59. 3 graduate students registered fall 1959.

Animal Sciences.—Dairy Husbandry. Production and manufacturing. Prerequisites for graduate study: 18 semester hours in agricultural subjects; 12 in biological science; 12 in chemistry. 7 professorial staff. Ph.D. program initiated 1958.

4 master's degrees awarded 1955-59. 7 graduate students registered fall 1959.

Animal Sciences.—Genetics. Interdepartmental program which includes Departments of Animal Husbandry, Poultry Husbandry, Dairy Husbandry, Physiology, and Zoology. Prerequisite for graduate study: major in one of the animal industry departments or in a biological science. 10 professorial staff. 2 Ph.D.'s awarded 1955-59.

Bacteriology. Prerequisites for graduate study: 18 semester hours of bacteriology beyond freshman level; 2 years of 1 foreign language. 6 professorial staff. Ph.D. program initiated 1957. 17 master's degrees awarded 1955-59. 11 graduate students registered fall 1959.

Biochemistry. — Medical. Prerequisites for graduate study: equivalent of 2 semester's credit in basic medical sciences; 1 year each of college physics, organic, inorganic, and physical chemistry, qualitative and quantitative analysis. 9 professorial staff. Ph.D. program initiated 1958. 2 master's degrees awarded 1955-59. 5 graduate students registered fall 1959.

Botany.—Plant Pathology. Ecology, morphology, mycology, pathology, physiology, taxonomy. Prerequisites for graduate study: major in botany; 1 year of zoology; 1 course in genetics; 2 years of 1 foreign language. 13 professorial staff. 12 master's degrees and 7 Ph.D.'s awarded 1955-59. 20 graduate students registered fall 1959.

Business Organization and Management. Accounting, banking, finance, insurance, statistics, marketing, personnel and labor, foreign trade, economic theory, public finance, transportation, public utilities. Prerequisite for graduate study: 30 hours in business organization and/or economics, of which 6 hours must be in principles of economics and 6 hours in basic accounting. 11 professorial staff. 37 master's degrees and 1 Ph.D. awarded 1955-59. 51 graduate students registered fall 1959.

Chemistry and Biochemistry. Inorganic, organic, analytical, or physical chemistry; biochemistry. Offered by Department of Chemistry. Prerequisites for graduate study: 18 semester hours of chemistry beyond freshman level; mathematics through integral calculus; 2 years of German, French, or Russian. 22 professorial staff. 58 master's degrees and 27 Ph.D.'s awarded 1955-59. 72 graduate students registered fall 1959.

Economics. Prerequisite for graduate study: 24 hours of economics, including 6 in principles of economics. 12 professorial staff. 21 master's degrees and 6 Ph.D.'s awarded 1955-59. 26 graduate students registered fall 1959.

Education.—Educational Psychology and Measurements. Psychometrics, special education and school psychology, counseling and student personnel, developmental psychology. Prerequisites for graduate study: 12 semester hours of English; 18 hours of professional education, including 3 in practice teaching; minimum of 18 hours in each of 2 teaching fields. 10 professorial staff. 28 master's degrees and 21 Ph.D.'s awarded 1955-59. 22 graduate students registered fall 1959.

Education.—School administration. Prerequisites for graduate study: 12 semester hours in English; 18 hours of professional education, including 3 in practice teaching; minimum of 18 hours in each of 2 teaching fields. 7 professorial staff. 9 master's degrees and 12 Ph.D.'s awarded 1955-59. 5 graduate students registered fall 1959.

Education.—Secondary. Prerequisites for graduate study: 12 semester hours of English; 18 of professional education courses, including 3 in practice teaching; minimum of 18 hours in each of 2 teaching fields. 10 professorial staff. 25 master's degrees and 5 Ph.D.'s awarded 1955-59. 14 graduate students registered fall 1959.

Engineering Mechanics. 11 professorial staff. Ph.D. program initiated 1960. 5 master's degrees awarded 1955-59. 11 graduate students registered fall 1959.

English. Prerequisites for graduate study: 27 hours of English beyond freshman composition, exclusive of courses in comparative literature, business English, journalism, and speech; 2 years in 1 foreign language. 17 professorial staff. 3 master's degrees and 36 Ph.D.'s awarded 1955-59. 37 graduate students registered fall 1959.

Entomology. Ecology, taxonomy, morphology, physiology, toxicology, medical and economic entomology, insect transmission of plant pathogens. Prerequisites for graduate study: major in entomology; introductory courses in botany, zoology, inorganic, and organic chemistry; usually 2 years in 1 foreign language. 8 professorial staff. Ph.D. program initiated 1958. 4 master's degrees awarded 1955-59. 13 graduate students registered fall 1959.

Geography. Concentration in natural science or social science aspect of geography. Prerequisites for graduate study: 18 semester hours in geography beyond freshman courses; 2 years in 1 foreign language. 5 professorial staff. 12 master's degrees and 10 Ph.D.'s awarded 1955-59. 14 graduate students registered fall 1959.

Geology. Specialization in any major division of geology, including paleontology. Prerequisite for graduate study: 18 semester hours in geology beyond freshman courses. For specialization in paleontology, preparation in biology and 2 years of foreign language are required. 8 professorial staff. 44 master's degrees and 2 Ph.D.'s awarded 1955-59. 27 graduate students registered fall 1959.

History. Ancient, medieval, English, modern European, American, Latin-American. Prerequisites for graduate study: 26 semester hours of history; 2 years of foreign language. 11 professorial staff. 33 master's degrees and 20 Ph.D.'s awarded 1955-59. 33 graduate students registered fall 1959.

Mathematics. Offered by the Department of Mathematics and Astronomy. Prerequisites for graduate study: 15 semester credits in mathematics beyond integral calculus; 2 years of 1 foreign language. 15 professorial staff. 24 master's degrees and 1 Ph.D. awarded 1955-59. 31 graduate students registered fall 1959.

Medical Sciences. Anatomy, biochemistry, internal medicine, microbiology, neurology and psychiatry, obstetrics and gynecology, orthopedic surgery, pathology, pediatrics, physiology and pharmacology, radiology. Interdepartmental area program which includes departments of medical sciences, both preclinical and clinical. Prerequisite for graduate study: 2 semester's credit in basic medical sciences. 25 professorial staff. 1 master's degree and 2 Ph.D.'s awarded 1955-59.

Pharmaceutical Science. Pharmacy, pharmaceutical chemistry, pharmacognosy, pharmacology. Interdepartmental area program which includes Departments of Pharmacy and Pharmaceutical Chemistry, Pharmacology, Pharmacognosy, Bacteriology, Chemistry. Prerequisite for graduate study: master's degree with major in pharmacy, pharmaceutical chemistry, pharmacology, or pharmacognosy. 6 professorial staff. Ph.D. program begun 1955. 2 Ph.D.'s awarded 1955-59. 2 graduate students registered fall 1959.

Philosophy. Prerequisites for graduate study: 18 semester credits of philosophy beyond introductory courses; 2 years of 1 foreign language. 4 professorial staff. 4 master's degrees and 5

Ph.D.'s awarded 1955-59. 11 graduate students registered fall 1959.

Physics. Prerequisites for graduate study: mathematics through integral calculus; minimum of 18 semester credits in physics beyond beginning courses; 2 years of 1 foreign language. 8 professorial staff. 20 master's degrees and 5 Ph.D.'s awarded 1955-59. 46 graduate students registered fall 1959.

Physiology and Pharmacology (Medical). Prerequisites for graduate study: equivalent of 2 semester credits in basic medical sciences. 6 professorial staff. 5 master's degrees and 5 Ph.D.'s awarded 1955-59. 2 graduate students registered fall 1959.

Political Science. — International Relations. American government (national, state, and local); political theory; comparative European governments; international law, organization, and relations; public administration; politics and public policy; public law. Prerequisites for graduate study: 18 semester credits of political science beyond introductory courses; 2 years of 1 foreign language. 9 professorial staff. 13 master's degrees and 5 Ph.D.'s awarded 1955-59. 17 graduate students registered fall 1959.

Psychology. Experimental, clinical. Prerequisites for graduate study: 18 semester credits of psychology beyond introductory courses; college algebra; statistics; 2 years of 1 foreign language; GRE or MAT. 9 professorial staff. 5 master's degrees and 18 Ph.D.'s awarded 1955-59. 36 graduate students registered fall 1959.

Romance Languages and Literatures. French and Spanish. Prerequisite for graduate study: minimum of 18 semester hours beyond sophomore courses in either French or Spanish. Ph.D. candidacy prerequisite: reading knowledge of German and Latin. 7 professorial staff. 10 master's degrees and 3 Ph.D.'s awarded 1955-59. 14 graduate students registered fall 1959.

Sociology. Sociology, criminology. Prerequisites for graduate study: 18 semester credits of sociology beyond beginning courses; 2 years of 1 foreign language. 5 professorial staff. 9 master's degrees and 5 Ph.D.'s awarded 1955-59. 16 graduate students registered fall 1959.

Zoology, Physiology, and Veterinary Science. Offered by Department of Zoology and Anatomy. Prerequisites for graduate study: 18 semester credits of zoology beyond introductory course; 2 years of 1 foreign language. 9 professorial staff.

11 master's degrees and 11 Ph.D.'s awarded 1955-59. 21 graduate students registered fall 1959.

New Hampshire, University of

DURHAM, NEW HAMPSHIRE

The Graduate School

Graduate instruction has been offered since 1893, and the first Ph.D. was conferred in 1896. The Graduate School was established in 1903 and reorganized in 1928, offering work at the master's level. Doctoral programs were reestablished later, and in 1957 Ph.D. degrees were again awarded. University is publicly controlled by the state. Both men and women are admitted.

One small residence hall is maintained for single graduate students; married graduate students eligible for accommodations in university-owned housing facilities.

Special facilities include: outstanding chemistry laboratories; excellent field and laboratory facilities for work in marine zoology; greenhouse and experimental farm facilities for botany and horticulture. Library contains approximately 270,000 volumes.

Residence requirement for Ph.D.: 3 years beyond bachelor's degree, of which a minimum of 1 full academic year must be spent in residence on campus.

ADMISSION REQUIREMENTS

For graduate study: bachelor's degree; cumulative GPA of not less than 2.5; achievement test in some cases. Recommended: GRE. For candidacy for Ph.D.: completion of substantial portion of course work with A or B grades; reading knowledge of 2 foreign languages (usually selected from French, German, and Russian); preliminary qualifying examinations; approval of dissertation subject.

Apply to Dean of the Graduate School by September 1 for fall semester; by January 1 for spring semester.

FEES AND FIRST-YEAR AID

No application fee. Tuition for state residents $380 per academic year; others $700. Special fees approximate $12 annually. Room (in dormitory) $200 per academic year. Approximate annual cost of board in college dining room $300. Apartments $35-$40 per month.

First-year aid available: 20 tuition scholarships; research assistantships, $1,600 plus tuition exemption; teaching assistantships, $1,600 plus tuition exemption. Total number of research and teaching assistantships varies from year to year, but averages about 60.

Apply to Dean of the Graduate School by March 1 or earlier.

FIELDS OF STUDY FOR THE PH.D.

Botany. Plant physiology and pathology. 8 professorial staff. 8 master's degrees and 4 Ph.D.'s awarded 1955-59. 7 graduate students registered fall 1959.

Chemistry. Organic, inorganic, physical. 10 professorial staff. 35 master's degrees and 8 Ph.D.'s awarded 1955-59. 35 graduate students registered fall 1959.

Horticulture. Prerequisites for graduate study: chemistry and plant science courses equivalent to those required for a major in horticulture. 5 professorial staff. 5 master's degrees and 2 Ph.D.'s awarded 1955-59. 5 graduate students registered fall 1959.

Zoology. Marine biology, physiology, taxonomy of various groups, parasitology, animal ecology, histology. Prerequisites for graduate study: 2 years of zoology; suitable training in botany, chemistry, mathematics, and physics. 9 professorial staff. 26 master's degrees and 1 Ph.D. awarded 1955-59. 25 graduate students registered fall 1959.

New Mexico Highlands University

LAS VEGAS, NEW MEXICO

Division of Graduate Studies

Graduate instruction at the master's level has been offered since 1930. Beginning in 1960, a new Ph.D. program in biophysical chemistry will be offered. Master's work in the related areas has been carried on for about 8 years with approximately 30 graduate students regularly enrolled. University is publicly controlled by the state. Both men and women are admitted.

University dormitory rooms available for single students; apartments for married students.

The Institute of Scientific Research has complete research facilities which are used by graduate staff and students. The Institute also works closely with the Division of Graduate Studies to provide graduate assistantships, consultants, and senior staff for lecture and seminar purposes. By cooperative agreement, certain facilities of the Los Alamos Scientific Laboratory are also available. Special laboratories for biophysics and biochemistry are provided. Library contains approximately 62,000 volumes.

Residence requirement for Ph.D.: 2 years; 24 quarter hours of graduate credit may be transferred from other institutions provided it is of A or B quality.

ADMISSION REQUIREMENTS

For graduate study: bachelor's degree; GPA of 2.85; fitness for graduate study in chosen field; approval by department, the Director, and Graduate Committee; 2 years of 1 foreign language; preliminary qualifying examinations in major fields. Recommended: GRE. For candidacy for Ph.D.: reading knowledge of 2 foreign languages (French, German, Russian); completion of at least half of course work; candidacy examination.

Apply to Office of Admissions 30 days prior to matriculation. All pertinent data should accompany application.

FEES AND FIRST-YEAR AID

No application fee; $5 matriculation fee after admission. Tuition for state residents $165 per year; others $270. Room (in dormitory) $255 per year; combined fee for room and board $770. Apartments $60 per month (includes utilities except electricity).

First-year aid available: approximately 10 tuition scholarships; approximately 30 research assistantships, $65 per month plus room, board, and tuition.

Apply to Director, Institute of Scientific Research, by April 1 for fall term.

FIELDS OF STUDY FOR THE PH.D.

Biophysical Chemistry. Biophysics, biochemistry, molecular biology. Offered by Departments of Biology, Chemistry, Physics, and Mathematics. Prerequisites for graduate study: major in chemistry or physics; minors in the other field and in biology; mathematics through calculus. 14 professorial staff. Ph.D. program begun 1960.

New Mexico Institute of Mining and Technology

SOCORRO, NEW MEXICO

Department of Graduate Study

Graduate work at the master's level has been offered since 1948. The program leading to the Ph.D. in geophysics was established in 1953, and the first Ph.D. was awarded in 1956. Institute is publicly controlled by the state. Both men and women are admitted.

Rooms in regular residence halls available for single graduate students; apartments for married students.

Library of approximately 39,000 volumes contains special library for the research and development division, consisting of domestic and foreign books, manuscripts, and journals in the fields of physics, geophysics, chemistry, and mathematics.

Residence requirement for Ph.D.: equivalent of 3 full years of study and research; amount of graduate credit which may be transferred from other institutions individually determined.

ADMISSION REQUIREMENTS

For graduate study: bachelor's degree; superior academic record indicating capacity for advanced study and research. Recommended: GRE. For candidacy for Ph.D.: B average in all graduate work; examination in German and 1 other foreign language; comprehensive examination; participation in graduate earth-science club; preliminary work on dissertation subject.

Apply to head of Department of Graduate Study, Campus Station, by March 1. Later applications considered if possible.

FEES AND FIRST-YEAR AID

No application fee. Tuition for state residents $110 per year; others $310. Special fees approximate $58 annually. Room with board $600 per year minimum. Apartments $33-$47 a month.

First-year aid available: 20 research assistantships, $1,700-$3,500. Part-time employment and ⅓-time research assistantships may also be arranged for graduate students.

Apply to head of the Department of Graduate Study, Campus Station, by March 1.

FIELDS OF STUDY FOR THE PH.D.

Geophysics. Physics of the earth; atmospheric physics; ground-water hydrology; certain aspects of geochemistry, geology, and extractive metallurgy. 21 professorial staff. 11 master's degrees and 1 Ph.D. awarded 1955-59. 29 graduate students registered fall 1959.

New Mexico State University

UNIVERSITY PARK, NEW MEXICO

The Graduate School

Although graduate instruction has been offered at the university since 1895, doctoral programs have been introduced quite recently. The Graduate School was organized in 1956, and the first Ph.D. awarded in 1960. The D.Sc. (with a major in one of the fields of engineering) is also conferred. Institution is publicly controlled by the state. Both men and women are admitted.

Rooms in college dormitories available for single graduate students; university-owned apartments for married students.

Special facilities include: physical science laboratory; research center; library of approximately 112,000 volumes. Proximity to White Sands Missile Range offers unusual opportunities for study in related fields.

Residence requirement for Ph.D.: 3 years of full-time study beyond bachelor's degree. 1 academic year after completion of 30 semester hours and 1 foreign language examination must be taken in residence at New Mexico State University. Summer and evening courses available.

ADMISSION REQUIREMENTS

For graduate study: bachelor's degree; satisfaction of departmental requirements. Recommended: GRE; MAT. For candidacy for Ph.D.: qualifying examinations in major and minor fields; examinations in 2 foreign languages; comprehensive preliminary examination; thesis subject approval

Apply to Dean of the Graduate School at least 1 month prior to registration. Transcripts in duplicate should be included with application.

FEES AND FIRST-YEAR AID

No application fee. Tuition for state residents $180 per academic year; others $360. Room (in dormitory) $180 per year. Approximate annual cost of board in college dining room $440. Apartments $30-$59 a month.

First-year aid available: about 20 teaching fellowships, $1,900-$2,500 (½-time for 9 months); about 15 research assistantships, $1,900-$2,500 (½-time for 9 months).

Apply to Dean of the Graduate School before April 1.

FIELDS OF STUDY FOR THE PH.D.

Mathematics. Algebra, topology, functional analysis. Prerequisite for graduate study: 12 hours above calculus. Recommended: 1 foreign language. 10 professorial staff. Ph.D. program initiated 1956. 66 master's degrees awarded 1955-59. 71 graduate students registered fall 1959.

Physics. Theoretical physics, solid-state physics and low-temperature phenomena, electromagnetic radiation. Prerequisites for graduate study: 16 semester hours of upper-division physics; 2 years of 1 foreign language. 10 professorial staff. Ph.D. program initiated 1956. 11 master's degrees awarded 1955-59. 51 graduate students registered fall 1959.

New Mexico, University of

ALBUQUERQUE, NEW MEXICO

The Graduate School

The Graduate School was founded in 1917 and has jurisdiction over all graduate programs. The first Ph.D. was awarded in 1947. The degrees of D.Sc. in Engineering and Ed.D. are also conferred. The university is publicly controlled by the state. Both men and women are admitted.

Separate residence halls maintained for graduate men and women; limited number of university-owned apartments available for married students (others are under construction).

Special facilities include: library of approximately 300,000 volumes; affiliation with Los Alamos Graduate Center for work in biology, chemistry, engineering, mathematics, and physics; affiliation with Los Alamos Scientific Laboratory for dissertation research in biology, chemistry, engineering, or physics; a special technical development program in engineering (conducted jointly with the Sandia Corporation); special contract research programs in various departments; proximity of various Southwestern anthropological sites; extensive microfilm acquisitions from Spanish and Mexican archives; bilingual programs serving teachers of Indian children.

Residence requirement for Ph.D.: 3 years beyond bachelor's degree. A minimum of 2 successive regular semesters (during which at least 12 semester hours shall be completed) must be spent in full-time residence study at the University of New Mexico. This requirement must be satisfied following completion of the master's degree. Summer and evening courses available.

ADMISSION REQUIREMENTS

For graduate study: bachelor's degree; overall average of B. Recommended: GRE and MAT; preparation in foreign languages. For candidacy for Ph.D.: master's degree or completion of 30 semester hours of graduate work (at least 6 of which must be taken in residence at the University of New Mexico); B average in all graduate work; qualifying examination; reading knowledge of 2 foreign languages; written and oral comprehensive examinations in major and minor fields; approval of thesis topic; recommendation of Committee on Graduate Studies and Graduate Dean.

Apply to Dean of the Graduate School by August 15 for fall semester; by January 1 for spring session; by May 15 for summer session.

FEES AND FIRST-YEAR AID

Transfer application fee $5. Tuition for state residents $246 per academic year; others $476. Special fees approximate $39 annually. Room (in dormitory) and board $724 per academic year (combined charge only). Apartments $68 per month.

First-year aid available: 6 tuition scholarships for foreign students; 13 fellowships, $1,800; numerous graduate assistantships allocated departmentally, $1,800.

Apply to Dean of the Graduate School by February 1.

FIELDS OF STUDY FOR THE PH.D.

Anthropology. Archaeology, ethnology, social anthropology, linguistics. Prerequisites for graduate study: at least 12 semester hours of advanced work in anthropology; GRE. 6 professorial staff. 12 master's degrees and 4 Ph.D.'s awarded 1955-59. 16 graduate students registered fall 1959.

Area Studies.—American. American literature, fine arts, and philosophy; American history, education, social thought, and institutions. Candidate emphasizes either American history or literature. Interdepartmental program administered by a permanent Committee on American Studies with membership drawn from cooperating departments. Prerequisite for graduate study: master's degree in history, English, education, sociology, political science, philosophy, or economics; strong preparation in history and English. 30 professorial staff. 6 Ph.D.'s awarded 1955-59. 5 graduate students registered fall 1959.

Area Studies.—Ibero-American. History of Latin America (Colonial or national), Brazilian or Spanish-American literature, a related field. Offered by Departments of History and Modern and Classical Languages. Prerequisites for graduate study: equivalent of a major in Spanish, inter-American affairs, or history; minimum of 15-18 hours of lower-division Spanish or equivalent experience. 7 professorial staff. Program begun 1959. 11 graduate students registered fall 1959.

Botany or Zoology. In botany: ecology, microbiology, morphology, taxonomy. In zoology: ichthyology, invertebrate mammalogy, physiology. Offered by Department of Biology. Prerequisites for graduate study: major in botany or zoology; 1 year of biology, including 1 semester each of invertebrate zoology, plant morphology, and physiology; 12 hours of upper-division undergraduate courses. 11 professorial staff. 26 master's degrees and 8 Ph.D.'s awarded 1955-59. 40 graduate students registered fall 1959.

Chemistry. Inorganic, organic, physical. Prerequisites for graduate study: 8 semester hours each of general, analytical, and physical chemistry; 10 semester hours of organic chemistry; 1 year of physics; mathematics through calculus; GRE during first year. Recommended: 2 years of German; second year physics; advanced calculus; 1 year French or Russian. 8 professorial staff. 6 master's degrees and 20 Ph.D.'s awarded 1955-59. 45 graduate students registered fall 1959.

Education. Foundations of education, curriculum and instruction, administration and supervision, pupil personnel services. Interdepartmental program offered by College of Education under direction of the Graduate School. Prerequisites for graduate study: broad general education background; major or minor in subject field; GRE; MAT. Ph.D. admission prerequisite: personal appearance before the Education Doctorate Committee; letters of recommendation; examples of graduate writing; some teaching experience and/or school administration. 22 professorial staff. Ph.D. program begun 1957. 297 master's degrees awarded 1955-59. 269 graduate students registered fall 1959. Ed.D. also awarded in this field; usually no language requirement for Ed.D.

English. British or American literature, linguistics. Department of English, which offers this program, also participates in American Studies program as a principal department. Prerequisites for graduate study: major in English; 2 years of a foreign language; GRE after entrance. Recommended: British history; classics. 13 professorial staff. 26 master's degrees and 12 Ph.D.'s awarded 1955-59. 44 graduate students registered fall 1959.

Geology. Mineralogy, petrology, structural or petroleum geology, sedimentology, stratigraphy, paleontology, micropaleontology, geomorphology, mineral deposits, petrography, aerial photography. Prerequisites for graduate study: 40 semester hours of geology; GRE Advanced Test in Geology. 7 professorial staff. Ph.D. program begun 1957. 31 master's degrees awarded 1955-59. 39 graduate students registered fall 1959.

History. United States: Southwest; Colonial America; Civil War. Latin America: Colonial Mexico; Latin America in the 20th century. Medieval Europe: Later Middle Ages. Early Modern Europe: Reformation; Enlightenment. Modern Europe: 20th century England; 20th century Russia. Department of History, which offers this program, also participates in American Studies and Ibero-American Studies programs. Prerequisites for graduate study: 30 semester hours of history; GRE. 9 professorial staff. 15 master's degrees and 5 Ph.D.'s awarded 1955-59. 42 graduate students registered fall 1959.

Mathematics. Analysis, algebra, applied mathematics, differential equations, summability theory, statistics. Offered by Department of Mathematics and Astronomy. Prerequisites for graduate study: 1 year each of modern algebra, advanced calculus, and advanced geometry; 1 semester of foundations; GRE during first year.

Recommended: 1 semester of topology. 13 professorial staff. Ph.D. program begun 1956. 11 master's degrees awarded 1955-59. 86 graduate students registered fall 1959.

Physics. Cosmic rays, nuclear or atmospheric physics, magnetohydrodynamics. Prerequisites for graduate study: major in physics or equivalent; GRE; departmental qualifying examination. 6 professorial staff. 20 master's degrees and 3 Ph.D.'s awarded 1955-59. 94 graduate students registered fall 1959.

Psychology. General experimental, physiological, or engineering psychology. Training in clinical psychology available (not clinical program as established by American Psychological Association). Prerequisites for graduate study: 12 semester hours of advanced work in psychology; GRE and MAT. 6 professorial staff. Ph.D. program begun 1960. 15 master's degrees awarded 1955-59. 22 graduate students registered fall 1959. New enrollment limited to 3

Spanish. Spanish literature or philology; Spanish-American, Portuguese and Brazilian, or French literature. Offered by Department of Modern and Classical Languages. Department also participates in program in Ibero-American Studies. Prerequisites for graduate study: major in Spanish; GRE during first year. Ph.D. candidacy prerequisites: French, German, and Latin in addition to Spanish. 9 professorial staff. 25 master's degrees and 6 Ph.D.'s awarded 1955-59. 39 graduate students registered fall 1959.

New School for Social Research

NEW YORK 11, NEW YORK

Graduate Faculty of Political and Social Science

Graduate Faculty in the New School for Social Research provides a program of advanced and integrated studies in the social sciences which has been offered since 1933. Scheduling of classes is designed to facilitate part-time graduate instruction. Programs lead to the degrees of M.A., Ph.D., and Master and Doctor of Social Science. The New School is privately controlled and nonsectarian. Both men and women are admitted.

No residence facilities are provided.

Residence requirement for Ph.D.: 60 points of graduate credit, of which at least 30 must be taken in residence at the New School for Social Research. Summer and evening courses available.

ADMISSION REQUIREMENTS

For graduate study: bachelor's degree in the liberal arts or sciences; satisfactory academic grades; specific training in field of proposed graduate study. For candidacy for Ph.D.: completion of 45 points of graduate work with grades averaging no lower than B; written qualifying examinations in several areas of major field; reading knowledge of 2 foreign languages.

Apply to Admissions Office, Graduate Faculty of Political and Social Science, New School for Social Research, 66 West 12th Street, New York 11, New York, by September 5 for fall term; by January 10 for spring term.

FEES AND FIRST-YEAR AID

No application fee. Tuition $35 per point (or $1,050 a year for full program of 30 points). Special fees approximate $14 per year.

First-year aid available: 40 institutional and contributed scholarships, full or part-time tuition; 5 teaching fellowships, $1,800-$2,200; grants-in-aid for full or partial tuition.

Apply to Chairman, Scholarship Committee, Graduate Faculty of Political and Social Science, New School for Social Research, 66 West 12th Street, New York 11, New York, by April 1.

FIELDS OF STUDY FOR THE PH.D.

Economics. Economic theory, econometrics, labor, international economics, economic history. 22 professorial staff. 39 master's degrees and 12 Ph.D.'s awarded 1955-59. 289 graduate students registered fall 1959.

Philosophy. History of philosophy, phenomenology, systematic philosophy. 9 professorial staff. 9 master's degrees and 1 Ph.D. awarded 1955-59. 173 graduate students registered fall 1959.

Philosophy—Psychology. This is a joint program. Degree must be taken in either philosophy or in psychology.

Political Science. Political philosophy, history of political thought, political institutions and government, international relations. 9 professorial staff. 30 master's degrees and 8 Ph.D.'s awarded 1955-59. 163 graduate students registered fall 1959.

Psychology. Experimental (learning and perception), social, motivation, or personality psychology. Prerequisite for graduate study: 15 credits of psychology. 8 professorial staff. 103 master's degrees and 14 Ph.D.'s awarded 1955-59. 230 graduate students registered fall 1959.

Sociology. Sociological theory, history of sociological thought. 10 professorial staff. 54 master's degrees and 23 Ph.D.'s awarded 1955-59. 280 graduate students registered fall 1959.

New York, State University of

ALBANY 1, NEW YORK

The State University of New York consists of 28 units of higher education distributed throughout the State of New York. It is publicly controlled by the state. Both men and women are admitted.

Programs leading to the Ph.D. degree are offered through the State University College of Forestry at Syracuse, the Downstate Medical Center in Brooklyn, and the Upstate Medical Center at Syracuse. The programs offered by these institutions are described below. *See also* Alfred University for a program leading to the Ph.D. in Ceramics offered by the State University College of Ceramics at Alfred. Also offered are: the Ed.D. degree (through the New York State College for Teachers at Albany) and the Med.Sc.D. in psychiatry (through the Downstate Medical Center in Brooklyn).

Residence requirement for Ph.D.: usually 2 or 3 years beyond bachelor's degree, of which at least 1 year must be taken in residence at institution awarding degree.

College of Forestry

Graduate instruction has been offered since 1911, and the first Ph.D. was awarded in 1918.

Residence facilities at Syracuse University may be used by graduate students of the State University College of Forestry. Summer and evening courses may be taken at Syracuse University, but not at the College of Forestry.

ADMISSION REQUIREMENTS

For graduate study: bachelor's degree; fitness for advanced study in chosen field. For candidacy for Ph.D.: reading knowledge of 2 foreign languages or 1 foreign language plus knowledge of statistics.

Apply to Associate Dean for Graduate Studies, State University College of Forestry at Syracuse, Syracuse 10, New York, at any time.

FEES AND FIRST-YEAR AID

No application fee. No tuition for residents of New York State; $300 per year for nonresidents. Special fees approximate $220 annually.

First-year aid available: 4 out-of-state tuition scholarships; 28 teaching fellowships, $1,500-$1,700 (for 9 months); 25 to 30 other fellowships, $2,100-$3,000 (for 12 months).

Apply to Associate Dean for Graduate Studies, State University College of Forestry at Syracuse, Syracuse 10, New York, by March 1.

FIELDS OF STUDY FOR THE PH.D.

Biological Sciences. Forest pathology, mycology, tree physiology, plant and animal ecology, genetics, forest entomology, insect physiology, invertebrate and vertebrate zoology, soil fauna, wildlife management. Offered by Departments of Forest Botany, Forest Entomology, and Forest Zoology. Recommended for graduate study: major in forestry or biological sciences. 20 professorial staff. 30 master's degrees and 11 Ph.D.'s awarded 1955-59. 28 graduate students registered fall 1959.

Physical Sciences. Chemistry of cellulose, wood and plant materials, polymer and macromolecular chemistry, paper and fiber chemistry, wood technology, and wood physics. Offered by Departments of Forest Chemistry, Pulp and Paper Technology, and Wood Products Engineering. Recommended for graduate study: major in physical sciences. 29 professorial staff. 69 master's degrees and 36 Ph.D.'s awarded 1955-59. 61 graduate students registered fall 1959.

Resource Management. Forest administration, mensuration, photogrammetry, silviculture forest tree improvement, forest soils, forestry economics, world forestry. Offered by Departments of Forestry Economics, Forest Management, Silviculture, and Landscape Architecture. Prerequisite for graduate study: major in forestry or biological sciences. 17 professorial staff. 46 master's

degrees and 10 Ph.D.'s awarded 1955-59. 38 graduate students registered fall 1959.

Downstate Medical Center

Unit has offered graduate instruction since 1956, and the first Ph.D. was awarded in 1960.

No residence facilities provided for graduate students.

Special facilities include: laboratory space; use of medical school's library, cafeteria, health services, etc.

Elective courses may be taken during the summer session.

ADMISSION REQUIREMENTS

For graduate study: bachelor's degree; good scholastic accomplishment; good character recommendations. For candidacy for Ph.D.: reading knowledge of 2 foreign languages (usually French, German, Russian); preliminary comprehensive examinations.

Apply to Director of Graduate Program at Downstate Medical Center, State University of New York, Brooklyn 3, New York, before July 1.

FEES AND FIRST-YEAR AID

No application fee. Tuition $200 for 12 months. Apartments in community rent for approximately $100 per month.

First-year aid available: teaching fellowships, $2,500-$3,000; other fellowships, $2,500-$3,000.

Apply to Director of Graduate Program, Downstate Medical Center, State University of New York, Brooklyn 3, New York, or to departmental chairman, as early as possible (with application for admission).

FIELDS OF STUDY FOR THE PH.D.

Anatomy. Growth and differentiation, analytical morphology, endocrinology, tissue culture and transplantation, functional neuroanatomy, hematology, human genetics. Prerequisites for graduate study: 6 hours of general biology or morphology; 1 advanced course in biology; mathematics through calculus; 8 hours of general chemistry; 6 hours of organic chemistry; college physics; qualitative analysis. Recommended: quantitative analysis; statistics. 10 professorial staff. Ph.D. program begun 1956. 1 master's degree awarded 1955-59. 4 graduate students registered fall 1959. Total enrollment limited to 6.

Bacteriology — Microbiology — Immunology. Infection, allergy, morphological and functional differences in major divisions of plant and animal kingdoms, ecological differences, techniques of field and laboratory investigations. Offered by Department of Microbiology and Immunology. Prerequisites for graduate study: major in biology, chemistry, or physics; 12 hours of biology; 4 hours of physical chemistry with laboratory work. 10 professorial staff. Ph.D. program begun 1956. 1 graduate student registered fall 1959. Total enrollment limited to 6.

Biochemistry. Peptide synthesis, intermediate metabolism of proteins and amino acids, metabolism of heme and related compounds, mineral metabolism, enzymes, membrane equilibria. Prerequisites for graduate study: 4 hours each of inorganic chemistry, qualitative analysis, elemental quantitative analysis, and qualitative organic chemistry; 10 hours each of organic and physical chemistry. Recommended: college physics; mathematics through calculus; statistics. 6 professorial staff. Ph.D. program begun 1956. 4 graduate students registered fall 1959. Total enrollment limited to 6-12.

Pharmacology. Mechanics of drug action, drug action at cellular level, pharmacology of cardiovascular system, pharmacology of muscle, biochemical aspects of drug action on electrophysiological phenomena. Prerequisites for graduate study: mathematics through calculus; 14 hours of chemistry (through organic and quantitative analysis); physical chemistry; physics; biology. 10 professorial staff. Ph.D. program begun 1956. 6 graduate students registered fall 1959. Total enrollment limited to 6-12.

Physiology. Neurophysiology, respiratory and cardiac physiology, endocrinology, medical physics, history of physiology. Prerequisites for graduate study: 12 hours of inorganic and organic chemistry and qualitative analysis; physics; mathematics through calculus; 12 hours of biology. Recommended: quantitative analysis; physical chemistry; qualitative organic chemistry; statistics; genetics; embryology; comparative anatomy. 14 professorial staff. Ph.D. program begun 1956. 1 master's degree awarded 1955-59. 6 graduate students registered fall 1959. Total enrollment limited to 6-12.

Physiology and Biophysics. Medical physics, electronics, ultrasonics, instrumentation. Offered by Department of Physiology. Prerequisites for graduate study: about the same as for entrance into medical school, with strength in physics, electronics, and mathematics. Recommended: statistics; biology. 14 professorial staff. Ph.D. program begun 1956. 1 master's degree awarded 1955-59. 1 graduate student registered fall 1959. Total enrollment limited to 6.

Upstate Medical Center

Graduate instruction (as part of State University) began in 1954, and first Ph.D. was awarded in 1958.

No residence facilities provided. Medical center facilities and facilities of Syracuse University are available to graduate students.

ADMISSION REQUIREMENTS

For graduate study: bachelor's degree. For candidacy for Ph.D.: reading knowledge of 2 foreign languages or competence in 1 foreign language and knowledge of statistics; qualifying examination.

Apply to Graduate School Office, Upstate Medical Center, State University of New York, Syracuse 10, New York, preferably by March 1.

FEES AND FIRST-YEAR AID

No application fee. Tuition $200 per academic year. Student activity fee $15-$20.

First-year aid available: 10 teaching fellowships, $2,000-$2,400; 6 to 8 other fellowships, $2,000-$3,300.

Apply to chairman of appropriate department, Upstate Medical Center, State University of New York, Syracuse 10, New York, by March 1.

FIELDS OF STUDY FOR THE PH.D.

Anatomy. Chemical studies in speciation, cytochemistry, development of behavior, developmental physiology, electron microscopy, experimental embryology, experimental neurology. Prerequisites for graduate study: 16 hours of chemistry; 6 hours each of biology, physics, English, and 1 foreign language. Recommended: additional training in physics, mathematics, chemistry, and biology. 7 professorial staff. 3 graduate students enrolled fall 1959. Total enrollment limited to 6.

Biochemistry. Nutrition, lipids, metabolic pathways, hemoglobin biosynthesis, choline interrelationships, insulin, thyroxin, steroids. Recommended for graduate study: B.S. in chemistry. Ph.D. candidacy prerequisites: 2 foreign languages; statistics. 9 professorial staff. 3 Ph.D.'s awarded 1955-59. 6 graduate students registered fall 1959.

Medical Microbiology. Medical bacteriology, virology, and parasitology. Offered by Department of Microbiology. Prerequisite for graduate study: adequate preparation in biology, general bacteriology, physics, and chemistry. 5 professorial staff. Ph.D. program begun 1955. 1 master's degree awarded 1955-59.

Pharmacology. Action of drugs on living matter; enzyme adaptations in mammals; obesity problem; renal and cardiac physiology and pharmacology; drug metabolism; relation of lipids to cell function; behavioral pharmacology. Prerequisites for graduate study: background in chemistry, biology, and physics; 1 foreign language. Recommended: statistics; physical chemistry; advanced organic chemistry. 6 professorial staff. Ph.D. program begun 1956. 2 Ph.D.'s awarded 1955-59. 4 graduate students registered fall 1959. New enrollment limited to 2.

Physiology. Neurophysiology, cardiovascular physiology, and renal physiology. Prerequisite for graduate study: major in biology or physics (engineering acceptable). Recommended: about 2 years of German, French, or Spanish. 5 professorial staff. 1 master's degree and 2 Ph.D.'s awarded 1955-59. 4 graduate students registered fall 1959. Total enrollment limited to 4.

New York University

NEW YORK 3, NEW YORK

The university received its charter in 1831. It is privately controlled and nonsectarian. Three separate units award the Ph.D.: the Graduate School of Arts and Sciences; the Graduate School of Business Administration; and the School of Education. Other doctorates conferred by the university include: J.S.D. (School of Law); D.Eng.S. (College of Engineering); Ed.D.

(School of Education); Med.Sc.D. (College of Medicine).

Graduate School of Arts and Sciences

The Graduate School of Arts and Sciences was established in 1886, and the first Ph.D. was awarded in 1887.

Dormitory space available for some graduate women and a very limited number of graduate men. No on-campus residence facilities provided for married students. Residence Bureau recommends rooms and apartments in community.

Special facilities include: library of approximately 1,100,000 volumes; language laboratories; Maison Française. Urban setting makes possible active collaboration with such institutions as the Metropolitan Museum of Art and the American Museum of Natural History. Unique research programs are conducted at the Institute of Fine Arts, the Institute of Mathematical Sciences, and the Research Center for Human Relations.

Residence requirement for Ph.D.: minimum of 3 years beyond bachelor's degree, of which at least 1 year must be spent in residence at New York University. Summer and evening courses available.

ADMISSION REQUIREMENTS

For graduate study: bachelor's degree; major or minor, with B average, in proposed field of study; letters of recommendation. Recommended: GRE. For candidacy for Ph.D.: completion of substantial portion of course work; reading knowledge of 2 foreign languages (usually French and German); preliminary examinations; departmental approval.

Apply to Committee on Admissions, Graduate School of Arts and Sciences, New York University, New York 3, New York, at least 1 month prior to opening of term.

FEES AND FIRST-YEAR AID

No application fee. Tuition $40 per point ($1,200 a year for full program). Special fees approximate $60 annually. Room (in dormitory) $270-$500 per academic year. Students may purchase meals in university cafeteria.

First-year aid available: approximately 20-25 full-tuition scholarships.

Apply to Dean, Graduate School of Arts and Sciences, New York University, New York 3, New York, by March 1.

FIELDS OF STUDY FOR THE PH.D.

Courses in the methodology of teaching are offered through the School of Education for those interested in a career of college teaching. Departmental assistantships offer opportunity to teach under supervision.

American Civilization. Development or state of society, institutions, thought and culture in America. Combined program offered by Departments of English, Philosophy, History, Government, Economics, Sociology, Journalism, Fine Arts, and Music. Prerequisite for graduate study: preparation in American subjects. 11 master's degrees and 8 Ph.D.'s awarded 1955-59. 56 graduate students registered fall 1959.

Anatomy. Gross anatomy, histology (microanatomy), neurology. Prerequisites for graduate study: 1 year each of mathematics and physics; 2 years of chemistry (including organic); general biology; comparative anatomy; embryology. Recommended: general physiology and genetics; calculus; physical chemistry. 8 professorial staff. 3 master's degrees and 6 Ph.D.'s awarded 1955-59. 6 graduate students registered fall 1959.

Biology. Biophysical or endocrine physiology, cytophysiology and cytochemistry, experimental vertebrate morphogenesis, protozoology. Prerequisites for graduate study: 3 years of biology; 1 year each of physics and mathematics; organic chemistry; French or German. Recommended: calculus and physical chemistry. 22 professorial staff. 85 master's degrees and 54 Ph.D.'s awarded 1955-59. 282 graduate students registered fall 1959.

Chemistry. Inorganic, organic, and physical chemistry; analytical chemistry, including microchemistry. Prerequisites for graduate study: 1 year each (with laboratory) of elementary chemistry (which may include qualitative analysis), quantitative analysis, organic and physical chemistry, calculus (preferably through differential equations); at least 1 course each in physics and German. 21 professorial staff. 46 master's degrees and 46 Ph.D.'s awarded 1955-59. 216 graduate students registered fall 1959.

Classics. Literature, ancient history, linguistics. Combined program in linguistics and comparative literature offered by Department of

Classics with other departments. Prerequisites for graduate study: general knowledge of classical civilization; reasonable competence in translating Latin or Greek prose and poetry. 8 professorial staff. 3 master's degrees and 2 Ph.D.'s awarded 1955-59. 8 graduate students registered fall 1959.

Comparative Literature. Program instituted by the language departments and approved by Committee on Comparative Literature. Prerequisites for graduate study: reading knowledge of 1 or 2 foreign languages. Ph.D. candidacy prerequisite: reading knowledge of 3 foreign languages (ancient or modern). Program initiated 1957. 8 graduate students registered fall 1959.

Economics. Economics theory and history of economics theories, statistics, economics and financial history, labor problems and social legislation, monopolies, business organization and marketing methods, public utilities or finance, money and banking, international economic relations. Prerequisite for graduate study: major in economics (or in another social science or business administration with a minor in economics). 21 professorial staff. 85 master's degrees and 17 Ph.D.'s awarded 1955-59. 204 graduate students registered fall 1959.

English. All fields of English and American literature; special strength in Renaissance, Milton, Age of Johnson, contemporary American novel, drama, poetry. Combined program with other departments in linguistics and comparative literature. 23 professorial staff. 163 master's degrees and 25 Ph.D.'s awarded 1955-59. 483 graduate students registered fall 1959.

Fine Arts. History of art from classical times to modern, including Far East; history of archaeology. Offered by Institute of Fine Arts. Prerequisite for graduate study: knowledge of general history of art and familiarity with chosen period. Recommended: languages necessary for work in special area of study. 17 professorial staff. 50 master's degrees and 14 Ph.D.'s awarded 1955-59. 97 graduate students registered fall 1959.

Geology. Stratigraphy, geophysics, micropaleontology, petrology, structural or petroleum geology, photogeology, paleontology. Prerequisites for graduate study: 28 points in geology; 1 year in each of 2 (chemistry, physics, biology); 1 year of mathematics. Recommended: ecology; botany; statistical methods for those specializing in micropaleontology. 9 professorial staff. 29 master's de-

grees awarded 1955-59. 58 graduate students registered fall 1959.

German. Literature and philology. Combined program in linguistics and comparative literatures with other language departments. Prerequisites for graduate study: grammar and composition; history of German literature. 6 professorial staff. 9 master's degrees and 6 Ph.D.'s awarded 1955-59. 33 graduate students registered fall 1959.

Government. Political behavior; political theory and philosophy; public administration, policy, or law; comparative government; international relations and world affairs; area studies. 27 professorial staff. 70 master's degrees and 24 Ph.D.'s awarded 1955-59. 221 graduate students registered fall 1959.

History. Europe (including England) from fall of Rome to 1500, Europe since 1500, England since 1485, early America and United States to 1828, United States since 1828, Latin America, modern Far East, urban-business history. Prerequisites for graduate study: major in history or 18 points supplemented by work in other social sciences. 19 professorial staff. 89 master's degrees and 24 Ph.D.'s awarded 1955-59. 260 graduate students registered fall 1959.

Mathematics. Analysis, applied mathematics, geometry, algebra, numerical analysis and computing, probability and statistics. Prerequisite for graduate study: advanced calculus. 33 professorial staff. 99 master's degrees and 62 Ph.D.'s awarded 1955-59. 587 graduate students registered fall 1959.

Meteorology and Oceanography. Climatology, atmospheric radiation, turbulence and physics, wave motions, hydrometeorology, cyclogenesis, hydrography. Prerequisite for graduate study: good background in mathematics and physics. 9 professorial staff. 5 master's degrees and 12 Ph.D.'s awarded 1955-59. 15 graduate students registered fall 1959.

Music. Musicology. Prerequisites for graduate study: knowledge of history of music; competence in harmony, counterpoint, orchestration, and analysis of the larger forms. Recommended: French; German; Latin; Italian. 5 professorial staff. 21 master's degrees and 7 Ph.D.'s awarded 1955-59. 38 graduate students registered fall 1959.

Pathology. General pathology, special and histological, neuropathology. Prerequisite for

graduate study: premedical or predental background. 12 professorial staff. 2 graduate students registered fall 1959.

Philosophy. Metaphysics, existentialism, Marxism, philosophy of history. Prerequisite for graduate study: knowledge of history of philosophy. 6 professorial staff. 22 master's degrees and 5 Ph.D.'s awarded 1955-59. 61 graduate students registered fall 1959.

Physics. Theoretical or solid-state physics, electrical distribution in gases, nuclear reactors or instrumentation, cosmic radiation, microwaves, relativity, fluid dynamics, photoconductivity, X-rays, properties of thin films, collision problems in theoretical physics, field theory, nuclear structure. Prerequisites for graduate study: major in physics; calculus and ordinary differential equations. 27 professorial staff. 63 master's degrees and 49 Ph.D.'s awarded 1955-59. 252 graduate students registered fall 1959.

Physiological Sciences. Biochemistry, microbiology, pharmacology, physiology, industrial toxicology. Offered by Departments of Biochemistry, Microbiology, Physiology and Pharmacology of the College of Medicine and Departments of Physiology and Biochemistry of the College of Dentistry. Prerequisite for graduate study: premedical or predental program. 27 professorial staff. 22 master's degrees and 18 Ph.D.'s awarded 1955-59. 17 graduate students registered fall 1959.

Psychology. General experimental, social and industrial, clinical and counseling psychology. Prerequisites for graduate study: 12 points in psychology, including 1 year of experimental; GRE Aptitude and Advanced Psychology Test; MAT. 50 professorial staff. 23 master's degrees and 82 Ph.D.'s awarded 1955-59. 275 graduate students registered fall 1959.

Public Administration. Administrative theory and practice, organization and method analysis, financial or personnel administration, labor and social security administration, international and comparative public administration, law enforcement and correctional administration; fiscal policy; planning and housing, public relations. Prerequisite for graduate study: work in government, political science, or social science. 24 professorial staff. 5 Ph.D.'s awarded 1955-59. 86 graduate students registered fall 1959.

Romance Languages and Literatures. French, Spanish, Italian, Portuguese, comparative Romance literature. Combined program offered by Department of Romance and Slavic Languages and Literatures with other language departments. Prerequisite for graduate study: competence in and knowledge of literature of appropriate language, and knowledge of the language itself. 13 professorial staff. 18 master's degrees and 7 Ph.D.s awarded 1955-59. 112 graduate students registered fall 1959.

Slavic Languages and Literatures. Russian language and literature. Offered by Department of Romance and Slavic Languages and Literatures. Prerequisite for graduate study: competence in and knowledge of literature and language. 2 professors. Program begun 1960.

Sociology and Anthropology. Sociological theory, social psychology or organization, cultural anthropology, applied sociology, cultures and peoples of Africa and Southeast Asia. 15 professorial staff. 36 master's degrees and 18 Ph.D.'s awarded 1955-59. 105 graduate students registered fall 1959.

Graduate School of Business Administration

The Graduate School of Business Administration was established in 1920, and awarded its first Ph.D. in 1938.

Nichols Hall, the new home of the division, was dedicated on January 27, 1960. It is air conditioned and incorporates the latest advances in educational construction, including a library, seminar rooms, classrooms, student lounges, and the faculty, and administrative offices of the school. Residence facilities are available at Washington Square.

Residence requirement for Ph.D.: 72 points of approved graduate courses, of which a minimum of 40 points must be completed at the Graduate School of Business Administration. Summer and evening courses available.

ADMISSION REQUIREMENTS

For graduate study: bachelor's degree; high scholastic average. Recommended: Admission Test for Graduate Study in Business. For candidacy for Ph.D.: foreign language examination; statistics examination; written and oral qualifying examinations in major and minor fields; approval of dissertation topic.

Apply to Chairman, Admissions Committee, Graduate School of Business Administration, New York University, 100 Trinity Place, New York 6, New York, prior to August 30 for fall semester; prior to January 1 for spring semester.

FEES AND FIRST-YEAR AID

Application fee $10. Tuition $80 for 2-point graduate courses; $160 for 4-point courses. Special fees approximate $20 annually.

First-year aid available: part-tuition scholarships of $2,500; teaching fellowships, $500-$2,500; other fellowships, $1,750-$3,600; research assistantships, $750-$1,880.

Apply to Chairman, Scholarship Committee, Graduate School of Business Administration, New York University, 100 Trinity Place, New York 6, New York, at the earliest possible date prior to term for which application is made.

FIELDS OF STUDY FOR THE PH.D.

Business Administration. Accounting, corporation finance and investments, economic and financial history, economic theory and history of economic thought, management, international finance and business, labor problems and industrial relations, domestic marketing, money and banking, public finance, public utilities and transportation, real estate and land economics, statistics, taxation, political economy, language. Offered by Departments of Accounting, Banking, Economics, Management, and Marketing. 135 professorial staff. 2,713 master's degrees and 91 Ph.D.'s awarded 1955-59. 5,200 graduate students registered fall 1959.

School of Education

Graduate study in education was offered by the School of Pedagogy about 1887. The name was formally changed to the present in 1920. Residence facilities are the same as those provided for the Graduate School of Arts and Sciences.

Special facilities include: statistical laboratory; science laboratory; home economics laboratory.

Residence requirement for Ph.D.: 3 years beyond bachelor's degree, of which 27 points must be taken under the auspices of the School of Education (full-time residence or study not required). Summer and evening courses available.

ADMISSION REQUIREMENTS

For graduate study: bachelor's or master's degree; B average. Recommended: GRE. For candidacy for Ph.D.: reading knowledge of 2 modern foreign languages or 1 language and statistics; comprehensive preliminary examination; departmental approval.

Apply to Committee on Admissions, School of Education, New York University, 100 Washington Square East, New York 3, New York, at least 3 months prior to date of desired entry.

FEES AND FIRST-YEAR AID

No application fee. Tuition $40 per point. University fee $15 per semester.

First-year aid available: limited number of scholarships; teaching fellowships with stipends up to $1,200.

Apply to Assistant Dean, School of Education, 100 Washington Square East, New York University, New York 3, New York, at least 6 months prior to date of desired entry.

FIELDS OF STUDY FOR THE PH.D.

Education. General administration of public school systems; adult, art, business, early childhood and elementary, English, higher, international relations, integrated, music, nurse, religious, safety, science, speech, vocational, or industrial arts education; communications in education; dramatic art; educational psychology or sociology; foreign language; guidance and personnel administration; Hebrew culture and education; history of physical, health, and recreation education; home economics; human relations; mathematics; philosophy of education; and physical therapy; secondary-school service; junior high school; senior high school; social studies and history; arts and crafts; occupational therapy; vocational rehabilitation.

North Carolina College at Durham

DURHAM, NORTH CAROLINA

The Graduate School

The Graduate School was organized in 1939. A program leading to the Ph.D. in Education was established in 1951, and the first degree was awarded in 1955. On this program there is close cooperation between North Carolina College and the University of North Carolina, including sharing of the university faculty with the college. Institution is publicly controlled by the state. Both men and women are admitted.

Graduate women live in new graduate dormitory; rooms in college dormitories available for graduate men. A section of the men's dormitory is reserved for married students, but no children are permitted.

Special facilities include: Bureau of Educational Research; statistics laboratory; audiovisual laboratory and recording unit; extensive facilities for training guidance workers and counselors; library of approximately 118,000 volumes.

Residence requirement for Ph.D.: 6 semesters of full-time work, of which 1 full academic year must be taken in residence at North Carolina College at Durham. Summer and evening courses available.

ADMISSION REQUIREMENTS

For graduate study: bachelor's degree; GRE. For candidacy for Ph.D.: master's degree; B average for at least 20 semester hours of graduate work in education; certification by major department; presentation of certificates of proficiency in 2 foreign languages; removal of any special conditions.

Apply to Dean of the Graduate School at least 30 days in advance of date of desired admission.

FEES AND FIRST-YEAR AID

No application fee. Tuition for state residents $130.50 a year; others $500. Special fees approximate $68.50 annually. Room (in dormitory) $110 per year. Approximate annual cost of board in college dining room $275.

First-year aid available: 15 research assistantships, $500-$600.

Apply to Dean of the Graduate School at any time.

FIELDS OF STUDY FOR THE PH.D.

Education. Supervision and administration, guidance, educational psychology, history and theory of education, elementary or secondary education. 8 professorial staff. 265 master's degrees and 3 Ph.D.'s awarded 1955-59. 75 graduate students registered fall 1959.

North Carolina State College

RALEIGH, NORTH CAROLINA

The Graduate School

State College is one of three divisions of the Consolidated University of North Carolina. Each branch of the Consolidated Graduate School is administered by a graduate dean who works in close association with the vice president in charge of graduate studies and research. Graduate instruction at State College, which has been offered since 1893, is organized to provide opportunity and facilities for advanced study and research in the fields of agriculture, engineering, forestry, technological education, and textiles. However, the full resources of the Consolidated University of North Carolina are available to all graduate students enrolled in any of the three branches of the Graduate School. Institution is publicly controlled by the state. Both men and women are admitted.

Rooms in dormitories available for single graduate students; a limited number of special apartment units for married students. No residence facilities provided for single women.

Special facilities include: Agricultural Experiment Station; Department of Engineering Research; Institute of Statistics; computing facilities including UNIVAC and IBM 650. Affiliation with Oak Ridge Institute of Nuclear Studies provides additional opportunities for research. Library of approximately 195,000 volumes includes special collections on entomology, textiles, design, architecture, engineering technology, agriculture and allied sciences.

Residence requirement for Ph.D.: 6 full semesters beyond bachelor's degree; at least 1 full year in continuous residence at the Consolidated University of North Carolina. Summer courses available.

ADMISSION REQUIREMENTS

For graduate study (with full standing): bachelor's degree; B average in major field. GRE or National Teachers Examination required for provisional admission. For candidacy for Ph.D.: reading knowledge of scientific literature in 2 modern foreign languages; qualifying comprehensive examinations (written and oral); approval of examining committee.

Apply to Dean of the Graduate School, North Carolina State College, 30 days in advance of date admission is desired.

FEES AND FIRST-YEAR AID

No application fee. Tuition for state residents $150 per academic year; others $500. Special fees approximate $136 per year. Room (in dormitory) for men $170 per academic year. Approximate annual cost of board in college dining room $500. Apartments $45-$70 a month.

First-year aid available: 259 teaching fellowships and research assistantships, $2,000-$2,400; 11 grants-in-aid, $1,000-$4,800.

Apply to Dean of the Graduate School, North Carolina State College, at any time.

FIELDS OF STUDY FOR THE PH.D.

Agricultural Economics. Theory, policy, farm management, land economics, marketing, economic development, and econometrics. 10 professorial staff. 18 master's degrees and 10 Ph.D.'s awarded 1955-59. 37 graduate students registered fall 1959.

Animal Industry. Animal nutrition, pathology, breeding, or husbandry; dairy husbandry, bacteriology, chemistry, or manufacturing; physiology of reproduction and lactation, rumen physiology; animal parasitology. Prerequisite for graduate study: bachelor's degree in bacteriology, dairy technology, chemistry, mathematics, animal science. Recommended: fundamental courses in mathematics, chemistry, physics, and biology. 31 professorial staff. 38 master's degrees and 20 Ph.D.'s awarded 1955-59. 51 graduate students registered fall 1959.

Botany and Bacteriology. Plant physiology, morphology, ecology, and systematic botany. 10 professorial staff. 10 master's degrees and 1 Ph.D. awarded 1955-59. 10 graduate students registered fall 1959.

Engineering.—Agricultural. Power and machinery, rural structures, soil and water conservation, rural electrification, agricultural processing. Prerequisite for graduate study: bachelor's degree in agricultural engineering. 6 professorial staff. Ph.D. program begun 1957. 14 master's degrees and 1 Ph.D. awarded 1955-59. 16 graduate students registered fall 1959.

Engineering.—Ceramic. Electrical ceramics, glass, vitreous enamels and coatings, structural clay products, refractories, whitewares, and materials associated with nuclear reactor and missile programs. Offered by Department of Mineral Industries. Prerequisite for graduate study: bachelor's degree in ceramic engineering or equivalent. 8 professorial staff. 5 master's degrees and 2 Ph.D.'s awarded 1955-59. 7 graduate students registered fall 1959.

Engineering.—Chemical. Fluid dynamics, heat transfer, distillation, diffusion, physical properties of binary liquid systems, liquid-liquid extraction, solid-liquid contacting. Prerequisite for graduate study: major in chemical engineering or allied area such as chemistry, metallurgy, or nuclear engineering. 6 professorial staff. 18 master's degrees and 7 Ph.D.'s awarded 1955-59. 18 graduate students registered fall 1959.

Engineering.—Civil. Sanitary engineering, soil mechanics, foundation engineering, structural engineering, and transportation engineering. Prerequisite for graduate study: B.S. in civil engineering. 10 professorial staff. Ph.D. program begun 1957. 18 master's degrees awarded 1955-59. 31 graduate students registered fall 1959.

Engineering.—Electrical. Electronics, automatic control, computers, power systems, electric network synthesis, and advanced electromagnetic theory. Prerequisites for graduate study: major in engineering or physics: Recommended: major in electrical engineering. 6 professorial staff. 19 master's degrees and 2 Ph.D.'s awarded 1955-59. 30 graduate students registered fall 1959.

Engineering.—Mechanical. Thermal sciences, including classical thermodynamics, heat transfer and transport phenomena, statistical thermodynamics, gas dynamics (aerothermochemistry, aerothermodynamics); mechanical sciences, such as principles of fluid motion, dynamics of compressible flow and viscous fluids, vibrations, mechanical transients, stress analysis, and applied mechanics. Prerequisite for graduate study: major in engineering. 15 professorial staff. Ph.D. program begun 1960. 19 master's degrees awarded 1955-59. 18 graduate students registered fall 1959.

Entomology. Taxonomy, toxicology, ecology, applied entomology. Prerequisite for graduate study: fundamental training in chemistry, mathematics, and biological science. Recommended: GRE. 13 professorial staff. 11 master's degrees and 9 Ph D 's awarded 1955-59. 15 graduate students registered fall 1959.

Field Crops. Plant breeding, weed control, forage crop production and crop production.

Prerequisite for graduate study: degree in agronomy, field crops, botany, biology, or related field. Recommended: chemistry through organic; mathematics through calculus. 25 professorial staff. 15 master's degrees and 11 Ph.D.'s awarded 1955-59. 28 graduate students registered fall 1959.

Forestry. Wood technology, silvics, genetics, forest management. Recommended for graduate study: bachelor's degree in forestry. 10 professorial staff. 32 master's degrees and 1 Ph.D. awarded 1955-59. 28 graduate students registered fall 1959.

Genetics. Cytology and cytogenetics, physiological and irradiation genetics, forest genetics, population genetics, and the application of quantitative genetics to breeding methodology. Prerequisites for graduate study: major in biology or agriculture. 10 professorial staff. 3 master's degrees and 8 Ph.D.'s awarded 1955-59. 15 graduate students registered fall 1959.

Physics. Nuclear physics, reactor theory. The Ph.D. is offered in both engineering physics and nuclear engineering. Prerequisite for graduate study: B.S. in engineering or physics. 12 professorial staff. 77 master's degrees and 7 Ph.D.'s awarded 1955-59. 46 graduate students registered fall 1959.

Plant Pathology. Fundamental work in phytopathology, including diseases caused by fungi, bacteria, nematodes, and viruses. Prerequisite for graduate study: basic training in biology. Recommended: GRE. 19 professorial staff. 9 master's degrees and 10 Ph.D.'s awarded 1955-59. 20 graduate students registered fall 1959.

Sociology.—Rural. Program includes study of a number of social sciences and students are required to take approximately 15 semester hours in the Department of Sociology at the University of North Carolina, Chapel Hill. 4 professorial staff. 4 master's degrees and 1 Ph.D. awarded 1955-59. 9 graduate students registered fall 1959.

Soils. Soil chemistry, physics, fertility, morphology, and microbiology. Prerequisites for graduate study: good background in basic sciences, including mathematics, physics, chemistry, and biological sciences; at least 16 semester hours in soils. 15 professorial staff. 13 master's degrees and 15 Ph.D.'s awarded 1955-59. 20 graduate students registered fall 1959

Statistics.—Experimental. Statistical genetics, sample survey theory and designs, experimental design, response surface studies, and econometrics. Prerequisite for graduate study: undergraduate calculus. Recommended: undergraduate (or master's) degree in mathematics, statistics, or some applied field. 15 professorial staff. 20 master's degrees and 24 Ph.D.'s awarded 1955-59. 33 graduate students registered fall 1959.

Zoology. Animal ecology and wildlife science. Prerequisite for graduate study: B.S. in some phase of biological sciences. 7 professorial staff. 11 master's and 1 Ph.D. awarded 1955-59. 11 graduate students registered fall 1959.

North Carolina, University of

CHAPEL HILL, NORTH CAROLINA

The Graduate School

Because this institution is a part of the Consolidated University of North Carolina, it is known also as the University of North Carolina at Chapel Hill. Graduate instruction has been offered since 1876, and the first Ph.D. was awarded in 1883. The Graduate School was organized in 1903 and now offers numerous Ph.D. programs. Programs leading to the Ed.D. and D.P.H. degrees are offered through the Schools of Education and Public Health, respectively. Institution is publicly controlled by the state. Both men and women are admitted.

Separate residence halls are maintained for single graduate students; married students eligible for apartments in university-owned housing development.

Special facilities include: library of 1,000,000 volumes; computation center; numerous institutes.

Residence requirement for Ph.D.: 6 semesters beyond bachelor's degree, of which 2 consecutive semesters must be taken in residence at the university. Summer courses available.

ADMISSION REQUIREMENTS

For graduate study: bachelor's degree; GPA of B or better in field of proposed graduate study; GRE. For candidacy for Ph.D.: approximately 40 semester hours of graduate study in major field and 18-24 in minor; examinations in 2 modern foreign languages; 2 years of resident graduate study; preliminary oral examination.

Apply to Dean of the Graduate School at least 30 days prior to date of desired entrance.

FEES AND FIRST-YEAR AID

No application fee. Tuition for state residents $150 per academic year; others $500. Special fees approximate $94 annually. Room (in residence hall) for men $171.50 per year; for women $220 a year. Approximate annual cost of board in college dining room $400-$480. Apartments in older prefabricated buildings $19-$35 per month; in new permanent apartments $60-$70.

First-year aid available: 10 scholarships, $2,100 plus tuition; approximately 400 teaching fellowships, $1,000-$2,000; approximately 30 other fellowships, $1,000-$3,000; approximately 100 research assistantships, $500-$2,500.

Apply to the Dean of the Graduate School by February 15.

FIELDS OF STUDY FOR THE PH.D.

Courses in the methodology of teaching offered in the School of Education. One summer course also available. There are also regular non-credit meetings of part-time instructors during the academic year.

Anthropology. Ethnology (with special emphasis on Latin America, Africa, Middle East, and South Asia); archaeology; linguistics. Offered by Department of Sociology and Anthropology. 26 professorial staff. 33 master's degrees and 25 Ph.D.'s awarded 1955-59. 15 graduate students registered fall 1959.

Bacteriology and Immunology. Bacterial physiology and metabolism, immunology, virology, medical mycology, clinical microbiology, allergic and infectious diseases. 6 professorial staff. 6 master's degrees and 2 Ph.D.'s awarded 1955-59. 12 graduate students registered fall 1959.

Biochemistry and Nutrition. Isolation of nucleic acids, proteins, and enzymes; metabolism of nucleic acids; metabolism of amino acids and proteins; synthesis and metabolism of phospholipids; antimetabolites; mechanism of calcification of bones and teeth; oxidative phosphorylation; mechanism of action of enzymes; mechanism of action of steroid hormones; isolation of factors concerned in the clotting of blood. 8 professorial staff. 1 master's degree and 1 Ph.D. awarded 1955-59. 14 graduate students registered fall 1959.

Botany. Mycology, plant physiology, cytology, anatomy and morphology, taxonomy, algology. 7 professorial staff. 8 master's degrees and 10 Ph.D.'s awarded 1955-59. 26 graduate students registered fall 1959.

Business Administration. Accounting, industrial management, marketing, personnel, finance, operations research, statistics. Joint program offered by School of Business Administration and Department of Economics. Prerequisite for graduate study: admission test or graduate study in business or GRE. 42 professorial staff. 112 master's degrees and 1 Ph.D. awarded 1955-59. 68 graduate students registered fall 1959.

Chemistry. Organic, inorganic, physical, or analytical chemistry; chemical physics. 17 professorial staff. 10 master's degrees and 34 Ph.D.'s awarded 1955-59. 74 graduate students registered fall 1959.

Chemistry.—Pharmaceutical. Offered by the School of Pharmacy. 4 professorial staff. 17 graduate students registered fall 1959 (including those in pharmacy).

Classics. Latin, Greek. 8 professorial staff. 3 master's degrees and 5 Ph.D.'s awarded 1955-59. 25 graduate students registered fall 1959.

Comparative Literature. Ancient or medieval literature; modern literatures of continental Europe, England, and America. Offered by Curriculum in Comparative Literature. Prerequisite for graduate study: broad undergraduate preparation in language. 6 professorial staff. 2 master's degrees and 1 Ph.D. awarded 1955-59. 7 graduate students registered fall 1959.

Economics. Economic theory, econometrics, economic history, international economics, labor, monetary theory, public finance, public policy, statistics, Soviet economics, economic fluctuations. Joint program offered by Department of Economics and School of Business Administration. 42 professorial staff. 8 master's degrees and 14 Ph.D.'s awarded 1955-59. 35 graduate students registered fall 1959.

Education. Elementary education, secondary education, administration and supervision, guidance and personnel, educational psychology, history and comparative education. Offered by School of Education. Prerequisites for graduate study: Ohio Psychological Test; Cooperative English Test; Class A teaching certificate for State of North Carolina. 34 professorial staff. 293 master's degrees and 26 Ph.D.'s awarded

1955-59. 350 graduate students registered fall 1959. Ed.D. degree also offered in this field.

English. Old English and Middle English language and literature, the Renaissance, English literature of the 17th and 18th centuries, English literature of the Romantic and Victorian periods, American literature, British and American literature of the 20th century. Prerequisite for Ph.D. candidacy: examination in Latin. 25 professorial staff. 108 master's degrees and 22 Ph.D.'s awarded 1955-59. 131 graduate students registered fall 1959.

French. Linguistics, medieval studies, modern literature. Offered by Department of Romance Languages. 16 professorial staff (combined with Spanish). 12 master's degrees and 14 Ph.D.'s awarded 1955-59. 42 graduate students registered fall 1959 (French and Spanish).

Geography. Urban, regional, and economic. Offered by Department of Geology and Geography. 10 professorial staff. 3 master's degrees and 2 Ph.D.'s awarded 1955-59. 6 graduate students registered fall 1959.

Geology. Mineralogy, petrology, geomorphology, stratigraphy, paleontology, structural geology, economic geology, geophysics. Offered by Department of Geology and Geography. 10 professorial staff. 13 master's degrees and 2 Ph.D.'s awarded 1955-59. 23 graduate students registered fall 1959.

German. Germanic linguistics and literature. Offered by Department of Germanic Language. 7 professorial staff. 3 Ph.D.'s awarded 1955-59. 11 graduate students registered fall 1959.

History. Ancient and medieval, modern European, English history with related work in European history, United States history, Latin-American history with related work in United States history, Russian history. 21 professorial staff. 47 master's degrees and 35 Ph.D.'s awarded 1955-59. 83 graduate students registered fall 1959.

Industrial Relations. Offered by Curriculum in Industrial Relations. Prerequisite for graduate study: major in psychology, economics and business administration, political science, sociology and anthropology, history, or education. 7 professorial staff. 4 master's degrees and 1 Ph.D. awarded 1955-59. 5 graduate students registered fall 1959.

Linguistics. Historical and comparative linguistic in Indo-European languages, structural linguistics. Offered by Curriculum in Linguistics.

Prerequisite for graduate study: broad preparation in languages. 9 professorial staff. 2 Ph.D.'s awarded 1955-59. 3 graduate students registered fall 1959.

Mathematics. Applied mathematics (including digital computing), differential equations, analysis, topology, algebra, number theory. 24 professorial staff. 40 master's degrees and 12 Ph.D.'s awarded 1955-59. 60 graduate students registered fall 1959.

Music. Musicology. Prerequisites for graduate study: GRE; diagnostic test in music. 8 professorial staff. 22 master's degrees and 6 Ph.D.'s awarded 1955-59. 26 graduate students registered fall 1959.

Pharmacy. Offered by School of Pharmacy. 7 professorial staff. 3 master's degrees and 9 Ph.D.'s awarded 1955-59. 17 graduate students registered fall 1959 (including pharmaceutical chemistry).

Philosophy. History of philosophy, area of epistemology and metaphysics, value theory (including ethics and aesthetics), logic, existential, and phenomenological philosophy. 6 professorial staff. 2 master's degrees and 4 Ph.D.'s awarded 1955-59. 29 graduate students registered fall 1959.

Physics. Experimental physics: certain areas of solid-state physics, low-temperature physics, molecular spectroscopy, nuclear physics, and cosmic rays. Theoretical physics: certain areas of solid-state theory, theory of nuclear structure, quantum field theory, and general relativity. 10 professorial staff. 7 master's degrees and 12 Ph.D.'s awarded 1955-59. 46 graduate students registered fall 1959.

Political Science. Government and politics in the United States, public administration, foreign and comparative government, international affairs, political theory and jurisprudence. 16 professorial staff. 25 master's degrees and 16 Ph.D.'s awarded 1955-59. 35 graduate students registered fall 1959.

Psychology. General-experimental, clinical, personality-social psychology; psychometrics. Prerequisites for graduate study: GRE; MAT. 22 professorial staff. 24 master's degrees and 22 Ph.D.'s awarded 1955-59. 53 graduate students registered fall 1959. New enrollment limited to 20.

Public Health. Public health education, biostatistics, sanitary engineering, parasitology. Offered by School of Public Health. Prerequisites for graduate study: broad training in the natural and social sciences; at least 1 year of related experience. 44 professorial staff. 379 master's degrees and 10 Ph.D.'s awarded 1955-59. D.P.H. also offered in this field.

Sociology. Sociology and rural sociology. Offered by Department of Sociology and Anthropology. 26 professorial staff. 33 master's degrees and 25 Ph.D.'s awarded in the combined fields 1955-59. 50 graduate students registered in sociology fall 1959.

Spanish. Spanish American studies, linguistics, medieval studies, modern literature. Offered by Department of Romance Languages. 16 professorial staff (combined with French). 8 master's degrees and 9 Ph.D.'s awarded 1955-59. 42 graduate students registered fall 1959 (French and Spanish).

Statistics. Theoretical statistics. Prerequisite for graduate study: advanced calculus. 7 professorial staff. 5 master's degrees and 17 Ph.D.'s awarded 1955-59. 50 graduate students registered fall 1959.

Zoology. General ecology, invertebrate zoology, cytology, embryology of invertebrates, cell physiology, hydrobiology, vertebrate zoology, genetics, marine ecology. 10 professorial staff. 16 master's degrees and 13 Ph.D.'s awarded 1955-59. 21 graduate students registered fall 1959.

North Dakota Agricultural College

FARGO, NORTH DAKOTA

The Graduate School

Graduate instruction at the master's level has been offered by the college since 1903. The Graduate School was organized in 1954, and the first Ph.D. programs approved in 1959. The institution is publicly controlled by the state. Both men and women are admitted.

Rooms in college dormitories available for single graduate students; brick and barracks-type apartment units and 2 trailer courts provided for married students.

Special facilities include: library of 130,000 volumes with special collections in chemistry, agriculture, engineering, home economics, and pharmacy; strong research facilities for work in plant sciences, chemistry, and animal science.

Residence requirement for Ph.D.: 3 years beyond bachelor's degree, of which 1 year beyond master's degree must be spent in residence at this college. Transfer of graduate credit arranged on individual basis by advisory committee. Summer and evening courses available.

ADMISSION REQUIREMENTS

For graduate study: bachelor's degree; GPA of 2.5; indications of ability to do high-quality advanced work. For candidacy for Ph.D.: reading proficiency in 2 foreign languages or proficiency in 1 language and 12 credits in course studies of direct value outside major or minors; comprehensive preliminary examination.

Apply to Office of Admissions and Records, or to Graduate Dean, before registration.

FEES AND FIRST-YEAR AID

Application fee $5. Tuition for state residents $120 per year; others $270. Special fees approximate $57 per year. Room (in dormitory) for men $195 per year; for women $180. Approximate annual cost of board in college dining room $600. Apartments $37-$80 a month.

First-year aid available: a number of scholarships with variable stipends; approximately 25 teaching fellowships, $1,500-$2,000; approximately 12 research assistantships, $1,500 (for 9 months) or $2,400 (for 12 months). Grants-in-aid in variable amounts also available.

Apply to chairman of appropriate department by March 15.

FIELDS OF STUDY FOR THE PH.D.

Three programs, each earning 3 semester hours of credit, are being developed to acquaint graduate students with teaching problems of the college instructor. These courses are designated as: Individual Appraisal Techniques; Higher Education in the United States; and Student Personnel Services.

Animal Science. Animal breeding, production, or nutrition. Offered by the Departments of Animal Industry, Dairy Husbandry, Poultry Husbandry, Veterinary Science, and Zoology. Prerequisite for graduate study: major in the animal sciences or equivalent. 15 professorial staff. Ph.D. program initiated 1959. 11 master's degrees awarded 1955-59. 6 graduate students registered fall 1959.

Chemistry.—Agricultural. Biochemistry and organic chemistry. Offered by Departments of Agricultural and Biological Chemistry and Organic Chemistry. Prerequisites for graduate study: 60 credits in chemistry, including courses in inorganic, analytical, organic, and physical chemistry; 2 years of college mathematics; 1 year of physics; reading knowledge of scientific German. 11 professorial staff. Ph.D. program initiated 1959. 54 master's degrees awarded 1955-59. 20 graduate students registered fall 1959.

Chemistry.—Pharmaceutical. 6 professorial staff. Ph.D. program initiated 1959. 4 master's degrees awarded 1955-59. 3 graduate students registered fall 1959.

Entomology.—Agricultural. Taxonomy, morphology, ecology, transmission of diseases, applied entomology. Prerequisite for graduate study: minor work in biological sciences and chemistry. 6 professorial staff. Ph.D. program initiated fall 1959. 7 master's degrees awarded 1955-59. 5 graduate students registered fall 1959.

Plant Science. Agronomy; botany; range ecology or management; grassland ecology; plant breeding, pathology or physiology; crop production; soil fertility or chemistry. Prerequisite for graduate study: 24 credits in major field. 25 professorial staff. Offered by Departments of Botany, Plant Pathology, and Soils and Agronomy. Ph.D. program initiated 1959. 18 master's degrees awarded 1955-59. 10 graduate students registered fall 1959.

North Dakota, University of

GRAND FORKS, NORTH DAKOTA

The Graduate School

Graduate instruction has been offered at the University of North Dakota since 1908, and the first Ph.D. was awarded in 1912. The Graduate School was organized in 1925 and now offers numerous Ph.D. programs. Programs leading to the Ed.D. degree in the fields of general education, elementary education, secondary education, school administration, business education, and guidance and counseling are also offered. Institution is publicly controlled by the state. Both men and women are admitted.

Rooms in college dormitories available for single graduate students. Apartments for married students are also available and preference is given to graduate teaching assistants.

Special facilities include: library of approximately 150,000 volumes, including large collections on the state and region; cooperation of oil industry and State Geological Survey in development of graduate geology program; cooperation of Bureau of Economic Research with Department of Business Education; cooperation of Ireland Cancer Research Laboratory for graduate work in medical sciences.

Residence requirement for Ph.D.: 3 years, of which 1 must be taken in residence at University of North Dakota. Summer and evening courses available.

ADMISSION REQUIREMENTS

For graduate study: bachelor's degree; GPA of 1.75 on 3-point scale; satisfaction of department requirements. For candidacy for Ph.D.: reading tests in French and German (another modern foreign language may be substituted for 1 of these); B average on all graduate work attempted; diagnostic and comprehensive examinations; approval of dissertation topic.

Apply to Dean of the Graduate School at any time.

FEES AND FIRST-YEAR AID

Application fee $5. Incidental (tuition) fee for state residents $120 per academic year; others $270. Special fees approximate $65 per year. Room (in dormitory) for men $146-$182 per year; for women $146-$164. Approximate annual cost of board in college dining room $405. Apartments $35-$85 per month.

First-year aid available: 30 tuition scholarships for state residents; 68 teaching fellowships, $1,800 for master's candidates and $2,100 for doctoral candidates; 25 research assistantships, $1,800-$2,200; 1 $1,000 scholarship; 1 alumni fellowship of $1,000.

Apply to Dean of the Graduate School by March 15 for teaching fellowships; no closing date for other types of aid.

FIELDS OF STUDY FOR THE PH.D.

Anatomy. Gross or developmental anatomy, general histology, neuroanatomy, endocrinology, histochemistry. Offered by Department of Anatomy with support by Departments of Biochem-istry, Physiology, and Pathology. Prerequisites for graduate study: general zoology; comparative anatomy; vertebrate embryology; inorganic, qualitative, quantitative, and organic chemistry; college physics; mathematics through trigonometry; German. Recommended: GRE or Medical College Admission Test; physical chemistry; French. 5 professorial staff. 5 master's degrees and 1 Ph.D. awarded 1955-59. 10 graduate students registered fall 1959. New registration limited to 5.

Biochemistry. General biochemistry, lipid chemistry, enzymes. Offered by Department of Biochemistry with support from Departments of Physiology and Pharmacology, Bacteriology, and Chemistry. Prerequisites for graduate study: general, analytical, organic, and physical chemistry; biology; ACS Test for Biochemistry for students entering with master's degree. Recommended: French and German. 4 professorial staff. 9 master's degrees and 5 Ph.D.'s awarded 1955-59. 8 graduate students registered fall 1959. New registration limited to maximum of 6.

Biology. Ecology, entomology, systematic botany. Offered by Department of Biology with support from Departments of Chemistry, Physics, Mathematics, Geology, Basic Medical Sciences. Prerequisite for graduate study: 30 hours work in biology. Recommended: French or German or both. 4 professorial staff. 2 master's degrees awarded 1955-59. 3 graduate students registered fall 1959. New registration limited to 3 a year (until 1961).

Business Education. Offered by Department of Business Education with support from Departments of Education, Business Administration, and other related fields. Prerequisite for graduate study: 15 hours of work in business education or business administration. 2 professorial staff. Ph.D. program initiated 1959. 26 master's degrees awarded 1955-59. 21 graduate students registered fall 1959.

Chemistry. Inorganic, analytical, organic, physical. Offered by Department of Chemistry with support from Departments of Biochemistry, Mathematics, and Physics. Prerequisite for graduate study: major in chemistry; mathematics through calculus; 1 year of physics; German; entrance tests. Recommended: French or Russian; physical chemistry. 10 professorial staff. Ph.D. program initiated 1959. 19 master's degrees awarded 1955-59. 8 graduate students registered fall 1959.

Education. General, elementary, secondary education; school administration; guidance and counseling. Offered by Department of Education with support from Departments of Philosophy and Psychology. Prerequisite for graduate study: 15 hours in education, including practice teaching; experience in administration and/or teaching; MAT; GRE Aptitude and Advanced Test; 1 year of statistics. 8 professorial staff. 379 master's degrees and 5 Ph.D.'s awarded 1955-59. 90 graduate students registered fall 1959. Ed.D. degree also awarded in this field.

Geology. Invertebrate paleontology, geomorphology, stratigraphy, glacial or economic geology. Prerequisite for graduate study: courses in general geology, mineralogy, structural geology, Petrography, optical mineralogy, geomorphology, sedimentology, paleontology, stratigraphy; summer field course; 1 year of physics; 1 year of chemistry; trigonometry. Recommended: calculus; physical chemistry; reading knowledge of French, German, or Russian. 6 professorial staff. Ph.D. program initiated 1960. 8 master's degrees awarded 1955-59. 13 graduate students registered fall 1959. New enrollment limited to 5.

History. Ancient and medieval, modern European, or American (including Latin-American, Western, and Great Plains) history; economic, social, and cultural history of United States and Europe. Prerequisite for graduate study: 21 credits in history. Recommended: other social sciences. 7 professorial staff. 13 master's degrees and 1 Ph.D. awarded 1955-59. 10 graduate students registered fall 1959.

Physiology and Pharmacology. Physiology, pharmacology. Offered by Department of Physiology and Pharmacology with support from Departments of Biochemistry and Anatomy. Prerequisites for graduate study: general biology; comparative anatomy; vertebrate embryology; inorganic, qualitative, quantitative, organic chemistry; college physics; trigonometry. Recommended: calculus; physical chemistry; French or German. 6 professorial staff. 5 master's degrees and 1 Ph.D. awarded 1955-59. 3 graduate students registered fall 1959. New registration limited to 6.

Psychology. General, experimental, clinical psychology; counseling and guidance. Offered by Department of Psychology with support from Department of Education. Prerequisites for graduate study: 18 hours of psychology, including personality dynamics, statistics, and experimental psychology; 1 year each of biology and algebra; MAT; GRE Aptitude and Advanced Tests. Recommended: French or German; advanced biology. 11 professorial staff. 12 master's degrees and 2 Ph.D.'s awarded 1955-59. 32 graduate students registered fall 1959.

North Texas State College

DENTON, TEXAS

Graduate School

Graduate instruction has been offered since 1935 at the master's level. A Ph.D. program in music was established in 1950, and the first Ph.D. was awarded in 1956. A program leading to the Ed.D. degree is offered by the School of Education. University is publicly controlled by the state. Both men and women are admitted.

Rooms in college dormitories available for single graduate students; no university-owned facilities are maintained for married students.

Library of approximately 340,000 volumes contains special music encyclopedias, directories, dictionaries, music scores, sheet music (including the major operas, oratorios, operettas, and cantatas), and several thousand records.

Residence requirement for Ph.D.: 3 years (90 hours) beyond bachelor's degree, at least 60 hours of which must be taken in residence at North Texas State College. Summer courses and limited number of evening courses available.

ADMISSION REQUIREMENTS

For graduate study: master's degree or equivalent; proficiency in instrument or voice; extensive course background in music; preliminary examinations. For candidacy for Ph.D.: reading knowledge of French and German plus Latin or other languages as necessitated by subject of dissertation; successful completion of 1 semester of doctoral work; approval of plan of study.

Apply to Dean of the Graduate School at least 30 days before date of desired entry.

FEES AND FIRST-YEAR AID

No application fee. Tuition for state residents $150 per academic year; others $450. Room (in dormitory) and board $480 per academic year.

First-year aid available: 10 teaching fellowships with stipend of $1,440.

Apply to the Dean of the School of Music in April or May for fall term.

FIELDS OF STUDY FOR THE PH.D.

Course in methods for the improvement of college teaching is offered for students interested in college teaching as a career.

Music. Musicology, composition, and music theory. Offered by the School of Music through the Graduate School. Prerequisites for graduate study: preliminary examinations include music theory (harmony, counterpoint, canon, fugue, orchestration); music history; music literature; research (an essay on an announced subject); piano, vocal, or instrumental solo with all parts. 23 professorial staff. 173 master's degrees and 5 Ph.D.'s awarded 1955-59. 60 graduate students registered fall 1959.

Northwestern University

EVANSTON AND CHICAGO, ILLINOIS

The Graduate School

Graduate instruction has been offered at Northwestern since about 1893, and the first Ph.D. was awarded in 1896. The Graduate School was organized in 1910. Programs of study leading to the Ph.D. are available in all departments of the College of Liberal Arts and in all professional schools of the university, except Law. A program leading to the Ed.D. degree is also administered by the Graduate School. The D.Mus. is offered through the School of Music. University is privately controlled and nonsectarian. Both men and women are admitted.

Apartments available for a limited number of married graduate students; off-campus Housing Offices recommend accommodations in community for single and married graduate students.

Special facilities include: library of approximately 1,372,000 volumes, with special collections on Africa, Japanese politics and government of the 20th century, French Revolution, Horace, papers of Charles Dawes, Spanish plays; computing center with digital and analogue computers; Van de Graaff accelerator; observatory; gas dynamics laboratory; Ipatieff high-pressure and catalytic laboratory; audiology and speech correction clinics; television and radio studios; program of African studies; transportation center; center for metropolitan studies; materials science center.

Residence requirement for Ph.D.: minimum of 3 years beyond bachelor's degree with 3 consecutive quarters (1 academic year) in full-time continuous study at Northwestern. Summer courses and a few evening courses available.

ADMISSION REQUIREMENTS

For graduate study: bachelor's degree; standing in upper half of graduating class. Recommended: GRE; knowledge of 1 foreign language. For candidacy for Ph.D.: completion of at least 1 year of graduate work; reading knowledge of at least 1 foreign language (others required in many departments); qualifying examination; departmental approval.

Apply to the Graduate School at least 5 weeks before date of desired entry.

FEES AND FIRST-YEAR AID

No application fee. Tuition $900 per academic year. Health service fee $15 per quarter. Rooms (in community) $10-$15 per week. Approximate annual cost of board in college dining room $480. First-year aid available: scholarships (some for tuition only, others for tuition plus $300): fellowships, $1,400 plus tuition; teaching assistantships with varying stipends available in some departments.

Apply by March 1 to the Graduate School, except that applications for scholarships and assistantships in the Schools of Engineering, Medicine, Journalism, Music, and Business should be directed to the individual school.

FIELDS OF STUDY FOR THE PH.D.

Anthropology. Ethnology (emphasis on aesthetics), culture and personality, archaeology, comparative politics, Africa, Asia, and Indian America. Offered by Department of Anthropology and Interdisciplinary Program of African Studies. Recommended for graduate study: some preparation in social sciences. Ph.D. candidacy prerequisite: 2 foreign languages or 1 language and statistics. 7 professorial staff. 12 master's degrees and 13 Ph.D.'s awarded 1955-59. 18 graduate students registered fall 1959. Total enrollment limited to 25.

Art. History of art and architecture. Prerequisite for graduate study: good foundation in history of art and the liberal arts. 6 professorial staff. 17 master's degrees and 1 Ph.D. awarded 1955-59. 3 graduate students registered fall 1959. Combined program with School of Education leading to the Ed.D. is also offered.

Astronomy. Observational astrophysics, scintillation of starlight, stellar spectroscopy, emission-line stars. Offered by Department of Astronomy, Dearborn Observatory. Prerequisite for graduate study: major in astronomy, physics, or mathematics. 2 professorial staff. 1 Ph.D. awarded 1955-59. 1 graduate student registered fall 1959.

Biochemistry.—Medical. Action of hormones or of enzymes and antibiotics, mineral metabolism, biosynthesis of proteins, radiobiology, studies of metabolism using radioactive isotopes, organic preparations, physical biochemistry, structure and metabolism of complex lipids, other aspects of metabolism. Prerequisites for graduate study: 1 year each of physics. organic, and physical chemistry; mathematics through calculus; qualitative and quantitative inorganic chemistry; reading knowledge of 1 foreign language approved by department. Recommended: more than 1 year of organic chemistry. 6 professorial staff. 9 master's degrees and 4 Ph.D.'s awarded 1955-59. 13 graduate students registered fall 1959.

Biology — Botany — Zoology. Anatomy or physiology (plant and animal), bacteriology, biochemistry, embryology, endocrinology, ecology, entomology, genetics, parasitology, protozoology, phycology, taxonomy, virology. Combined program offered by Departments of Biological Sciences and Chemistry and the Chicago Museum of Natural History. Prerequisite for graduate study: good background in biology and in chemistry or mathematics. Ph.D. candidacy prerequisite: reading knowledge of 2 foreign languages. 14 professorial staff. 67 master's degrees and 16 Ph.D.'s awarded 1955-59. 29 graduate students registered fall 1959.

Business Administration. Finance, marketing, production, accounting, statistics, sales management, banking, industrial relations, administration, transportation, investment finance. Offered by School of Business. 60 professorial staff. 715 master's degrees and 19 Ph.D.'s awarded 1955-59. 587 graduate students registered fall 1959.

Chemistry. Analytical, inorganic, organic, or physical chemistry; biochemistry. Combined program in Chemical Physics offered with Department of Physics. Prerequisites for graduate study: general, analytical, organic, and physical chemistry; general physics; calculus. Ph.D. candidacy prerequisite: German plus French or Russian. 20 professorial staff. 33 master's degrees and 100 Ph.D.'s awarded 1955-59. 85 graduate students registered fall 1959.

Classics. Latin and Greek language and literature; Greek and Roman history. Combined program in ancient history offered with History Department; minor fields in related areas such as English, Romance languages, German literature, philosophy, art. Prerequisites for graduate study: background in classical literature and ancient history; Greek or Latin. Recommended: French or German. Ph.D. candidacy prerequisites: Greek and Latin; reading knowledge of French and German. 4 professorial staff. 6 master's degrees and 1 Ph.D. awarded 1955-59. 6 graduate students registered fall 1959.

Dentistry. Oral surgery, orthodontics, periodontics, pedodontics, prosthetic dentistry, bacteriology, chemistry, anatomy, dental materials, pathology, physiology, and pharmacology. Combined program offered by Departments of Oral Surgery, Orthodontics, Periodontics, Pedodontics, Prosthetic Dentistry, and Basic Science. Prerequisite for graduate study: baccalaureate or D.D.S. 24 professorial staff. 63 master's degrees awarded 1955-59. 50 graduate students registered fall 1959. Enrollment limited to 10 in orthodontics and 6 each in other fields.

Economics. Economic theory or development, history, public finance, money and banking, international trade, institutional organization and prices, labor economics, statistics and econometrics, economics of transportation. Doctoral candidates may elect 1 field from the other social sciences or from the School of Business. Combined programs with the Transportation Center and Program of African Studies. Prerequisites for graduate study: major in economics or another social science (high calibre students admitted with only introductory mathematics or a major in mathematics. Ph.D. candidacy prerequisite: reading knowledge of 2 foreign languages or competence in 1 language and training in mathematics through calculus. 17 professorial staff. 29 master's degrees and 10 Ph.D.'s awarded

1955-59. 37 graduate students registered fall 1959.

Education. School administration, elementary or secondary education, guidance and counseling, curriculum, educational psychology. Offered by the School of Education and the Graduate School. A cooperative program in the philosophy of education is offered with the Departments of Philosophy and Psychology in the College of Liberal Arts. Special programs for liberal arts graduates lead to the master's degree. 18 professorial staff plus those in liberal arts. 883 master's degrees and 84 Ph.D.'s awarded 1955-59. Ed.D. degree is also awarded. 139 graduate students registered fall 1959.

Engineering. — Chemical. Thermodynamics, transport properties, fluid mechanics, heat transfer, applied reaction kinetics. Prerequisites for graduate study: major in engineering or physical sciences; strong background in chemistry, physics, and mathematics. Ph.D. candidacy prerequisite: reading proficiency in German or Russian. 9 professorial staff. 30 master's degrees and 21 Ph.D.'s awarded 1955-59. 41 graduate students registered fall 1959. New enrollment limited to approximately 25.

Engineering.—Civil. Structural engineering or mechanics, fluid or soil mechanics, transportation and traffic, planning, sanitary engineering, water resources. Cooperative programs with Departments of Theoretical and Applied Mechanics and Department of Science Engineering. Prerequisite for graduate study: major in engineering. 16 professorial staff. 100 master's degrees and 9 Ph.D.'s awarded 1955-59. 52 graduate students registered fall 1959.

Engineering.—Electrical. Antennas, communication circuits, microwaves, electrophysiology, control systems, information and data processing, computers, logical design, machinery, network synthesis and analysis, power-system analysis, semiconductors, information theory, magnetic amplifiers, tube and high-vacuum research, properties of solid state. Prerequisite for graduate study: major in engineering. Ph.D. candidacy prerequisite: 2 foreign languages (French, German, Russian). 10 professorial staff. 71 master's degrees and 22 Ph.D.'s awarded 1955-59. 132 graduate students registered fall 1959.

Engineering.—Industrial. Operations research and management science, information systems analysis and design, work study, processing and automation. Offered by Department of Industrial Engineering, Technological Institute. 8 professorial staff. Ph.D. program begun 1958. 6 master's degrees awarded 1955-59. 19 graduate students registered fall 1959.

Engineering.—Mechanical. Thermodynamics, heat transfer, gas dynamics, aerothermochemistry, transport phenomena, stress analysis, elasticity, kinematics, dynamics and vibrations, controls and instrumentation, theoretical and applied mechanics, statistical mechanics, rehology, viscoelasticity, magnetohydrodynamics, plasma physics, aerothermoelasticity. Prerequisite for graduate study: B.S. in engineering, physics, chemistry, mathematics, or astronomy. Ph.D. candidacy prerequisite: German or Russian and 1 other appropriate foreign language. 14 professorial staff. 46 master's degrees and 12 Ph.D.'s awarded 1955-59. 50 graduate students registered fall 1959.

Engineering.—Nuclear. Use of pulsed neutron techniques in the solution of reactor design problems, reactor theory, applied mathematics. Offered by Department of Engineering Sciences. Prerequisite for graduate study: B.S. in engineering, science, or mathematics. 4 professorial staff. Program begun 1959. 2 graduate students registered fall 1959.

Engineering.—Theoretical and Applied Mechanics. Mechanics of solids and fluids, theory of elasticity, structural mechanics, fluid dynamics, experimental stress analysis. Offered by Departments of Civil and Mechanical Engineering. Ph.D. candidacy prerequisite: German and another foreign language (usually French). 13 professorial staff. 3 master's degrees and 3 Ph.D.'s awarded 1955-59. 2 graduate students registered fall 1959.

English. Chaucer and Middle English literature; Renaissance and 17th century, 18th or 20th century, English Romantic, or Victorian literature; American literature; linguistics and history of the language. Ph.D. candidacy prerequisite: 2 foreign languages (usually French and German). 22 professorial staff. 139 master's degrees and 44 Ph.D.'s awarded 1955-59. 91 graduate students registered fall 1959.

Geography. Regional geography of Anglo-America, Latin America, Asia, Europe, or Africa; economic, urban, transportation, or political geography; physiography; cartography. Combined program offered by Department of Geography, Program of African Studies, and the Transportation Center. Prerequisite for graduate study: training in geography, including 1 year each in physical and economic geography. Recommended: 1 year mathematics; at least 1 course in statistics; 2 years of a foreign language. Ph.D. candidacy prerequisites: 2 foreign languages or 1 language and an advanced course in statistics. 7 professorial staff. 47 master's degrees and 19 Ph.D.'s awarded 1955-59. 23 graduate students registered fall 1959.

Geology. Regional stratigraphic analysis, sedimentology, petrology, structure and petrology of the Precambrian, statistical analysis in geologic problems, glaciology. Prerequisites for graduate study: courses in general and historical geology, paleontology, mineralogy, petrology, and structural geology. Preference given to students with strong backgrounds in mathematics and related sciences. 6 professorial staff. 18 master's degrees and 9 Ph.D.'s awarded 1955-59. 20 graduate students registered fall 1959. Total enrollment limited to 20.

German. German language and literature. Prerequisite for graduate study: major in German or equivalent. Ph.D. candidacy prerequisite: reading knowledge of French. 7 professorial staff. 21 master's degrees and 4 Ph.D.'s awarded 1955-59. 12 graduate students registered fall 1959.

History. American, English, European, Far Eastern, or World History. Combined program offered by Departments of History, Anthropology, Economics, and Political Science. Prerequisite for graduate study: training in history and allied disciplines. Recommended: 1 foreign language; training in an allied field in humanities or social sciences. 13 professorial staff. 86 master's degrees and 21 Ph.D.'s awarded 1955-59. 58 graduate students registered fall 1959.

Journalism. Journalism and public affairs, journalistic management, social aspects of mass communications, communications research. Offered by School of Journalism and the Graduate School. Ph.D. candidacy prerequisites: M.S. in journalism or equivalent; 2 years of professional experience in some field of journalism. 11 professorial staff. 206 master's degrees and 1 Ph.D. awarded 1955-59. 83 graduate students registered fall 1959.

Mathematics. Analysis, algebra, algebraic or differential geometry, functional or numerical analysis, probability and statistics, topology. Prerequisite for graduate study: major in mathe-

matics. Recommended: foundations of real variables; linear algebra. Ph.D. candidacy prerequisites: M.S. in mathematics or equivalent; French, German, or Russian. 20 professorial staff. 37 master's degrees and 7 Ph.D.'s awarded 1955-59. 49 graduate students registered fall 1959.

Metallurgy—Materials Science. Mechanical, chemical, physical metallurgy; ceramics; metal physics. Prerequisite for graduate study: major in engineering, physics, chemistry, or mathematics. Ph.D. candidacy prerequisite: 2 foreign languages. 6 professorial staff. 9 master's degrees and 3 Ph.D.'s awarded 1955-59. 34 graduate students registered fall 1959.

Microbiology.—Medical. Medical bacteriology, virology, mycology, parasitology. Prerequisite for graduate study: major in microbiology. Ph.D. candidacy prerequisite: master's degree in microbiology. 7 professorial staff. 6 master's degrees and 3 Ph.D.'s awarded 1955-59. 7 graduate students registered fall 1959. Total enrollment limited to 8-10.

Music. Music education, music history and literature, theory. Prerequisites for graduate study: minimum of 75 quarter hours in general education; adequate grounding in field of specialization. Ph.D. candidacy prerequisite: French and German. 13 professorial staff. 413 master's degrees and 22 Ph.D.'s awarded 1955-59. 99 graduate students registered fall 1959.

Pharmacology. Mode of action or metabolism of drugs, drug antagonism, chemotherapy, physiological basis for drug therapy. Prerequisites for graduate study: general, organic, and biological chemistry; zoology; general physics; mathematics through algebra. Recommended: physical chemstry; biophysics; mathematics beyond algebra; personal interview. Ph.D. candidacy prerequisites: 2 foreign languages; statistics. 8 professorial staff. 7 master's degrees and 3 Ph.D.'s awarded 1955-59. 4 graduate students registered fall 1959. New enrollment limited to 8.

Philosophy. Full programs offered in all areas with particular strength in metaphysics, epistemology, ethics, theory of value, philosophical anthropology, history of philosophy, contemporary philosophy, and contemporary continental thought. Combined program in philosophy of education offered with Department of Education. Recommended for graduate study: major in philosophy or closely related area; at least 1 foreign language; GRE. Ph.D. candidacy prerequisite: 2 foreign languages. 7 professorial staff.

12 master's degrees and 9 Ph.D.'s awarded 1955-59. 12 graduate students registered fall 1959.

Physics. Nuclear, high-energy particle, solid-state, or low-temperature physics; optical spectroscopy and interferometry; statistical theory. Combined program in chemical physics conducted jointly with Chemistry Department. Prerequisite for graduate study: equivalent of a physics major or an engineering degree. Recommended: GRE; 2 foreign languages; strong background in mathematics. Ph.D. candidacy prerequisite: reading knowledge of 2 foreign languages. 15 professorial staff. 28 master's degrees and 18 Ph.D.'s awarded 1955-59. 38 graduate students registered fall 1959.

Physiology. Respiratory, cardiovascular, gastro-intestinal, neural, and endocrine fields in mammalian physiology. Offered by Physiology Department of the Medical School. Recommended for graduate study: background in chemistry, physics, and mathematics. 7 professorial staff. 4 master's degrees and 2 Ph.D.'s awarded 1955-59. 1 graduate student registered fall 1959. Total enrollment limited to 15.

Political Science. International relations, comparative or community politics, political behavior, law and politics. Cooperative activity with Program in African Studies. Prerequisite for graduate study: preparation in political science or another social science. Recommended: at least 1 foreign language; statistics; GRE. 14 professorial staff. 19 master's degrees and 16 Ph.D.'s awarded 1955-59. 38 graduate students registered fall 1959.

Psychology. Clinical, experimental, physiological, and social psychology. Prerequisites for graduate study: major in field; 1 foreign language; MAT. Recommended: mathematics. 16 professorial staff. 24 master's degrees and 34 Ph.D.'s awarded 1955-59. 55 graduate students registered fall 1959. New enrollment limited to approximately 15.

Romance Languages. Romance philology; French, Spanish, and Italian language and literature. Combined programs offered occasionally with Departments of German, English, and Education. Prerequisites for graduate study: major in language and literature of choice; at least 2 Romance languages. Recommended: some knowledge of Latin. 16 professorial staff. 29 master's degrees and 9 Ph.D.'s awarded 1955-59. 17 graduate students registered fall 1959.

Sociology. Social organization, including stratification and institutions, social psychology, research methodology and statistics, systematic sociology and theory, urban sociology and ecology. Combined program offered by Departments of Psychology, Anthropology, and Speech, Center of Metropolitan Studies (geography), Program of African Studies, and Transportation Center. Prerequisites for graduate study: major in a social science; introductory course in statistics; reading knowledge of 1 foreign language. 9 professorial staff. 9 master's degrees and 11 Ph.D.'s awarded 1955-59. 20 graduate students registered fall 1959.

Speech.—Communicative Disorders. Preparation for research, teaching, or clinical work in audiology, language pathology, and speech pathology. Research and training opportunities integrated with medical and dental facilities in Chicago area. Prerequisite for graduate study: major in biological, physical, or social sciences, education, psychology, or communicative disorders. 11 professorial staff.

Speech.—Education. Elementary, secondary, college. Combined program offered by Departments of Education and Speech Education. Prerequisite for graduate study: preparation in speech and closely related areas. Recommended: courses in education and psychology. 3 professorial staff. 20 graduate students registered fall 1959. Ed.D. degree also awarded in this field.

Speech.—Interpretation. Historical and critical study of the esthetic principles governing oral performance of literary texts, together with training in performance. Prerequisite for graduate study: major in speech or major in literature with some training in speech. 4 professorial staff.

Speech.—Public Address and Group Communication. Rhetoric, history of public address, argumentation, persuasion, communication theory, general semantics, group processes. Prerequisite for graduate study: preparation in speech and history, philosophy, English and/or psychology. 8 professorial staff. 20 graduate students registered fall 1959.

Speech.—Radio, Television, and Film. History and criticism. Prerequisite for graduate study: preparation in speech or in closely related areas. Recommended: some experience in educational or commercial broadcasting. 5 professorial staff. 16 graduate students registered fall 1959.

Speech.—Theatre. Dramatic production combined with dramatic literature and theatre history. Prerequisites for graduate study: preparation in dramatics and related areas by means of course work and extracurricular participation. 10 professorial staff. 35 graduate students registered fall 1959.

Notre Dame, University of

NOTRE DAME, INDIANA

The Graduate School

Although some graduate programs were offered earlier and the first Ph.D. was conferred in 1912, graduate instruction did not become a regular part of the curriculum until 1918 when the Graduate School was formally established. In addition to the Ph.D., the D.Sc. in Engineering Science is awarded through the School of Engineering Science and the D.S.M. through the Mediaeval Institute. University is privately controlled and is conducted by the Holy Cross Fathers of the Roman Catholic Church. During the academic year, enrollment is restricted to men and sisters; lay women may be admitted to summer sessions.

Residence facilities available for priests, brothers, and sisters. Unmarried students find accommodations in homes in community. University-owned apartments available for married graduate students.

Special facilities include: library of approximately 530,000 volumes, including archives for American Catholic Church history and Mediaeval Library of the Mediaeval Institute; germ-free life facilities in Biology Department; radiation chemistry equipment of all kinds.

Residence requirement for Ph.D.: minimum of 3 years beyond bachelor's degree or 2 years beyond a master's degree earned elsewhere. Special approval required for transfer of any graduate credit after master's degree. Summer courses available.

ADMISSION REQUIREMENTS

For graduate study: bachelor's degree; major in field of proposed study; satisfactory academic record; GRE Aptitude and Advanced Tests; placement tests in some science departments. Recommended: college courses in German, French, or other modern foreign language. For candidacy for Ph.D.: reading knowledge of French and German (or approved substitutes); candidacy examinations.

Apply to Dean of the Graduate School by June 1.

FEES AND FIRST-YEAR AID

No application fee. Matriculation fee $10. Tuition $1,000 per academic year. Room in community approximately $300 per academic year. Meals in cafeteria average $15 per week. Unfurnished apartments $33 per month plus utilities.

First-year aid available: 30 tuition scholarships; 100 teaching fellowships and laboratory assistantships, $1,600-$2,000 plus tuition; 10 other fellowships, $1,500 plus tuition; 6 research assistantships, $1,000-$1,600 plus tuition; 30 grants-in-aid, $300-$900. There are also opportunities for student employment and loans.

Apply to Dean of the Graduate School by March 15. November or January GRE scores should be enclosed with application.

FIELDS OF STUDY FOR THE PH.D.

No courses specifically in the methodology of teaching are offered, but briefing sessions are held for teaching fellows. Nearly all students have had classroom experience by the time Ph.D. is awarded.

Area Studies.—American. American history, government, or literature. The studies in government and literature stress historical backgrounds and interdisciplinary contact. Offered by Departments of English, History, and Political Science. 5 professorial staff. 1 master's degree awarded 1955-59.

Area Studies.—Soviet Policy and Eastern Europe. Russia, East Central Europe. Offered by departments of Political Science, History, and Modern Languages. Prerequisites for graduate study: 18 hours in political science; reading knowledge of Russian. 6 professorial staff. 15 master's degrees and 4 Ph.D.'s awarded 1955-59. 4 graduate students registered fall 1959.

Biology. Gnotobiotics and microbiology, ecology, physiology, structural or developmental biology. Prerequisites for graduate study: 4 semesters of chemistry; 2 each of mathematics and physics; 2 of general botany or zoology; 18 semester hours of biological sciences. 17 professorial staff. Ph.D. programs in gnotobiotics and microbiology begun 1957. 38 master's degrees and 17 Ph.D.'s awarded

1955-59. 33 graduate students registered fall 1959.

Chemistry. Analytical, biological, inorganic, organic, physical, polymer, or radiation chemistry. Prerequisites for graduate study: major in chemistry; 2 years of 1 modern foreign language. 17 professorial staff. 62 master's degrees and 82 Ph.D.'s awarded 1955-59. 72 graduate students registered fall 1959.

Economics. General economics, industrial relations. Prerequisite for graduate study: 18 credit hours in economics. Recommended: undergraduate courses in philosophy and mathematics. 11 professorial staff. Ph.D. program begun 1956. 33 master's degrees awarded 1955-59. 10 graduate students registered fall 1959.

Education. Guidance, administration, history and philosophy, or general education. Prerequisite for graduate study: 12 hours of education. 6 professorial staff. 227 master's degrees and 6 Ph.D.'s awarded 1955-59.

Engineering.—Mechanical. Heat transfer vibrations, thermodynamics, and control engineering. Prerequisites for graduate study: major in mechanical engineering. Ph.D. program begun 1960. 12 professorial staff. 16 master's degrees awarded 1955-59. 12 graduate students registered fall 1959.

Engineering.—Metallurgical. Physical and extractive metallurgy, the sintering of metals and ceramics, solid-state transformations, preferred orientations, phase equilibria, X-ray diffraction, dislocations. Offered by Department of Metallurgical Engineering. Prerequisite for graduate study: major in metallurgical engineering or in physics. 5 professorial staff. 12 master's degrees and 6 Ph.D.'s awarded 1955-59. 15 graduate students registered fall 1959.

Engineering Science. Broad spectrum in the engineering sciences, such as applied mechanics; basic electrical theory; science of materials; systems engineering; or mass, momentum, and heat transfer. Prerequisite for graduate study: background in engineering science. 7 professorial staff. Ph.D. program initiated in 1958. 15 master's degrees awarded 1955-59. 22 graduate students registered fall 1959.

English. English literature (mediaeval, Renaissance, and 19th century), American literature, linguistics. Prerequisite for graduate study: 24 semester hours of English. Recommended: 2 or more years of French, German, and Latin. 24 professorial staff. 135 master's degrees and 10

Ph.D.'s awarded 1955-59. 58 graduate students registered fall 1959.

History. Major in United States or modern Europe; minor in Middle Ages or Latin America. Prerequisite for graduate study: major in history. 19 professorial staff. 73 master's degrees and 9 Ph.D.'s awarded 1955-59. 28 graduate students registered fall 1959.

Mathematics. Algebra, number theory, analysis, topology. Prerequisite for graduate study: strong major in mathematics. 13 professorial staff. 56 master's degrees and 11 Ph.D.'s awarded 1955-59. 41 graduate students registered fall 1959.

Mediaeval Studies. Mediaeval intellectual history of France; mediaeval education (the universities). Degree offered is D.S.M., but student may take Ph.D. by meeting requirement of appropriate department. Offered by Mediaeval Institute. Prerequisites for graduate study: appropriate courses in history, literature, and philosophy; good knowledge of Latin, French, and German. 9 professorial staff. 1 master's degree and 2 Ph.D.'s awarded 1955-59. 2 graduate students registered fall 1959.

Philosophy. Symbolic logic, history of philosophy, philosophy of nature, metaphysics, philosophy of science, moral philosophy. Prerequisites for graduate study: courses in logic, philosophy of nature (cosmology and psychology), ancient and modern philosophy; reading knowledge of Latin. Recommended: Greek, French, and German. 14 professorial staff. 38 master's degrees and 13 Ph.D.'s awarded 1955-59. 36 graduate students registered fall 1959.

Physics. Theoretical, surface, solid-state, and nuclear physics. 17 professorial staff. 20 master's degrees and 19 Ph.D.'s awarded 1955-59. 65 graduate students registered fall 1959.

Political Science. Political theory, American or comparative government, international relations, constitutional law, political parties. Prerequisite for graduate study: 18 hours of political science. 8 professorial staff. 39 master's degrees and 7 Ph.D.'s awarded 1955-59. 29 graduate students registered fall 1959.

Sociology. General sociology; correctional administration (M.A. only). Prerequisites for graduate study: 18 hours of social science, including 9 in sociology. Recommended: courses in theory and methods. 9 professorial staff. 53 master's degrees and 4 Ph.D.'s awarded 1955-59. 22 graduate students registered fall 1959.

Occidental College

LOS ANGELES 41, CALIFORNIA

Intercollegiate Program of Graduate Studies

Graduate instruction has been offered at the master's level at Occidental since 1922, and in 1951 the Intercollegiate Program of Graduate Studies was established. This began an association of Occidental with six other colleges in the area (Pomona, Claremont Men's, Scripps, Claremont Graduate School, Redlands, and Whittier) for the purpose of offering Ph.D. programs in English and comparative literature, history, and political economy. The first Ph.D. was awarded at Occidental in 1957. The college is privately controlled and nonsectarian, though an affiliation is maintained with the United Presbyterian Church. Both men and women are admitted.

No dormitory facilities provided; apartments available on campus.

Residence requirement for Ph.D.: 3 years with a minimum of 1 year on campus. Evening courses and a few summer courses available.

ADMISSION REQUIREMENTS

For graduate study: bachelor's degree; 3.0 GPA or better; MAT. Recommended: minimum proficiency in 2 languages; teaching experience. For candidacy for Ph.D.: examination indicating high degree of reading proficiency in 2 languages, including ability to read poetry; preliminary examinations.

Apply to Chairman, Department of English and Comparative Literature, as early as possible.

FEES AND FIRST-YEAR AID

Application fee $10. Tuition $700 per academic year. Approximate annual cost of board in college dining room $480. Apartments $36 per month.

First-year aid available: scholarships (based on merit and need), $700-$2,000.

Apply to Chairman, Department of English and Comparative Literature, as early as possible and no later than March 1.

FIELDS OF STUDY FOR THE PH.D.

Seminars and teaching internships are provided to increase effectiveness of the candidate as a teacher.

Comparative Literature. Genres: epic; lyric poetry; drama; novel. Periods: medieval; Renaissance; Romantic; modern. Offered by Occidental Department of English and Comparative Literature. Preliminary examination for candidacy includes 5 fields: literary figure; literary genre; literary period; an area of literary criticism; related nonliterary field. 7 professorial staff on campus; others in associated colleges. 4 master's degrees and 1 Ph.D. awarded 1955-59. New registration limited to about 7.

Ohio State University

COLUMBUS 10, OHIO

The Graduate School

Graduate instruction has been offered at Ohio State University since 1894, and the first Ph.D. was awarded in 1909. The Graduate School, which administers graduate work throughout the campus, was established 1911. Institution is publicly controlled by the state. Both men and women are admitted.

Single graduate students find accommodations in private rooming houses and in the university residence halls; married students live in residence halls and in privately-owned apartments or houses in the community.

Library of approximately 1,300,000 volumes contains special collections on American literature, Civil War, geology, history of monastic orders, history of medicine, Homeric linguistics, Reformation history, secondary school curricula, 17th century Spanish drama, welding. Affiliation with Argonne National Laboratory provides additional opportunities for research. Portions of Ph.D. programs may be completed at other state universities in Ohio.

Residence requirement for Ph.D.: 3 years, of which 1 year of full-time work must be done on campus (interpreted as minimum of 10 quarter hours during 3 or 4 consecutive quarters). Summer and evening courses available.

ADMISSION REQUIREMENTS

For graduate study: bachelor's degree; 2.70 GPA for all collegiate work; adequate undergraduate major; general test. GRE required for applicants with GPA under 2.70. For candidacy for Ph.D.: B average in all graduate work; dictionary reading knowledge of 2 modern foreign languages (usually French, German, Russian, or Spanish) or thorough reading knowledge of 1; written and oral general comprehensive examinations.

Apply to University Examiner, 190 North Oval Drive, Columbus 10, Ohio, 10 days before opening of quarter.

FEES AND FIRST-YEAR AID

Application fee $5. Tuition for state residents $300 per academic year; others $675. Room (in dormitory) for men $294 per year; for women $264. Approximate annual cost of board in college dining room $500. Apartments $85-$95 per month.

First-year aid available: teaching fellowships, $1,500 and up; other fellowships, $1,900-$3,000; research assistantships, $1,800 and up.

Apply to Dean of Graduate School by February 15 for fellowships; to chairmen of departments by April 1 for assistantships.

FIELDS OF STUDY FOR THE PH.D.

A 2-credit graduate school course on college teaching is offered several times a year to prospective teachers. Departmental seminars are held for teaching assistants.

Accounting. Advanced principles of accounting, cost accounting, financial statement analysis, economic statistics, management accounting, auditing principles and procedures, business controls, advance auditing, government accounting. Prerequisites for graduate study: major in accounting; 9 quarter hours of business law; Admission Test for Graduate Study in Business. 14 professorial staff. 22 master's degrees and 4 Ph.D.'s awarded 1955-59. 25 graduate students registered fall 1959.

Agronomy. Soil fertility, management, chemistry, physics, or biology; physical chemistry of soils; soil genesis and morphology; soil conservation; seed production; field crop management, ecology, and breeding; weed control; experimental methods of agronomy. Combined program offered by Department of Agronomy with Ohio Agricultural Experiment Station and 13 district and county experiment farms. Prerequisites for graduate study: courses in mathematics, chemistry, agricultural chemistry, physics, botany, genetics, geology; working knowledge of field crops. 17 professorial staff. 25 master's degrees

and 24 Ph.D.'s awarded 1955-59. 42 graduate students registered fall 1959.

Anatomy. Human and comparative anatomy, embryology, neurology, histology, histochemistry. Prerequisite for graduate study: preclinical medical sciences. 15 professorial staff. 11 master's degrees and 3 Ph.D.'s awarded 1955-59. 15 graduate students registered fall 1959.

Animal Sciences.—Dairy Science. Animal nutrition and genetics, dairy production. Prerequisite for graduate study: courses in biology, physiology, mathematics, and agricultural biochemistry. 8 professorial staff. 13 master's degrees and 11 Ph.D.'s awarded 1955-59. 10 graduate students registered fall 1959.

Animal Sciences.—Dairy Technology. Dairy plant management, market milk, concentrated milk products, ice cream, cheese, technical control of dairy products, nutrition and food technology, dairy chemistry, dairy bacteriology, dairy engineering. Interdepartmental seminars in cooperation with Institute of Nutrition and Food Technology. 6 professorial staff. 11 master's degrees and 6 Ph.D.'s awarded 1955-59. 12 graduate students registered fall 1959.

Animal Sciences.—General. Animal nutrition, genetics, and production; meats. Prerequisites for graduate study: for animal nutrition, agricultural or biological chemistry; for animal genetics, college zoology, 2 years of study in types and breeding of livestock, and collateral work in principles of breeding, feeding, and management. 15 professorial staff. 17 master's degrees and 5 Ph.D.'s awarded 1955-59. 13 graduate students registered fall 1959.

Animal Sciences.—Poultry Science. Poultry genetics, marketing, nutrition, physiology, metabolism, processing, marketing, plant management, poultry products technology. Prerequisites for graduate study: 10 hours biological sciences; 20 hours physical and/or social sciences. Recommended: economics. 8 professorial staff. 6 master's degrees and 10 Ph.D.'s awarded 1955-59. 8 graduate students registered fall 1959.

Bacteriology. Veterinary bacteriology, pathogenic bacteriology, dairy bacteriology, pathogenic protozoology, serology, sanitary bacteriology, food microbiology, medical bacteriology, filterable viruses, immunology. Combined program offered by Bacteriology Department and Institute of Nutrition and Food Technology. Prerequisite for graduate study: ability in bacteriology and allied sciences. 12 professorial staff.

41 master's degrees and 23 Ph.D.'s awarded 1955-59. 38 graduate students registered fall 1959.

Biochemistry.—Agricultural. Biological chemistry, nutrition and metabolism, chemistry of foods and food processing, plant chemistry, biochemistry preparation, enzymes, animal biochemistry, dairy chemistry. Combined program offered by Department of Agricultural Biochemistry, Institute of Nutrition and Food Technology, and other allied departments. Prerequisite for graduate study: equivalent of major in chemistry, including 1 year each in analytical, organic, and physical chemistry, 1 year of biochemistry, and pertinent courses in botany and zoology. 12 professorial staff. 10 master's degrees and 21 Ph.D.'s awarded 1955-59. 12 graduate students registered fall 1959.

Botany and Plant Pathology. Physiology, morphology, anatomy, pathology, mycology, ecology, genetics, taxonomy. Prerequisites for graduate study: general botany; general zoology; local flora; plant physiology, anatomy, and pathology; ecology; organic, biological, or agricultural chemistry. 30 professorial staff. 26 master's degrees and 35 Ph.D.'s awarded 1955-59. 46 graduate students registered fall 1959.

Business Organization. Core of courses in administration of business enterprises, major functions of business and control, and 24 hours of specialized work. Prerequisite for graduate study: Admission Test for Graduate Study in Business. 37 professorial staff. 161 master's degrees and 44 Ph.D.'s awarded 1955-59. 216 graduate students registered fall 1959.

Chemistry. Organic, physical, and advanced analytical chemistry; instrumental analysis; inorganic microanalysis; spectroscopic analysis, etc. Prerequisites for graduate study: courses in chemistry (general inorganic chemistry, qualitative and quantitative analysis, introductory organic and physical chemistry, and laboratory work); broad general courses. 27 professorial staff. 74 master's degrees and 139 Ph.D.'s awarded 1955-59. 178 graduate students registered fall 1959.

Chemistry.—Physiological. Physiological, organic, and physical chemistry; pharmacology. Combined program offered by Department of Physiological Chemistry and Institute of Nutrition and Food Technology. Prerequisites for graduate study: laboratory work and fundamental courses in general chemistry; qualitative and quantitative analysis; organic chemistry; biology; ability to read biochemical papers in French and German. 14 professorial staff. 14 master's degrees and 4 Ph.D.'s awarded 1955-59. 24 graduate students registered fall 1959.

Classical Languages. Literary, linguistic, social, historical, economic, or other aspects of ancient civilization. Auxiliary fields in archaeology, bibliography, ancient history, paleography, epigraphy, or metrics. A combined degree is offered in ancient history and literature. Prerequisite for graduate study: major in classical languages. 7 professorial staff. 3 master's degrees and 2 Ph.D.'s awarded 1955-59. 9 graduate students registered fall 1959.

Economics. Economic theory and history, labor relations, labor and government, social insurance, money, credit, banking, monetary fiscal policy, public control, economic statistics, econometrics, business fluctuations, national income, accounting, economic systems (planning and reform), welfare economics. Prerequisites for graduate study: basic courses in economics plus courses in 5 other areas, such as accounting anthropology, business organization, geography, history, mathematics, philosophy, political science, psychology, or sociology; broad liberal training; acquaintance with European and American history. 22 professorial staff. 21 master's degrees and 19 Ph.D.'s awarded 1955-59. 46 graduate students registered fall 1959.

Economics (Agricultural) and Rural Sociology. Farm organization and management, marketing farm products, rural sociology, farm prices, land use, agricultural policy, farm taxation, farm science. Prerequisite for graduate study: fundamental courses in economics or sociology. 24 professorial staff. 68 master's degrees and 23 Ph.D.'s awarded 1955-59. 76 graduate students registered fall 1959.

Education. Educational administration, elementary education, guidance, higher education and teacher training, philosophy and history of education, research, school library science, secondary education (teaching of English, foreign language, mathematics, science, social studies, speech), special and adult education, vocational and practical arts education, workshops, field experience. Combined program offered by Department of Education and Bureau of Educational Research. Prerequisites for graduate study: familiarity with areas of education required for certification to teach in Ohio public schools; student teaching courses or 1-2 years of successful teaching experience. 84 professorial staff. 568 master's degrees and 150 Ph.D.'s awarded 1955-59. 632 graduate students registered fall 1959.

Education.—Agricultural. Agricultural education (teaching aids, farming programs, curriculum, adult education, FFA, state administration and supervision of vocational agriculture), research. Combined program offered by Department of Agricultural Education with Colleges of Education and of Agriculture. Prerequisites for graduate study: 1 year of successful experience as teacher of vocational agriculture; 3 areas of specialization in addition to major field (2 in education or agriculture). 9 professorial staff. 36 master's degrees and 18 Ph.D.'s awarded 1955-59. 48 graduate students registered fall 1959.

Engineering. — Aeronautical. Aerodynamics, propulsion, structures. Prerequisite for graduate study: major in aeronautical engineering. 8 professorial staff. 25 master's degrees and 3 Ph.D.'s awarded 1955-59. 71 graduate students registered fall 1959.

Engineering.—Ceramic. Ceramic and glass engineering and technology, abrasives, electrical and technical ceramics, vitreous enamels, structural clay products, refractories, whitewares, technical design of ceramic equipment. Prerequisites for graduate study: major in ceramic engineering or technology or courses in qualitative and quantitative chemical analysis, physical chemistry, thermochemical mineralogy, mathematics through calculus, physics (with laboratory work). 7 professorial staff. 19 master's degrees and 6 Ph.D.'s awarded 1955-59. 14 graduate students registered fall 1959.

Engineering.—Chemical. Elements of chemical engineering and operations, measurements and control, thermodynamics, economy, chemical technology, chemical process development, industrial chemistry and chemical engineering, petroleum engineering. Prerequisite for graduate study: training in chemical engineering. 13 professorial staff. 69 master's degrees and 22 Ph.D.'s awarded 1955-59. 67 graduate students registered fall 1959.

Engineering.—Civil. Structural, sanitary, and highway engineering; transportation; soil mechanics and foundations. Prerequisites for graduate study: major in some branch of engineering or fundamental engineering sciences (mathematics, mechanics, chemistry); plane surveying theory; field practice; engineering drawing or equivalent. 12 professorial staff. 40 master's degrees and 1 Ph.D. awarded 1955-59. 37 graduate students registered fall 1959.

Engineering.—Electrical. Electrical machinery, circuits, communications, radiation, and instruments; power systems; alternating current apparatus; small motors; electronics; electron tubes; servomechanism; industrial electronics; electronic optics; betatron studies. 27 professorial staff. 76 master's degrees and 19 Ph.D.'s awarded 1955-59. 203 graduate students registered fall 1959.

Engineering.—Industrial. Methods and standards, personnel, production engineering, safety engineering, planning and control, plant layout and design, system analysis and design, operations research. Prerequisites for graduate study: major in industrial or mechanical engineering or courses in mathematics, physics, chemistry, engineering drawing, mechanics. 11 professorial staff. 45 master's degrees and 10 Ph.D.'s awarded 1955-59. 35 graduate students registered fall 1959.

Engineering.—Mechanical. Thermodynamics, heat transfer, fluid mechanics, internal combustion power, steam power, environmental control, machine design. Prerequisite for graduate study: major in mechanical engineering or its equivalent. 16 professorial staff. 45 master's degrees and 11 Ph.D.'s awarded 1955-59. 75 graduate students registered fall 1959.

Engineering Mechanics. Advanced experimental methods, advanced dynamics, hydrodynamics and fluid mechanics, mechanics of earth action, applied elasticity, strength of materials, vibrations, plasticity, plates and shells. Prerequisites for graduate study: major in engineering, mathematics, or physics; 4 courses in engineering mechanics; 1 approved foreign language. 7 professorial staff. 6 master's degrees and 3 Ph.D.'s awarded 1955-59. 21 graduate students registered fall 1959.

Engineering. — Metallurgical. Metallurgical and mining engineering. Prerequisites for graduate study: chemistry, physics, metallurgy; background courses in metallurgical engineering. 9 professorial staff. 28 master's degrees and 9 Ph.D.'s awarded 1955-59. 59 graduate students registered fall 1959.

English. Academic (research) or professional study (teaching). Prerequisites for graduate study: major in English. 31 professorial staff. 61

master's degrees and 21 Ph.D.'s awarded 1955-59. 66 graduate students registered fall 1959.

Fine and Applied Arts. History of art; painting; sculpture; ceramics; art education. 28 professorial staff. 44 master's degrees and 19 Ph.D.'s awarded 1955-59. 42 graduate students registered fall 1959.

Geography. Physical geography (geology, climatology, soil sciences, ecology, etc.); cultural geography (social sciences, history, political science, anthropology, sociology). Prerequisites for graduate study: major in geography or 40 hours in geography and closely allied fields; training in systematic geomorphology and physiography of some geographical area; knowledge of fundamental concept of economics. 11 professorial staff. 12 master's degrees and 11 Ph.D.'s awarded 1955-59. 15 graduate students registered fall 1959.

Geology. Stratigraphy (paleontology), stratigraphy (structural geology), geomorphology, glacial geology and quartenary stratigraphy, petrography, mineralogy, ore deposits. Courses in geodetic science, geodesy, and photogrammetry offered in cooperation with Institute of Geodesy, Photogrammetry, and Cartography. Prerequisites for graduate study: major in geology or 30 hours of geology; mineralogy plus chemistry, mathematics, physics, and biology; field experience. 19 professorial staff. 62 master's degrees and 19 Ph.D.'s awarded 1955-59. 73 graduate students registered fall 1959.

German. Linguistics or literature. Prerequisites for graduate study: wide reading in classical and modern literature; proper preparation for specialized work in German; knowledge of Romance language; working knowledge of Latin or Greek. 6 professorial staff. 9 master's degrees and 6 Ph.D.'s awarded 1955-59. 21 graduate students registered fall 1959.

History. Ancient Oriental and Greek history; Roman history; the Middle Ages (including English history to 1485); Renaissance and Reformation (1300-1643); European history (1648-1815, 1789-1870, and since 1870); expansion of Europe; history of England (1485-1763 and since 1763), the Near East; United States history; constitutional history of England and the United States; United States foreign relations; Latin America. Allied fields are anthropology, economics, political science, philosophy, and literature. Prerequisite for graduate study: major in history or equivalent. 20 professorial staff. 59

master's degrees and 25 Ph.D.'s awarded 1955-59. 78 graduate students registered fall 1959.

Home Economics. Food and nutrition (dietetics), home economics education, family and child development, food and nutrition, home management, textiles and clothing. Offered by Department of Home Economics in cooperation with Institute on Child Development and Family Life and Institute of Nutrition and Food Technology. Prerequisite for graduate study: major in home economics or the equivalent, with basic courses in 3 related areas such as biological sciences, education, fine arts, physical science, and social sciences. 33 professorial staff. 111 master's degrees and 10 Ph.D.'s awarded 1955-59. 57 graduate students registered fall 1959.

Horticulture and Forestry. Pomology, vegetable crops, floriculture and ornamental horticulture, products and processing (canning, freezing, fermentation, dehydration). Prerequisites for graduate study: preparation in field; acquaintance with important biological principles underlying the production and processing of horticultural crops. Recommended: plant physiology; biochemistry; plant breeding; plant nutrition; botany; genetics; statistics; soil physics and chemistry; physical and spectroscopic chemistry; techniques of research. 12 professorial staff. 25 master's degrees and 34 Ph.D.'s awarded 1955-59. 29 graduate students registered fall 1959.

Mathematics. Prerequisite for graduate study: 45 quarter hours of college mathematics. Recommended: background in physics, engineering, or fields using mathematics. 35 professorial staff. 39 master's degrees and 11 Ph.D.'s awarded 1955-59. 96 graduate students registered fall 1959.

Mineralogy. Crystallography, thermochemical and microscopic mineralogy, petrography. Prerequisites for graduate study: fundamental courses in crystallography and mineralogy; quantitative analysis; physical chemistry; general courses in physics. To specialize in petrology, student must have taken physical and historical geology. 4 professorial staff. 3 master's degrees and 2 Ph.D.'s awarded 1955-59. 5 graduate students registered fall 1959.

Music. History and literature; theory and composition. A combined program in music education is also offered by Departments of Music and Education. Prerequisites for graduate study: broad preparation in all fields of music; placement tests in theory, history, and performance during first quarter. 28 professorial staff. Ph.D. program begun 1959. 83 master's degrees awarded 1955-59. 37 graduate students registered fall 1959.

Optometry.—Physiological Optics. Physiological optics, physical optics, anatomy of eye and nervous system, physiology of vision, psychology of vision. Prerequisites for graduate study: mathematics through differential and integral calculus; physics; zoology; anatomy; physiology; psychology; physiological optics. 6 professorial staff. 9 master's degrees and 3 Ph.D.'s awarded 1955-59. 5 graduate students registered fall 1959.

Pathology. Pathologic anatomy, clinical pathology. Prerequisites for graduate study: for pathologic anatomy, M.D. or thorough training in laboratory work, autopsy technique, surgical pathology; for clinical pathology, major in chemistry or bacteriology, courses equivalent to 4th year curriculum in medical technology, 1 year in hospital laboratory, and qualification for certification by Board of Medical Technology. 6 professorial staff. 8 master's degrees awarded 1955-59. 21 graduate students registered fall 1959.

Pharmacy. Pharmaceutical chemistry, pharmacognosy, pharmacology. Prerequisites for graduate study: degree in pharmacy. 13 professorial staff. 20 master's degrees and 20 Ph.D.'s awarded 1955-59. 37 graduate students registered fall 1959.

Philosophy. History of philosophy, logic, epistemology and metaphysics, ethics. Prerequisite for graduate study: major in philosophy or equivalent. Recommended: aesthetics; philosophy of religion and science; social philosophy. 14 professorial staff. 3 master's degrees and 3 Ph.D.'s awarded 1955-59. 11 graduate students registered fall 1959.

Physical Education. Prerequisites for graduate study: courses in professional education; human anatomy or physiology; physical and health education. 26 professorial staff. 90 master's degrees and 13 Ph.D.'s awarded 1955-59. 53 graduate students registered fall 1959.

Physics and Astronomy. Classical mechanics, electromagnetic theory, quantum and statistical mechanics, modern physics, some field of specialization in physics. Prerequisites for graduate study in physics: physics; chemistry; mathematics through differential equations; elementary and intermediate principles of classical and modern physics. For astronomy-astrophysics: obser-

vational astronomy; theoretical and celestial mechanics; physical optics and atomic physics; mathematical methods in physics. 47 professorial staff. 61 master's degrees and 54 Ph.D.'s awarded 1955-59. 169 graduate students registered fall 1959.

Physiology. Neuroanatomy and histology, physiological chemistry or biochemistry, advanced physiology, laboratory, research. Prerequisites for graduate study: organic chemistry; general physics and biological sciences (including comparative anatomy); physical chemistry. Recommended: calculus and statistics. 19 professorial staff. 8 master's degrees and 17 Ph.D.'s awarded 1955-59. 22 graduate students registered fall 1959.

Political Science. Political theory and jurisprudence, foreign governments and comparative political institutions, American government and politics, state and local government, public opinion, parties and pressure groups, public administration, public law, international law and relations. Prerequisites for graduate study: broad grasp of information and concepts in political science; acquaintance with relevant aspects of allied disciplines. 16 professorial staff. 19 master's degrees and 16 Ph.D.'s awarded 1955-59. 43 graduate students registered fall 1959.

Psychology. Clinical or counseling psychology, research and experimental psychology. Combined program offered by Department of Psychology and Institute on Child Development and Family Life. Prerequisite for graduate study: major in psychology or equivalent. 49 professorial staff. 112 master's degrees and 140 Ph.D.'s awarded 1955-59. 210 graduate students registered fall 1959.

Romance Languages. Linguistic or literary Romance languages. Prerequisite for graduate study: command of major language; courses in literature. Recommended: French; Italian; Portuguese; Spanish. 19 professorial staff. 16 master's degrees and 14 Ph.D.'s awarded 1955-59. 35 graduate students registered fall 1959.

Social Work. Community organization, social casework, social group work, corrections, rehabilitation of the handicapped, social work research, public welfare administration. Prerequisites for graduate study: fundamental courses in psychology, economics, sociology, political science, and history. 29 professorial staff. 102

master's degrees and 2 Ph.D.'s awarded 1955-59. 103 graduate students registered fall 1959.

Sociology and Anthropology. Sociology: theory, race relations, social organization and planning, the family, criminology and penology, educational sociology and penology, educational sociology and ecology, research methodology. Anthropology: physical anthropology, archaeology, ethnology, social anthropology. Prerequisite for graduate study: major in sociology or equivalent. 23 professorial staff. 24 master's degrees and 35 Ph.D.'s awarded 1955-59. 37 graduate students registered fall 1959.

Speech. Rhetoric, public address and discussion, history and theory of the theater and play production, radio and television programming, speech science, general speech education. Combined programs in related fields offered by Departments of Speech, Psychology, Education, and Physics. Prerequisites for graduate study: 40 hours of speech and related field; ability to write and speak with clarity and good usage. 26 professorial staff. 83 master's degrees and 63 Ph.D.'s awarded 1955-59. 90 graduate students registered fall 1959.

Veterinary Anatomy. Anatomical techniques, veterinary endocrinology, research. Prerequisite for graduate study: D.V.M. 2 professorial staff. 1 master's degree and 1 Ph.D. awarded 1955-59.

Veterinary Medicine. Minor problems, ophthalmology, research. Prerequisite for graduate study: D.V.M. 2 professorial staff. 1 master's degree and 2 Ph.D.'s awarded 1955-59. 2 graduate students registered fall 1959.

Veterinary Parasitology. Literature, classification, morphology, life histories, and economic importance of parasites. Prerequisite for graduate study: D.V.M. 1 professor. 4 master's degrees awarded 1955-59. 1 graduate student registered fall 1959.

Veterinary Pathology. Pathology technique, advanced systematics pathology, veterinary surgical pathology, animal oncology. Prerequisite for graduate study: D.V.M. 3 professorial staff. 8 master's degrees and 5 Ph.D.'s awarded 1955-59. 3 graduate students registered fall 1959.

Veterinary Physiology and Pharmacology. Prerequisite for graduate study: D.V.M. 3 professorial staff. 3 master's degrees and 1 Ph.D. awarded 1955-59. 5 graduate students registered fall 1959.

Veterinary Preventive Medicine. Veterinary preventive medicine, veterinary public health

(transmission of diseases from animal to man), improvement of food hygiene. Prerequisites for graduate study: D.V.M. 3 professorial staff. 4 master's degrees, and 2 Ph.D.'s awarded 1955-59.

Veterinary Surgery. Surgery, sterility, research. Prerequisite for graduate study: D.V.M. 4 professorial staff. 2 master's degrees awarded 1955-59. 2 graduate students registered fall 1959.

Zoology and Entomology. Animal behavior, ecology, embryology, genetics, invertebrate zoology, ornithology, parasitology, physiological zoology, protozoology, vertebrate zoology, wildlife conservation. Combined program offered by Department of Zoology and Entomology with Ohio Agricultural Experiment Station and Institute of Genetics. 45 professorial staff. 58 master's degrees and 58 Ph.D.'s awarded 1955-59. 85 graduate students registered fall 1959.

Ohio University

ATHENS, OHIO

Graduate College

Graduate instruction has been offered at Ohio University since 1822, but the Graduate College was not organized until 1936. The first Ph.D. was awarded in 1959. The university is publicly controlled by the state. Both men and women are admitted.

Single graduate students find accommodations in private residences and in university housing adjacent to main campus; apartment units available for married graduate students (located approximately 2 miles from university with free hourly commuter bus service).

Library of approximately 288,000 volumes contains special collections on history of university and on Northwest territory, as well as historical books in chemistry and other applied sciences.

Residence requirement for Ph.D.: 6 semesters beyond bachelor's degree, at least 2 of which must be taken in continuous residence on campus.

ADMISSION REQUIREMENTS

For graduate study: bachelor's degree; 2.5 overall undergraduate GPA with 3.0 GPA in area of proposed study. Recommended: GRE. For candidacy for Ph.D.: reading knowledge of 2 foreign languages or competence in 1 language and 1 approved research tool (languages are usually French, German, or Russian); comprehensive examinations; recommendation of Advisory Committee; selection of dissertation topic.

Apply to the Graduate College at least 1 month in advance of date of desired entry.

FEES AND FIRST-YEAR AID

No application fee. Matriculation fee $10. Tuition for state residents $300 per academic year; others $600. Room in university-owned buildings $288 per academic year. Approximate annual cost of board in college dining room $468. Apartments $42 per month including utilities (new units to be available 1960-61 will be higher).

First-year aid available: scholarships, $500; teaching fellowships, $2,200-$3,000; research assistantships, $1,800-$3,000; graduate assistantships, $1,800-$2,000.

Apply to Graduate College by March 1.

FIELDS OF STUDY FOR THE PH.D.

Each doctoral program includes elective courses or seminars designed to assist the prospective college teacher.

Chemistry. Analytical, inorganic, organic, and physical chemistry; radiochemistry. Prerequisites for graduate study: 8 semester hours of quantitative analysis; 10 of organic chemistry; 6 of physical calculus and physics. 11 professorial staff. 18 master's degrees and 1 Ph.D. awarded 1955-59. 22 graduate students registered fall 1959.

Education. School administration, guidance and counseling, elementary education. Prerequisites for graduate study: courses qualifying students for teacher certification; GRE. 26 professorial staff. Ph.D. program initiated 1959. 278 master's degrees awarded 1955-59. 61 graduate students registered fall 1959.

Physics. Cosmic rays; solid-state, theoretical, and nuclear physics; other areas. Prerequisites for graduate study: major in physics; mathematics through integral calculus. 11 professorial staff. Ph.D. program initiated 1959. 13 master's degrees awarded 1955-59. 16 graduate students registered fall 1959.

Speech. Public address, speech and hearing therapy. Prerequisite for graduate study: 18 semester hours of basic speech courses, including public address, speech and hearing therapy, and phonetic audiology. 23 professorial staff. Ph.D. program initiated 1958. 29 master's degrees awarded 1955-59. 31 graduate students registered fall 1959.

Oklahoma State University of Agriculture and Applied Science

STILLWATER, OKLAHOMA

Graduate School

Graduate courses have been offered at Oklahoma State University since 1910. The Graduate School was organized in 1929, and the first Ph.D. was conferred in 1948. Ph.D. programs are offered in a number of areas on campus and a Ph.D. program in the field of chemical thermodynamics is offered in conjunction with the Petroleum Research Station of the U.S. Bureau of Mines in Bartlesville, Oklahoma. The Ed.D. degree is also conferred. University is publicly controlled by the state. Both men and women are admitted.

Single graduate students may live in university residence halls; married students in university-owned apartments.

Special facilities include: library of approximately 425,000 volumes; computer center; radiation and radioisotopes laboratory.

Residence requirement for Ph.D.: 6 semesters of full-time graduate study beyond bachelor's degree, of which 1 academic year of the last 2 must be spent in continuous residence on campus. Summer and evening courses available.

ADMISSION REQUIREMENTS

For graduate study: bachelor's degree; satisfactory academic record; appropriate background for field of proposed study; acceptance by department. Recommended (required by some departments): GRE. For candidacy for Ph.D.: completion of main areas of approved plan of study; approval of Advisory Committee; dictionary reading knowledge of 2 foreign languages, or thorough reading knowledge of 1 foreign language, or dictionary reading knowledge of 1 foreign language and competence in a research technique or related field of knowledge; qualifying examinations.

Apply to Dean, Graduate School, at any time.

FEES AND FIRST-YEAR AID

No application fee. Tuition and fees for state residents $6 per credit hour; others $15 per credit hour. No other fees. Room (in dormitory) for men $252-$348 per academic year; for women $240-$320. Approximate annual cost of board in college dining room $240. Apartments $45-$75 per month (with utilities).

First-year aid available: scholarships, $50-$500; teaching fellowships, $1,200-$3,000; other fellowships, $600-$3,000; research assistantships, $1,500-$3,600. Ample loan funds available at low rate of interest.

Apply to Dean, Graduate School, by March 1 (later applications will be considered if there are vacancies).

FIELDS OF STUDY FOR THE PH.D.

Minor in higher education is available to candidates for the Ph.D. It consists of a unit of 10 semester credit hours of related course work in philosophy, organization and function of higher education, and methods of teaching in college. A seminar for prospective college teachers is also available.

Animal Breeding. Genetics and physiology of reproduction of cattle, sheep, swine, and poultry. Combined program offered by Departments of Animal Husbandry, Dairying, and Poultry Science. Prerequisites for graduate study: major in animal husbandry, dairying, or poultry science; 13 hours of chemistry; 12 of basic biological sciences. Recommended: additional courses in basic biological sciences, chemistry, and mathematics. 7 professorial staff. 25 master's degrees and 7 Ph.D.'s awarded 1955-59. 18 graduate students registered fall 1959.

Animal Nutrition. Animal nutrition, biochemistry, physiology, statistics. Combined program offered by Departments of Animal Husbandry, Biochemistry, Dairying, and Poultry Science. Prerequisites for graduate study: major in animal science or chemistry; 13 hours of chemistry, including organic; 12 of basic biological sciences. 32 professorial staff. 24 master's degrees and 13 Ph.D.'s awarded 1955-59. 20 graduate students registered fall 1959.

Botany. Plant ecology, taxonomy, or physiology; cytology. Offered by Department of Bot-

any and Plant Pathology. 16 professorial staff. 20 master's degrees and 2 Ph.D.'s awarded 1955-59. 17 graduate students registered fall 1959.

Chemistry. Biochemistry; analytical, organic, or physical chemistry. Offered by Departments of Chemistry and Biochemistry. Prerequisites for graduate study: major in chemistry; 1 year each in general, analytical, organic, and physical chemistry; mathematics; physics entrance examinations. Recommended: additional chemistry, physics, mathematics, and biology. 18 professorial staff. 54 master's degrees and 18 Ph.D.'s awarded 1955-59. 58 graduate students registered fall 1959.

Economics. Economic history and institutions, economic theory or development, business and economic policy, international or labor economics, public finance, money and banking. Prerequisite for graduate study: major in economics or related field. Recommended: 1 foreign language; calculus. 12 professorial staff. Ph.D. program begun 1958. 8 master's degrees awarded 1955-59. 15 graduate students registered fall 1959.

Economics.—Agricultural. Agricultural marketing; agricultural prices and policy; production economics and farm management; land economics; finance and appraisal. Prerequisite for graduate study: major in agricultural economics or equivalent. 16 professorial staff. 45 master's degrees and 4 Ph.D.'s awarded 1955-59. 31 graduate students registered fall 1959.

Engineering.—Agricultural. Stress analysis; structural and machine design; electrical applications; agricultural hydrology and hydraulics; water, wind erosion, and evaporation control; water purification; irrigation; micrometeorology; cooling, drying, processing, and storage of agricultural products; environmental control for livestock production. Prerequisites for graduate study: agricultural engineering curriculum or mathematics through differential equations; physics; theoretical and applied engineering mechanics; thermodynamics; adequate working knowledge of agricultural engineering. 8 professorial staff. Ph.D. program begun 1957. 15 master's degrees and 1 Ph.D. awarded 1955-59. 11 graduate students registered fall 1959.

Engineering.—Chemical. 5 professorial staff. 22 master's degrees and 5 Ph.D.'s awarded 1955-59. 26 graduate students registered fall 1959.

Engineering.—Civil. Engineering mechanics; soil mechanics and foundations; structural, hydraulic, transportation or sanitary engineering.

Prerequisite for graduate study: major in civil, general, architectural, or mechanical engineering. 11 professorial staff. 45 master's degrees and 1 Ph.D. awarded 1955-59. 42 graduate students registered fall 1959.

Engineering.—Electrical. Prerequisite for graduate study: the completion of an electrical engineering curriculum. 7 professorial staff. 52 master's degrees and 7 Ph.D.'s awarded 1955-59. 60 graduate students registered fall 1959.

Engineering.—General. Basic courses from civil, electrical, industrial and mechanical engineering. Prerequisite for graduate study: completion of an engineering curriculum. 40 professorial staff. 3 master's degrees awarded 1955-59. 35 graduate students registered fall 1959.

Engineering.—Industrial. Management, work measurement, operations research, industrial control, systems design. Offered by School of Industrial Engineering and Management. Prerequisite for graduate study: completion of an engineering curriculum. 6 professorial staff. 46 master's degrees and 1 Ph.D. awarded 1955-59. 45 graduate students registered fall 1959.

Engineering.—Mechanical. Heat transfer, gas dynamics, thermodynamics, aeronautical or petroleum engineering, and fluid power and controls. 17 professorial staff. 65 master's degrees and 3 Ph.D.'s awarded 1955-59. 68 graduate students registered fall 1959.

Entomology. Prerequisite for graduate study: 32 semester credit hours in zoology and entomology. 6 professorial staff. 20 master's degrees and 4 Ph.D.'s awarded 1955-59. 21 graduate students registered fall 1959.

Mathematics. Mathematics and statistics. Prerequisite for graduate study: major in mathematics. Recommended: reading proficiency in at least 1 modern foreign language; undergraduate study in field of application. 18 professorial staff. 61 master's degrees and 6 Ph.D.'s awarded 1955-59. 68 graduate students registered fall 1959.

Microbiology. Bacterial physiology, anatomy, nutrition, or genetics; dairy, food, or general microbiology; veterinary bacteriology; immunochemistry. Offered by Department of Bacteriology. Prerequisite for graduate study: major in a basic science with equivalent of a minor in bacteriology. 8 professorial staff. Ph.D. program begun 1960. 4 master's degrees awarded 1955-59. 8 graduate students registered fall 1959.

Physics. Solid-state, acoustics, nuclear, or theoretical physics. Prerequisites for graduate study: 24 semester hours of physics above basic courses; mathematics through differential equations. 13 professorial staff. 16 master's degrees awarded 1955-59. 28 graduate students registered fall 1959.

Physiology. Physiology of reproduction, endocrinology. Offered by Department of Physiology and Pharmacology. Prerequisite for graduate study: courses in anatomy, inorganic and organic chemistry, histology, physics, and physiology. 4 professorial staff. Ph.D. program begun 1955. 6 master's degrees awarded 1955-59. 7 graduate students registered fall 1959.

Plant Breeding and Genetics. Plant breeding, genetics, cytology, taxonomy. Offered by Departments of Agronomy and Horticulture. Prerequisites for graduate study: biological science background; departmental entrance examination. Recommended: basic background in botany, chemistry, and genetics. 17 professorial staff. 49 master's degrees and 5 Ph.D.'s awarded 1955-59. 37 graduate students registered fall 1959.

Psychology. General, experimental, industrial, psychology; counseling and guidance; mental retardation; physiological and comparative or experimental-clinical psychology. Combined program in educational psychology offered by Departments of Psychology and Education. Prerequisite for graduate study: GRE and MAT. Recommended: background in social or biological science or mathematics. 8 professorial staff. Ph.D. program begun 1958. 10 master's degrees awarded 1956-59. 34 graduate students registered fall 1959. The Ed.D. degree is also awarded in this field.

Soil Science. Soil chemistry, physics, genesis and morphology, or fertility and management. Offered by Department of Agronomy. Prerequisite for graduate study: biological and physical science background. Recommended: 22 hours of chemistry; 8-10 of physics; mathematics through calculus. 11 professorial staff. Ph.D. program begun 1959. 35 master's degrees awarded 1955-59. 21 graduate students registered fall 1959.

Veterinary Parasitology. Pathology, general parasitology, entomology, biochemistry, physiology. Prerequisite for graduate study: training in basic and/or applied biological sciences. 3 professors. Ph.D. program begun 1955. 2 graduate students registered fall 1959. New enrollment limited to 3.

Veterinary Pathology. Histopathology; surgical, biochemical, viral, or experimental pathology; hematology; bactopathology. Prerequisite for graduate study: D.V.M. or completion of undergraduate courses in veterinary pathology. 6 professorial staff. Program begun 1958. 1 graduate student registered fall 1959.

Wildlife Conservation. Wildlife management, ecology, fisheries biology, limnology. Offered by Department of Zoology. Prerequisites for graduate study: 32 hours of zoology (including physiology and entomology) or 40 hours of biology or science; entrance test. 23 professorial staff. 9 master's degrees and 8 Ph.D.'s awarded 1955-59. 8 graduate students registered fall 1959.

Zoology. Ornithology, parasitology, limnology, invertebrate zoology, ecology, ichthyology, mammalogy, protozoology, genetics, cytology, embryology. Prerequisites for graduate study: 32 hours of zoology (including physiology and entomology) or 40 hours of biology or science; entrance test. Recommended: 1 summer at a biological station, preferably marine. 16 professorial staff. 8 master's degrees and 4 Ph.D.'s awarded 1955-59. 17 students registered fall 1959.

Oklahoma, University of

NORMAN, OKLAHOMA

The Graduate College

Graduate instruction has been offered at the university since 1899, and the Graduate College was organized in 1909. First Ph.D. was awarded in 1929. The university also confers the Ed.D. and D.B.A. degrees. Institution is publicly controlled by the state. Both men and women are admitted.

Rooms in dormitories available for single graduate students; university-owned apartments for married students.

Special facilities include: library of approximately 700,000 volumes, including special collections in the history of science and Southwest history; museum; observatory; computer laboratory; biological station at Lake Texoma. Cooperative program with Oak Ridge Institute of Nuclear Science affords additional opportunities for research in this area.

Residence requirement for Ph.D.: 3 years beyond bachelor's degree, of which 1 year (or 30 of last 60 hours) must be taken in residence at the University of Oklahoma. Summer courses available.

ADMISSION REQUIREMENTS

For graduate study: bachelor's degree; B average in all previous work. For candidacy for Ph.D.: reading knowledge of 2 foreign languages, 1 of which must be French or German; general examination.

Apply to Director of Admissions, Office of Admissions and Records, 1 month prior to date of desired admission.

FEES AND FIRST-YEAR AID

No application fee. Tuition $6 per credit hour for state residents; $15 for others. Room (in dormitory) for men $152-$260 for 9 months; women $260. Approximate annual cost of board in college dining room $350. Apartments $52.50-$65 per month.

First-year aid available: $10,000 available for tuition scholarships; 248 teaching fellowships, $1,800-$2,000; 13 research assistantships, variable stipends.

Apply to Dean of the Graduate College or appropriate department chairmen by March 1.

FIELDS OF STUDY FOR THE PH.D.

Biochemistry. Offered by Biochemistry Department of Medical School. Prerequisites for graduate study: 8 hours each of general and organic chemistry; 4 each of physical and quantitative; 8 each of biology and physics. 9 professorial staff. Ph.D. program begun 1956. 4 master's degrees and 5 Ph.D.'s awarded 1955-59. 8 graduate students registered fall 1959.

Chemistry. Analytical, inorganic, organic, and physical chemistry; biochemistry. Prerequisites for graduate study: 8-10 hours each of general, organic, analytical, and physical chemistry; 8-10 of physics; 8 of calculus. 15 professorial staff. 29 master's degrees and 21 Ph.D.'s awarded 1955-59. 37 graduate students registered fall 1959.

Economics. Prerequisites for graduate study: major in economics or business; 6 hours of accounting; 3 hours each of business statistics, business law, business management, finance, and marketing. 9 professorial staff. 13 master's degrees and 8 Ph.D.'s awarded 1955-59. 27 graduate students registered fall 1959.

Education. Elementary, secondary, business, and health education; measurement; history and philosophy of education; psychology; guidance Prerequisites for graduate study: undergraduate degree in education; Advanced GRE. 30 professorial staff. 971 master's degrees and 93 Ph.D.'s awarded 1955-59. 343 graduate students registered fall 1959. The Ed.D. degree is also awarded in this field (no language requirement).

Engineering.—Chemical. Prerequisites for graduate study: a major in chemical engineering; 6 hours of advanced mathematics beyond differential and integral calculus; 6 hours of advanced work in physics, chemistry, or other engineering subjects. 9 professorial staff. 32 master's degrees and 3 Ph.D.'s awarded 1955-59. 30 graduate students registered fall 1959.

Engineering Sciences. Combined program offered by all divisions of the College of Engineering. Prerequisites for graduate study: bachelor's degree in a field of engineering. Program begun 1957. 8 graduate students registered fall 1959.

English. Medieval period, 16th century, 17th century, contemporary American literature, linguistics. Prerequisite for graduate study: 27 hours of English, including composition, English and American literature, and English language. 16 professorial staff. 51 master's degrees and 10 Ph.D.'s awarded 1955-59. 62 graduate students registered fall 1959.

Geology. General geology, paleontology, mineralogy, and petrography. Prerequisites or graduate study: 30 hours of geology, including physical, historical, and advanced general geology; mineralogy; paleontology; elementary courses in chemistry, physics, mechanical drawing, and surveying; Advanced GRE. 23 professorial staff. 162 master's degrees and 6 Ph.D.'s awarded 1955-59. 73 graduate students registered fall 1959.

Government. Theory, public law, national government, international government. Prerequisites for graduate study: 9-12 hours of government; 9-16 hours of other social sciences; statistics; college algebra; accounting. 12 professorial staff. 19 master's degrees and 2 Ph.D.'s awarded 1955-59. 18 graduate students registered fall 1959.

History. American, European, general. Prerequisite for graduate study: 20 hours of history. 16 professorial staff. 19 master's degrees and 9 Ph.D.'s awarded 1955-59. 42 graduate students registered fall 1959.

Mathematics. Prerequisite for graduate study: 12 hours of mathematics. 11 professorial staff. 24 master's degrees and 8 Ph.D.'s awarded 1955-59. 32 graduate students registered fall 1959.

Medical Sciences. Anatomy, bacteriology, biochemistry, pathology, physiology, pharmacology, preventive medicine, and public health. Offered by School of Medicine. Prerequisites for graduate study: vary with field of concentration, but should include biology, chemistry, physics, and courses in special field. 50 professorial staff. 20 master's degrees and 24 Ph.D.'s awarded 1955-59. 49 graduate students registered fall 1959.

Modern Languages. French, Spanish. Prerequisites for graduate study: 25 hours in the language; beginning Latin; European history. 17 professorial staff. 3 master's degrees awarded 1955-59. 12 graduate students registered fall 1959.

Physics. Molecular spectroscopy, electrical discharges, shock waves, cosmic waves, solid-state physics, general physics. Prerequisites for graduate study: 30 hours of physics; differential and integral calculus; differential equations; general chemistry. 11 professorial staff. 15 master's degrees and 15 Ph.D.'s awarded 1955-59. 39 graduate students registered fall 1959.

Plant Sciences. Taxonomy, morphology, genetics, bacteriology, ecology, physiology. Prerequisite for graduate study: 20 hours in biological work in addition to general botany. 10 professorial staff. 13 master's degrees and 6 Ph.D.'s awarded 1955-59. 19 graduate students registered fall 1959.

Preventive Medicine and Public Health. Medical protozoology, medical helminthology, medical entomology, epidemiology, biostatistics, public health. Prerequisites for graduate study: 15 hours of biology; 12 of chemistry; 8 of physics. 9 professorial staff. Ph.D. program begun 1956. 1 master's degree and 1 Ph.D. awarded 1955-59. 9 graduate students registered fall 1959.

Psychology. Clinical and experimental-theoretical psychology. Prerequisites for graduate study: elements of psychology; experimental psychology; statistics; GRE; MAT. 9 professorial staff. 18 master's degrees and 16 Ph.D.'s awarded 1955-59. 41 graduate students registered fall 1959.

Speech. Speech arts, speech sciences. Prerequisite for graduate study: 20 hours of speech, including fundamentals of speech, phonetics, and bases of speech behavior. 13 professorial staff. 16 master's degrees and 2 Ph.D.'s awarded 1955-59. 28 graduate students registered fall 1959.

Zoology. Comparative physiology, vertebrate physiology, fisheries biology, herpetology, embryology, parasitology, ornithology, limnology, entomology, protozoology, human genetics. Prerequisites for graduate study: 24 hours of biology, college algebra, physics, organic chemistry. 15 professorial staff. 14 master's degrees and 8 Ph.D.'s awarded 1955-59. 32 graduate students registered fall 1959.

Oregon State College

CORVALLIS, OREGON

The Graduate School

The first master's degree was awarded by Oregon State College in 1875 and the first Ph.D. in 1935. The Graduate School was established in 1946. Prior to this, graduate instruction had been under the jurisdiction of the Committee on Advanced Degrees (1910-31) and the Graduate Division (1932-45). At present Ph.D.'s are awarded in many areas and the Ed.D. degree is also conferred. University is publicly controlled by the state. Both men and women are admitted.

Rooms in university dormitories reserved for graduate women and 1 floor reserved in men's dormitory for graduate men; university-owned and privately-owned apartments maintained for married students.

Special facilities include: library of approximately 365,000 volumes; museum; cyclotron; electron microscope; digital computer; forest products laboratory; experimental forests; arboretum; agricultural experiment station.

Residence requirement for Ph.D.: 3 years of full-time work beyond bachelor's degree, of which at least 1 year (usually the last) must be spent in residence on campus. Summer courses available.

ADMISSION REQUIREMENTS

For graduate study: bachelor's degree; GPA of 2.5 or better; appropriate background for program selected; qualifying entrance examinations. For candidacy for Ph.D.: reading knowledge of German and French (another language may be substituted for French upon petition); comprehensive preliminary examinations (written and oral) in major and minor fields.

Apply to the Office of the Registrar by August 31 for fall term (after that date, a late fee of $10 is required).

FEES AND FIRST-YEAR AID

No application fee. Tuition $90 per quarter; no additional fee for out-of-state students. Room (in dormitory) $670 per year for double room; $790 for single room. Approximate annual cost of board in college dining room $450. Apartments $42 a month (1 bedroom); $42-$48 (2 bedrooms).

First-year aid available: teaching fellowships, $1,800-$2,000; other fellowships, $1,800-$2,000; research assistantships, $1,400-$1,800.

Apply to head of major department by April 1.

FIELDS OF STUDY FOR THE PH.D.

A minor graduate program in college and university teaching has been established, and any candidate for a Ph.D. degree may include this in his graduate program. Maturity, background, and sincerity of purpose are principal prerequisites; there are no course prerequisites in professional education. Core of this minor consists of 5 courses: The College Student (3 hours); College and University Teaching (3 hours); American Higher Education (3 hours); seminar on teaching procedure (hours to be arranged); College Teaching Studies (3 hours).

Bacteriology and Hygiene. Dairy, food, industrial, pathogenic, or soil bacteriology; hygiene and sanitation; physiology of bacteria; virology; bacteriology of water and sewage. 8 professorial staff. 21 master's degrees and 9 Ph.D.'s awarded 1955-59. 18 graduate students registered fall 1959.

Botany. Cytology, ecology, morphology, mycology, plant pathology, physiology, systematic botany. 18 professorial staff. 8 master's degrees and 29 Ph.D.'s awarded 1955-59. 39 graduate students registered fall 1959.

Chemistry. Analytical, forest products, inorganic, organic, or physical chemistry; biochemistry (including agricultural); radiochemistry (organic and inorganic); 32 professorial staff. 51 master's degrees and 47 Ph.D.'s awarded 1955-59. 107 graduate students registered fall 1959.

Dairy and Animal Husbandry. Dairy production, nutrition, reproduction, physiology, wool technology, livestock management, range management, genetics (emphasis on animal husbandry). 17 professorial staff. 14 master's degrees and 10 Ph.D.'s awarded 1955-59. 14 graduate students registered fall 1959.

Economics.—Agricultural. Agricultural marketing, policy, finance, or prices; production economics; land economics; farm management. 13 professorial staff. 25 master's degrees and 5 Ph.D.'s awarded 1955-59. 24 graduate students registered fall 1959.

Engineering.—Chemical. 6 professorial staff. 11 master's degrees and 4 Ph.D.'s awarded 1955-59. 14 graduate students registered fall 1959.

Engineering.—Civil. Highway, hydraulic, sanitary, or structural engineering. 13 professorial staff. 15 master's degrees and 2 Ph.D.'s awarded 1955-59. 10 graduate students registered fall 1959.

Engineering.—Electrical. Electrical engineering, communication, control, computers, electronics and power. 10 professorial staff. 12 master's degrees and 1 Ph.D. awarded 1955-59. 19 graduate students registered fall 1959.

Engineering. — Industrial — Industrial Arts. Production control, plant layout, materials handling, methods analysis, work simplification, operations research and related industrial engineering problems. 3 graduate students registered fall 1959.

Engineering.—Mechanical. Aeronautics, applied mechanics, metallurgy and materials, heat and power, automotive design. 14 professorial staff. 24 master's degrees and 1 Ph.D. awarded 1955-59. 13 graduate students registered fall 1959.

Entomology. General, applied, forest, or systematic entomology; insect toxicology. 13 professorial staff. 17 master's degrees and 11 Ph.D.'s awarded 1955-59. 21 graduate students registered fall 1959.

Family Life and Home Administration. Child development and family relationships. 7 professorial staff. 9 master's degrees and 1 Ph.D. awarded 1955-59. 10 graduate students registered fall 1959.

Farm Crops. Plant breeding, weed control, cultural methods and production, seed technology, genetics, range management. 10 professorial staff. 11 master's degrees and 6 Ph.D.'s awarded 1955-59. 19 graduate students registered fall 1959.

Fish and Game Management. Wildlife management and fisheries. 8 professorial staff. 46 master's degrees awarded 1955-59. 19 graduate students registered fall 1959.

Food and Dairy Technology. Food technology, dairy technology; food science. 14 professorial staff. 15 master's degrees and 8 Ph.D.'s awarded 1955-59. 13 graduate students registered fall 1959.

Foods and Nutrition. Foods or nutrition. 7 professorial staff. 3 master's degrees and 2 Ph.D.'s awarded 1955-59. 8 graduate students registered fall 1959.

Forest Management. Silviculture; forest genetics, management, economics, or photogrammetry; tree physiology; fire control. 15 professorial staff. 35 master's degrees awarded 1955-59. 19 graduate students registered fall 1959.

Genetics. All principal phases. Course work drawn from biological departments of the Schools of Science and Agriculture. 13 professorial staff. 3 master's degrees and 11 Ph.D.'s awarded 1955-59. 9 graduate students registered fall 1959.

Geology. Economic and areal geology, geomorphology, petrology, invertebrate paleontology, micropaleontology, sedimentology, stratigraphy. 7 professorial staff. 12 master's degrees awarded 1955-59. 11 graduate students registered fall 1959.

Horticulture. Pomology, vegetable crops, ornamental horticulture. 10 professorial staff. 4 master's degrees and 7 Ph.D.'s awarded 1955-59. 6 graduate students registered fall 1959.

Mathematics. Analysis, algebra, geometry and applied mathematics, numerical analysis, computer science and technology. 14 professorial staff. 17 master's degrees and 12 Ph.D.'s awarded 1955-59. 41 graduate students registered fall 1959.

Pharmacy. Pharmacy, pharmaceutical analysis and pharmacology, pharmacognosy. 7 professorial staff. 3 master's degrees awarded 1955-59. 5 graduate students registered fall 1959.

Physics. Nuclear, theoretical, or applied physics; meteorology; photography; electronics. 11 professorial staff. 30 master's degrees and 8 Ph.D.'s awarded 1955-59. 34 graduate students registered fall 1959.

Poultry Husbandry. Nutrition, breeding, reproduction physiology and management. 4 professorial staff. 1 master's degree awarded 1955-59. 2 graduate students registered fall 1959.

Science.—General. Broad Ph.D. program in general science for teachers in small liberal arts college and in colleges of education who do not desire or need highly specialized training of a departmental degree. Minimum of 25 hours in each of 3 science fields and a fourth field, including the college teaching minor and certain pertinent courses in education, are normally required. Thesis research may be in a field of science or in teaching of a science in college. 6 professorial staff. 151 master's degrees and 1 Ph.D. awarded 1955-59. 68 students registered fall 1959.

Soils. Soil fertility, physics, chemistry, or genesis; irrigation; forest soils. 9 professorial staff. 18 master's degrees and 5 Ph.D.'s awarded 1955-59. 23 graduate students registered fall 1959.

Zoology. Cellular biology, embryology and anatomy, genetics, invertebrate zoology and parasitology, natural history and ecology, physiology. 11 professorial staff. 14 master's degrees and 13 Ph.D.'s awarded 1955-59. 28 graduate students registered fall 1959.

Oregon, University of

EUGENE, OREGON

The University of Oregon was organized in 1876 and began offering graduate instruction in 1899. Present Ph.D. programs on the Eugene campus are administered by the Graduate School. The Medical School, located in Portland, also awards the Ph.D. The Ed.D. degree is awarded through the School of Education and the School of Health and Physical Education; the D.B.A. through the School of Business Administration. University is publicly controlled by the state. Both men and women are admitted.

The Graduate School

Founded in 1900; awarded first Ph.D. in 1926.

A few rooms available in university dormitories for women graduate students; none for men. University maintains 1-, 2-, and 3-bedroom apartments for married students.

Residence requirement for Ph.D.: 3 years beyond bachelor's degree, of which 1 year must be spent in full-time study on campus. Summer courses available.

ADMISSION REQUIREMENTS

For graduate study: bachelor's degree; 2.5 GPA; adequate preparation in field of proposed graduate study. For candidacy for Ph.D.: completion of substantial portion of course work with satisfactory grades; examinations in 2 foreign languages; qualifying examination; comprehensive examinations.

Apply to Dean of the Graduate School at least 1 month before date of desired entry.

FEES AND FIRST-YEAR AID

Application fee $10. Tuition $270 per academic year. Special fees approximate $20 annually. Room (in dormitory) for women $240 a year. Approximate annual cost of board in college dining room $510. Apartments $38-$75 monthly.

First-year aid available: teaching fellowships, $1,400-$2,000; research assistantships, $1,100-$1,800.

Apply to Dean of the Graduate School by March 1.

FIELDS OF STUDY FOR THE PH.D.

Anthropology. Cultural anthropology, culture dynamics, New World archaeology. Recommended for graduate study: 2 years of 1 foreign language, preferably German; basic preparation in anthropology. 5 professorial staff. 5 master's degrees and 1 Ph.D. awarded 1955-59. 20 graduate students registered fall 1959.

Biology. Genetics, animal physiology (general and comparative), botany ecology, molecular biology. Recommended for graduate study: major in biology, botany, or zoology; courses in mathematics, chemistry, and physics; 2 years of French or German. 17 professorial staff. 24 master's degrees and 10 Ph.D.'s awarded 1955-59. 44 graduate students registered fall 1959.

Chemistry, Physical, organic chemistry; biochemistry. Prerequisite for graduate study: major in chemistry. 10 professorial staff. 12 master's degrees and 16 Ph.D.'s awarded 1955-59. 35 graduate students registered fall 1959.

Economics. Economic theory, history, or development; money and banking; international, labor, or mathematical economics; public finance; history of economic thought; government regulation of business. Prerequisite for graduate study: background in economics and allied fields. Recommended: GRE. 16 master's degrees and 7 Ph.D.'s awarded 1955-59. 34 graduate students registered fall 1959.

Education. School administration; psychological services; counseling, and testing; elementary, secondary, or special education. Offered by the School of Education. Prerequisite for graduate study: MAT. 16 professorial staff. 1,024 master's degrees and 95 doctorates awarded 1955-59. 52 graduate students registered fall 1959.

English. English philology, history of the English language. English or American literature. Recommended for graduate study: work in Latin, French, German. 15 professorial staff. 24 master's degrees and 5 Ph.D.'s awarded 1955-59. 30 graduate students registered fall 1959.

Geography. Geography of Latin America or the Far East, physical geography, statistical methodology in geographical research. Recommended for graduate study: statistics; 1 foreign language. 5 professorial staff. Program begun 1960.

Geology. Mineralogy, petrology, stratigraphy, paleontology. Prerequisites for graduate study: major in geology or equivalent; GRE. Recommended: 1 language, preferably German. 6 professorial staff. Ph.D. program begun 1956. 15 master's degrees awarded 1955-59. 28 graduate students registered fall 1959.

History. European, American, Far Eastern. Prerequisite for graduate study: major in history or equivalent. Recommended: reading knowledge of 2 foreign languages. 14 professorial staff. 4 master's degrees and 1 Ph.D. awarded 1955-59. 51 graduate students registered fall 1959.

Mathematics. Analysis, algebra and number theory, mathematical statistics, topology. Prerequisite for graduate study: major or minor in mathematics. 13 professorial staff. 22 master's degrees and 10 Ph.D.'s awarded 1955-59. 41 graduate students registered fall 1959.

Physical Education. Administration or scientific basis of physical education, growth and development, corrective physical education, health education. Offered by School of Health and Physical Education. Prerequisites for graduate study: major in field; MAT; 2 years of successful experience in teaching or related work. 12 professorial staff. 106 master's degrees and 19 Ph.D.'s awarded 1955-59. 65 graduate students registered fall 1959. The Ed.D. degree is also awarded in this field.

Physics. Atomic spectroscopy, nuclear physics (especially beta ray spectroscopy), solid-state physics, ultrasonics, X-rays. 9 professorial staff. 24 master's degrees and 7 Ph.D.'s awarded 1955-59. 32 graduate students registered fall 1959.

Political Science. Political theory, public law or administration, comparative government, politics, international relations. Prerequisite for graduate study: major in political or other related social science. Recommended: language competence; statistical skill. 7 professorial staff. 28 master's degrees and 5 Ph.D.'s awarded 1955-59. 35 graduate students registered fall 1959.

Psychology. Experimental psychology (learning and perception in human beings), comparative psychology, psychology of personality, psychological measurement, clinical psychology (child and adult), counseling psychology, rehabilitation counseling. Prerequisites for graduate study: major in psychology or equivalent; MAT or GRE. Recommended: German and French or Russian; course in statistics. 17 professorial staff. 36 master's degrees and 11 Ph.D.'s awarded 1955-59. 64 students registered fall 1959.

Romance Languages. French and Spanish literatures (students usually major in one and minor in the other). Offered by Department of Foreign Languages. Prerequisite for graduate study: major in French, Spanish, or Romance languages. Recommended: reading knowledge of German, Latin and Italian; GRE. 10 professorial staff. 15 master's degrees and 1 Ph.D. awarded 1955-59. 25 graduate students registered fall 1959.

Sociology. Social psychology or stratification, marriage and the family, deviant behavior, population and ecology, methodology, general theory, organization of societies, belief and value systems, industrial sociology, community organization and analysis, formal organizations. Prerequisites for graduate study: background in sociology; MAT. Recommended: reading knowledge of at least 1 foreign language; basic course in statistics. 9 professorial staff. 8 master's degrees and 3 Ph.D.'s awarded 1955-59. 28 graduate students registered fall 1959.

Speech. Rhetoric and public address, radio and television, speech pathology, theater. 13 professorial staff. Ph.D. program begun 1958. 33 master's degrees awarded 1955-59. 14 graduate students registered fall 1959.

Medical School

The Medical School is located in Portland, Oregon, and is administratively an autonomous unit in the Oregon State System of Higher Education. Its Dean reports independently to the

State Board of Higher Education; its budget is separate; and it controls its own graduate activities independently of the University of Oregon. Graduate instruction has been offered since 1921, and the first Ph.D. was awarded in 1942.

No residence facilities provided for graduate students; rooms and apartments available in community.

Medical School maintains its own library on the Medical School campus. It currently contains more than 69,000 volumes and subscribes to over 1,300 periodicals.

Residence requirement for Ph.D.: minimum of 6 academic terms.

ADMISSION REQUIREMENTS

For graduate study: bachelor's degree; satisfactory academic record; acceptance by department of proposed graduate study. Recommended: subjects and credits as required for admission to the Medical School; reading knowledge of 1 or 2 modern foreign languages. For candidacy for Ph.D.: reading knowledge of 2 modern foreign languages; qualifying examinations.

Apply to Office of the Registrar, University of Oregon Medical School, Portland 1, Oregon, at least 3 months prior to date of desired registration.

FEES AND FIRST-YEAR AID

Application fee $5. Tuition $237 per academic year for graduate students registered for 7 or more term hours. Students registered for 6 term hours or less pay $11 per term hour ($22 term minimum). Room and board in community averages $1,000 per year. Apartments $75-$110 per month.

First-year aid available: all graduate student stipends are obtained from training and research grants and vary from $1,000-$2,400 per year depending on level of training of student and on the degree sought.

FIELDS OF STUDY FOR THE PH.D.

Anatomy. Neuroanatomy and embryology, endocrinology, experimental teratology. Prerequisites for graduate study: biology or zoology; comparative anatomy; chemistry; physics. Recommended: zoology; histology; microtechnique; physiology; anthropology; embryology; biochemistry; 1 modern foreign language. Ph.D. candidacy prerequisite: statistics. 5 professorial staff.

5 master's degrees awarded 1955-59. 5 graduate students registered fall 1959.

Bacteriology.—Medical. Medical bacteriology, immunology. Recommended for graduate study: bacteriology; biochemistry; genetics. 3 professorial staff. 7 master's degrees and 1 Ph.D. awarded 1955-59. 2 graduate students registered fall 1959.

Biochemistry. Lipid, carbohydrate, protein, or muscle metabolism; neurochemistry; bone growth and development; biochemistry of connective tissue; oxidative enzyme systems. Prerequisite for graduate study: at least 1 year of biology or zoology. Recommended: major in chemistry; German, French or Russian; differential and integral calculus; physical chemistry. 10 professorial staff. 22 master's degrees and 5 Ph.D.'s awarded 1955-59. 11 graduate students registered fall 1959.

Physiology. Neurophysiology; renal, respiratory, gastro-intestinal and cardiac physiology. Prerequisite for graduate study: thorough grounding in mathematics, physics, and chemistry beyond usual B.S. requirements. 4 professorial staff. 10 master's degrees awarded 1955-59. 5 graduate students registered fall 1959.

Paper Chemistry, The Institute of

APPLETON, WISCONSIN

The Institute was organized in 1929 to provide for the graduate education of men for positions of industrial leadership, primarily in the pulp and paper field. First Ph.D. was conferred in 1933. Degrees are granted by Lawrence College upon recommendation of the Institute faculty. The Board of Trustees is composed of leading executives in the pulp and paper industry and representatives of Lawrence College. Only men are admitted.

Two dormitories available for single students; dormitory-apartment buildings for 36 married students. Facilities include 6 buildings on 32-acre campus. Dard Hunter Paper Museum contains very fine collection illustrating the art of papermaking from its invention to present.

Residence requirement for Ph.D.: 4 years of study under guidance of Institute is normally required; at least 2 years must be taken in residence at the Institute.

ADMISSION REQUIREMENTS

For graduate study: bachelor's degree, usually in chemistry or chemical engineering (majors in other sciences or engineering may qualify); 5 letters of recommendation; personal interview. Recommended: reading knowledge of German; differential equations; 2 years of physics; GRE; Selective Service College Qualification Test. For candidacy for Ph.D.: M.S. from Institute; reading knowledge of technical German; successful completion of Preparation for Research program.

Apply to Dean of Admissions by March 15.

FEES AND FIRST-YEAR AID

No application fee. Tuition $900 per year. Special fees approximate $60 annually. Room (in dormitory) $225 a year. Approximate annual cost of board in college dining room $450. Apartments $70 a month (heat and utilities furnished).

First-year aid available: 25 scholarships with stipends of $2,220 for single students, $2,400 for married students, and $2,800 for married students with children.

Apply to Dean of Admissions by March 15.

FIELDS OF STUDY FOR THE PH.D.

Physical Science. Combined program in chemistry, chemical engineering and technology, physics and mathematics. Independent research required. 36 professorial staff. 65 master's degrees and 37 Ph.D.'s awarded 1955-59. 72 graduate students registered fall 1959. New enrollment limited to 25.

Pennsylvania State University

UNIVERSITY PARK, PENNSYLVANIA

The Graduate School

Graduate instruction was first offered in 1862, and for many years was carried on under the direction of a committee of the University Senate. The Graduate School was organized in 1922 and granted its first Ph.D. in 1926. At present the Ph.D. is offered in 68 areas, and in 24 of these the Ed.D. degree is also conferred. The latter is also awarded in 4 areas in which the Ph.D. is not given: biological science; higher education; music education; and physical science. The university is publicly controlled by the state. Both men and women are admitted.

Single graduate students find accommodations in Graduate Hall, Grange Hall, and in private homes in community; university-owned 1- and 2-bedroom apartment units available for married graduate students. Apartments also available in community.

Special facilities include: the United States regional pasture research laboratory; animal calorimeter; climatometer; cryogenic laboratory; X-ray and crystal analysis laboratory; ordnance research laboratory and water tunnel for naval ordnance and fundamental hydraulics research; nuclear reactor; ionosphere research laboratory; petroleum research laboratory; gamma radiation laboratory for studies in radiation biology; speech and hearing clinic.

Residence requirement for Ph.D.: equivalent of 3 academic years of graduate work, of which at least 2 semesters must be spent in residence at the University Park campus with at least half time devoted to graduate study. Many summer courses and a few evening courses available.

ADMISSION REQUIREMENTS

For graduate study: bachelor's degree; junior-senior GPA of 2.5 (certain departments may require higher average). For candidacy for Ph.D.: reading knowledge of at least 2 foreign languages (usually French and German); acceptance by major department; candidacy examination.

Apply to Dean of the Graduate School, 103 Willard Building, Pennsylvania State University, University Park, Pennsylvania, at least 6 weeks in advance of date of desired entry.

FEES AND FIRST-YEAR AID

Application fee $10. Tuition for state residents $480 per academic year; others $960. Room (in dormitory) and board $802 per academic year in single room; $762 in double room. Apartments $65-$82.50 (1 bedroom) and $75-$92.50 (2 bedroom).

First-year aid available: scholarships in varying amounts; graduate teaching assistantships, tuition plus $657-$3,375 per academic year (amount depends on service rendered and on training); graduate research assistantships, tuition plus $657-$3,375 for 12-month period; about 800 other teaching and research appointments with varying stipends; 40 grants-in-aid, full tuition with privilege of working 10 hours per week.

Apply to Dean of the Graduate School early in November for assistantships and grants-in-aid for the following year. Write to department head for information on scholarships and many privately-sponsored fellowships in the sciences. For information on residence hall counselorships in either men's or women's residence halls, write to Dean of Men or Dean of Women by March 1.

FIELDS OF STUDY FOR THE PH.D.

Any doctoral candidate looking forward to college teaching as a career may minor in higher education.

Agricultural and Biological Chemistry. Plant metabolism and photosynthesis, intermediary metabolism, nucleic acids, proteins, carbohydrates, lipides, enzymes, vitamins, animal or poultry nutrition, clinical chemistry, endocrinology, pesticides. Prerequisites for graduate study: at least 1 year each of general, analytical, organic, and physical chemistry, and general physics; mathematics through integral calculus. Recommended: biology; biochemistry; foreign languages. 11 professorial staff. 21 master's degrees and 18 Ph.D.'s awarded 1955-59. 32 graduate students registered fall 1959.

Agricultural Economics. Offered by Department of Agricultural Economics and Rural Sociology. Prerequisites for graduate study: 3 credits each in agricultural economics and economics plus 3 additional credits in 1 of these. 13 professorial staff. 35 master's degrees and 6 Ph.D.'s awarded 1955-59. 29 graduate students registered fall 1959. Ed.D. also awarded in this field.

Agricultural Education. Minors may be taken in any of the areas of agricultural technology or in 1 of the other fields of education. Prerequisite for graduate study: 18 semester hours in professional education courses, including educational psychology and practice teaching in vocational agriculture or certification to teach vocational agriculture. 3 professorial staff. 58 master's degrees and 9 Ph.D.'s awarded 1955-59. 60 graduate students registered fall 1959. Ed.D. also awarded in this field.

Agronomy. Soil chemistry, conservation, classification, fertility, mineralogy, or physics; breeding of corn, small grains, and forage plants; forage or turf management; potato or tobacco culture; weed control; ecology of crops and pas-tures. Facilities available for X-ray diffraction, infrared, and petrographic investigations of soils. Prerequisites for graduate study: basic courses in chemistry, mathematics, physics, and biological sciences. 21 professorial staff. 35 master's degrees and 25 Ph.D.'s awarded 1955-59. 30 graduate students registered fall 1959. Ed.D. also awarded in this field.

Animal Husbandry. Animal production or breeding, meats. Prerequisite for graduate study: curriculum in animal husbandry or related animal science. 4 professorial staff. 6 master's degrees and 1 Ph.D. awarded 1955-59. 11 graduate students registered fall 1959.

Animal Nutrition. Energy metabolism. Prerequisites for graduate study: courses in animal nutrition or equivalent; completion of requirements for graduate work in agricultural and biological chemistry. 3 professorial staff. 1 graduate student registered fall 1959.

Art Education. Prerequisite for graduate study: major in art education. Ph.D. candidacy prerequisite: 2 years of successful teaching experience. 6 professorial staff. 101 master's degrees and 2 Ph.D.'s awarded 1955-59. 276 graduate students registered fall 1959. Ed.D. also awarded in this field.

Bacteriology. Bacterial physiology; soil, food, or industrial microbiology; immunology; virology. Research in animal disease in cooperation with Department of Veterinary Science. Prerequisites for graduate study: 20 semester hours of chemistry, including quantitative analysis and organic chemistry; 20 hours of biological science, including 8 of microbiology. Additional chemistry credits may be substituted for part of biology requirement. 12 professorial staff. 1 master's degree and 19 Ph.D.'s awarded 1955-59. 25 graduate students registered fall 1959. Ed.D. also awarded in this field.

Botany. Plant anatomy, cytology, ecology, genetics, morphology, mycology, physiology, plant pathology, taxonomy. Offered by Department of Botany and Plant Pathology. Prerequisites for graduate study: 27 credits in botany or 21 in botany and 6 in biological science. 13 professorial staff. 10 master's degrees and 9 Ph.D.'s awarded 1955-59. 9 graduate students registered fall 1959. Ed.D. also awarded in this field.

Business Administration. Accounting, banking and finance, insurance and real estate, management, marketing, transportation and trade. Prerequisites for graduate study: minimum of 18 acceptable credits in accounting, commerce, economics, and business statistics, including at least 6 in economics and 3 in business statistics; Admission Test for Graduate Study in Business. 20 professorial staff. 38 master's degrees awarded 1955-59. 63 graduate students registered fall 1959. Both Ph.D. and Ed.D. may be earned in this field.

Business Education. Training in the secondary school and college teaching of bookkeeping, secretarial, clerical, general business, retailing, and related subjects. Prerequisites for graduate study: 18 credits in education and psychology; 30 in business and business education subjects. Recommended: general education in the social and behavioral sciences, and in the humanities. 2 professors. 38 master's degrees awarded 1955-59. 49 graduate students registered fall 1959. Both Ph.D. and Ed.D. may be earned in this field.

Ceramic Technology. Clay mineralogy, phase diagram and related studies, ferrite and ferroelectric studies, glass technology, high-temperature reaction kinetics. Prerequisites for graduate study: major in ceramics or a related physical science; differential and integral calculus; physics; chemistry. 5 professorial staff. 15 master's degrees and 12 Ph.D.'s awarded 1955-59. 16 graduate students registered fall 1959. Ed.D. also awarded in this field.

Chemistry. Analytical, inorganic, organic, physical, or petroleum chemistry. Prerequisites for graduate study: at least 1 year in each: general, analytical, organic, and physical chemistry, and general physics; mathematics through integral calculus; reading knowledge of at least 1 foreign language (preferably German); placement examinations. 40 professorial staff. 60 master's degrees and 88 Ph.D.'s awarded 1955-59. 134 graduate students registered fall 1959. Ed.D. also awarded in this field.

Child Development and Family Relationships. Child development, family relationships. Guidance and development of children, relationships among various members of the family, problems of all stages of the family cycle, nursery school or parental education, education for home and family living in the schools, work with children and families in community agencies. Prerequisites for graduate study: minimum of 6 credits in physical and biological sciences; 12 in social sciences (including a basic course in sociology and 1 in psychology); 6 in child development and family relationships. 5 professorial staff. In

child development: 8 master's degrees and 1 Ph.D. awarded 1955-59; 10 graduate students registered fall 1959. In family relationships: 8 master's degrees awarded 1955-59; 13 graduate students registered fall 1959.

Clinical Speech. Speech correction or audiology. Offered by Department of Educational Services. Prerequisites for graduate study: 27 semester hours in clinical speech and hearing, education, and psychology, including at least 9 hours in speech correction and/or audiology. 5 professorial staff. 50 master's degrees and 6 Ph.D.'s awarded 1955-59. 78 graduate students registered fall 1959. Ed.D. degree is also awarded in this field.

Clothing and Textiles. Textile area stresses background natural sciences; clothing area stresses background social sciences. Prerequisites for graduate study: strong foundation and good record in home economics, chemistry, sociology, economics or psychology. 5 professorial staff. 13 master's degrees and 3 Ph.D.'s awarded 1955-59. 31 graduate students registered fall 1959.

Comparative Literature. Languages and literatures, both ancient and modern; comparative literature. Interdepartmental major administered by a special committee. Prerequisite for graduate study: good knowledge of foreign languages. 4 graduate students registered fall 1959.

Counseling in Education. College student or pupil personnel administration, supervision, or rehabilitation. Prerequisites for graduate study: minimum 27 credits in economics, education, psychology, sociology, and physiology or anatomy, with credits in at least 3 of these areas. 3 professorial staff. 125 master's degrees awarded 1955-59. 290 graduate students registered summer 1959 and fall 1959. Both Ph.D. and Ed.D. may be earned in this field.

Dairy Science. Dairy products manufacture, chemistry of milk and dairy products, dairy cattle nutrition or management, physiology of reproduction. Minor usually taken in agricultural and biological chemistry, bacteriology, zoology, or agricultural economics. Prerequisites for graduate study: major in dairy science or a related science; algebra; general physics. 10 professorial staff. 29 master's degrees and 9 Ph.D.'s awarded 1955-59. 19 graduate students registered fall 1959. Ed.D. also awarded in this field.

Economics. Business statistics, economic theory, labor, international economics, government economic policy, money, credit, and public finance. Prerequisites for graduate study: 6 credits in economic principles; 9 in social sciences; either 3 in statistics or 6 in mathematics. 18 professorial staff. 9 master's degrees and 1 Ph.D. awarded 1955-59. 18 graduate students registered fall 1959.

Educational Administration. Doctoral programs prepare for positions as supervising principal, assistant superintendent, and superintendent of schools. Minors in educational foundations or a field outside of education. Offered by Department of Educational Services. Prerequisites for graduate study: 18 credits in education and psychology; 1 year of teaching experience. Recommended: background in the social and behavioral sciences and in the humanities. Ph.D. candidacy prerequisite: 2 years of teaching experience. 13 professorial staff. 290 master's degrees awarded 1955-59. 240 graduate students registered fall 1959. Both Ph.D. and Ed.D. may be earned in this field.

Elementary Education. Training as kindergarten or elementary school teachers, curriculum specialist. Prerequisite for graduate study: 18 credits in elementary education, including teaching experience. 8 professorial staff. 320 master's degrees awarded 1955-59. 493 graduate students registered fall 1959. Both Ph.D. and Ed.D. may be earned in this field.

Engineering. — Aeronautical. Classical and modern hydro-, aero- and gas-dynamics, including aerochemistry and magnetohydrodynamics; structures; aeroelasticity; turbo-machinery; advanced propulsion; low-speed flight. Prerequisites for graduate study: major in science, mathematics, or engineering; courses in fluid and solid mechanics and in intermediate mathematical analysis. 3 professorial staff. 4 master's degrees and 1 Ph.D. awarded 1955-59. 11 graduate students registered fall 1959.

Engineering.—Chemical. Phase equilibria, thermodynamics, unit operations or processes, nuclear chemical engineering, petroleum technology, rheology, lubrication. Prerequisites for graduate study: 24 semester hours of chemical engineering, including stoichiometry, industrial chemistry, unit operations, thermodynamics, plant design, kinetics or chemical engineering problems; 14 semester hours of engineering, including basic courses in engineering mechanics, electrical engineering, or mechanical engineering; chemistry through 1 year of physical chemistry;

mathematics through differential equations. 11 professorial staff. 17 master's degrees and 10 Ph.D.'s awarded 1955-59. 15 graduate students registered fall 1959.

Engineering.—Civil. Structures, hydraulics, transportation or sanitary engineering, and surveying. Offered by Department of Civil and Sanitary Engineering. Prerequisite for graduate study: major in civil engineering. 9 professorial staff. 16 master's degrees and 3 Ph.D.'s awarded 1955-59. 15 graduate students registered fall 1959.

Engineering.—Electrical. Information theory, microwave theory and techniques, networks, computers, control, power conversion, servomechanisms, tubes and transistors, dynamical machine analysis, power dispatching, relay protection, wave propagation. Prerequisites for graduate study: major in engineering or science; courses in electrical circuits, machinery, and electronics. 15 professorial staff. 41 master's degrees and 2 Ph.D.'s awarded 1955-59. 67 graduate students registered fall 1959.

Engineering.—Mechanical. Heat transfer, advanced machine design, internal combustion engines, machine dynamics, gas turbines and gas dynamics, lubrication, automatic control systems, power generation and utilization. Prerequisite for graduate study: major in mechanical engineering or equivalent. 10 professorial staff. 30 master's degrees and 5 Ph.D.'s awarded 1955-59. 24 graduate students registered fall 1959.

Engineering Mechanics. Dynamics and vibrations, theory of elasticity and strength of materials, experimental stress analysis, theory of plasticity, solid-state mechanics, mechanical properties of materials, fluid mechanics. Prerequisites for graduate study: major in engineering or science; courses in statics, dynamics, and strength of materials. 9 professorial staff. 29 master's degrees and 7 Ph.D.'s awarded 1955-59. 47 graduate students registered fall 1959.

Engineering.—Mining. Mine property valuation and economics of mining engineering, mechanization and mine plant, development and exploitation methods, production engineering and operational analysis, environmental control, rock mechanics. Prerequisites for graduate study: major in mining engineering or related field. 3 professorial staff. 10 master's degrees awarded 1955-59. 9 graduate students registered fall 1959.

Engineering.—Petroleum and Natural Gas.

Experimental and theoretical studies of water flooding and newer methods for displacing oil from porous media, methods for calculating reservoir performance, scaled laboratory studies of reservoir phenomena, drilling and well completion problems. Prerequisites for graduate study: major in the field, or 20 credits of chemistry and physics, 6 of geology, 15 of engineering science, and mathematics through integral calculus. 5 professorial staff. 29 master's degrees and 8 Ph.D.'s awarded 1955-59. 25 graduate students registered fall 1959.

English. English or American literature, philology, or rhetoric. Prerequisites for graduate study: 24 credits in English, or 18 credits exclusive of survey and freshman courses. 23 professorial staff. 61 master's degrees and 18 Ph.D.'s awarded 1955-59. 91 graduate students registered fall 1959. Ed.D. also awarded in this field.

Entomology. Apiculture, ecology, economic entomology, morphology, physiology, insect resistances of plants, taxonomy, toxicology of insecticides. Offered by Department of Zoology and Entomology. Prerequisites for graduate study: 24 credits in entomology or zoology and related biological sciences; chemistry through organic. Recommended: physics and mathematics. 9 professorial staff. 4 master's degrees and 1 Ph.D. awarded 1955-59. 4 graduate students registered fall 1959.

Foods and Nutrition. Preparation for high school or college teaching, research, adult program leadership. Prerequisites for graduate study: 9 credits in organic and inorganic chemistry; 3 in biological chemistry; 3 in bacteriology; 9 in social sciences; 10 in foods and nutrition; 3 in psychology. 8 professorial staff. 20 master's degrees and 3 Ph.D.'s awarded 1955-59. 16 graduate students registered fall 1959.

Fuel Technology. Chemistry and combustion of solid, liquid, and gaseous fuels. Prerequisite for graduate study: major in chemistry, chemical engineering, physics, or fuel technology. 6 professorial staff. 14 master's degrees and 16 Ph.D.'s awarded 1955-59. 28 graduate students registered fall 1959.

Genetics and Breeding. Theoretical and applied genetics. Offered by interdepartmental committee from the biological and certain agricultural fields. Prerequisites for graduate study: minimum of 15 credits in basic biology; 15 in the areas of chemistry, mathematics, and physics.

Ph.D. program begun 1958. 2 master's degrees awarded 1955-59. 5 graduate students registered fall 1959.

Geochemistry. Crystal chemistry, phase equilibria, element distribution and affiliations, geochemical prospecting, cosmochemistry, isotope, high-temperature, and high-pressure geochemistry. Offered by Department of Geochemistry and Geophysics. Prerequisites for graduate study: introductory courses in chemistry, physics, geology, and mineralogy; 12 semester hours of intermediate work in 1 or a combination of chemistry, physics, and geological science; mathematics through integral calculus. 11 professorial staff. 7 master's degrees and 12 Ph.D.'s awarded 1955-59. 22 graduate students registered fall 1959.

Geography. Physical, human, political or economic geography; cartography; regional geography. Prerequisites for graduate study: for physical geography; 18 credits in geography and 20 in mathematics and biological and physical sciences (including 6 in geology); for human, political, or economic geography, 18 credits in geography and 20 in social sciences (including 3 in economics). 5 professorial staff. 22 master's degrees and 4 Ph.D.'s awarded 1955-59. 24 graduate students registered fall 1959.

Geology. Stratigraphy, paleontology, paleobotany, palynology, regional and structural geology, geomorphology, coal or metalliferous geology. Prerequisites for graduate study: 25 credits in chemistry, physics, mathematics, and biological sciences; 18 credits in geology and mineralogy. 8 professorial staff. 15 master's degrees and 3 Ph.D.'s awarded 1955-59. 40 graduate students registered fall 1959.

Geophysics. Geophysical prospecting, seismology, gravity, well logging, radioactive age determinations, tectonics. Offered by Department of Geochemistry and Geophysics. Prerequisites for graduate study: introductory courses in chemistry, physics, geology, and mineralogy; 12 semester hours of intermediate work in 1 or a combination of chemistry, physics, and geological sciences; mathematics through differential equations. 11 professorial staff. 6 master's degrees and 6 Ph.D.'s awarded 1955-59. 9 graduate students registered fall 1959.

German. German literature or philology. Prerequisite for graduate study: 18 credits in German. 6 professorial staff. 5 master's degrees and 1 Ph.D. awarded 1955-59. 8 graduate students registered fall 1959.

History. Ancient; medieval; early modern or modern European; colonial, 19th century, or modern American; British; Russian; Latin American; Far Eastern; European or American political, economic, diplomatic, or social and cultural. Prerequisites for graduate study: history of Europe from ancient times to present; history of America from its discovery to present; work in cognate field. 15 professorial staff. 25 master's degrees and 3 Ph.D.'s awarded 1955-59. 54 graduate students registered fall 1959.

Home Economics.—Education. Curriculum development; evaluation; teaching at elementary, secondary, adult, or higher education levels; supervision; administration in colleges; research. Prerequisites for graduate study: approximately 50 semester hours of work in home economics education, education and/or psychology, aspects of home economics, or physical, biological, and social sciences. 3 professorial staff. 23 master's degrees and 1 Ph.D. awarded 1955-59. 22 graduate students registered fall 1959. Ed.D. also awarded in this field.

Home Economics.—General. Program designed for teachers in secondary schools or small colleges and others who wish to be proficient in several areas of home economics. Prerequisites for graduate study: 6 credits in each of 3 areas of home economics. Professors are from various home economics departments. 22 master's degrees and 1 Ph.D. awarded 1955-59. 28 graduate students registered fall 1959. Ed.D. also awarded in this field.

Home Management and Family Economics. Family management practices, their effects upon members of the family unit, and interaction of such practices with local and national economy. 4 professorial staff. 14 master's degrees awarded 1955-59. 9 graduate students registered fall 1959.

Horticulture. Propagation, production, processing, breeding, nutrition, and other physiological studies of horticultural crop species; landscape design. Prerequisite for graduate study: basic courses in chemistry, mathematics, and biological sciences. Students of landscape architecture must also have basic courses in art and architecture and a minimum of 30 credits in landscape architecture. 13 professorial staff. 18 master's degrees and 8 Ph.D.'s awarded 1955-59. 18 graduate students registered fall 1959.

Industrial Arts Education. Preparation for teaching, supervision, administration, or teacher education. Prerequisite for graduate study: major in industrial arts. 5 professorial staff. 37 master's degrees awarded 1955-59. 68 graduate students registered fall 1959. Both Ph.D. and Ed.D. may be earned in this field.

Mathematics. Function or number theory, abstract algebra, topology, statistics, numerical analysis, mathematical logic. Prerequisite for graduate study: at least 2 courses beyond integral calculus. 25 professorial staff. 21 master's degrees and 4 Ph.D.'s awarded 1955-59. 92 graduate students registered fall 1959.

Metallurgy. Chemical, physical, or mechanical metallurgy, or the science of metals. Prerequisites for graduate study: major in metallurgy, chemistry, physics, or related engineering field. 6 professorial staff. 16 master's degrees and 13 Ph.D.'s awarded 1955-59. 15 graduate students registered fall 1959. Ed.D. also awarded in this field.

Meteorology. Aerosol and cloud physics: various phases of dynamic meteorology, including turbulence and atmospheric circulation, atmospheric optics, macro- and microclimatology, agricultural or synoptic meteorology, or meteorological instrumentation. Prerequisites for graduate study: mathematics through differential equations; 1 year physics; 12 credits in meteorology. 5 professorial staff. 25 master's degrees and 6 Ph.D.'s awarded 1955-59. 21 graduate students registered fall 1959. Ed.D. also awarded.

Mineral Economics. Economics of exploration for, and extraction, beneficiation and utilization of, ferrous and nonferrous metals, nonmetallics, fuels, and ground water; property evaluation; analysis of mineral data; influence of technological advances on mineral economics. Prerequisites for graduate study: 24 credits in chemistry, physics, and mathematics; 12 in geology, mineralogy, or biological sciences; 9 in mineral economics, economics, commerce, or geography; 6 in mining, metallurgy, petroleum engineering, ceramics, or industrial engineering. 2 professors. 13 master's degrees awarded 1955-59. 5 graduate students registered fall 1959.

Mineral Preparation. Fundamentals of gravity, electrical and chemical methods of beneficiating natural mineral deposits, properties of specific minerals as related to beneficiation. Prerequisites for graduate study: major in chemistry, physics, mathematics or in an engineering field such as mining, metallurgy, ceramics, fuel technology, or mechanical, electrical, or civil engineering; 6 credits in mineral preparation. 2 professors. 17 master's degrees and 1 Ph.D. awarded 1955-59. 9 graduate students registered fall 1959.

Mineralogy and Petrology. Igneous, sedimentary or metamorphic petrology; mineralogy; crystal chemistry; X-ray, clay, and ore mineralogy; applications of statistics in earth sciences. Offered by Department of Mineralogy. Prerequisites for graduate study: mathematics through integral calculus; chemistry through quantitative analysis; 10 credits of general physics; 30 of geology, petrology, and mineralogy, including microscopial petrography. 6 professorial staff. 16 master's degrees and 10 Ph.D.'s awarded 1955-59. 14 graduate students registered fall 1959.

Philosophy. History of philosophy, logic and scientific methods, value theory. Prerequisite for graduate study: major or strong minor in philosophy. 6 professorial staff. Ph.D. program begun 1958. 3 master's degrees awarded 1955-59. 16 graduate students registered fall 1959.

Physical Education. History, philosophy, and principles; applied science (physiology of exercise, kinesiology, body mechanics); organization and administration; objectives, programs, methods, and evaluation; adaptives and correctives; health; athletics (intramural and interschool). Offered by College of Physical Education and Athletics. Prerequisites for graduate study: 24-36 semester hours in professional health and physical education; 18-24 in education and psychology. 10 professorial staff. 91 master's degrees and 4 Ph.D.'s awarded 1955-59. 134 graduate students registered fall 1959. Ed.D. also awarded in this field.

Physics. Visible and infrared spectroscopy; crystal structure; field emission; acoustics; biophysics; electronics; shock waves, physics of high polymers; high-pressure, low-temperature, nuclear, or solid-state physics; various phases of theoretical physics. Prerequisite for graduate study: major in physics or allied field. 30 professorial staff. 47 master's degrees and 33 Ph.D.'s awarded 1955-59. 107 graduate students registered fall 1959. Ed.D also awarded in field.

Plant Pathology. Plant diseases caused by fungi, bacteria, or viruses and their control. Offered by Department of Botany and Plant Pathology. Prerequisites for graduate study: minimum of 27 credits in botany, plant pathology, and biological science, of which not more than 6 may be in biological science. 13 professorial staff. 2 master's degrees and 3 Ph.D.'s awarded 1955-59. 17 graduate students registered fall 1959.

Political Science. American or comparative government, political theory, international relations. Prerequisite for graduate study: minimum of 12 credits in field or equivalent. 9 professorial staff. 8 master's degrees and 4 Ph.D.'s awarded 1955-59. 26 graduate students registered fall 1959.

Poultry Husbandry. Poultry nutrition, management, products, or breeding; animal behavior. In each area the program consists of a joint major between the Department of Poultry Husbandry and 1 or more basic science departments. Prerequisite for graduate study: major in 1 of the basic sciences. 8 professorial staff. 5 master's degrees and 2 Ph.D.'s awarded 1955-59. 3 graduate students registered fall 1959.

Psychology. Clinical, educational and developmental, experimental and general, school, industrial and business, or social psychology; psychological measurements and statistics. Prerequisite for graduate study: minimum of 12 credits in the field. 28 professorial staff. 90 master's degrees and 86 Ph.D.'s awarded 1955-59. 78 graduate students registered fall 1959. Ed.D. also awarded in this field.

Recreation Education. History, philosophy and principles; administration and supervision; planning areas and facilities; program content and application; surveys and appraisals; principles of the group process; research. Students may prepare for administrative positions in public recreation systems, industries, hospitals, camps, or private agencies, or for leadership of special groups in a particular activity. Offered by College of Physical Education and Athletics. Prerequisites for graduate study: major in recreation, sociology, music, physical education, fine or industrial arts, theater arts, or related field. 7 professorial staff. 9 master's degrees awarded 1955-59. 16 graduate students registered summer 1959.

Romance Languages and Literatures. Student concentrating in French or Spanish may choose second area as minor. Prerequisite for graduate study: 24 credits of post-intermediate work in language and literature. 10 professorial staff. 21 master's degrees and 2 Ph.D.'s awarded 1955-59. 13 graduate students registered fall 1959.

Rural Sociology. Offered by Department of Agricultural Economics and Rural Sociology. Prerequisite for graduate study: 3 credits each in rural sociology and sociology, and 3 additional credits in either field. 9 professorial staff. 15 master's degrees and 9 Ph.D.'s awarded 1955-59. 12 graduate students registered fall 1959. Ed.D. also awarded in this field.

Secondary Education. Prerequisite for graduate study: 18 credits in education and psychology, including practice teaching in an area appropriate to major. Recommended: 2 years of successful teaching experience. 11 professorial staff. 141 master's degrees awarded 1955-59. 193 graduate students registered summer 1959. Both Ph.D. and Ed.D. may be earned in this field.

Sociology. Prerequisites for graduate study: 12 credits in sociology; minimum 7 in other social sciences. Recommended: broad background in arts and sciences. 11 professorial staff. 12 master's degrees and 8 Ph.D.'s awarded 1955-59. 19 graduate students registered fall 1959. Ed.D. also awarded in this field.

Speech. Speech arts, radio and television, rhetoric and public address, speech science, or speech pathology and audiology. Prerequisite for graduate study: 12 credits in speech, including a beginning public speaking course and speech science with group discussion and persuasion. 12 professorial staff. 21 master's degrees and 7 Ph.D.'s awarded 1955-59. 48 graduate students registered fall 1959. Ed.D. also awarded.

Vocational Industrial Education. Preparation for teaching, supervision, administration, or teacher education. Offered by Department of Industrial Education. Prerequisite for graduate study: major in industrial arts education. 5 professorial staff. 12 master's degrees awarded 1955-59. 18 graduate students registered fall 1959. Both Ph.D. and Ed.D. may be earned in this field.

Zoology. Animal behavior, bioacoustics, ecology, endocrinology, fishery biology, genetics, histology, ichthyology, invertebrate zoology or physiology, wildlife management. Prerequisites for graduate study: 24 credits in zoology and related biological sciences; chemistry through organic. Recommended: physics and mathematics. 9 professorial staff. 32 master's degrees and 3 Ph.D.'s awarded 1955-59. 28 graduate students registered fall 1959.

Pennsylvania, University of

PHILADELPHIA 4, PENNSYLVANIA

Graduate School of Arts and Sciences

The Graduate School was established in 1882 and awarded its first Ph.D. in 1889. The University is privately controlled and nonsectarian. Both men and women are admitted.

Other doctoral degrees awarded by the institution include: Ed.D. (School of Education); D.S.W. (School of Social Work); Med.Sc.D. (Graduate School of Medicine); and J.S.D. (Law School).

Rooms in dormitories available for single graduate students; no residence facilities for married students.

Special facilities include: library of approximately 1,570,000 volumes; departmental libraries; museum containing archaeological and ethnological collections from all continents; foundations for insurance education and child development; institutes of local and state government and of foreign policy; South Asia regional studies program; center for human relations; arboretum; observatories; Univac computer.

Residence requirement for Ph.D.: 1 year during which 12 semester credits must be earned in 2 successive terms. Minimum of 54 credits must be earned for Ph.D., of which 30 must be completed at the University of Pennsylvania.

ADMISSION REQUIREMENTS

For graduate study: bachelor's degree or equivalent; satisfactory academic record; 3 letters of recommendation; approval of Dean of Graduate School upon advice of various departments. For candidacy for Ph.D.: satisfactory completion of at least 18 semester credits of graduate work in residence at the university; knowledge of 2 modern foreign languages; preliminary examination.

Apply to Admissions Officer by September 1 for a fall term; by January 1 for a spring term; by June 1 for summer session.

FEES AND FIRST-YEAR AID

Application fee $5. Tuition $1,200 per academic year. Special fees approximate $110 annually. Room (in dormitory) $350 per academic year. Board in the college dining room averages about $600 per academic year.

First-year aid available: about 45 tuition scholarships; about 200 teaching fellowships, $500-$2,000 plus tuition; about 50 other fellowships, $500-$5,000 plus tuition; about 50 research assistantships, $1,000-$4,000 plus tuition.

Apply to the Graduate School of Arts and Sciences by February 18th.

FIELDS OF STUDY FOR THE PH.D.

American Civilization. American history and literature, anthropology, political science, race relations, philosophy, fine arts, comparative cultures. Prerequisites for graduate study: background in American history and literature; GRE. 2 professors plus others from related departments. 50 master's degrees and 21 Ph.D.'s awarded 1955-59. 75 graduate students registered fall 1959.

Anatomy. Experimental embryology, histochemistry, neuroanatomy, neurophysiology. 10 professorial staff. 4 Ph.D.'s awarded 1955-59. 5 graduate students registered fall 1959.

Anthropology. Cultural or physical anthropology, prehistoric archaeology. Prerequisites for graduate study: major in a liberal arts field; ability to read 1 foreign language. 14 professorial staff. 17 master's degrees and 13 Ph.D.'s awarded 1955-59. 47 graduate students registered fall 1959.

Area Studies.—South Asian. Offered by Departments of South Asia Regional Studies, Oriental Studies, Linguistics, History, Economics, Sociology, Political Science, and Geography. Prerequisites for graduate study: course in modern India and Pakistan; 1 language of South Asia; 1 modern European language; 1 social science. 14 professorial staff. 17 master's degrees and 2 Ph.D.'s awarded 1955-59. 19 graduate students registered fall 1959.

Art History. American art. Prerequisites for graduate study: major in art; 1 foreign language. 4 professorial staff. 6 master's degrees awarded 1955-59. 21 graduate students registered fall 1959.

Astronomy. Eclipsing variable stars; developments in instrumentation, especially in photoelectric photometry; studies of stellar scintillation and atmospheric turbulence; stellar photometry in the infrared; galactic structure by radioastronomy techniques. Prerequisite for graduate study: major in astronomy, physics, mathematics or engineering. Recommended: courses in mathematics, physics, and astronomy; 1 foreign language. 5 professorial staff. 2 master's degrees and 2 Ph.D.'s awarded 1955-59. 12 graduate students registered fall 1959.

Biochemistry. Intermediary metabolism, biochemistry of muscle or of viruses and nucleic acids, physical biochemistry. Prerequisites for graduate study: inorganic, qualitative, quantitative, organic, and physical chemistry; calculus; physics; biology; 1 foreign language. 20 professorial staff. 4 master's degrees and 15 Ph.D.'s awarded 1955-59. 20 graduate students registered fall 1959. New enrollment limited to 10-12.

Biophysics and Physical Biochemistry. Mechanism of enzyme action; electron transfer and phosphorylation in relation to respiration and photosynthesis; energy transfer processes in metabolic and functional activity; metabolic responses of muscles; metabolic regulations in animal and plant cells and tissues; enzyme purification and kinetics in vitro and in vive with emphasis on mitochondria and their constituent cytochromes; application of analog and digital computers to metabolic regulations; spectrophotometric, magnetometric, fluorometric, and electron spin resonance techniques. Offered by the Johnson Foundation. Prerequisite: major in chemistry, physics, physical chemistry, or biochemistry. 6 professorial staff. 4 Ph.D.'s awarded 1955-60. 3 graduate students registered fall 1959.

Botany. Plant physiology or taxonomy, developmental plant morphology. Offered by Graduate Group in Botany, Division of Biology. Prerequisites for graduate study: training in mathematics, physics, chemistry, and biology; GRE. 10 professorial staff. 7 Ph.D.'s awarded 1955-59.

Chemistry. Analytical-inorganic, organic, or physical chemistry. Prerequisites for graduate study: major in chemistry (43 or more credits); intermediate and advanced language (German preferred). 20 professorial staff. 59 master's degrees and 76 Ph.D.'s awarded 1955-59. 129 graduate students registered fall 1959. Total enrollment limited to about 150.

City Planning. Urban growth and structure, economics, demography and migration, renewal, or design; public policy formation and decision making; history of cities; housing; transportation; history of cities in urban areas. Offered by the Group Committee on City Planning. Prerequisite for graduate study: GRE. Recommended: introduction to design or to statistics; mathematics through calculus; introductory courses in at least 3 social sciences. Ph.D. candidacy prerequisite: M.C.P. or equivalent. 10 professorial staff plus those in affiliated departments. 72 master's degrees and 2 Ph.D.'s awarded 1955-59. 66 graduate students registered fall 1959. Ph.D. candidates limited to total of 15.

Classical Archaeology. Classical Greece and Rome, Bronze Age Greece, Etruria, Cyprus, Anatolia, architecture, sculpture, painting, inscriptions, Bronze Age, minor arts, history as represented by the monuments. Cooperative program with Bryn Mawr College (students supplement their work with courses offered there). Prerequisites for graduate study: major in classics, ancient history, or fine arts (with emphasis on ancient); (Greek; Latin, French, or German). Recommended: ancient history; Greek and Latin literature; history and archaeology of Egypt, Mesopotamia, Anatolia, and Iran. 5 professorial staff (including 2 at Bryn Mawr). 5 master's degrees awarded 1955-59. 7 graduate students registered fall 1959.

Classical Studies. Greek, Latin, classical linguistics. Prerequisites for graduate study: 4 years of Greek plus some Latin or 4 years of Latin plus some Greek; courses in history, English, philosophy, and modern languages. Recommended: courses in the classical background; French or German. 5 professorial staff. 13 master's degrees and 6 Ph.D.'s awarded 1955-59. 26 graduate students registered fall 1959.

Economics.—Applied. Economic statistics, finance, marketing, risk and insurance, transportation and public utilities, international commerce, business and organization, labor and industrial relations, economic geography. Offered by Department of Economics. 58 professorial staff.

Economics.—General. Economic history, development, and systems. Offered by Department of Economics, Wharton School of Finance and Commerce. 16 professorial staff. Ph.D. program begun 1958. 58 master's degrees and 66 Ph.D.'s awarded in economics (general and applied) 1955-59. 49 graduate students registered fall 1959.

Economics.—History. American, European, or Asiatic economic history. Combined program offered by Departments of Economics and History. 1 Ph.D. awarded 1955-59. 7 graduate students registered fall 1959.

Education. Elementary or secondary education, foundations or history of education. 17 pro-

fessorial staff. 2 master's degrees and 11 Ph.D.'s awarded 1955-59. 10 graduate students registered fall 1959. The Ed.D. degree is also awarded in this field.

Engineering.—Chemical. Interphase transfer, properties of materials at high pressures, process dynamics, biological engineering, reaction kinetics. 6 professorial staff. 17 master's degrees and 6 Ph.D.'s awarded 1955-59. 51 graduate students registered fall 1959.

Engineering.—Civil. Structures, soils, fluids, elastic theory. 5 professorial staff. 46 master's degrees awarded 1955-59. 50 graduate students registered fall 1959.

Engineering.—Electrical. Electrical communication, control and instrumentation, computers and computing, electromedical, or general electrical engineering. Prerequisites for graduate study: major in electrical engineering, except in cases where previous education warrants admission for a particular speciality. 30 professorial staff. 218 master's degrees and 19 Ph.D.'s awarded 1955-59. 1,015 graduate students registered fall 1959.

Engineering.—Mechanical. Vibrations, aerodynamics, thermodynamics, mechanics of rigid bodies, turbomachinery, lubrication, gas dynamics. Prerequisite for graduate study: major in field. 6 professorial staff. 74 master's degrees awarded 1955-59. 85 graduate students registered fall 1959.

Engineering.—Metallurgical. Physical, chemical, or mechanical metallurgy; materials science. Recommended for graduate study: major in metallurgy, physics, or chemistry. 7 professorial staff. 15 master's degrees and 4 Ph.D.'s awarded 1955-59. 45 graduate students registered fall 1959.

English. Any 3 major periods in English or American literature, philology, folklore. Prerequisite for graduate study: French or German. 26 professorial staff. 119 master's degrees and 68 Ph.D.'s awarded 1955-59. 211 graduate students registered fall 1959.

French or Spanish Literature—Romance Linguistics. French or Spanish literature, Romance linguistics. Offered by Department of Romance Languages. Prerequisite for graduate study: major in language of the major field. Recommended: knowledge of other Romance languages plus German and Latin. 10 professorial staff. 23 master's degrees and 15 Ph.D.'s awarded 1955-59. 69 students registered fall 1959.

German. Philology, literature. Offered by Department of Germanic Languages and Literature. Prerequisites for graduate study: major in field; courses in writing and conversation, history of the German language, and survey of German literature. Recommended: knowledge of French, and of the literature, history, and philosophy of other languages (especially English). 8 professorial staff. 14 master's degrees and 8 Ph.D.'s awarded 1955-59. 23 graduate students registered fall 1959.

History. Ancient, medieval, early modern or modern European, British, American, Latin-American, Far Eastern. 15 professorial staff. 85 master's degrees and 36 Ph.D.'s awarded 1955-59. 129 graduate students registered fall 1959.

Immunology. Antibody formation, streptococcal immunology. Offered by Department of Public Health and Preventive Medicine. Prerequisites for graduate study: major in biology or chemistry; reading ability in French or German. 3 professorial staff. 3 Ph.D.'s awarded 1955-59. New enrollment limited to 3.

International Relations. Basic courses: international politics; law and organization; economics; diplomacy; geography. Functional fields: international law and organization; public administration and finance or commerce; foreign relations and diplomacy; population. Regional studies: South Asia; Far or Middle East; Soviet Union; Latin America; Western and Central Europe; British Commonwealth; American civilization. Offered by International Relations Group Committee. Prerequisite for graduate study: preparation in economics, history, and political science. Recommended: 1 or more foreign languages. 32 professorial staff. 41 master's degrees and 5 Ph.D.'s awarded 1955-59. 35 graduate students registered fall 1959.

Linguistics. Historical, descriptive, or mathematical linguistics; historical linguistics theory; Indo-European comparative grammar; reconstruction from unrecorded languages; acoustic phonetics. Recommended: background in linguistics, anthropology, logic, mathematics, computers, or programming. 4 professorial staff. 11 master's degrees and 8 Ph.D.'s awarded 1955-59. 31 graduate students registered fall 1959.

Mathematics. Classical analysis (real and complex variables), number or approximation theory, algebra, algebraic geometry, topology, topological groups. Prerequisite for graduate study: strong preparation in mathematics. Rec-

ommended: competence in at least 1 foreign language (French, German, Russian); background in physics. 16 professorial staff. 35 master's degrees and 20 Ph.D.'s awarded 1955-59. 67 graduate students registered fall 1959.

Medical Microbiology. Microbiology, immunology, virology, microbial genetics and physiology, pathogenesis of infectious diseases. Prerequisites for graduate study: courses in inorganic, organic, and analytical chemistry; courses in biology and physics; mathematics through calculus. 22 professorial staff. 23 master's degrees and 41 Ph.D.'s awarded 1955-59. 33 graduate students registered fall 1959.

Music. Musicology and theory of music. Prerequisites for graduate study: entrance examination in music history and theory of music. Recommended: Latin; French; German; strong background in history for musicology majors; experience in composition for theory majors. 6 professorial staff. 11 master's degrees and 6 Ph.D.'s awarded 1955-59. 12 graduate students registered fall 1959.

Oriental Studies. Languages, history and archaeology, law, literature. Prerequisites for graduate study: equivalent of 2-3 years in either a language or historical branch of the major field; French or German; equivalent of 3 years of Hebrew for those concentrating on Hebrew Studies. 14 professorial staff. 8 master's degrees and 7 Ph.D.'s awarded 1955-59. 29 graduate students registered fall 1959.

Parasitology. Study of the major animal parasite groups (helminthic, protozoan and arthropod). Prerequisites for graduate study: courses in biology, botany, zoology (including introductory parasitology), mathematics, physics, and chemistry. Recommended: introductory or general course in entomology. Ph.D. candidacy prerequisite: reading knowledge of 1 foreign language. 1 professor. 2 master's degrees and 1 Ph.D. awarded 1955-59.

Pathology. Research and teaching in all aspects of disease with attention to morphologic, physiologic, and chemical characteristics. Offered by Department of Pathology, School of Medicine. Prerequisites for graduate study: inorganic, organic, physical chemistry; quantitative and qualitative analysis; physics; mathematics; biology; reading knowledge of 1 foreign language. Recommended: GRE or Medical College Admission Test; additional science courses. 15 professorial staff. 4 master's degrees and 1 Ph.D.

awarded 1955-59. Ph.D. program begun 1955. 8 graduate students registered fall 1959. Total enrollment limited to 12.

Pharmacology. Mechanisms of action of drugs and other chemicals on biological systems. Prerequisites for graduate study: major in chemistry, biology or physics; courses in general inorganic, organic, analytical, and physical chemistry; physics; mathematics through calculus. Recommended: zoology; biology. 6 professorial staff. 2 Ph.D.'s awarded 1955-59. 1 graduate student registered fall 1959. Total enrollment limited to 3.

Philosophy. History of philosophy, logic, philosophy of science, ethics, aesthetics, theory of knowledge. Prerequisite for graduate study: some courses in philosophy. 9 professorial staff. 11 master's degrees and 9 Ph.D.'s awarded 1955-59. 40 graduate students registered fall 1959.

Physics. High- or low-energy nuclear or solid-state physics; materials sciences. Prerequisites for graduate study: equivalent of major in physics; mathematics, including some calculus; 1 course in chemistry. Recommended: additional mathematics. 23 professorial staff. 16 master's degrees and 86 Ph.D.'s awarded 1955-59. 157 graduate students registered fall 1959.

Physiology.—General. Nonclinical areas of physiology with emphasis on physiology of animals and plants on cellular level. Prerequisite for graduate study: training in biology, mathematics, physics, and chemistry. 3 professorial staff. 7 graduate students registered fall 1959. Ph.D. program will be discontinued after 1960-61.

Physiology.—Medical and Veterinary. Heart and circulation, respiration, digestion, metabolism, temperature regulation, endocrinology, muscular and neurophysiology, sensation, comparative physiology, physiological psychology, animal behavior. Offered by Graduate Group in Physiology. Recommended for graduate study: physical chemistry, calculus, mammalian or comparative anatomy, advanced physics. 11 professorial staff. 6 master's degrees and 10 Ph.D.'s awarded 1955-59. 17 graduate students registered fall 1959. New enrollment limited to 6.

Political Science. American or comparative government, public administration and finance, international relations, political theory. 18 professorial staff. 40 master's degrees and 23 Ph.D.'s awarded 1955-59. 73 graduate students registered fall 1959.

Psychology. Experimental, mathematical, physiological, social, clinical, or industrial psychology. Prerequisites for graduate study: 1 year of mathematics and/or statistics; 1 laboratory course in psychology; GRE. Recommended: courses in biology, physics, chemistry, mathematics, and psychology. 18 professorial staff. 43 master's degrees and 41 Ph.D.'s awarded 1955-59. 40 graduate students registered fall 1959. New enrollment limited to about 20.

Regional Science. Economics of location; spatial interaction; regional and interregional theory and methods of analysis, including social accounting, input-output, linear programming, and general equilibrium models; population and gravity and potential models of human interaction; transportation and land use. Prerequisites for graduate study: 1 year each of intermediate theory in a social science field; statistics; calculus or equivalent. 5 professorial staff. Program begun 1956. 1 Ph.D. awarded 1956-59. 5 graduate students registered fall 1959.

Slavic and Baltic Studies. Russian and Polish language and literature, Balto-Slavic philology. Prerequisites for graduate study: 3 years of Russian; placement examination in Russian. Recommended: Russian history and other area subjects. 5 professorial staff. 13 master's degrees and 17 Ph.D.'s awarded 1955-59. 14 graduate students registered fall 1959.

Sociology. Demography; social disorganization, including criminology; society and the individual. Prerequisite for graduate study: major or adequate preparation in field. Recommended: statistics; language preparation. 15 professorial staff. 19 master's degrees and 19 Ph.D.'s awarded 1955-59. 53 graduate students registered fall 1959.

Virology. Viral immunology, host-virus interactions, tumor viruses, epidemiology of virus diseases. Offered by Department of Public Health and Preventive Medicine and also by Department of Medical and General Microbiology. Prerequisites for graduate study: biology; organic and inorganic chemistry; physics; bacteriology. Recommended: histology and anatomy; calculus; physical chemistry. 6 professorial staff. 3 graduate students registered fall 1959.

Zoology. Behavior, developmental biochemistry, cellular physiology, embryology, genetics, protozoology, vertebrate paleontology, ecology, population genetics. Offered by Graduate Group in Zoology, Division of Biology. Prerequisites for graduate study: general work in zoology; related biological sciences; chemistry; mathematics;

physics. 12 professorial staff. 13 master's degrees and 13 Ph.D.'s awarded 1955-59. 31 graduate students registered fall 1959.

Philadelphia College of Pharmacy and Science

PHILADELPHIA 4, PENNSYLVANIA

The Graduate School

Master of Science degree has been awarded since 1926, the date of organization of the Graduate School. From 1933 through 1957 the D.Sc. was conferred in pharmacy, but since 1958 the Ph.D. has been awarded in this field. The college is privately controlled and nonsectarian. Both men and women are admitted.

Rooms in Women's Residence Hall available for women graduate students; single men and married students find accommodations in private homes, apartments, and residence hotels in community.

Residence requirement for Ph.D.: 3 years beyond bachelor's degree. Work may be done on part-time basis, but at least 1 year of resident study (in which full assignment is carried) must be taken at this institution.

ADMISSION REQUIREMENTS

For graduate study: bachelor's degree in pharmacy or equivalent; average of 80 per cent or better in undergraduate work; recommendations from major professors; qualifying examinations administered by college prior to registration. Recommended: courses in differential and integral calculus, physical chemistry, German, and French; GRE. For candidacy for Ph.D.: master's degree or equivalent in chosen field; qualifying examinations at discretion of Graduate Committee; examinations to demonstrate reading knowledge of French and German (another language may be substituted for French under certain circumstances); preliminary examinations in major and 2 minor fields of study; demonstrated ability for research.

Apply to Secretary of the Graduate Committee, Philadelphia College of Pharmacy and Science, 43rd Street and Kingsessing Avenue, Philadelphia 4, Pennsylvania, at any time.

FEES AND FIRST-YEAR AID

No application fee. Tuition $800 per academic year. Room and board (for women only) $600 per academic year (2 meals for 5 days a week). Rooms in private homes in community range from $350-$500 per academic year.

First-year aid available: 12 teaching assistantships, $1,600-$1,800 plus remission of all fees.

Apply to Secretary of the Graduate Committee, Philadelphia College of Pharmacy and Science, 43rd Street and Kingsessing Avenue, Philadelphia 4, Pennsylvania, at any time.

FIELDS OF STUDY FOR THE PH.D.

Pharmacy. Pharmaceutical chemistry, pharmaceutical research and product development, pharmacology, pharmacognosy, and other biological sciences. Combined program offered by Departments of Pharmacy, Chemistry, Pharmacology, Biology, and Bacteriology. 28 professorial staff. Ph.D. program initiated 1958 (D.Sc. from 1933). 40 master's degrees and 10 doctorates awarded 1955-59. 29 graduate students registered fall 1959.

Pittsburgh, University of

PITTSBURGH 21, PENNSYLVANIA

The Graduate Faculty

Graduate instruction has been offered since 1852, and the first Ph.D. awarded in 1887. In 1913 a Graduate School was established, to be succeeded in 1957 by the Graduate Faculty as part of a general revision of the university structure. In addition to the Ph.D., the following doctoral degrees are awarded: Ed.D., D.Sc. in Engineering, D.S.W., D.P.H., and D.Sc. in Hygiene. The university is privately controlled and nonsectarian. Both men and women are admitted.

Rooms in dormitories available for single graduate students; no residence facilities for married students.

Special facilities include: library of approximately 900,000 volumes; observatory; radiation laboratory; Laboratory of Field Biology.

Residence requirement for Ph.D.: 6 terms of full-time work or equivalent; last 3 in residence at University of Pittsburgh. New 3-term academic calendar (September 1-July 31) permits students to complete residence requirements in 2 calendar years by attending all 3 terms. Summer and evening courses also available.

ADMISSION REQUIREMENTS

For graduate study: bachelor's degree and evidence of qualifications for advanced study. Recommended: 2 years college-level study of 1 foreign language; GRE Aptitude and Advanced Tests. For candidacy for Ph.D.: master's degree or equivalent of 1 year of graduate work; reading knowledge of 1 foreign language at a high level of proficiency (additional languages or other tools of research may be required by individual schools, divisions, or departments); preliminary examination; approval of dissertation subject.

Apply to Office of the Dean of school or division administering the program by August 1 for fall trimester; by December 1 for winter trimester; by March 15 for spring trimester; by June 1 for summer session.

FEES AND FIRST-YEAR AID

Application fee $10. Tuition $840 for 2 trimesters. Special fees approximate $96 for 2 trimesters. Room (in dormitory) $175 per trimester. Approximate cost of board in college dining room $175-$250 per trimester.

First-year aid available: tuition and university fee scholarships, $926-$1,404; teaching fellowships, $2,100-$2,800; 50 other fellowships, $2,000-$3,700; 50 research assistantships, $2,100-$2,800; 150 graduate assistantships, $1,800-$2,850. The official responsible for the aid and the date of application varies with type of aid. Details given in Bulletin of Graduate Faculty.

FIELDS OF STUDY FOR THE PH.D.

Anatomy. Aging. Offered by Department of Anatomy, School of Medicine. Prerequisites for graduate study: 1 year of physics; chemistry including analytical and organic; mathematics through calculus; 2 years of biology, including 1 in specialized area. 10 professorial staff. Ph.D. program initiated 1957. 1 master's degree awarded 1955-59. 8 graduate students registered fall 1959.

Anthropology. Social organization, ethnography, linguistics culture change, applied anthropology. Prerequisites for graduate study: training in social sciences; 1 foreign language. 10

professorial staff. Ph.D. program initiated 1956. 1 graduate student registered fall 1959.

Bacteriology. Microbial genetics, physiology, or biochemistry; general microbiology; host-parasite relationships. Offered by Department of Biological Sciences. Prerequisite for graduate study: major in field; general physics; analytical geometry; introduction to calculus. Recommended: 2 years of 1 foreign language; qualitative and quantitative analysis; immunology. 3 professorial staff. 14 master's degrees and 8 Ph.D.'s awarded 1955-59. 13 graduate students registered fall 1959. Enrollment limited to approximately 15.

Biochemistry. Isolation, metabolism, nutrition, endocrinology. Combined program offered by the Biochemistry Department of the School of Medicine and the Department of Biochemistry and Nutrition of the Graduate School of Public Health. Prerequisites for graduate study: major in chemistry; reading knowledge of 1 modern foreign language. Recommended: biology. 13 professorial staff. 7 master's degrees and 6 Ph.D.'s awarded 1955-59. 28 graduate students registered fall 1959.

Biophysics. Biophysical properties of plant, animal, and bacterial viruses; biological effects of radiation; physical chemistry of nucleic acids and proteins; bioluminescence; biohydrodynamics; psychological physics; molecular or theoretical biophysics. Prerequisites for graduate study: 1 year each of botany and geology; 2 years of physics; mathematics through calculus; general, analytical, organic, and physical chemistry; at least 1 modern foreign language. 7 professorial staff. 7 master's degrees and 6 Ph.D.'s awarded 1955-59. 12 graduate students registered fall 1959.

Botany. Plant ecology, physiology of growth regulators, morphology and morphogenesis. Offered by Department of Biological Sciences. Prerequisites for graduate study: major in field; general physics; analytical geometry; introduction to calculus. Recommended: 2 years in 1 foreign language; course in plant growth and development; genetics; evolution. 3 professorial staff. 5 master's degrees and 1 Ph.D. awarded 1955-59. 7 graduate students registered fall 1959.

Business Administration. Accounting, marketing and advertising, industrial economics or management, industrial relations and personnel management, finance and managerial forecasting, real estate, insurance, transportation and public utilities, statistics and business variations. Offered by School of Business Administration. Recommended for graduate study: Admission Test for Graduate Study in Business (ETS). 26 professorial staff. Ph.D. program initiated 1957. 331 master's degrees and 1 Ph.D. awarded 1955-59. 254 graduate students registered fall 1959.

Chemistry. Analytical, inorganic, organic, physical chemistry; chemical physics, chemical crystallography; nuclear and radiation chemistry. Prerequisites for graduate study: general, organic, analytical, and physical chemistry; general physics; mathematics through integral calculus. Recommended: additional physics; inorganic chemistry. 21 professorial staff. 29 master's degrees and 58 Ph.D.'s awarded 1955-59. 118 graduate students registered fall 1959.

Classics. Greek, Latin. Prerequisites for graduate study: major in classics; competent reading of Greek and Latin; reading knowledge of French and German (or Italian); competence in Greek, Latin, and prose composition. Recommended: Greek and Roman civilization; historical and cultural development of Greek and Latin literature; courses in histories of Greek and Latin adventures. Ph.D. candidacy prerequisites: Greek and Latin plus French and German. 2 professors. 7 master's degrees and 1 Ph.D. awarded 1955-59. 10 graduate students registered fall 1959.

Dentistry. Anesthesiology, oral surgery, orthodontics, pedontics, periodontics, prosthodontics. Prerequisite for graduate study: D.D.S. 32 professorial staff. 29 master's degrees awarded 1955-59. 33 graduate students registered fall 1959.

Economics. Economic theory or history, international trade, government and business, labor and allied fields, transportation, growth, industrial mobilization, public finance. Prerequisite for graduate study: major in economics. Recommended: mathematics. 11 professorial staff. 63 master's degrees and 27 Ph.D.'s awarded 1955-59. 72 graduate students registered fall 1959.

Education. Business, elementary, religious, secondary, special, and vocational education; health, physical, safety, and recreation education; foundations of education; educational administration; guidance, supervision, and administration. Combined program with faculty from all departments in School of Education and with Department of Psychology for program for preparation of school psychologists. Prerequisites for graduate study: professional courses in education and psychology as required by each department;

3 years of successful teaching experience or equivalent. 36 professorial staff. 1,897 master's degrees and 199 Ph.D.'s awarded 1955-59. 900 graduate students registered fall 1959.

Engineering.—Chemical. Heat, mass, or momentum transfer; kinetics; catalysis; control theory; thermodynamics. Prerequisite for graduate study: major in chemical engineering. 3 professorial staff. 31 master's degrees and 6 Ph.D.'s awarded 1955-59. 54 graduate students registered fall 1959.

Engineering.—Electrical. Control, circuits, power systems and machinery, electronics. Prerequisites for graduate study: major in electrical engineering; 1 foreign language. 27 professorial staff. 87 master's degrees and 6 Ph.D.'s awarded 1955-59. 213 graduate students registered fall 1959.

Engineering.—Mechanical. Heat transfer, stress analysis, vibration, thermodynamics, fluid mechanics. Prerequisite for graduate study: major in mechanical engineering. 20 professorial staff. 88 master's degrees and 2 Ph.D.'s awarded 1955-59. 144 graduate students registered fall 1959.

Engineering.—Metallurgical. Physical and process or solid-state metallurgy, thermodynamics, graduate X-ray diffraction, high-temperature alloys, alloys for nuclear and atomic uses. Offered by Metallurgical Engineering Department, School of Mines. Prerequisite for graduate study: major in metallurgical engineering. 7 professorial staff. 8 master's degrees and 5 Ph.D.'s awarded 1955-59. 48 graduate students registered fall 1959. Total enrollment limited to 50.

English. English or American literature; linguistics. Prerequisites for graduate study: minimum 24 hours in English courses beyond freshman year; French and German. Recommended: Latin and Greek. 13 professorial staff. 146 master's degrees and 13 Ph.D.'s awarded 1955-59. 126 graduate students registered fall 1959.

Fine Arts. Art history, inconology, connoisseurship. Prerequisite for graduate study: major in field of humanities with some history of art. Recommended: 1 foreign language. 5 professorial staff. 10 master's degrees and 2 Ph.D.'s awarded 1955-59. 8 graduate students registered fall 1959.

Geography. Economic, physical, regional (Africa, Asia). Prerequisite for graduate study: major in geography or equivalent. 6 professorial staff. Ph.D. program initiated 1959. 35 master's degrees awarded 1955-59. 16 graduate students registered fall 1959.

Geology. Sedimentation, stratigraphy, petrography, petroleum geology, paleontology. Prerequisites for graduate study: general physics and chemistry; mathematics through calculus; mineralogy; petrology; invertebrate paleontology; physical, historical, structural, field, and economic geology. Recommended: qualitative and quantitative analysis; general biology; petroleum engineering; geomorphology. 4 professorial staff. 30 master's degrees and 1 Ph.D. awarded 1955-59. 15 graduate students registered fall 1959.

History. Ancient, medieval, modern Europe, English, United States, Latin America. Prerequisites for graduate study: major in any social science; 12 history credits. Recommended: reading knowledge of French or German. 12 professorial staff. 91 master's degrees and 16 Ph.D.'s awarded 1955-59. 78 graduate students registered fall 1959.

Mathematics. Projective differential geometry; partial differential equations; mathematical statistics; numerical analysis; probability, summability, or group theory; topology; lie algebras; geometry of the complex domain; applied mathematics. Prerequisite for graduate study: minimum of 24 mathematics credits, including at least 12 credits beyond elementary calculus. 18 professorial staff. 84 master's degrees and 23 Ph.D.'s awarded 1955-59. 175 graduate students registered fall 1959.

Microbiology. Immunology, immunochemistry, virology, microbial biochemistry, physiology, and genetics. Prerequisites for graduate study: college algebra; trigonometry; analytical geometry; introductory calculus; general biology; special biology (to be selected from zoology, botany, genetics, embryology, cytology, bacteriology); physics; chemistry. 8 professorial staff. Ph.D. program initiated 1958. 14 master's degrees and 8 Ph.D.'s awarded 1955-59. 13 graduate students registered fall 1959.

Modern Languages and Literatures. French literature (all periods); French language; Spanish literature (primarily Latin-American and modern Peninsular); Spanish language; comparative Romance linguistics; Romance literatures. Prerequisites for graduate study: proficiency in language tools; 1 year course in literature of major language. Recommended: Latin; courses in history and civilization of country of major language; survey and problem course in

literature; residence and study abroad. Ph.D. candidacy prerequisites: 2 Romance languages; German; Latin in many cases. 13 professorial staff. Ph.D. program initiated 1959. 25 master's degrees and 6 Ph.D.'s awarded 1955-59. 20 graduate students registered fall 1959.

Music. Historical musicology, music theory. Prerequisites for graduate study: major in music; 1 foreign language. Recommended: a second language. 5 professorial staff. Ph.D. program initiated 1960. 5 master's degrees awarded 1955-59. 1 graduate student registered fall 1959.

Nursing Education. Nursing education, nursing service administration, psychiatric nursing service, administration or education. Combined programs offered by Department of Nursing Education in cooperation with Departments of Psychology and Psychiatry or Education and Chemistry. Prerequisite for graduate study: major in nursing. 24 professorial staff. 127 master's degrees and 2 Ph.D.'s awarded 1955-59. 71 graduate students registered fall 1959.

Pathology. Immunopathology, immunochemistry, cancer research, endocrinology, histochemistry, radiobiology, tissue culture. Prerequisite for graduate study: comprehensive background in field, including courses in gross and microscopic anatomy, neuroanatomy, biochemistry, physiology, microbiology, pathology, mathematics, biology, physics, and chemistry. 5 professorial staff. Program initiated 1960.

Pharmacology. Cardiovascular and psychopharmacology. Offered by Department of Pharmacology, School of Pharmacy. Prerequisites for graduate study: general, organic, and analytical chemistry; biology; mathematics through calculus; comparative anatomy. 3 professorial staff. Ph.D. program initiated 1958. 9 master's degrees and 1 Ph.D. awarded 1955-59. 9 graduate students registered fall 1959. Total enrollment limited to 12.

Pharmacology. Cardiovascular pharmacology, psychopharmacology. Offered by Department of Physiology and Pharmacology, School of Medicine, and Department of Pharmacology, School of Pharmacy. Prerequisites for graduate study: 1 year each of general, organic, and physical chemistry, physics, general biology, special biology, and pharmacology; mathematics through calculus. 10 professorial staff. Ph.D. program initiated 1958. 8 master's degrees and 1 Ph.D. awarded 1955-59. 10 graduate students registered fall 1959.

Pharmacy. Physical pharmacy, pharmaceutical chemistry. Prerequisite for graduate study: B.S. in pharmacy. 3 professorial staff. 15 master's degrees and 6 Ph.D.'s awarded 1955-59. 18 graduate students registered fall 1959.

Pharmacy Administration. Economics of the pharmaceutical industry, administration of retail pharmacies, drug marketing. Prerequisites for graduate study: degree in pharmacy; courses in economics, law, accounting, marketing, and administration. 1 professor. 1 master's degree and 2 Ph.D.'s awarded 1955-59. 6 graduate students registered fall 1959.

Philosophy—History and Philosophy of Science. Philosophy of religion or of science, social philosophy, history of philosophy, logic, ethics, metaphysics. Prerequisites for graduate study: courses in history of philosophy, logic, and ethics; 2 foreign languages. 5 professorial staff. Ph.D. program initiated 1960. 17 master's degrees and 4 Ph.D.'s awarded in philosophy 1955-59. 18 graduate students registered fall 1959.

Physics. Nuclear, solid-state, atomic, theoretical, or upper-atmosphere physics; X-ray crystallography; spectroscopy. Prerequisites for graduate study: differential equations; intermediate course in chief areas of classical physics. Recommended: 2 years of French, German, or Russian. 25 professorial staff. 20 master's degrees and 21 Ph.D.'s awarded 1955-59. 103 graduate students registered fall 1959.

Political Science. Comparative government; American government (national, state, local); international relations; law and organization; political theory or behavior; public administration, policy, and processes. Prerequisite for graduate study: course work in political science. 15 professorial staff. 22 master's degrees and 8 Ph.D.'s awarded 1955-59. 37 graduate students registered fall 1959.

Psychology. Experimental, physiological, industrial and personnel, social, clinical, developmental, or educational psychology. Prerequisites for graduate study: 12 credits in psychology; MAT. 15 professorial staff. 37 master's degrees and 47 Ph.D.'s awarded 1955-59. 75 graduate students registered fall 1959.

Sociology. Sociological theories and methods; social groups, structure, processes, control, and problems; community and population. Prerequisite for graduate study: major in sociology. 10 professorial staff. 21 master's degrees and 13

Ph.D.'s awarded 1955-59. 35 graduate students registered fall 1959.

Speech. Rhetoric and public address; speech pathology and audiology; theater and dramatic art. Prerequisite for graduate study: GRE or MAT. 13 professorial staff. 12 master's degrees awarded 1955-59. 17 graduate students registered fall 1959.

Zoology. Ecology, limnology, tissue culture, physiology, genetics, morphology of vertebrates and invertebrates, microtechnique. Offered by Biological Sciences Department. Prerequisites for graduate study: major in field; general physics; analytical geometry and introduction to calculus; 2 years of 1 foreign language; ecology of animal and cell; genetics and physiology. 7 professorial staff. 31 master's degrees and 15 Ph.D.'s awarded 1955-59. 31 graduate students registered fall 1959.

Portland, University of

PORTLAND, OREGON

The Graduate School

Graduate instruction has been offered since 1936, although the Graduate School was not formally organized until 1946. First Ph.D. was awarded in 1951. Ph.D. programs in two areas are offered at the present time, and the Ed.D. is awarded by the Department of Education. University is privately controlled and is related to the Roman Catholic Church. Both men and women admitted.

No special residence facilities are provided for graduate students, but they may live in regular university dormitories if space is available.

The university sponsors a psychological services center which is designed to afford practical experience for students in psychology. Library contains approximately 70,000 volumes.

Residence requirement for Ph.D.: 60 hours beyond master's degree, of which minimum of 48 must be taken in residence at the University of Portland. 6 to 8 hours of graduate credit may be transferred at master's level; 8 to 12 at the doctoral level. Summer and evening courses available.

ADMISSION REQUIREMENTS

For graduate study: bachelor's degree; B

average in each of the specialization and related areas; 12 hours of pertinent undergraduate instruction; 1 language (French, German, or Russian); GRE for all graduate students; MAT for graduate students in psychology. For candidacy for Ph.D.: master's degree; passing of qualifying examinations; acceptance of a thesis proposal. 2 of 3 languages (French, German, or Russian) required before degree is awarded.

Apply to Dean of the Graduate School at least 2 months before admission is desired.

FEES AND FIRST-YEAR AID

No application fee. Tuition $20 per credit per semester hour. Room (in dormitory) and board in college dining room $330 per semester.

First-year aid available: 10 scholarships, $250-$1,000; 7 teaching fellowships, tuition plus $100 per month; 2 other fellowships, one covering tuition only and the other tuition plus $100 per month; 3 research assistantships, with stipends ranging from $75-$150 per month.

Apply to Dean of the Graduate School by April 1 for fall term.

FIELDS OF STUDY FOR THE PH.D.

Education.—Administration. Prerequisite for graduate study: several years of administrative experience. 9 professorial staff. Ph.D. program initiated 1958. 119 master's degrees awarded 1955-59. 140 graduate students registered fall 1959.

Psychology. Clinical and experimental. Prerequisite for graduate study: courses in statistics, mathematics, history, and abnormal psychology. Recommended: laboratory courses in biology and physics. 9 professorial staff. 16 master's degrees and 7 Ph.D.'s awarded 1955-59. 42 graduate students registered fall 1959. Department attempts to accept approximately 10 students at the master's level and 5 students at the doctoral level each fall.

Princeton University

PRINCETON, NEW JERSEY

The Graduate School

Graduate instruction has been offered at Princeton since 1877, and the first Ph.D. awarded in 1884. The Graduate School was organized in 1901. Graduate instruction is offered in the arts and sciences and in engineering and architecture. University is privately controlled and nonsectarian. Only men are admitted.

Princeton is a residential graduate school; 212 students live in the Graduate College, 58 in the Graduate College annexes. Graduate student apartments accommodate 225 married couples and families.

Special facilities include: library of approximately 1,570,000 volumes containing many valuable collections in particular areas; art museum; Aeronautical Science Research Center; nuclear accelerators; nuclear fusion projects.

Residence requirement for Ph.D.: minimum of 1 year of full-time study in residence at Princeton. Graduate School does not operate on a system of semester-hour credits, and there is no mechanical provision for satisfying any portion of the degree requirements by transfer of units of credit. Level of achievement is the criterion of the speed with which a student may proceed to an advanced degree.

ADMISSION REQUIREMENTS

For graduate study: bachelor's degree in a broad program of general education; high scholastic standing; letters of recommendation. Reading knowledge of 2 foreign languages is normally necessary for carrying on graduate studies; usually these are French and German, but other languages may be substituted where permissible and advisable. In general, admission is only to candidacy for the Ph.D. degree, except in Engineering, School of Architecture, Art and Archaeology, Music, and the Woodrow Wilson School. The M.A. is granted as an incidental degree awarded to those who pass the Ph.D. general examination, which is normally taken after 2 years of graduate study and fulfillment of the language requirements. As the number of students who can be enrolled in any program is strictly limited, all applications are considered on a competitive basis; students are required to make a strong affirmative case in regard to their academic qualifications and fitness for graduate work.

Apply to Dean of the Graduate School by February 21 for fall term (only time of entrance).

FEES AND FIRST-YEAR AID

Application fee $5. Tuition $1,250 per academic year. Rooms in residence halls $200-$475 annually. Approximate annual cost of board in college dining room $595. Apartments $45-$48 per month.

First-year aid available: scholarships, $1,250; assistantships, $2,450 plus rebate of $500 on tuition; other fellowships, $1,250-$2,650; research assistantships, $2,450 plus $500 rebate on tuition; grants-in-aid up to $1,250. Application for financial support is a part of the regular application procedure.

FIELDS OF STUDY FOR THE PH.D.

The courses in the methodology of college teaching are provided through individual departments.

Architecture. Offered by School of Architecture. 15 professorial staff. 55 master's degrees and 1 Ph.D. awarded 1955-59. 30 graduate students registered fall 1959.

Art and Archaeology. 16 professorial staff. 15 master's degrees and 21 Ph.D.'s awarded 1955-59. 16 graduate students registered fall 1959.

Astronomy. 7 professorial staff. 8 Ph.D.'s awarded 1955-59. 5 graduate students registered fall 1959.

Biology. 14 professorial staff. 14 master's degrees and 23 Ph.D.'s awarded 1955-59. 14 graduate students registered fall 1959.

Chemistry. 20 professorial staff. 39 master's degrees and 47 Ph.D.'s awarded 1955-59. 68 graduate students registered fall 1959.

Chinese Art and Archaeology. Combined program offered by Department of Art and Archaeology and Department of Oriental Studies. Ph.D. program begun 1959.

Classical Archaeology. Combined program offered by Department of Classics and Department of Art and Archaeology. 4 graduate students registered fall 1959.

Classics. 17 professorial staff. 7 master's degrees and 15 Ph.D.'s awarded 1955-59. 23 graduate students registered fall 1959.

Economics and Sociology. Offered by Department of Economics and Sociology (as of the academic year 1960-61, this department will be divided into 2 separate departments). 34 professorial staff. 35 master's degrees and 35 Ph.D.'s awarded 1955-59. 47 graduate students registered fall 1959.

Engineering.—Aeronautical. 12 professorial staff. 68 master's degrees and 14 Ph.D.'s awarded

1955-59. 46 graduate students registered fall 1959.

Engineering.—Chemical. 10 professorial staff. 35 master's degrees and 14 Ph.D.'s awarded 1955-59. 33 graduate students registered fall 1959.

Engineering.—Civil. 9 professorial staff. 42 master's degrees and 2 Ph.D.'s awarded 1955-59. 19 graduate students registered fall 1959.

Engineering.—Electrical. 12 professorial staff. 47 master's degrees and 5 Ph.D.'s awarded 1955-59. 42 graduate students registered fall 1959.

Engineering.—Geological. 8 professorial staff. 3 master's degrees awarded 1955-59. 3 graduate students registered fall 1959.

Engineering.—Mechanical. 9 professorial staff. 21 master's degrees and 2 Ph.D.'s awarded 1955-59. 19 graduate students registered fall 1959.

English. 32 professorial staff. 23 master's degrees and 34 Ph.D.'s awarded 1955-59. 32 graduate students registered fall 1959.

European and Near Eastern History. Combined program offered by Department of History and Department of Oriental Studies. Ph.D. program begun 1955.

Geology. 11 professorial staff. 13 master's degrees and 34 Ph.D.'s awarded 1955-59. 31 graduate students registered fall 1959.

Germanic Languages and Literatures. Until 1958, the department was part of the Department of Modern Languages. 9 professorial staff. 13 master's degrees and 17 Ph.D.'s awarded 1955-58 by Department of Modern Languages. 3 master's degrees and 1 Ph.D. awarded 1958-59. 8 graduate students registered fall 1959.

History. 26 professorial staff. 20 master's degrees and 19 Ph.D.'s awarded 1955-59. 33 graduate students registered fall 1959.

Mathematics. 23 professorial staff. 29 master's degrees and 56 Ph.D.'s awarded 1955-59. 64 graduate students registered fall 1959.

Music. 9 professorial staff. 26 master's degrees and 4 Ph.D.'s awarded 1955-59. 21 graduate students registered fall 1959.

Oriental Studies. 12 professorial staff. 16 master's degrees and 12 Ph.D.'s awarded 1955-59. 16 graduate students registered fall 1959.

Philosophy. 10 professorial staff. 4 master's degrees and 10 Ph.D.'s awarded 1955-59. 13 graduate students registered fall 1959.

Physics. 27 professorial staff. 38 master's degrees and 59 Ph.D.'s awarded 1955-59. 76 graduate students registered fall 1959.

Plastics. 5 professorial staff. 25 master's degrees awarded 1955-59. Ph.D. degrees included in Chemical Engineering. 9 graduate students registered fall 1959.

Political and Near East Studies. Combined program offered by Department of Politics and Department of Oriental Studies. Ph.D. program begun 1958.

Politics. 19 professorial staff. 41 master's degrees and 33 Ph.D.'s awarded 1955-59. 50 graduate students registered fall 1959.

Psychology. 14 professorial staff. 17 master's degrees and 25 Ph.D.'s awarded 1955-59. 27 graduate students registered fall 1959.

Public and International Affairs. Offered by Woodrow Wilson School of Public and International Affairs. 18 professorial staff. 59 master's degrees awarded 1955-59. 39 graduate students registered fall 1959.

Religion. 10 professorial staff. Ph.D. program begun 1955. 9 master's degrees and 2 Ph.D.'s awarded 1955-59. 17 graduate students registered fall 1959.

Romance Languages and Literatures. French, Italian, Portuguese, Spanish. Until 1958, the department was part of the Department of Modern Languages. 18 professorial staff. 13 master's degrees and 17 Ph.D.'s awarded 1955-58 by the Department of Modern Languages. 6 master's degrees and 3 Ph.D.'s awarded 1958-59. 15 graduate students registered fall 1959.

Purdue University

LAFAYETTE, INDIANA

The Graduate School

The Graduate School was organized in 1929, although graduate instruction was authorized in some departments in 1925. First Ph.D. was awarded in 1928. In general, advanced degree programs have been limited to the pure and applied sciences. Cooperation among the disciplines has been encouraged through establishment of interdisciplinary committees, thus providing great flexibility in the organization of the re-

sources of the Graduate School around new areas of research interest. Purdue and Ball State Teachers College jointly sponsor a Ph.D. program in guidance. University is publicly controlled by the state. Both men and women are admitted.

Single graduate men live in single and double rooms in Harrison Courts; women in the Purdue Graduate Women's Club. A large number of furnished and unfurnished apartments are available for married students.

Special facilities include: library of approximately 475,000 volumes; engineering experiment station; agricultural experiment station; statistical and computing laboratory; central isotope storage and processing laboratory; refrigeration and climate control laboratory.

Residence requirement for Ph.D.: minimum of 6 semesters, 2 of which must be completed at Purdue. Summer courses available.

ADMISSION REQUIREMENTS

For graduate study: bachelor's degree; scholastic record indicating ability to pursue advanced study and research; adequate preparation in chosen field of study. For candidacy for Ph.D.; substantial completion of course requirements; reading knowledge of 2 foreign languages, usually selected from French, German, and Russian (another language or additional course work may occasionally be substituted for 1 language).

Apply to Dean of the Graduate School by August 15 for fall term; by January 1 for spring term; by May 15 for summer session.

FEES AND FIRST-YEAR AID

No application fee. No tuition for state residents; fees $240 a year. Nonresidents pay tuition of $615 which includes fees. Room (in dormitory) for men $270-$390 for 2 semesters; women $325-$375. Approximate annual cost of board in college dining room $600. Apartments $78-$93 per month.

First-year aid available: 75 scholarships, $400-$500; 519 teaching fellowships, $900-$2,700; 245 other fellowships, $1,500-$3,000; 606 research assistantships, $900-$2,700. 110 residence counselors and 50 administrative assistants are employed at varying stipends. The foregoing aid is also open to second- and third-year students.

Apply to the Dean of the Graduate School or to the head of department in major field before April 1 if possible.

FIELDS OF STUDY FOR THE PH.D.

Agronomy. Soil fertility and plant nutrition; soil chemistry, mineralogy, genesis, or microbiology; plant genetics and breeding; crop physiology and ecology. Prerequisite for graduate study: courses in agronomy, biology, chemistry, and physics. 28 professorial staff. 47 master's degrees and 26 Ph.D.'s awarded 1955-59. 85 graduate students registered fall 1959.

Animal Science. Animal genetics, nutrition, physiology, and production. 12 professorial staff. 15 master's degrees and 11 Ph.D.'s awarded 1955-59. 23 graduate students registered fall 1959.

Biochemistry. Biological or agricultural chemistry, plant biochemistry, animal chemistry and nutrition. Prerequisites for graduate study: orientation examinations. 12 professorial staff. 38 master's degrees and 39 Ph.D.'s awarded 1955-59. 68 graduate students registered fall 1959.

Biological Sciences. Bacteriology, biophysics, plant science, and zoology. Combined program offered by Departments of Biology, Bacteriology, Biophysics, Plant Science, and Zoology. In bacteriology, the Agricultural Experiment Station and the Schools of Agriculture, Chemical Engineering, and Metallurgical Engineering cooperate. Prerequisites for graduate study: for bacteriology, courses in microbiology and other aspects of biology and chemistry; for biophysics, elementary physics, differential and integral calculus, physical chemistry, and elementary biology; for plant science, basic courses in field; for zoology, training in zoology and courses in general, analytical, organic chemistry, general physics, and 1 foreign language. 28 professorial staff. 59 master's degrees and 67 Ph.D.'s awarded 1955-59. 103 graduate students registered fall 1959.

Botany and Plant Pathology. Plant pathology, physiology, or genetics; soil and agricultural microbiology. Prerequisites for graduate study: courses in basic plant and physical sciences; analytical and organic chemistry; physics. 21 professorial staff. 15 master's degrees and 12 Ph.D.'s awarded 1955-59. 32 graduate students registered fall 1959.

Chemistry. Analytical, biological, inorganic, organic, and physical chemistry. Prerequisites for graduate study: 35 semester hours in chemistry, including general, organic, and physical chemistry; qualitative and quantitative analysis; mathe-

matics through integral calculus; 1 year of physics; orientation examinations. 30 professorial staff. 130 master's degrees and 144 Ph.D.'s awarded 1955-59. 286 graduate students registered fall 1959.

Dairy Science. Dairy production majors offered in breeding and genetics and in nutrition and physiology; dairy manufacturing major in dairy microbiology. Prerequisite for graduate study: knowledge of the basic sciences. 11 professorial staff. 10 master's degrees and 3 Ph.D.'s awarded 1955-59. 11 graduate students registered fall 1959.

Economics. Industrial economics and relations. Prerequisites for graduate study: preparation in basic areas of economics; mathematics through calculus; GRE. 29 professorial staff. 21 master's degrees and 1 Ph.D. awarded 1955-59. 43 graduate students registered fall 1959.

Economics.—Agricultural. Farm management and production economics, farm work simplification; agricultural marketing, prices and statistics, finance or policy. Prerequisite for graduate study: courses in farm management, marketing, principles of economics, money and banking, and statistics. 29 professorial staff. 57 master's degrees and 23 Ph.D.'s awarded 1955-59. 66 graduate students registered fall 1959.

Education. Guidance, educational administration, secondary education. Prerequisites for graduate study: courses which qualify student for teacher's license. 57 professorial staff. 307 master's degrees and 13 Ph.D.'s awarded 1955-59. 216 graduate students registered fall 1959.

Engineering. — Aeronautical. Aerodynamics, structures, dynamics, aerolasticity, propulsion. Prerequisites for graduate study: major in engineering; strong mathematics and physics background. 16 professorial staff. 40 master's degrees and 8 Ph.D.'s awarded 1955-59. 26 graduate students registered fall 1959.

Engineering.—Chemical. Unit or nuclear processes, fluid dynamics, high polymers, pressure measurements, heat transfer, distillation, absorption and extraction, thermodynamics, applied reaction kinetics, process dynamics and control. Prerequisites for graduate study: B.S. in chemical engineering or equivalent or major in science or other engineering fields with adequate preparation in chemistry, mathematics, and physics. 14 professorial staff. 61 master's degrees and 20 Ph.D.'s awarded 1955-59. 60 graduate students registered fall 1959.

Engineering.—Civil. Transportation, structural, sanitary engineering; soil mechanics; surveying and mapping (for a master's degree or as a minor in the Ph.D. program); hydrology; hydraulics; mechanics of fluids; engineering geology. Prerequisites for graduate study: major in civil engineering or equivalent or major in other fields of engineering or science with adequate preparation in mathematics, physical sciences, geology, and economics. 37 professorial staff. 124 master's degrees and 20 Ph.D.'s awarded 1955-59. 122 graduate students registered fall 1959.

Engineering.—Electrical. High-voltage and lightning protection; communication engineering; electronics; power generation, transmission, and distribution; electrical machine design; electrical machinery; automatic control mechanisms. Prerequisites for graduate study: major in electrical engineering or equivalent or major in science or other fields of engineering with sufficient courses in mathematics, physics, chemistry, and economics. 33 professorial staff. 147 master's degrees and 29 Ph.D.'s awarded 1955-59. 145 graduate students registered fall 1959.

Engineering.—Industrial. Ph.D. candidacy prerequisites: master's degree in industrial engineering or equivalent; GRE. 14 professorial staff. 48 master's degrees and 4 Ph.D.'s awarded 1955-59. 37 graduate students registered fall 1959.

Engineering.—Mechanical. Heat transmission; thermodynamics; refrigeration; fluid mechanics; internal combustion engines; air conditioning; power-plant engineering, including nuclear power; gas turbines; rockets and jet propulsion; dynamics of machinery; kinematics; machine design; regulators and control systems. Prerequisites for graduate study: major in engineering; training in mathematics and physics. 33 professorial staff. 124 master's degrees and 36 Ph.D.'s awarded 1955-59. 113 graduate students registered fall 1959.

Engineering.—Metallurgical. Thermodynamics, structure and diffraction, elastic and plastic behavior of solids, diffusionless transformations, internal friction and dislocation theory, X-ray diffraction, metallurgical thermodynamics and kinetics, diffusion, oxidation mechanisms, solution rates and rate processes in liquid metals, irreversible thermodynamics, nuclear metallurgy, physical ceramics, solidification of metals. Pre-

requisites for graduate study: major in metallurgical engineering or equivalent or major in science or another field of engineering with sufficient courses in mathematics, physics, and chemistry. 10 professorial staff. 16 master's degrees and 9 Ph.D.'s awarded 1955-59. 20 graduate students registered fall 1959.

Engineering.—Nuclear. Prerequisite for graduate study: major in engineering or engineering science. 8 professorial staff. Ph.D. program initiated 1958. 7 master's degrees awarded 1955-59.

Engineering Sciences. Broad plan of study, including work in most areas represented by classical mechanics, elasticity, plasticity, fluid mechanics, thermodynamics, heat transfer, nuclear engineering, modern physics, chemistry, systems analysis and synthesis, electrical science, and modern computers. Plan of study must also include mathematics and physics. Prerequisites for graduate study: major in engineering: good background in mathematics and physics; GRE. 20 professorial staff. 57 master's degrees and 8 Ph.D.'s awarded 1955-59. 67 graduate students registered fall 1959.

Entomology. Behavior, biological control, ecology, morphology, taxonomy, physiology, toxicology, applied entomology, nematology, vertebrate pests. Prerequisite for graduate study: training in entomology, botany, chemistry, zoology, physics, and plant pathology. 17 professorial staff. 12 master's degrees and 1 Ph.D. awarded 1955-59. 20 graduate students registered fall 1959.

Home Economics. Food and nutrition. Prerequisite for graduate study: major in home economics or sufficient background in related sciences. 8 professorial staff. 46 master's degrees and 6 Ph.D.'s awarded 1955-59. 47 graduate students registered fall 1959.

Horticulture. Plant genetics and breeding, physiology or nutrition; food technology. Prerequisite for graduate study: basic courses in botany and plant physiology, chemistry, entomology, genetics, physics, mathematics, and horticulture. 16 professorial staff. 26 master's degrees and 16 Ph.D.'s awarded 1955-59. 27 graduate students registered fall 1959.

Mathematics. Algebra, topology, analysis, applied mathematics, mathematical and applied statistics. Offered by Department of Mathematics and Statistics. A program leading to the Ph.D.

in mathematics education is offered in cooperation with the Division of Education and the Department of Psychology. Prerequisite for graduate
study: mathematics, including differential equations and advanced calculus. 29 professorial staff.
119 master's degrees and 29 Ph.D.'s awarded
1955-59. 115 graduate students registered fall
1959.

Pharmacy. Pharmaceutical chemistry, pharmacology and pharmacognosy, bionucleonics.
Prerequisite for graduate study: major in pharmacy or equivalent, including courses in biology,
chemistry, or pharmacy. 15 professorial staff. 51
master's degrees and 57 Ph.D.'s awarded 1955-
59. 66 graduate students registered fall 1959.

Physics. X-rays; electron diffraction or microscopy; spectroscopy; physics of the solid-state or
of high-energy particles; electronics; cosmic rays;
nuclear, low-temperature, or theoretical physics;
certain aspects of applied physics. Prerequisite
for graduate study: major in physics or related
science. 36 professorial staff. 30 master's degrees
and 29 Ph.D.'s awarded 1955-59. 101 graduate
students registered fall 1959.

Poultry Science. Genetics, nutrition, physiology, poultry products technology. Prerequisite
for graduate study: courses in biology, chemistry,
economics, physiology, mathematics, genetics,
and poultry science. 10 professorial staff. 23 master's degrees and 12 Ph.D.'s awarded 1955-59.
28 graduate students registered fall 1959.

Psychology. Industrial, applied social, clinical,
counseling, school clinical, educational, or child
psychology. Prerequisites for graduate study:
major in psychology or equivalent; training in
mathematics and basic sciences; GRE. 24 professorial staff. 101 master's degrees and 122 Ph.D.'s
awarded 1955-59. 134 graduate students registered fall 1959.

Sociology. Sociological theory, research methods, sociology of the family, industrial sociology,
social organization and structure, social problems. Prerequisites for graduate study: 12 credits
in sociology; GRE. 10 professorial staff. 18 master's degrees and 3 Ph.D.'s awarded 1955-59.
28 graduate students registered fall 1959.

Speech. Speech pathology, audiology, voice
science, discussion, persuasion, public address.
Prerequisites for graduate study vary in accord-
ance with major selected, but ability to speak
clearly and effectively before groups is expected
of all candidates. 21 professorial staff. 47 mas-

ter's degrees and 15 Ph.D.'s awarded 1955-59.
62 graduate students registered fall 1959.

Veterinary Science and Medicine. Animal
anatomy, physiology, pathology, parasitology,
microbiology, or surgery. Prerequisite for graduate study: degree from a veterinary college or
equivalent or major in another field with good
training in biological sciences. 14 professorial
staff. 9 master's degrees and 6 Ph.D.'s awarded
1955-59. 22 graduate students registered fall
1959.

Radcliffe College

CAMBRIDGE 38, MASSACHUSETTS

Graduate School of Arts and Sciences

Radcliffe College was founded 1879 with the
primary objective of making Harvard University
instruction available to women. The first graduate students were admitted in that year, and the
first Ph.D. awarded in 1902. Radcliffe is a
separately incorporated institution, but all instruction is offered by the Harvard University
Faculty of Arts and Sciences. Radcliffe and Harvard students attend the same classes, take the
same examinations, enjoy the same privileges,
and are subject to the same academic rules and
regulations. Women are awarded a Radcliffe
degree, but the diploma is signed by the president
of Harvard as well as the president of Radcliffe.
In the 10-year period, 1950-1959, Radcliffe has
awarded 303 Ph.D.'s The university is privately-
controlled and nonsectarian.

Radcliffe Graduate Center houses 107 graduate students, and 2 small dormitories house 25.

All laboratories, museums, and other facilities
of Harvard University are open to Radcliffe
graduate students.

Residence requirement for Ph.D.: 2 years of
study (8 full courses, which need not necessarily
be taken within the compass of two academic
years). Summer courses toward the Ph.D. may
be taken at Harvard Summer School but not at
Radcliffe.

ADMISSION REQUIREMENTS

Bachelor's degree or the equivalent and undergraduate record of distinction are required. Lan-

guage requirements vary with program selected, but students are expected to have had college courses in foreign languages. GRE and MAT required for social relations and psychology. Entrance examinations are given for admission in the field of music. General or qualifying examination must be taken before a student may do independent research on thesis.

Apply to Dean of the Graduate School, Radcliffe College, 10 Garden Street, Cambridge 38, Massachusetts, by February 1.

FEES AND FIRST-YEAR AID

Application fee $10. Tuition $1,250 per academic year. Health fee $68. Average charge for room is $475 per academic year. Approximate annual cost of full board in college dining room $600; partial board plan $450.

First-year aid available: a few teaching fellowships in natural science or language fields are open to first-year students, stipend $840-$1,050; about 40 other fellowships, $1,000-$2,500; a few research assistantships, $800-$1,000. Loans up to $1,000 available.

For fellowships, apply to Dean of the Graduate School, Radcliffe College, 10 Garden Street, Cambridge 38, Massachusetts, by February 1. For teaching fellowships and research assistantships, apply to appropriate department chairman.

FIELDS OF STUDY FOR THE PH.D.

A noncredit course for prospective college teachers is given biannually in the evening without charge. It consists of lectures by faculty members, conferences, and speech training and practice.

See Harvard University for full information about Ph.D. programs available.

Redlands, University of

REDLANDS, CALIFORNIA

Intercollegiate Program of Graduate Studies

Graduate instruction was offered at the University of Redlands from 1909 through 1911 and then not again until 1935. The first Ph.D. was awarded in 1957. Redlands cooperates with six other colleges in the area (Occidental, Pomona, Claremont Men's, Scripps, Claremont Graduate School, and Whittier) for the purpose of offering Ph.D. programs in English and comparative literature, history, and political economy. Redlands awards the Ph.D. in comparative literature only. The university is privately controlled and related to the Baptist Church. Both men and women are admitted.

No on-campus housing facilities are provided for graduate students.

Residence requirement for Ph.D.: minimum of 3 years of study, including 1 on campus. Summer courses and a few evening courses are available.

ADMISSION REQUIREMENTS

For graduate study: bachelor's degree; 2.5 average in upper-division work and 2.75 average in major field; GRE Aptitude and Advanced Tests. For candidacy for Ph.D.: reading knowledge of 2 modern foreign languages. MAT required in some cases.

Apply to Director of Admissions at any time.

FEES AND FIRST-YEAR AID

Application fee $10. Tuition $900 per academic year. Approximate annual cost of board in college dining room $450. Apartments (in community) $20-$55 per month.

First-year aid available: scholarships (in intercollegiate program) $700-$2,200; a few teaching fellowships, $700.

Apply to Dean of Graduate Studies by March 1.

FIELDS OF STUDY FOR THE PH.D.

A teaching internship is a normal part of the doctoral program in the Intercollegiate Program of Graduate Studies.

Comparative Literature. An integrative program designed to develop good college classroom teachers. Offered by Division of Languages and Literature. Prerequisites for graduate study: high scholastic promise; interest in an integrative approach. The entire faculty in pertinent fields and related fields in the 7 cooperating colleges available for teaching in this program. 21 master's degrees and 2 Ph.D.'s awarded 1955-59. 15 graduate students registered fall 1959.

Rensselaer Polytechnic Institute

TROY, NEW YORK

The Graduate School

Founded in 1824, Rensselaer at once engaged in graduate instruction. In 1835 it conferred the M.A. degree and, in 1835, the first degree in science and engineering in any English-speaking country. The Graduate School was formally organized in 1913 and the first Ph.D. was awarded in 1917. It now offers the Ph.D. in several fields, and also the Doctor of Engineering Science. The Institute is privately controlled and nonsectarian. Both men and women are admitted, but students are predominantly men.

Dormitory accommodations provided for single graduate students; limited number of apartments for married students; no residence facilities for women.

Special facilities include: library of approximately 85,000 volumes; computing center with digital and analog equipment; cobalt-60 unit; radio astronomy observatory; betatron; Cockroft-Walton accelerator; nuclear chemistry laboratory; surface chemistry laboratory; subcritical uranium and reflector assembly; powder metallurgy laboratory; building research laboratory.

Residence requirement for Ph.D.: 1 year or equivalent (30 credit hours) must be done in residence on campus.

ADMISSION REQUIREMENTS

For graduate study: bachelor's degree; high scholastic standing (usually not less than B average); adequate preparation for advanced study in chosen field (records of applicants will be evaluated by department of their major subject); GRE in some cases. For candidacy for Ph.D.: reading knowledge of French, German, or Russian (for certain departments a second foreign language is required); satisfaction of 45 credit course requirements; candidacy examination; approval of advisory committee and major department.

Apply to Director of Admissions at any time, but preferably by March 1.

FEES AND FIRST-YEAR AID

No application fee. Tuition $40 per credit hour. Special fees approximate $72 annually.

Room (in dormitory) for men $280 per academic year. Approximate annual cost of board in college dining room $528 per academic year. Apartments $55 per month (excluding electricity).

First-year aid available: approximately 20 scholarships, $1,200; 130 teaching fellowships, $2,525-$2,825; approximately 24 other fellowships, $600-$2,500 plus tuition; 35 research assistantships, $2,525-$2,825.

Apply to Director of Admissions by March 1, simultaneously with application for admission.

FIELDS OF STUDY FOR THE PH.D.

A course in college teaching is offered which includes consideration of various aspects of teaching, including practice sessions.

Chemistry. Analytical, inorganic, organic, physical, colloid, nuclear, medicinal chemistry. Prerequisite for graduate study: major in chemistry. 14 professorial staff. 18 master's degrees and 36 Ph.D.'s awarded 1955-59. 67 graduate students registered fall 1959.

Engineering.—Aeronautical. Aerodynamics, astronautics, propulsion, or structures. Aeroelasticity inactive at present. Prerequisites for graduate study: major in engineering or science. 5 professorial staff. 33 master's degrees and 3 Ph.D.'s awarded 1955-59. 10 graduate students registered fall 1959.

Engineering.—Chemical. Thermodynamics and fluid dynamics, mass transfer, heat transfer, kinetics, fibre science and technology. Prerequisite for graduate study: major in chemical engineering. 7 professorial staff. 36 master's degrees and 12 Ph.D.'s awarded 1955-59. 45 graduate students registered fall 1959.

Engineering.—Civil. Structural or foundation engineering, soil mechanics. Prerequisite for graduate study: major in civil engineering or equivalent. 12 professorial staff. 69 master's degrees and 2 Ph.D.'s awarded 1955-59. 68 graduate students registered fall 1959.

Engineering.—Electrical. Gaseous electronics, control, microwave electronics. Prerequisites for graduate study: major in electrical engineering or physics; qualifying examination in electrical engineering; mathematics; physics. 13 professorial staff. 59 master's degrees and 4 Ph.D.'s awarded 1955-59. 91 graduate students registered fall 1959.

Engineering.—Mechanical. Heat transfer and thermodynamics, automatic control, design. Prerequisite for graduate study: major in mechanical engineering. 5 professorial staff. 41 master's degrees and 2 Ph.D.'s awarded 1955-59. 51 graduate students registered fall 1959.

Geology and Geophysics. Geophysics, seismology, petrology, petrography, stratigraphy, sedimentation. Prerequisites for graduate study: major in geology; good background in chemistry, physics, and mathematics. 7 professorial staff. 3 master's degrees awarded 1955-59. 12 graduate students registered fall 1959.

Mathematics. Applied mathematics, analysis, mathematical logic. Prerequisite for graduate study: at least 4 years of college mathematics. Recommended: 1 year each of physics and mechanics; 1 or 2 more years of mathematics; reading knowledge of German and French or Russian. 15 professorial staff. 23 master's degrees and 1 Ph.D. awarded 1955-59. 38 graduate students registered fall 1959. New enrollment limited to 25.

Mechanics. 5 professorial staff. 31 master's degrees and 5 Ph.D.'s awarded 1955-59. 18 graduate students registered fall 1959.

Metallurgy. Metal physics, welding, mechanical metallurgy, composite materials, nuclear materials, corrosion, metallography, alloy theory, kinetics of reactions, melting, solidification, structure of solids. Recommended: course work in physical metallurgy. Ph.D. candidacy prerequisites: GRE; German. 15 professorial staff. 63 master's degrees and 22 Ph.D.'s awarded 1955-59. 76 graduate students registered fall 1959.

Microbiology. Microbial or radiation genetics; intermediary metabolism, cytological and histological organization. Cooperative program offered by Department of Biology (Rensselaer) and Albany Medical College. Prerequisites for graduate study: major in microbiology; 2 years each of calculus, physics, physical and organic chemistry; 2 foreign languages. 8 professorial staff. Ph.D. program initiated 1957. 2 master's degrees awarded 1955-59. 2 graduate students registered fall 1959.

Physics. Nuclear or solid-state physics, scatterings of wave and particles, astrophysics and meteorology. Prerequisite for graduate study: major in physics. 20 professorial staff. 63 master's degrees and 8 Ph.D.'s awarded 1955-59. 91 graduate students registered fall 1959.

Rhode Island, University of

KINGSTON, RHODE ISLAND

Division of Graduate Studies

The first master's degree was awarded by the University of Rhode Island in 1907. In 1943 the Division of Graduate Studies was organized, and in 1960 the first Ph.D. was awarded. The university is publicly controlled by the state. Both men and women are admitted.

Single graduate students live in residential halls; married students in university-owned apartments.

Library contains approximately 174,000 volumes.

Residence requirement for Ph.D.: 6 units beyond bachelor's degree, 2 of which must be taken in consecutive semesters on campus.

ADMISSION REQUIREMENTS

For graduate study: bachelor's degree; B average or better. Recommended (required under certain conditions): GRE or MAT. For candidacy for Ph.D.: completion of first 4 units of study; proficiency examinations in 2 foreign languages (or 1 language and another research tool); comprehensive examination.

Apply to Dean of Graduate Studies by March 15.

FEES AND FIRST-YEAR AID

No application fee. Tuition for state residents $300 per academic year; others $600. Special fees approximate $10 annually. Room (in dormitory) for men $260-$300 per year; for women $350-$380. Approximate annual cost of board in college dining room $400. Apartments (unfurnished) $75-$95 per month; furnished $81-$101.

First-year aid available: 30 tuition scholarships; 50 teaching fellowships, $1,700 and up; 8 other fellowships, $1,500-$2,500; 21 research assistantships, $1,700 and up.

Apply to Dean, Division of Graduate Studies, by March 15.

FIELDS OF STUDY FOR THE PH.D.

Biological Oceanography. General marine biology, plankton biology, fisheries biology, invertebrates. Offered at Narragansett Marine Laboratory. Prerequisites for graduate study: major in biology; approval of director of the laboratory and Dean of the Graduate School. 7 professorial staff. Ph.D. program initiated 1958. 6 master's degrees awarded 1955-59. 11 graduate students registered fall 1959.

Biological Sciences. Agronomy, animal and poultry husbandry, animal pathology, developmental biology, ecology, endocrinology, entomology-acarology, general bacteriology, horticulture, invertebrate zoology, ornithology, parasitology, physiology (general and vertebrate), physiological ecology, plant cytology, serology, taxonomy, vertebrate biology. Combined program offered by the Departments of Agronomy, Animal and Poultry Husbandry, Animal Pathology, Bacteriology, Botany, Horticulture, Pharmacognosy, Pharmacology, Plant Pathology, and Zoology. Programs in pharmacognosy and pharmacology are offered (under *Pharmaceutical Sciences*) jointly with the Department of Pharmacy. Prerequisite for graduate study: major in a biological science or closely related field. 35 professorial staff. Ph.D. program initiated 1959. 41 master's degrees awarded 1955-59. 38 graduate students registered fall 1959.

Chemistry. Inorganic (metal chelates, coordination compounds, salts); analytical (flame photometry, gas chromatography, analyses); organic (reaction mechanisms, polymers, syntheses); physical (decomposition of metal oxides, catalysis, electrochemistry). Prerequisites for graduate study: major in chemistry; French or German. 10 professorial staff. Ph.D. program initiated 1958. 19 master's degrees awarded 1955-59. 3 Ph.D.'s awarded 1960. 17 graduate students registered fall 1959. Total registration limited to 25.

Engineering.—Chemical. Heat, mass, or momentum transfer; process dynamics; thermodynamics; distillation; crystallization; phase equilibria. 6 professorial staff. Ph.D. program initiated 1959. 9 master's degrees awarded 1955-59. 6 graduate students registered fall 1959.

Pharmaceutical Sciences. Medicinal chemistry, chemical and physical methods of drug analysis, synthesis, biosynthesis and drug plant chemical isolation studies, fermentation studies, toxicology and pharmacology, molecular structure and pharmacological problems. Offered by Departments of Pharmacy, Pharmaceutical Chemistry, Pharmacognosy, and Pharmacology. Recommended for graduate study: major in pharmacy, chemistry, or biology; 1 foreign language. 11 pro-

fessorial staff. Ph.D. program intiated 1958. 1 Ph.D. awarded 1960. 16 graduate students registered fall 1959.

Rice University*

HOUSTON 1, TEXAS

Committee on Graduate Instruction

Graduate study and research have been emphasized at Rice since its opening in 1912. A graduate division was established in 1915, and the first Ph.D. was awarded in 1918. University is privately controlled and nonsectarian. Both men and women are admitted.

A few rooms for single graduate students available in residential colleges; no residence facilities provided for married students.

Library of approximately 355,000 volumes includes extensive files of scientific and technical journals.

Residence requirement for Ph.D.: 3 years; no transfer of credits allowed.

ADMISSION REQUIREMENTS

For graduate study: bachelor's degree; record of high scholarship in advanced undergraduate work. Recommended: GRE. For candidacy for Ph.D.: examinations indicating reading knowledge of French and German (or other approved language); completion of 36 hours of graduate study with high standing; departmental preliminary examinations.

Apply to chairman of appropriate department by March 15 or earlier.

FEES AND FIRST-YEAR AID

No application fee or tuition. Special fees approximate $124 annually. Room (in dormitory) and board for men $945 per academic year; for women $995.

First-year aid available: 58 institute fee scholarships; 151 teaching fellowships, $1,500-$1,800; 34 other fellowships, $500-$3,000; 10 research assistantships, $3,000-$5,500.

Apply to chairman of appropriate department by March 15 or earlier.

---

* Name officially changed on July 1, 1960, from Rice Institute to William Marsh Rice University.

FIELDS OF STUDY FOR THE PH.D.

Biology. Parasitology, endocrinology, cellular physiology, microanatomy, genetics. Prerequisites for graduate study: major in biological sciences; chemistry through organic; general physics; 1 year college mathematics. 6 professorial staff. 7 master's degrees and 10 Ph.D.'s awarded 1955-59. 13 graduate students registered fall 1959.

Chemistry. Physical chemistry: theoretical, thermodynamics, microwave, colloid, crystallography. Organic: natural products, physical organic. Prerequisite for graduate study: 4 to 6 courses in chemistry. 10 professorial staff. 10 master's degrees and 12 Ph.D.'s awarded 1955-59. 20 graduate students registered fall 1959.

Economics and Business Administration. Economic theory, economic thought and history, mathematical economics, quantitative methods, labor and industrial organization, monetary theory and policy, international trade and finance, and managerial economics. 7 professorial staff. Program begun 1960.

Engineering.—Chemical. Thermodynamics, kinetics, heat and mass transfer, or nuclear engineering. 8 professorial staff. 10 master's degrees and 6 Ph.D.'s awarded 1955-59. 41 graduate students registered fall 1959.

Engineering.—Civil. Structures. Prerequisite for graduate study: major in civil engineering. 7 professorial staff. Ph.D. program begun 1959. 3 master's degrees awarded 1955-59. 19 graduate students registered fall 1959.

Engineering.—Mechanical. Theoretical and applied mechanics; physical metallurgy; fluid dynamics and hydrodynamics; thermodynamics and heat transfer. Prerequisite for graduate study: German. 10 professorial staff. Ph.D. program begun 1956. 30 master's degrees awarded 1955-59. 23 graduate students registered fall 1959.

English. Middle English, Renaissance and Elizabethan, 17th, 18th, 19th centuries. Prerequisite for graduate study: work in some foreign language other than Spanish. 11 professorial staff. 20 master's degrees and 5 Ph.D.'s awarded 1955-59. 38 graduate students registered fall 1959.

French. French literature (18th, 19th, and 20th centuries). Offered by Department of Romance Languages. Prerequisite for graduate study: major in French. Ph.D. candidacy prerequisite: M.A. in French, or French and Spanish. 7 professorial staff. 6 master's degrees and 2 Ph.D.'s awarded 1955-59. 26 graduate students registered fall 1959.

Geology. Geochemistry, geophysics, geobiology. Prerequisite for graduate study: major in geology, physics, or chemistry. 6 professorial staff. 23 master's degrees and 8 Ph.D.'s awarded 1955-59. 37 graduate students registered fall 1959.

History. Medieval, 17th and 18th century English, early national period American, American South, American Civil War. Prerequisite for graduate study: 4 to 6 advanced courses in history. 8 professorial staff. 6 master's degrees and 3 Ph.D.'s awarded 1955-59. 13 graduate students registered fall 1959.

Mathematics. Analysis (real variable, complex variable, partial differential equations), topological algebra, number theory. Prerequisite for graduate study: work in mathematics indicating ability for advanced and original work. 8 professorial staff. 12 master's degrees and 7 Ph.D.'s awarded 1955-59. 29 graduate students registered fall 1959.

Philosophy. Ethics, philosophy of religion, history of philosophy, metaphysics. Prerequisites for graduate study: major in philosophy or related field; French or German. 4 professorial staff. Ph.D. program begun 1960. 4 master's degrees awarded 1955-59. 5 graduate students registered fall 1959.

Physics. Nuclear and solid state. Prerequisite for graduate study: major in physics or electrical engineering. 11 professorial staff. 44 master's degrees and 26 Ph.D.'s awarded 1955-59. 58 graduate students registered fall 1959.

Rochester, University of

ROCHESTER 20, NEW YORK

The Graduate School

Although graduate instruction has been offered at Rochester since about 1850, it developed slowly until the 1920's. Then, with the establishment of the School of Medicine and Dentistry and the Eastman School of Music, the expansion of university library facilities, and the increased provision of equipment and fellowships for research in the College of Arts and Science, graduate work developed more rapidly. The first Ph.D. was awarded in 1925. In 1957 a reorganization of graduate work took place which resulted in decentralization of most of the administrative control of graduate work. At present each of the colleges or schools in the university administers its own graduate program and is responsible for recommending candidates for master's degrees. Policies, standards, and facilities for work toward the Ph.D. are under the general scrutiny of a University Council on Graduate Studies, which recommends candidates for this degree. The Ed.D. degree is conferred through the College of Education and the A.Mus.D. degree through the Eastman School of Music. The University is privately controlled and nonsectarian. Both men and women are admitted.

Most graduate students find accommodations in privately-owned facilities, but single students may be admitted to undergraduate dormitories if space is available.

Special facilities include: library of approximately 675,000 volumes, including several important collections of personal papers and an outstanding music library; 2 cyclotrons; 4 electron microscopes; a 2-million-volt X-ray; radio telescope (through Associated Universities, Inc.); association with Brookhaven National Laboratories (through Associated Universities, Inc.); cine-fluorographic equipment; biological laboratories of the Atomic Energy Commission; computing center with IBM 650; subcritical reactor; analog computer equipment; nuclear magnetic resonance spectrophotometer; art gallery; Strong Memorial Hospital.

Residence requirement for Ph.D.: minimum of 3 years (90 semester hours) of study beyond bachelor's degree, of which at least 1 year (2 consecutive semesters) must be spent in full-time resident study at the University of Rochester. Summer and evening courses available for full-time students.

ADMISSION REQUIREMENTS

For graduate study: graduation from college, scientific school, or music school of good standing; satisfactory evidence of ability to pursue graduate study with profit; acceptance by individual college or academic department. Recommended: GRE. For candidacy for Ph.D.: satisfactory completion of substantial portion of course work; reading knowledge of at least 1 modern foreign language (most departments require 2 languages); qualifying examination.

Apply to Secretary of Graduate Admissions Office, Office of Admissions, Administration Building, by September 5.

FEES AND FIRST-YEAR AID

No application fee. Tuition: Eastman School of Music $1,225; School of Medicine and Dentistry $1,250; all other schools $1,275. Annual health fee $25. If available, room (in dormitory) for men $250-$295 per academic year; $260-$300 for women. Approximate annual cost of board in college dining room $500.

First-year aid available: scholarships, up to full tuition; teaching assistantships, $1,500 and up; fellowships, $1,000 and up; research assistantships, $1,500 and up. Grants-in-aid also available. In addition to stipends noted above, tuition is waived in almost all cases.

Apply by March 1 to Associate Dean for Graduate Studies in the school or college in which graduate work is to be done.

FIELDS OF STUDY FOR THE PH.D.

Some departments hold regular seminars or other functions on methodologies and skills in teaching for their graduate students. Other departments require supervised teaching experience as part of the Ph.D. program.

Anatomy. Morphology, histochemistry, histopathology, nutritional deficiencies, muscular dystrophy, cytology, neurophysiology. Offered by Department of Anatomy, School of Medicine and Dentistry. Prerequisite for graduate study: major in biology or in chemistry and biology. Ph.D. candidacy prerequisite: reading knowledge of 2 foreign languages. 6 professorial staff. 1 master's degree and 3 Ph.D.'s awarded 1955-59. 3 graduate students registered fall 1959. New enrollment limited to 2.

Bacteriology. Virology, microbial physiology, general medical or oral microbiology, animal parasitology, immunochemistry. Offered by Department of Bacteriology, School of Medicine and Dentistry. Prerequisites for graduate study: major in microbiology, general biology, or chemistry; at least 1 year each of general, analytical, and organic chemistry, mathematics, physics, and biology; basic training in French and German. Recommended: physical chemistry. 8 professorial staff. 9 master's degrees and 5 Ph.D.'s awarded 1955-59. 10 graduate students registered fall 1959. New enrollment limited to 2.

Biochemistry. Nucleic acid and cytochemistry, isolation of oxidative enzymes, chromatography and identification of heme prosthetic groups, chromatography, identification and biosynthesis of phospholipides, oxidative phosphorylation. Offered by Department of Biochemistry, School of Medicine and Dentistry. Prerequisites for graduate study: major in chemistry or biology with advanced work in the other field; calculus. Recommended: statistics; genetics; other chemistry courses. 14 professorial staff. 2 master's degrees and 15 Ph.D.'s awarded 1955-59. 15 graduate students registered fall 1959. New enrollment limited to 5.

Biology. Experimental embryology or cytology, viral biochemical and drosophila genetics, submicroscopic morphology, photosynthesis, nonenzymatic synthesis, plant and visual biochemistry, plant ecology. Offered by Department of Biology, College of Arts and Science. Prerequisites for graduate study: 8 terms of biology, zoology, or botany; mathematics through elementary calculus; 1 year of physics; 2 semesters of organic chemistry. Recommended: advanced training in mathematics, physics, and chemistry. 11 professorial staff. 5 master's degrees and 8 Ph.D.'s awarded 1955-59. 22 graduate students registered fall 1959. New enrollment limited to approximately 6.

Biophysics. Biological effects of ionizing radiations, distribution in nature of naturally radioactive substances, investigation of possible uses of antibodies as carriers of radiation for therapy, metabolic studies in mammals using radioactive tracers, electron microscopy. Offered by Department of Radiation Biology, School of Medicine and Dentistry. Prerequisite for graduate study: major in physics. Recommended: elementary courses in chemistry and biology; 2 years of mathematics. 2 master's degrees and 9 Ph.D.'s awarded 1955-59. 3 graduate students registered fall 1959. New enrollment limited to 2.

Chemistry. Organic and physical. Offered by Department of Chemistry, College of Arts and Science. Prerequisites for graduate study: minimum of at least 1 year in each of general, analytical, organic, and physical chemistry; 2 years of mathematics, including 1 year of differential and integral calculus; 1 year of physics; ability to read German chemical literature; proficiency examination. 12 professorial staff. 4 master's degrees and 58 Ph.D.'s awarded 1955-59. 62 graduate students registered fall 1959. New enrollment limited to 20-22.

Economics. Econometrics, international or mathematical economics, economic development with emphasis on Far East. Offered by Department of Economics, College of Arts and Science. Recommended for graduate study: background in economics and mathematics. 8 professorial staff. Ph.D. program begun 1959. 4 master's degrees awarded 1955-59. 21 graduate students registered fall 1959. New enrollment limited to 10.

Engineering.—Chemical. Rheology of suspensions, properties of glass, bonding strength of adhesives, 2-phase fluid flow, flocculation and aggregation of particulate matter, heat transfer, gas dispersion and mass transfer, molecular distillation, agitation, filtration. Offered by Department of Chemical Engineering, College of Engineering. Prerequisites for graduate study: major or equivalent in chemical engineering or major in chemistry with deficiencies; proficiency examination. Recommended: reading knowledge of 1 foreign language, preferably German or Russian; GRE. 7 professorial staff. 16 master's degrees and 3 Ph.D.'s awarded 1955-59. 19 graduate students registered fall 1959. New enrollment limited to 3.

Engineering. — Electrical. Servomechanisms, transistor and solid state devices, acoustics, network theory, biomedical engineering. Offered by Department of Engineering, College of Engineering. Prerequisite for graduate study: major in field or background in physics or engineering. 5 professorial staff. Ph.D. program begun 1959. 6 master's degrees awarded 1955-59. 47 graduate students registered fall 1959. New enrollment limited to approximately 15.

English. English and American literature; also, through supervised teaching, the development of equal competence in teaching and scholarship. Offered by Department of English, College of Arts and Science. Prerequisites for graduate study: English concentration; French or German. 15 professorial staff. 23 master's degrees and 2 Ph.D.'s awarded 1955-59. 50 graduate students registered fall 1959. New enrollment limited to 10.

Geology. Paleontology, stratigraphy, micropaleontology, structural geology, sedimentation, petrology. Offered by Department of Geology and Geography, College of Arts and Science. Prerequisites for graduate study: basic courses in physics, chemistry, mathematics, paleontology, mineralogy, and (for students specializing on paleontology or stratigraphy) elementary biology. 4 professorial staff. 14 master's degrees and 1 Ph.D. awarded 1955-59. 11 graduate students registered fall 1959. New enrollment limited to approximately 1.

History. American history with emphasis on training of college and university teachers. Offered by Department of History, College of Arts and Science. Prerequisite for graduate study: 24-30 hours of work in history. 8 professorial staff. 30 master's degrees and 15 Ph.D.'s awarded 1955-59. 45 graduate students registered fall 1959. New enrollment limited to 10.

Mathematics. Analysis (functional, measure theory, Fourier analysis, complex variables), algebra, point set topology, numerical analysis. Offered by Department of Mathematics, College of Arts and Science. Prerequisite for graduate study: major in mathematics or equivalent. 14 professorial staff. 13 master's degrees and 4 Ph.D.'s awarded 1955-59. 16 graduate students registered fall 1959. New enrollment limited to 8.

Music.—Composition. Offered by Department of Composition, Eastman School of Music. Prerequisites for graduate study: 18 hours of composition; 12 of lower-division theory; 12 of upper-division counterpoint and orchestration; experience in writing larger forms; theory placement examination. 12 professorial staff. 29 master's degrees and 35 Ph.D.'s awarded 1955-59. 20 graduate students registered fall 1959. New enrollment limited to 5. A.Mus.D. also awarded in this field.

Music.—Education. Offered by Department of Music Education, Eastman School of Music. Prerequisites for graduate study: major in public school music; Seashore talent and theory placement tests. Recommended: 2 years of teaching. 12 professorial staff. 80 master's degrees awarded 1955-59. 23 graduate students registered fall 1959. New enrollment limited to 3.

Music.—Musicology. Offered by Department of Musicology, Eastman School of Music. Prerequisites for graduate study: 10 hours in history of music, including 4 of upper-division courses; 18 hours of theory, including 6 of upper-division; reading knowledge of French and German; theory and music history placement examinations. 12 professorial staff. 17 master's degrees and 5 Ph.D.'s awarded 1955-59. 10 graduate students registered fall 1959. New enrollment limited to 2.

Music.—Theory. Offered by Department of Theory, Eastman School of Music. Prerequisites for graduate study: 24 hours of theory, including 10 of upper-division courses; theory placement examination. Recommended: 1 year each of counterpoint and orchestration. 12 professorial staff. 76 master's degrees and 28 Ph.D.'s awarded 1955-59. 39 graduate students registered fall 1959. New enrollment limited to 4.

Optics. Radiometry, including solar radiation and optical problems of the atmosphere; photometry and problems related to the mechanism of vision; design, building, and testing of optical instruments; vacuum spectroscopy; microspectroscopy; optical constants of transparent materials and metals. Offered by Institute of Optics. A combined program in solid-state physics is offered with the Department of Physics. Prerequisite for graduate study: major in physics or engineering or advanced work in physics and mathematics. 15 professorial staff. 24 master's degrees and 8 Ph.D.'s awarded 1955-59. 35 graduate students registered fall 1959. New enrollment limited to 6.

Pathology. Neoplasia and relation to changes in connective tissue, connective tissue metabolism, problems in bone resorption. Offered by Department of Pathology, School of Medicine and Dentistry. Prerequisite for graduate study: D.D.S., D.M.D. or M.D. degree. 5 professorial staff. 5 Ph.D.'s awarded 1955-59. 2 graduate students registered fall 1959. New enrollment limited to 1.

Pharmacology and Toxicology. Cell physiology, bone or drug metabolism, studies of the effects of radiation and radioactive material on cellular metabolism, pharmacodynamics and biological effects of inhaled materials, neuropharmacology. Offered by Department of Pharmacology and Toxicology, School of Medicine and Dentistry. Prerequisite for graduate study: major in chemistry or biology or a premedical course. Recommended: heredity; comparative or chordate anatomy; general physics; French; German. 18 professorial staff. 7 master's degrees and 10 Ph.D.'s awarded 1955-59. 8 graduate students registered fall 1959. New enrollment limited to 2.

Philosophy. History of modern philosophy, theory of knowledge or of value, logic, philosophy of science, metaphysics. Preparation for a career in teaching philosophy is an essential part of the Ph.D. program. Offered by Department of Philosophy, College of Arts and Science. Prerequisite for graduate study: 3 years of philosophy or equivalent. 4 professorial staff. Ph.D. program begun 1959. 6 master's degrees awarded 1955-59. 7 graduate students registered fall 1959. New enrollment limited to 4-5.

Physics. Experimental and theoretical research in low or high energynuclear physics, particle physics, cosmic rays, and astrophysics. Offered by Department of Physics and Astronomy, College of Arts and Science. Prerequisite for graduate study: advanced work in physics and mathematics. 23 professorial staff. 33 master's degrees and 41 Ph.D.'s awarded 1955-59. 67 graduate students registered fall 1959. New enrollment limited to 18. (The foregoing figures include Physics and Astronomy and Physics and Optics.)

Physics and Astronomy. Theoretical and observational work in astrophysics. Offered by Department of Physics and Astronomy, Colleges of Arts and Science. Prerequisites for graduate study: advanced work in physics and mathematics; placement examination. 23 professorial staff. For degrees awarded 1955-59, see *Physics.*

Physics and Optics. Experimental and theoretical research in optics and solid-state physics with special attention to the optical and electron properties of solids. Offered by Department of Physics and Astronomy, College of Arts and Science. Prerequisite for graduate study: advanced work in physics and mathematics; placement examination. 23 professorial staff. For degrees awarded 1955-59, see *Physics.*

Physiology. Biological transport, kidney or cardiovascular physiology, fluid and electrolyte balance, endocrinology, neurophysiology, digestive functions. Offered by Department of Physiology, School of Medicine and Dentistry. Prerequisites for graduate study: equivalent of B.S. degree in premedical sciences; biology; comparative anatomy; physics; calculus; organic and physical chemistry; quantitative analysis. 14 professorial staff. 7 master's degrees and 14 Ph.D.'s awarded 1955-59. 9 graduate students registered fall 1959. New enrollment limited to 5.

Psychology. General experimental, physiological, social, clinical, vision, audition, or applied experimental psychology. Offered by Department of Psychology, College of Arts and Science. Prerequisites for graduate study: substantial preparation in field, including 1 course each in psychology and statistics; GRE and MAT. Recommended: biology; chemistry; physics; sociology; mathematics. 12 professorial staff. 2 master's degrees and 41 Ph.D.'s awarded 1955-59. 45 grad-

uate students registered fall 1959. New enrollment limited to 12.

Radiation Biology. Biological effects of radiation, behavior and effects of radioactive materials, tracer chemistry, other areas in collaboration with other departments. Offered by Department of Radiation Biology, School of Medicine and Dentistry. Prerequisite for graduate study: training in biology or chemistry. 42 professorial staff. 80 master's degrees and 12 Ph.D.'s awarded 1955-59. 52 graduate students registered fall 1959. New enrollment limited to 9.

Rockefeller Institute

NEW YORK 21, NEW YORK

In 1901 John D. Rockefeller founded The Rockefeller Institute for Medical Research. The charter was amended in 1954 to make the Institute a part of the University of the State of New York. At this time the scope of activities was significantly extended to include graduate education in the natural sciences, with special emphasis on the life sciences. The Institute was given authority to grant the advanced degrees of Ph.D. and Med.-Sc.D. In 1958 name was changed to The Rockefeller Institute, thus recognizing the increased scope of its activities. The Institute is privately controlled and nonsectarian. Both men and women are admitted.

One of the distinguishing characteristics of The Rockefeller Institute is the flexible and personal nature of its organization; its many independent groups of scientists are built around individuals rather than being collected into the conventional departments related to specified areas of knowledge. Faculty of nearly 200 represents many fields of biology, medicine, and the related physical sciences. Students who are candidates for the Ph.D. or Med.Sc.D. degree are limited at present to about 75. This organization provides freedom for faculty and students to study and do research in any field of science they choose without regard for the inhibiting restrictions of departmental barriers.

The graduate students residence hall provides 49 single rooms and 28 suites for married students on 3 of its 4 floors. Recreational and athletic facilities are provided on the first floor and basement. 14 well-equipped buildings provide excellent facilities for research, teaching, and the social lives of faculty, students, and staff.

Residence requirement for Ph.D.: minimum of 3 years. Students are encouraged to spend as many as 12 months in residence at 2 or 3 other universities (in this and other countries) to widen their associations and intellectual horizons.

ADMISSION REQUIREMENTS

For graduate study: bachelor's or M.D. degree; competence in mathematics, physics, chemistry, and some area of the biological sciences; exceptional promise for scientific teaching and investigation. Admission to the Institute or the awarding of a fellowship is usually made on nomination by an appropriate officer or professor of science of the college or university in which the candidate has had his undergraduate work or medical education.

Apply to the President of the Institute at any time.

FEES AND FIRST-YEAR AID

At present 15 fellowships, tenable for terms of 3 years, are awarded each year to applicants who show exceptional promise for scientific research and investigation.

FIELDS OF STUDY FOR THE PH.D.

Editor's Note: It is the opinion of those with whom we corresponded at the Rockefeller Institute, that its Ph.D. programs do not lend themselves to description in the format selected for this volume. For this reason, we are reproducing below the information in the form supplied by the institute.

Each student is requested to plan his graduate study and research so that some competence in the basic sciences is the foundation upon which he builds his program of specialized study.

A suitable foundation of graduate study in the areas of science listed in Table I is required of all candidates for the Ph.D. degree. Adequate performance demands some knowledge of the mathematics of physics and chemistry based upon calculus, differential equations and the theory of probability. The particular pattern of emphasis will reflect the individual's plans for a more limited area of technical and professional competence—that is, of professional specialization. Such individual programs are planned by consultation first with the Dean of Graduate

Studies and thereafter with appropriate faculty members.

Table I: Physics, Physical Chemistry, Organic Chemistry, Biophysics, Biochemistry, Molecular Biology, Cellular Biology, Organism Biology

The areas of specialization listed in Table II are illustrative of individual programs actually accomplished or in progress. The list is not exhaustive, for the complexions are as numerous as the graduate students and often change during an individual's graduate years.

Table II: Microbiology, Comparative Physiology, Cytology, Embryology, Protozoology, Developmental Biology, Neurophysiology, Ecology, Virology, Genetics, Endocrine Physiology, Immunology

Wherever appropriate the above areas of specialization can emphasize plants or animals. A graduate program can also emphasize the medical aspects of such areas of specialization. In addition, the group of biological disciplines tabulated in Table I are appropriate areas of specialization. Specialization in such areas requires intensive work in physical sciences that goes far beyond that expected as a foundation for all graduate students. For example, a student specializing in biochemistry should do advanced work in organic chemistry or physical chemistry and preferably in both.

Opportunities for laboratory experience and for thesis research are provided in the laboratories of the institute. These are: animal pathology, biochemical genetics, biochemistry, biophysics, biosynthesis, cytology, developmental biology, ecology, endocrine physiology, general physiology, genetics, history of science, human biology, immunology, neurophysiology, parasitology, pathology, physical chemistry, physiology of reproduction, plant pathology, and spectroscopy.

The Rockefeller Institute is not organized into departments but is composed of laboratories in which scientists with common interests work together. Therefore, there may be several laboratories listed under one of the previous categories, each with its own particular approach to the pertinent general area of biology. This arrangement presents a wide variety of opportunity for graduate students seeking research experience. Working directly with experienced investigators is, for many students, a natural pathway toward a problem worthy of investigation for a thesis. A student can develop a broad professional competence by choosing a problem for his thesis that requires research in several different laboratories. There is no need to confine his research methods to those prevailing in particular laboratories. Indeed, a student undertaking a composite research program is making the maximum effective use of the opportunities provided by the faculty of the Institute.

Rutgers—The State University

NEW BRUNSWICK, NEW JERSEY

Graduate School

Rutgers has offered graduate instruction since 1876 and awarded its first Ph.D. degree in 1884. The Graduate School was organized in 1912. At present the Ph.D. is awarded in a number of fields, and the Ed.D. degree is also conferred through the School of Education. The university is publicly controlled by the state. Both men and women are admitted.

Limited dormitory facilities are provided for single graduate men and women; 186 apartments for married students.

Special facilities include: agricultural experiment station; engineering experiment station; research bureaus (biological, mineral, economic, and government); institute of politics; institute of microbiology. Library contains approximately 863,000 volumes.

Residence requirement for Ph.D.: minimum of 3 years of full-time graduate study (or its equivalent) beyond bachelor's degree; not more than 1 year of graduate credit may be transferred, and at least 1 year must be spent in full-time graduate study at Rutgers.

ADMISSION REQUIREMENTS

For graduate study: bachelor's degree; standing in upper half of graduating class; 3 letters of recommendation; approval of department chairman and Dean of the Graduate School. GRE or MAT required of applicants with grade average below B. For candidacy for Ph.D.: reading knowledge of 2 foreign languages; completion of major portion of course requirements; qualifying examination.

Apply to Director of Admissions by August 15 for fall term; by January 15 for spring term; and by May 30 for summer session.

FEES AND FIRST-YEAR AID

Application fee $10. Tuition $400 per year. Special fees approximate $27 annually. Room (in dormitory) for men $300 per academic year; for women $300-$320. Meals in college dining room average $12-$15 per week. Apartments $51, $61, and $71 per month.

First-year aid available: small number of tuition scholarships; limited number of teaching fellowships, $2,052; limited number of research assistantships, $2,052.

For tuition scholarships, apply to Dean of the Graduate School by March 1 for fall term, by December 1 for spring term. For teaching fellowships and research assistantships, apply to the chairman of the appropriate department.

FIELDS OF STUDY FOR THE PH.D.

A 1-term noncredit seminar on the training of college teachers is offered. A 6-credit seminar on higher education will be offered for the first time in 1960-61.

Animal Science.—Dairy. Animal genetics, physiology, or nutrition, dairy chemistry, and bacteriology. Offered by Department of Dairy Science. Prerequisites for graduate study: courses in organic and inorganic chemistry, mathematics, physics, biology, and nutrition. 9 professorial staff. 10 master's degrees and 6 Ph.D.'s awarded 1955-59. 16 graduate students registered fall 1959.

Animal Science.—Poultry. Nutrition, pathology, physiology. Offered by Department of Poultry Science. Prerequisite for graduate study: background in mathematics, chemistry, and physiology. 6 professorial staff. 5 master's degrees and 5 Ph.D.'s awarded 1955-59. 13 graduate students registered fall 1959.

Applied and Mathematical Statistics. Design of experiments and regression analysis. Offered by Statistics Center. Prerequisite for graduate study: minimum of 1 year of calculus. Recommended: higher algebra; advanced calculus; introductory courses in statistics. 5 professorial staff. Ph.D. program begun 1959. 69 master's degrees awarded 1955-59. 132 graduate students registered fall 1959. New enrollment limited to approximately 4 or 5.

Bacteriology. Bacterial nutrition or metabolism, epidemiology, enzymology, immunology, pathogenic organisms. Prerequisites for graduate study: 2 terms each of English composition, mathematics (including calculus), inorganic chemistry, organic chemistry; 1 term analytical chemistry. Recommended: French, German, or Russian; physics, animal or plant physiology; 2 terms general biology; 1 term genetics; 3 terms bacteriology; GRE. 4 professorial staff. 27 master's degrees and 10 Ph.D.'s awarded 1955-59. 22 graduate students registered fall 1959. Total enrollment limited to about 23.

Biochemistry and Nutrition. Nutrition. Offered by Department of Agricultural Biochemistry. (Program integrated with Department of Physiology and Biochemistry.) Prerequisite for graduate study: broad scientific background with emphasis on chemistry. 4 professorial staff. 3 master's degrees and 7 Ph.D.'s awarded 1955-59. 12 graduate students registered fall 1959. New enrollment limited to 12-15.

Botany. Morphology, radiobiology, physiology, phycology, genetics, taxonomy, bryology, ecology, phytoserology. Prerequisites for graduate study: major in plant science or biology; chemistry through organic. 8 professorial staff. 7 master's degrees and 15 Ph.D.'s awarded 1955-59. 19 graduate students registered fall 1959.

Ceramics. Physics of high temperatures with emphasis on physical chemistry, inorganic structures, and electronic physics. Offered by School of Ceramics. Prerequisites for graduate study: degree in ceramics, ceramic engineering, chemistry, physics, or other material science; emphasis on mathematics. Recommended: GRE. 5 professorial staff. 4 master's degrees and 10 Ph.D.'s awarded 1955-59. 28 graduate students registered fall 1959. Total enrollment limited to about 30.

Chemistry. Inorganic, analytical, organic, physical, or nuclear chemistry. Offered by School of Chemistry. Prerequisite for graduate study: major in chemistry. Recommended: German. 11 professorial staff. 24 master's degrees and 48 Ph.D.'s awarded 1955-59. 74 graduate students registered fall 1959. Total enrollment limited to about 70.

Economics. Economic theory or history; international, labor, or monetary economics; public finance. Recommended for graduate study: GRE. 8 professorial staff. 17 master's degrees and 7 Ph.D.'s awarded 1955-59. 39 graduate students registered fall 1959.

Engineering.—Civil and Sanitary. Structures, applied mechanics, soils or sanitary engineering. Offered by Department of Civil Engineering. 6 professorial staff. Ph.D. program begun 1960. 13 master's degrees awarded 1955-59. 7 graduate students registered fall 1959.

Engineering.—Electrical. Microwave electronics, solid-state devices, instrumentation and control. Prerequisites for graduate study: B.S. in electrical engineering or equivalent. 7 professorial staff. Ph.D. program begun 1956. 45 master's degrees awarded 1955-59. 50 graduate students registered fall 1959.

English. Most periods of English and American literature. Prerequisite for graduate study: reading knowledge of French, German, Latin, or Greek. Recommended: GRE Aptitude and Advanced Tests. 20 professorial staff. 32 master's degrees and 8 Ph.D.'s awarded 1955-59. 90 graduate students registered fall 1959.

Entomology. Economic entomology, insect toxicology or morphology. Prerequisite for graduate study: at least 40 credit hours in mathematics and basic sciences. Recommended: 2 foreign languages; 65 credits in basic sciences. 11 professorial staff. 6 master's degrees and 15 Ph.D.'s awarded 1955-59. 27 graduate students registered fall 1959.

Farm Crops. Plant breeding, crop or turf management, weed control. Prerequisites for graduate study: courses in chemistry, physics, botany, and mathematics. Recommended: agronomy. 11 professorial staff. 16 master's degrees and 11 Ph.D.'s awarded 1955-59. 21 graduate students registered fall 1959.

Food Science. Basic studies on physiological, chemical, and microbiological changes in foods. Prerequisites for graduate study: inorganic and organic chemistry; qualitative and quantitative analysis; physics; 1 year of mathematics; some biological science; French or German. Recommended: calculus; physical chemistry. 4 professorial staff. 12 master's degrees and 13 Ph.D.'s awarded 1955-59. 22 graduate students registered fall 1959.

Geology. Macro- and micropaleontology, sedimentology, optical mineralogy and petrology, petrofabrics, structure, economic geology. Prerequisites for graduate study: concentration or major in geology; 2 years of a foreign language. Recommended: GRE or general examination after first year of graduate study. 7 professorial staff. 12 master's degrees and 9 Ph.D.'s awarded

1955-59. 20 graduate students registered fall 1959. New enrollment limited to 10.

German Language and Literature. Modern German literature, literature of Classicism and Romanticism, Old and Middle High German. Prerequisites for graduate study: major or half-major in German; 1 other foreign language (Latin or French preferred). Ph.D. candidacy prerequisite: M.A. in German (30 credits in graduate courses). 9 professorial staff. Ph.D. program begun 1959. 9 master's degrees awarded 1955-59. 21 graduate students registered fall 1959.

History. Western medieval; Byzantine; American and European diplomatic, intellectual, economic, and political; several fields of British History. Recommended for graduate study: GRE. 13 professorial staff. 24 master's degrees and 1 Ph.D. awarded 1955-59. 82 graduate students registered fall 1959.

Horticulture. Floriculture, ornamentals, pomology, vegetables, breeding and nutrition, plant physiology. Prerequisite for graduate study: GRE or MAT. Recommended: physics; plant physiology; organic chemistry; mathematics; botany. 23 professorial staff. 38 master's degrees and 18 Ph.D.'s awarded 1955-59. 30 graduate students registered fall 1959.

Library Service. Librarianship. Offered by Graduate School of Library Service. Ph.D. candidacy prerequisites: master's degree in library service. 11 professorial staff. Ph.D. program begun 1959. 7 graduate students registered fall 1959.

Mathematics. Algebra, analysis, topology. Prerequisite for graduate study: 30 or more credits in mathematics, including 6 in advanced calculus. 29 professorial staff. 20 master's degrees and 3 Ph.D.'s awarded 1955-59. 50 graduate students registered fall 1959. Ph.D. enrollment limited to 20.

Microbiology. Animal virology, antibiotics, chemistry of microbial products, general microbiology, immunology and immunochemistry, medical bacteriology, microbial biochemistry and physiology, microbial engineering or genetics, mycology and taxonomy. Offered by Institute of Microbiology. Prerequisite for graduate study: GRE. 16 professorial staff. 10 master's degrees and 18 Ph.D.'s awarded 1955-59. 26 graduate students registered fall 1959.

Microbiology. — Agricultural. Ecology and physiology of microorganisms (bacteria, viruses, actinomycetes, fungi, algae, protozoa, small invertebrates). Accent on microorganisms as converters of organic and mineral substances in nature-soil, water and in association with animals and plants. Prerequisites for graduate study: background in chemistry, biology, physics, mathematics, and geology; reading knowledge of at least 1 foreign language. 2 professors. 1 master's degree and 10 Ph.D.'s awarded 1955-59. 8 graduate students registered fall 1959.

Pharmaceutical Sciences. Physical pharmacy; pharmaceutical formulations, engineering, analysis, or synthesis. Offered by Department of Pharmacy and Pharmaceutical Chemistry. Prerequisites for graduate study: B.S. in pharmacy; mathematics through calculus. Recommended: GRE. 13 professorial staff. Ph.D. program begun 1958. 15 master's degrees awarded 1955-59. 22 graduate students registered fall 1959. Total enrollment limited to approximately 30.

Physics. Solid-state and liquid-state physics (superconductivity, superfluidity, properties of materials at very low temperature, nuclear magnet resonance); nuclear physics (high-energy nuclear physics, nuclear emulsions); theoretical physics (general theory of solid and liquid state), nuclear physics, physics of fundamental particles. Recommended for graduate study: minimum 1 year each in 2 foreign languages (French, German, Russian). 14 professorial staff. 6 master's degrees and 16 Ph.D.'s awarded 1955-59. 45 graduate students registered fall 1959. New enrollment limited to 20-30.

Physiology and Biochemistry. Protein nutrition (general and in relation to cancer); culture and analysis of heart muscle cells; mammalian mitochondrial cytochromes (purification and characterization). Prerequisites for graduate study: chemistry through quantitative analysis; mathematics through integral calculus; 1 year of physics; 4 to 6 semesters of biology; French or German. Recommended: physical chemistry. 3 professorial staff. 25 master's degrees and 17 Ph.D.'s awarded 1955-59. 28 graduate students registered fall 1959. Ph.D. candidacy enrollment limited to 6 per year.

Plant Pathology. Virus diseases; mycology; effect of air pollution on vegetation; fruit, vegetable, ornamental, and turf diseases. Prerequisites for graduate study: degree in biological sciences or agriculture; courses in botany, plant physiology, bacteriology, and inorganic, and organic chemistry. Recommended: French and German; qualitative and quantitative analysis; genetics. 7 professorial staff. 1 master's degree and 6 Ph.D.'s awarded 1955-59.

Plant Physiology. Inorganic chemistry (particularly micro-nutrient element nutrition); metals in physiology and chemistry of enzymes; plant growth regulators. Prerequisite for graduate study: degree in a biological science (preferably plant science), chemistry, or biochemistry. Recommended: French, German, or Russian; mathematics through calculus; analytical, organic, or physical chemistry; biochemistry; botany (anatomy, morphology, cytology, histology); nuclear radio-isotope physics. 3 professorial staff. 1 master's degree and 3 Ph.D.'s awarded 1955-59. 4 graduate students registered fall 1959.

Political Science. American national government; state and local government; constitutional law; citizenship, parties, and politics; public administration; political philosophy; international politics; foreign governments (Europe and the Commonwealth); government and politics of the Far East. 39 master's degrees and 6 Ph.D.'s awarded 1955-59. 69 graduate students registered fall 1959.

Psychology. General experimental and clinical. Prerequisites for graduate study: experimental psychology plus supporting courses; MAT. Recommended: mathematics and other sciences; GRE. 14 professorial staff. 7 master's degrees and 2 Ph.D.'s awarded 1955-59. 50 graduate students registered fall 1959.

Romance Languages. French, Spanish, and Spanish-American literature. Prerequisite for graduate study: 24 hours of credit in major language; comprehensive examination in its language and literature. Ph.D. candidacy prerequisites: Latin; German; second Romance language. 16 professorial staff. Ph.D. program begun 1959. 9 master's degrees awarded 1955-59. 52 graduate students registered fall 1959.

Sanitation. Chemistry, biochemistry, biology, and microbiology of water and air pollution, sewage, and industrial waste treatment. Offered by Departments of Sanitation with other courses taken in Departments of Chemistry, Biochemistry, Biology, Microbiology, and Sanitary Engineering. Prerequisite for graduate study: major

in chemistry, biological disciplines, or sanitary engineering. 5 professorial staff. 4 master's degrees and 10 Ph.D.'s awarded 1955-59. 11 graduate students registered fall 1959.

Soils. Soil chemistry, fertility physics, genesis, morphology, and mineralogy. Prerequisites for graduate study: inorganic and organic chemistry; mathematics; physics; botany; plant physiology; bacteriology; geology. Recommended: courses in soils. 7 professorial staff. 5 master's degrees and 25 Ph.D.'s awarded 1955-59. 21 graduate students registered fall 1959.

Zoology. Ecology (fresh-water, aquatic, terrestrial, marine); endocrinology; embryology; parasitology; serology (systematic, forensic, experimental). Prerequisites for graduate study: 1 year each of mathematics and physics; 2½ years of chemistry; 6 years of biology. 9 professorial staff plus those in related departments. 27 master's degrees and 22 Ph.D.'s awarded 1955-59. 50 graduate students registered fall 1959.

St. Bonaventure University

ST. BONAVENTURE, NEW YORK

School of Graduate Studies

Graduate instruction has been offered at St. Bonaventure since 1928, and the first Ph.D. was awarded in 1933. The School of Graduate Studies was organized in 1941. At present, the Ph.D. is awarded through the Department of Biology and in the Franciscan Institute, a graduate institute of specialized research and instruction in medieval history, philosophy, and theology. The university is privately controlled and is conducted by the Franciscan Fathers (Province of the Holy Name) of the Roman Catholic Church. Both men and women are admitted.

No on-campus residence facilities are provided for either single or married graduate students.

Special facilities include: Franciscan Institute with special library facilities, including a 10,000-volume collection of Franciscana, incunabula, and manuscripts dealing chiefly with the Scholastic period; university library of approximately 130,000 volumes; special radioactive materials and tracer technique laboratory.

Residence requirement for Ph.D.: 3 years of full-time study or equivalent beyond bachelor's degree, with at least two years in residence at St. Bonaventure. Summer and evening courses available.

ADMISSION REQUIREMENTS

For graduate study: bachelor's degree; well above average rank in undergraduate work as a whole; completion with superior rank of at least 18 semester hours in field of proposed study; GRE. For candidacy for Ph.D.: satisfactory completion of substantial portion of course work; satisfaction of language requirement; qualifying examinations; approval of major professor and Dean of School of Graduate Studies.

Apply to the Graduate Office by August 15 for fall term; by January 1 for spring term; by June 1 for summer session. Summer and evening courses available.

FEES AND FIRST-YEAR AID

No application fee. Matriculation fee $10. Tuition $22 per semester hour credit. Special fees approximate $10 annually. Approximate annual cost of board in college dining room $480.

First-year aid available: 14 graduate assistantships, $1,300 plus remission of tuition for 18 semester hours of graduate credit and remission of general academic fees.

Apply to head of major department at least 30 days before opening of term, preferably earlier.

FIELDS OF STUDY FOR THE PH.D.

Biology. Natural history, gross and microscopic anatomy, microbiology. Prerequisites for graduate study: 18-24 semester hours of work in zoology, botany, anatomy, histology, embryology or genetics, bacteriology, biology, chemistry, physics, mathematics, education, or philosophy; 12 hours of English; 6 of social science. Ph.D. candidacy prerequisites: examinations in 2 modern foreign languages. 6 professorial staff. 7 master's degrees and 3 Ph.D.'s awarded 1955-59. 9 graduate students registered fall 1959.

Philosophy. Offered by Philosophy Department of the Franciscan Institute. Prerequisite for graduate study: reading knowledge of classical languages. 7 professorial staff. 16 master's degrees and 4 Ph.D.'s awarded 1955-59. 4 graduate students registered fall 1959.

St. John's University
JAMAICA 32, NEW YORK

Founded as St. John's College in 1870, the university is conducted by the Congregation of the Mission of the Roman Catholic Church. Graduate instruction has been offered since the early 1900's, and the first Ph.D. was awarded in 1959. Ph.D. programs are offered in the Graduate School of Arts and Sciences and the Graduate Division, School of Education. The Ed.D. degree is also awarded through the latter division and the J.S.D. through the School of Law. Both men and women are admitted.

Graduate School of Arts and Sciences

The Graduate School of Arts and Sciences was established in 1914 and awarded its first Ph.D. degree in 1939.

No university-owned residence facilities are maintained for graduate students; university Placement Director recommends rooms and apartments in community.

Special facilities include: Philosophy of Science Institute, inaugurated in 1958 to suggest methods of arriving at universal syntheses of knowledge; Freedom Institute, inaugurated in 1959 to study the international communist conspiracy and recommend measures for counteraction; Institute of Asian Studies, inaugurated in 1959 (but not in operation until 1960) to provide opportunities for intensive study of Chinese language and a broad background of understanding of the cultures of the Far East. Facilities of Marine Biological Laboratory and Brookhaven National Laboratory are utilized for study and research in appropriate fields. Internship program in public administration in Department of Political Science provides opportunity for students to work directly with public officials on federal, state, and local levels of government. Library contains approximately 174,000 volumes.

Residence requirement for Ph.D.: 2 years beyond master's degree (24 semester hours of course work). 6 graduate credits may be transferred toward master's degree; the amount which may be transferred towards the Ph.D. is individually determined.

ADMISSION REQUIREMENTS

For graduate study: bachelor's degree; acceptable preparation in major field. For candidacy for Ph.D.: master's degree; reading knowledge of French and German (another language or research tool may be substituted for 1 language); comprehensive examinations.

Apply to the Registrar by April 15.

FEES AND FIRST-YEAR AID

No application fee. Tuition $30 per semester hour for nonscience courses; $32 for science courses. Special fees approximate $25 annually; additional fees for laboratory science courses.

First-year aid available: several tuition scholarships, $2,000-$2,400 plus remission of tuition and $400 a year for each dependent; research assistantships, $1,500-$2,300 plus remission of tuition; grants-in-aid, $200-$700.

Apply to the Dean of the Graduate School of Arts and Sciences by March 1 for scholarships, fellowships, and assistantships; to Chairman of the Committee on Scholarships for grants-in-aid. GRE Aptitude and Advanced Tests required of all applicants for assistantships and fellowships.

FIELDS OF STUDY FOR THE PH.D.

The English Department offers a formal course on the theory and pedagogy of literature. Other departments offer conference and seminars on college teaching. Students interested in teaching have an opportunity to gain experience by teaching certain undergraduate courses under the direction of the departmental chairman.

Area Studies.—Asian. Combined program offered by Departments of History, Political Science, and Philosophy, and Institute in Asian Studies. Prerequisites for graduate study: courses in the social sciences; a modern foreign language and/or linguistics. Ph.D. program initiated 1960.

Area Studies.—World Affairs. Communist areas, Asia, Middle East. Combined program offered by Departments of History, Political Science, and Philosophy, Institute in Asian Studies, and the Freedom Institute. Prerequisite for graduate study: 24 semester hours of history. Program initiated 1960.

Biology. Parasitology, physiology, microbiology, zoology. Prerequisites for graduate study: 3 years of biology; 2 of chemistry; 1 of physics. 8 professorial staff. 58 master's degrees and 3

Ph.D.'s awarded 1955-59. 81 graduate students registered fall 1959.

Chemistry. Analytical, inorganic, organic, physical. Prerequisite for graduate study: courses in chemistry, physics, and mathematics. 8 professorial staff. Ph.D. program initiated 1957. 28 master's degrees awarded 1955-59. 61 graduate students registered fall 1959.

English. Origins and medieval literature; literatures of the Renaissance, Restoration and the 18th and 19th centuries; American literature; contemporary literature and criticism. Prerequisite for graduate study: 24 semester hours of English. 5 professorial staff. 46 master's degrees and 16 Ph.D.'s awarded 1955-59. 146 graduate students registered fall 1959.

History. Europe to 1914; Europe in the 20th century; America 1492-1865; America 1865-1914; America since 1900; war and peace in the 20th century. Prerequisite for graduate study: 24 semester hours of history. 3 professorial staff. 65 master's degrees and 12 Ph.D.'s awarded 1955-59. 83 graduate students registered fall 1959.

Philosophy. Ancient, medieval, modern and contemporary, systematic and textual philosophy. Prerequisite for graduate study: major in Scholastic philosophy. 8 professorial staff. 29 master's degrees awarded 1955-59. 20 graduate students registered fall 1959.

Physics. Experimental, theoretical. Prerequisite for graduate study: major in physics, applied physics, engineering, or related field. 11 professorial staff. Ph.D. program initiated 1958. 1 master's degree awarded 1955-59. 22 graduate students registered fall 1959.

Political Science. International law and relations, comparative government, political theory. Prerequisite for graduate study: background in political science. 2 professorial staff. Ph.D. program initiated 1957. 3 master's degrees awarded 1955-59. 20 graduate students registered fall 1959.

Sociology. Sociology, industrial sociology, sociology and social work. Prerequisites for graduate study: 24 semester hours in sociology or social science. 1 professor. Program was in social sciences, but department was reorganized to sociology during 1959-60. More faculty will be available 1960-61. 4 master's degrees and 4 Ph.D.'s awarded in social sciences 1955-59. 22 graduate students registered fall 1959.

Graduate Division, School of Education

Division was organized in 1955 and granted first Ph.D. in 1956. Prior to this time, the Graduate Department of Education was part of the Graduate School of Arts and Sciences. Program leading to the Ph.D. offered in 4 areas, and the Ed.D. degree is also conferred in each of these areas.

No residence facilities available for graduate students.

Special facilities include Reading and Speech Clinic and affiliation with St. Vincent's Hospital Clinic and Foundling Hospital, both in New York City. Public and private schools are used for internship and observation purposes. Cooperative test data in the Diocese of Brooklyn, Rockville Center, and New York City used for research purposes (55,000 tests given during spring 1960).

Residence requirements are the same as for the Graduate School of Arts and Sciences.

ADMISSION REQUIREMENTS

For graduate study: bachelor's degree; 18 undergraduate credits in professional education; 2 years of general education; MAT; GRE; 4 qualifying examinations. For candidacy for Ph.D.: master's degree or equivalent; reading knowledge of French and German (advanced statistics may be substituted for 1 language); completion of 12 semester hours of graduate work.

Apply to the Office of the Registrar at least 1 semester prior to date of desired entry.

FEES AND FIRST-YEAR AID

No application fee. Tuition $30 per credit. Special fees approximate $25 annually.

First-year aid available: 7 teaching fellowships, $2,000.

Apply to the Director, Graduate Division, School of Education, by April 15.

FIELDS OF STUDY FOR THE PH.D.

Administration and Supervision. Elementary or secondary school principalship, school business administration, instructional staff supervision. Recommended for graduate study: 2 years of teaching or administrative experience. 1 professorial staff. 44 master's degrees and 4 Ph.D.'s awarded 1955-59. 148 graduate students registered fall 1959.

Elementary Education. Teaching, reading, curriculum. 4 professorial staff. 7 master's degrees awarded 1955-59. 65 graduate students registered fall 1959.

Guidance. Elementary and secondary school guidance personnel services. Recommended for graduate study: experience in the field of personnel services. 3 professorial staff. 54 master's degrees and 6 Ph.D.'s awarded 1955-59. 104 graduate students registered fall 1959.

Psychology. School psychologist. Ph.D. candidacy prerequisite: master's degree in psychology or equivalent. 4 professorial staff. Ph.D. program begun 1958. 19 master's degrees and 3 Ph.D.'s awarded 1955-59. 50 graduate students registered fall 1959.

St. Louis University

ST. LOUIS 10, MISSOURI

Graduate School

Graduate instruction has been offered at St. Louis University since 1832, and the first Ph.D. was awarded in 1883. The Graduate School was formally organized in 1924 and has jurisdiction over all graduate programs. The university is a Roman Catholic institution conducted by the Jesuits. Both men and women are admitted.

Residence halls available for single graduate students; no residence facilities for married students.

Special facilities include: library of approximately 508,000 volumes, which includes a new central library, The Pius XII Memorial Library, and the Knights of Columbus Vatican Microfilm Library (12,000,000 Vatican manuscript pages); center for human relations training and research; curriculum laboratory; 3 seismological stations; meteorological observatory; bureau for institutional research; The James Henry Yalen Scientific Computing Center; counseling and guidance center; the Valentine B. Reis biological station. Affiliations with Midwest Library Center and Argonne National Laboratory provide additional opportunities for study and research. University maintains largest Catholic medical center in the world.

Residence requirement for Ph.D.: minimum of 3 years beyond bachelor's degree, including

1 year of full-time residence at St. Louis University.

ADMISSION REQUIREMENTS

For graduate study: bachelor's degree or equivalent; academic record showing evidence of ability and preparation for pursuit of graduate studies; letters of recommendation; qualifying examination in most departments. Recommended: GRE. For candidacy for Ph.D.: satisfaction of language requirements; preliminary examination; approval of dissertation subject.

Apply to Dean of Graduate School, St. Louis University, 221 North Grand Boulevard, St. Louis 3, Missouri, at least 4 weeks before opening of session for which admission is desired.

FEES AND FIRST-YEAR AID

Application fee $10. Tuition $25-$30 a semester hour, depending on department; cost of full program ranges from $450-$600 per academic year. Special fees vary according to program selected. Room (in dormitory) for men $274 per academic year; other rooms average $360 per year. Room (in dormitory) and board (breakfast and dinner) for women $704 per year; room alone $360. Approximate annual cost of board in college dining room $525.

First-year aid available: teaching fellowships and research assistantships, $1,500-$2,000 ($3,000 in biochemistry). These do not include remission of tuition and fees. There are service scholarships for full or partial remission of tuition. Academic and clerical employment available.

Apply to Dean of Graduate School, St. Louis University, 221 North Grand Boulevard, St. Louis 3, Missouri, early in semester previous to registration.

FIELDS OF STUDY FOR THE PH.D.

Anatomy. Anatomy, neuroanatomy, histology, embryology. Prerequisite for graduate study: major in biology or equivalent, including lower-division courses in chemistry, biology, and physics and 18 semester hours of upper-division biology, including comparative embryology. Ph.D. candidacy prerequisites: 2 languages (German, French, Russian). 4 professorial staff. 9 master's degrees and 6 Ph.D.'s awarded 1955-59. 2 graduate students registered fall 1959. Program suspended for the present.

Biochemistry. Steroid or bile acid metabolism, enzymes, tissue enzyme systems, nutrition. Prerequisites for graduate study: major in chemistry or equivalent, including lower-division courses in chemistry, mathematics, and physics and 40 hours of upper-division courses in chemical principles, organic and advanced analytical chemistry, physical and inorganic chemistry, and chemical literature. Recommended: previous work in biology, including comparative. Ph.D. candidacy prerequisites: German and French. 11 professorial staff. 5 master's degrees and 11 Ph.D.'s awarded 1955-59. 23 graduate students registered fall 1959.

Biology. General or comparative physiology, morphology, genetics, cytology, protozoology. Prerequisites for graduate study: major in biology or equivalent including lower-division courses in biology, chemistry, and physics and 18 semester hours of upper-division biology, including comparative anatomy and embryology. Ph.D. candidacy prerequisites: 2 languages (French, German, Russian). Recommended: full summer season at seaside or fresh-water laboratory in study or research. 6 professorial staff. 8 master's degrees and 11 Ph.D.'s awarded 1955-59. 18 graduate students registered fall 1959.

Business Administration. Programs include all commerce fields. Offered by Department of Management and supervised by an interdepartmental committee. Prerequisite for graduate study: B.S. in commerce. Ph.D. candidacy prerequisites: any 2 of following: German; French; Russian; course sequence in methodology. 8 professorial staff. 103 master's degrees and 10 Ph.D.'s awarded 1955-59. 71 graduate students registered fall 1959.

Chemistry. Analytical, inorganic, organic, and physical chemistry, with research facilities for organic synthesis, kinetics of organic reactions, molecular spectra, properties of solutions, dielectric constants, X-ray spectroscopy, chemistry of the hydrides of boron. Prerequisites for graduate study: lower-division courses in chemistry, mathematics, and physics; 40 hours of upper-division courses in chemical principles, organic and advanced analytical chemistry, physical, and organic chemistry, and chemical literature. Ph.D. candidacy prerequisites: 2 languages (German, French, Russian). 9 professorial staff. 65 master's degrees and 27 Ph.D.'s awarded 1955-59. 54 graduate students registered fall 1959.

Economics. Preparation for careers in government, industry, and teaching. Department participates in program leading to Ph.D. in Business Administration. Prerequisites for graduate study: 18 semester hours of upper-division work, including introductory statistics, intermediate economic analysis, national income and business fluctuations, economic development of the United States, or economic history since the industrial revolution. Recommended: money and banking; labor economics and competition; pricing policy and market structure. Ph.D. candidacy prerequisites: any 2 of following: French; German; Russian; course sequence in methodology. 11 professorial staff. 26 master's degrees and 9 Ph.D.'s awarded 1955-59. 28 graduate students registered fall 1959.

Education. Guidance and counseling; administration; supervision at primary, secondary, and university levels; teacher training; curriculum. Prerequisites for graduate study: 18 semester hours of upper-division courses, including philosophy of education and introduction to tests and measurements. Ph.D. candidacy prerequisites: any 2 of following: French; German; course sequence in methodology; Russian. 16 professorial staff. 315 master's degrees and 16 Ph.D.'s awarded 1955-59. 178 graduate students registered fall 1959.

English. Middle Ages, Renaissance, Renaissance drama, Restoration and 18th century, 19th century, American or modern literature, literary criticism, novel and drama. Prerequisites for graduate study: 18 semester hours of upper-division courses, including Chaucer, Shakespeare, 18th and 19th century, American literature, practical criticism. Recommended: 12 semester hours of Latin or Greek or both. Ph.D. candidacy prerequisites: 2 languages (French, German, Italian, Latin, Spanish, Russian). 15 professorial staff. 57 master's degrees and 10 Ph.D.'s awarded 1955-59. 57 graduate students registered fall 1959.

Geophysics. Geophysics, meteorology, seismology. Offered by Department of Geophysics and Geophysical Engineering. Prerequisite for graduate study: substantial preparation in field. Ph.D. candidacy prerequisites: 2 languages (French, German, Russian). 9 professorial staff. 36 master's degrees and 5 Ph.D.'s awarded 1955-59. 35 graduate students registered fall 1959.

Greek and Latin. Greek, Latin; minors in classical antiquities, Greek, Latin, and linguistics.

Offered by Department of Classical Languages. Prerequisites for graduate study: 18 semester hours of upper-division courses, including (for Greek) Greek historical writers, poets, dramatists, and 1 course in classical antiquities or (for Latin) history of Latin literature, 1 literary course, and 1 course in classical antiquities. Ph.D. candidacy prerequisites: 2 languages (German, French, Italian, Russian, Spanish). 7 professorial staff. 42 master's degrees and 4 Ph.D.'s awarded 1955-59. 19 graduate students registered fall 1959.

Health Organization Research. Experimental interdepartmental program planned under a U.S. Public Health Service grant to prepare thoroughly prepared researchers in behavioral sciences for hospitals and other health organizations. Program requires 3 to 5 years. Recommended prerequisites: introduction to statistics; courses in economics, sociology, psychology, business administration, and human relations. Ph.D. candidacy prerequisites: any 2 of following: German; French; Russian; Spanish; course sequence in methodology. Ph.D. program begun 1958. 10 graduate students registered fall 1959.

History. Medieval, modern European, American, intellectual. Prerequisites for graduate study: 18 semester hours of upper-division courses, including 1 in Middle Ages, 2 in modern European, 2 in United States. Ph.D. candidacy prerequisites: any 2 of following: French; German; Spanish; Russian; course sequence in methodology. 13 professorial staff. 92 master's degrees and 12 Ph.D.'s awarded 1955-59. 91 graduate students registered fall 1959.

Mathematics. Topology, number theory, mathematical statistics, algebra, analysis. Prerequisites for graduate study: 18 semester hours in upper-division courses in mathematics. Ph.D. candidacy prerequisites: 2 languages (French, German, Russian). 5 professorial staff. 34 master's degrees and 12 Ph.D.'s awarded 1955-59. 46 graduate students registered fall 1959.

Microbiology. Virology, including bacteriophages; bacterial metabolism and physiology; immunology and serology; microbial genetics; medical microbiology; tissue culture; biochemistry of normal and virus-infected cells in tissue culture. Prerequisites for graduate study: thorough training in biology, physics, chemistry, and mathematics; course in biochemistry. Ph.D. candidacy prerequisites: 2 languages (French, German, Russian). 6 professorial staff. 2 Ph.D.'s

awarded 1955-59. 4 graduate students registered fall 1959.

Pathology. Virology and cancer research. Prerequisite for graduate study: M.D. degree. Ph.D. candidacy prerequisites: 2 languages (French, German, Russian). Recommended: 1 year of clinical internships after M.D. 6 professorial staff. 2 graduate students registered fall 1959.

Pharmacology. Prerequisite for graduate study: 18 hours of upper-division courses. Ph.D. candidacy prerequisites: 2 languages (French, German, Russian). 5 professorial staff. 1 master's degree and 2 Ph.D.'s awarded 1955-59. 2 graduate students registered fall 1959.

Philosophy. History of Western philosophy, all principal areas of systematic philosophy. Prerequisites for graduate study: 18 semester hours of upper-division in philosophy. Ph.D. candidacy prerequisite: 3 languages (French, German, Latin). 22 professorial staff. 35 master's degrees and 20 Ph.D.'s awarded 1955-59. 49 graduate students registered fall 1959.

Physics. Nuclear physics (many phases in cooperation with Argonne National Laboratory), solid-state physics, beta and gamma rays, spectroscopy, slow neutron scattering, properties of semiconductors, photoelectric emission, X-ray and electron diffraction, electron microscopy, structure of thin films, theoretical physics, dirac equation, nuclear magnetic effects, microwave absorption, field theory, X-ray microscopy. Prerequisites for graduate study: courses in general physics and chemistry, algebra, geometry, trigonometry, and differential and integral calculus; 18 semester hours of upper-division courses in physics. Ph.D. candidacy prerequisites: 2 languages (French, German, Russian). 9 professorial staff. 20 master's degrees and 17 Ph.D.'s awarded 1955-59. 43 graduate students registered fall 1959.

Physiology. Central and peripheral circulation, blood coagulation, sympathetic nervous system, regulation of body temperatures, microwave irradiation. Prerequisite for graduate study: adequate training in biology, chemistry, and physics. Ph.D. candidacy prerequisites: 2 languages (French, German, Russian). 6 professorial staff. 1 master's degree and 2 Ph.D.'s awarded 1955-59. 5 graduate students registered fall 1959.

Political Science. Prerequisites for graduate study: 18 semester hours of upper-division courses in field, including American government,

history of political thought, international relations, comparative government. Ph.D. candidacy prerequisites: any 2 of following: French; German; Russian; Spanish, course sequence in methodology. 6 professorial staff. 10 master's degrees and 3 Ph.D.'s awarded 1955-59. 31 graduate students registered fall 1959.

Sociology. Social theory and sociological synthesis, social organization and demography, social psychology, marriage and the family, social disorganization and problems, social anthropology. Offered by Department of Sociology and Anthropology. Prerequisites for graduate study: 18 semester hours of upper-division courses in sociology and related fields. Ph.D. candidacy prerequisites: any 2 of the following: French; German; Italian; Spanish; course sequence in methodology. 8 professorial staff. 42 master's degrees and 6 Ph.D.'s awarded 1955-59. 22 graduate students registered fall 1959.

Spanish. Spanish and Latin-American studies with minors in both Latin-American area studies and Portuguese-Brazilian studies. Third minor in French, comparative literature, English, classics, or German is recommended. Prerequisites for graduate study: 18 semester hours of upper-division courses, including 6 of survey of the literature or equivalent and 6 of advanced composition; acquaintance with Latin and with history of the country. Ph.D. candidacy prerequisites: Portuguese; Italian; French; German; Latin. 8 professorial staff. Ph.D. program begun 1958. 7 master's degrees awarded 1955-59. 16 graduate students registered fall 1959.

St. Mary's College

NOTRE DAME, INDIANA

School of Sacred Theology

Graduate instruction at the doctoral level was initiated in 1943 to give religious teachers, as well as lay teachers, the opportunity to become better qualified as teachers of Sacred Doctrine, especially on the secondary-school or college level. The first Ph.D. was awarded in 1946. St. Mary's is privately controlled and is conducted by the Congregation of the Sisters of the Holy Cross, Roman Catholic Church. Only women are admitted to this institution.

Room and board available for graduate students. Library of approximately 58,000 volumes contains a special collection on Dante.

Residence requirement for Ph.D.: usually 3 years.

ADMISSION REQUIREMENTS

For graduate study: bachelor's degree; background in philosophy; Latin. Recommended: French or German; 9-12 hours in philosophy.

Apply to the Dean, School of Sacred Theology, at any time.

FEES AND FIRST-YEAR AID

No application fee; $10 matriculation fee. Tuition $270 per academic year. Room and board $600 per year.

First-year aid available: 2 scholarships covering all expenses; limited number of teaching fellowships, variable stipends.

Apply to Dean, School of Sacred Theology, at any time.

FIELDS OF STUDY FOR THE PH.D.

Sacred Doctrine. Dogmatic and moral theology, scripture. Offered by the School of Sacred Theology. 10 professorial staff. 80 master's degrees and 23 Ph.D.'s awarded 1955-59. 23 graduate students registered fall 1959.

Smith College

NORTHAMPTON, MASSACHUSETTS

Committee on Graduate Study of Smith College

Graduate instruction has been offered at Smith since 1879, and the first Ph.D. was awarded in 1882. The Committee on Graduate Study was organized in 1906. The institution is privately controlled and nonsectarian. Degrees are awarded only to women, but both men and women may register for graduate study.

Although Smith is authorized to grant the Ph.D., it has done so infrequently in recent years. Emphasis is placed on the various master's degrees. A new cooperative Ph.D. program has been established with the University of Massachusetts, Amherst College, and Mount Holyoke College. Under this plan work may be done at any or all

of the above schools with the "Home School" being the one where thesis and research is done. Programs have been organized in chemistry and biology to date. Requirements for admission are the same as those for the University of Massachusetts.

Two dormitories are maintained for graduate women. There are no special residence facilities for men or for married graduate students.

Library contains about 430,000 volumes and has unusual facilities and special collections in music and art. There is a strong teaching fellowship program in sciences, music, and theater.

Requirement for doctorate: 3 years, including at least 1 year in another institution. Maximum of 6 semester hours of graduate credit may be transferred toward the M.A.; requirements flexible for higher degrees.

ADMISSION REQUIREMENTS

For graduate study: bachelor's degree; undergraduate record of honors calibre; reading knowledge of 1 modern language. GRE recommended.

Apply at any time to Committee on Graduate Study.

FEES AND FIRST-YEAR AID

No application fee. Tuition $700 a year. Special fees approximate $25 annually. Annual cost of board and room in dormitory $950.

First-year aid available: 6 to 10 scholarships, $1,000-$1,800; approximately 20 teaching fellowships, $1,800-$1,900; 6 tuition scholarships.

Apply to the Committee on Graduate Study before February 15.

South Carolina, Medical College of

CHARLESTON 16, SOUTH CAROLINA

Committee on Graduate Studies

Graduate studies in the basic medical sciences have been offered since 1949, and the first Ph.D. was awarded in 1952. College is publicly controlled by the state. Both men and women are admitted.

Housing for male graduate students is available in the Alumni Memorial House. No residence facilities provided for single women or for married students.

The varied teaching and research facilities of the laboratories and hospital of the Medical College of South Carolina are available to graduate students.

Residence requirement for Ph.D.: 3 academic years beyond bachelor's degree. The amount of graduate credit which may be transferred from other institutions is individually determined. Summer courses available.

ADMISSION REQUIREMENTS

For graduate study: B.S., B.A., or M.D. degree; B average or better in natural and physical sciences, including mathematics; adequate preparation in chosen field; GRE; personal interview; recommendation of department in which graduate work is to be done. For candidacy for Ph.D.: completion of course work; reading knowledge of 2 foreign languages (usually French and German); qualifying examination.

Apply to Chairman, Committee on Graduate Studies, at any time.

FEES AND FIRST-YEAR AID

No application fee. Tuition $80.50 per academic year. Special fees approximate $12 annually. Room (in Alumni Memorial House) for men $225 per school year. Approximate annual cost of board in college cafeteria $450.

General information and advice concerning the various fellowships available may be obtained from the Chairman of the Committee on Graduate Studies.

FIELDS OF STUDY FOR THE PH.D.

No formal courses in the methodology of teaching are offered, but practice teaching under supervision is encouraged.

Anatomy. Microcirculation in living animals in health and disease, endocrinology, neuroanatomy, growth and development of the normal Rhesus monkey. 5 professorial staff. 3 master's degrees and 2 Ph.D.'s awarded 1955-59. 3 graduate students registered fall 1959.

Chemistry. Chemistry of proteins, hemoglobin, and amino acids; methods for blood analysis; analytical instrumentation. 4 professorial staff. 1 master's degree and 3 Ph.D.'s awarded 1955-59. 1 graduate student registered fall 1959.

Microbiology. 4 professorial staff. 1 master's degree awarded 1955-59. This department is not accepting students at the present time, although it is contributing teaching, research, and cooperation in the training of graduate students in other departments.

Pathology. 6 professorial staff. This department is not accepting students at the present time although it is contributing teaching, research, and cooperation in the training of graduate students of other departments.

Pharmacology. Cardiovascular pharmacology. Offered by Department of Pharmacology and Therapeutics in collaboration with the clinical Departments of Surgery, Medicine, and Anesthesiology. 5 professorial staff. 3 master's degrees and 3 Ph.D.'s awarded 1955-59. 5 graduate students registered fall 1959.

Physiology. Circulation and respiration (especially control), neuropharmacology, and enzymology. Prerequisites for graduate study: courses in biology, physics, and inorganic and organic chemistry. Recommended: comparative anatomy; physical chemistry; electronics. 5 professorial staff. 1 master's degree and 1 Ph.D. awarded 1955-59. 2 graduate students registered fall 1959.

South Carolina, University of

COLUMBIA 1, SOUTH CAROLINA

The Graduate School

Although graduate instruction was offered at the University of South Carolina as early as 1812, and the first Ph.D. awarded in 1891, the Graduate School was not formally organized until 1923. The doctoral program was discontinued in 1933 and reorganized in 1944. University is publicly controlled by the state. Both men and women are admitted.

Special dormitories maintained for graduate men and women; limited number of family units available for married students.

Special facilities include: library of over 400,000 volumes; excellent collection of Colonial and state archives. Cooperative arrangements with Oak Ridge National Laboratories and Savannah River installation of the Atomic Energy Commission provide additional opportunities for study and research in these areas.

Residence requirement for Ph.D.: minimum of 3 years beyond bachelor's degree, of which 1 year (the last) must be spent in residence at the University of South Carolina. Summer courses available.

ADMISSION REQUIREMENTS

For graduate study: bachelor's degree; satisfactory academic record; GRE. For candidacy for Ph.D.: reading knowledge of 2 foreign languages, of which 1 must be French or German (Ph.D. in education requires only 1 foreign language); written and oral qualifying examinations.

Apply to Dean of the Graduate School by July 1 for fall term; by December 1 for spring term.

FEES AND FIRST-YEAR AID

No application fee. Tuition for state residents $120 per academic year; others $350. Special fees approximate $150 annually. Room (in dormitory) $170 per academic year. Board in college cafeteria averages $350 per year. Apartments $38-$54 per month.

First-year aid available: 35 teaching fellowships, $600-$1,800; 10 other fellowships, $300-$2,300; 10 research assistantships, $1,000-$2,000.

Apply to the Dean of the Graduate School by February 1.

FIELDS OF STUDY FOR THE PH.D.

Biology. Botany (plant morphology or taxonomy), vertebrate embryology, regeneration (cellular behavior), physiology, cytology, ichthyology (taxonomy). Prerequisites for graduate study: 35 semester credits in biology and 8 in general chemistry; recommendation of major professor. 7 professorial staff. 7 master's degrees and 2 Ph.D.'s awarded 1955-59. 17 graduate students registered fall 1959. Total enrollment limited to 20.

Chemistry. Organic, physical. Prerequisite for graduate study: major in chemistry. 9 professorial staff. 17 master's degrees and 6 Ph.D.'s awarded 1955-59. 26 graduate students registered fall 1959.

Education. Elementary or secondary education, educational administration, psychological services in education (reading, guidance, and measurement). Prerequisite for graduate study: GRE Aptitude Test and Advanced Test in Education. Offered by the School of Education. 12

professorial staff. 298 master's degrees and 6 Ph.D.'s awarded 1955-59. 16 full-time and 124 part-time graduate students registered fall 1959.

English. All periods of English literature, including modern; American literature. Offered by Department of English. A Southern culture program is offered in conjunction with the Department of History. Prerequisites for graduate study: major in literature or equivalent; letters of recommendation. 19 professorial staff. 13 master's degrees and 3 Ph.D.'s awarded 1955-59. 23 graduate students registered fall 1959.

History. Modern European, British, United States, or diplomatic history. Prerequisites for graduate study: major in history; letters of recommendation. Ph.D. candidacy prerequisite: master's degree with thesis. 13 professorial staff. 16 master's degrees and 5 Ph.D.'s awarded 1955-59. 27 graduate students registered fall 1959.

Mathematics. Algebra, analysis, topology. Prerequisite for graduate study: major in mathematics or equivalent. Ph.D. candidacy prerequisite: master's degree in mathematics or equivalent. 9 professorial staff. Ph.D. program begun 1960. 10 master's degrees awarded 1955-59. 8 graduate students registered fall 1959.

Physics. Mathematical and theoretical, chemical, or neutron physics. Prerequisite for graduate study: major in general physics or in theoretical mathematical physics. 6 professorial staff. Ph.D. program begun 1958. 8 master's degrees awarded 1955-59. 6 graduate students registered fall 1959. Total enrollment limited to 10.

South Dakota State College of Agriculture and Mechanic Arts

BROOKINGS, SOUTH DAKOTA

Graduate Division

The college has offered graduate instruction at the master's level since 1891, but the Graduate Division was not formally organized until 1957. First Ph.D. was awarded in 1958. Institution is publicly controlled by the state. Both men and women are admitted.

Rooms in dormitories and private homes available for single graduate students; college-

and privately-owned apartments for married students.

Residence requirement for Ph.D.: minimum of 3 academic years of full-time work (135 quarter hours) beyond bachelor's degree, of which 75 quarter hours must be earned in residence at this institution. 45 credits must be earned during the academic year. Summer courses and a few evening courses available.

ADMISSION REQUIREMENTS

For graduate study: bachelor's degree; B average or better for last 2 years of undergraduate study (for unconditional admission); acceptance by department and approval of Dean of the Graduate Division. For candidacy for Ph.D.: substantial completion of course work; reading knowledge of 2 foreign languages (or 1 foreign language and proficiency in a collateral field); written and oral preliminary examinations.

Apply to Dean of the Graduate Division at least 1 month prior to date of desired entry.

FEES AND FIRST-YEAR AID

Matriculation fee of $5 must accompany application. Tuition for state residents $198 per academic year; others $366. Special fees approximate $48 annually. Room (in dormitory) $144-$216 per academic year. Rooms in private homes cost $5-$6 per week. Meals in college dining room average $10 per week. College-owned apartment units for married students $25-$65 a month.

First-year aid available: research and teaching assistantships, $1,500-$2,000.

Apply to head of appropriate department at any time.

FIELDS OF STUDY FOR THE PH.D.

Agricultural Economics. Offered by Department of Economics. Prerequisites for graduate study: 36 credits in the social sciences, including 24 in the field of economics and at least 1 course in statistics. 19 professorial staff. Ph.D. program begun 1955. 34 master's degrees and 1 Ph.D. awarded 1955-59. 11 graduate students registered fall 1959.

Agronomy. Soils, crops. Prerequisite for graduate study: at least 20 credits in either soils or crops. 18 professorial staff. Ph.D. program begun 1955. 24 master's degrees and 1 Ph.D. awarded 1955-59. 24 graduate students registered fall 1959.

Animal Husbandry. Nutrition, animal breeding. Prerequisite for graduate study: at least 20 credits in animal husbandry. 15 professorial staff. Ph.D. program begun 1955. 16 master's degrees awarded 1955-59. 15 graduate students registered fall 1959.

Animal Science. Combined program offered by Departments of Animal, Dairy and Poultry Husbandry, Entomology-Zoology, Bacteriology; and Chemistry. 39 professorial staff. Ph.D. program begun 1955. 1 Ph.D. awarded 1955-59. 4 graduate students registered fall 1959.

Biochemistry. Offered by Chemistry Department. Prerequisites for graduate study: major in chemistry; qualifying examination in some cases. 13 professorial staff. Ph.D. program begun 1958. 2 master's degrees awarded 1955-59.

Plant Science. Combined program offered by Departments of Agronomy, Botany, Plant Pathology, Horticulture, Bacteriology, Entomology-Zoology, and Chemistry. 31 professorial staff. Ph.D. program begun 1955. 2 graduate students registered fall 1959.

Social Science. Combined program offered by Departments of Economics, Rural Sociology, History, Political Science, and Education and Psychology. 24 professorial staff. Ph.D. program begun 1955. 1 graduate student registered fall 1959.

South Dakota, State University of

VERMILLION, SOUTH DAKOTA

The Graduate School

Graduate instruction at the master's level has been available since 1911, and the Graduate School was organized in 1929. A Ph.D. program was initiated in 1956. Institution is publicly controlled by the state. Both men and women are admitted.

A program leading to the Ed.D. is offered by the School of Education.

Single graduate students may live in college dormitories; university-operated apartments and trailer units available for married students.

Residence requirement for Ph.D.: 2 academic years; a maximum of 24 semester hours of graduate credit may be transferred from other institutions. Summer courses available.

ADMISSION REQUIREMENTS

For graduate study; bachelor's degree. For candidacy for Ph.D.: proficiency examinations in 2 modern foreign languages (usually French and German); preliminary examinations in major and minor fields.

Apply to departmental chairman 6 to 8 months in advance of fall registration.

FEES AND FIRST-YEAR AID

No application fee. Tuition for state residents $198 per year; others $366. Special fees approximate $60 per year. Room (in dormitory) $145 per year. Approximate annual cost of board in college dining room $304. Apartments rent for approximately $65 per month.

First-year aid available: teaching fellowships $1,800; research assistantships, $2,200-$2,400.

Apply to departmental chairman in fall or winter preceding year of registration.

FIELDS OF STUDY FOR THE PH.D.

Anatomy. Gross anatomy, histology, embryology, neuroanatomy. 4 professorial staff. Ph.D. program initiated 1956. 4 master's degrees awarded 1955-59. 2 graduate students registered fall 1959. New enrollment limited to 3 or 4.

Bacteriology. Medical bacteriology, immunology, virology, bacterial physiology and metabolism. Minor field is usually biochemistry. Prerequisites for graduate study: adequate preparation in basic physical and biological sciences, including chemistry (through organic), physics, mathematics, and zoology or botany; 1 foreign language. Recommended: undergraduate courses in biochemistry, bacteriology, calculus, and genetics. Some deficiencies may be made up after admission to program. Ph.D. candidacy prerequisites: 2 years of graduate work; approval of thesis topic. 4 professorial staff. 13 master's degrees awarded 1955-59. 8 graduate students registered fall 1959. Enrollment limited to 6.

Biochemistry. Enzymes, amino acids, vitamins, hormones, X-ray diffraction, isotopic technics. Prerequisites for graduate study: general chemistry, qualitative analysis, quantitative analysis, organic chemistry. Recommended: 2 years of modern foreign language; physical chemistry. Ph.D. prerequisites: physical chemistry; approval of thesis topic by faculty advisory committee. 3 professorial staff. Ph.D. program initiated 1956. 6 master's degrees awarded 1955-59. 4 graduate students registered fall 1959. New enrollment limited to 8 or 9.

Physiology and Pharmacology. Physiology, pharmacology. Prerequisites for graduate study: chemistry, physics, and zoology. 5 professorial staff. Ph.D. program initiated 1957. 6 master's degrees awarded 1957-59. 6 graduate students registered fall 1959.

Southern California, University of

LOS ANGELES 7, CALIFORNIA

Graduate School

In 1910 a graduate department was organized in the College of Letters, Arts, and Sciences. The year 1920 saw the beginning of a Graduate School of Arts and Sciences, which 3 years later became the Graduate School of the university. The first Ph.D. was awarded in 1927. Other doctoral degrees conferred include: D.B.A. (School of Business Administration); Ed.D. (School of Education); D.M.A. (School of Music); D.P.A. (School of Public Administration); and D.S.W. (School of Social Work). University is privately controlled and nonsectarian. Both men and women are admitted.

Dormitory rooms available for 74 graduate women and 160 graduate men. 44 studio apartments maintained for married students with no children; 27 apartments for couples with one child.

Special facilities include: library of approximately 866,000 volumes; the Allan Hancock Foundation for research in marine biology and related sciences which includes a marine laboratory ship among its facilities.

Residence requirement for Ph.D.: minimum of 3 academic years beyond bachelor's degree, of which 1 year (normally the last) must be spent in residence at the University of Southern California. Summer and evening courses available.

ADMISSION REQUIREMENTS

For graduate study: bachelor's degree; evidence of ability to do acceptable graduate work; strong personal qualifications, including good moral character and sound health; GRE before or at time of admission; departmental tests. For candidacy for Ph.D.: reading knowledge of 2 foreign languages (usually selected from French, German, and Russian); completion of substantial portion of course work with satisfactory grades; qualifying examinations; recommendation of Guidance Committee.

Apply to Office of Admissions at least 6 weeks before date of desired entry.

FEES AND FIRST-YEAR AID

Application fee $10. Tuition $32 per unit ($640-$960 for a normal course load for 1 academic year). Student health service fee $20 a year. Room (in dormitory) $320 per academic year. Approximate annual cost of board in college dining room: $530 for women, $550 for men. Unfurnished apartments $30-$32.50 per month; furnished $45-$55.

First-year aid available: 20 fellowships, waiver of up to 14 units of tuition; 134 teaching fellowships, $1,732-$2,312; 75 other fellowships, $350-$2,900; variable number of research assistantships with stipends in varying amounts.

Apply to head of appropriate department or to Dean of the Graduate School by February 15.

FIELDS OF STUDY FOR THE PH.D.

Four courses in the methodology of teaching are offered at the graduate level: Procedures in Junior College Instruction; Problems of College Teaching; Curriculum Development in the Undergraduate College; Field Work in Higher Education.

Anatomy. Medical anatomy. Prerequisites for graduate study: courses in anatomy, biochemistry and nutrition, medical microbiology, pharmacology, and physiology. 8 professorial staff. 1 Ph.D. awarded 1955-59. 4 graduate students registered fall 1959.

Bacteriology. Bacteriology, physiology, metabolism, cytology of bacteria, serology and immunology, food or public health bacteriology. Prerequisites for graduate study: chemistry through 1 year of biochemistry; 25-30 units of advanced bacteriology. Recommended: additional work in chemistry such as physical chemistry. 5 professorial staff. 17 master's degrees and 13 Ph.D.'s awarded 1955-59. 25 graduate students registered fall 1959. Total enrollment limited to 25.

Biochemistry. Offered by Department of Biochemistry and Nutrition. Prerequisites for gradu-

ate study: general, analytical, organic, and physical chemistry; mathematics through calculus; physics, zoology, or bacteriology; general biochemistry. 9 professorial staff. 2 master's degrees and 8 Ph.D.'s awarded 1955-59. 30 graduate students registered fall 1959.

Biology. Cytology, embryology, vertebrate natural history and taxonomy, anatomy, mammalian physiology, cellular physiology, protozoology, parasitology, ecology, plant morphology, taxonomy, ecology and physiology. Prerequisites for graduate study: major in biology, botany, or zoology, or equivalent; GRE Advanced Test in Biology. 8 professorial staff. 22 master's degrees and 14 Ph.D.'s awarded 1955-59. 39 graduate students registered fall 1959.

Chemistry. Colloid and polymer, inorganic, organic, physical chemistry, prerequisites for graduate study: major in chemistry; GRE Advanced Test in Chemistry. 16 professorial staff. 18 master's degrees and 35 Ph.D.'s awarded 1955-59. 42 graduate students registered fall 1959.

Comparative Literature. Each candidate selects for emphasis and concentration a century, a movement, and a genre. Offered by Department of Comparative Literature with the cooperation of several departments of national literatures. Prerequisites for graduate study: knowledge of at least 2 modern foreign languages or 1 modern and 1 ancient language; oral interview. 9 professorial staff. 3 master's degrees and 6 Ph.D.'s awarded 1955-59. 13 graduate students registered fall 1959.

Economics. Economic theory or history; history of economic thought; money, banking, and credit; government finance and fiscal policy; labor or international economics; economics of development; economic fluctuations and forecasting; economic organization and planning; industrial organization; urban and regional economics and statistics. Offered by Department of Economics in cooperation with School of Business Administration. Prerequisite for graduate study: major in economics or 18 upper-division units in economics. Ph.D. candidacy prerequisite: master's thesis in economics or equivalent research and writing experience. 9 professorial staff. 60 master's degrees and 22 Ph.D.'s awarded 1955-59. 62 graduate students registered fall 1959.

Education. School administration, elementary education, guidance, music education, physical education, educational psychology, secondary and higher education, social and philosophical foundations. Prerequisites for graduate study: 18 units of upper-division nonprofessional education courses. 60 professorial staff. 2,504 master's degrees and 245 Ph.D.'s awarded 1955-59. 1,651 graduate students registered fall 1959. Ed.D. degree is also awarded in this field.

Engineering.—Chemical. Unit operations or processes; thermodynamics; kinetics, electrochemistry. 4 professorial staff. 32 master's degrees awarded 1955-59. 47 graduate students registered fall 1959.

Engineering.—Civil, Industrial, Mechanical, Petroleum, Aeronautical. Low-density fluid mechanics, shock wave-boundary layer interaction, propulsion system, supersonic diffuser instability, aircraft stability and control, boundary layer control and supercirculation, hypersonic aerodynamics, hydraulics, structures, sanitary engineering, operations research, statistical control, plant layout and material handling, engineering economy, business systems (engineering and data processing), methods and work measurement, process and tool engineering, thermodynamics and heat transfer, mechanical design, physical metallurgy, drilling fluids, relative permeability and capillary pressure, secondary recovery. Cooperative program offered by Departments of Civil Engineering, Industrial Engineering, Mechanical Engineering, Petroleum Engineering, and Aeronautical Engineering. 20 professorial staff. 1,013 master's degrees and 2 Ph.D.'s awarded 1955-59. 30 graduate students registered fall 1959.

Engineering.—Electrical. Circuit analysis and synthesis, communication theory, computers and controls, electromagnetic engineering, electronics and electron devices, electromechanical systems, power and machinery. 8 professorial staff. Ph.D. program begun 1955. 384 master's degrees and 3 Ph.D.'s awarded 1955-59. 337 graduate students registered fall 1959.

English. Prerequisite for graduate study: at least 24 units in English; 6 in history, philosophy, or religion. 16 professorial staff. 78 master's degrees and 15 Ph.D.'s awarded 1955-59. 110 graduate students registered fall 1959.

French. French language or literature, Romance philology. Prerequisite for graduate study: major in French. Recommended: good background in humanities, especially Latin. 5 professorial staff. 12 master's degrees and 5 Ph.D.'s

awarded 1955-59. 11 graduate students registered fall 1959.

Geology. General, structural, and marine geology; invertebrate paleontology; micropaleontology; desert and engineering geology. Prerequisite for graduate study: major in geology. 9 professorial staff. 16 master's degrees and 6 Ph.D.'s awarded 1955-59. 60 graduate students registered fall 1959. Total enrollment limited to 60.

German. Modern literature, classic period, Germanic philology. Prerequisite for graduate study: major in German; Latin is required for those majoring in classics. 4 professorial staff. 5 master's degrees and 3 Ph.D.'s awarded 1955-59. 24 graduate students registered fall 1959.

History. Medieval history, early modern or contemporary Europe, intellectual and cultural history of Europe, English history, British Empire, Latin-America, Colonial and early national United States, 19th or 20th century United States, intellectual and cultural history of the United States, United States diplomatic history, Western United States, California, Far East, Middle East, Russia, China, Afro-Asian studies. 12 professorial staff. 53 master's degrees and 28 Ph.D.'s awarded 1955-59. 100 graduate students registered 1959.

Mathematics. Modern geometry, algebraic topology, homotopy theory, algebraic and analytic number theory, Banach spaces, boundary value problems of partial differential equations, stability theory in ordinary differential equations, convex bodies. Prerequisite for graduate study: major in mathematics; examinations in prerequisites. 10 professorial staff. 16 master's degrees and 7 Ph.D.'s awarded 1955-59. 200 graduate students (including those in the evening classes) registered fall 1959.

Microbiology. Microbiology (including bacteriology); immunology; virology; genetics (microbial); biophysics (including electron microscopy); biochemistry (microbial or cellular metabolism). Offered by Department of Medical Microbiology. Prerequisite for graduate study: adequate preparation in mathematics (calculus) and physical sciences (physics and chemistry). Recommended: basic courses in biology (especially genetics) and physical chemistry. Ph.D. program begun 1956. 3 master's degrees and 1 Ph.D. awarded 1955-59. 3 graduate students registered fall 1959.

Music. Musicology. Prerequisite for graduate study: music graduate entrance examinations.

Ph.D. candidacy prerequisite: M.A. in music history and literature. 23 professorial staff. 12 master's degrees and 13 Ph.D.'s awarded 1955-59. 17 graduate students registered fall 1959.

Pharmacology. Cellular or cardiac pharmacology, biochemistry. Prerequisite for graduate study: courses in biology or chemistry. 6 professorial staff. 2 master's degrees and 4 Ph.D.'s awarded 1955-59. 3 graduate students registered fall 1959.

Pharmacy. Pharmaceutical chemistry, pharmacognosy, pharmacology, pharmacy. Offered by School of Pharmacy. Prerequisite for graduate study: preparation in field. 9 professorial staff. 19 master's degrees awarded 1955-59. 11 graduate students registered fall 1959. Total enrollment limited to 12.

Philosophy. History of philosophy, epistemology, metaphysics, value (theory, ethics, aesthetics), mathematical logic. Offered by School of Philosophy. Prerequisite for graduate study: personal interview. 5 professorial staff. 2 master's degrees and 1 Ph.D. awarded 1955-59. 23 graduate students registered fall 1959.

Physical Education. Health education, physical education, or recreation; administration (teaching or leadership); curriculum or program; problem solving or research; evaluation; field experience; professional preparation; history or philosophy. Prerequisites for graduate study: acceptable undergraduate preparation; MAT or equivalent. A nationally standardized test in physical education currently being considered. Recommended: acceptable professional experience. 11 professorial staff. 65 master's degrees and 24 Ph.D.'s awarded 1955-59. 62 graduate students registered fall 1959. Ed.D. degree is also awarded in this field.

Physics. Prerequisite for graduate study: major in physics with superior grades in mathematics and physics. Ph.D. candidacy prerequisite: GRE Advanced Test in Physics. 12 professorial staff. 20 master's degrees and 10 Ph.D.'s awarded 1955-59. 72 graduate students registered fall 1959.

Physiology. Medical physiology. Prerequisite for graduate study: basic premedical sciences (because of space limitations, M.D. students have preference). 4 professorial staff. 6 Ph.D.'s awarded 1955-59. 6 graduate students registered fall 1959.

Political Science. Political theory; comparative government; public law; American government; political parties, public opinion, and political dynamics; international relations; public administration. Offered by the Department of Political Science in cooperation with the faculties of the School of International Relations and the School of Public Administration. Prerequisites for graduate study: 18 upper-division units in political science; GRE Advanced Test in Government. 22 professorial staff. 30 master's degrees and 22 Ph.D.'s awarded 1955-59. 50 graduate students registered fall 1959.

Psychology. Theoretical, clinical, or industrial psychology; psychological measurement. Prerequisites for graduate study: 18 upper-division course units in field, including elementary experimental and physiological psychology, elementary statistical measurements, and history or systems of psychology. Recommended: courses in biological, physical, and social sciences, mathematics, perception, learning, motivation, and advanced statistics. 15 professorial staff. 23 master's degrees and 47 Ph.D.'s awarded 1955-59. 99 graduate students registered fall 1959. New enrollment limited to 30.

Religion. Archaeology, Bible, church history, history of Christian thought, philosophy or psychology of religion, theology, world religions. Offered by the Graduate School of Religion. Prerequisites for graduate study: 18 upper-division credits in religion; screening examinations. 11 professorial staff. 32 master's degrees and 35 Ph.D.'s awarded 1955-59. 66 graduate students registered fall 1959.

Sociology. Social psychology, social theory, demography and population, social research, social organization and disorganization. Prerequisites for graduate study: major in sociology or another social science; screening examination by department. 8 professorial staff. 25 master's degrees and 14 Ph.D.'s awarded 1955-59. 98 graduate students registered fall 1959. Total enrollment limited to 100.

Spanish. Language (philology or linguistics), literature (Spanish or Spanish-American). Offered by Department of Spanish and Italian. Prerequisite for graduate study: major in Spanish or equivalent. 5 professorial staff. 11 master's degrees and 8 Ph.D.'s awarded 1955-59. 42 graduate students registered fall 1959.

Speech. Public address, oral interpretation, speech and hearing pathology. 8 professorial staff.

97 master's degrees and 47 Ph.D.'s awarded 1955-59. 50 graduate students registered fall 1959.

Southern Illinois University

CARBONDALE, ILLINOIS

The Graduate School

Graduate instruction has been offered at the university since 1944. The Graduate School, which was organized in 1949, has jurisdiction over the graduate programs offered at the several campuses of the university. The first Ph.D. was awarded in 1959. The Ph.D. is the only doctoral degree awarded by Southern Illinois, but 1 year beyond the master's degree in education may be taken here and applied toward the Ed.D. degree at Indiana University. Institution is publicly controlled by the state. Both men and women are admitted.

Limited dormitory space available for single graduate students. University-owned apartments and a trailer court maintained for married students.

Special facilities include a library of approximately 350,000 volumes containing special collections on Abraham Lincoln, Walt Whitman, and James Joyce.

Residence requirement for the Ph.D.: minimum of 3 years beyond bachelor's degree, of which 2 must be taken in residence at Southern Illinois. Summer and evening courses available.

ADMISSION REQUIREMENTS

For graduate study: bachelor's degree; C+ average (higher in some departments); approval of major department. For candidacy for Ph.D.: completion of 48 hours of course work with satisfactory grades; competence in 2 foreign languages or in 1 language and statistics; preliminary examinations.

Apply to Director of Admissions at least 3 months in advance of date of desired entry.

FEES AND FIRST-YEAR AID

No application fee. Tuition for state residents $150 per academic year; others $300. Room (in dormitory) $240 per academic year. Approximate annual cost of board in college dining room $480. Apartments $60-$90 per month.

First-year aid available: tuition scholarships; teaching assistantships, $180-$210 per month; fellowships, $120 per month; research assistantships, $125-$175 per month.

For fellowships and scholarships, apply to Dean of the Graduate School by March 15; for assistantships, to departmental chairman.

FIELDS OF STUDY FOR THE PH.D.

Courses in the methodology of teaching are offered through the Department of Higher Education. In addition, several doctoral departments offer courses in the teaching of their disciplines.

Anthropology. Cultural anthropology of Meso-America, northern Mexico, and the Southwest; Southeast Asia-Oceania; Africa; linguistics; archaeology. Recommended for graduate study: major in anthropology; 1 foreign language. 9 professorial staff. Program begun 1960. 10 graduate students registered.

Education.—Administration and Supervision. Administration and social foundations. Prerequisites for graduate study: National Teachers Examination and MAT. Ph.D. candidacy prerequisites: acceptance by College of Education Examining Committee; 2 years of administrative experience. 12 professorial staff. Ph.D. program begun 1959. 305 master's degrees awarded 1955-59. 87 graduate students registered fall 1959.

Education.—Elementary. Reading, curriculum and supervision, administration, science or general methods in the elementary school. Ph.D. candidacy prerequisites: M.A. or M.S. in elementary education or related field; experience in elementary schools; statistics and 1 foreign language. 8 professorial staff. Ph.D. program begun 1959. 83 master's degrees awarded 1955-59. 45 graduate students registered fall 1959.

Education.—Secondary. Secondary school as an institution, curriculum of secondary school, secondary school student. Cooperative program offered by Department of Secondary Education and all departments offering work representing secondary teaching fields. Prerequisites for graduate study: National Teachers Examination and MAT. Ph.D. candidacy prerequisites: master's degree with background in education. 5 professorial staff. Ph.D. program begun 1957. 35 master's degrees awarded 1955-59. 40 graduate students registered fall 1959.

Guidance. Educational psychology, measurements, or statistics; theory and practice of counseling, theories of learning, clinical guidance, group guidance. Prerequisites for graduate study: major in education or equivalent; teacher certification; English Proficiency and Ohio Psychological Examinations. Recommended: 1 year of professional experience. Ph.D. candidacy prerequisites: M.S. in field or equivalent; 2 years of professional experience; MAT and National Teachers Examination; 1 modern foreign language; proficiency in statistical design and analysis. 7 professorial staff. Ph.D. program begun 1960. 150 master's degrees awarded 1955-59. 160 graduate students registered fall 1959.

Health Education. School health or community health education. Prerequisite for graduate study: major in health education or related field. 8 professorial staff. Ph.D. program begun 1960. 18 master's degrees awarded 1955-59. 20 graduate students registered fall 1959.

Microbiology and Genetics. Genetics and biochemistry of yeasts. Offered by Department of Microbiology. 4 professorial staff. Program begun 1959. 18 graduate students registered fall 1959. Total enrollment limited to 20.

Physical Education. Physical education and allied fields, psychological foundations of education, curriculum, philosophy of education, tools of research, independent research. Ph.D. candidacy prerequisites: master's degree or equivalent; thesis or research paper; Ohio Psychological Test; MAT. 6 professorial staff. Ph.D. program begun 1960. 74 master's degrees awarded 1955-59. 31 graduate students registered fall 1959.

Physiology. Human or cellular physiology, pharmacology. Prerequisites for graduate study: knowledge of 1 foreign language; GRE; qualifying examination. 3 professorial staff. Ph.D. program begun 1960. 12 master's degrees awarded 1955-59. 10 graduate students registered fall 1959.

Political Science. American, comparative, or state and local government; political theory; international relations; public administration or law; dynamics of politics. Offered by Department of Government. Recommended for graduate study: major in political science; foreign languages. Ph.D. candidacy prerequisite: master's degree or equivalent in field. 20 professorial staff. Ph.D. program begun 1958. 20 master's degrees awarded 1955-59. 39 graduate students registered fall 1959.

Psychology. Clinical, industrial, counseling psychology. Prerequisites for graduate study: B— average; MAT; GRE (including Advanced Test in Psychology). Recommended: basic courses in psychology; mathematics; social, physical, and biological sciences. 15 professorial staff. Ph.D. program begun 1957. 14 master's degrees awarded 1955-59. 43 graduate students registered fall 1959.

Speech. History and criticism of rhetoric and public address, contemporary problems in communication. Prerequisite for graduate study: major in speech or equivalent. Recommended: strong background in languages, literature, and social sciences. 8 professorial staff. Ph.D. program begun 1959. 13 master's degrees awarded 1955-59. 17 graduate students registered fall 1959.

Speech Correction, Pathology, and Audiology. Ph.D. candidacy prerequisite: master's degree. 7 professorial staff. 28 master's degrees and 1 Ph.D. awarded 1955-59. 18 graduate students registered fall 1959.

Zoology. Mammalogy, ecology, parasitology, embryology, entomology, anatomy, limnology, ichthyology, ornithology, fish and game management, herpetology, vertebrate paleontology. Prerequisites for graduate study: B average in all previous course work; 1 year of foreign language; Ohio Psychological and English Proficiency Examinations. Recommended: GRE. Ph.D. candidacy prerequisites: 2 foreign languages plus statistics. 12 professorial staff. Program begun 1959. 8 graduate students registered fall 1959.

Southern Methodist University

DALLAS 22, TEXAS

The Graduate School

The Graduate School was one of the 4 schools named in the original university charter of 1911. Graduate instruction at the master's level was begun in 1915. A doctoral program in economics was approved in 1957, and it is anticipated that the first Ph.D. will be awarded in 1962. A faculty committee is currently studying the feasibility of offering doctoral studies in earth sciences. University is privately controlled and related to the Methodist church. Both men and women are admitted.

A cooperative program between the Southern Methodist University Law School and Latin-American universities leads to the D.C.L. degree. This program is not administered by the Graduate School.

Graduate students find accommodations in dormitories, fraternities, and in private homes in community. 1 dormitory with 67 efficiency apartments is maintained for married graduate students without children.

Special facilities include: library of approximately 477,000 volumes; computing laboratory with Univac 1103.

Residence requirement for Ph.D.: 3 years beyond bachelor's degree, of which 2 must be spent in full-time residence on campus.

ADMISSION REQUIREMENTS

For graduate study: bachelor's degree; superior academic record; minimum of 12 advanced hours of credit in major field; GRE. For candidacy for Ph.D.: examinations in 2 fields and in 1 foreign language.

Apply to Dean of the Graduate School at least 2 months prior to date of desired registration. Late applications will be considered if vacancies exist.

FEES AND FIRST-YEAR AID

Application fee $10. Tuition $650 per academic year. Special fees approximate $75 annually. Room (in dormitory) $250 per academic year. Approximate annual cost of board in college dining room $440. Efficiency apartments $270 per semester.

First-year aid available: 4 scholarships, $2,650; 5 teaching fellowships, $2,400; 1 or 2 research assistantships, $1,200-$1,800.

Apply to Dean of the Graduate School by March 20 for fall term.

FIELDS OF STUDY FOR THE PH.D.

Economics. Economic theory, mathematical economics, statistics and econometrics, history of economic thought (philosophy and economic history are associated fields), international economics and economic development (particularly in Latin America), monetary and fiscal theory and policy, industrial organization. Recommended for graduate study: mathematics through

calculus. 13 professorial staff. Ph.D. program begun 1959. 9 master's degrees awarded 1955-59. 12 graduate students registered fall 1959. Total enrollment in each year should not exceed 15.

Stanford University

STANFORD, CALIFORNIA

Committee on Graduate Study

Graduate instruction has been offered at Stanford since its establishment in 1891. First Ph.D. was awarded in 1894. Other doctoral degrees awarded are: Ed.D. (School of Education) and J.S.D. (School of Law). University is privately controlled and nonsectarian. Both men and women are admitted.

Separate dormitories maintained for graduate men and women; apartments in Stanford and Escondido Villages for married students.

Special facilities include: library of approximately 1,400,000 catalogued volumes; Hopkins Marine Station at Pacific Grove, California; Hoover Institution on War, Revolution, and Peace; special laboratories for study in high voltage, electronics, nuclear engineering, physics, biophysics, and microwaves; Stanford Medical Center; computer center, including IBM 650 and Burroughs 220.

Residence requirement for Ph.D.: minimum of 3 years of graduate study beyond bachelor's degree; at least 1 year and final units of credit must be taken at Stanford. Summer courses and a few evening courses available.

ADMISSION REQUIREMENTS

For graduate study: bachelor's degree; credentials indicating ability and promise; intention to become a candidate for an advanced degree or for teaching and administrative credentials, or to pursue research or professional courses. Some departments require GRE. School of Medicine requires Medical College Admission Test. Graduate School of Business requires Admission Test for Graduate Study in Business. For candidacy for Ph.D.: completion of substantial portion of course work with satisfactory grades; satisfaction of major department's required preliminary procedures (usually qualifying examinations); fulfillment of at least 1 of the 2 language requirements; certification by major department.

Apply to Office of Admissions, except for admission to School of Law, School of Medicine, and Graduate School of Business. These schools should be addressed directly. Applications for physics program should be received by February 15; for psychology program by June 1; for other programs by August 1 (except business and medicine).

FEES AND FIRST-YEAR AID

Application fee $5. Tuition $1,005 per academic year. Room (in dormitory) for men $225-$345 a year; for women $300. Approximate cost of board in college dining room $435 per academic year for 5-day week; $555 for 7-day week. Apartments in Stanford Village $46-$65 per month; in Escondido Village $85-$105.

First-year aid available: scholarships and fellowships, $500-$3,000; assistantships, $405-$1,650 (taxable); research assistantships, up to $2,250 (taxable); grants-in-aid, up to $1,005.

Apply to Financial Awards Office by February 15.

FIELDS OF STUDY FOR THE PH.D.

A 4-unit course is offered in fall and spring terms for those planning careers in teaching, research, or administration in American higher education. It is called Introduction to American Higher Education, and explores European and American historical backgrounds for the purpose of comprehending the current scene and planning for the future.

Anatomy. Offered by Department of Anatomy in School of Medicine. Programs combining work in anatomy and other fields of biology or medicine may be arranged. Instruction is primarily for students of medicine, but a few other qualified students may be admitted. 7 professorial staff. 2 Ph.D.'s awarded 1955-59. 3 graduate students registered fall 1959.

Anthropology. Cultural or physical anthropology, prehistoric archaeology, linguistics. Offered by Department of Anthropology in School of Humanities and Sciences. Prerequisites for graduate study: major in anthropology or equivalent; introductory course in statistics. 8 professorial staff. 17 master's degrees and 2 Ph.D.'s awarded 1955-59. 15 graduate students registered fall 1959.

Area Studies.—Hispanic American. Cultural rather than geographical study of Spain, Portugal, and Latin America; Spanish and Portuguese languages; political, social, and economic growth of Hispanic world. Interdepartmental program administered under Graduate Division Special Programs, with many departments contributing to faculty. Prerequisites for graduate study: reading, writing, and oral knowledge of Spanish or Portuguese and reading knowledge of the other. 8 master's degrees and 1 Ph.D. awarded 1955-59. 10 graduate students registered fall 1959.

Bacteriology. Offered by Department of Medical Microbiology in the School of Medicine. Prerequisites for graduate study: completion of premedical sciences program; quantitative analysis. 7 professorial staff. 13 master's degrees and 8 Ph.D.'s awarded 1955-59. 13 graduate students registered fall 1959.

Biological Sciences. General and experimental biology, natural history, marine biology and oceanography. Offered by Department of Biological Sciences in the School of Humanities and Sciences. Recommended for graduate study: GRE. 22 professorial staff. 30 master's degrees and 49 Ph.D.'s awarded 1955-59. 44 graduate students registered fall 1959.

Biophysics. X-ray and electron microscopy and microspectroscopy, electron paramagnetic resonance spectroscopy, biophysical studies on cell physiology. Most of required course work is in the Departments of Physics, Chemistry, and Biological Sciences. Program is conducted under the guidance of an advisory committee in the Biophysics Laboratory of the School of Medicine. Laboratory staff gives courses in biophysics designed to integrate the 3 fundamental disciplines, as well as courses on specialized biophysical techniques. 9 professorial staff. Program begun 1959. 4 graduate students registered fall 1959.

Business. Offered by the Graduate School of Business for students interested in teaching, professional research in business, or further specialization in business subjects. 945 master's degrees and 16 Ph.D.'s awarded 1955-59. 398 graduate students registered fall 1959.

Chemistry — Biochemistry — Chemical Engineering. Offered by Department of Chemistry and Chemical Engineering. 15 professorial staff. 43 master's degrees (33 in chemistry and 10 in chemical engineering) and 56 Ph.D.'s (all in chemistry) awarded 1955-59. 54 graduate students registered in chemistry program fall 1959; 8 other graduate students registered in chemical engineering.

Classics. Latin and Greek languages, literature, history, and archaeology. Offered by Department of Classics in School of Humanities and Sciences. Prerequisite for graduate study: major in Latin and/or Greek or equivalent. Recommended: reading knowledge of French or German. 7 professorial staff. 1 master's degree awarded 1955-59. 6 graduate students registered fall 1959.

Economics. 15 professorial staff. 72 master's degrees and 17 Ph.D.'s awarded 1955-59. 69 graduate students registered fall 1959.

Education. General school administration; elementary, secondary, or higher education; junior college; guidance; philosophy and/or history of education; overseas and/or comparative education; psychological foundations of education; health education; general curriculum; child development; teacher or secondary education; special curriculum. Offered by School of Education. Prerequisite for graduate study: GRE. 42 professorial staff. 1,022 master's degrees and 40 Ph.D.'s awarded 1955-59. 344 graduate students registered fall 1959. The Ed.D. degree is also conferred in this field.

Engineering.—Aeronautical. Aircraft design or structures; aerodynamics; physical aspects of aeronautics. Prerequisites for graduate study: training in fields of aerodynamics, aircraft structures, and mathematics. 15 professorial staff. 24 master's degrees and 1 Ph.D. awarded 1955-59. 82 graduate students registered fall 1959.

Engineering.—Civil. Civil engineering administration; hydraulic, structural, or construction engineering; public works administration. Recommended for graduate study: degree in civil engineering. 15 professorial staff. 205 master's degrees and 10 Ph.D.'s awarded 1955-59. 83 graduate students registered fall 1959.

Engineering. — Electrical. Administration, communication theory, electron tubes, illumination, microwaves, network theory, radio science, solid-state electronics, theory of systems, and transistor electronics. 35 professorial staff. 374 master's degrees and 94 Ph.D.'s awarded 1955-59. 415 graduate students registered fall 1959.

Engineering.—Industrial. Engineering statistics or economy, data processing. 7 professorial staff. 89 master's degrees and 1 Ph.D. awarded 1955-59. 55 students registered fall 1959.

Engineering.—Mechanical. Power generation; engineering design; instrumentation and controls; thermodynamic processes, including nuclear energy problems; mechanical engineering research and development. Prerequisite for graduate study: degree in engineering or equivalent. 12 professorial staff. 105 master's degrees and 9 Ph.D.'s awarded 1955-59. 118 graduate students registered fall 1959.

Engineering Mechanics. Solid and fluid mechanics; programs of study in advanced mechanics for mechanical, aeronautical, and civil engineers. 4 professorial staff. 45 master's degrees and 23 Ph.D.'s awarded 1955-59. 73 graduate students registered fall 1959.

Engineering.—Metallurgical. Offered by Department of Metallurgical Engineering in the School of Mineral Sciences. 5 professorial staff. 17 master's degrees and 3 Ph.D.'s awarded 1955-59. 25 graduate students registered fall 1959.

Engineering.—Mineral. Mining engineering and mineral processing. Offered by Department of Mineral Engineering in the School of Mineral Sciences. 2 professorial staff. 5 master's degrees awarded 1955-59. 7 graduate students registered fall 1959.

Engineering.—Petroleum. Exploration and development, production and reservoir engineering, field processing, and appraisal. Offered by Department of Petroleum Engineering in the School of Mineral Sciences. 3 professorial staff. 36 master's degrees awarded 1955-59. 9 graduate students registered fall 1959.

English. English literature, English philology. 19 professorial staff. 63 master's degrees and 40 Ph.D.'s awarded 1955-59. 109 graduate students registered fall 1959.

Food Research. Study of production, distribution, and consumption of food. Offered by the Food Research Institute. Prerequisite for graduate study: usually a bachelor's degree in economics or agricultural economics. 11 professorial staff. 13 master's degrees and 4 Ph.D.'s awarded 1955-59. 11 graduate students registered fall 1959.

French. Linguistics or literature. Offered by Department of Modern European Languages. 7 professorial staff. 2 master's degrees and 4 Ph.D.'s awarded in 1955-59. 21 graduate students registered fall 1959.

Geology. Geology, geochemistry. Offered by Department of Geology in the School of Mineral Sciences. Recommended for graduate study: 1 modern foreign language, preferably German. 17

professorial staff. 87 master's degrees and 42 Ph.D.'s awarded 1955-59. 56 graduate students registered fall 1959.

Geophysics. Fundamentals of geology, mathematics, physics, and engineering. Offered by the Department of Geophysics in the School of Mineral Sciences. Prerequisite for graduate study: German. 5 professorial staff. 8 master's degrees and 2 Ph.D.'s awarded 1955-59. 12 graduate students registered fall 1959.

German. Linguistics, literature. Offered by Department of Modern European Languages. 5 professorial staff. 5 master's degrees and 6 Ph.D.'s awarded 1955-59. 17 graduate students registered fall 1959.

History. European, British, United States, or Latin-American history; the Far East. 18 professorial staff. 60 master's degrees and 44 Ph.D.'s awarded 1955-59. 55 graduate students registered fall 1959.

Mass Communications Research. This program is one of the Graduate Division Special Programs and is presented through the Department of Communication and Journalism in cooperation with other appropriate departments. Program includes courses in statistics, learning, perception, social psychology and organization, social structure, and methodology of the behavioral sciences. 6 Ph.D.'s awarded 1955-59. 6 graduate students registered fall 1959.

Mathematics. Prerequisite for graduate study: major in mathematics. 24 professorial staff. 36 master's degrees and 19 Ph.D.'s awarded 1955-59. 92 graduate students registered fall 1959.

Music. Prerequisite for graduate study: major in music; ability to play the piano with moderate facility. 9 professorial staff. 26 master's degrees and 3 Ph.D.'s awarded 1955-59. 34 graduate students registered fall 1959. A program leading to the Ed.D. with concentration in music education is also offered in cooperation with the School of Education.

Pharmacology. Offered by Department of Pharmacology in the School of Medicine. Instruction is primarily for students of medicine, but individual Ph.D. programs may be worked out by qualified students with department faculty. No candidates accepted for master's degree. 6 professorial staff. 2 Ph.D.'s awarded 1955-59. 1 graduate student registered fall 1959.

Philosophy. Prerequisite for graduate study: GRE. 8 professorial staff. 7 master's degrees and

2 Ph.D.'s awarded 1955-59. 27 graduate students registered fall 1959.

Physics. High-energy, nuclear, low-temperature, or theoretical physics; nuclear induction; microwave spectroscopy; microwaves; biophysics. Degree may be obtained in physics or applied physics. 18 professorial staff. 61 master's degrees and 59 Ph.D.'s awarded 1955-59. 107 graduate students registered fall 1959.

Physiology. Offered by Department of Physiology in the School of Medicine. Prerequisite for graduate study: preference given to students who have substantial background in mathematics, chemistry, physics, and biology. 3 professorial staff. 4 master's degrees and 5 Ph.D.'s awarded 1955-59. 7 graduate students registered fall 1959.

Political Science. Domestic politics, foreign affairs. Prerequisite for graduate study: courses in political science and other social science subjects. 16 professorial staff. 43 master's degrees and 17 Ph.D.'s awarded 1955-59. 37 graduate students registered fall 1959.

Psychology. Clinical, counseling, departmental, social and personality, or physiological and comparative psychology; perception and learning; psychometrics. Prerequisites for graduate study: intention to earn Ph.D. degree (except for those specializing in preschool area); GRE. 20 professorial staff. 24 master's degrees and 42 Ph.D.'s awarded 1955-59. 59 graduate students registered fall 1959. Enrollment is very strictly limited; balance is maintained between clinical and nonclinical majors.

Sociology. Prerequisites for graduate study: major in sociology; elementary course in statistics. 9 professorial staff. 24 master's degrees and 3 Ph.D.'s awarded 1955-59. 16 graduate students registered fall 1959.

Spanish. Linguistics or literature. Offered by Department of Modern European Languages. 3 professorial staff. 12 master's degrees and 3 Ph.D.'s awarded 1955-59. 20 graduate students registered fall 1959.

Special Programs. Provided by the Graduate Division for unusually well-qualified students whose plans do not fall within the province of any one department. A chairman and an advisory committee are selected from the various departments representing student's field of interest. 1 master's degree and 9 Ph.D.'s awarded 1955-59 (including 6 in mass communications research and 1 in Hispanic American studies). 13 graduate students registered fall 1959.

Speech and Drama. Theater and drama, rhetoric and public address. Prerequisites for graduate study: training in speech and drama; GRE Aptitude and Advanced Tests. 10 professorial staff. 69 master's degrees and 29 Ph.D.'s awarded 1955-59. 42 graduate students registered fall 1959.

Speech Pathology and Audiology. Speech correction, hearing, and speech science. Student specializes in 1 of the fields, but is expected to acquire background in the other 2. Offered by the Division of Speech Pathology and Audiology in the School of Medicine. 5 professorial staff. Ph.D. program begun 1957. 7 master's degrees and 7 Ph.D.'s awarded 1955-59. 28 graduate students registered fall 1959.

Statistics. Mathematical theory of statistics and probability. Prerequisite for graduate study: mathematical background, including calculus. 15 professorial staff. 50 master's degrees and 16 Ph.D.'s awarded 1955-59. 85 graduate students registered fall 1959.

Stevens Institute of Technology

HOBOKEN, NEW JERSEY

Graduate Studies Program

Graduate instruction was inaugurated at Stevens about 1875, and the first Ph.D. was awarded in 1877. Graduate degree work was then dropped for a time, but was reestablished in 1930 at the master's degree level. Programs leading to the Ph.D. were started in 1955. The D.Sc. is also awarded in the fields of mechanics and chemical engineering. Institute is privately controlled and nonsectarian. Both men and women are admitted.

Some dormitory rooms and a limited number of small apartments available for graduate students.

Special facilities include: experimental towing tank laboratory for ship models and seaplanes; powder metallurgy laboratory; general facilities in physics, chemistry, and mechanical engineering for theoretical and experimental work (including Collins Cyrostat, infra-red spectroscopy); library of approximately 40,000 volumes.

Residence requirement for Ph.D.: 3 years beyond bachelor's degree, with at least 1 year in residence at Stevens. Evening courses available.

ADMISSION REQUIREMENTS

For graduate study: bachelor's degree; standing in upper third of graduating class or GRE; qualifying examinations in major field. For candidacy for Ph.D.: examinations in German and (usually) 1 other language; written and oral preliminary examinations.

Apply to Director of Admissions by September 1 for the fall term; by January 1 for the spring term.

FEES AND FIRST-YEAR AID

Application fee $10; registration $10. Tuition $1,080 per academic year. Approximate annual cost of board in college dining room $380.

First-year aid available: 28 teaching fellowships, $1,750-$2,000 plus ½ tuition; 6 other fellowships, $900-$1,600 plus tuition; 20 research assistantships, $1,750-$2,000 plus ½ tuition. Loan fund also available.

Apply to Dean of Graduate Studies by March 1.

FIELDS OF STUDY FOR THE PH.D.

Chemistry. Spectroscopy, radiation chemistry of gases and solids, physico-chemical optics, chemistry of natural products or of organic sulphur compounds, diffusion of gases and liquids through membranes, polymer chemistry, structure of concentrated solutions, mechanisms of photosynthesis. Offered by Department of Chemistry and Chemical Engineering. Prerequisites for graduate study: Courses in analytical, organic, and physical chemistry. 8 professorial staff. Ph.D. program begun 1955. 33 master's degrees and 1 Ph.D. awarded 1957-59. 103 graduate students registered fall 1959.

Mathematics. Applied mathematics, analysis. Prerequisites for graduate study: courses in analytic geometry, calculus, and elementary differential equations; 1 other term of mathematics. 8 professorial staff. Ph.D. program begun 1955. 28 master's degrees awarded 1955-59. 38 graduate students registered fall 1959.

Physics. Plasma physics, particle acceleration by plasma betatron, general relativity, classical limit of quantum theory, properties of helium at low temperature, superconductivity, elementary particle physics-nuclear emulsion technique, scattering theory. 15 professorial staff. Ph.D. program initiated 1955. 24 master's degrees awarded 1955-59. 103 students registered fall 1959.

Syracuse University

SYRACUSE 10, NEW YORK

Graduate School

The Graduate School, which has jurisdiction over all doctorate programs except those offered by the College of Forestry and the College of Education, was established in 1912. Graduate courses, however, have been offered since 1874 with the first Ph.D. being awarded in 1876. Programs have been greatly expanded since 1930. Syracuse is nonsectarian and privately controlled. Both men and women are admitted.

Other doctorates conferred by the institution are: Ed.D. (School of Education); D.P.A. (Maxwell School and the Graduate School); D.S.S. (Maxwell School and the Graduate School). The College of Business has been authorized to award the D.B.A., but this program is not yet in operation. The College of Forestry of the State University of New York is located on the Syracuse campus and cooperates in many programs; its offerings are described in the exhibit for the State University of New York.

Residence facilities for men include a graduate section in new dormitory, 2 apartment houses, and graduate cottages. Women students accommodated in university-owned or approved housing. 540 units available for married students in housing section; additional units being acquired.

Special facilities include: library of approximately 440,000 volumes; several statistics laboratories; electric network analyser; computer center; psychological research center; hearing and speech center; reading laboratory; museum of natural science; and research institute which coordinates and administers sponsored research.

Requirements for doctorate: 2 academic years, exclusive of dissertation; at least 1 year in residence in Syracuse. Summer and evening courses available in some fields.

ADMISSION REQUIREMENTS

For graduate study with full standing: bachelor's degree with major in field chosen for graduate study; department or field prerequisites; evidence of scholarly capabilities; 1.5 to 2.0 average (on 3.0 scale). Recommended (required in some departments): foreign languages; MAT, CAVD, or GRE. Provisional standing is at discretion of major department and the Dean. For candidacy for Ph.D.: 2 years of advanced study; tool requirements (usually foreign languages); qualifying examinations; 1 year of residence.

Apply to Dean of the Graduate School by May 15 for summer or fall terms for all programs except forestry (State University of New York), social science (Maxwell School), or School of Education.

FEES AND FIRST-YEAR AID

Application fee $10. Tuition $1,080 per academic year for work in physical sciences, engineering, or mathematics; $720 in other programs (figures based on 12-credit hour load per semester; credit hour rates are $45 and $30 respectively). Special fees approximate $96 annually. Annual cost of rooms (in dormitory) $432 for 36 weeks; $624 for 52 weeks. Annual cost of board in college dining room: $472 for 36 weeks; $708 for 52 weeks. Apartments $43-$48 (temporary housing); $95-$108 (permanent housing).

First-year aid available: 10 to 15 scholarships, $900-$1,350; approximately 200 teaching fellowships, $1,500-$2,200; approximately 40 other fellowships, $1,900-$2,500; approximately 200 research assistantships, $1,500-$3,300; loan funds available.

For scholarships and fellowships, apply to Dean of the Graduate School not later than March 1; for assistantships, to department chairmen not later than March 15.

FIELDS OF STUDY FOR THE PH.D.

Two courses on the methodology of college teaching are available: Teaching of Social Science in Higher Education, and Teaching of Science in Higher Education. Other higher education courses are offered by the School of Education.

Anthropology. Physical, social, and cultural anthropology; primitive societies. Offered by Department of Sociology and Anthropology. 4 professorial staff. 3 master's degrees and 1 Ph.D. awarded 1955-59. 3 graduate students registered fall 1959.

Audiology and Speech Pathology. Speech and hearing disorders; hearing aids and auditory training; anatomy, physiology, and pathology of hearing mechanisms; advanced clinical practice in speech and hearing therapy; neurological bases of physical disabilities; neuropathologies of speech and language. Offered by Department of Special Education. Prerequisites: MAT;

CAVD; technical preparation in the field. 4 professorial staff. 18 master's degrees and 5 Ph.D.'s awarded 1955-59. 11 graduate students registered fall 1959.

Bacteriology and Botany. Bacteriology, botany, genetics, microbiology. 14 professorial staff. 21 master's degrees and 8 Ph.D.'s awarded 1955-59. 25 graduate students registered fall 1959.

Chemistry and Biochemistry. Organic and inorganic chemistry, quantitative analysis, physical chemistry, crystallography, chemical kinetics, analytical chemistry, quantum mechanics, plant and animal biochemistry. Chemistry offered by Department of Chemistry; Biochemistry by Biochemistry Committee. Recommended for graduate study: German and another foreign language. Required for biochemistry: general, analytical, organic, and physical chemistry; mathematics through integral calculus; appropriate preparation in the biological sciences. 30 professorial staff. 17 master's degrees and 32 Ph.D.'s awarded 1955-59. 58 graduate students registered fall 1959.

Communications. Principles, history, or law of communications; advertising. Offered by the School of Journalism. Recommended for graduate study: statistics; foreign languages. 7 professorial staff. Ph.D. program begun 1956. 66 master's degrees awarded 1955-59. 60 graduate students registered fall 1959.

Economics. Theory, method, and history of doctrine; labor and labor law; finance; public economy; organization of industry; economic history and systems; Russian economics; international economics; economic development; cognate fields. Recommended for graduate study: mathematics, foreign languages, or alternative tools. 11 professorial staff. 43 master's degrees and 22 Ph.D.'s awarded 1955-59. 65 graduate students registered fall 1959.

Education. Adult, art, audiovisual, business elementary, or English education; evaluation, measurement, and statistics; arithmetic; guidance and personnel; higher education; home economics, foreign language, mathematics, or music education; physical and health education; reading; secondary; school psychologist; science, social studies, or special education. Prerequisites for graduate study: review and acceptance by School of Education; MAT and CAVD. Recommended: foreign languages and advanced mathematics. 65 professorial staff. 1,000 master's degrees and 50 Ph.D.'s awarded 1955-59. 1,429 graduate students registered fall 1959. In some special fields, enrollment limited according to available faculty.

Engineering.—Chemical. Unit operations, reaction kinetics, thermodynamics, corrosion, electrochemistry, process dynamics. Offered by College of Engineering. 6 professorial staff. 23 master's degrees and 10 Ph.D.'s awarded 1955-59. 33 graduate students registered fall 1959.

Engineering.—Electrical. Network theory, electromagnetic theory, electronic circuits, information theory, control systems, antennas, nonlinear circuit theory. Offered by College of Engineering. 18 professorial staff. 91 master's degrees and 11 Ph.D.'s awarded 1955-59. 679 graduate students registered fall 1959.

Engineering.—Mechanical. Thermodynamics, power plants, mechanics of materials, electricity, heat transfer, fluid dynamics, plasticity. Offered by College of Engineering. 11 professorial staff. Ph.D. program begun 1958. 22 master's degrees awarded 1955-59. 132 graduate students registered fall 1959.

English. Anglo-Saxon and history of the English language; Middle Ages; 1500-1600; 1600-1700; 1700-1800; 1800-1914; 1914 to present; American literature and culture 1600-1870; American literature and culture 1871-present; history of criticism; history of ideas; influence of classics; influence of science; a major figure and his reputation and influence. 16 professorial staff. 28 master's degrees and 10 Ph.D.'s awarded 1955-59. 86 graduate students registered fall 1959.

Geography. Geographic technique, history of geographic thought, regional fields, topical fields. 9 professorial staff. 28 master's degrees and 14 Ph.D.'s awarded 1955-59. 41 graduate students registered fall 1959.

German. History of the German language, German civilization, Old and Middle High German, German literature and philosophy. 5 professorial staff. 5 master's degrees awarded 1955-59. 5 graduate students registered fall 1959.

History. Ancient history, history of Western Europe or England, Russian or Soviet history, history of Great Britain and the Commonwealth, American history. 10 professorial staff. 12 master's degrees and 8 Ph.D.'s awarded 1955-59. 46 graduate students registered fall 1959.

Home Economics. Family living and child development, foods and nutrition, home economics education. 7 professorial staff. 12 master's degrees awarded 1955-59. 4 graduate students registered fall 1959.

Humanities Program in College Teaching. Two humanities fields normally chosen by regular departmental Ph.D. candidates; 3 "synthetic" fields which cut across the traditional boundaries of departments. Offered by Humanities Committee on College Teaching. Prerequisite for graduate study: broad foundation in the humanities. Ph.D. candidacy prerequisite: apprenticeship in college teaching. Interdepartmental staff. 3 Ph.D. degrees awarded 1955-59. 13 graduate students registered fall 1959.

Mathematics. Analysis, differential or integral equations, functional analysis, Hilbert space theory, probability theory, algebra, number theory, geometry, topology, lie groups, applied mathematics. 21 professorial staff. 21 master's degrees and 9 Ph.D.'s awarded 1955-59. 188 graduate students registered fall 1959.

Philosophy. Logic, metaphysics, history of philosophy, ethics, aesthetics, political philosophy, philosophy of religion. 6 professorial staff. 5 master's degrees and 2 Ph.D.'s awarded 1955-59. 10 graduate students registered fall 1959.

Physics. Experimental physics: low-temperature, magnetic resonance, molecular beams, solid-state, surface phenomena, spectroscopy (including infrared), high-energy. Theoretical physics: high-energy, relativistic field theory, statistical mechanics, solid-state. 18 professorial staff. 43 master's degrees and 27 Ph.D.'s awarded 1955-59. 197 graduate students registered fall 1959.

Political Science.—General. Comparative government, parties and politics, political theory, international law and relations, public law, public administration. Recommended for graduate study: foreign languages, statistics. 21 professorial staff. 29 master's degrees and 15 Ph.D.'s awarded 1955-59. 54 graduate students registered fall 1959.

Political Science.—International Relations. Areas of geographical concentration, international organization and administration, international economics, American foreign service, diplomatic history, cultural relations, international law. Offered by International Relations Committee. Interdepartmental staff. 15 master's degrees and 4 Ph.D.'s awarded 1955-59. 8 graduate students registered fall 1959.

Psychology. Social, educational, experimental or physiological psychology; diagnostic tests and counseling; clinical psychology; psychology of maturity and old age; child, adolescent, or behavior psychology. Prerequisite for graduate study: MAT. Recommended: statistics, foreign language. 15 professorial staff. 25 master's degrees and 33 Ph.D.'s awarded 1955-59. 72 graduate students registered fall 1959.

Romance Languages. French, Italian, Spanish languages and literatures. Recommended for graduate study: other foreign languages. 8 professorial staff. 6 master's degrees and 4 Ph.D.'s awarded 1955-59. 20 graduate students registered fall 1959.

Science Teaching. Bacteriology and botany, chemistry, geology, mathematics, physics, experimental psychology, zoology. Offered by the Committee on Program for Preparation of College Teachers of Science. Prerequisite for graduate study: broad background in science. Prerequisite for Ph.D. candidacy: apprenticeship in college teaching. Interdepartmental staff. 51 master's degrees and 11 Ph.D.'s awarded 1955-59. 67 graduate students registered fall 1959.

Sociology. Theory of sociology, social organization and control, industrial sociology, cultural relations, urbanization, family behavior, demography, criminology, social psychology. Offered by Department of Sociology and Anthropology. Recommended for graduate study: statistics; foreign languages. 11 professorial staff. 6 master's degrees and 1 Ph.D. awarded 1955-59. 18 graduate students registered fall 1959.

Solid-State Science and Technology. Solid-state theory, electromagnetic theory, quantum mechanics, thermodynamics, physical metallurgy, heat transfer, plasticity, physics of solids, chemistry of solids, elasticity, crystallography. Offered by Committee on Solid State Science and Technology. Recommended for graduate study: foreign languages; mathematics. Interdepartmental staff. Ph.D. program initiated 1958. 1 Ph.D. awarded 1958-59. 6 graduate students registered fall 1959.

Zoology. Neurophysiology, physiological genetics, cytology, physiology of enzymes, experimental embryology, physiology of nutrition, protobiology, parasitology, histophysiology. 12 professorial staff. 11 master's degrees and 7 Ph.D.'s awarded 1955-59. 50 graduate students registered fall 1959.

Temple University

PHILADELPHIA 22, PENNSYLVANIA

The Graduate School

Graduate instruction has been offered at Temple since 1946, and the first Ph.D. was awarded in 1950. The Graduate School, which was organized in 1960, is administered by a dean under policy established by a graduate board composed of representatives from the faculties of the schools and colleges engaged in graduate instruction.

The Ph.D. is awarded in several fields, and programs leading to the Ed.D. and Med.Sc.D. degrees are offered through the Teachers College and Medical School, respectively. University is privately controlled (but state-aided) and is non-sectarian. Both men and women are admitted.

Rooms in dormitories available for single graduate students. No university-owned residence facilities are provided for married students, but apartments are available in community.

Special facilities include: library of approximately 480,000 volumes which has contemporary publications in all fields of study in which the Ph.D. is offered; new science building (opened fall 1960) which has the most modern facilities for study and research.

Residence requirement for Ph.D.: 3 years beyond bachelor's degree, of which 1 must be taken in residence at Temple. Summer and evening courses available.

ADMISSION REQUIREMENTS

For graduate study: bachelor's degree; evidence of ability to pursue graduate work (i.e., grades in upper quarter of graduating class or records showing distinguished work in special field); adequate preparation for study in proposed field; acceptance by department. GRE may be required. For candidacy for Ph.D.: completion of residence requirement; reading knowledge of 2 foreign languages; preliminary examination.

Apply to Dean of the Graduate School at any time.

FEES AND FIRST-YEAR AID

No application fee. Tuition $820 per academic year. Laboratory fees approximate $50 annually. Room (in dormitory) for men $270 per year; for women $350. Approximate annual cost of board in college dining room $430.

First-year aid available: teaching fellowships in all departments; other fellowships and scholarships.

Apply to head of appropriate department at any time.

FIELDS OF STUDY FOR THE PH.D.

Courses in the methodology of college teaching are available through the Department of English.

Anatomy. Offered by the Medical School. Prerequisites for graduate study: 12 hours of biology, including 8 in zoological subjects; 16 of chemistry; 6 of foreign languages; 6 of mathematics; 8 of physics. 8 professorial staff.

Chemistry. Organic, physical, inorganic, or analytical chemistry; biochemistry. Offered by the Medical School. Prerequisites for graduate study: general, organic, and physical chemistry; qualitative and quantitative analysis; 1 year of advanced chemistry; physics; differential and integral calculus; reading knowledge of German. 11 professorial staff. 50 graduate students registered fall 1959.

English. Program is intended as preparation for college teaching, research and critical writing, or other occupations calling for advanced literary studies. Candidates may concentrate exclusively on English or may pursue studies in the relation of English and American literature to other branches of the humanities. Prerequisite for graduate study: superior ability in English and related subjects. 51 professorial staff. 6 graduate students registered fall 1959.

Microbiology. Offered by Medical School. Prerequisites for graduate study: 12 semester hours of biology; 16 of chemistry; 6 of foreign language; 6 of mathematics; 8 of physics. 6 professorial staff. 3 graduate students registered fall 1959.

Pharmacology. Analytical chemistry, physical chemistry, humanities. Offered by Medical School. Prerequisites for graduate study: 12 semester hours of biology; 16 of chemistry; 6 of foreign language; 6 of mathematics; 8 of physics. 5 professorial staff.

Pharmacy. Pharmacy, pharmaceutical chemistry, pharmacology. Offered by School of Pharmacy. Prerequisites for graduate study: major in pharmacy; qualifying examination.

Physics. Acoustics, ultrasonics, solid-state physics, X-ray diffraction, nucleonics, magnetics, optics, micrometeorites, magnetohydrodynamics. Prerequisites for graduate study: major in physics; GRE. 16 professorial staff. 105 graduate students registered fall 1959.

Physiological Chemistry. Offered by the Medical School. Prerequisites for graduate study: 12 semester hours in biology; 16 in chemistry; 6 in foreign language; 6 in mathematics; 8 in physics. 6 professorial staff. 4 graduate students registered fall 1959.

Physiology. Offered by the Medical School. Prerequisites for graduate study: 12 semester hours of biology; 16 of chemistry; 6 of foreign language; 6 of mathematics; 8 of physics. 8 professorial staff. 3 graduate students registered fall 1959.

Psychology. Clinical and counseling psychology, psychology of reading, the general field. Prerequisite for graduate study: GRE. Ph.D. candidacy prerequisites: master's degree in psychology; maturity; satisfactory personal qualifications. 32 professorial staff. 150 graduate students registered fall 1959.

Tennessee, University of

KNOXVILLE 16, TENNESSEE

Graduate School

Graduate instruction has been offered since 1872, and the first Ph.D. was awarded in 1886. The Graduate School was organized in 1944. University is publicly controlled by the state. Both men and women are admitted.

Allied divisions offering doctoral degrees: School of Biological Sciences at Memphis, Tennessee offers Ph.D. in anatomy, bacteriology, chemistry, pathology, pharmacology, and physiology; the Oak Ridge Branch of the university offers the Ph.D. in chemical engineering, chemistry, mathematics, metallurgy, and physics. The Ed.D. degree may be earned in the fields of educational administration and supervision, curriculum and instruction, and home economics education.

Rooms and dormitories available for single graduate men and women; university-owned apartments for married students.

Special facilities include: library of approximately 600,000 volumes; university hospital and medical research center. Affiliation with Oak Ridge Institute of Nuclear Studies offers additional opportunities for research. TVA central headquarters is located in Knoxville.

Residence requirement for Ph.D.: minimum of 3 academic years beyond bachelor's degree, of which 1 academic year (normally the last) must be taken in residence on campus. Summer and evening courses available.

ADMISSION REQUIREMENTS

For graduate study: bachelor's degree; satisfactory academic record; preparation in field of proposed study; acceptance by department. Recommended: GRE; proficiency in at least one language. For candidacy for Ph.D.: completion of substantial portion of course work with satisfactory grades; reading knowledge of 2 modern foreign languages; preliminary examinations; research ability; approval of dissertation topic.

Apply to Graduate School Office as early as possible. Application for admission to program in psychology must be received by April 15.

FEES AND FIRST-YEAR AID

No application fee. Tuition for state residents $225 for 9 months; others $525. Room (in dormitory) for men $62.50-$85 per quarter; for women $50-$85. Approximate annual cost of board in college dining room $375. Apartments $65 per month.

First-year aid available: 24 scholarships, $2,000-$2,400; 54 teaching fellowships, $1,600-$2,400; 180 other fellowships, $1,000-$1,700; 93 research assistantships (at Knoxville), $1,800-$3,600. Loans will not be made to new students until after the opening of their second quarter of satisfactory work.

Apply to head of major department before April 15. For loans, apply to University Treasurer's Office.

FIELDS OF STUDY FOR THE PH.D.

Noncredit seminars and senior faculty supervision are offered in some departments to improve teaching assistants' methodology.

Anatomy. Neuroanatomy, embryology, teratology, physiology of reproduction, endocrines, histochemistry, tooth development, carcinogenesis, fine structure. 12 professorial staff. 2 master's degrees and 1 Ph.D. awarded 1955-59. 4 graduate students registered fall 1959. New enrollment limited to 4.

Bacteriology. Physiology and metabolism; pathogenic bacteriology; virology; immunology; industrial, sanitary, food, or soils bacteriology. Prerequisites for graduate study: major in biological science; minor in chemistry; 1 year of bacteriology; knowledge of statistics. Recommended: 1 year each of mathematics and physics. 4 professorial staff. 12 master's degrees and 9 Ph.D.'s awarded 1955-59. 17 graduate students registered fall 1959.

Biochemistry. Intermediary or microbial metabolism, nutrition, clinical methods, hematopoiesis. Offered by Division of Chemistry. Prerequisites for graduate study: general and advanced courses in organic chemistry, quantitative and physical chemistry; biology; mathematics through calculus. 12 professorial staff. 8 master's degrees and 8 Ph.D.'s awarded 1955-59. 7 graduate students registered fall 1959.

Botany. Bryology, cytology, ecology, genetics, morphology, mycology, physiology, taxonomy, anatomy. Recommended for graduate study: major in some field of biology. 6 professorial staff. 19 master's degrees and 8 Ph.D.'s awarded 1955-59. 17 graduate students registered fall 1959. Total enrollment limited to 18.

Chemistry. Analytical, inorganic, organic, or physical chemistry; biochemistry. Prerequisite for graduate study: 1 year each of general, analytical, organic, and physical chemistry. 16 professorial staff. 48 master's degrees and 38 Ph.D.'s awarded 1955-59. 118 graduate students registered fall 1959.

Engineering.—Chemical. Advanced work in thermodynamics, transfer and rate processes, and system dynamics. Offered by Department of Chemical and Metallurgical Engineering. Prerequisite for graduate study: major in chemical engineering. Recommended: strong background in mathematics and physical chemistry. 4 professorial staff. 20 master's degrees and 7 Ph.D.'s awarded 1955-59. 51 graduate students registered fall 1959.

Engineering.—Metallurgical. Physical metallurgy. Offered by Department of Chemical and Metallurgical Engineering. Prerequisite for graduate study: major in metallurgical engineering or equivalent. 6 professorial staff. 14 master's degrees and 3 Ph.D.'s awarded 1955-59. 47 graduate students registered fall 1959.

Engineering Science. Mechanics of solids or liquids, thermodynamics, transfer and rate mechanisms, electromagnetic or circuit theory, nature and properties of materials. Offered by Engineering College through Engineering Science Committee. Prerequisites for graduate study: major in engineering; placement examination. 25 professorial staff. Ph.D. program begun 1960. 2 master's degrees awarded 1955-59. 5 graduate students registered fall 1959.

English. English literature and language, American literature. Prerequisite for graduate study: major in English or equivalent. Recommended: 2 foreign languages. 21 professorial staff. 39 master's degrees and 8 Ph.D.'s awarded 1955-59. 46 graduate students registered fall 1959.

Entomology. Ecology, economic entomology, physiology, taxonomy. Offered by Department of Zoology and Entomology. Prerequisites for graduate study: 12 quarter hours each of general zoology or biology, general entomology, or general chemistry; 3 quarter hours of economic or medical entomology; 1 course in mathematics. 2 professors. 3 master's degrees and 1 Ph.D. awarded 1955-59. 8 graduate students registered fall 1959.

Geography. Regional: North or South America; systematic: economic geography, land-use planning. Offered by Department of Geology and Geography. Prerequisites for graduate study: major in field or wide background in earth sciences and social sciences; 1 year of physical geography or physical geology. 10 master's degrees and 3 Ph.D.'s awarded 1955-59. 12 graduate students registered fall 1959. New enrollment limited to 2-5.

Geology. Economic or structural geology, mineralogy and petrology, stratigraphic and historical geology. Offered by Department of Geology and Geography. Prerequisites for graduate study: major in field; qualifying examination. 5 professorial staff. 41 master's degrees awarded 1955-59. 23 graduate students registered fall 1959.

History. Middle Ages, modern Europe, Latin-American or English history, various specialties in American history. Ph.D. awarded in either social sciences or humanities. Prerequisite for graduate study: major in history. Recommended: competence in French and German; survey courses in economics, political science, sociology. 9 professorial staff. Ph.D. program begun 1955. 16 master's degrees awarded 1955-59. 25 graduate students registered fall 1959.

Mathematics. Algebra, analysis, topology,

probability theory. Prerequisite for graduate study: major in mathematics. Recommended: reading knowledge of French or German. 6 professorial staff. 9 master's degrees and 8 Ph.D.'s awarded 1955-59. 111 graduate students registered fall 1959.

Nutrition.—Foods and Nutrition. Prerequisites for graduate study: courses in quantitative analysis, organic chemistry, mathematics, physiology, bacteriology, and foods and nutrition. 11 professorial staff. Ph.D. program begun 1960. 46 master's degrees awarded 1955-59. 11 graduate students registered fall 1959.

Pathology and Bacteriology. Human and experimental pathology, pathogenic bacteria and viruses. Offered by Division of Pathology and Microbiology. Recommended for graduate study: as much chemistry as possible. 10 professorial staff. 12 master's degrees and 5 Ph.D.'s awarded 1955-59. 10 graduate students registered fall 1959.

Pharmacology. Cardiovascular or autonomic nervous system drugs, general pharmacology. 8 professorial staff. 1 master's degree and 4 Ph.D.'s awarded 1955-59. 9 graduate students registered fall 1959. New enrollment limited to 2.

Physics. Theoretical physics (nuclear, plasma, molecular); textile, low-temperature, or high-energy physics; infrared, optical, or Gamma-ray spectroscopy; low-energy nuclear physics. Prerequisite for graduate study: major in physics or equivalent. Recommended: GRE. 14 professorial staff. 19 master's degrees and 16 Ph.D.'s awarded 1955-59. 96 graduate students registered fall 1959.

Physiology and Biophysics. Gastrointestinal, cardiovascular, or respiratory physiology; lipid metabolism; neurophysiology; endocrinology. Offered by Department of Physiology. Recommended for graduate study: training and special aptitude in physics, mathematics, and chemistry. 14 professorial staff. 4 master's degrees and 5 Ph.D.'s awarded 1955-59. 12 graduate students registered fall 1959.

Political Science. Public administration, political parties. Recommended for graduate study: major in political science. 9 professorial staff. 17 master's degrees and 1 Ph.D. awarded 1955-59. 10 graduate students registered fall 1959.

Psychology. Clinical or general experimental psychology; industrial psychology and psychometrics. Prerequisites for graduate study: biology; algebra; statistics; measurements; social or abnormal psychology; learning; MAT. Recommended: broad background in psychology; mathematics, including calculus. 10 professorial staff. 13 master's degrees and 31 Ph.D.'s awarded 1955-59. 66 graduate students registered fall 1959.

Radiation Biology. Biochemistry, biophysics, cytology, ecology, electron microscropy, embryology, genetics, hematology, immunology, oncology, parasitology, pathology, physiology, tissue culture. Offered by Institute of Radiation Biology. Prerequisites for graduate study: 30 quarter hours of biological sciences; 9 of mathematics; 12 each of organic and inorganic chemistry and general physics. 43 professorial staff. Ph.D. program begun 1956. 3 master's degrees awarded 1955-59. 13 graduate students registered fall 1959.

Sociology. Community, urban, and regional sociology; industrial and occupational sociology; demography; deviant behavior; marriage and the family; social psychology or organization. Prerequisite for graduate study: major in sociology or equivalent. Recommended: foreign languages and mathematics. 6 professorial staff. Ph.D. program begun 1959. 6 master's degrees awarded 1955-59. 24 graduate students registered fall 1959.

Zoology. Cytology, ecology, embryology, genetics, herpetology, ichthyology, mammalogy, ornithology, parasitology, physiology, radiation biology. Offered by Department of Zoology and Entomology. Prerequisites for graduate study: 12 quarter hours each of general zoology or biology and of general chemistry; 18 quarter hours of advanced zoology; 1 course in mathematics. 9 professorial staff. 14 master's degrees and 6 Ph.D.'s awarded 1955-59. 26 graduate students registered fall 1959.

Texas, Agricultural and Mechanical College of

COLLEGE STATION, TEXAS

The Graduate School

Graduate instruction at the master's level was begun in 1914, and the Graduate School was organized in 1924. First Ph.D. was awarded in 1940. Institution is publicly controlled by the state. Only men are admitted.

Sections of college dormitories reserved for single graduate students; limited number of college-owned apartments available for married students.

Special facilities include: library of approximately 360,000 volumes; Data Processing Center; Nuclear Science Center which includes an AGN-201 nuclear training reactor and a swimming pool reactor; ocean-going research vessel and station for oceanographic research.

Residence requirement for Ph.D.: 6 semesters of full-time graduate study or equivalent beyond bachelor's degree, 2 semesters of which must be taken in residence on campus. Summer courses available and 1 summer session, in which 12 hours of work are taken, may be applied toward residence requirement.

ADMISSION REQUIREMENTS

For graduate study: bachelor's degree; academic record showing promise of ability to pursue advanced study; adequate preparation in chosen field. Recommended: GRE. Some departments require comprehensive examination covering basic work in major field. For candidacy for Ph.D.: completion of a minimum of 64 hours of work beyond master's degree with satisfactory grades; reading knowledge of French and German or approved substitute; written and oral preliminary examinations.

Apply to Director of Admissions and Registrar well in advance of semester in which admission is desired.

FEES AND FIRST-YEAR AID

No application fee. Tuition for state residents $100 per academic year; others $400. Special fees approximate $46 annually. Student activity fee of $23.80 is optional. Room (in dormitory) $128 per academic year. Approximate annual cost of board in college dining room $348. Apartments $42.50-$65 per month (utilities included).

First-year aid available: 100 teaching fellowships, $1,500-$1,800 for 9 months; 20 to 30 other fellowships carrying varying stipends; 50 to 75 research assistantships, $1,800-$2,400 per year. Grants-in-aid in varying amounts also available.

Apply to Dean of Graduate Studies by March 1 for following year.

FIELDS OF STUDY FOR THE PH.D.

Agronomy. Soil or field crop science; plant breeding; pasture and turf management; soil physics, chemistry, or mineralogy. 28 professorial staff. 35 master's degrees and 2 Ph.D.'s awarded 1955-59. 17 graduate students registered fall 1959.

Animal Breeding. Combined program offered by Departments of Animal Husbandry and Genetics. 26 professorial staff. 6 master's degrees and 8 Ph.D.'s awarded 1955-59. 5 graduate students registered fall 1959.

Animal Husbandry. Physiology of reproduction, animal nutrition or breeding, meats. 14 professorial staff. 15 master's degrees and 3 Ph.D.'s awarded 1955-59. 13 graduate students registered fall 1959.

Animal Nutrition. Combined program offered by Departments of Biochemistry and Nutrition, Animal Husbandry, Dairy Science, and Poultry Science. 12 professorial staff. 7 master's degrees and 8 Ph.D.'s awarded 1955-59. 4 graduate students registered fall 1959.

Animal Parasitology. Combined program offered by Departments of Entomology, Biology, and Veterinary Parasitology. 7 professorial staff. 1 master's degree awarded 1955-59.

Biochemistry and Nutrition. Biochemistry and nutrition, animal nutrition, poultry science, plant chemistry. 12 professorial staff. 15 master's degrees and 22 Ph.D.'s awarded 1955-59. 23 graduate students registered fall 1959.

Biology. Vertebrate or invertebrate zoology, plant morphology, embryology, cytology, parasitology. 16 professorial staff. 4 graduate students registered fall 1959.

Botany. Offered by Department of Biology. 16 professorial staff. 1 master's degree awarded 1955-59. 3 graduate students registered fall 1959.

Chemistry. Analytical, inorganic, organic, and physical chemistry. 17 professorial staff. 29 master's degrees and 14 Ph.D.'s awarded 1955-59. 34 graduate students registered fall 1959.

Dairy Science. Dairy manufactures or production, food technology. 6 professorial staff. 5 master's degrees and 3 Ph.D.'s awarded 1955-59. 5 graduate students registered fall 1959.

Economics. — Agricultural. Farm management, land economics, agricultural marketing and policy, administration. Combined program offered by Departments of Agricultural Economics and Sociology. 18 professorial staff. 22 master's degrees and 7 Ph.D.'s awarded 1955-59. 28 graduate students registered fall 1959.

Engineering.—Chemical. Chemical engineering, chemical thermodynamics, applied nuclear energy, corrosion, electrochemical processes, inorganic or organic chemical technology, instrumentation, kinetics and reactor design, nuclear fuels and processes, petroleum refining, petrochemical or vegetable oil technology, plastics, water treatment. 3 professorial staff. 26 master's degrees and 3 Ph.D.'s awarded 1955-59. 13 graduate students registered fall 1959.

Engineering.—Civil. Soil mechanics; structures; hydraulic; highway, hydraulic, or municipal engineering. 21 professorial staff. 67 master's degrees and 2 Ph.D.'s awarded 1955-59. 47 graduate students registered fall 1959.

Engineering.—Electrical. Electronic components for analog computers, power systems and machinery, communications, electrical machinery, electronics, high-frequency systems, servomechanisms. 10 professorial staff. 29 master's degrees and 3 Ph.D.'s awarded 1955-59. 28 graduate students registered fall 1959.

Engineering. — Geological. 11 professorial staff. 1 master's degree awarded 1955-59.

Engineering.—Mechanical. Heat, power, and thermodynamics; fluid mechanics; heat transfer; mechanical design; mechanics and machine design; metallurgy; nuclear power; power generation. 13 professorial staff. 20 master's degrees and 2 Ph.D.'s awarded 1955-59. 28 graduate students registered fall 1959.

Engineering.—Nuclear. 4 professorial staff. Program begun 1959. 6 graduate students registered fall 1959.

Engineering.—Petroleum. Natural gas, production, drilling engineering, economics and valuation or petroleum economics, production methods or engineering, reservoir equilibrium and mechanics, subsurface engineering problems, transportation and field processing. 6 professorial staff. 29 master's degrees and 2 Ph.D.'s awarded 1955-59. 17 graduate students registered fall 1959.

Entomology. Economic entomology, insect physiology and toxicology, morphology, agriculture. 12 professorial staff. 10 master's degrees and 10 Ph.D.'s awarded 1955-59. 23 graduate students registered fall 1959.

Food Technology. Combined program offered by Departments of Dairy Science and Horticulture. 16 professorial staff. 1 master's degree awarded 1955-59. 2 graduate students registered fall 1959.

Genetics. Genetics, animal or plant breeding. 12 professorial staff. 4 master's degrees and 7 Ph.D.'s awarded 1955-59. 4 graduate students registered fall 1959.

Geology. Economic geology, geochemistry, mineralogy, paleontology, petrology. Offered by Department of Geology and Geophysics. 11 professorial staff. 38 master's degrees and 1 Ph.D. awarded 1955-59. 26 graduate students registered fall 1959.

Geophysics. Offered by Department of Geology and Geophysics. 11 professorial staff. 1 master's degree awarded 1955-59. 3 graduate students registered fall 1959.

Horticulture. Fruit or vegetable production, fruit and vegetable processing, food technology. 10 professorial staff. 9 master's degrees and 4 Ph.D.'s awarded 1955-59. 7 graduate students registered fall 1959.

Mathematics. Algebra, analysis, pure or applied mathematics, number theory, statistics. 11 professorial staff. 6 master's degrees awarded 1955-59. 20 graduate students registered fall 1959.

Meteorology. Offered by Department of Oceanography and Meteorology. 7 professorial staff. Ph.D. program begun 1958. 23 master's degrees awarded 1955-59. 16 graduate students registered fall 1959.

Microbiology. Offered by Department of Biology. 16 professorial staff.

Oceanography. Offered by Department of Oceanography and Meteorology. 10 professorial staff. 21 master's degrees and 15 Ph.D.'s awarded 1955-59. 33 graduate students registered fall 1959.

Oil Seed Technology. Offered by Department of Chemical Engineering. 3 professorial staff.

Physics. Acoustics, atomic physics; biophysics; electricity and magnetism; liquid-state, nuclear solid-state, molecular, or theoretical physics; mechanics; thermodynamics. 10 professorial staff. 14 master's degrees and 7 Ph.D.'s awarded 1955-59. 32 graduate students registered fall 1959.

Physiology of Reproduction. Combined program offered by Departments of Animal Husbandry, Biology, Dairy Science, Genetics, and Poultry Science. 57 professorial staff. 1 master's degree and 2 Ph.D.'s awarded 1955-59. 3 graduate students registered fall 1959.

Plant Breeding. Combined program offered by Departments of Genetics, Agronomy, Floriculture, and Horticulture. 51 professorial staff. 5 master's degrees and 10 Ph.D.'s awarded 1955-59. 6 graduate students registered fall 1959.

Plant Physiology and Pathology. 15 professorial staff. 7 master's degrees and 12 Ph.D.'s awarded 1955-59. 15 graduate students registered fall 1959.

Plant and Soil Science. Offered by Department of Agronomy. 28 professorial staff.

Poultry Science. Nutrition, breeding, marketing, management. 9 professorial staff. 22 master's degrees and 9 Ph.D.'s awarded 1955-59. 23 graduate students registered fall 1959.

Range Management. Offered by Department of Range and Forestry. 8 professorial staff. 18 master's degrees and 16 Ph.D.'s awarded 1955-59. 10 graduate students registered fall 1959.

Soil Chemistry. Offered by Department of Agronomy. 28 professorial staff. 3 Ph.D.'s awarded 1955-59. 1 graduate student registered fall 1959.

Soil Physics. Offered by Department of Agronomy. 28 professorial staff. 2 master's degrees and 4 Ph.D.'s awarded 1955-59. 2 graduate students registered fall 1959.

Veterinary Medicine and Surgery. 3 professorial staff. 2 master's degrees awarded 1955-59. 6 graduate students registered fall 1959.

Veterinary Pathology. 3 professorial staff. 5 master's degrees and 2 Ph.D.'s awarded 1955-59. 3 graduate students registered fall 1959.

Veterinary Public Health. 1 professor.

Wildlife Management. Vertebrate systematics, vertebrate ecology. 5 professorial staff. 2 master's degrees and 2 Ph.D.'s awarded 1955-59. 5 graduate students registered fall 1959.

Zoology. Offered by Department of Biology. 16 professorial staff. 6 master's degrees and 3 Ph.D.'s awarded 1955-59. 10 graduate students registered fall 1959.

Texas Technological College

LUBBOCK, TEXAS

The Graduate School

Graduate instruction was first offered in 1927, and the Graduate School was formally organized in 1937. First Ph.D. was awarded in 1952. A program leading to the Ed.D. degree is also offered. Institution is publicly controlled by the state. Both men and women are admitted.

Rooms in dormitories are available for single students; apartments in community for married students.

Special facilities include: library of 277,500 volumes, including good files of 18th and 19th century English magazines, "Southwest Collection" of published and unpublished material on the development of West Texas, microfilm items of 16th and 17th century English literature; electron microscope; mass spectrometer; infrared and ultraviolet spectrometers; Testing and Counseling Center; infrahuman, primate, and sub-human laboratories; State Hospital for psychiatric service.

Requirement for doctorate: 3 academic years of work; 1 full year in residence at this institution. Summer and evening courses available.

ADMISSION REQUIREMENTS

For graduate study: bachelor's degree; above-average undergraduate record; GRE Aptitude Test. Recommended: GRE Advanced Tests. For candidacy for Ph.D.: reading knowledge of 2 foreign languages; qualifying examination.

FEES AND FIRST-YEAR AID

No application fee. Tuition $100 a year for state residents; $400 for others. Special fees approximate $60 annually; additional fees for laboratory courses. Room (in dormitory) and board averages $590-$655 per academic year (subject to change without notice).

First-year aid available: 5 or more teaching fellowships in each department, $1,500-$2,400; 2 other fellowships, $1,000-$1,800; research assistantships in chemistry, stipend usually $2,000.

Apply to head of department by April 1.

FIELDS OF STUDY FOR THE PH.D.

Department of English offers a course in the theory and practice of college teaching. Department of History has informal seminar in which problems of college teaching are discussed.

Chemistry. Inorganic, organic, analytical, physical. 8 professorial staff. 10 master's degrees and 4 Ph.D.'s awarded 1955-59. 33 graduate students registered fall 1959.

English. English and American literature. 10 professorial staff. 22 master's degrees and 5 Ph.D.'s awarded 1955-59. 34 graduate students registered fall 1959.

History. American history with special emphasis on the West and Southwest. 12 professorial staff. 14 master's degrees and 3 Ph.D.'s awarded 1955-59. 29 graduate students registered fall 1959.

Psychology. General, counseling, experimental. Prerequisites: MAT; GRE Advanced Test in Psychology. 8 professorial staff. 23 master's degrees and 3 Ph.D.'s awarded 1955-59. 62 graduate students registered fall 1959.

Texas, University of

AUSTIN, TEXAS

The Graduate School

Graduate work at the master's level was first offered in 1883. The Graduate School was organized in 1910, and the first Ph.D. conferred in 1915. At present Ph.D. programs are offered on the Austin Campus, at the University of Texas Medical Branch in Galveston, and at Southwestern Medical School in Dallas. The Ed.D. degree is also awarded. All work is under the jurisdiction of the Graduate School. University is publicly controlled by the state. Both men and women are admitted.

Single graduate students find accommodations in university dormitories and in private homes or apartments; married graduate students in university-operated and privately-operated apartments.

Special facilities include: library of approximately 1,290,000 volumes; Balcones Research Center; defense research laboratory; computation center; interdepartmental laboratories; Hogg Foundation for Mental Health; bureau of business research; institute of Latin-American studies; institute of marine science. The MacDonald Observatory at Fort Davis, Texas, is operated jointly by the University of Texas and the University of Chicago in a program of which the Yerkes Observatory at Williams Bay, Wisconsin, is also a component.

Residence requirement for Ph.D.: usually at least 3 years beyond bachelor's degree, of which 2 semesters (or the equivalent in summer session or part-time study) must be spent in residence at the University of Texas. Summer courses available.

ADMISSION REQUIREMENTS

For graduate study: bachelor's degree; 2.0 GPA on all work of junior and senior level previously taken; appropriate preparation in field of proposed graduate study; GRE. For candidacy for Ph.D.: master's degree or equivalent of 1 long session of full-time graduate work; 1 semester or 1 entire summer's work in residence; recommendation of Committee on Graduate Study in student's major area on basis of qualifying examinations or other methods; approval of Dean. Reading knowledge of 2 foreign languages must be demonstrated by beginning of student's last full year of graduate work.

Apply to Registrar and Director of Admissions at least 30 days prior to date of desired entry.

FEES AND FIRST-YEAR AID

No application fee. Tuition for state residents $50 per semester; others $200. Special fees approximate $50 annually. Room (in dormitory or community) ranges from $10 to $45 per month for men. Room (in dormitory) and board for women $90-$150 per month. Board alone averages about $52 per month. Apartments $25-$125 per month.

First-year aid available: variable number of scholarships and fellowships, $1,800-$2,400; approximately 500 teaching fellowships, $1,600-$2,000; departmental and area fellowships with varying stipends; about 300 research assistantships carrying stipends in varying amounts.

Apply to chairman of appropriate department by March 1.

FIELDS OF STUDY FOR THE PH.D.

Anatomy. Electron microscopy; autoradiography; experimental, comparative, and anatomical neurology; tissue culture and phase cinematography; histochemistry; experimental endocrinology. Offered at the Medical Branch at Galveston and at the Southwestern Medical School at Dallas. Recommended for graduate study: premedical courses; mathematics through calculus. 14 professorial staff (in the 2 branches). 6 master's degrees and 4 Ph.D.'s awarded 1955-59. 12 graduate students registered fall 1959.

Area Studies.—Latin-American. An interdepartmental program, with prerequisite of a bachelor's degree in an appropriate area. 12 master's degrees and 18 Ph.D.'s awarded 1955-59.

Astronomy. Photoelectric photometry, theoretical astrophysics, stellar spectroscopy, galactic and extragalactic research, planetary and lunar studies, auroral physics, electronic instrumentation. Offered by Astronomy Departments of the University of Texas and the University of Chicago. Ph.D. candidacy prerequisites: minor in physics; 1 year (usually the second) in residence at Yerkes Observatory. 5 professorial staff. Ph.D. program begun 1959. 1 graduate student registered fall 1959. No master's degree offered in this field.

Bacteriology. Medical and public health bacteriology, immunology, physiology and biochemistry of bacteria and other micro-organisms, general and food bacteriology, mycology, viruses. Prerequisite for graduate study: preparation in chemistry, biology, and microbiology. 8 professorial staff. 49 master's degrees and 33 Ph.D.'s awarded 1955-59. 35 graduate students registered fall 1959.

Biochemistry. Offered by Department of Biochemistry and Nutrition at the Medical Branch at Galveston and by Department of Biochemistry at Southwestern Medical School at Dallas. For offerings in biochemistry at Main University, *see* Chemistry. 12 professorial staff (in the 2 branches). 2 master's degrees and 1 Ph.D. awarded 1955-59. 6 graduate students registered fall 1959.

Biology. Offered within the Departments of Bacteriology, Botany, and Zoology.

Botany. Physiology, plant biochemistry, genetics, cytology, anatomy, taxonomy, ecology, morphology. Prerequisites for graduate study: 24 semester hours in botany with at least 12 in advanced work; courses in biology, chemistry, physics, and mathematics. 10 professorial staff. 5 master's degrees and 6 Ph.D.'s awarded 1955-59. 26 graduate students registered fall 1959.

Business Administration. Accounting, statistics, finance, management, marketing, resources, retailing, transportation. Prerequisites for graduate study: 12 semester hours of economics, including economic history of the United States and advanced economic theory; 27 semester hours of business administration or equivalent. 58 professorial staff. 230 master's degrees and

46 Ph.D.'s awarded 1955-59. 168 graduate students registered fall 1959.

Chemistry. Analytical, biological, inorganic, organic, or physical. Prerequisites for graduate study: 24 semester hours in chemistry, including 6 each in general, organic, and physical chemistry, and quantitative analysis; at least 12 of the 24 hours must be in advanced courses. 29 professorial staff. 75 master's degrees and 112 Ph.D.'s awarded 1955-59. 149 graduate students registered fall 1959.

Classical Languages. Authors and literary genres in classical, Hellenistic, and Biblical Greek and in classical and medieval Latin; historical grammar; epigraphy; research materials of classical philology. 5 professorial staff. 18 master's degrees and 3 Ph.D.'s awarded 1955-59. 10 graduate students registered fall 1959.

Economics. Economic theory and its history; economic history, development, and resources; international, labor, or Latin-American economics; money and banking; public finance; social control of industry. Prerequisites for graduate study: 1 course each in economic and social statistics and in prices and economic organization. 13 professorial staff. 41 master's degrees and 18 Ph.D.'s awarded 1955-59. 39 graduate students registered fall 1959.

Education. Curriculum and instruction, educational administration, educational psychology, history and philosophy of education, physical and health education. 52 professorial staff. 645 master's degrees and 94 Ph.D.'s awarded 1955-59. 336 graduate students registered fall 1959. Ed.D. degree also awarded.

Engineering.—Aerospace. Aerothermodynamics of air and gas flows at all speeds, structural analysis of flight vehicles, dynamics of flight vehicles, flight propulsion. Prerequisite for graduate study: major in field or equivalent. 2 professors. 18 master's degrees and 2 Ph.D.'s awarded 1955-59. 11 graduate students registered fall 1959.

Engineering.—Chemical. 8 professorial staff. 42 master's degrees and 23 Ph.D.'s awarded 1955-59. 55 graduate students registered fall 1959.

Engineering.—Civil. Structures, hydraulics, sanitary engineering, soil mechanics, materials, photogrammetry, highways. 14 professorial staff. 57 master's degrees and 5 Ph.D.'s awarded 1955-59. 38 graduate students registered fall 1959.

Engineering. — Electrical. Electromagnetic fields, circuit and system analysis, power systems. Prerequisite for graduate study: major in field or equivalent. 12 professorial staff. 71 master's degrees and 11 Ph.D.'s awarded 1955-59. 53 graduate students registered fall 1959.

Engineering.—Mechanical. Fluid mechanics, heat transfer, thermodynamics and combustion, gas turbines, jet propulsion, internal combustion engines, power, kinematics, lubrication, mechanical design, vibrations, industrial and production engineering, metallurgy and materials, refrigeration and air conditioning. Prerequisites for graduate study: strong background in mathematics (through differential equations and calculus); chemistry; physics; mechanics; materials; thermodynamics; electrical circuits and electronics; mechanical design. 19 professorial staff. 61 master's degrees and 9 Ph.D.'s awarded 1955-59. 42 graduate students registered fall 1959.

Engineering Mechanics. Vibration, elasticity, plasticity, fluid mechanics, dynamics, stress analysis. Prerequisites for graduate study: courses in engineering mechanics, mechanical engineering, and mathematics. 6 professorial staff. 7 master's degrees and 4 Ph.D.'s awarded 1955-59. 11 graduate students registered fall 1959.

Engineering.—Petroleum. Exploration, development, reservoir or gas engineering, evaluation, engineering economy, transportation of crude oil and natural gas, conservation. Prerequisite for graduate study: minimum of 22 semester hours in major field. 6 professorial staff. 34 master's degrees and 2 Ph.D.'s awarded 1955-59. 32 graduate students registered fall 1959.

English. English and American literature, comparative literature, criticism, history of ideas, folklore, language and linguistics, bibliography and methods of research, creative and technical writing, teaching of English at college level. 40 professorial staff. 126 master's degrees and 52 Ph.D.'s awarded 1955-59. 140 graduate students registered fall 1959.

Geology. Field, structural, or marine geology; vertebrate and invertebrate paleontology and biostratigraphy; micropaleontology; sedimentary or igneous and metamorphic petrology; geochemistry; clay mineralogy; economic geology of the metals and nonmetals. Prerequisites for graduate study: a course in biology (for biogeologists), in calculus (for physical geologists), in sedimentation (for those interested in sedimentary petrology), or in geology of fluids (for those interested

in water or petroleum). 20 professorial staff. 113 master's degrees and 13 Ph.D.'s awarded 1955-59. 91 graduate students registered fall 1959.

Germanic Languages. Germanic literature and culture before or after 1500; Germanic linguistics and philology. Prerequisite for graduate study: major in field. Recommended: Latin or Greek (required for linguistics or older literature). 9 professorial staff. 15 master's degrees and 11 Ph.D.'s awarded 1955-59. 23 graduate students registered fall 1959.

Government. American or comparative government, international relations, political theory, public administration, public law. 13 professorial staff. 23 master's degrees and 11 Ph.D.'s awarded 1955-59. 36 graduate students registered fall 1959.

History. Latin-American, United States, or European history. Prerequisites for graduate study: liberal preparation, with broad knowledge of European and American history; competence in languages needed to support program. 18 professorial staff. 70 master's degrees and 40 Ph.D.'s awarded 1955-59. 92 graduate students registered fall 1959.

Linguistics. Descriptive or historical linguistics. Combined program offered by Departments of Classical Languages, English, Germanic Languages, and Romance Languages. 10 professorial staff. Program begun 1959. 11 graduate students registered fall 1959.

Mathematics. Analysis, geometry, number theory and algebra, differential geometry, tensor or numerical analysis, theory of relativity, mathematical physics, probability, statistics, theory and programming of high-speed computers. 16 professorial staff. 81 master's degrees and 23 Ph.D.'s awarded 1955-59. 128 graduate students registered fall 1959.

Microbiology. Bacteriology, immunology, virology, protozoology, mycology, helminthology. Offered by Departments of Bacteriology (Main University) and Microbiology (medical branches). Prerequisite for graduate study: adequate preparation in chemistry, biology, and microbiology. Recommended: inorganic chemistry; organic chemistry or biochemistry; physics; pathogenic bacteriology. 15 professorial staff (in the 2 branches). Ph.D. program begun 1958. 3 master's degrees awarded 1955-59. 9 graduate students registered fall 1959.

Musicology. Applied music, music education, musicology, music history and literature, music theory, composition and theory. Offered by Department of Music. 22 professorial staff. 122 master's degrees awarded 1955-59. 60 graduate students registered fall 1959.

Pharmacology. Offered by the Department of Pharmacology and Toxicology at the Medical Branch at Galveston. Prerequisite for graduate study: individual students and programs must have special prior approval of Dean of Graduate School. 7 professorial staff (in the 2 branches). 2 Ph.D.'s awarded 1955-59.

Pharmacy. Theoretical pharmacy and formulation, hospital or industrial pharmacy, pharmacy administration, pharmacognosy, pharmaceutical chemistry, pharmacology. Ph.D. candidacy prerequisites: German plus 1 other foreign language. 12 professorial staff. 15 master's degrees and 1 Ph.D. awarded 1955-59. 11 graduate students registered fall 1959.

Philosophy. Aesthetics, epistemology, ethics, history of philosophy, logic, metaphysics, philosophy of religion or of science, value theory. 8 professorial staff. 8 master's degrees and 5 Ph.D.'s awarded 1955-59. 27 graduate students registered fall 1959.

Physics. Acoustics; atomic and molecular spectroscopy or quantum mechanics; radiation biophysics; nuclear, solid-state, or theoretical physics; X-rays. Prerequisites for graduate study: approximately 27 hours past sophomore level of physics or equivalent; 12 semester hours of mathematics; 1 advanced course in mechanics and 1 in electricity and magnetism. 20 professorial staff. 52 master's degrees and 54 Ph.D.'s awarded 1955-59. 99 graduate students registered fall 1959.

Physiology. Hematology; renal or gastrointestinal physiology; neurophysiology; respiration; heart, circulation, lymph; endocrinology; temperature control. Offered at the Medical Branch at Galveston and at Southwestern Medical School at Dallas. Recommended for graduate study: advanced courses in physics, chemistry, and biology. 13 professorial staff (in the 2 branches). 4 master's degrees and 5 Ph.D.'s awarded 1955-59. 9 graduate students registered fall 1959. Total enrollment limited to 12.

Psychology. Clinical, experimental, physiological, and social psychology. A program in counseling psychology is administered by the Departments of Psychology and Educational Psychology. Prerequisites for graduate study: 3 letters of recommendation from teachers in psychology;

18 hours in basic psychology courses. 19 professorial staff. 56 master's degrees and 58 Ph.D.'s awarded 1955-59. 84 graduate students registered fall 1959.

Romance Languages. French, Italian, Portuguese, or Spanish language and literature; Romance philology and linguistics. 21 professorial staff. 23 master's degrees and 11 Ph.D.'s awarded 1955-59. 25 graduate students registered fall 1959.

Sociology. History of sociology and sociological theory, research methods, human ecology and demography, collective behavior and social change, sociology of institutions, social organization and disorganization. 13 professorial staff. 20 master's degrees and 8 Ph.D.'s awarded 1955-59. 24 graduate students registered fall 1959.

Zoology. Cytology and genetics, environmental and systematic zoology, physiology and biophysics. Ph.D. candidacy prerequisite: GRE Advanced Test in Biology. Recommended: at least 1 summer course in marine biology at a coastal station. 19 professorial staff. 43 master's degrees and 42 Ph.D.'s awarded 1955-59. 66 graduate students registered fall 1959.

Texas Woman's University

DENTON, TEXAS

The Graduate School

Graduate instruction has been offered at Texas Woman's University since 1930, the year the Graduate School was formally organized. First Ph.D. was awarded in 1953. The Ed.D. degree is also conferred. The Graduate Council administers the program, which is taught by faculty members of, or cooperating with, the College of Household Arts and Sciences or the College of Health, Physical Education, and Recreation, under the direction of the Dean of Graduate Studies. University is publicly controlled by the state. Only women are admitted.

A graduate center is maintained in downtown Denton for single graduate students; some apartments available for married students. There are also limited facilities for married couples and for women without husbands but with small children.

Special facilities include: library of approximately 141,000 volumes; body fluids research laboratory; Stark Laboratory for Human Nutrition Research; fibre and textile institute; detergency research laboratories; electron microscope; bone density microdensitometric assembly; animal laboratory; experimental kitchens and housing units; power laundry and drycleaning plant; subcritical nuclear reactor; university nursing centers in Dallas and Houston.

Residence requirement for Ph.D.: 3 full years beyond bachelor's degree, of which 1 year (preferably the last) must be spent in residence on campus. Summer courses available.

ADMISSION REQUIREMENTS

For graduate study: bachelor's degree; good undergraduate record; undergraduate major or equivalent in field of proposed graduate study (qualifying tests for those lacking appropriate major); evidence of maturity and good health. Recommended: GRE. For candidacy for Ph.D.: reading knowledge of 2 foreign languages; preliminary oral and written examinations; approval of student's advisory committee.

Apply to Dean of Admissions—Registrar, Drawer A, Texas Woman's University, University Hill Station, Denton, Texas, at any time.

FEES AND FIRST-YEAR AID

No application fee. Tuition for state residents $100 per academic year; others $400. Special fees approximate $52 annually. Room (in graduate student center) $324-$600 per academic year. Limited cafeteria service available. Apartment rentals vary.

First-year aid available: a few scholarships, $100-$300; a few teaching fellowships, $1,000-$3,000; a few other fellowships with a wide range of stipends; a number of research assistantships (in the College of Household Arts and Sciences only) with a wide range of stipends. A few grants-in-aid also available. There are some industry-sponsored fellowships and federal loans which may be applied for.

Apply to the appropriate college or the Student Aid Committee, Drawer A, Texas Woman's University, University Hill Station, Denton, Texas, by June 15.

FIELDS OF STUDY FOR THE PH.D.

Courses in professional responsibilities, role and duties of the teacher, history and principles of discipline, and methodology of instruction are offered. These are optional in the College of Household Arts and Sciences and compulsory in the College of Health, Physical Education, and Recreation.

Child Development and Nursery Education. Child development; nursery education; family living, life problems, or economics; mental testing; parent-teacher relationship; creative arts in nursery education; housing, equipment, and management; the preschool child; advanced child development. Offered by College of Household Arts and Sciences. Prerequisite for graduate study: knowledge of statistics. 12 professorial staff. 5 master's degrees and 1 Ph.D. awarded 1955-59. 6 graduate students registered fall 1959.

Clothing and Textiles. Clothing construction, costume design, textiles and related arts, textile design, fabric analysis and comparative study, textiles and textile technology or research, draping, history of textiles, detergency or cotton research. Offered by College of Household Arts and Sciences. Prerequisite for graduate study: knowledge of statistics. 19 professorial staff. 14 master's degrees and 16 Ph.D.'s awarded 1955-59. 14 graduate students registered fall 1959.

Costume Design. Costume or textile design; tailoring; draping; merchandising; clothing construction; fabric research; fashion illustration; fashion illustration and costume design; fabrics, fibres, and leather; patterns; children's clothing; color, weave, and texture in apparel. Offered by College of Household Arts and Sciences. Prerequisite for graduate study: knowledge of statistics. 14 professorial staff. 14 master's degrees and 16 Ph.D.'s awarded 1955-59. 14 graduate students registered fall 1959.

Dance and Related Arts. Dance; accompaniment for movement; dance for children; history and philosophy of dance; teaching of dance; ethnic, folk, or modern dance; labanotation; theories and practices in teaching of dance; drama and dance, music and dance, speech and dance. Offered by College of Health, Physical Education, and Recreation. 9 professorial staff. 3 master's degrees and 1 Ph.D. awarded 1955-59. 5 graduate students registered fall 1959.

Family Living and Economics. Family living, economics, life problems, budgets, dynamics, relations, or counseling; family and the child; agrarian and urban family economics; management in family living and house residence. Offered by College of Household Arts and Sciences. Prerequisite for graduate study: knowledge of statistics. 17 professorial staff. 1 Ph.D. awarded 1955-59. 5 graduate students registered fall 1959.

Foods and Nutrition.—Dietetics and Institution Administration. Nutrition; foods; food preparation or services; meal management; food service in nursery school; experimental or demonstration cookery; food research; dietetics; bionutrition and its application; child nutrition; nutrition and geriatrics; nutrition and radiation medicine; nutrition and bone density; assessing human nutrition; institution management, organization, and equipment; institution purchasing and management; institution administration research; public food service; hospital and institution food service. Offered by College of Household Arts and Sciences. Prerequisite for graduate study: knowledge of chemistry and biology. 28 professorial staff. 17 master's degrees and 6 Ph.D.'s awarded 1955-59. 18 graduate students registered fall 1959.

Health and Physical Education. Health, safety, or driver education; adaptive physical education; school health. Offered by College of Health, Physical Education, and Recreation. 7 professorial staff. 1 master's degree and 1 Ph.D. awarded 1955-59. 4 graduate students registered fall 1959.

Health, Physical Education, and Recreation. 21 professorial staff. 28 master's degrees and 1 Ph.D. awarded 1955-59. 21 graduate students registered fall 1959.

Home Economics Education and Home Demonstration. Home economics education, home demonstration, teaching home economics, vocational home economics, the home economics supervisor; curriculum in home economics; cooperative extension work. Offered by College of Household Arts and Sciences. Recommended for graduate study: knowledge of statistics and chemistry. 18 professorial staff. 36 master's degrees and 7 Ph.D.'s awarded 1955-59. 39 graduate students registered fall 1959.

Home Economics.—General. All areas, exclusive of those listed elsewhere under College of Household Arts and Sciences. Recommended for graduate study: chemistry and statistics. 47 professorial staff. 36 master's degrees and 7 Ph.D.'s awarded 1955-59. 21 graduate students registered fall 1959.

Home Management, Housing, Household Equipment, and Family Economics. Home management, supervision of and residence in home management house, research in home management, housing, household equipment, housing and family economics. Offered by College of Household Arts and Sciences. Recommended for graduate study: economics. 7 professorial staff. 1 master's degree and 1 Ph.D. awarded 1955-59. 6 graduate students registered fall 1959.

Physical Education. Sports, history and principles, tests and measurements, supervision, coaching. Offered by College of Health, Physical Education, and Recreation. 9 professorial staff. 8 master's degrees and 1 Ph.D. awarded 1955-59. 9 graduate students registered fall 1959.

Recreation, Recreation Therapy, and Recreation Administration. Recreation, recreation therapy, recreation administration or skills, camping, program planning, recreation and camping in schools, field work in recreation, industrial or hospital recreation. Offered by College of Health, Physical Education, and Recreation. 8 professorial staff. 1 master's degree and 1 Ph.D. awarded 1955-59. 4 graduate students registered fall 1959.

Textiles and Textile Technology. Textiles; history of or research in textiles; textile technology, testing, or detergency; textiles and clothing. Offered by College of Household Arts and Sciences. Recommended for graduate study: statistics; chemistry. 19 professorial staff. 5 master's degrees and 4 Ph.D.'s awarded 1955-59. 4 graduate students registered fall 1959.

Toledo, University of

TOLEDO 6, OHIO

Division of Graduate Study

At the master's level, graduate instruction has been offered at the University of Toledo since 1912. Graduate work is offered in Arts and Sciences, Business Administration, Education, and Engineering. Doctoral programs leading to the Ph.D. in Education and the Ed.D. degrees were begun in February of 1960. No doctorates have as yet been awarded. The university is publicly controlled by the city of Toledo. Both men and women are admitted.

Rooms in university dormitories available for single graduate students; apartments for married students.

Library contains approximately 230,000 volumes. Use is often made of the special industrial facilities of Toledo for research in engineering, the basic sciences, and in business. The special facilities of the Toledo Museum of Art are also used.

Residence requirement for Ph.D.: minimum of 3 years (90 semester graduate hours) beyond bachelor's degree, of which 2 consecutive semesters must be spent in full-time resident study at the University of Toledo. Summer and evening courses available.

ADMISSION REQUIREMENTS

For graduate study: bachelor's degree; GPA of 1.5 (on 3.0 scale); adequate preparation to undertake graduate work; GRE; evidence of research ability; recommendations. For candidacy for Ph.D.: master's degree in education; reading knowledge of 2 foreign languages; completion of substantial portion of course work with 2.0 average; comprehensive examination; recommendation of major adviser.

Apply to Division of Graduate Study at any time.

FEES AND FIRST-YEAR AID

No application fee. Tuition $21 per credit hour. Matriculation fee $10. There are also a few other special fees. Room (in dormitory) $210 per academic year. Meals available in college cafeteria at about $2 per day. Apartments $45 per month.

First-year aid available: about 40 teaching fellowships or graduate assistantships, $2,000-$4,000; 6 research fellowships, $2,000-$2,500; usually 6 research assistantships, $2,000 and up; grants-in-aid also available. A few instructorships are open to exceptional graduate students who are willing to limit their graduate work to ¼ time.

Apply to Division of Graduate Study by February 1.

FIELDS OF STUDY FOR THE PH.D.

Education. Program is appropriate for subject matter specialists who wish to teach in colleges and universities. Students concentrate their work in major and minor fields of study, with 1 such area being selected outside the professional course work. Areas possible as primary or secondary fields are: general school administration; guidance and counseling; curriculum (elementary, secondary, or higher and teacher education); foundations of education. Possible secondary fields are: art or business education; language arts or English; library science; physical education; science or social studies education. Offered by College of Education through the Division of Graduate Study. Ed.D. degree is also awarded (no language requirement, and research is oriented toward matters of immediate professional concern rather than toward the extension of the frontiers of knowledge).

Tufts University

MEDFORD 55, MASSACHUSETTS

Tufts was founded in 1852 as a liberal arts college and has now grown into a small modern university. Ph.D. programs are now offered through the Graduate School of Arts and Sciences and the Fletcher School of Law and Diplomacy (administered by Tufts with the cooperation of Harvard University). The university is privately controlled and nonsectarian. Both men and women are admitted.

Graduate School of Arts and Sciences

Graduate instruction has been offered at Tufts since 1876. The Graduate School of Arts and Sciences was established in 1892, and the first Ph.D. awarded in 1895. In practice, graduate instruction was largely limited to master's programs until 1955. Doctoral programs in the medical and dental sciences draw on the faculties and facilities of the Schools of Medicine and Dental Medicine, but are administered by the Graduate School of Arts and Sciences.

Limited number of dormitory rooms available for single graduate students. No residence facilities provided for married graduate students.

Library of approximately 305,000 volumes contains over 40,000 government documents, a collection in humanities and sciences, and departmental collections in chemistry, physics, and engineering.

Residence requirement for Ph.D.: 3 academic years beyond bachelor's degree, including at least 1 full year in residence at Tufts.

ADMISSION REQUIREMENTS

For graduate study: bachelor's degree; satisfactory academic record; recommendations. GRE required for M.A., M.S., and Ph.D. applicants; recommended for others. For candidacy for Ph.D.: completion of major part of course work with A and B grades; reading knowledge of 2 modern foreign languages; approval of department; qualifying examination.

Apply to Dean of the Graduate School of Arts and Sciences by April 1.

FEES AND FIRST-YEAR AID

No application fee. Tuition $40 per credit hour. Room (in dormitory) for men $290-$320 per year.

First-year aid available: 5 tuition scholarships for each program; teaching fellowships, up to $2,160 plus tuition; research assistantships, up to $2,160 plus tuition.

Apply to Dean of Graduate School of Arts and Sciences by April 1 (with application for admission).

FIELDS OF STUDY FOR THE PH.D.

Supervised apprentice teaching and associated seminar to be included in the humanistic studies program which will begin 1961-62.

Biochemistry. Nucleic acids; proteins; enzymology; amino-acid, lipid, or carbohydrate metabolism. Prerequisites for graduate study: background in chemistry; general experimental physics; general biology. 9 professorial staff. Ph.D. program begun 1955. 1 master's degree and 3 Ph.D.'s awarded 1955-59. 11 graduate students registered fall 1959.

Biology. Insect neurophysiology or behavior, photobiology, radiobiology. Prerequisite for graduate study: physics and chemistry (preferably above elementary level). 10 professorial staff. Ph.D. program begun 1959. 3 master's degrees awarded 1955-59. 4 graduate students registered fall 1959. Total enrollment limited to 4.

Chemistry. Synthesis of conjugated dienes, organic structural determinations, mechanisms of ozonolysis, relationships between conforma-tion and reactivity, cyclohexane stereochemistry, syntheses of bicyclo- and polycyclo-systems, properties and structure of gas-metal systems, phase rule studies, melting-point calorimetry, high-temperature heat capacity, reactions of heterocyclic systems, molecular spectroscopy, theoretical molecular structure, synthesis of inorganic hydrides and fluorides, lithium chemistry, defect structures, mechanism of adsorption, high-temperature and high-pressure X-ray diffraction, lattice energy of metallic compounds, enzymatic cleavage of proteins. Prerequisite for graduate study: major in chemistry. Recommended: MAT; reading knowledge of German. 9 professorial staff. Ph.D. program begun 1958. 23 master's degrees awarded 1955-59. 9 graduate students registered fall 1959.

Microbiology. Virology, chemotherapy of infection. Prerequisites for graduate study: general physics, biology, and chemistry. 5 professorial staff. Ph.D. program begun 1959.

Pharmacology. Biochemical pharmacology, mechanism of drug action at the enzymatic level. Prerequisites for graduate study: biology (preferably including microbiology and genetics); chemistry, including general inorganic, organic, and physical chemistry and qualitative and quantitative analysis; mathematics through calculus; physics. 5 professorial staff. Ph.D. program begun 1955. 2 master's degrees and 3 Ph.D.'s awarded 1955-59. 3 graduate students registered fall 1959. Total enrollment limited to 10.

Physics. Experimental and theoretical, solid-state, and high-energy physics. Prerequisite for graduate study: training in physics, mathematics, or electrical engineering. Recommended: reading knowledge of 2 foreign languages (French, German, Russian). 8 professorial staff. Ph.D. program begun 1957. 8 master's degrees awarded 1955-59. 9 graduate students registered fall 1959.

Physiology. Radio-biology, intermediary metabolism, electron transport, oxidative phosphorylation, diabetes, muscle physiology. Prerequisites for graduate study: background in biology, physics, inorganic and organic chemistry, and qualitative and quantitative analysis. 6 professorial staff. Ph.D. program begun 1957. 1 Ph.D. awarded 1957-59. 6 graduate students registered fall 1959.

Psychology. Perception (especially in vision), EEG, physiological or social psychology, learning, motivation, human engineering. Prerequisites for graduate study: basic science and mathematics; 12-15 hours in psychology; MAT. 10 professorial staff. Ph.D. program begun 1957. 11 master's degrees awarded 1955-59. 24 graduate students registered fall 1959.

Sociology. Social control, criminology. Recommended for graduate study: major in sociology. Ph.D. candidacy prerequisite: GRE. 5 professorial staff. 3 master's degrees awarded 1955-59. 7 graduate students registered fall 1959.

Fletcher School of Law and Diplomacy

Fletcher School of Law and Diplomacy was founded in 1933 as the first graduate school in the United States devoted exclusively to the study of international affairs. First Ph.D. was awarded in 1940. Originally the school was jointly administered by Tufts College and Harvard University, but this plan was modified to provide for administration by Tufts with cooperation by Harvard. Under the cooperative arrangement, students take approved courses at Harvard, with reciprocal privileges for Harvard graduate students at Fletcher.

Graduate residence houses provided for both single men and women; no university-owned housing for married students, but apartments are available in community.

Library contains over 80,000 volumes devoted primarily to study of international affairs and related fields.

Residence requirement for Ph.D.: 3 years beyond bachelor's degree, with 2 full years in residence at Fletcher. Summer courses (at Harvard Summer School) available.

ADMISSION REQUIREMENTS

For graduate study: bachelor's degree with high standing; good preparation in economics, history, and political science; reading knowledge of 1 modern foreign language. Recommended: GRE. For candidacy for Ph.D.: master's degree at Fletcher; completion of second year in residence at Fletcher; reading knowledge of second modern foreign language with written examinations in 2 languages; written and oral examinations covering fields of study.

Apply to Registrar, Fletcher School of Law and Diplomacy, Tufts University, Medford 55, Massachusetts, by February 15.

FEES AND FIRST-YEAR AID

Application fee $10. Tuition $1,250 per academic year. Room (in dormitory) $280 per academic year. Approximate annual cost of board in college dining room $560.

First-year aid available: Fletcher and Clayton scholarships, up to $2,500; Fletcher and Clayton fellowships, $1,250-$2,500. Grants-in-aid and numerous teaching assistantships also available in varying amounts for second- and third-year students.

Apply to Registrar, Fletcher School of Law and Diplomacy, Tufts University, Medford 55, Massachusetts, by February 15.

FIELDS OF STUDY FOR THE PH.D.

International Affairs. International law, organization, politics, trade and commercial policies, finance, or economics; American or European diplomacy; special regional and topical studies. 19 professorial staff. 45 M.A.'s, 20 M.A.L.D.'s and 10 Ph.D.'s awarded 1959-60. 88 graduate students registered fall 1959. New enrollment limited to 50.

Tulane University

NEW ORLEANS 18, LOUISIANA

The Graduate School

Graduate instruction has been offered at Tulane since 1883, and the first Ph.D. was awarded in 1887. In 1925 the Faculty of Graduate Studies became the present Graduate School. At present the Ph.D. is awarded in 24 areas and, in addition, the Graduate Faculty has recently approved programs in Italian, social work, mechanical engineering, and chemical engineering. The D.P.H. and J.S.D. degrees are offered through the School of Medicine and the School of Law, respectively.

Graduate men live in residence halls and in rooms in private homes; married students in modern air-conditioned apartment building on campus or in private apartments off campus. No residence facilities provided for single graduate women.

Special facilities include: library of approximately 633,000 volumes; biophysics laboratory; urban life research institute; American universities field staff; Middle American Research Institute; geology summer camp in Mexico. Affiliation maintained with Oak Ridge Institute of Nuclear Studies.

Residence requirement for Ph.D.: normally a student may expect to complete minimum course requirements (48 semester hours) in 2 years and to complete dissertation in third year. As much as 24 hours of graduate credit may be accepted for work done elsewhere. Limited number of summer courses available.

ADMISSION REQUIREMENTS

For graduate study: bachelor's degree; adequate preparation in proposed field of specialization; B average or better in undergraduate work; personal interview whenever possible; GRE in some departments. For candidacy for Ph.D.: reading knowledge of 2 foreign languages (usually French and German); completion of course requirements; qualifying examination; recommendation of major department; dissertation prospectus.

Apply to Dean of the Graduate School, usually by March 1 for the following year.

FEES AND FIRST-YEAR AID

No application fee. Tuition $640 per academic year. Special fees approximate $110 annually. Room (in residence halls) for men $265-$325 per academic year. Rent for 1-bedroom apartment $70 per month; for 2-bedroom $80, for 3-bedroom $90.

First-year aid available: scholarships; teaching fellowships and research assistantships in some fields. Scholarship stipends are based on merit and need. Long-term loans at 3% interest also available. Plans for financial assistance over whole period of study are worked out for each student by department head and Dean.

Apply to Dean of the Graduate School by March 1 for following academic year.

FIELDS OF STUDY FOR THE PH.D.

Some courses in the methodology of teaching are offered by certain departments. All departments, however, give careful attention to providing supervised teaching experience for each Ph.D. student. Departments also provide general orientation to the academic profession for Ph.D. students.

Anatomy, Histochemistry, and Human Genetics. Cancer research, electron microscopy, experimental and descriptive embryology, experimental neurology, gross anatomy, histochemistry, histology, human genetics. Offered by Department of Anatomy. Prerequisites for graduate study: adequate background in biology, basic physics, and organic chemistry. Recommended: GRE; 2 years of French and/or German; genetics; embryology. 9 professorial staff. 3 master's degrees and 3 Ph.D.'s awarded 1955-59. 2 graduate students registered fall 1959.

Anthropology. Archaeology, cultural anthropology. Offered by Department of Sociology and Anthropology. 6 professorial staff. Program begun 1958. 9 graduate students registered fall 1959. Total enrollment limited to 25.

Biochemistry. Prerequisites for graduate study: major in chemistry or in biology with strong chemistry background; at least 1 modern foreign language; GRE. 18 professorial staff. 1 master's degree and 5 Ph.D.'s awarded 1955-59. 23 graduate students registered fall 1959. Total enrollment limited to 25.

Chemistry. Analytical, inorganic, organic, or physical chemistry. Prerequisites for graduate study: major in chemistry; courses in calculus and physics. Recommended: biology; advanced physics and mathematics; German plus French or Russian. 11 professorial staff. 25 master's degrees and 27 Ph.D.'s awarded 1955-59. 29 graduate students registered fall 1959.

Economics. Economic theory, history, or development; international economics; mathematical economics and econometrics; money and banking; public finance; labor; resources; social control of industry. Prerequisites for graduate study: strong background in economics; GRE. Recommended: courses in economic theory, statistics, and mathematics; 1 foreign language. 8 professorial staff. 13 master's degrees and 1 Ph.D. awarded 1955-59. 30 graduate students registered fall 1959. Total enrollment limited to 30.

English. History of the English language; medieval or English Renaissance literature; 17th, 18th, or 19th century English literature; American literature; Modern English and American literature. Prerequisite for graduate study: 18-24 hours of advanced English courses. Recommended: GRE; knowledge of French and German. Ph.D. candidacy prerequisite: M.A. in English and 24 additional graduate hours. 17 professorial staff. 45 master's degrees and 9

Ph.D.'s awarded 1955-59. 50 graduate students registered fall 1959.

French. French literature of the Middle Ages, the Renaissance, or the 17th, 19th, or 20th centuries; French linguistics. Offered by Department of French and Italian. Prerequisites for graduate study: major in French or equivalent; at least 1 other Romance language. Recommended: German; Latin. 9 professorial staff. 4 master's degrees and 7 Ph.D.'s awarded 1955-59. 20 graduate students registered fall 1959.

Geology. Areal and regional geography, stratigraphy, invertebrate paleontology (including micropaleontology), sedimentation, geophysics. Prerequisites for graduate study: major in geology: GRE Advanced Test in Geology; comprehensive placement examination. Recommended: French or German; mathematics through calculus; general chemistry, physics, and/or zoology. Ph.D. candidacy prerequisites: graduate field geology or a mapping dissertation. 6 professorial staff. Ph.D. program begun 1960. 1 master's degree awarded 1955-59. 12 graduate students registered fall 1959. Total enrollment limited to 18.

German. Theory and history of the German drama; classical, or 19th or 20th century German literature. Prerequisites for graduate study: 2 foreign languages; GRE; qualifying examination. Recommended: elementary Latin; European and English history and culture. 5 professorial staff. Ph.D. program begun 1958. 2 master's degrees awarded 1955-59. 6 graduate students registered fall 1959.

History. United States history with emphasis on cultural history and the South; Latin American with emphasis on the Caribban area; modern European with emphasis on Germany, France, England and intellectual history. Prerequisite for graduate study: GRE during first semester; recommendations from professors; language proficiency. 20 professorial staff. 23 master's degrees and 4 Ph.D.'s awarded 1955-59. 42 graduate students registered fall 1959. Total enrollment limited to 50.

Mathematics. Algebra, topology, topological algebra, applications of topology to analysis, functional analysis, ergodic or graph theory, Banach algebras, periodic functions, geometry of numbers, diophantine approximation, complex variables, algebraic geometry. Prerequisite for graduate study: major in mathematics or equivalent. 10 professorial staff. 11 master's degrees and

9 Ph.D.'s awarded 1955-59. 37 graduate students registered fall 1959.

Microbiology. Medical microbiology, immunology, mycology, microbial metabolism. Prerequisite for graduate study: GRE. 7 professorial staff. 6 Ph.D.'s awarded 1955-59. 13 graduate students registered fall 1959.

Parasitology. Helminthology, protozoology, medical entomology, malacology. Offered by Department of Tropical Medicine and Public Health. Prerequisites for graduate study: major in biology, zoology, microbiology, or chemistry; 1 foreign language; GRE. Recommended: histology; biochemistry. 5 professorial staff. 9 master's degrees and 7 Ph.D.'s awarded 1955-59. 9 graduate students registered fall 1959. Total enrollment limited to 8-10.

Pharmacology. Chemical constitution and pharmacologic activity, drug metabolism, drug enzyme interactions, neuropharmacology. Offered by Department of Pharmacology, School of Medicine. Prerequisite for graduate study: major in biology, chemistry, general science, or pharmacy. 6 professorial staff. Ph.D. program begun 1956. 1 master's degree and 1 Ph.D. awarded 1955-59. 8 graduate students registered fall 1959. Enrollment limited.

Philosophy. Epistemology, metaphysics, philosophy of religion, American philosophy. Prerequisite for graduate study: GRE. 10 professorial staff. 12 master's degrees awarded 1955-59. 21 graduate students registered fall 1959.

Physics. Nuclear, theoretical, or solid-state physics. Prerequisites for graduate study: courses in general physics, electricity or electrical measurements, mechanics, heat and thermodynamics, and optics; 6 additional hours of credit in specialized courses such as contemporary or theoretical physics, atomic and nuclear physics, and acoustics; calculus and differential equations. 9 professorial staff. Ph.D. program begun 1959. 4 master's degrees awarded 1955-59. 17 graduate students registered fall 1959.

Physiology. Physiology of nervous or cardiovascular-renal system, radiobiology, capillary permeability, lymph and lymphatics, cellular physiology. Offered by Department of Physiology, School of Medicine. Prerequisites for graduate study: biology; chemistry through organic; mathematics through calculus; physics. Recommended: statistics; psychology. 6 professorial staff. 1 master's degree and 1 Ph.D. awarded 1955-59. 20 students registered fall 1959.

Political Science. American political institutions, comparative government, legal studies, international relations, political behavior or theory, public administration. Prerequisite for graduate study: GRE Aptitude and Advanced Tests. Recommended: 12 semester hours in political science. 10 professorial staff. 6 master's degrees awarded 1955-59. 20 graduate students registered fall 1959.

Psychodynamics. Program designed to give complete psychiatric training to a limited number of clergymen, who are encouraged to return to their seminaries to teach the material to candidates for the ministry. Offered by Department of Psychiatry and Neurology, School of Medicine. Prerequisites for graduate study: intense psychiatric and psychological screening by faculty of department; B.D. degree; letters of recommendation from candidate's church and seminary. 36 professorial staff. Program begun 1959. 1 graduate student registered fall 1959. (As this is an experimental program, no further candidates will be considered until fall 1961; enrollment will be limited to 3.)

Psychology. General-experimental psychology with emphasis on learning, motivation, physiological psychology, perception. Prerequisite for graduate study: GRE. 10 professorial staff. 17 master's degrees and 14 Ph.D.'s awarded 1955-59. 28 graduate students registered fall 1959. Total enrollment limited to 35.

Sociology. Social organization, social psychology. Offered by Department of Sociology and Anthropology. Prerequisite for graduate study: 1 year of statistics. Recommended: 1 year each of cultural anthropology and social psychology; mathematics. 6 professorial staff. 3 master's degrees and 3 Ph.D.'s awarded 1955-59. 22 graduate students registered fall 1959. Total enrollment limited to 25.

Spanish. Spanish and Spanish-American literatures, philology, American Spanish. Offered by Department of Spanish and Portuguese. Prerequisite for graduate study: major in field. Recommended: GRE. Ph.D. candidacy prerequisites: reading knowledge examinations in 4 languages other than the major. 7 professorial staff. 10 master's degrees and 9 Ph.D.'s awarded 1955-59. 29 graduate students registered fall 1959.

Theatre. Theatre production, history, or theory; dramatic literature and criticism. Offered by Department of Theatre and Speech. Prerequisites for graduate study: approximately 24 hours in theatre and allied fields; GRE. 5 professorial staff. Ph.D. program begun 1959. 9 master's degrees awarded 1955-59. 25 graduate students registered fall 1959. Total enrollment limited to 30.

Zoology. Aquatic, fishery, or insect biology; cytology; ecology; evolution; embryology; genetics; herpetology; histology; ichthyology; mammalogy; morphology; parasitology; physiology; protozoology; systematics. Prerequisites for graduate study: major in zoology or biology; GRE. Ph.D. candidacy prerequisite: 1 year as teaching laboratory assistant. 15 professorial staff. 13 master's degrees and 8 Ph.D.'s awarded 1955-59. 27 graduate students registered fall 1959. Total enrollment limited to 30.

Union College and University

SCHENECTADY, NEW YORK

The component institutions of Union College and University include: Union College; Albany Medical College; Albany Law School; Dudley Observatory; Albany College of Pharmacy. At present the Ph.D. degree may be earned only through the Albany Medical College. The university is privately controlled and nonsectarian. Both men and women are admitted.

Albany Medical College

The Graduate School of Albany Medical College was founded in 1951 and the first Ph.D. was awarded in 1956. Departments of Biochemistry and Microbiology have a working arrangement with Rensselaer Polytechnic Institute whereby graduate students at either institution may take courses for credit at the other.

No university-owned residence facilities; rooms and apartments available in community.

Active research laboratories in the New York State Department of Health, Division of Laboratories and Research, as well as in the nearby Veterans' Administration Hospital, are open to graduate students and are staffed by individuals who participate in the graduate teaching program.

Residence requirement for Ph.D.: 90 semester hours beyond bachelor's degree, of which no more than 30 hours may be transferred from other graduate institutions.

ADMISSION REQUIREMENTS

For graduate study: bachelor's degree; superior scholastic achievement; courses in biology, chemistry, organic chemistry, and physics. Recommended: physical chemistry; GRE; proficiency in 1 modern foreign language. For candidacy for Ph.D.: reading knowledge of 2 modern foreign languages; qualifying examinations.

Apply to Registrar's Office, Albany Medical College, Albany 8, New York, at any time.

FEES AND FIRST-YEAR AID

No application fee. Tuition $1,200 per academic year. Registration fee $5. Health fee $10. Average cost of single room in community $9 per week. Meals in hospital cafeteria average $2 a day.

First-year aid available: tuition scholarships; research assistantships in some departments, $2,000-$2,800; student assistantships, $1,800-$2,400. Grants-in-aid of $2,500-$3,500 obtainable by properly qualified individuals. All of these are in addition to tuition remission.

Apply to Registrar's Office, Albany Medical College, Albany 8, New York, at the time application for admission is made.

FIELDS OF STUDY FOR THE PH.D.

No special courses in the methodology of college teaching are offered, but effective teaching and exposition is fostered and developed increasingly during candidate's tenure as student.

Anatomy. Histology, cytology, and cytochemistry of the endocrine glands; cytology and physiology of the reproductive system; neuroendocrinology; electron microscopy. Recommended for graduate study: courses in embryology, genetics, comparative anatomy, and mathematics. 7 professorial staff.

Biochemistry. Intermediary metabolism of carbohydrates, fats and proteins; enzymology; biological oxidations; biochemistry and metabolism of steroid hormones; protein physicochemistry and biosynthesis. Prerequisite for graduate study: major in chemistry, including physical chemistry. Recommended: more than average training in mathematics and biology. 10 professorial staff. 2 master's degrees and 1 Ph.D. awarded 1955-59. 8 graduate students registered fall 1959. New enrollment limited to 5.

Microbiology. Bacteriology and mycology, virology, inmunochemistry, bacterial metabolism, microbial genetics. Prerequisite for graduate study: training in biology and chemistry, including physical chemistry. Recommended: courses in embryology and genetics. 7 professorial staff. 1 master's degree awarded 1955-59. 4 graduate students registered fall 1959.

Pathology. Pathological chemistry, experimental pathology, electron microscopy. Recommended for graduate study: courses in comparative anatomy, embryology, and genetics. 6 professorial staff. 1 Ph.D. awarded 1955-59. 1 graduate student registered fall 1959.

Pharmacology. Nature and mechanism of drug action, isolation and investigation of new therapeutic agents, isotope techniques in pharmacology. Prerequisites for graduate study: qualitative and quantitative analysis; GRE. Recommended: comparative anatomy; genetics; mathematics. 4 professorial staff. 1 master's degree and 1 Ph.D. awarded 1955-59. 2 graduate students registered fall 1959. New enrollment limited to 4.

Physiology. Vascular system and smooth muscle physiology, environmental physiology, renal system, membrane permeability and bioelectricity, cardiac function. Prerequisites for graduate study: physical chemistry; introductory calculus; biology or zoology. Recommended: additional physics courses; comparative anatomy; histology. 4 professorial staff. 1 graduate student registered fall 1959. New enrollment limited to 4.

Union Theological Seminary

NEW YORK, NEW YORK

Union Theological Seminary is an interdenominational seminary founded in 1836 for the training of Protestant ministers and teachers of religion and theology. A joint committee representing Union Theological Seminary and Columbia University directs a course leading to a Ph.D. in religion granted by the latter.

The program involves several Columbia departments such as religion, classics, economics, history, anthropology, languages, etc. Both men and women are admitted.

Seminary also awards the Th.D. and the S.M.D. degrees. A program leading to the Ed.D. degree with religion as the area of specialization may be undertaken through Teachers College of Columbia University.

Dormitories available for single students; both dormitories and apartments for married students.

Residence requirement for doctorate: 2 years after a B.A. with a religion major (but 1 additional semester is usually needed); between 1 and 2 years after B.D. or M.A. in religion. Summer and evening courses available at Columbia.

ADMISSION REQUIREMENTS

Outstanding college record and a religion major. No advance credit given except for B.D. or M.A. in religion. German and French; other languages where necessary.

General examination after 1 year of study. Field examination after 1½ or 2 years of study.

Apply before February 1 to Director of Graduate Studies.

FEES AND FIRST-YEAR AID

Application fee $10. Tuition: $37 a point at Union Theological Seminary; $40 a point at Columbia. Room (in dormitory) $200 per person per year. Student apartments $500-$1,080 per year.

Available to first-year students: scholarships for able students, ranging from $300 to $1,500. Number given annually varies. Need of student is considered. Most aid is given by Union Theological Seminary; one large scholarship annually by Columbia.

Apply before February 1 to Director of Graduate Studies.

FIELDS OF STUDY FOR THE PH.D.

Religion. Bible, philosophy of religion and ethics, history of religion, religion and society. Prerequisites: practically all candidates take a survey course in history of religion and in history of philosophy; for Bible studies, Greek and Hebrew; others depending upon area of study. Professorial staff (both institutions) 40. 60 master's degrees and 40 Ph.D.'s awarded 1955-59. 50 graduate students registered fall 1959.

Utah State University of Agriculture and Applied Science

LOGAN, UTAH

School of Graduate Studies

The university is Utah's land-grant institution, chartered in 1888. It includes 7 colleges and the School of Graduate Studies. Graduate instruction has been offered since 1917, and the present Graduate School was organized in 1945. First Ph.D. was awarded in 1950. A program leading to the Ed.D. degree is offered through the College of Education. The university is publicly controlled by the state. Both men and women are admitted.

Single graduate students live in residence halls; married students in trailer courts and in university-owned and privately-owned apartments.

Special facilities include: library of approximately 240,000 volumes; Division of University Research; agricultural experiment station; engineering experiment station.

Residence requirement for Ph.D.: 3 years beyond bachelor's degree, of which the last must be spent in residence at Utah State University. Summer courses available.

ADMISSION REQUIREMENTS

For graduate study: bachelor's degree; B average; 3 letters of recommendation; approval of major department; qualifying examinations; GRE Aptitude Test and Advanced Tests. For candidacy for Ph.D.: completion of substantial portion of course work; reading knowledge of at least 1 foreign language (second language optional with department); comprehensive examination.

Apply to Dean, School of Graduate Studies, at least 3 months in advance of date of desired entry.

FEES AND FIRST-YEAR AID

No application fee. Tuition $264 per academic year. Special fees approximate $41 annually. Room (in residence halls) $255 per academic year. Approximate annual cost of board in college dining room $540.

First-year aid available: teaching fellowships,

$1,500; other fellowships, $2,000; research assistantships, $1,000-$2,400.

Apply to Dean, School of Graduate Studies, by March 15.

FIELDS OF STUDY FOR THE PH.D.

Courses in the methodology of teaching are offered in certain departments.

Animal Husbandry. Animal breeding or nutrition, physiology of reproduction, nutrition and biochemistry. 7 professorial staff. 16 master's degrees and 4 Ph.D.'s awarded 1955-59. 9 graduate students registered fall 1959.

Chemistry. Physical or organic chemistry. Prerequisite for graduate study: reading knowledge of German. Ph.D. candidacy prerequisites: German plus French or Russian. 10 professorial staff. Ph.D. program begun 1959. 12 master's degrees awarded 1955-59. 7 graduate students registered fall 1959.

Engineering.—Electrical. Radio propagation, computers and servomechanisms, transistor physics and circuitry. Prerequisite for graduate study: major in field. Ph.D. candidacy prerequisite: M.S. in field or equivalent. 9 professorial staff. Ph.D. program begun 1960. 5 master's degrees awarded 1955-59. 17 graduate students registered fall 1959.

Entomology. Agricultural entomology, insect control or biology. Offered by Department of Zoology, Entomology, and Physiology. Prerequisite for graduate study: major in entomology or closely related field. 10 professorial staff. 6 master's degrees and 3 Ph.D.'s awarded 1955-59. 6 graduate students registered fall 1959.

Fluid Mechanics and Hydraulics—Irrigation and Drainage. Offered by Department of Civil and Irrigation Engineering. Prerequisite for graduate study: major in civil or agricultural engineering. 12 professorial staff. 19 master's degrees and 4 Ph.D.'s awarded 1955-59. 30 graduate students registered fall 1959. Total enrollment limited to 30.

Horticulture. Vegetable crops, pomology, floriculture, food technology. 7 professorial staff. 11 graduate students registered fall 1959.

Nutrition and Biochemistry. Effects of toxic and nontoxic substances on digestion and metabolism of farm animals, atmospheric pollution, cholesterol metabolism, amino-acid metabolism, other physiological processes related to nutrition.

Combined program offered by Departments of Biochemistry, Animal Husbandry, Dairy Husbandry, Poultry Husbandry, and Foods and Nutrition. 10 professorial staff. Ph.D. program begun 1957. 1 master's degree and 1 Ph.D. awarded 1955-59. 5 graduate students registered fall 1959.

Physiology. Endocrinology, cellular physiology, microscopic anatomy. Offered by Department of Zoology, Entomology, and Physiology. Prerequisite for graduate study: major in physiology, zoology, or other biological science. Recommended: mathematics through calculus; 1 year of physics; general, qualitative, quantitative, and organic chemistry; biochemistry; general bacteriology; 1 year of a foreign language. Ph.D. candidacy prerequisite: M.S. in physiology or equivalent. 3 professorial staff. Ph.D. program begun 1959. 3 master's degrees awarded 1955-59. 4 graduate students registered fall 1959.

Plant Physiology. Plant physiology, plant biochemistry and enzymes, water relations, mineral nutrition. Offered by Department of Botany and Plant Pathology. Prerequisites for graduate study: training in botany, zoology, mathematics, and chemistry; written and oral examinations. Recommended: physics; agronomy; statistics. 6 professorial staff. Ph.D. program begun 1957. 6 master's degrees awarded 1955-59. 5 graduate students registered fall 1959.

Range Management. Range or watershed management, range livestock nutrition, plant ecology. Prerequisite for graduate study: biological science background. Recommended: range management major. 6 professorial staff. 11 master's degrees and 4 Ph.D.'s awarded 1955-59. 13 graduate students registered fall 1959. Ph.D. enrollment limited to about 5.

Sociology. Social theory, social organizations and institutions, social psychology or pathology, social work, research methods and statistics, population. Offered by Department of Sociology and Social Work in cooperation with Departments of Child Development and Family Living, Psychology, Economics, and Political Science. Prerequisites for graduate study: major in sociology or equivalent. Ph.D. candidacy prerequisites: 2 foreign languages. 23 professorial staff. 13 master's degrees and 1 Ph.D. awarded 1955-59. 6 graduate students registered fall 1959.

Soil Science. Soils related to irrigation. Offered by Department of Agronomy. Recommended for graduate study: 1 foreign language. 8 professorial staff. 25 master's degrees and 5 Ph.D.'s awarded 1955-59. 15 graduate students registered fall 1959.

Wildlife Management—Environmental Biology. Wildlife ecology, limnology, animal behavior. Prerequisite for graduate study: major in biological science. Ph.D. candidacy prerequisite: M.S. in a biological field. 6 professorial staff. 28 master's degrees and 7 Ph.D.'s awarded 1955-59. 31 graduate students registered fall 1959.

Zoology. Genetics, parasitology, vertebrate zoology. Offered by Department of Zoology, Entomology, and Physiology. Prerequisite for graduate study: major in biology, zoology, or related field. 8 professorial staff. Ph.D. program begun 1955. 9 master's degrees and 1 Ph.D. awarded 1955-59. 9 graduate students registered fall 1959.

Utah, University of

SALT LAKE CITY 12, UTAH

Graduate School

Although advanced degrees were granted as early as 1894, graduate work was not formally organized until 1908. The Graduate Division was established in 1917, reorganized on a more advanced level in 1925, and established as a Graduate School in 1946. The first Ph.D. was conferred in 1947. The Ed.D. degree is also awarded. University is publicly controlled by the state. Both men and women are admitted.

Single graduate students are accommodated in residence halls; married students in Stadium Village.

Special facilities include: library of approximately 355,000 volumes; numerous museums; art gallery; Utah Symphony; Center for Intercultural Studies; electron microscopes; powerful optical microscopes; nuclear magnetic resonance spectrometer; datatron 205 high-speed digital computer; mass spectrometers; X-ray fluorescence equipment; high-pressure and high-temperature equipment.

Residence requirement for Ph.D.: minimum of 3 years beyond bachelor's degree, of which 1 of last 2 years must be spent in continuous residence at the University of Utah. Summer and evening courses available.

ADMISSION REQUIREMENTS

For graduate study: bachelor's degree; B average; departmental approval; entrance examinations when required by departments. For candidacy for Ph.D.: reading knowledge of French and German or other approved languages; preliminary examinations in major and minor fields.

Apply to Office of Admissions, Registrar, at least 30 days before date of registration.

FEES AND FIRST-YEAR AID

No application fee. Tuition for state residents $255 per academic year; others $435. Room (in dormitory) $175 per academic year. Approximate annual cost of board in college dining room $450. Apartments in Stadium Village $32 per month (until June 1961); after this date new housing will be available at approximately $75 per month.

First-year aid available: departmental teaching fellowships, $1,800-$2,100; approximately 12 university research fellowships, $1,200; departmental research assistantships, $1,800-$2,100.

Apply to head of major department or to Dean of Graduate School. Applications for university research fellowships should be received by January 1; for teaching fellowships and research assistantships by March 1.

FIELDS OF STUDY FOR THE PH.D.

Anatomy. Anatomy, histology, neurology, hematology, endocrinology. Recommended for graduate study: major in biology and minor in chemistry preferred; other acceptable minors are biochemistry, physiology, and/or endocrinology. 6 professorial staff. 3 master's degrees and 4 Ph.D.'s awarded 1955-59. 7 graduate students registered fall 1959. Total enrollment limited to 8.

Anthropology. Cultural anthropology, archaeology, linguistics. Prerequisite for graduate study: oral admissions examination. 4 professorial staff. Ph.D. program begun 1956. 2 master's degrees awarded 1955-59. 14 graduate students registered fall 1959.

Bacteriology. Basic, medical, or sanitary bacteriology; immunology and serology; mycology; virology; tissue culture. Offered by Department of Bacteriology, College of Medicine. Prerequisite for graduate study: major in biological or physical sciences. Recommended: 15-25 hours in biology; 40-50 in chemistry; 40-45 in bacteriology. 8 professorial staff. 5 master's degrees and

12 Ph.D.'s awarded 1955-59. 22 graduate students registered fall 1959. Total enrollment limited to 25.

Biochemistry. Endocrinology, enzymology, protein chemistry, intermediary metabolism, nucleic acid chemistry. Prerequisites for graduate study: chemistry (organic and physical); physics (1-year course with laboratory); mathematics through calculus; zoology (comparative anatomy); reading knowledge of French or German. 16 professorial staff. 1 master's degree and 9 Ph.D.'s awarded 1955-59. 11 graduate students registered fall 1959.

Botany. Plant ecology or physiology. Prerequisites for graduate study: major in botany or closely related field; GRE Advanced Test in Biology. Recommended: 1 year each of mathematics and chemistry. 3 professorial staff. 10 master's degrees and 2 Ph.D.'s awarded 1955-59. 9 graduate students registered fall 1959.

Business and Commerce. Accounting, banking and finance, management, marketing. Cooperative program offered by Departments of Accounting, Management, and Marketing. Prerequisite for graduate study: major in business. 18 professorial staff. Ph.D. program begun 1957. 79 master's degrees awarded 1955-59. 50 graduate students registered fall 1959.

Chemistry. Analytical, inorganic, organic, physical. Prerequisites for graduate study: major in chemistry; ACS Placement Examination. Recommended: German and French. 13 professorial staff. 9 master's degrees and 43 Ph.D.'s awarded 1955-59. 50 graduate students registered fall 1959.

Economics. Economic history; economic theory and the history of economic doctrines; economic resources and population; economic planning and comparative economic systems; statistics and mathematical methods in economics; money, banking, and business cycles; public finance; international economics; labor; transportation and public utilities; government and business. Prerequisite for graduate study: major in economics. Recommended: proficiency in mathematics and 2 languages. 15 professorial staff. Ph.D. program begun 1957. 8 master's degrees awarded 1955-59. 22 graduate students registered fall 1959.

Education.—Elementary and Secondary. 16 professorial staff. 30 master's degrees awarded 1955-59. 3 graduate students registered fall 1959. Both Ph.D. and Ed.D. degrees awarded in field.

Educational Administration. History and philosophy of education, education and the contemporary scene, school law or finance, American school buildings, public relations, personnel administration. Prerequisites for graduate study: GRE Advanced Test in Education; MAT; English usage test; social science test. 5 professorial staff. 91 master's degrees and 4 Ph.D.'s awarded 1955-59. 124 graduate students registered fall 1959. Ph.D. candidates limited to 5 per year. The Ed.D. degree is also awarded in this field.

Educational Psychology. Counseling, reading, school psychology, rehabilitation counseling, measurement and evaluation, research. Prerequisite for graduate study: GRE or MAT. Ph.D. candidacy prerequisite: M.A. in field. 9 professorial staff. 40 master's degrees and 4 Ph.D.'s awarded 1955-59. 60 graduate students registered fall 1959. The Ed.D. degree is also awarded in this field.

Engineering.—Ceramic. Chemistry and physics of nonmetallic solids at temperatures above 500° C. Prerequisite for graduate study: major in field or in allied area of physical science or engineering. Recommended: interview; recommendations. 3 professorial staff. 1 master's degree and 2 Ph.D.'s awarded 1955-59. 9 graduate students registered fall 1959.

Engineering.—Chemical. Fluid dynamics, heat transfer, chemical kinetics, thermodynamics. Prerequisite for graduate study: major in a physical science or a branch of engineering. Recommended: 1 year of mathematics beyond calculus. 5 professorial staff. 4 master's degrees and 4 Ph.D.'s awarded 1955-59. 20 graduate students registered fall 1959.

Engineering.—Civil. Fluid mechanics. Prerequisites for graduate study: major in field; departmental qualifying examination. Recommended: 1 year of mathematics beyond calculus. 4 professorial staff. Ph.D. program begun 1960. 11 master's degrees awarded 1955-59. 6 graduate students registered fall 1959.

Engineering.—Electrical. Computers, microwaves, control and feedback, circuits. Prerequisite for graduate study: departmental qualifying examination. 6 professorial staff. 40 master's degrees and 7 Ph.D.'s awarded 1955-59. 55 graduate students registered fall 1959.

Engineering.—Fuels. Physical chemistry of fuels and their chemical products. Prerequisite for graduate study: major in chemical, mechanical, or fuels engineering or in chemistry, fuel technology, mathematics, metallurgy, or physics. Recommended: reading knowledge of German or Russian. 3 professorial staff. 1 master's degree and 7 Ph.D.'s awarded 1955-59. 7 graduate students registered fall 1959.

Engineering.—Mechanical. Thermodynamics and nuclear engineering, applied mechanics and design, fluid dynamics and heat transfer. Prerequisites for graduate study: equivalent of major in mechanical, nuclear, or aeronautical engineering or in applied mechanics; GRE. 7 professorial staff. Ph.D. program begun 1958. 9 master's degrees awarded 1955-59. 28 graduate students registered fall 1959.

Engineering.—Mining and Geological. Geomechanics, geochemistry, efficiency studies, expiration, trace elements, flow of plastic and solid materials. Prerequisite for graduate study: major in mining or geological engineering. 4 professorial staff. 12 master's degrees and 2 Ph.D.'s awarded 1955-59. 14 graduate students registered fall 1959.

English. Drama, poetry, fiction or nonfiction of any 3 recognized periods of American or English literary history. A program in linguistics is offered in collaboration with Departments of Languages and Anthropology, and one in comparative literature with Department of Languages. Prerequisite for graduate study: major in English, French, or German. Recommended: 15 hours of Latin. 19 professorial staff. 12 master's degrees and 3 Ph.D.'s awarded 1955-59. 30 graduate students registered fall 1959.

Experimental Biology. Cellular or general physiology; sample current problems; various aspects of photosynthesis, radiation biology, mechanical properties of biological materials, energy metabolism, membrane permeability. Prerequisites for graduate study: 2 years each of biology and chemistry; 1 year each of mathematics and physics; GRE Aptitude and Advanced Tests. Recommended: calculus. 4 professorial staff. 8 master's degrees and 2 Ph.D.'s awarded 1955-59. 4 graduate students registered fall 1959.

French—German—Spanish. Offered by Department of Languages. Prerequisites for graduate study: admittance examination. 15 professorial staff. 3 Ph.D.'s awarded 1955-59.

Genetics. Speciation in plants, human genetics. Offered by Department of Genetics and Cytology. Prerequisites for graduate study: major in a biological or related science; French and/or German; GRE. Recommended: chemistry through organic,

1 year of physics, mathematics through algebra. 3 professorial staff. 6 master's degrees and 1 Ph.D. awarded 1955-59. 7 graduate students registered fall 1959.

Geology. Economic or structural geology, paleontology, micropaleontology, stratigraphy. Prerequisites for graduate study: major in science; GRE. 7 professorial staff. 26 master's degrees and 9 Ph.D.'s awarded 1955-59. 22 graduate students registered fall 1959. Total enrollment limited to 25-35.

Geophysics. Exploration geophysics, earth physics. Prerequisite for graduate study: major in geophysics, physics, geology, mathematics, or allied field. 3 professorial staff. 12 master's degrees and 5 Ph.D.'s awarded 1955-59. 14 graduate students registered fall 1959.

Health, Physical Education, and Recreation. Prerequisite for graduate study: preliminary qualifying examination. 11 professorial staff. 30 master's degrees and 1 Ph.D. awarded 1955-59. 19 graduate students registered fall 1959. The Ed.D. degree is also awarded in this field.

History. Prerequisite for graduate study: major in field. 8 professorial staff. 15 master's degrees awarded 1955-59. 12 graduate students registered fall 1959.

Mathematics. Topology, analysis (especially differential equations), algebra. Prerequisite for graduate study: major in mathematics or at least 28 quarter hours beyond calculus. Recommended: reading knowledge of French, German, or Russian; GRE. 17 professorial staff. 21 master's degrees and 2 Ph.D.'s awarded 1955-59. 52 graduate students registered fall 1959.

Metallurgy. Mineral dressing, production or physical metallurgy. Offered by Department of Metallurgy and Metallurgical Engineering. Prerequisite for graduate study: major in metallurgical or chemical engineering, physics, chemistry, or any science or engineering area specializing in physics and chemistry. 12 professorial staff. 12 master's degrees and 19 Ph.D.'s awarded 1955-59. 28 graduate students registered fall 1959.

Mineralogy. Mineralogy, petrology, geochemistry, chemistry, mathematics, physics, geological engineering, ceramics, metallurgy. Prerequisites for graduate study: calculus; 1 year each of chemistry and physics; geophysics; geology. 3 professorial staff. 3 master's degrees and 7 Ph.D.'s awarded 1955-59. 8 graduate students registered fall 1959. Total enrollment limited to about 8 or 10.

Music. Composition, theory, musicology. 7 professorial staff. 18 master's degrees and 3 Ph.D.'s awarded 1955-59. 14 graduate students registered fall 1959.

Pharmacology. Convulsive disorders and anticonvulsants; brain excitability and drugs; respiration, cough, emesis, fever, and the action of drugs; autonomic drugs; action of drugs on the heart; kidney function and diuretics; drug receptor theory; structure-activity relationship; electrolyte transport mechanisms; spinal cord functions and the actions of drugs. Prerequisites for graduate study: courses in general biology or zoology, inorganic and organic chemistry, quantitative analysis, algebra, and physics. Recommended: German plus French or Russian; GRE; courses in physical chemistry, calculus, analytic geometry, zoology or cellular physiology, and logic. 7 professorial staff. 5 Ph.D.'s awarded 1955-59. 5 graduate students registered fall 1959. New enrollment limited to 4, total enrollment to 12.

Pharmacy. Pharmacy, pharmacology, pharmaceutical chemistry, pharmacognosy, pharmacy administration. Prerequisite for graduate study: major in pharmacy. Recommended: mathematics through calculus. 4 professorial staff. 5 master's degrees and 5 Ph.D.'s awarded 1955-59. 10 graduate students registered fall 1959. Total enrollment limited to 10.

Philosophy. Methodology, epistemology, metaphysics, social philosophy, ethics, logic, aesthetics, philosophy of religion, history of philosophy. Prerequisites for graduate study: comprehensive examination; broad background in humanistic fields. 5 professorial staff. 7 master's degrees awarded 1955-59. 6 graduate students registered fall 1959.

Physics. Solid-state, cosmic ray, or cloud physics; spectroscopy; light diffraction. Prerequisite for graduate study: major in physics. Recommended: at least 1 foreign language. 11 professorial staff. 1 master's degree and 20 Ph.D.'s awarded 1955-59. 47 graduate students registered fall 1959.

Physiology. Neurophysiology, renal physiology. Prerequisites for graduate study: mathematics through differential calculus; organic chemistry; qualitative and quantitative analysis; physics; zoology; comparative anatomy. Recommended: physical chemistry; advanced physics; mathematics. 7 professorial staff. 1 Ph.D. awarded 1955-59. Enrollment limited to about 2.

Political Science. International law, relations, and organization; constitutional law; public administration; comparative government; political theory; political parties and politics. 7 professorial staff. 20 master's degrees and 9 Ph.D.'s awarded 1955-59. 17 graduate students registered fall 1959.

Psychology. Clinical, counseling, general and experimental, physiological and comparative, child and developmental, industrial-personnel, or social psychology; measurement and statistics. Prerequisite for graduate study: competence in written English. Recommended: basic preparation in psychology; French or German. 15 professorial staff. 32 master's degrees and 21 Ph.D.'s awarded 1955-59. 80 graduate students registered fall 1959.

Sociology. Basic theory and methodology, community and societal organization; marriage, family, and kinship; criminology. Prerequisite for graduate study: major in sociology or equivalent. 8 professorial staff. 7 master's degrees and 6 Ph.D.'s awarded 1955-59. 13 graduate students registered fall 1959.

Speech and Theatre Arts. General speech, theatre and ballet, speech science, radio and TV. Prerequisite for graduate study: major in field. Recommended: MAT. 21 professorial staff. 8 Ph.D.'s awarded 1955-59. 35 graduate students registered fall 1959.

Zoology and Entomology. Mammalogy, ornithology, protozoology, nematology, ichthyology, entomology, herpetology, limnology, ecology, parasitology, embryology, conservation, arachnology. Prerequisites for graduate study: GRE Aptitude and Advanced Tests. 21 professorial staff. 33 master's degrees and 4 Ph.D.'s awarded 1955-59. 40 graduate students registered fall 1959.

Vanderbilt University

NASHVILLE 5, TENNESSEE

The Graduate School

Graduate instruction has been part of the program at Vanderbilt since the founding of the university in 1875. First Ph.D. was awarded in 1879. The present Graduate School was established in 1935. University is privately controlled and nonsectarian. Both men and women are admitted.

Affiliations are maintained with the Oak Ridge Institute of Nuclear Studies, the Bill Wilkerson Hearing and Speech Foundation, George Peabody College for Teachers, and the Scarritt College for Christian Workers. The last 2 affiliations are part of a program of cooperation in the service of higher education.

Residence halls maintained for single graduate students; small apartments for married students.

Special facilities include: library of approximately 760,000 volumes; institute of research and training in the social sciences; institute of economic development; Dyer Observatory; Learned Laboratories (a new 9-story structure housing facilities for medical and science research).

Residence requirement for Ph.D.: 3 academic years beyond bachelor's degree, of which a minimum of 1 year must be taken in residence at Vanderbilt (3 years of residence preferred). Summer courses available.

ADMISSION REQUIREMENTS

For graduate study: bachelor's degree; overall average of B and not less than B in courses leading to field of graduate concentration; completion of courses of study approximately equivalent to those required at Vanderbilt; 2 years of 1 foreign language at college level; MAT. Recommended: GRE. For candidacy for Ph.D.: reading knowledge of French and German or approved substitute; written and oral comprehensive qualifying examinations; recommendation of student's advisory committee.

Apply to Graduate School between October 1 and June 1.

FEES AND FIRST-YEAR AID

No application fee. Tuition $750 per academic year. Special fees approximate $100 annually. Room (in residence hall) for men $150-$270 a year; for women $170. Approximate annual cost of board in college dining room $445. Apartments $45-$57 a month.

First-year aid available: scholarships, $500-$2,250; teaching fellowships, $1,000-$2,400; other fellowships, $750-$3,500; research assistantships, $1,000-$3,500; teaching assistantships, $500-$1,500.

Apply to the Graduate School by February 15.

FIELDS OF STUDY FOR THE PH.D.

A course in the nature and history of the American college is open to all graduate students without degree credit. No other courses in the methodology of teaching are provided, but there is strong emphasis on the supervision of teaching assistants.

Anatomy. Histology, neuroanatomy, neurophysiology, hematology. Prerequisites for graduate study: basic courses in biology and physics; general and organic chemistry. Recommended: embryology; comparative anatomy. 3 professorial staff. 4 graduate students registered fall 1959.

Biochemistry. Metabolism, nutrition, physical or irradiation biochemistry, enzymology, bioorganic chemistry, biochemistry of genetics and growth. Prerequisites for graduate study: general, organic, and physical chemistry; qualitative and quantitative analysis; mathematics through calculus; 1 course in physics. 10 professorial staff. 3 master's degrees and 2 Ph.D.'s awarded 1955-59. 11 graduate students registered fall 1959.

Biology. Bacteriology, cellular physiology, entomology, botany, genetics, limnology, microbiology, invertebrate zoology, mycology, plant taxonomy-ecology, plant physiology, theoretical biology, vertebrate taxonomy. Prerequisites for graduate study: major in biology; fundamental work in zoology, botany, and bacteriology. Recommended: chemistry through organic; 1 course in physics. 13 professorial staff. 16 master's degrees and 13 Ph.D.'s awarded 1955-59. 24 graduate students registered fall 1959.

Chemistry. Inorganic, analytical, organic, or physical chemistry; metallurgy; radiochemistry. Prerequisites for graduate study: 1 year each of inorganic, analytical, organic, and physical chemistry (1 year each of calculus and physics or physical chemistry). 9 professorial staff. 22 master's degrees and 23 Ph.D.'s awarded 1955-59. 31 graduate students registered fall 1959.

Comparative Literature. 3 literatures selected from English, French, German, Greek, Latin, Spanish. Combined program offered by Departments of Classics, English, Germanic Languages and Russian, and Romance Languages. Prerequisites for graduate study: German, French, and Latin. 1 Ph.D. awarded 1955-59. 12 graduate students registered fall 1959.

Economics—Business Administration. Economics of agriculture, organization and control of industry, labor and social security, international economics, economic fluctuations or development, public finance, public utilities and transportation, econometrics. Prerequisites for graduate study: major in economics; courses in intermediate economic theory. 21 professorial staff. 46 master's degrees and 7 Ph.D.'s awarded 1955-59. 54 graduate students registered fall 1959.

English. Old or Middle English, Renaissance, Neoclassic, 19th century, American, or Southern literature; 20th century English and American literature; English or American language. Prerequisites for graduate study: major in English; 1 foreign language. 18 professorial staff. 87 master's degrees and 27 Ph.D.'s awarded 1955-59. 68 graduate students registered fall 1959.

German. Germanic philology, older German literature, German literature of the 18th, 19th, or 20th centuries. Offered by Department of Germanic Languages and Russian. Prerequisites for graduate study: major in German; reading knowledge of French. 5 professorial staff. Ph.D. program begun 1959. 2 master's degrees awarded 1955-59. 1 graduate student registered fall 1959.

History. United States, English (especially 17th century), Brazil, modern European (especially diplomatic). Prerequisite for graduate study: major in history. 13 professorial staff. 37 master's degrees and 14 Ph.D.'s awarded 1955-59. 50 graduate students registered fall 1959.

Mathematics. Geometry, abstract algebra, topology, analysis. Prerequisites for graduate study: mathematics through intermediate calculus plus some of the following: differential equations; matrix theory; theory of equations; projective geometry; advanced calculus; introduction to modern algebra. Recommended: French and German. 14 professorial staff. 19 master's degrees and 3 Ph.D.'s awarded 1955-59. 19 graduate students registered fall 1959.

Microbiology. Virology, medical microbiology, immunology. Prerequisites for graduate study: chemistry; physics; bacteriology. Recommended: experience in clinical bacteriology. 4 professorial staff. 2 master's degrees and 2 Ph.D.'s awarded 1955-59. 2 graduate students registered fall 1959.

Pharmacology. Antimetabolites, barbiturates, auricular fibrillation, nucleoproteins, cancer chemotherapy. Prerequisite for graduate study: major in biology or chemistry. Recommended: advanced organic chemistry; mathematics through calculus; physical chemistry. 6 professorial staff. 1 master's degree and 3 Ph.D.'s

awarded 1955-59. 9 graduate students registered fall 1959.

Philosophy. History of philosophy, metaphysics and theory of knowledge, theory of value (ethics, aesthetics, religion, law). 6 professorial staff. Program to be resumed in 1960.

Physics and Astronomy. Nuclear physics or theory, ultrasonics, molecular spectroscopy, astronomy (photoelectric photometry and galactic structure), biophysics, elementary particle physics, theory of elementary particles. Prerequisites for graduate study: 26 hours or more in field; mathematics through differential calculus. Recommended: chemistry; mathematics beyond differential equations. 14 professorial staff. 58 master's degrees and 16 Ph.D.'s awarded 1955-59. 74 graduate students registered fall 1959.

Physiology. Cellular and metabolic problems in physiology. Prerequisite for graduate study: major in biology or chemistry. 5 professorial staff. 4 master's degrees and 2 Ph.D.'s awarded 1955-59. 5 graduate students registered fall 1959.

Political Science. Political theory and methodology, political behavior and organization, international politics, public administration or law, comparative government. Prerequisites for graduate study in a combined program: minor field of 18 hours in other departments, or equivalent course time in 2 or more social sciences relevant to the major. 12 professorial staff. 13 master's degrees and 1 Ph.D. awarded 1955-59. 17 graduate students registered fall 1959.

Psychology. General, experimental, physiological, social, clinical, counseling, or industrial psychology. Prerequisite for graduate study: major in field. Recommended: biology; mathematics; sociology. 12 professorial staff. 21 master's degrees and 15 Ph.D.'s awarded 1955-59. 47 graduate students registered fall 1959.

Religion. Biblical, theological, or historical studies. Combined program offered by Departments of Religion, History, and Philosophy. Prerequisite for graduate study: liberal arts degree. Recommended: B.D. degree or equivalent. 14 professorial staff. 4 master's degrees and 21 Ph.D.'s awarded 1955-59. 48 graduate students registered fall 1959.

Sociology. Social psychology or social organization (especially community), research methods, population and human ecology. Prerequisites for graduate study: elementary social statistics; introduction to field research and to population and human ecology; introductory and advanced social psychology; social organization; cultural anthropology. Recommended: mathematics through calculus. 7 professorial staff. 2 master's degrees and 6 Ph.D.'s awarded 1955-59. 8 graduate students registered fall 1959.

Vermont, University of, and State Agricultural College

BURLINGTON, VERMONT

The Graduate College

Graduate instruction has been offered since before 1883, and first Ph.D. was awarded in 1915. The Graduate College was organized in 1952. Institution is a state-controlled university and land-grant college. Both men and women are admitted.

No residence facilities provided by university; accommodations available in community.

Library contains about 250,000 volumes.

Residence requirement for Ph.D.: minimum of 75 hours graduate study, of which at least 50 must be earned in residence at this institution.

ADMISSION REQUIREMENTS

For graduate study: bachelor's degree; B+ average in major and not less than B— for general average; recommendations; GRE where appropriate. For candidacy for Ph.D.: 1 year of successful graduate study in residence. Knowledge of German and 1 other foreign language required before degree is awarded.

Apply to Dean of The Graduate College by March 15 for fall term.

FEES AND FIRST-YEAR AID

Application fee of $35 is refundable to student on leaving. Tuition for state residents, up to $420; others, up to $1,040. Special fees approximate $30 annually. Rooms in community for single students average $300 annually; board in college dining room $500. Apartments in town average $65-$90 per month.

First-year aid available: 6 fellowships, $500-$2,400 plus tuition; 2 teaching fellowships, $1,800 plus tuition; 4 other fellowships, $2,000-$3,600 plus tuition; 2 research fellowships, $1,800 plus tuition.

Apply to Dean of The Graduate College by March 1 for fall term.

FIELDS OF STUDY FOR THE PH.D.

Courses in the methodology of teaching planned for near future.

Biochemistry. Enzymology, plant biochemistry, nutrition, metabolism, microbiology. Biochemistry is offered in College of Medicine; agricultural biochemistry in College of Agriculture. 13 professorial staff. Ph.D. program initiated 1958. 5 master's degrees awarded 1955-59. 8 graduate students registered fall 1959. New enrollment limited to 6.

Pharmacology. Cardio-vascular physiology and pharmacology, pharmaco-chemistry, histochemistry, the autonomic nervous system, effects of radiation on biological function. 8 professorial staff. Ph.D. program initiated 1959. 3 master's degrees awarded 1955-59. 5 graduate students registered fall 1959. New annual enrollment limited to 4.

Physiology and Biophysics. Cardiac contraction, respiratory control, auditory mechanisms, intercellular clotting mechanisms. 8 professorial staff. Ph.D. program initiated 1960. 3 master's degrees awarded 1955-59. 2 graduate students registered fall 1959. New annual enrollment limited to 4.

Virginia, Medical College of

RICHMOND 19, VIRGINIA

School of Graduate Studies

A program of graduate studies leading to research degrees has been in operation since 1934. First Ph.D. was awarded in 1952. In 1957 the School of Graduate Studies was constituted. Most programs lead to the Ph.D. degree, but a D.Sc. may be awarded to certain candidates. College is publicly controlled by the state. Both men and women are admitted.

Single graduate students live in new student residence hall; married students in 60-apartment Diesel housing unit.

The graduate school program is conducted within the environment of a research-oriented teaching medical center. Library contains approximately 63,000 volumes.

Residence requirement for Ph.D.: minimum of 3 years beyond bachelor's degree. No specific limit is placed on amount of graduate credit which may be transferred. No summer or evening courses available, but graduate students work full 12-month period.

ADMISSION REQUIREMENTS

For graduate study: bachelor's degree or more than its equivalent; satisfactory academic record; 3 letters of recommendation; personal interview. Recommended: GRE. For candidacy for Ph.D.: satisfactory completion of all formal course work; examinations in French and German or approved substitutes; comprehensive qualifying examinations.

Apply to Dean of Graduate Studies at any time.

FEES AND FIRST-YEAR AID

No application fee. Tuition for state residents $200 per year; others $250. Special fees approximate $67 annually. Single room (in dormitory) $450 for 9 months, $500 for 12 months; double room $248 each for 9 months, $261 each for 12 months. Students pay for own meals in college dining room. Apartments $45-$59 per month.

First-year aid available: 1 scholarship, $1,800. Various fellowships and assistantships available in separate departments with stipends ranging from $1,800 to $2,400.

Apply to Dean of Graduate Studies or to chairman of major department at any time.

FIELDS OF STUDY FOR THE PH.D.

No courses in the methodology of teaching are provided, but each graduate student is given actual experience in teaching through teaching students in laboratories and giving special lectures and seminars.

Anatomy. Embryology, neuroanatomy, histochemistry. 12 professorial staff. 3 graduate students registered fall 1959.

Biochemistry. Minor work offered in physiology, bacteriology, physical chemistry, or pharmacology. 7 professorial staff. 3 graduate students registered fall 1959.

Biology. Genetics, biology, statistics. Offered by Department of Biology and Genetics. 2 pro-fessorial staff. 1 graduate student registered fall 1959.

Biophysics. Biophysics, biometry, and statistics. Offered by Department of Biophysics and Biometry. 8 professorial staff. Ph.D. program begun 1957. 3 graduate students registered fall 1959.

Pathology. Minor work offered in anatomy, dental research, physiology, or biochemistry. 8 professorial staff. 1 graduate student registered fall 1959.

Pharmaceutical Chemistry. Minors offered in pharmacology, biochemistry, physical chemistry, or physiology. Offered by Department of Chemistry and Pharmaceutical Chemistry. 2 master's degrees and 3 Ph.D.'s awarded 1955-59. 5 graduate students registered fall 1959.

Pharmacology. Minors offered in biology, biochemistry, or biophysics. 16 professorial staff. 8 Ph.D.'s awarded 1959. 5 graduate students registered fall 1959.

Physiology. Minors offered in biochemistry, biophysics, or pharmacology. 7 professorial staff. 2 master's degrees awarded 1955-59. 3 graduate students registered fall 1959.

Virginia Polytechnic Institute

BLACKSBURG, VIRGINIA

The Graduate School

Graduate instruction was begun about 1882, and the Graduate School was formally organized in 1928. First Ph.D. was conferred in 1942. Institute is publicly controlled by the state. Both men and women are admitted.

Most graduate students find rooms or apartments in community. A limited number of rooms are available for them in college dormitories and in a university club for men.

Special facilities include: library of approximately 252,000 volumes; a 650 computer; Argonaut reactor; agricultural and engineering experiment stations.

Residence requirement for Ph.D.: minimum of 3 academic years of full-time graduate study beyond bachelor's degree, of which 1 (the last) must normally be taken in continuous residence at Virginia Polytechnic Institute. Summer courses available.

ADMISSION REQUIREMENTS

For graduate study: bachelor's degree; approval by a graduate admissions committee, including head of the major department, Director of Admissions, and Director of Graduate Study. Recommended: GRE; previous training in 2 modern foreign languages; letters of recommendation. For candidacy for Ph.D.: approval of study program and thesis outline; qualifying examinations in major and minor fields; reading knowledge of 2 modern foreign languages.

Apply to Director of Graduate Study at least 1 month in advance of date of desired entry.

FEES AND FIRST-YEAR AID

No application fee. Tuition $285 per academic year. Room, board, and laundry $450 per academic year (when available).

First-year aid available: 32 fellowships, $1,350-$2,400 per academic year; 75 assistantships, $145-$175 per month; 72 research assistantships, $145-$190 per month.

Apply to Director of Graduate Study or to department head by March 20.

FIELDS OF STUDY FOR THE PH.D.

No courses in the methodology of teaching are offered at doctoral level, but teaching experience may be obtained through assistantships and instructorships.

Agronomy. Genetics of field crops, crop management, soils. 13 professorial staff. Ph.D. program begun 1959. 5 master's degrees awarded 1955-59. 18 graduate students registered fall 1959.

Bacteriology. Physiology; rumen nutrition and cellulose utilization; soil, dairy, or food bacteriology. Offered by Department of Biology. 3 professorial staff. 8 master's degrees and 6 Ph.D.'s awarded 1955-59. 5 graduate students registered fall 1959.

Biochemistry and Nutrition. Intermediary metabolism, mineral elements in biological systems, isolation of compounds of biological significance from natural sources, microbial nutritional requirements of animals. Recommended for graduate study: physical chemistry and calculus. 7 professorial staff. Program begun 1959. 23 graduate students registered fall 1959. New enrollment limited to approximately 10.

Botany. Mycology (especially water fungi), taxonomy (especially Virginia flora), plant physiology (cooperative with another department). Offered by Department of Biology. 3 professorial staff. 8 master's degrees and 6 Ph.D.'s awarded 1955-59. 5 graduate students registered fall 1959.

Chemistry. Analytical, inorganic, nuclear, organic, or physical chemistry; polymers. 10 professorial staff. 23 master's degrees and 9 Ph.D.'s awarded 1955-59. 21 graduate students registered fall 1959.

Economics.—Agricultural. Farm management; production economics; economic theory; agricultural marketing, policy, or credit; land economics; econometrics; international trade. Offered by Department of Agricultural Economics and Rural Sociology. 14 professorial staff. 12 master's degrees awarded 1955-59. 5 graduate students registered fall 1959.

Engineering. — Aeronautical. Aerodynamics, mechanics of space flight, aeroelasticity, missile dynamics, energy systems for space operations, magnetoaerodynamics. 4 professorial staff. Ph.D. program begun 1959. 12 master's degrees awarded 1955-59. 16 graduate students registered fall 1959.

Engineering.—Chemical. Electrochemical processing, mass and heat transfer, instrumentation and control, waste treatment and utilization on ultrasonics molecular distillation, process design. 4 professorial staff. 33 master's degrees and 14 Ph.D.'s awarded 1955-59. 21 graduate students registered fall 1959.

Engineering Mechanics—Applied Mechanics. Mechanics of solids and fluids, vibration, dynamics, stress analysis, engineering materials. Offered by Department of Engineering Mechanics. 7 professorial staff. 36 master's degrees and 5 Ph.D.'s awarded 1955-59. 27 graduate students registered fall 1959.

Engineering.—Sanitary. Water pollution control, water treatment, water supply development. Combined program offered by Departments of Civil Engineering, Chemical Engineering, and Biology. 8 professorial staff. 10 master's degrees awarded 1955-59. 2 graduate students registered fall 1959.

Entomology. Physiology and biochemistry of insects; biology and ecology of insects; external parasites and transmission of arthropod-borne diseases; toxicology of insecticides; biology, morphology, and genetics of resistance; taxonomy of selected groups of arthropods. 9 professorial staff. 6 master's degrees and 2 Ph.D.'s awarded 1955-59. 8 graduate students registered fall 1959.

Genetics. Cytogenetics, physiological genetics. Offered by Department of Biology. 1 professor (plus those in other departments). 8 master's degrees and 6 Ph.D.'s awarded 1955-59. 5 graduate students registered fall 1959.

Geological Sciences. Stratigraphy, structural or economic geology, petrology, paleontology, geophysics, geochemistry. Recommended for graduate study: scores on U.S. Geological Survey Civil Service Test. 8 professorial staff. 14 master's degrees and 6 Ph.D.'s awarded 1955-59. 23 graduate students registered fall 1959. Total enrollment limited to 35.

Horticulture and Food Technology. Plant physiology as applied to horticultural crops, soil and irrigation, fertilization and plant nutrition, post-harvest physiology of fruits and vegetables, fruit and vegetable crop breeding and cytological studies, food technology and processing of fruits and vegetables. 10 professorial staff. Ph.D. program begun 1959. 12 master's degrees awarded 1955-59. 7 graduate students registered fall 1959.

Mathematics. Applied mathematics, topology, functional analysis. 7 professorial staff. Program begun 1959. 11 graduate students registered fall 1959.

Physics. Solid-state or nuclear physics. 10 professorial staff. Ph.D. program begun 1956. 20 master's degrees awarded 1955-59. 39 graduate students registered fall 1959.

Statistics. Inference, stochastic processes, design of experiments, multivariate analysis, linear programming, nonparametric statistics, biometrics. Recommended for graduate study: advanced calculus; matrix algebra. 8 professorial staff. 50 master's degrees and 19 Ph.D.'s awarded 1955-59. 37 graduate students registered fall 1959.

Wildlife Management. Forestry, vertebrate natural history, basic land management, biological sciences. Combined program offered by Departments of Forestry and Wildlife and Biology. 14 professorial staff. 7 master's degrees and 3 Ph.D.'s awarded 1955-59. 10 graduate students registered fall 1959.

Zoology. Invertebrate zoology, ichthyology, limnology. Offered by Department of Biology. 4 professorial staff. 8 master's degrees and 6 Ph.D.'s awarded 1955-59. 5 graduate students registered fall 1959.

Virginia, University of
CHARLOTTESVILLE, VIRGINIA

Graduate School of Arts and Sciences

First post-graduate department was instituted in 1859. Programs leading to the Ph.D. were begun in 1880, and the first such degree was awarded in 1885. Other doctoral degrees now conferred are: Ed.D. (School of Education); J.S.D. (School of Law); D.Sc. (School of Engineering). The university is publicly controlled by the state. Both men and women are admitted.

Residence halls maintained for single graduate students; temporary housing available for married students, and new apartments are being planned.

Special facilities include: library of approximately 926,000 volumes; art museum; observatory; institute for political economy; Thomas Jefferson Institute in History; Mountain Lake Biological Station; Blandy Experimental Farm (with facilities for nuclear radiation of plants); 2 Van de Graaff generators; solid-state physics laboratory; nuclear reactor.

Residence requirement for Ph.D.: at least 3 sessions (6 semesters) of full-time graduate study, of which 2 sessions must be taken in residence at the University of Virginia. Summer sessions (at the master's level only) are available.

ADMISSION REQUIREMENTS

For graduate study: bachelor's degree; GPA of B for last 2 undergraduate sessions; favorable recommendation of departmental chairman; adequate preparation in field of proposed graduate study (academic credits must have been earned within 10 years of application). Recommended: reading knowledge of French and German; GRE Verbal, Quantitative, and Advanced Subject Tests. For candidacy for Ph.D.: completion of substantial portion of course work; reading knowledge of French and German. Preliminary examinations may be required by individual departments.

Apply to Dean of the Graduate School, Box 3025 University Station, Charlottesville, Virginia, by August 1.

FEES AND FIRST-YEAR AID

No application fee. Tuition for state residents $270 per academic year; others $540. Special fees total $74 per year. Room (in dormitory) for men $200-$285 per academic year; for women $225-$275. Approximate annual cost of board in college dining room $600. Apartments $36.50-$44 per month.

First-year aid available: 12-15 scholarships, $250-$1,000; 90 half-time teaching fellowships, $1,400-$1,900; 45 other fellowships, $1,200-$1,500 plus tuition; 10 research assistantships, $1,500-$1,800. There are also a limited number of special fellowships with stipends up to $2,500.

For fellowships, apply to Dean of the Graduate School by February 28; for teaching fellowships apply to chairman of appropriate department.

FIELDS OF STUDY FOR THE PH.D.

No programs in the methodology of teaching are offered, but informal instruction is provided by faculty members of the department.

Anatomy. Gross anatomy, neuroanatomy. Prerequisites for graduate study: thorough grounding in general biology; basic work in chemistry. Recommended: mathematics; psychology; physics. 5 professorial staff. Ph.D. program begun 1955.

Astronomy. Celestial mechanics, astrophysics, spectroscopy. Prerequisite for graduate study: background in mathematics and physics. 3 professorial staff. 1 master's degree and 2 Ph.D.'s awarded 1955-59. 2 graduate students registered fall 1959.

Biochemistry. Prerequisite for graduate study: thorough grounding in chemistry, biology, physics, and mathematics. 4 professorial staff. Ph.D. program begun 1955. 2 graduate students registered fall 1959.

Biology. Biology, botany, zoology, genetics, radiation biology, parasitology. Prerequisite for graduate study: major in biology, chemistry, geology, or physics. 10 professorial staff. 24 master's degrees and 16 Ph.D.'s awarded 1955-59. 21 graduate students registered fall 1959.

Chemistry. Analytical, organic, physical-organic (solid-state), or theoretical physics. Prerequisite for graduate study: major in chemistry with background in organic, inorganic, and analytical chemistry. 14 professorial staff. 37 master's degrees and 18 Ph.D.'s awarded 1955-59. 42 graduate students registered fall 1959.

Classics. Greek or Latin language and literature; paleography, especially of medieval manuscripts. Prerequisites for graduate study: major in classics (12 hours of specified courses are required for Greek and Latin). 3 professorial staff. 1 Ph.D. awarded 1955-59. 2 graduate students registered fall 1959.

Economics. Economic or monetary theory, accounting, international or resource economics, economic growth, public finance, political economy. Prerequisite for graduate study: background courses in economics, commerce, and political science. Recommended: calculus. 11 professorial staff. 21 master's degrees and 18 Ph.D.'s awarded 1955-59. 38 graduate students registered fall 1959.

Education. Curricula and administration in elementary, secondary, and junior college levels; correction of speech, hearing, and reading difficulties; education of gifted children and mentally retarded; guidance and counseling; tests and measurement, music education. Offered by School of Education and Graduate School of Arts and Sciences. Prerequisites for graduate study: major in education; background in psychology. 25 professorial staff. 39 master's degrees and 4 Ph.D.'s awarded 1955-59. 3 graduate students registered fall 1959. Ed.D. degree also awarded in this field.

Engineering. — Chemical. Thermodynamics, catalysis, petroleum refining, diffusional processes, absorption and extraction. Prerequisite for graduate study: major in chemistry or chemical engineering. 10 professorial staff. Ph.D. program begun 1956. 12 master's degrees awarded 1955-59. 9 graduate students registered fall 1959.

Engineering.—Electrical. Power system analysis and operation, microwave and radiation engineering, electrical network synthesis, servomechanisms, transistors, electromagnetic field theory. Prerequisite for graduate study: major in physics or electrical engineering with minor in mathematics. 10 professorial staff. Ph.D. program begun 1958. 11 master's degrees awarded 1955-59. 24 graduate students registered fall 1959.

Engineering.—Nuclear. Nuclear reactors, biological effects of radiations. Prerequisite for graduate study: thorough background in biology, chemistry, physics, and mathematics. 8 professorial staff. Ph.D. program begun 1958. 1 master's degree awarded 1955-59. 15 graduate students registered fall 1959.

Engineering Physics. Nuclear and atomic engineering. Combined program offered by School of Engineering and Department of Physics. Prerequisite for graduate study: major in physics or engineering physics, with minor in mathematics. 6 professorial staff. Ph.D. program begun 1955. 1 master's degree awarded 1955-59. 9 graduate students registered fall 1959.

English. English and American literature, criticism, bibliographical studies, Old and Middle English; certain courses in rhetoric, Gothic, and Icelandic. Prerequisites for graduate study: minimum of 30 semester hours of English; some Latin. 12 professorial staff. 41 master's degrees and 7 Ph.D.'s awarded 1955-59. 31 graduate students registered fall 1959.

Foreign Affairs—International Relations. International law and organization; diplomatic history; area studies (United States, Western Europe, Soviet Union and Eastern Europe, Latin America, South Asia, Africa). Offered by Department of Foreign Affairs. Prerequisites for graduate study: background in economics and commerce, history, political science, sociology, anthropology, or in most of these; major language in field of area study. 12 professorial staff. Ph.D. program begun 1959. 48 master's degrees awarded 1955-59. 26 graduate students registered fall 1959.

History. Medieval and modern European history, Soviet and Eastern Europe, South Asia, United States, Central and South America. Prerequisite for graduate study: major in history, with some background in economics and political science. 11 professorial staff. 29 master's degrees and 17 Ph.D.'s awarded 1955-59. 50 graduate students registered fall 1959.

Mathematics. Topology. Prerequisite for graduate study: major in mathematics. Recommended: reading knowledge of Russian. 9 professorial staff. 17 master's degrees and 8 Ph.D.'s awarded 1955-59. 20 graduate students registered fall 1959.

Microbiology. Physiology of bacteria, viruses and rickettsiae, immunology. Prerequisite for graduate study: thorough background in biology and chemistry. 4 professorial staff. Program begun 1955. 6 graduate students registered fall 1959.

Pharmacology. Prerequisite for graduate study: general background in biology and chemistry. Recommended: basic physics. 3 professorial staff. Ph.D. program begun 1955. 1 Ph.D. awarded 1955-59.

Philosophy. Classic systems in the history of philosophy, metaphysics, epistemology, logic, ethics, philosophical analysis, philosophy of science. Prerequisite for graduate study: major in field. 6 professorial staff. 14 master's degrees and 7 Ph.D.'s awarded 1955-59. 14 graduate students registered fall 1959.

Physics. Nuclear or solid-state physics. Prerequisites for graduate study: major in physics; mathematics through calculus. 11 professorial staff. 57 master's degrees and 35 Ph.D.'s awarded 1955-59. 65 graduate students registered fall 1959.

Physiology. Prerequisite for graduate study: thorough grounding in biology, chemistry, and physics. 4 professorial staff. Program begun 1955.

Political Science. American or comparative government, public law or administration, political theory, American political party system. Prerequisite for graduate study: major in field with background in history and economics. 7 professorial staff. 1 master's degree and 4 Ph.D.'s awarded 1955-59. 10 graduate students registered fall 1959.

Psychology. Experimental psychology with emphasis on learning; animal behavior; the senses; physiological psychology. Prerequisite for graduate study: major in field with basic work in biology, chemistry, and physics. 8 professorial staff. 9 master's degrees and 8 Ph.D.'s awarded 1955-59. 12 graduate students registered fall 1959.

Romance Languages. French, Spanish, Portuguese, and Italian languages and literatures; philology of Romance languages. Prerequisites for graduate study: major in language of the special field; basic work in 1 or more related languages. 11 professorial staff. 3 Ph.D.'s awarded 1955-59. 13 graduate students registered fall 1959.

Washington State University

PULLMAN, WASHINGTON

The Graduate School

University began offering graduate instruction early in the present century, but The Graduate School was not organized until 1922. The first Ph.D. was awarded in 1929. At present Ph.D. programs are offered in a number of fields, and the Ed.D. degree is also conferred through The

Graduate School. University is publicly controlled by the state. Both men and women are admitted.

Graduate dormitories are provided for single graduate students; university-owned apartments for married students.

Special facilities include: agricultural experiment station; division of industrial research; computer center; bureau of economics and business research. Library contains approximately 650,000 volumes.

Residence requirement for Ph.D.: 3 years beyond bachelor's degree, of which 32 semester hours must be completed in residence on campus prior to preliminary examination. Summer courses available.

ADMISSION REQUIREMENTS

For graduate study: bachelor's degree; superior academic record; qualifying examinations in some departments. For candidacy for Ph.D.: completion of 32 semester hours of graduate work in residence; satisfaction of language requirement; 2 examinations prior to preliminary examination; general preliminary examination.

Apply to Dean, The Graduate School, at least one month prior to date of desired entry. Foreign students must apply at least six months in advance.

FEES AND FIRST-YEAR AID

No application fee. Tuition for state residents $60 per year; others $200. Incidental fees $153 per year for state residents; $300 for others. Room (in dormitory) $300 a year. Approximate annual cost of board in college dining room $420. Apartments $37-$85 per month.

First-year aid available: teaching assistantships, $2,000; fellowships, $1,500-$2,400; research assistantships, $2,000.

Apply to Dean, The Graduate School, by March 15.

FIELDS OF STUDY FOR THE PH.D.

Agronomy. Farm crops and soil science. Prerequisites for graduate study: for emphasis on crops, general physics and plant physiology, mathematics, organic chemistry, genetics, soils, and agronomy; for emphasis on soils, general microbiology, plant physiology, mathematics, geology, soils, chemistry, physics, agronomy, and forestry or horticulture. Ph.D. candidacy prerequisites: French or Spanish (either but not both) and German or Russian. 21 professorial

staff. 21 Ph.D.'s awarded 1955-59. 30 graduate students registered fall 1959.

Animal Science. Animal nutrition, applied genetics, dairy manufacturing. Combined program offered by Departments of Animal Science, Dairy Science, and Poultry Science. Prerequisites for graduate study: courses in general agriculture, nutrition and/or genetics, general zoology, quantitative analysis, organic chemistry, and mathematics. Ph.D. candidacy prerequisites: French or Spanish (either but not both) and German or Swedish. 19 professorial staff. 7 Ph.D.'s awarded 1955-59. 8 graduate students registered fall 1959.

Bacteriology. Medical bacteriology in selected areas. Prerequisites for graduate study: general microbiology; medical bacteriology and epidemiology; quantitative analysis; organic chemistry; introductory botany; introductory zoology. Ph.D. candidacy prerequisites: 2 foreign languages (French, German, Russian). 3 professorial staff. 15 master's degrees and 5 Ph.D.'s awarded 1955-59. 15 graduate students registered fall 1959.

Botany. Plant physiology, genetics, systematic botany, ecology. Prerequisites for graduate study: general and systematic botany; plant physiology; organic chemistry; microtechnique; genetics. Ph.D. candidacy prerequisites: French or Spanish (either but not both) and German or Swedish. 6 professorial staff. 6 master's degrees and 12 Ph.D.'s awarded 1955-59. 16 graduate students registered fall 1959.

Chemistry. Physical and inorganic chemistry, and biochemistry. Prerequisites for graduate study: 40 semester hours in chemistry, including inorganic, qualitative, quantitative, organic, and physical chemistry; 8 hours of physics; mathematics through calculus; reading knowledge of scientific German or French. Ph.D. candidacy prerequisites: 2 foreign languages (French, German, Russian). 18 professorial staff. 17 master's degrees and 23 Ph.D.'s awarded 1955-59. 38 graduate students registered fall 1959.

Economics.—Agricultural. Farm and ranch management, agricultural business and marketing. Prerequisites for graduate study: economics through economic theory; 15-18 semester hours of agricultural economics; statistics and accounting; 15 semester hours of general agriculture. Ph.D. candidacy prerequisites. French or Spanish (either but not both) and German or Russian. 9 professorial staff. 7 master's degrees awarded 1955-59. 4 graduate students registered fall 1959.

Economics.—General. Business cycles, labor, transportation, government and business. Prerequisites for graduate study: money and banking; business fluctuations; federal, state, and local finance; taxation; 15 semester hours in approved electives. Ph.D. candidacy prerequisites: French or Spanish (either but not both) and German or Russian. 10 professorial staff. Ph.D. program begun 1958. 5 master's degrees awarded 1955-59. 14 graduate students registered fall 1959.

Education. Educational administration and curriculum. Prerequisites for graduate study: requirements leading to certification; teaching experience. Ph.D. candidacy prerequisites: French or Spanish (either but not both) and German or Swedish. 11 professorial staff. 125 master's degrees and 6 Ph.D.'s awarded 1955-59. 62 graduate students registered fall 1959. The Ed.D. degree is also awarded.

Entomology. Systematic and economic entomology. Offered by Department of Zoology. Prerequisites for graduate study: systematic biology; introductory entomology; organic chemistry. Ph.D. candidacy prerequisites: 2 foreign languages (French, German, Russian). 8 professorial staff. 7 master's degrees and 7 Ph.D.'s awarded 1955-59. 7 graduate students registered fall 1959.

Food Technology. Microbiology and processing of foods. Combined program offered by Departments of Animal Science, Poultry Science, Foods and Nutrition, Dairy Science, and Horticulture. Prerequisites for graduate study: general and organic chemistry; quantitative analysis; general microbiology; mathematics; physics. Ph.D. candidacy prerequisites: French or Spanish (either but not both) and German or Swedish. 12 professorial staff. 2 master's degrees and 4 Ph.D.'s awarded 1955-59. 8 graduate students registered fall 1959.

Genetics. Fundamental genetics, applied plant and animal genetics. Combined program offered by the Departments of Agronomy, Animal Science, Botany, Chemistry, Dairy Science, Horticulture, Poultry Science, and Zoology. Prerequisites for graduate study: botany or zoology; genetics; 2 semesters of general chemistry; 1 semester of organic chemistry; 1 semester of physics. Ph.D. candidacy prerequisites: French or Spanish (either but not both) and German or Russian. 10 professorial staff. 2 Ph.D.'s awarded 1955-59. 3 graduate students registered fall 1959.

Geology. Stratigraphy and mineralogy. Prerequisites for graduate study: general geology through historical geology; field methods and structures; 1 year each of chemistry, mathematics, and physics. Ph.D. candidacy prerequisites: 2 languages selected from French, German or Swedish (either but not both), Russian. 3 professorial staff. 9 master's degrees and 2 Ph.D.'s awarded 1955-59. 13 graduate students registered fall 1959.

History. American, Northwest, and European history. Prerequisites for graduate study: basic training in European, English, and American history; related background in literature and social studies. Ph.D. candidacy prerequisites: French or Spanish (either but not both) and German. 6 professorial staff. 12 master's degrees and 3 Ph.D.'s awarded 1955-59. 10 graduate students registered fall 1959.

Horticulture. Pomology. Prerequisites for graduate study: plant physiology; general bacteriology; organic chemistry; quantitative analysis; fruit insects. Ph.D. candidacy prerequisites: French or Spanish (either but not both) and German. 15 professorial staff. 5 Ph.D.'s awarded 1955-59. 7 graduate students registered fall 1959.

Mathematics. Algebra, analysis, geometry, topology, statistics, and applied mathematics. Prerequisites for graduate study: 12 semester hours beyond calculus. Ph.D. candidacy prerequisites: 2 languages (French, German, Russian). 12 professorial staff. 6 master's degrees awarded 1955-59. 17 graduate students registered fall 1959.

Pharmacy. Pharmaceutical chemistry and pharmacy. Prerequisite for graduate study: B.S. in pharmacy. Ph.D. candidacy prerequisites: French and German. 6 professorial staff. 3 master's degrees and 1 Ph.D. awarded 1955-59. 7 graduate students registered fall 1959.

Physical Education. Experimental physical education. Prerequisites for graduate study: not less than 30 semester hours of physical education, including kinesiology, tests and measurements, general microbiology, and human physiology. Ph.D. candidacy prerequisites: 2 languages selected from French, German or Swedish (either but not both), Russian. 7 professorial staff. Ph.D. program begun 1957. 70 master's degrees awarded 1955-59. 20 graduate students registered fall 1959.

Physics. Experimental work, theoretical physics, biophysics. Prerequisites for graduate study:

general and atomic physics; mechanics; heat and thermodynamics; electricity and magnetism; optics; differential equations; chemistry. Ph.D. candidacy prerequisites: 2 languages (French, German, Russian). 4 professorial staff. 6 master's degrees and 6 Ph.D.'s awarded 1955-59. 13 graduate students registered fall 1959.

Plant Pathology. Mycology. Prerequisites for graduate study: course in plant science; 1 year each of inorganic chemistry, elementary botany, elementary zoology, physics, and German; 1 semester each of bacteriology, plant physiology, systematic botany, general plant pathology, entomology, college algebra, organic chemistry, and report writing or advanced composition. Ph.D. candidacy prerequisites: 2 languages selected from French, Italian or Spanish (either but not both), German. 16 professorial staff. 7 Ph.D.'s awarded 1955-59. 14 graduate students registered fall 1959.

Political Science. Public administration and political theory. Prerequisites for graduate study: 12 semester hours of political science; strong preparation in other social studies. Ph.D. candidacy prerequisites: French or Spanish (either but not both) and German or Russian. 5 professorial staff. 4 master's degrees awarded 1955-59. 4 graduate students registered fall 1959.

Psychology. Experimental, clinical, and general psychology. Prerequisites for graduate study: minimum of 18 semester hours of psychology, including 3 hours in statistics and a course in experimental psychology. Ph.D. candidacy prerequisites: 2 languages selected from French, German or Swedish (either but not both), Russian. 8 professorial staff. 23 master's degrees and 8 Ph.D.'s awarded 1955-59. 41 graduate students registered fall 1959.

Sociology. General and rural sociology, social statistics. Prerequisites for graduate study: not less than 18 semester hours in sociology, including elementary social statistics. Ph.D. candidacy prerequisites: French or Spanish (either but not both) and German or Swedish. 15 professorial staff. 12 master's degrees and 6 Ph.D.'s awarded 1955-59. 16 graduate students registered fall 1959.

Veterinary Science. Veterinary microbiology and pathology. Offered by College of Veterinary Medicine. Prerequisites for graduate study: organic chemistry; general physics; comparative vertebrate anatomy; comparative physiology. Ph.D. candidacy prerequisites: French or Spanish

(either but not both) and German or Russian. 13 professorial staff. Ph.D. program begun 1957. 3 master's degrees awarded 1955-59. 7 graduate students registered fall 1959.

Zoology. Experimental embryology, systematic zoology, zoophysiology. Prerequisites for graduate study: general zoology; systematic biology or histology; embryology; organic chemistry; elementary mathematics. Ph.D. candidacy prerequisites: 2 languages (French, German, Russian). 10 professorial staff. 5 master's degrees and 7 Ph.D.'s awarded 1955-59. 29 graduate students registered fall 1959.

Washington University

ST. LOUIS 30, MISSOURI

Graduate School of Arts and Sciences

The Graduate School of Arts and Sciences was established about 1898 to administer the graduate work leading to the degrees of Master of Arts and Doctor of Philosophy. The first Ph.D. was awarded in 1911. Other doctoral degrees conferred include: D.Sc. (Sever Institute of Technology); D.S.W. (George Warren Brown School of Social Work); Ed.D. (Graduate School of Arts and Sciences through the Graduate Institute of Education); D.B.A. (School of Business Administration). The university is privately controlled and nonsectarian. Both men and women are admitted.

Programs leading to the Ph.D. are offered in conjunction with the Central Institute for the Deaf and with the following divisions of Washington University: School of Business Administration; School of Medicine; Sever Institute of Technology (graduate engineering).

Rooms in university dormitories available for single graduate students; no residence facilities for married students. New residence halls for men and women are being planned.

Special facilities include: Ridgley Library with many notable collections; special libraries and school libraries; John M. Olin Library ('under construction'); Washington University art collection; Wulfing coin collection; photographic and other materials from Washington University excavations in Greece; collection of photographs of works of art of the 15th and 16th centuries; radiological institute; the Oscar Johnson Institute; electronic analog computer; electronic 650 digital computer; complete statistical facilities for social science and other research; facilities for research in radiochemistry, nuclear and paramagnetic resonance, optical spectroscopy, beta and gamma spectroscopy, X-ray crystallography, low-temperature studies, physical electronics, nuclear reactions, cyclotron, betatron, cosmic ray, cloud chamber and emulsions, and theoretical physics; laboratory facilities for X-ray diffraction, spectrography, differential thermal analysis, and geophysical equipment.

Residence requirement for Ph.D.: 3 years beyond bachelor's degree, with at least 1 year in residence at Washington University. Summer and evening courses available.

ADMISSION REQUIREMENTS

For graduate study: bachelor's degree; B average in undergraduate work; recommendation of major department. Recommended: proficiency in 2 modern foreign languages. For candidacy for Ph.D.: evidence of superior academic achievement; qualifying examinations.

Apply to Dean of the Graduate School of Arts and Sciences by September 7 for fall term; by January 15 for spring term; by June 1 for summer school.

FEES AND FIRST-YEAR AID

No application fee. Tuition $750 per academic year. Room (in dormitory) for men $300 per academic year; room and board for women $650-$800. Approximate annual cost of board in college dining room $450.

First-year aid available: tuition scholarships; teaching fellowships and research assistantships, $690-$2,500; other fellowships, $450-$2,500. Traineeships are available in psychology, sociology, and molecular biology.

Apply to appropriate department for assistantships, to Dean of the Graduate School for other types of aid. Applications should be received by March 1.

FIELDS OF STUDY FOR THE PH.D.

Various departments have programs designed to increase the effectiveness of the doctoral candidate as a college teacher. Sometimes these are informal programs; in other cases they are special courses in methodology.

Anatomy. Prerequisite for graduate study: adequate foundation in comparative anatomy, embryology, and general physiology. 13 professorial staff. 1 master's degree and 4 Ph.D.'s awarded 1955-59.

Art and Archaeology. Greek and Roman art and archaeology; Renaissance, modern and contemporary, or Far Eastern art. Prerequisites for graduate study: minimum of 18 units in art and archaeology. Recommended: 2 or more courses in European and American history. 4 professorial staff. 4 master's degrees and 1 Ph.D. awarded 1955-59. 11 graduate students registered fall 1959.

Audiology. Physical and architectural acoustics, electro- or psycho-acoustics, auditory biophysics, neurophysiology of audition, education of the deaf, speech and phonetics. Combined program offered by Departments of Anatomy, Education, Electrical Engineering, Psychiatry and Neurology, Otolaryngology, Physiology, Psychology, and Zoology. Prerequisites for graduate study: at least elementary courses in biology, physics, psychology, and mathematics. Recommended for auditory biophysics or neurophysiology students: knowledge of the principles of inorganic and organic chemistry, including practice in the elements of volumetric analysis. 9 professorial staff. 4 master's degrees awarded 1955-59. 2 graduate students registered fall 1959.

Biochemistry. Intermediary metabolism and related problems, mechanism of enzyme action, hormonal regulation of enzyme activity. Offered by Department of Biological Chemistry. Prerequisites for graduate study: general, analytical, organic, and physical chemistry; physics. 6 professorial staff. 2 Ph.D.'s awarded 1955-59. 3 graduate students registered fall 1959.

Biology.—Molecular. Physical, chemical, and biological analysis of cellular constituents, of inheritance, growth, and differentiation processes, and of metabolism as related to higher plants and animals, microorganisms, and viruses. Combined program offered by Departments of Botany, Chemistry, Physics, and Zoology. Prerequisite for graduate study: major in biology, chemistry, or physics. 10 professorial staff. Program begun 1959. 6 graduate students registered fall 1959.

Botany Taxonomy, physiology, genetics, mycology, economic botany, paleobotany. Offered by Henry Shaw School of Botany. 11 professorial staff. 13 master's degrees and 13 Ph.D.'s awarded

1955-59. 14 graduate students registered fall 1959.

Business Administration. Accounting, finance, marketing, personnel, production. Offered by School of Business Administration. Prerequisites for graduate study: 18 units in business administration and economics; ETS Admission Test for Graduate Study in Business; 6 hours of graduate-level statistics or qualifying examination in this field. 20 professorial staff. 1 graduate student registered fall 1959.

Chemistry. Inorganic, analytical, organic, or physical chemistry; radiochemistry; nuclear and paramagnetic resonance; spectroscopy; X-ray crystallography; low-temperature studies. Prerequisites for graduate study: minimum of 24 units in organic, analytical, physical, and inorganic chemistry; 6 units of physics; mathematics through integral calculus. 11 professorial staff. 13 master's degrees and 31 Ph.D.'s awarded 1955-59. 42 graduate students registered fall 1959.

Classics. Greek and Latin languages and literatures; linguistics; ancient archaeology, history, and philosophy. Prerequisite for graduate study: major in Greek or Latin or equivalent. 5 professorial staff. 4 master's degrees and 1 Ph.D. awarded 1955-59. 1 graduate student registered fall 1959.

Economics. International or labor economics, regional economic development. Prerequisite for graduate study: foundation in economic theory, history of economics, and statistical inference. 8 professorial staff. 13 master's degrees and 1 Ph.D. awarded 1955-59. 18 graduate students registered fall 1959.

Education. Offered by Graduate Institute of Education. Prerequisite for graduate study: MAT. 16 professorial staff. 374 master's degrees and 26 Ph.D.'s awarded 1955-59. 313 graduate students registered fall 1959.

Engineering.—Electrical. Networks and electro-mechanics; servomechanisms and electrical power transmission; servomechanisms and electrical machinery; electronics; electro-acoustics; electronics-communications. Prerequisite for graduate study: good background in mathematics and physics. 5 professorial staff. 3 graduate students registered fall 1959.

English. Conventional areas in English and American literature. Prerequisite for graduate study: 24 hours of upperclass courses in English and American literature. 18 professorial staff. 27

master's degrees and 5 Ph.D.'s awarded 1955-59. 40 graduate students registered fall 1959.

Geology. Geochemistry, geomorphology, geophysics, clay mineralogy, micropaleontology, engineering geology, petrogenesis and mineral deposits. Offered by Department of Geology and Geological Engineering. Prerequisites for graduate study: minimum of 18 hours in geology; chemistry through quantitative analysis; mathematics through calculus; physics. 10 professorial staff. 30 master's degrees and 6 Ph.D.'s awarded 1955-59. 20 graduate students registered fall 1959.

German. Prerequisites for graduate study: 18 units in German, including introduction to German literature. 5 professorial staff. 1 master's degree and 1 Ph.D. awarded 1955-59. 5 graduate students registered fall 1959.

History. American: Western, recent, the South, intellectual. European: institutional and social history of 17th and 18th centuries. English: modern. Prerequisite for graduate study: minimum of 18 units in history. 8 professorial staff. 17 master's degrees awarded 1955-59. 28 graduate students registered fall 1959.

Mathematics. Topics in algebra and analysis, theory and practice of operation of electronic computer. Prerequisite for graduate study: thorough basic preparation in field. 16 professorial staff. 3 master's degrees and 2 Ph.D.'s awarded 1955-59. 35 graduate students registered fall 1959.

Music. History and literature of music; analysis of harmony, form, style and orchestration; written harmony and counterpoint. Prerequisites for graduate study: strong background in music, with performance ability in at least 1 medium at advanced level. 12 professorial staff. Ph.D. program begun 1957. 24 master's degrees awarded 1955-59. 41 graduate students registered fall 1959.

Pathology. Experimental pathology. Prerequisites for graduate study: courses in histology, anatomy, biological chemistry, bacteriology, and physiology. 7 professorial staff. 1 Ph.D. awarded 1955-59. 4 graduate students registered fall 1959.

Pharmacology. Prerequisite for graduate study: strong background in biological chemistry and physiology. 7 professorial staff. 3 Ph.D.'s awarded 1955-59. 10 graduate students registered fall 1959.

Philosophy. Logic and philosophy of science; history of philosophy, ethics, social philosophy, aesthetics, philosophy of religion, and theory of value; metaphysics and theory of knowledge. Prerequisites for graduate study: courses in logic, ethics, history of philosophy, and other preparation in field; broad background in liberal arts and sciences. 6 professorial staff. 5 master's degrees awarded 1955-59. 8 graduate students registered fall 1959.

Physics. Nuclear, solid-state, low-temperature, and theoretical physics; cosmic rays and high-energy particles; nuclear and electronic magnetic resonance; physical electronics; beta and gamma spectroscopy. Prerequisites for graduate study: 4 years each of physics and mathematics; 2 to 3 years of chemistry. 16 professorial staff. 10 master's degrees and 31 Ph.D.'s awarded 1955-59. 44 graduate students registered fall 1959.

Physiology. Electrical manifestations of nerve and muscle; physical properties of muscle; respiration; kidney. Offered by Department of Physiology, School of Medicine. Prerequisite for graduate study: training in physics, general and organic chemistry, general biology, and physical and biological chemistry. 8 professorial staff. 4 graduate students registered fall 1959.

Political Science. All major branches of political science. Prerequisite for graduate study: strong background in political science and the social sciences. 8 professorial staff. 12 master's degrees and 3 Ph.D.'s awarded 1955-59. 16 graduate students registered fall 1959.

Psychology. General experimental (including physiological and comparative) and clinical psychology; gerontological or industrial psychology; psychological aspects of mental retardation. Prerequisite for graduate study: strong background in field. 16 professorial staff. 15 master's degrees and 28 Ph.D.'s awarded 1955-59. 78 graduate students registered fall 1959.

Romance Languages. French: medieval literature and linguistics; Renaissance; 17th century classicism; 19th century realism, naturalism, and symbolism; contemporary literature. Spanish: Golden Age of drama and Cervantes; 19th century novelists; contemporary literature. Prerequisites for graduate study: 12 units in advanced courses in the language chosen, including general introduction to its literature. 7 professorial staff. 17 master's degrees and 1 Ph.D. awarded 1955-59. 6 graduate students registered fall 1959.

Sociology and Anthropology. Community organization, urban or industrial sociology, ecology and demography, culture and personality, cul-

tural change and economic development, general theory, comparative institutions (especially Far East, Africa, Latin America, and U.S.), research methods, administrative behavior. Prerequisite for graduate study: major in sociology-anthropology or equivalent. 12 professorial staff. 20 master's degrees and 10 Ph.D.'s awarded 1955-59. 19 graduate students registered fall 1959.

Speech and Hearing. Anatomy and physiology of speech and hearing, pathology of speech and hearing, tests and measurements of the deaf, psychoacoustics, electroacoustics, applied audiology, training of deaf or speech defectives. Prerequisites for graduate study: major in field; adequate preparation in anatomy or physiology, psychology, and education. 8 professorial staff. 15 master's degree awarded 1955-59. 2 graduate students registered fall 1959.

Zoology. Evolution, genetics, ecology, neurophysiology, experimental or physiological embryology, comparative endocrinology. Prerequisites for graduate study: minimum of 18 hours in zoology; 1 year of physics or organic chemistry. Recommended: at least 1 summer at a seashore laboratory in study of marine life. 9 professorial staff. 7 master's degrees and 6 Ph.D.'s awarded 1955-59. 16 graduate students registered fall 1959.

Washington, University of

SEATTLE 5, WASHINGTON

The Graduate School

Graduate instruction was begun at the University of Washington in 1885, and the Graduate School was organized in 1911. First Ph.D. was awarded in 1914. The Ed.D. and D.B.A. degrees are also conferred. University is publicly controlled by the state. Both men and women are admitted.

Limited space in university dormitories available for graduate students; 303 apartment units available for married students with children; 145 units for childless couples. Office of Student Residences maintains listing of suitable housing in community.

Special facilities include: library of over 1,000,000 volumes; museum of history and industry; art gallery; observatory; state museum;

bureau of business research; child development institute; child health center; clinic for child study; Far Eastern and Russian Institute; fisheries research institute; institute of forest products; Friday Harbor Laboratories (marine biology, zoology, fisheries, microbiology, oceanography, meteorology); center for graduate study at Hanford (nuclear science and engineering); bureau of government research; engineering experiment station; population research; psychiatric clinic; institute of public affairs; research computer center with IBM 650 and 704 computers; nuclear piles; public opinion laboratory; cosmic ray research laboratory; laboratory of radiation biology.

Residence requirement for Ph.D.: minimum of 3 academic years, 2 of which must be taken at the University of Washington, with at least 1 year in continuous full-time residence. Summer courses available.

ADMISSION REQUIREMENTS

For graduate study: bachelor's degree; GPA of 3.00 in senior year for full standing (between 2.75 and 3.00 for provisional standing); necessary prerequisites for work in chosen graduate field. For candidacy for Ph.D.: successful completion of 2 full years of graduate study; reading knowledge of 2 foreign languages related to major field of study; recommendation of student's supervisory committee; general examination.

Apply to Director of Admissions or to Dean of the Graduate School by August 1 for fall term; by December 1 for winter term; by March 1 for spring term; by May 15 for summer term.

FEES AND FIRST-YEAR AID

No application fee. Tuition and incidental fees for state residents $213 per academic year; others $498. Room (in dormitory) and board for men $225 per quarter (in double room); for women $240 per quarter in single room and $205-$225 in double room. Approximate annual cost of board in college dining room $540-$600 for 9 months (on 5-day basis). Apartments $48-$85 per month.

First-year aid available: scholarships in varying amounts; about 359 teaching assistantships, $2,025 per academic year; fellowships with stipends in various amounts; about 266 research assistantships, $2,025 per academic year. There are also about 53 predoctoral associateships avail-

able to those having a master's degree; stipend $2,275 per academic year.

For teaching and research assistantships and predoctoral associateships, apply to departmental chairman; for scholarships, to Director of Student Financial Aids. Appointments are usually made about March 15; application should be received at least 4 to 6 weeks before this date.

FIELDS OF STUDY FOR THE PH.D.

Anatomy. Cytology, cytochemistry, electron microscopy, microspectroscopy, X-ray diffraction, reproductive physiology, histology, neuroanatomy, gross anatomy, embryology, radioactive tracer biology, molecular anatomy, special optical approaches to structural studies. Prerequisite for graduate study: major in biology, chemistry, physics, or mathematics (or M.D., D.D.S., or D.V.M. degree). Recommended: at least 1 foreign language; mathematics through calculus; more than 1 year of physics. 12 professorial staff. 1 Ph.D. awarded 1955-59. 2 graduate students registered fall 1959.

Anthropology. Archaeology, ethnology, linguistics, physical or social anthropology, areal programs (polar, Pacific Northwest, Oceania, Asia), comparative political systems or religions. Asian program is offered in cooperation with Far Eastern and Russian Institute. Recommended for graduate study: reading proficiency in 2 foreign languages (French and German preferred). 15 professorial staff. 12 master's degrees and 6 Ph.D.'s awarded 1955-59. 35 graduate students registered fall 1959.

Area Studies.—Far Eastern and Russian Studies. China, Inner Asia, Japan, Russia. Combined program offered by Departments of Anthropology, Economics, Geography, History, Philosophy, Political Science, and Far Eastern and Slavic Languages and Literature. Prerequisite for graduate study: knowledge of language of country being studied. 23 professorial staff. 27 master's degrees and 9 Ph.D.'s awarded 1955-59. 63 graduate students registered fall 1959.

Biochemistry. Physical, lipide, or physiological biochemistry; protein chemistry; enzymology; biological control mechanisms; intermediary metabolism; nucleic acids and viruses; X-ray crystallography. Prerequisite for graduate study: major in chemistry or equivalent (or major in biological sciences with chemistry as a minor). 8 professorial staff. 5 master's degrees and 17

Ph.D.'s awarded 1955-59. 30 graduate students registered fall 1959.

Botany. Taxonomy, morphology, mycology, plant physiology, algology, ecology, genetics. Prerequisite for graduate study: major in botany. Recommended: chemistry through organic; mathematics, including calculus; 1 year of physics. 8 professorial staff. 10 master's degrees and 2 Ph.D.'s awarded 1955-59. 17 graduate students registered fall 1959.

Chemistry. Analytical, inorganic, nuclear, organic, or physical chemistry. Prerequisites for graduate study: major in chemistry; at least 1 foreign language. 20 professorial staff. 36 master's degrees and 90 Ph.D.'s awarded 1955-59. 125 graduate students registered fall 1959.

Classics. Classical languages and literatures; ancient philosophy. Prerequisite for graduate study: major in Greek, Latin, or classics. Recommended: reading knowledge of French and German. 7 professorial staff. Ph.D. program begun 1960. 3 master's degrees awarded 1955-59. 4 graduate students registered fall 1959.

Economics. Economic theory or history; money, banking, and cycles; government regulations; labor economics; public finance; international trade; national economies; statistics and econometrics. Recommended for graduate study: reading knowledge of 2 foreign languages; mathematics through calculus. 15 professorial staff. 32 master's degrees and 17 Ph.D.'s awarded 1955-59. 44 graduate students registered fall 1959.

Education. Educational administration and supervision; educational methods or psychology; college teaching; curriculum; elementary or special education; guidance and counseling; history and philosophy of education. Prerequisite for graduate study: adequate background in professional education. Recommended: GRE; MAT. Ph.D. candidacy prerequisites: 2 years' teaching experience; recommendations from previous institutions and employers. 14 professorial staff. 191 master's degrees and 53 Ph.D.'s awarded 1955-59. 211 graduate students registered fall 1959.

Engineering.—Aeronautical. Aerodynamics, dynamics, or structures. 7 professorial staff. Ph.D. program begun 1959. 31 master's degrees awarded 1955-59. 70 graduate students registered fall 1959.

Engineering.—Chemical. Transport processes, diffusion, nuclear engineering, ion exchange, heat or mass transfer, corrosion, fluidized beds, cellulose and lignin, electrochemistry. Recommended for graduate study: major in field. 8 professorial staff. 30 master's degrees and 15 Ph.D.'s awarded 1955-59. 69 graduate students registered fall 1959.

Engineering.—Civil. Hydraulics and fluid mechanics; engineering or soil mechanics; sanitary, structural, or transportation engineering. Prerequisite for graduate study: major in civil engineering or engineering mechanics. 21 professorial staff. 70 master's degrees awarded 1955-59. 74 graduate students registered fall 1959.

Engineering.—Electrical. Electronics; communications, solid-state, or circuit theory; control systems; computers; microwaves. 25 professorial staff. 44 master's degrees and 2 Ph.D.'s awarded 1955-59. 171 graduate students registered fall 1959.

Engineering.—Mechanical. Thermodynamics, heat transfer, fluid flow, theoretical and experimental stress analysis, elasticity and plasticity. Prerequisite for graduate study: major in mechanical engineering or equivalent. 18 professorial staff. Ph.D. program begun 1959. 14 master's degrees awarded 1955-59. 150 graduate students registered fall 1959.

English. English and American literature, comparative and general literature. Prerequisite for graduate study: major in English or equivalent. Recommended: proficiency in French and German. 40 professorial staff. 96 master's degrees and 42 Ph.D.'s awarded 1955-59. 134 graduate students registered fall 1959.

Far Eastern and Slavic Languages and Literature. China, Inner Asia, Japan, Russia. Prerequisite for graduate study: major in appropriate language or the equivalent. 17 professorial staff. 15 master's degrees and 4 Ph.D.'s awarded 1955-59. 31 graduate students registered fall 1959.

Fisheries. Marine or freshwater fisheries biology, fisheries technology, invertebrate fisheries. Offered by College of Fisheries. Prerequisites for graduate study: major in fisheries or related field; broad training in basic sciences. 9 professorial staff. 20 master's degrees and 15 Ph.D.'s awarded 1955-59. 37 graduate students registered fall 1959.

Forestry. Forest management: soils; tree nutrition; ecology; silviculture; genetics; influences; mensuration; management; recreation; photogrammetry; policy. Forest products: basic wood technology; plywood; gluing; preservation; synthetic boards; mechanical properties; and saw-milling. Prerequisite for graduate study: major in forestry or related science. 12 professorial staff. 27 master's degrees and 6 Ph.D.'s awarded 1955-59. 33 graduate students registered fall 1959. Total enrollment limited to 35.

Genetics. Genetics of microorganisms, medical genetics. Recommended for graduate study: strong background in chemistry, physics, biology, and mathematics; knowledge of French and German. 5 professorial staff. Program begun 1960. 3 graduate students registered fall 1960. New enrollment limited to 3.

Geography. Regional geography (Anglo-America, Far East, Soviet Union), economic geography, cartography. Recommended for graduate study: strong liberal arts background; at least 1 language; some geography; at least 1 other social science (preferably geology or meteorology); mathematics. 12 professorial staff. 27 master's degrees and 17 Ph.D.'s awarded 1955-59. 35 graduate students registered fall 1959.

Geology. Petrology, paleontology, structural or engineering geology, stratigraphy, geomorphology. Prerequisite for graduate study: major in field. Recommended: reading knowledge of French or German. Ph.D. candidacy prerequisites: M.S. in geology; ETS Advanced Test in Geology. 9 professorial staff. 22 master's degrees and 17 Ph.D.'s awarded 1955-59. 37 graduate students registered fall 1959.

Germanics. German literature or philology. Offered by Department of Germanic Languages and Literature. Prerequisite for graduate study: major in German. Recommended: European history; philosophy; courses in the arts; an additional foreign language. 9 professorial staff. 6 master's degrees and 1 Ph.D. awarded 1955-59. 11 graduate students registered fall 1959.

History. Ancient, medieval, Renaissance, modern European, English, or American history; history of science. Offered by Department of History, partially in cooperation with Department of Far Eastern and Slavic Languages and Literature. Prerequisites for graduate study: major in history; languages. 14 professorial staff. 42 master's degrees and 17 Ph.D.'s awarded 1955-59. 122 graduate students registered fall 1959.

Linguistics. Nature, comparison, or analysis and description of languages (Indo European, Altaic, Chinese, Japanese and Korean, Southeast Asian, American Indian, American English dialect). Prerequisite for graduate study: advanced

work in 2 foreign languages. Recommended: Latin; Greek. 6 professorial staff. 2 Ph.D.'s awarded 1955-59. 5 graduate students registered fall 1959.

Mathematics. Analysis, topology, algebra, differential geometry, mathematical statistics. Prerequisite for graduate study: at least 15 hours' mathematics beyond calculus. Recommended: French, German, or Russian; general physics; 20-25 hours of mathematics beyond calculus. 35 professorial staff. 30 master's degrees and 24 Ph.D.'s awarded 1955-59. 115 graduate students registered fall 1959.

Meteorology and Climatology. Large or small scale meteorology, polar meteorology, energy transfer, instrument development, bioclimatology, cloud physics, upper atmosphere. Prerequisites for graduate study: major in physical science or mathematics; diagnostic test at entrance. Recommended: courses in modern physics, differential equations, vector analysis; reading knowledge of Russian or German. 7 professorial staff. 17 master's degrees and 6 Ph.D.'s awarded 1955-59. 35 graduate students registered fall 1959.

Microbiology. General microbiology, bacterial and animal virology, immunology, microbial metabolism and physiology, microbial genetics, medical mycology. Offered by Department of Microbiology, School of Medicine. Prerequisites for graduate study: major in microbiology, biology, or physical sciences; 1 year of a foreign language. 9 professorial staff. 17 master's degrees and 18 Ph.D.'s awarded 1955-59. 21 graduate students registered fall 1959. Total enrollment limited to about 20.

Music. Musicology; theory and composition. Offered by School of Music. Prerequisites for graduate study: cultural background in humanities, social sciences, and sciences; broad knowledge of music theory and literature; proficiency in general musicianship, including piano. 29 professorial staff. 44 master's degrees awarded 1955-59. 37 graduate students registered fall 1959.

Oceanography. Biological, geological, chemical, or physical oceanography. Prerequisites for graduate study: major in field, or in a natural or exact science; chemistry through quantitative analysis; mathematics through calculus, 1 year of physics; 1 quarter each of zoology and geology. Recommended: reading knowledge of French, German, or Russian. 7 professorial staff. 8 master's degrees and 3 Ph.D.'s awarded 1955-59. 28 graduate students registered fall 1959.

Pharmacology. Skeletomuscular, cardiovascular, smooth muscle, or gastrointestinal pharmacology; central nervous system; anticoagulants; psychopharmacology. Offered by Department of Pharmacology, School of Medicine. Prerequisite for graduate study: major in zoology, chemistry, physics, pharmacy, psychology, or physiology. Recommended: physical chemistry; mathematics through calculus; knowledge of electronics. 8 professorial staff. 4 master's degrees and 4 Ph.D.'s awarded 1955-59. 4 graduate students registered fall 1959. Total enrollment limited to 10.

Pharmacy. Pharmacy, pharmaceutical chemistry, pharmacognosy. Offered by College of Pharmacy. Prerequisites for graduate study: major in pharmacy or in a biological or physical science; mathematics placement test. Recommended: courses in physical or qualitative organic chemistry, calculus, biochemistry, and statistical methods (plant physiology for pharmacognosy majors). 11 professorial staff. 10 master's degrees and 14 Ph.D.'s awarded 1955-59. 19 graduate students registered fall 1959.

Philosophy. Logic, epistemology, metaphysics, ethics, aesthetics, history of philosophy, social philosophy, philosophy of religion or science, semantics. Prerequisite for graduate study: major in field. 7 professorial staff. 11 master's degrees and 8 Ph.D.'s awarded 1955-59. 22 graduate students registered fall 1959.

Physics. Atomic and molecular, high-energy, low-temperature, nuclear, solid-state, or theoretical physics; cosmic rays; gaseous electronics; magnetic resonance; spectroscopy. Prerequisites for graduate study: upper-division courses in electricity and magnetism, optics, properties of matter, and atomic and nuclear physics; introduction to mathematical physics; mathematics through analysis. Recommended: 2 foreign languages; partial differential equations. 26 professorial staff. 33 master's degrees and 25 Ph.D.'s awarded 1955-59. 144 graduate students registered fall 1959.

Physiology and Biophysics. Neurophysiology, cardiovascular and respiratory physiology, biophysics, physiological psychology, behavioral neurophysiology. Prerequisite for graduate study: major in zoology, psychology, chemistry, engineering, or physics (or an M.D. degree). Degree in psychology required for physiological psychology; in physics for biophysics. Recommended:

French; German; mathematics; physics. 11 professorial staff. Ph.D. program in physiological psychology begun 1959. 2 master's degrees and 8 Ph.D.'s awarded 1955-59. 26 graduate students registered fall 1959. Total enrollment limited to 30.

Political Science. Political theory, public law or administration, international law and relations, comparative government, state and local government, American government and politics. Offered by Departments of Political Science and Far Eastern Languages and Literatures. Prerequisite for graduate study: major in field or equivalent. Recommended: foreign languages. 14 professorial staff. (Department of Political Science). 41 master's degrees and 16 Ph.D.'s awarded 1955-59. 50 graduate students registered fall 1959.

Psychology. Measurement and evaluation, social psychology and personality, clinical or developmental psychology, physiological and comparative psychology. Joint degree in psychology and physiology offered in cooperation with Department of Physiology. Prerequisites for graduate study: mathematics; physics; chemistry; biology; social sciences; 2 courses in psychology; MAT. 17 professorial staff. 45 master's degrees and 45 Ph.D.'s awarded 1955-59. 88 graduate students registered fall 1959. New enrollment limited to approximately 25.

Romance Languages and Literature. Romance languages: French, Spanish, or Italian literature; Romance linguistics. Language teacher training and supervision: French or Spanish language, literature, and culture; psychology of language; theoretical and applied linguistics; research in language teaching. Prerequisite for graduate study: major or equivalent in French, Spanish, or Italian. Recommended: knowledge of Latin; history courses related to major and minor literatures. 14 professorial staff. Ph.D. in teacher training and supervision begun 1959. 14 master's degrees and 13 Ph.D.'s awarded 1955-59. 27 graduate students registered fall 1959.

Sociology. Sociological theory; research methods and statistics; ecology and demography; social interaction; social institutions and organization; social disorganization or criminology. Prerequisite for graduate study: major in field. Recommended: GRE. 15 professorial staff. 15 master's degrees and 20 Ph.D.'s awarded 1955-59. 57 graduate students registered fall 1959.

Speech. Rhetoric and public address, speech correction and hearing. Prerequisite for graduate study: major in field or minimum of 35 quarter credits of approved course work. 16 professorial staff. 18 master's degrees and 2 Ph.D.'s awarded 1955-59. 42 graduate students registered fall 1959.

Zoology. Cellular or comparative physiology, cytology, ecology, embryology, entomology, herpetology, mammalogy, morphology, ornithology, protozoology, systematic zoology (primarily invertebrate). Prerequisites for graduate study: particularly good record in biological or physical sciences; 1 year each of physics and organic chemistry. 13 professorial staff. 12 master's degrees and 9 Ph.D.'s awarded 1955-59. 34 graduate students registered fall 1959.

Wayne State University

DETROIT 2, MICHIGAN

Division of Graduate Instruction and Research

The Division of Graduate Instruction and Research was created in 1959, replacing the former Graduate School which was organized in 1932. It is the central unit for overall administration of graduate work at the university. Of significance in the general reorganization is the increase in the number of areas in which the Ph.D. is awarded. New programs are available in the Departments of Biology, Economics, Chemical and Metallurgical Engineering, and Engineering Mechanics. The College of Education, which formerly offered only the Ed.D. on the doctoral level, is now authorized to admit students to Ph.D. programs as well. The university is publicly controlled by the state. Both men and women are admitted.

Dormitories are available for graduate men and women; 1 apartment building for women over 21 years of age; 3 apartment houses and 1 housing project for married graduate students. Library contains approximately 620,000 volumes, with special collections in chemistry, medicine, labor, philology, Judaica and Hebraica, and Michigan and Detroit. Location in industrial Detroit provides many and varied opportunities for study and research.

Residence requirement for Ph.D.: minimum of 3 years of full-time graduate work, of which 2 successive semesters or 3 terms must be spent in full-time residence at Wayne State University. Summer and evening courses available.

ADMISSION REQUIREMENTS

For graduate study: bachelor's degree; B average or better for doctoral applicants (students with overall graduate average of 2.6 may be accepted on adviser's recommendation); adequate preparation and ability to pursue graduate work in chosen field; acceptance by department. Nonresidents of Michigan may be accepted only if such admission does not prevent acceptance of a qualified Michigan resident, and if it is not a probationary classification. Some departments require GRE, MAT, or performance tests. For candidacy for Ph.D.: proficiency examinations in 2 foreign languages normally required; qualifying examination; approval of plan of work.

Apply to the Graduate Division by August 1 for fall semester; by December 15 for spring semester; by May 15 for summer session.

FEES AND FIRST-YEAR AID

No application fee. Students pay fees on the basis of credit hours elected; maximum for state residents $352 per academic year. Nonresidents of Michigan pay an additional fee per credit hour of work elected; maximum $300. Room (in dormitory) $113-$243 per 20-week period. Meals available in college-operated cafeteria. Apartments for single women $165-$300 per 20-week period. Apartments for married students $62-$90 per month; accommodation in housing project $28-$70 per month depending on income.

First-year aid available: 56 Board of Governors graduate professional scholarships covering all course fees except nominal and nonresident fees; variable number of research assistantships carrying stipends in varying amounts; 2 awards which cover all fees except nonresident fees.

Apply to the Administrative Officer, Graduate Division, for scholarships and awards; to chairman of appropriate department for assistantships and associateships. Applications should normally be received in April or May; in the case of assistantships, the date is set by individual departmental chairmen.

FIELDS OF STUDY FOR THE PH.D.

Special program in which student is instructed in research procedures, assessment and evaluation of research designs, and design construction is available.

Anatomy. Neuroanatomy, neurophysiology, morphology, physical anthropology, electron microscopy, microscopic or experimental anatomy, cytology, embryology. Prerequisites for graduate study: biology and chemistry. 7 professorial staff. 1 Ph.D. awarded 1955-59. 2 graduate students registered fall 1959.

Biology. Bacteriology, botany, zoology. Prerequisites for graduate study: major in biology or a subdivision; courses in genetics, morphology, and physiology; supporting courses in physics, chemistry, and mathematics; GRE, including Advanced Test in Biology. 18 professorial staff. Ph.D. program begun 1958. 27 master's degrees awarded 1955-59. 32 graduate students registered fall 1959.

Chemistry. Biochemistry; analytical, inorganic, organic, or physical chemistry. 20 professorial staff. 43 master's degrees and 67 Ph.D.'s awarded 1955-59. 103 graduate students registered fall 1959.

Economics. 18 professorial staff. Ph.D. program begun 1960. 9 master's degrees awarded 1955-59. 27 graduate students registered fall 1959.

Education. General, elementary, or secondary administration and supervision; curriculum development; educational sociology; evaluation and research; guidance and counseling; history and philosophy of education; audio-visual, industrial, special or teacher education. Offered by College of Education. Prerequisites for graduate study: 3 years of teaching experience; MAT; GRE. 75 full-time professorial staff and several times this number of part-time personnel. Ph.D. program begun 1960. Ed.D. degree awarded prior to this time. 2,056 master's degrees awarded 1955-59. 2,150 graduate students registered fall 1959. At present, 6 new graduate students accepted each year. Ed.D. is also awarded in this field.

Educational Psychology. Ph.D. candidacy prerequisites: master's degree with major in field or equivalent; entrance examinations; demonstrated proficiency as teacher of educational psychology at college level. 11 professorial staff. 110 master's degrees and 1 Ph.D. awarded 1955-59. 394 graduate students registered fall 1959.

Engineering.—Chemical. 6 professorial staff. Ph.D. program begun 1959. 27 master's degrees awarded 1955-59. 39 graduate students registered fall 1959.

Engineering Mechanics. Elasticity, plasticity, strength of materials, dynamics and vibrations, fluid mechanics, nonlinear mechanics. 11 professorial staff. Ph.D. program begun 1960. 13 master's degrees awarded 1955-59. 54 graduate students registered fall 1959.

Engineering.—Metallurgical. 4 professorial staff. Ph.D. program begun 1959. 12 master's degrees awarded 1955-59. 24 graduate students registered fall 1959.

English. American or English literature, literary criticism, linguistic studies in Middle and modern English. Prerequisites for graduate study: good background in liberal arts; GRE. 32 professorial staff. 41 master's degrees and 1 Ph.D. awarded 1955-59. 145 graduate students registered fall 1959.

History. Europe and Asia, the Americas. 22 professorial staff. Ph.D. program begun 1956. 25 master's degrees awarded 1955-59. 78 graduate students registered fall 1959. Ph.D. students accepted only when awarded teaching fellowships. Department has only 2 a year.

Mathematics. Pure or applied mathematics, mathematical statistics. Prerequisites for graduate study: 9 hours beyond calculus; analytic geometry. 26 professorial staff. 25 master's degrees and 4 Ph.D.'s awarded 1955-59. 87 graduate students registered fall 1959.

Microbiology. Prerequisites for graduate study: basic bacteriology and physics; 1 year of mathematics (preferably through calculus); chemistry through organic; quantitative analysis; GRE. 7 professorial staff. 5 master's degrees and 1 Ph.D. awarded 1955-59. 7 graduate students registered fall 1959.

Modern Languages. Offered by Departments of French, German, and Spanish. Prerequisites for graduate study: A.B. in major language or equivalent; approximately 20 semester hours in minor language (1 of the other 2 languages); working knowledge of Latin for majors in French or Spanish. 19 professorial staff. Ph.D. program begun 1956. 4 graduate students registered fall 1959. No master's degree awarded in this field.

Physics. Solid-state, theoretical, or nuclear physics. 12 professorial staff. 25 master's degrees and 1 Ph.D. awarded 1955-59. 29 graduate students registered fall 1959.

Physiological Chemistry. Offered by Department of Physiological Chemistry, School of Medicine. Prerequisites for graduate study: comparative anatomy; mathematics through calculus. 9 professorial staff. 3 master's degrees and 7 Ph.D.'s awarded 1955-59. 9 graduate students registered fall 1959.

Physiology and Pharmacology. Prerequisites for graduate study: major in science; courses in biology, general and organic chemistry, and physics; 2 years of a language (usually German). Recommended: courses in embryology, physiology, comparative anatomy, histology, quantitative and qualitative analysis, and mathematics. 8 professorial staff. 8 master's degrees and 7 Ph.D.'s awarded 1955-59. 14 graduate students registered fall 1959.

Psychology. General-theoretical, clinical, industrial, or social psychology. 11 professorial staff. 26 master's degrees and 2 Ph.D.'s awarded 1955-59. 66 graduate students registered fall 1959. Total Ph.D. enrollment limited to 10 per year. Students may enter only in September.

Sociology. Social disorganization, social psychology, urban sociology. Offered by Department of Sociology and Anthropology. 19 professorial staff. 21 master's degrees and 2 Ph.D.'s awarded 1955-59. 53 graduate students registered fall 1959.

Speech. Public speaking, speech science and correction, radio and TV, interpretative reading, general speech. Prerequisites for graduate study: major in speech; ability to write effectively; speaking and reading performance test; GRE. 19 professorial staff. 56 master's degrees and 4 Ph.D.'s awarded 1955-59. 87 graduate students registered fall 1959. New enrollment limited to 10.

West Virginia University

MORGANTOWN, WEST VIRGINIA

The Graduate School

First master's degree was awarded at West Virginia in 1873, and first Ph.D. in 1902. The Graduate School was formally established in 1930 and has jurisdiction over all graduate programs of the university. In addition to the Ph.D., it awards the Ed.D. degree through the College of Educa-

tion. The university is publicly controlled by the state. Both men and women are admitted.

Single graduate students live in university dormitories or in private homes; married graduate students in private homes. University-owned apartments for married graduate students under construction.

Residence requirement for Ph.D.: minimum of 3 years of full-time graduate work beyond bachelor's degree, with at least 36 weeks of full-time graduate study in residence at West Virginia University. Summer and evening courses available.

ADMISSION REQUIREMENTS

For graduate study: bachelor's degree; good scholastic record; recommendations. For candidacy for Ph.D.: master's degree or equivalent; reading knowledge of 2 modern foreign languages (usually French and German); qualifying examinations (either oral or written or both).

Apply to the Registrar as early as possible.

FEES AND FIRST-YEAR AID

No application fee. Tuition for state residents $212 per academic year; others $542. Special fees vary according to department. Room (in dormitory) and board $540-$700 per academic year. Meals in campus cafeteria slightly under commercial rate for those who do not live in dormitories.

First-year aid available: teaching and research assistantships in many fields; industrial fellowships in science and engineering.

Apply to head of department, preferably by March 1; applications will be considered as long as vacancies exist.

FIELDS OF STUDY FOR THE PH.D.

Agricultural Microbiology. Combined program offered by Departments of Plant Pathology, Bacteriology, and Entomology. Prerequisite for graduate study: 30 hours of biology. Recommended: 1 foreign language. 11 professorial staff. Program begun 1959. 4 graduate students registered fall 1959.

Agronomy and Genetics. Soil science, crop science, genetics. Prerequisites for graduate study: 2 years of chemistry; courses in algebra, physics, botany, and geology. Recommended: trigonometry; calculus. 8 professorial staff. 15 master's degrees awarded 1955-59. 10 graduate students registered fall 1959.

Bacteriology. Pathogenic microbiology, immunology, bacterial physiology, mycology, virology. Offered by Department of Microbiology. Prerequisites for graduate study: organic chemistry; mathematics. Recommended: French or German. 4 professorial staff. Ph.D. program begun 1959. 4 master's degrees awarded 1955-59. 6 graduate students registered fall 1959.

Biochemistry. Vitamin or protein metabolism, enzyme kinetics. Prerequisites for graduate study: fundamentals of biology and chemistry. 4 professorial staff. 4 master's degrees awarded 1955-59. 5 graduate students registered fall 1959. New enrollment limited to 8.

Biochemistry.—Agricultural. Nutritional biochemistry, ruminant nutrition, antioxidants for lipids, biological antioxidants, antibiotics. Offered by Department of Agricultural Biochemistry and Nutrition. Prerequisites for graduate study: strong training in chemistry; departmental orientation examinations. Recommended: 1 year or more of biology. Ph.D. candidacy prerequisite: M.S. or equivalent. 10 professorial staff. 3 master's degrees and 5 Ph.D.'s awarded 1955-59. 5 graduate students registered fall 1959.

Botany—Zoology. Animal physiology; plant taxonomy, anatomy, or cytotaxonomy; ecology. Offered by Department of Biology. Prerequisites for graduate study: about 24 hours of credit in the field. 11 professorial staff. 27 master's degrees and 3 Ph.D.'s awarded 1955-59. 30 graduate students registered fall 1959.

Chemistry. Organic, analytical, inorganic, or physical chemistry. Prerequisites for graduate study: major in chemistry; 12-18 hours of foreign language; examinations. Recommended: mathematics beyond calculus. 13 professorial staff. 21 master's degrees and 11 Ph.D.'s awarded 1955-59. 28 graduate students registered fall 1959.

Engineering.—Chemical. General chemical, ceramic, metallurgical, or nuclear engineering. 7 professorial staff. 19 master's degrees and 10 Ph.D.'s awarded 1955-59. 21 graduate students registered fall 1959.

Geology. Petrography, stratigraphy, economic geology, paleontology, paleobotany. Prerequisites for graduate study: B.S. in geology; basic courses in physics, mathematics, and chemistry. 12 semester hours of 1 foreign language; comprehensive test. Recommended: mathematics through calculus. 6 professorial staff. 24 master's degrees and 2 Ph.D.'s awarded 1955-59. 11 graduate students registered fall 1959.

History. Medieval and Renaissance Europe; history of Europe (1500-1815 or 1789-present); English history (1066-1714 or 1688-present); British Imperial, Far Eastern, Latin-American, or American diplomatic history; history of the United States (1492-1783, 1763-1865, or 1850-present); local and regional problems. Prerequisites for graduate study: concentrations in history and cognate fields. 10 professorial staff. 21 master's degrees and 4 Ph.D.'s awarded 1955-59. 23 graduate students registered fall 1959.

Pharmacology. Chemotherapy, cardiovascular pharmacology, autonomic drugs, quantitative studies of catechdamines, calcium metabolism, parathyroids. Offered by Department of Pharmacology, School of Medicine. Prerequisite for graduate study: B.S. in pharmacy, zoology, or chemistry. 4 professorial staff. Ph.D. program begun 1959. 8 master's degrees awarded 1955-59. 5 graduate students registered fall 1959. New enrollment limited to about 6.

Physics. Paramagnetic resonance, ferromagnetics, nuclear physics, electromagnetic theory. Prerequisites for graduate study: B.S. in physics or engineering; entrance examination. Recommended: mathematics through differential equations. 8 professorial staff. Ph.D. program begun 1958. 13 master's degrees awarded 1955-59. 21 graduate students registered fall 1959.

Physiology. Offered by Department of Physiology, Medical Center. Prerequisite for graduate study: scholastic standing equivalent to that required for admission to School of Medicine. 3 professorial staff. Ph.D. program begun 1959. 1 master's degree awarded 1955-59. 2 graduate students registered fall 1959.

Plant Pathology. Combined program offered by Departments of Plant Pathology, Bacteriology, and Entomology. Prerequisite for graduate study: 30 hours of biology. Recommended: knowledge of a foreign language. 11 professorial staff. 11 master's degrees and 12 Ph.D.'s awarded 1955-59. 12 graduate students registered fall 1959.

Political Science. Ph.D. candidacy prerequisites: M.A. or equivalent. 9 professorial staff. Program begun 1960.

Psychology. General experimental or clinical psychology. Prerequisites for graduate study: courses in experimental psychology and statistics; GRE or MAT. Ph.D. candidacy prerequisite: M.A. or equivalent. 8 professorial staff. Ph.D.

program begun 1958. 13 master's degrees awarded 1955-59. 15 graduate students registered fall 1959. Total enrollment limited to 16.

Western Reserve University

CLEVELAND 6, OHIO

The Graduate School

Although a few advanced degrees were given earlier, the Graduate School was not formally organized until 1926. The first Ph.D. was awarded in 1928. The Ed.D. and the D.S.W. degrees are also conferred. The university is privately controlled and nonsectarian. Both men and women are admitted.

A limited number of rooms are available in university dormitories for graduate students; no residence facilities provided on campus for married students.

Library contains approximately 750,000 volumes. Affiliation with Institute of Music, Museum of Art, Case Institute of Technology, and Museum of Natural History provide additional opportunities for study and research.

Residence requirement for Ph.D.: minimum of 3 years beyond bachelor's degree, 1 year of which must be spent in residence on campus. Summer and evening courses available.

ADMISSION REQUIREMENTS

For graduate study: bachelor's degree; 2.5 (C+) average; major in field of proposed graduate study. For candidacy for Ph.D.: a minimum of 66 semester hours of graduate work; examinations in 2 foreign languages (usually French and German); preliminary or general examinations.

Apply to University Admissions Office by August 15, January 15, or May 15 for term beginning one month later.

FEES AND FIRST-YEAR AID

No application fee. Tuition $32 per credit hour ($960 a year for full program). Special fees approximate $15 yearly. Room (in dormitory) and board total $348.50 per semester.

First-year aid available: 20 tuition scholarships available for first-year students. Graduate assistantships and fellowships available in most departments.

Apply to University Admissions Office by March 1.

FIELDS OF STUDY FOR THE PH.D.

American Culture. Combined program offered by full staffs of Departments of English, History, Sociology, Philosophy, Art, Economics, Education, and Political Science. 19 master's degrees and 6 Ph.D.'s awarded 1955-59. 21 graduate students registered fall 1959.

Anatomy. Offered by Department of Anatomy, School of Medicine. 6 professorial staff. 2 master's degrees and 2 Ph.D.'s awarded 1955-59.

Art. 6 professorial staff. 40 master's degrees and 2 Ph.D.'s awarded 1955-59. 42 graduate students registered fall 1959.

Biochemistry. Offered by Department of Biochemistry, School of Medicine. 17 professorial staff. 2 master's degrees and 19 Ph.D.'s awarded 1955-59. 12 graduate students registered fall 1959.

Biology. Botany, zoology. Prerequisite for graduate study: major in biology. 8 professorial staff. 16 master's degrees and 5 Ph.D.'s awarded 1955-59. 27 graduate students registered fall 1959.

Chemistry. Inorganic, organic, physical. 13 professorial staff. 63 master's degrees and 44 Ph.D.'s awarded 1955-59. 103 graduate students registered fall 1959.

Economics. 5 professorial staff. 7 master's degrees and 1 Ph.D. awarded 1955-59. 28 graduate students registered fall 1959.

Education. 15 professorial staff. 657 master's degrees and 16 Ph.D.'s awarded 1955-59. 687 graduate students registered fall 1959. Ed.D. degree also awarded in this field (no language requirements).

English. Literature and linguistics. 20 professorial staff. 61 master's degrees and 15 Ph.D.'s awarded 1955-59. 76 graduate students registered fall 1959.

History. 10 professorial staff. 50 master's degrees and 8 Ph.D.'s awarded 1955-59. 91 graduate students registered fall 1959.

Library Science. Offered by School of Library Science in cooperation with a subject-matter department in the Graduate School. Prerequisites for graduate study: professional degree from a school of library science and adequate preparation to do graduate work in a subject-matter field. Ph.D. candidacy prerequisite: 36 hours beyond professional degree. 44 master's degrees awarded 1955-59. 6 graduate students (beyond professional degree) registered fall 1959.

Mathematics. 7 professorial staff. Ph.D. program begun 1959. 2 master's degrees awarded 1955-59. 24 graduate students registered fall 1959.

Microbiology. Offered by Department of Microbiology, School of Medicine. Prerequisite for graduate study: major in biology or chemistry. 8 professorial staff. 6 Ph.D.'s awarded 1955-59. 7 graduate students registered fall 1959.

Pathology. Offered by Department of Pathology, School of Medicine. Prerequisite for graduate study: major in biology or chemistry. 7 professorial staff. 2 master's degrees awarded 1955-59. 1 graduate student registered fall 1959.

Pharmacology. Offered by Department of Pharmacology, School of Medicine. Prerequisite for graduate study: appropriate science courses. 9 professorial staff. 4 graduate students registered fall 1959.

Physics. 9 professorial staff. Ph.D. program begun 1955. 7 master's degrees awarded 1955-59. 31 graduate students registered fall 1959.

Physiology. Offered by Department of Physiology, School of Medicine. Prerequisite for graduate study: major in biology. 8 professorial staff. 1 master's degree and 2 Ph.D.'s awarded 1955-59. 8 graduate students registered fall 1959.

Political Science. 6 professorial staff. 23 master's degrees and 1 Ph.D. awarded 1955-59. 12 graduate students registered fall 1959.

Psychology. General, industrial, or clinical psychology. Prerequisite for graduate study: MAT. 18 professorial staff. 51 master's degrees and 60 Ph.D.'s awarded 1955-59. 66 graduate students registered fall 1959. Total registration in clinical program limited to 30.

Religion. History of religion, literature of the Bible. 2 professorial staff. 4 master's degrees awarded 1955-59. 18 graduate students registered fall 1959.

Romance Languages. French and Spanish. Prerequisites for graduate study: major in French or Spanish and minor in other language. Ph.D. candidacy prerequisites: reading knowledge of 2 additional languages, usually German and Latin. 9 professorial staff. 61 master's degrees and 7 Ph.D.'s awarded 1955-59. 61 graduate students registered fall 1959.

Sociology. 6 professorial staff. 11 master's degrees awarded 1955-59. 29 graduate students registered fall 1959.

Speech and Dramatic Arts. Speech, dramatic arts, and combined program. Offered by Departments of Speech and Dramatic Arts. 9 professorial staff. 46 master's degrees and 7 Ph.D.'s awarded 1955-59. 27 graduate students registered fall 1959.

Speech and Hearing Therapy. Prerequisites for graduate study: appropriate courses in psychology, education, and physiology; MAT. 5 professorial staff. 43 master's degrees and 8 Ph.D.'s awarded 1955-59. 36 graduate students registered fall 1959.

Statistics. Prerequisite for graduate study: major in mathematics or statistics. 3 professorial staff. Ph.D. program begun 1957. 3 master's degrees awarded 1955-59. 11 graduate students registered fall 1959.

Wisconsin, University of

MADISON, WISCONSIN

The Graduate School

Graduate work at the university began informally about 1880, and the first Ph.D. was awarded in 1892. In 1904 the Graduate School was established. University is publicly controlled by the state. Both men and women are admitted.

Single graduate students live in university-approved rooms in lodging houses and private homes near campus; married students find accommodations in 648 university-owned and privately-owned apartments.

Special facilities include: library of approximately 1,500,000 volumes (figure includes all libraries on campus and the State Historical Society Library); National Agricultural Extension Center for Advanced Studies; numerical analysis laboratory; Army Mathematics Center; instrumentation laboratory; electron microscope; observatory; arboretum; Lake Laboratories. Affiliations with Forest Products Laboratory, State Historical Society, and Legislative Reference Bureau provide additional facilities for research.

Residence requirement for Ph.D.: minimum of 3 academic years, of which at least 1½ years must be spent in residence at the University of

Wisconsin with a minimum of 1 year of continuous residence. Summer and late afternoon courses available.

ADMISSION REQUIREMENTS

For graduate study: bachelor's degree; 2.75 GPA; major or equivalent in field of proposed graduate study; 70 semester hours of academic work outside undergraduate major, with appropriate subject matter distribution. Recommended: GRE. For candidacy for Ph.D.: reading knowledge of 2 foreign languages, 1 of which must be French or German; comprehensive preliminary examination in major field; approval of scope of proposed minor field; approval of proposed thesis subject.

Apply to Dean of the Graduate School at least 6 weeks in advance of date of desired entry.

FEES AND FIRST-YEAR AID

No application fee. General fee (required of all students) $110 per semester. Nonresidents of the state of Wisconsin pay an additional $190 per semester. Summer session fee (8 weeks): $80 for state residents; $110 for others. Room (in dormitory) and board for women $770-$800 per academic year. Apartments $72-$85 per month.

First-year aid available: scholarships, $500-$1,100; fellowships, $1,500-$2,500; research assistantships, $1,790 per academic year; teaching assistantships, $1,950 per academic year. Summer appointments are in addition to above.

Apply to Dean of the Graduate School or chairman of department by February 15.

FIELDS OF STUDY FOR THE PH.D.

Many departments have informal programs for teaching assistants; courses in teaching are offered for credit towards advanced degrees in several departments.

Agriculture and Extension Education—Home Economics. Administration, education, home economics. Offered by National Agricultural Extension Center for Advanced Study. 12 professorial staff. Ph.D. program begun 1955. 92 master's degrees and 29 Ph.D.'s awarded 1955-59. 64 graduate students registered fall 1959.

Agronomy. Vegetable control, crop physiology or ecology, biometry. Joint Ph.D. programs may be arranged with Departments of Botany, Genetics, Biochemistry, Plant Pathology, and Soils. Prerequisites for graduate study: 12 credits in agronomy and plant breeding; 1 semester each of organic chemistry or biochemistry and of mathematics; 1 year of physics or equivalent. 21 professorial staff. 31 master's degrees and 35 Ph.D.'s awarded 1955-59. 37 graduate students registered fall 1959.

Anatomy. Human and comparative morphology, embryology, neuroanatomy, medical genetics. Prerequisites for graduate study: preparation in zoology; 1 semester each of organic chemistry or biochemistry and of mathematics; 1 year of physics or equivalent. 7 professorial staff. 9 master's degrees and 10 Ph.D.'s awarded 1955-59. 6 graduate students registered fall 1959.

Animal Sciences.—Animal Husbandry. Animal nutrition, genetics, or physiology. Combined program offered by Departments of Animal Husbandry, Biochemistry, Zoology, Genetics, Physiology, and Bacteriology. Prerequisites for graduate study: preparation in zoology and physiology; 1 semester each of organic chemistry or biochemistry and of mathematics; 1 year of physics or equivalent. 9 professorial staff. 18 master's degrees and 5 Ph.D.'s awarded 1955-59. 19 graduate students registered fall 1959.

Animal Sciences.—Dairy Husbandry. Dairy cattle nutrition, physiology, breeding, or management. Offered by Department of Dairy Husbandry. Combined programs also offered with Departments of Biochemistry and Genetics. Prerequisites for graduate study: major in biology; 1 semester each of organic chemistry or biochemistry and of mathematics; 1 year of physics or equivalent. 11 professorial staff. 23 master's degrees and 13 Ph.D.'s awarded 1955-59. 19 graduate students registered fall 1959.

Animal Sciences.—Poultry Husbandry. Ph.D. offered as joint degree with Biochemistry, Genetics, or other departments. Prerequisites for graduate study: major in poultry husbandry; 1 semester each of organic chemistry or biochemistry and of mathematics; 1 year of physics or equivalent. 6 professorial staff. 4 master's degrees and 6 Ph.D.'s awarded 1955-59. 11 graduate students registered fall 1959.

Anthropology. Archaeology, cultural or physical anthropology. Prerequisite for graduate study: major in anthropology. Ph.D. candidacy prerequisite: master's degree in anthropology normally required. 5 professorial staff. 5 master's degrees and 2 Ph.D.'s awarded 1955-59. 19 graduate students registered fall 1959.

Art and Art Education. Combined program offered by Departments of Art and Education. Prerequisites for graduate study: preparation in art, art education, and education; portfolio of art work to be examined. 16 professorial staff. 76 master's degrees awarded 1955-59. 49 graduate students registered fall 1959.

Art History. Ancient, medieval, Far East, Renaissance. Prerequisites for graduate study: 26 credits in art history; working knowledge of at least 1 foreign language. Ph.D. candidacy prerequisite: working knowledge of collections in at least 1 major United States museum. 4 professorial staff. 5 master's degrees and 3 Ph.D.'s awarded 1955-59. 12 graduate students registered fall 1959.

Astronomy. Photometry and spectrophotometry of stars, galactic structure, interstellar matter, eclipsing of binaries, radiation from stars. Prerequisites for graduate study: 2 years of physics; mathematics through calculus. 5 professorial staff. 2 master's degrees and 3 Ph.D.'s awarded 1955-59. 8 graduate students registered fall 1959.

Bacteriology. Microbiology of animal diseases, dairy products, foods, industrial fermentations, soil, water or sewage, determinative bacteriology, physiology of microorganisms, viruses and bacteriophages, molds and yeasts. Offered by Department of Bacteriology. Combined programs also offered with Departments of Dairy and Food Industries, Soils, Genetics, Veterinary Sciences, Plant Pathology, Medical Microbiology, Botany, and Zoology. Prerequisites for graduate study: 1 semester each of organic chemistry or biochemistry and of mathematics; 1 year of physics or equivalent. Ph.D. candidacy prerequisite: teaching experience (usually part-time for 2 semesters). 10 professorial staff. 69 master's degrees and 47 Ph.D.'s awarded 1955-59. 72 graduate students registered fall 1959.

Biochemistry. Studies on different classes of compounds, various forms of living organisms, organic and physical methods applied to natural products. Offered by Department of Biochemistry. Combined programs also offered with Departments of Bacteriology, Genetics, Physical Chemistry, Dairy Husbandry, Poultry Husbandry, Animal Husbandry, and Agronomy. Prerequisites for graduate study: 1 semester each of organic chemistry or biochemistry and of mathematics; 1 year of physics or equivalent. 16 professorial staff. 80 master's degrees and 107 Ph.D.'s awarded 1955-59. 104 graduate students registered fall 1959.

Biophysics. Ultracentrifugation, electrophoresis, diffusion, radioactive tracers, mass spectrometry, electron microscopy, light scattering. New program offered by Departments of Physics and Biochemistry. 4 professorial staff.

Botany. Anatomy and morphology of plants, algology, bryology, cytology and cytogenetics, ecology, lichenology, mycology, physiology, plant geography, taxonomy. Offered by Department of Botany. Combined programs also offered with Departments of Agronomy, Bacteriology, Biochemistry, Chemistry, Entomology, Forestry and Wildlife Management, Genetics, Geology, Horticulture, Physics, Plant Pathology, Soils, and Zoology. Prerequisites for graduate study: 21 credits in botany; 1 course in zoology; 1 semester each of organic chemistry or biochemistry and of mathematics; 1 year of physics or equivalent. 16 professorial staff. 42 master's degrees and 37 Ph.D.'s awarded 1955-59. 66 graduate students registered fall 1959.

Chemistry. General, inorganic, analytical, organic, physical, and theoretical chemistry. Prerequisites for graduate study: 1 year each of general, analytical, organic, and physical chemistry; 1 year of physics; mathematics through calculus. 27 professorial staff. 68 master's degrees and 147 Ph.D.'s awarded 1955-59. 219 graduate students registered fall 1959.

Chemistry.—Physiological. Protein fractionation and characterization, intermediary metabolism, enzymology. Prerequisites for graduate study: major in chemistry; 1 semester each of organic chemistry or biochemistry and of mathematics; 1 year of physics or equivalent. 5 professorial staff. 1 master's degree and 8 Ph.D.'s awarded 1955-59. 15 graduate students registered fall 1959.

Chemistry.—Sanitary. Chemistry of water pollution, water or waste treatment, air sanitation. Prerequisites for graduate study: major in chemistry; 1 semester each of organic chemistry or biochemistry and of mathematics; 1 year of physics or equivalent. 5 professorial staff. Program reactivated fall 1960 after a lapse of several years.

Classics. Greek, Latin. Cooperative program with University of Iowa. Prerequisite for graduate study: 24 credits each of Greek and of Latin beyond elementary courses. 5 professorial staff.

18 master's degrees and 2 Ph.D.'s awarded 1955-59. 5 graduate students registered fall 1959.

Commerce. Accounting, finance, industrial management, labor marketing, public utilities and transportation, real estate, risk and insurance, statistics. Combined program offered by School of Commerce in cooperation with Department of Economics. Prerequisite for graduate study: preparation equivalent to B.B.A. 35 professorial staff. 229 master's degrees and 18 Ph.D.'s awarded 1955-59. 111 graduate students registered fall 1959.

Comparative Literature. Prerequisites for graduate study: major in comparative literature; reading knowledge of several foreign languages. 4 professorial staff. 2 master's degrees and 1 Ph.D. awarded 1955-59. 8 graduate students registered fall 1959.

Dairy and Food Industries. Dairy or food industry. Prerequisite for graduate study: major and preparation in chemistry and biology. 13 professorial staff. 32 master's degrees and 25 Ph.D.'s awarded 1955-59. 38 graduate students registered fall 1959.

Economics. Economic theory, institutions, or history; economic problems of underdeveloped areas; agricultural or international economics; industrial organization and public policy toward industry; finance; labor; public utilities; statistics and econometrics. Prerequisite for graduate study: 30 credits in economics. 21 professorial staff. 84 master's degrees and 91 Ph.D.'s awarded 1955-59. 73 graduate students registered fall 1959.

Economics.—Agricultural. General agricultural or land economics, farm management, marketing, prices and agricultural data. Combined program offered by Departments of Agricultural Economics and Economics. Prerequisite for graduate study: 24 credits in economics. 20 professorial staff. 53 master's degrees and 48 Ph.D.'s awarded 1955-59. 41 graduate students registered fall 1959.

Education. Educational foundations, curricula, administration and supervision, counseling and guidance, elementary or secondary education, audio-visual instruction. Combined programs possible with all subject matter fields at secondary school level and with Departments of Music, Physical Education, Political Science, Psychology, and Sociology. Prerequisites for graduate study: equivalent of University Teacher's Certificate. 48 professorial staff. 901 master's degrees and 118

Ph.D.'s awarded 1955-59. 279 graduate students registered fall 1959.

Engineering.—Chemical. Unit operations, reaction rates, applied thermodynamics, process control, electrochemistry, biochemical operations, analog computing, plastics. Offered by Department of Chemical Engineering. Combined program also offered with Departments of Chemistry and Biochemistry. Prerequisite for graduate study: major in chemical engineering. 11 professorial staff. 73 master's degrees and 36 Ph.D.'s awarded 1955-59. 62 graduate students registered fall 1959.

Engineering.—Civil. Highway, hydraulics, municipal, sanitary, or structural engineering; surveying. Prerequisite for graduate study: major in civil engineering. 13 professorial staff. 64 master's degrees and 11 Ph.D.'s awarded 1955-59. 112 graduate students registered fall 1959.

Engineering.—Electrical. Photometry, servomechanisms, circuit or power system analysis, computer systems, gaseous and solid electronics, ultra-high frequencies and microwaves, special instrumentation. Prerequisite for graduate study: major in electrical engineering. 23 professorial staff. 126 master's degrees and 39 Ph.D.'s awarded 1955-59. 223 graduate students registered fall 1959.

Engineering.—Mechanical. Stress analysis, manufacturing methods, motion and time study, heat transmission, air conditioning and refrigeration, steam power, internal combustion engines. Prerequisite for graduate study: major in mechanical engineering. 24 professorial staff. 99 master's degrees and 12 Ph.D.'s awarded 1955-59. 158 graduate students registered fall 1959.

Engineering Mechanics. Analytical or materials. Prerequisite for graduate study: major in engineering mechanics. 9 professorial staff. 6 master's degrees and 11 Ph.D.'s awarded 1955-59. 36 graduate students registered fall 1959.

Engineering. — Mining and Metallurgical. Mineral economics or dressing, many phases of metallurgy. Prerequisite for graduate study: major in mining and metallurgy. 8 professorial staff. 40 master's degrees and 7 Ph.D.'s awarded 1955-59. 34 graduate students registered fall 1959.

English. Prerequisites for graduate study: 24 credits of upper-division English, including a 2-semester course in Shakespeare, 1 semester of Old English, 1 course in Chaucer or Milton (or 1 of these and a period of English before 1900), and 19th century American or English literature.

21 professorial staff. 148 master's degrees and 98 Ph.D.'s awarded 1955-59. 213 graduate students registered fall 1959.

Entomology. Insecticides, toxicology, taxonomy, physiology, nutrition, ecology, disease transmission, biological control, insect-plant relations, insect resistance in plants, apiculture. Offered by Department of Entomology. Combined programs also offered with Departments of Genetics, Plant Pathology, and Zoology. Prerequisites for graduate study: major in entomology or equivalent; 1 semester each of organic chemistry or biochemistry and of mathematics; 1 year of physics or equivalent. 17 professorial staff. 31 master's degrees and 34 Ph.D.'s awarded 1955-59. 32 graduate students registered fall 1959.

Forestry and Wildlife Management. Offered by Department of Forestry in cooperation with Departments of Botany, Zoology or other biological science departments. Prerequisites for graduate study: major in an appropriate biological science; 1 semester each of organic chemistry or biochemistry and of mathematics; 1 year of physics or equivalent. 5 professorial staff. 12 master's degrees and 3 Ph.D.'s awarded 1955-59. 12 graduate students registered fall 1959.

French and Italian. Language, phonetics, diction, literature, literary history, linguistics, civilization. Prerequisite for graduate study: major in French or Italian. 12 professorial staff. 55 master's degrees and 17 Ph.D.'s awarded 1955-59. 38 graduate students registered fall 1959.

Genetics. Human, animal, bacterial, or plant genetics. Offered by Department of Genetics. Combined programs also offered with Departments of Agronomy, Animal Husbandry, Bacteriology, Biochemistry, Botany, Horticulture, Mathematical Statistics, Medical Genetics, Medical Microbiology, Plant Pathology, Poultry Husbandry, Dairy Husbandry, and Zoology. Prerequisites for graduate study: major in genetics; 1 semester each of organic chemistry or biochemistry and of mathematics; 1 year of physics or equivalent. 19 professorial staff. 35 master's degrees and 45 Ph.D.'s awarded 1955-59. 36 graduate students registered fall 1959.

Geography. Systematic and cultural geography, regional or historical geography, cartography and air photo interpretation. Prerequisite for graduate study: major in geography. 13 professorial staff. 58 master's degrees and 19 Ph.D.'s awarded 1955-59. 12 graduate students registered fall 1959.

Geology. Structural, metamorphic, or economic geology; paleontology and petroleum geology; stratigraphy; sedimentation; mineralogy and petrology; geomorphology and glacial geology; geophysics; X-ray. Prerequisite for graduate study: major in geology. 13 professorial staff. 91 master's degrees and 47 Ph.D.'s awarded 1955-59. 77 graduate students registered fall 1959.

German. Literature, linguistics. Prerequisite for graduate study: major in German. Ph.D. candidacy prerequisite: knowledge of Latin or Greek. 8 professorial staff. 14 master's degrees and 11 Ph.D.'s awarded 1955-59. 13 graduate students registered fall 1959.

History. Ancient, medieval, modern European, or United States history; American civilization; Britain and the British Empire. Combined program offered by Departments of History and Education. Prerequisite for graduate study: major in history. Ph.D. candidacy prerequisite: master's degree in history or equivalent. 22 professorial staff. 167 master's degrees and 74 Ph.D.'s awarded 1955-59. 230 graduate students registered fall 1959.

Home Economics. Human nutrition, experimental foods, family economics. Offered by Department of Home Economics. Combined programs also offered with Departments of Biochemistry and Education, and agricultural extensions. Prerequisite for graduate study: major in home economics; 1 semester each of organic chemistry or biochemistry, and of mathematics; 1 year of physics or equivalent. 23 professorial staff. 85 master's degrees and 15 Ph.D.'s awarded 1955-59. 42 graduate students registered fall 1959.

Horticulture. Ph.D. offered as joint major with Departments of Agronomy, Bacteriology, Biochemistry, Botany, Dairy and Food Industries, Entomology, Genetics, Plant Pathology, or Soils. Prerequisite for graduate study: major in horticulture. 15 professorial staff. 16 master's degrees and 6 Ph.D.'s awarded 1955-59. 16 graduate students registered fall 1959.

Industrial Relations. Public policy, organizational or interpersonal behavior. Administered by a committee from the Departments of Commerce, Economics, Sociology, Psychology, and Journalism. Prerequisites for graduate study: major in liberal arts, business administration, engineering, or other appropriate field; statistics or mathematics. 15 professorial staff. Ph.D. program begun 1957. 6 master's degrees and 3 Ph.D.'s awarded

1955-59. 19 graduate students registered fall 1959.

Journalism. Ph.D. offered as a joint program with another selected department or as a degree in mass communications. Prerequisite for graduate study: major in journalism. 12 professorial staff. 31 master's degrees awarded 1955-59 (including those in mass communications). 8 Ph.D.'s awarded through program in mass communications. 36 graduate students registered fall 1959 (including mass communications).

Linguistics. Comparative Indo-European linguistics. Prerequisites for graduate study: Latin and Greek (reading knowledge of 1 and elementary knowledge of other); French, German, Russian (reading knowledge of 2); 1 course in general phonetics. Ph.D. candidacy prerequisite: 6 credits in Sanskrit. 14 professorial staff. 1 Ph.D. awarded 1955-59. 1 graduate student registered fall 1959.

Mass Communications. Administered by a committee from the Departments of Journalism, Agricultural Journalism, Psychology, Sociology, and Speech. Ph.D. candidacy prerequisite: master's degree in journalism, agricultural journalism or equivalent. 5 professorial staff. 8 Ph.D.'s awarded 1955-59. (For master's degrees awarded, and for graduate students registered fall 1959, see program in journalism.)

Mathematics. Algebra, analysis, foundations, geometry, topology, applied mathematics. Prerequisite for graduate study: 15 semester hours of mathematics beyond calculus. 24 professorial staff. 136 master's degrees and 21 Ph.D.'s awarded 1955-59. 123 graduate students registered fall 1959.

Meteorology. Theory and practice as related to agriculture, engineering, and earth sciences. Prerequisites for graduate study: major or equivalent preparation in calculus, basic physics, and basic meteorology. 4 professorial staff. 12 master's degrees and 1 Ph.D. awarded 1955-59. 22 graduate students registered fall 1959.

Microbiology.—Medical. Prerequisites for graduate study: major in microbiology or bacteriology; 1 semester each of organic chemistry or biochemistry and of mathematics; 1 year of physics or equivalent. 5 professorial staff. 8 master's degrees and 12 Ph.D.'s awarded 1955-59. 14 graduate students registered fall 1959.

Music. Ph.D. given as joint degree with other departments, primarily with Department of Education. Prerequisites for graduate study: courses in music history and literature, music theory, and applied music. 21 professorial staff. 45 master's degrees and 2 Ph.D.'s awarded 1955-59. 36 graduate students registered fall 1959.

Oncology. Prerequisite for graduate study: major in chemistry, medical science or biology, or M.D. degree. 7 professorial staff. 11 master's degrees and 12 Ph.D.'s awarded 1955-59. 22 graduate students registered fall 1959.

Pathology. Ph.D. offered as joint degree with Departments of Bacteriology, Biochemistry, Physiology, Physiological Chemistry, Pharmacology, Veterinary Science, or Zoology. Prerequisite for graduate study: preparation in pathology and medical microbiology. 7 professorial staff. 2 master's degrees and 5 Ph.D.'s awarded 1955-59. 4 graduate students registered fall 1959.

Pharmacology. Pharmacology, toxicology, psycho-pharmacology. Prerequisites for graduate study: background courses in biology; 1 semester each of organic chemistry or biochemistry and of mathematics; 1 year of physics. 5 professorial staff. 2 master's degrees and 10 Ph.D.'s awarded 1955-59. 21 graduate students registered fall 1959.

Pharmacy. History of pharmacy, pharmaceutical chemistry, pharmacy administration, pharmacognosy. Prerequisite for graduate study: major in pharmacy. 13 professorial staff. 25 master's degrees and 40 Ph.D.'s awarded 1955-59. 21 graduate students registered fall 1959.

Philosophy. Logic, history of philosophy, ethics, aesthetics, epistemology, metaphysics. Prerequisite for graduate study: major in philosophy. 9 professorial staff. 13 master's degrees and 6 Ph.D.'s awarded 1955-59. 17 graduate students registered fall 1959.

Physical Education.—Women. Curriculum, dance, kinesiology, measurement, motor development, physiological effects of motor activities and relaxation. Offered by Department of Physical Education—Women. Combined programs also offered with Departments of Anatomy, Education, and Physiology. Prerequisite for graduate study: major in physical education or dance. 10 professorial staff. 50 master's degrees and 5 Ph.D.'s awarded 1955-59. 33 graduate students registered fall 1959.

Physics. Theoretical, nuclear, meson, solid-state, or low-temperature physics; atomic and molecular spectroscopy; X-rays; gaseous electronics; thermionics. Prerequisite for graduate study: major in physics. 21 professorial staff. 97

master's degrees and 57 Ph.D.'s awarded 1955-59. 148 graduate students registered fall 1959.

Physiology. Prerequisites for graduate study: major in biology or medical science; 1 semester each of organic chemistry or biochemistry and of mathematics; 1 year of physics or equivalent. 12 professorial staff. 5 master's degrees and 7 Ph.D.'s awarded 1955-59. 9 graduate students registered fall 1959.

Plant Pathology. Nematology and other main branches. Prerequisites for graduate study: major in plant pathology or botany; 1 semester each of organic chemistry or biochemistry and of mathematics; 1 year of physics or equivalent. 23 professorial staff. 27 master's degrees and 55 Ph.D.'s awarded 1955-59. 65 graduate students registered fall 1959.

Political Science. Political theory, comparative government, international relations, international law and organization, American political institutions, public administration or law, politics, public policy. Prerequisite for graduate study: major in political science. 16 professorial staff. 65 master's degrees and 27 Ph.D.'s awarded 1955-59. 54 graduate students registered fall 1959.

Psychology. Experimental, social, industrial, animal, physiological, or clinical psychology. Prerequisite for graduate study: major in psychology. Ph.D. candidacy prerequisite: M.S. in psychology or equivalent. 17 professorial staff. 65 master's degrees and 47 Ph.D.'s awarded 1955-59. 86 graduate students registered fall 1959.

Science.—History. History of science through Newton; the natural sciences since Leonardo and Vesalius, and the evolution of scientific institutions; the physical sciences since Newton; history of chemistry, pharmacy, or medicine. Prerequisites for graduate study: major in a science, history of science, history, philosophy, or classics. 5 professorial staff. 4 master's degrees and 3 Ph.D.'s awarded 1955-59. 13 graduate students registered fall 1959.

Sociology. Theory; social organization, disorganization, or psychology; methods and statistics; rural sociology; population. Prerequisite for graduate study: major in sociology. Ph.D. candidacy prerequisite: M.S. in sociology. 13 professorial staff. 29 master's degrees and 27 Ph.D.'s awarded 1955-59. 45 graduate students registered fall 1959.

Sociology.—Rural. Ph.D. offered as joint degree with Department of Sociology. Prerequisite for graduate study: major in sociology. Ph.D. candidacy prerequisite: M.S. in sociology or rural sociology. 7 professorial staff. 14 master's degrees and 13 Ph.D.'s awarded 1955-59. 16 graduate students registered fall 1959.

Soils. Soil fertility, chemistry, physics, conservation, forest soils, and soil survey. Prerequisites for graduate study: major in soils; 1 semester each of organic chemistry or biochemistry and of mathematics; 1 year of physics or equivalent. 20 professorial staff. 47 master's degrees and 48 Ph.D.'s awarded 1955-59. 53 graduate students registered fall 1959.

Spanish and Portuguese. Language, literature, civilization. Prerequisite for graduate study: major in Spanish. Ph.D. candidacy prerequisite: reading knowledge of French, German, and Latin. 11 professorial staff. 69 master's degrees and 15 Ph.D.'s awarded 1955-59. 50 graduate students registered fall 1959.

Speech. Rhetoric and public address, theater and interpretation, speech pathology and audiology, speech science or pedagogy, radio and television. Prerequisite for graduate study: major in speech. 17 professorial staff. 97 master's degrees and 43 Ph.D.'s awarded 1955-59. 76 graduate students registered fall 1959.

Statistics. General statistics, theory, design of experiments. Prerequisites for graduate study: major in mathematics, or major in a basic science with appropriate background in mathematics. Ph.D. candidacy prerequisite: M.S. in statistics from Wisconsin or equivalent preparation. 4 professorial staff. Program begun 1960.

Veterinary Science. Bacteriology, parasitology, pathology, and physiology as applied to the veterinary field. Prerequisite for graduate study: D.V.M. or equivalent preparation; 1 semester each of organic chemistry or biochemistry and of mathematics; 1 year of physics or equivalent. 12 professorial staff. 23 master's degrees and 13 Ph.D.'s awarded 1955-59. 26 graduate students registered fall 1959.

Zoology. Comparative anatomy or histology, comparative and general physiology, cytology, endocrinology, fishery ecology, hydrobiology, animal behavior or serology, ornithology, parasitology, protozoology. Offered by Department of Zoology. Combined programs also offered with Departments of Wildlife Management, Genetics, Anatomy, Entomology, and Veterinary Science. Prerequisites for graduate study: major in zoology; GRE; 1 semester each of organic chemistry or biochemistry and of mathematics; 1 year of physics or equivalent. 18 professorial staff. 49 master's degrees and 61 Ph.D.'s awarded 1955-59. 111 graduate students registered fall 1959.

Worcester Polytechnic Institute

WORCESTER 9, MASSACHUSETTS

Graduate Study Program

The Graduate Study Program is administered by the Dean of Faculty, the Graduate Study Committee, and the heads of the degree-granting departments. Graduate instruction has been offered since 1897, with the first doctorate being awarded in 1904. Institution is privately controlled and nonsectarian. Both men and women are admitted, but students are predominantly men.

Rooms for men are available in dormitories.

Research facilities include: Van de Graaff accelerator; a nuclear reactor (pool-type); computers; library of approximately 45,000 volumes.

Residence requirement for Ph.D.: 3 years beyond bachelor's degree, of which at least 1 year must be taken in residence at this institution. Usually no more than 10 semester credits may be transferred from other graduate institutions; exceptions must be approved by department head and Graduate Study Committee. Summer work on campus for thesis research only. Limited number of evening courses are offered.

ADMISSION REQUIREMENTS

For graduate study: bachelor's degree; undergraduate record of B or better; approval of course of study by department head and Graduate Study Committee. For candidacy for Ph.D.: comprehensive examination. Scientific reading knowledge of 2 foreign languages must be demonstrated before degree is awarded.

Apply to Dean of Faculty or department head at any time.

FEES AND FIRST-YEAR AID

No application fee. Tuition $1,100 per year. Rooms (in dormitory) for men $375-$450 per year. Approximate annual cost of board in college dining room $480.

First-year aid available: 6 tuition scholarships, up to full tuition; 15 half-time teaching fellowships, $1,600 plus tuition; 4 other fellowships, $2,200 plus tuition; 8 research assistantships, $1,600 plus tuition.

Apply to Dean of Faculty or department head before April 1.

FIELDS OF STUDY FOR THE PH.D.

Chemistry. Solid-state and synthetic organic chemistry, biochemistry, metal surfaces, colloid chemistry, and infrared spectroscopy. Program arranged on individual basis by Department of Chemical Engineering and Chemistry. Prerequisite for graduate study: major in chemistry. 5 professorial staff. 5 graduate students registered fall 1959.

Engineering.—Chemical. Reaction kinetics, diffusion, turbulence, combustion, heat transmission, process control, and nuclear chemical engineering. Program arranged on individual basis by Department of Chemical Engineering and Chemistry. Prerequisite for graduate study: major in chemical engineering. 6 professorial staff. 18 master's degrees awarded 1955-59. 10 graduate students registered fall 1959.

Physics. Nuclear physics, nuclear magnetic resonance, X-ray diffraction, physical optics, absorption and emission spectroscopy. Program arranged on individual basis by Department of Physics. Prerequisite for graduate study: major in physics. 12 professorial staff. 3 master's degrees awarded 1955-59. 9 graduate students registered fall 1959.

Wyoming, University of

LARAMIE, WYOMING

The Graduate School

Graduate degrees were first given in 1897, but the Graduate School was not formally organized until 1946. The first Ph.D. was awarded in 1947. In addition to the Ph.D. programs (which are emphasized in those fields where the University of Wyoming has unique advantages), a program leading to the Ed.D. is offered by the Graduate Study Division of the College of Education through the Graduate School. The university is publicly controlled by the state. Both men and women are admitted.

Single graduate students may live in university dormitories; university housing provided for married graduate students.

Special facilities include: library of approximately 262,000 volumes; herbarium; vertebrate and invertebrate paleontological museums; research facilities at Jackson Hole Station; summer camp facilities for instruction and research in geology, botany, and zoology.

Residence requirement for Ph.D.: minimum of 3 academic years, at least 4 semesters of which must be spent in residence at the University of Wyoming (including 2 during the regular academic year). Summer and evening courses available.

ADMISSION REQUIREMENTS

For graduate study: bachelor's degree; demonstrated ability to do superior work in major and cognate fields. For candidacy for Ph.D.: master's degree or completion of 20 hours of course work; departmental approval; reading knowledge of French and German (statistics or Russian may be substituted if recommended by student's advisory committee).

Apply to Section on Admissions, Office of the Registrar, at least 4 weeks prior to date of desired entry.

FEES AND FIRST-YEAR AID

No application fee. Tuition for state residents $245 per academic year; others $507. Room (in dormitory) for men $145 per academic year (2 to a room); for women $87-$280. Approximate annual cost of board in college dining room $400. Apartments $43.65-$53.65 per month plus utilities.

First-year aid available: 6 scholarships covering majority of fees; teaching fellowships in all fields, $1,000-$2,000 (modal figure $1,503); fellowships in American studies and geology, $1,500-$2,500; 10 research assistantships in agriculture, $1,000-$2,500; grants-in-aid for geology students, $500-$1,000.

Apply by February 1 as follows: for assistantships, to the Graduate School Office; for American Studies fellowships, to Office of Director, American Studies Program; for geology fellowships, to the Office of the Head of the Geology Departments.

FIELDS OF STUDY FOR THE PH.D.

Course in the methodology of teaching offered through the Graduate School carries credit of 1 hour per semester. Student enrolls in major field. During first semester there are lectures and discussion to orient the prospective teacher in areas other than his major field; during second semester student works with major professor in field as he does on a research program.

Agriculture. Animal science (including animal husbandry, dairy, poultry, and wool technology); plant science (including crops and soils, entomology, plant pathology, and range management). 28 professorial staff. 65 master's degrees and 9 Ph.D.'s awarded 1955-59. 35 graduate students registered fall 1959.

Chemistry. Organic chemistry (para-Claisen rearrangement, mechanism of ozonization); biochemistry; biosynthetic methods for aromatic compounds; cancer; analytical use of synthetic resins; physical oxidation with periodates; inorganic chemistry; complex component of metal halides with phosphorous oxychloride; reduction of metal sulfides; silicate chemistry; radiological chemistry. Prerequisites for graduate study: qualifying examinations to determine adequacy of preparation in general, analytical, organic, and physical chemistry. Recommended: general physics; calculus. 11 professorial staff. 8 master's degrees and 3 Ph.D.'s awarded 1955-59. 18 graduate students registered fall 1959.

Engineering.—Civil. Structural design and analysis, water resources, hydrology, transportation, aerodosy, meteorology, engineering materials, fluid mechanics, soil mechanics. Prerequisites for Ph.D. candidacy: M.S. in civil engineering; mathematics through partial differential equations. 8 professorial staff. Ph.D. program initiated 1958. 14 master's degrees awarded 1955-59. 15 graduate students registered fall 1959.

Geology. Stratigraphy, structural geology, geomorphology, vertebrate or invertebrate paleontology, mineral deposits. Prerequisites for graduate study: 30 semester hours of geology; 10 of chemistry; 10 of mathematics; 8 of physics. Recommended: general, historical, and structural geology; mineralogy; geomorphology; invertebrate paleontology; stratigraphy. 8 professorial staff. 79 master's degrees and 5 Ph.D.'s awarded 1955-59. 27 graduate students registered fall 1959.

Zoology and Physiology. Ecology, parasitology, physiology, wildlife conservation and management. 12 professorial staff. Ph.D. program begun 1957. 24 master's degrees awarded 1955-59. 21 graduate students registered fall 1959.

Yale University

NEW HAVEN, CONNECTICUT

The Graduate School

Provision for graduate study at Yale was made as early as 1732, and a special department for graduate study was established in 1847. First Ph.D. was awarded in 1861. The university is privately controlled and nonsectarian. Only men are admitted to the undergraduate college; both men and women to all graduate schools except the School of Forestry and the School of Engineering.

Other doctorates conferred by the university include: D.P.H. (School of Medicine); D.Eng. (School of Engineering); D.F. (School of Forestry); J.S.D. (School of Law); D.F.A. (School of Drama).

Separate residence halls maintained for single graduate students; apartments in university-owned buildings available for married students.

Special facilities include: library of over 4,000,000 volumes; professional school libraries; natural history museum; art gallery; Institute of Human Relations; child study center; electron accelerator; heavy-particle-ion accelerator; observatory (including branch at Mount Stromlo, Canberra, Australia in conjunction with Columbia University). Affiliations with Brookhaven National Laboratory and with Bishop Museum in Honolulu offer additional opportunities for research.

Residence requirement for Ph.D.: minimum of 3 years.

ADMISSION REQUIREMENTS

For graduate study: bachelor's degree; distinguished undergraduate record; French or German; letters of recommendation; GRE in some departments. Foreign students may be required to take English proficiency test. For candidacy for Ph.D.: reading knowledge of French and German (some departments also require Latin or other languages); general oral and written examinations; approval of dissertation subject.

Apply to Director of Admissions, Graduate School, by February 1.

FEES AND FIRST-YEAR AID

Application fee $10. Tuition $1,000 ($1,350 beginning 1961-62) per academic year. Room (in residence hall) for men $250-$400 per academic year; for women $425 for single room, $300 for double room. Cost of board in college dining room: $253.50 for fall term; $217 for spring term. Apartments $43-$65 per month.

First-year aid available: scholarships, $1,000; laboratory assistantships, $1,700 plus tuition; fellowships, $1,000-$3,000; research assistantships, variable stipend.

Apply to Director of Admissions, Graduate School, by February 1.

FIELDS OF STUDY FOR THE PH.D.

Several departments offer courses in the methodology of teaching or supervised training in teaching. Assistantships in instruction open to third-year students.

Anatomy. Prerequisite for graduate study: major in the biological sciences. 6 professorial staff. 2 Ph.D.'s awarded 1955-59. 3 graduate students registered fall 1959.

Anthropology. Archaeology; linguistics; physical anthropology; ethnology, including social anthropology and culture and personality. Prerequisite for graduate study: GRE Aptitude Test. 12 professorial staff. 3 master's degrees and 20 Ph.D.'s awarded 1955-59. 19 graduate students registered fall 1959.

Area Studies.—African. Not a degree program. Students enroll in history, economics, political science, or other appropriate discipline. Advisory Committee on African Studies counsels students, but degree is awarded in major discipline.

Area Studies.—American. Offered by Department of American Studies. Prerequisite for graduate study: broad preparation in humanities and social sciences. 15 professorial staff. 16 Ph.D.'s awarded 1955-59. 22 graduate students registered fall 1959.

Art.—History. History of art. Prerequisites for graduate study: knowledge of history of architecture, painting, and sculpture; acquaintance with fundamental principles of art criticism; GRE. 11 professorial staff. 15 master's degrees and 13 Ph.D.'s awarded 1955-59. 26 graduate students registered fall 1959.

Astronomy. Radio astronomy, astrophysics. Prerequisites for graduate study: mathematics and physics; GRE. 6 professorial staff. 1 master's degree and 4 Ph.D.'s awarded 1955-59. 6 graduate students registered fall 1959.

Biochemistry. Prerequisites for graduate study: general, analytical, physical, and organic chemistry; background in physics and general biology. 14 professorial staff. 5 master's degrees and 11 Ph.D.'s awarded 1955-59. 22 graduate students registered fall 1959.

Biophysics. Physics and chemistry of viruses, physics of cellular processes, biological action of ionizing radiation, X-ray structural analysis, ultraviolet action and absorption, genetic studies with radioactive tracers, bacterial transforming-principle studies, theoretical biophysics, electron microscopy. Prerequisite for graduate study: major in physics, biology, or chemistry or a combination of these subjects. 10 professorial staff. 2 master's degrees and 13 Ph.D.'s awarded 1955-59. 21 graduate students registered fall 1959.

Botany. Morphology, physiology, mycology, taxonomy, cytotaxonomy, ecology, paleobotany, genetics, cytology. Prerequisites for graduate study: background in botany, including morphology, genetics, physiology, and taxonomy; mathematics; physics; chemistry; zoology. 12 professorial staff. 21 master's degrees and 17 Ph.D.'s awarded 1955-59. 22 graduate students registered fall 1959.

Chemistry. Reaction mechanisms and kinetics; natural products, sterols, pigments, photoperoxides; methods of separating organic mixtures, chromatography, oxidation-reduction polymers; gas kinetics, high-temperature reactions; nuclear chemistry and systematics of nuclear fission; structure of natural products, organic reaction mechanisms; synthesis, mechanism of organic reactions, tracer studies; synthesis of natural products, carbohydrates, reaction mechanism; polymers, dielectrics, nonaqueous solutions; small rings, pyrolysis and air oxidation; statistical and quantum mechanics, protein physical chemistry; transport and thermodynamic properties of mixtures, diffusion, Soret effect; theoretical chemistry and physics; conductance and compressibilities of strong electrolytes; high field conductance, activity coefficients, physical chemistry of sodium in liquid ammonia; nuclear magnetic resonance and organic reaction mechanisms; physical chemistry of proteins and polymers, biochemistry, immunochemistry; calorimetry, physical chem-

istry of proteins, enzyme kinetics; hemoglobin, metal complexes, mechanism of inorganic and enzymic reactions; natural products, physical methods in structure determination; nuclear and radiochemistry, mechanism of high-energy reactions. Prerequisites for graduate study: general, analytical, organic, and physical chemistry; physics; mathematics through calculus. 18 professorial staff. 91 master's degrees and 83 Ph.D.'s awarded 1955-59. 88 graduate students registered fall 1959.

Classical Languages and Literatures. Greek or Latin literature, ancient history, classical archaeology, historical and comparative grammar. Prerequisites for graduate study: proficiency in Greek and Latin; GRE Aptitude Test. Ph.D. candidacy prerequisites: French and German. 15 professorial staff. 24 master's degrees and 13 Ph.D.'s awarded 1955-59. 26 graduate students registered fall 1959.

Comparative Literature. Prerequisites for graduate study: background in literature and literary history; Latin or Greek in addition to French and German. Ph.D. candidacy prerequisites: ability to read literary works in 2 foreign languages; course in philology or linguistics. 5 professorial staff. 8 Ph.D.'s awarded 1955-59. 17 graduate students registered fall 1959.

Economics. Economic theory or history, quantitative methods, market organization and public policy, labor economics and industrial relations, money and banking, economics of the public sector, international trade and finance; structure and growth of national economies; international and foreign economics. Prerequisites for graduate study: mathematics, including differential and integral calculus; statistics; GRE. Recommended: major in economics; courses in psychology, history, and other social sciences. 40 professorial staff. 124 master's degrees and 29 Ph.D.'s awarded 1955-59. 84 graduate students registered fall 1959.

Engineering.—Chemical. Prerequisites for graduate study: courses in mathematics, physics, chemistry, and fundamentals of chemical engineering. 5 professorial staff. 4 master's degrees and 5 Ph.D.'s awarded 1955-59. 3 graduate students registered fall 1959.

Engineering.—Civil. Prerequisites for graduate study: courses in mathematics, mechanics, chemistry, physics, and fundamentals of engineering. 9 professorial staff.

Engineering.—Electrical. Relationships of mathematics, mechanics, physics, and electrical engineering; techniques of modern engineering. Prerequisites for graduate study: mathematics; physics; engineering sciences. 17 professorial staff. 1 master's degree and 10 Ph.D.'s awarded 1955-59. 3 graduate students registered fall 1959.

Engineering.—Mechanical. Heat transfer, analytical mechanics, thermodynamics. Prerequisite for graduate study: fundamental subjects of mechanical engineering, with suitable foundation in mathematics and physics. 10 professorial staff. 2 Ph.D.'s awarded 1955-59. 2 graduate students registered fall 1959.

Engineering.—Metallurgical. Solid-state sciences, structure and properties of liquid alloys, phase transformation and fracture in steels, plasticity of nonmetallic crystals, oxidation reactions and diffusion, order-disorder transformations, X-ray investigation of stacking faults in metal and alloy crystals, structure of liquid metals. Offered by Department of Metallurgy. Prerequisites for graduate study: working knowledge of calculus and differential equations, physical chemistry, physics, crystallography, and the basic principles of physical metallurgy. 5 professorial staff.

English. English literature, literary criticism or history, history of the English language, philology. Prerequisites for graduate study: knowledge of English literature; broad preparation in humanities; GRE. 26 professorial staff. 132 master's degrees and 75 Ph.D.'s awarded 1955-59. 112 graduate students registered fall 1959.

Foreign Area Studies. Not a Ph.D. degree program. Advisory Committee on Foreign Area Studies will counsel students enrolled in history, economics, international relations, or political science with intent to emphasize area studies. 45 professorial staff. Degree awarded in major discipline in which student is enrolled.

Forestry. Forest pathology, genetics, or ecology; silviculture; finance, mensuration, and management; wood technology. Prerequisites for graduate study: courses in botany, mathematics, and economics; GRE. 25 professorial staff. 1 master's degree and 20 Ph.D.'s awarded 1955-59. 15 graduate students registered fall 1959.

French. French literature and philology. Offered by Department of Romance Languages and Literatures. Prerequisites for graduate study: major in French; ability to speak, read, and write the language; broad preparation in humanities.

11 professorial staff. 9 master's degrees and 36 Ph.D.'s awarded 1955-59. 60 graduate students registered fall 1959.

Geology. Mineralogy and crystallography, petrology, structural or economic geology, geomorphology and Pleistocene geology, paleontology, stratigraphy, sedimentology, geochemistry. Prerequisites for graduate study: physical and field geology; mineralogy; petrology; paleontology; physics; chemistry; mathematics through trigonometry and analytic geometry; GRE. Recommended: elementary biology for students majoring in paleontology or stratigraphy. 18 professorial staff. 32 master's degrees and 33 Ph.D.'s awarded 1955-59. 31 graduate students registered fall 1959.

German. Literature, linguistics and philology. Offered by Department of Germanic Languages and Literatures. Prerequisites for graduate study: ability to read difficult German; facility in writing and speaking German; general acquaintance with German literature; French; GRE. Ph.D. candidacy prerequisite: reading knowledge of a Scandinavian language. 6 professorial staff. 19 master's degrees and 6 Ph.D.'s awarded 1955-59. 18 graduate students registered fall 1959.

History. American, Chinese, medieval, or intellectual history; history of Western or of non-Western civilizations; foreign policy and diplomacy. Prerequisite for graduate study: major in history, with broad cultural background in humanities and social sciences. 35 professorial staff. 78 master's degrees and 32 Ph.D.'s awarded 1955-59. 89 graduate students registered fall 1959.

International Relations. International politics, comparative government and regional politics, methods and instruments of control, economics of international affairs, American and European diplomatic history and foreign policies. Prerequisites for graduate study: preferably a major in political science or history, with courses in economics, but students with broad preparation in social sciences and humanities may qualify; GRE. 26 professorial staff. 55 master's degrees and 22 Ph.D.'s awarded 1955-59. 35 graduate students registered fall 1959.

Italian. Italian literature. Offered by Department of Romance Languages and Literatures. Prerequisites for graduate study: training in Romance languages with adequate preparation in Italian. 2 professorial staff. 1 master's degree and 2 Ph.D.'s awarded 1955-59. 1 graduate student registered fall 1959.

Languages and Literatures.—Indic and Far Eastern. Indic, Iranian, Chinese, Tibetan, Mongolian, Korean, Japanese, Malayo-Polynesian, Burmese, Siamese, or Vietnamese languages. 12 professorial staff. 1 master's degree and 2 Ph.D.'s awarded 1955-59. 5 graduate students registered fall 1959.

Languages and Literatures.—Near Eastern. Cuneiform or West Semitic studies; Old or New Testament, Arabic, Near Eastern archaeology. Prerequisite for graduate study: GRE. Recommended: major in classics, history, linguistics, philosophy, or religion. 8 professorial staff. 1 master's degree and 6 Ph.D.'s awarded 1955-59. 7 graduate students registered fall 1959.

Linguistics. Linguistic or grammatical theory; comparative grammar; Indo-European, Indic, Iranian, Greek, Italic, Celtic, Germanic, Slavic, Near Eastern, Far Eastern, and Pacific languages. Prerequisites for graduate study: strong preparation in languages and literature; Latin and Greek in addition to French and German. Ph.D. candidacy prerequisite: knowledge of structure of 1 language outside Indo-European family. 20 professorial staff. 13 master's degrees and 9 Ph.D.'s awarded 1955-59. 16 graduate students registered fall 1959.

Mathematics. Algebra, analysis, topology. 15 professorial staff. 16 master's degrees and 31 Ph.D.'s awarded 1955-59. 44 graduate students registered fall 1959.

Medieval Studies. Not a degree program. Students enroll in history, literature, classics, or other appropriate discipline. Advisory Committee on Medieval Studies counsels the students, but degree is awarded in major discipline.

Microbiology. Microbiology, virology, parasitology, immunochemistry. Prerequisites for graduate study: preparation in biology, mathematics, physics, and chemistry (including 1 year of organic chemistry). 14 professorial staff. 7 master's degrees and 11 Ph.D.'s awarded 1955-59. 20 graduate students registered fall 1959.

Music.—History. History of music. Prerequisites for graduate study: history and theory of music; general background in humanities, particularly literature and history; GRE. 6 professorial staff. 3 master's degrees and 6 Ph.D.'s awarded 1955-59. 22 graduate students registered fall 1959.

Pharmacology. Prerequisite for graduate study: scientific background, including biology and chemistry. 16 professorial staff. 1 master's degree and 3 Ph.D.'s awarded 1955-59. 5 graduate students registered fall 1959.

Philosophy. History of philosophy, logic, philosophy of science, philosophy of religion, aesthetics, ethics, theory of value, metaphysics and theory of knowledge. Prerequisites for graduate study: basic preparation in philosophy; broad cultural training; GRE. 19 professorial staff. 57 master's degrees and 43 Ph.D.'s awarded 1955-59. 84 graduate students registered fall 1959.

Physics. Theoretical, nuclear, or low-temperature physics; quantum mechanics. Prerequisites for graduate study: major in physics; fundamentals of chemistry: working knowledge of calculus and differential equations. 39 professorial staff. 86 master's degrees and 70 Ph.D.'s awarded 1955-59. 111 graduate students registered fall 1959.

Physiology. Prerequisites for graduate study: biology and physics; general, analytical, physical, and organic chemistry; GRE. Recommended: knowledge of comparative anatomy and elementary histology. 11 professorial staff. 2 Ph.D.'s awarded 1955-59. 3 graduate students registered fall 1959.

Political Science. Political theory, comparative government, politics and policy formation, public administration, public law, international politics and organization. Prerequisites for graduate study: major in political science with broad preparation in social sciences; GRE. 20 professorial staff. 47 master's degrees and 23 Ph.D.'s awarded 1955-59. 46 graduate students registered fall 1959.

Psychology. Experimental or clinical psychology; social psychology, personality, and abnormal behavior; child development. Prerequisites for graduate study: basic courses in theoretical and experimental psychology; GRE Aptitude Test. Recommended: experimental training in physical science and biology; social sciences; mathematics through calculus; statistics; philosophy; history of science. Ph.D. candidacy prerequisite: certification of competence in research methods, including statistics. 26 professorial staff. 39 master's degrees and 46 Ph.D.'s awarded 1955-59. 55 graduate students registered fall 1959.

Public Health. Program being reorganized. Announcement of areas of concentration and structure of program will be made within a year or so. 42 professorial staff. 13 master's degrees and 3 Ph.D.'s awarded 1955-59. 1 graduate student registered fall 1959.

Religion. Comparative religion, Old or New Testament, Biblical theology, history of Christianity, theology (historical, philosophical, or contemporary), Christian or social ethics, sociology of religion, Christian education. Prerequisites for graduate study: orientation in fields of historical and contemporary religion, including introductory courses in comparative religion, Old and New Testament literature, history of Christianity, theology, and philosophy of religion. 34 professorial staff. 70 master's degrees and 80 Ph.D.'s awarded 1955-59. 79 graduate students registered fall 1959.

Russian. Slavic literature and linguistics. Offered by Department of Slavic Languages and Literatures. Prerequisite for graduate study: competence in Russian language. Ph.D. candidacy prerequisites: another non-Russian Slavic language; French and German. 9 professorial staff. Ph.D. program begun 1958. 1 master's degree awarded 1955-59. 6 graduate students registered fall 1959.

Science and Medicine.—History. Offered by Department of History of Science and Medicine. Recommended for graduate study: basic preparation in science or history; courses in the history and philosophy of science; intellectual history. 7 professorial staff. Ph.D. program begun 1960.

Sociology. Social stratification or conflict; small group research; medical sociology. Prerequisite for graduate study: major in sociology preferred, but those with broad preparation in the social sciences accepted. 14 professorial staff. 21 master's degrees and 18 Ph.D.'s awarded 1955-59. 35 graduate students registered fall 1959.

Spanish. Spanish literature and philology. Offered by Department of Romance Languages and Literatures. Prerequisites for graduate study: ability to speak, read, and write Spanish; broad preparation in humanities. Ph.D. candidacy prerequisites: Latin, French, and German. 5 professorial staff. 6 master's degrees and 6 Ph.D.'s awarded 1955-59. 11 graduate students registered fall 1959.

Theatre.—History. Offered by Department of History of the Theatre. Prerequisites for graduate study: background in humanities; GRE. 7 professorial staff. 7 Ph.D.'s awarded 1955-59. 5 graduate students registered fall 1959.

Zoology. Vertebrate and invertebrate zoology, genetics, morphology, physiology, histology, embryology. Prerequisites for graduate study: knowledge of the elements of botany, chemistry, mathematics (including elementary calculus), and physics. 20 professorial staff. 7 master's degrees and 21 Ph.D.'s awarded 1955-59. 37 graduate students registered fall 1959.

Yeshiva University
NEW YORK 33, NEW YORK

Yeshiva University evolved from a merger of 2 Orthodox Jewish theological seminaries, Yeshiva Eitz Chaim, and the Rabbi Isaac Elchanan Theological Seminary. It achieved university status in 1945. At present, Ph.D. programs are offered through the following divisions: Bernard Revel Graduate School; Harry Fischel School for Higher Jewish Studies (programs offered in summer session only); Sue Golding Graduate Division of Medical Sciences; Graduate School of Mathematical Sciences. The Graduate School of Education formerly offered both the Ph.D. and the Ed.D. degrees, but is now undergoing administrative reorganization and will announce its new programs at a later time. University is privately controlled under Orthodox Jewish auspices. Both men and women are admitted.

Bernard Revel Graduate School

Division was organized in 1937 and awarded its first Ph.D. in 1958. It also confers the D.H.L. and Ed.D. degrees.

University residence hall maintained for single graduate men; no residence facilities for women or for married students.

Residence requirement for Ph.D.: students must complete a minimum of 15 full courses in residence at Yeshiva. Summer courses offered under the auspices of the Harry Fischel School for Higher Jewish Studies. Evening courses also available.

ADMISSION REQUIREMENTS

For graduate study: bachelor's degree; broad knowledge of Jewish studies. Recommended:

preparation in Talmud. For candidacy for Ph.D.: master's degree or equivalent in area of specialization; reading knowledge of Hebrew, plus German and French or an approved substitute; approval of matriculation by faculty committee.

Apply to Director of Admissions, Bernard Revel Graduate School, Yeshiva University, Amsterdam Avenue and 186th Street, New York 33, New York, at least 30 days before beginning of new semester.

FEES AND FIRST-YEAR AID

Application fee $10. Tuition $30 per course. Special fees approximate $50 annually. Room (in residence hall) for single men $350 per year. Approximate annual cost of board in college dining room $700.

First-year aid available: scholarships, $100-$400 per semester; fellowships, $2,500-$3,000 per year.

Apply to Director of Admissions at the time application for admission is filed.

FIELDS OF STUDY FOR THE PH.D.

Jewish Studies. Bible; Jewish history, literature, and philosophy; Rabbinic and Talmudic studies; Semitic languages and literatures. 12 professorial staff. 16 master's degrees and 1 Ph.D. awarded 1955-59. 135 graduate students registered fall 1959.

Sue Golding Graduate Division of Medical Sciences

Graduate instruction has been offered in this division since 1956.

Abraham Mazer residence hall provides housing for 291 graduate and medical students; limited number of apartments available for married students.

All of the basic science and clinical facilities of the Albert Einstein College of Medicine of Yeshiva University are available to the graduate students in this division.

Residence requirement for Ph.D.: at least 3 years of graduate study beyond bachelor's degree, 2 of which must be taken in residence at the Sue Golding Graduate Division.

ADMISSION REQUIREMENTS

For graduate study: bachelor's degree; acceptance by department; recommendations. Recommended: GRE; knowledge of 2 modern foreign languages. For candidacy for Ph.D.: successful completion of formal course work; satisfaction of departmental language requirements (usually a reading knowledge of French and German); preliminary qualifying examinations.

Apply to chairman of appropriate department at any time. The division is located at the Medical Center, Eastchester Road and Morris Park Avenue, Bronx 61, New York.

FEES AND FIRST-YEAR AID

No application fee. Tuition $1,000 per academic year for students taking 12 hours or more per week per semester; $40 per weekly hour per semester for students taking 11 hours or less per week per semester. A charge of $25 per semester is made for thesis work. Registration fee and student hospital insurance total approximately $45 per year. Room (in residence hall) $400 on 10-month basis; $430 on annual basis. Apartments $90 per month. Students pay for own meals in college dining room.

First-year aid available: training fellowships, $1,800-$4,000 per year.

For additional information, write to Administrative Secretary, Sue Golding Graduate Division of Medical Sciences, Yeshiva University, Eastchester Road and Morris Park Avenue, Bronx 61, New York.

FIELDS OF STUDY FOR THE PH.D.

Anatomy and Genetics. Neuroendocrinology, mammalian genetics. Offered by Department of Anatomy. Prerequisite for graduate study: preparation in zoology, general principles of biology, physiology, embryology, genetics, histology, bacteriology, physics, and inorganic and organic chemistry. 13 professorial staff. Program begun 1956. 5 graduate students registered fall 1959. Total enrollment limited to 6.

Biochemistry. Intermediary metabolism, enzymology, lipid and protein chemistry, endocrinology, immunochemistry. Prerequisites for graduate study: major in chemistry, including physical and advanced organic chemistry; background in general biology; mathematics through calculus. 25 professorial staff. Program begun 1956. 4 graduate students registered fall 1959. New enrollment limited to 4 per year.

Microbiology and Immunology. Experimental hypersensitivity, microbial biochemistry and genetics, tissue culture, specific infectious disease agents. Offered by Department of Microbiology and Immunology. Prerequisites for graduate study: basic qualification in biological, chemical, and physical sciences; personal interview. 6 professorial staff. Program begun 1958.

Pathology. Application of physical methods, such as fluorescent tagging and isotope tagging; electron microscopy; endocrine physiology in stress; tissue culture; histochemistry; experimental oncology research; connective tissue studies. Offered by Department of Pathology. Prerequisites for graduate study: concentration in biological and chemical sciences; grounding in mathematics and physics; 1 modern foreign language; GRE; interview. 15 professorial staff. Program begun 1958. 1 graduate student registered fall 1959.

Pharmacology. Neuropharmacology, psychopharmacology, renal pharmacology. Prerequisite for graduate study: preparation in which emphasis has been placed on biological, chemical, and physical sciences; preference given to those who have majored in biochemistry, biophysics, chemistry, or zoology. 7 professorial staff. Program begun 1956. 5 graduate students registered fall 1959. New enrollment limited to 2 or 3.

Physiology. Neurophysiology, renal and body fluid physiology, physiology of circulation, developmental or cellular physiology. Prerequisite for graduate study: major in biology, physics, mathematics, or chemistry. 12 professorial staff. Program begun 1956. 2 graduate students registered fall 1959. New enrollment limited to 1 or 2 students per year.

Graduate School of Mathematical Sciences

Established in 1958 as an outgrowth of the Institute of Mathematics, which was organized by Yeshiva University in 1945.

Residence requirement for Ph.D.: 90 credits beyond bachelor's degree, 60 credits beyond master's degree. A minimum of 24 of the 30 credits required for the master's degree must be taken in residence at the Graduate School of Mathematical Sciences. For a Ph.D., a minimum of 24 credits of course work, in addition to comprehensive examination and thesis, must be taken in residence.

ADMISSION REQUIREMENTS

For graduate study: bachelor's degree; preparation in mathematics or physics. Matriculative students who seek acceptance for the Ph.D. are required to file a special application, pass the examinations, and meet other prescribed conditions.

Apply to the Office of Admissions, Yeshiva University, Amsterdam Avenue and 186th Street, New York 33, New York, as early as possible in the semester preceding that in which entry is desired.

FEES AND FIRST-YEAR AID

Admission fee $10. Tuition $30 per credit. Special fees approximate $60 annually.

FIELDS OF STUDY FOR THE PH.D.

Mathematics and Physics.

APPENDIXES

Appendix I: Doctoral Degrees Awarded by American Universities and Colleges

*Indicates doctoral degree is offered.
– Indicates doctoral degree is not offered.

	Institution*	Ph.D.†	Ed.D.	D.B.A.	D.Mus. & A.Mus.D.	D.Mus.Ed.	D.P.A.	D.P.H.	D.Phys.Ed.	D.R.E. & Ed.R.D.	D.S.W.	Eng.D. & D.Sc.Eng.§	J.S.D.	Med.Sc.D.	S.T.D.	Th.D.	Named on p. 438
								Other Doctorates‡									
Alab.	Alabama, Univ. of, p. 64	★	★	–	–	–	–	–	–	–	–	–	–	–	–	–	–
	Auburn Univ., p. 74	★	★	–	–	–	–	–	–	–	–	–	–	–	–	–	–
Alas.	Alaska, Univ. of, p. 66	★	–	–	–	–	–	–	–	–	–	–	–	–	–	–	–
Ariz.	Arizona State Univ.	–	★	–	–	–	–	–	–	–	–	–	–	–	–	–	–
	Arizona, Univ. of, p. 69	★	★	–	★	–	–	–	–	–	–	–	–	–	–	–	–
Ark.	Arkansas, Univ. of, p. 72	★	★	–	–	–	–	–	–	–	–	–	–	–	–	–	–
Calif.	Berkeley Baptist Divinity School	–	–	–	–	–	–	–	–	–	–	–	–	–	–	★	–
	California Inst. of Tech., p. 94	★	–	–	–	–	–	–	–	–	–	–	–	–	–	–	–
	California, Univ. of, p. 95	★	★	–	–	–	–	★	–	–	★	★	★	–	–	–	(1)
	Claremont Coll., p. 123	★	–	–	–	–	–	–	–	–	–	–	–	–	–	–	–
	Medical Evangelists, Coll. of, p. 229	★	–	–	–	–	–	–	–	–	–	–	–	–	–	–	–
	Occidental Coll., p. 290	★	–	–	–	–	–	–	–	–	–	–	–	–	–	–	–
	Pacific, Coll. of the	–	★	–	–	–	–	–	–	–	–	–	–	–	–	–	–
	Pacific School of Religion	–	–	–	–	–	–	–	–	–	–	–	–	–	–	★	–
	Redlands, Univ. of, p. 330	★	–	–	–	–	–	–	–	–	–	–	–	–	–	–	–
	San Francisco Theol. Seminary	–	–	–	–	–	–	–	–	–	–	–	–	–	–	★	–
	Southern Calif., Univ. of, p. 354	★	★	★	★	–	★	–	–	–	★	–	–	★	–	–	–
	Stanford Univ., p. 360	★	★	–	–	–	–	–	–	–	–	–	–	★	–	–	–
Colo.	Colorado School of Mines	–	–	–	–	–	–	–	–	–	–	★	–	–	–	–	–
	Colorado State Coll.	–	★	–	–	–	–	–	–	–	–	–	–	–	–	–	–
	Colorado State Univ., p. 127	★	★	★	–	–	–	–	–	–	–	–	–	–	–	–	–
	Colorado, Univ. of, p. 128	★	★	★	★	–	–	–	–	–	–	–	–	–	–	–	–
	Denver, Univ. of, p. 143	★	★	–	–	–	–	–	–	–	–	–	–	–	–	–	–
	Iliff School of Theol.	–	–	–	–	–	–	–	–	–	–	–	–	–	–	★	–
Conn.	Connecticut, Univ. of, p. 136	★	–	–	–	–	–	–	–	–	–	–	–	–	–	–	–
	Hartford Seminary Foundation, p. 168	★	–	–	–	–	–	–	–	★	–	–	–	–	–	–	–
	Yale Univ., p. 426	★	–	–	–	–	★	–	–	–	–	★	★	–	–	–	(2)
Del.	Delaware, Univ. of, p. 141	★	–	–	–	–	–	–	–	–	–	–	–	–	–	–	–
D. C.	American Univ., p. 68	★	★	–	–	–	–	–	–	–	–	–	–	–	★	–	(3)
	Catholic Univ. of America, p. 111	★	–	–	–	–	–	–	–	★	★	–	–	–	★	–	(3)
	George Washington Univ., p.160	★	★	–	–	–	–	–	–	★	★	–	–	–	–	–	(4)
	Georgetown Univ., p. 163	★	–	–	–	–	–	–	–	–	–	–	–	★	–	–	–
	Howard Univ., p. 176	★	–	–	–	–	–	–	–	–	–	–	–	–	–	–	–
Fla.	Florida State Univ., p. 150	★	★	–	★	★	–	–	★	–	–	–	–	–	–	–	–
	Florida, Univ. of, p. 153	★	★	–	–	–	–	–	–	–	–	–	–	–	–	–	–
	Miami, Univ. of, p. 229	★	–	–	–	–	–	–	–	–	–	–	–	–	–	–	–
Ga.	Emory Univ., p. 149	★	–	–	–	–	–	–	–	–	–	–	–	–	–	–	–
	Georgia Inst. of Tech., p. 164	★	–	–	–	–	–	–	–	–	–	–	–	–	–	–	–
	Georgia, Univ. of, p. 166	★	★	–	–	–	–	–	–	–	–	–	–	–	–	–	–
Hawaii	Hawaii, Univ. of, p. 173	★	–	–	–	–	–	–	–	–	–	–	–	–	–	–	–
Idaho	Idaho, Univ. of, p. 177	★	★	–	–	–	–	–	–	–	–	–	–	–	–	–	–
Ill.	Chicago Lutheran Theol. Seminary	–	–	–	–	–	–	–	–	–	–	–	–	–	★	–	–
	Chicago, Univ. of, p. 113	★	–	–	–	–	–	–	–	–	–	–	–	★	–	–	(4)
	Illinois Inst. of Tech., p. 178	★	–	–	–	–	–	–	–	–	–	–	–	–	–	–	–
	Illinois, Univ. of, p. 179	★	★	★	★	★	–	–	–	–	–	–	★	–	–	–	–

*Boldface type indicates institutions having exhibits in this volume; lightface type indicates the institutions which do not offer programs leading to the Ph.D., but which do award other doctoral degrees.

† For details on fields of study leading to the Ph.D., *see* the individual exhibits in this volume or the Index to Fields of Study for the Ph.D., p. 445.

‡ The Ph.D. is also awarded in many of the areas in which other doctoral degrees may be earned. Consult the Index to Fields of Study for the Ph.D., p. 445, for such information.

§ This category also includes the D.Sc. in any of the fields of engineering and such degrees as the Doctor of Civil Engineering, the Doctor of Mechanical Engineering, etc.

State	Institution*	Ph.D.†	Ed.D.	D.B.A.	D.Mus. & A.Mus.D.	D.Mus.Ed.	D.P.A.	D.P.H.	D.Phys.Ed.	D.R.E. & Ed.R.D.	D.S.W.	Eng.D. & D.Sc.Eng.§	J.S.D.	Med.Sc.D.	S.T.D.	Th.D.	Named on p. 438
Ill.—Contd.	Loyola Univ., p. 218	★	★	–	–	–	–	–	–	–	–	–	–	–	★	–	–
	Northwestern Univ., p. 283	★	★	–	★	–	–	–	–	–	–	–	–	–	–	–	–
	Southern Illinois Univ., p. 358	★	–	–	–	–	–	–	–	–	–	–	–	–	–	–	–
Ind.	Indiana Univ., p. 185	★	★	★	★	★	–	–	★	–	–	–	–	–	–	–	(5)
	Notre Dame, Univ. of, p. 288	★	–	–	–	–	–	–	–	–	–	–	★	–	–	–	(6)
	Purdue Univ., p. 326	★	–	–	–	–	–	–	–	–	–	–	–	–	–	–	–
	St. Mary's Coll., p. 349	★	–	–	–	–	–	–	–	–	–	–	–	–	–	–	–
Iowa	Iowa, State Univ. of, p. 190	★	–	–	–	–	–	–	–	–	–	–	–	–	–	–	–
	Iowa State Univ. of Sc. and Tech., p. 196	★	–	–	–	–	–	–	–	–	–	–	–	–	–	–	–
Kan.	Kansas State Univ., p. 205	★	–	–	–	–	–	–	–	–	–	–	–	–	–	–	–
	Kansas, Univ. of, p. 207	★	★	–	–	–	–	–	–	–	–	–	–	–	–	–	–
Ky.	Kentucky, Univ. of, p. 210	★	★	–	–	–	–	–	–	★	–	–	–	–	–	–	–
	Louisville, Univ. of, p. 216	★	–	–	–	–	–	–	–	–	–	–	–	–	–	–	–
	Southern Baptist Theol. Seminary	–	–	–	–	–	–	–	–	★	–	–	–	–	–	★	(7)
La.	Louisiana State Univ., p. 213	★	★	–	–	–	–	–	–	★	–	–	–	–	–	–	–
	New Orleans Baptist Theol. Seminary	–	–	–	–	–	–	–	–	★	–	–	–	–	–	★	–
	Tulane Univ., p. 383	★	–	–	–	–	–	★	–	–	–	–	★	–	–	–	–
Maine	Maine, Univ. of, p. 219	★	–	–	–	–	–	–	–	–	–	–	–	–	–	–	–
Md.	Johns Hopkins Univ., p. 199	★	–	–	–	–	–	★	–	–	–	–	–	★	–	–	(8)
	Maryland, Univ. of, p. 221	★	★	–	–	–	–	–	–	–	–	–	–	–	–	–	–
	St. Mary's Seminary and Univ.	–	–	–	–	–	–	–	–	–	–	–	–	–	★	–	–
	Woodstock Coll.	–	–	–	–	–	–	–	–	–	–	–	–	–	★	–	–
Mass.	Boston Coll., p. 77	★	★	–	–	–	–	–	–	–	–	–	–	–	★	–	–
	Boston Univ., p. 78	★	★	–	★	–	–	–	–	–	–	–	–	–	★	–	–
	Brandeis Univ., p. 81	★	–	–	–	–	–	–	–	–	★	–	–	–	–	–	–
	Clark Univ., p. 125	★	–	–	–	–	–	–	–	–	–	–	–	–	–	–	–
	Harvard Univ., p. 169	★	★	★	–	–	★	★	–	–	–	–	★	★	–	★	(8)
	Lowell Tech. Inst., p. 217	★	–	–	–	–	–	–	–	–	–	–	–	–	–	–	–
	Massachusetts Coll. of Pharmacy, p. 225	★	–	–	–	–	–	–	–	–	–	–	–	–	–	–	–
	Massachusetts Inst. of Tech., p. 226	★	–	–	–	–	–	–	–	–	–	★	–	–	–	–	(9)
	Massachusetts, Univ. of, p. 227	★	–	–	–	–	–	–	–	–	–	–	–	–	–	–	–
	Radcliffe Coll., p. 329	★	–	–	–	–	–	–	–	–	–	–	–	–	–	–	–
	Smith Coll., p. 350	★	–	–	–	–	–	–	–	–	–	–	–	–	–	–	–
	Springfield Coll.	–	–	–	–	–	–	–	★	–	–	–	–	–	–	–	–
	Tufts Univ., p. 381	★	★	–	–	–	–	–	–	–	–	–	–	–	–	–	–
	Worcester Polytech. Inst., p. 424	★	–	–	–	–	–	–	–	–	–	–	–	–	–	–	–
Mich.	Michigan State Univ., p. 231	★	★	★	–	★	–	–	★	–	–	–	–	★	–	–	(10)
	Michigan, Univ. of, p. 235	★	★	–	★	–	–	★	–	–	–	–	★	–	–	–	–
	Wayne State Univ., p. 412	★	★	–	–	–	–	–	–	–	–	–	–	–	–	–	–
Minn.	Minnesota, Univ. of, p. 242	★	★	–	–	–	–	–	–	–	–	–	–	–	–	–	–
Miss.	Mississippi Southern Coll., p. 250	★	★	–	–	–	–	–	–	–	–	–	–	–	–	–	–
	Mississippi State Univ., p. 251	★	–	–	–	–	–	–	–	–	–	–	–	–	–	–	–
	Mississippi, Univ. of, p. 252	★	★	–	–	–	–	–	–	–	–	–	–	–	–	–	–
Mo.	Kansas City, Univ. of, p. 204	★	–	–	★	–	–	–	–	–	–	–	–	–	–	–	–
	Missouri, Univ. of, p. 253	★	★	–	–	–	–	–	–	–	–	–	–	–	–	–	–
	St. Louis Univ., p. 346	★	–	–	–	–	–	–	–	–	–	–	–	–	–	–	–
	Washington Univ., p. 404	★	★	★	–	–	–	–	–	–	★	★	–	–	–	–	–
Mont.	Montana State Coll., p. 257	★	★	–	–	–	–	–	–	–	–	–	–	–	–	–	–
	Montana State Univ., p. 258	★	★	–	–	–	–	–	–	–	–	–	–	–	–	–	–
Neb.	Nebraska, Univ. of, p. 259	★	★	–	–	–	–	–	–	–	–	–	–	–	–	–	–
N. H.	New Hampshire, Univ. of, p. 262	★	–	–	–	–	–	–	–	–	–	–	–	–	–	–	–
N. J.	Drew Univ., p. 144	★	–	–	–	–	–	–	–	–	–	–	–	–	–	★	–
	Princeton Theol. Seminary	–	–	–	–	–	–	–	–	–	–	–	–	–	–	★	–
	Princeton Univ., p. 324	★	–	–	–	–	–	–	–	–	–	–	–	–	–	–	–
	Rutgers Univ., p. 340	★	★	–	–	–	–	–	–	–	–	–	–	–	–	–	–
	Stevens Inst. of Tech., p. 364	★	–	–	–	–	–	–	–	–	–	★	–	–	–	–	–
N. M.	New Mexico Highlands Univ., p. 262	★	–	–	–	–	–	–	–	–	–	–	–	–	–	–	–
	New Mexico Inst. of Mining and Tech., p. 263	★	–	–	–	–	–	–	–	–	–	–	–	–	–	–	–
	New Mexico State Univ., p. 264	★	–	–	–	–	–	–	–	–	–	★	–	–	–	–	–
	New Mexico, Univ. of, p. 264	★	★	–	–	–	–	–	–	–	–	★	–	–	–	–	–
N. Y.	Adelphi Coll., p. 63	★	–	–	–	–	–	–	–	–	–	–	–	–	–	–	–
	Alfred Univ., p. 67	★	–	–	–	–	–	–	–	–	–	★	–	–	–	–	–
	Brooklyn, Polytech. Inst. of, p. 85	★	–	–	–	–	–	–	–	–	–	★	–	–	–	–	–

* Boldface type indicates institutions having exhibits in this volume; lightface type indicates the institutions which do not offer programs leading to the Ph.D., but which do award other doctoral degrees.

† For details on fields of study leading to the Ph.D., *see* the individual exhibits in this volume or the Index to Fields of Study for the Ph.D., p. 445.

‡ The Ph.D. is also awarded in many of the areas in which other doctoral degrees may be earned. Consult the Index to Fields of Study for the Ph.D., p. 445, for such information.

§ This category also includes the D.Sc. in any of the fields of engineering and such degrees as the Doctor of Civil Engineering, the Doctor of Mechanical Engineering, etc.

Columns under the heading **Other Doctorates‡**: Ed.D., D.B.A., D.Mus. & A.Mus.D., D.Mus.Ed., D.P.A., D.P.H., D.Phys.Ed., D.R.E. & Ed.R.D., D.S.W., Eng.D. & D.Sc.Eng.§, J.S.D., Med.Sc.D., S.T.D., Th.D.

Institution*	Ph.D.†	Ed.D.	D.B.A.	D.Mus. & A.Mus.D.	D.Mus.Ed.	D.P.A.	D.P.H.	D.Phys.Ed.	D.R.E. & Ed.R.D.	D.S.W.	Eng.D. & D.Sc.Eng.§	J.S.D.	Med.Sc.D.	S.T.D.	Th.D.	Named on p. 438
N. Y.—Contd. Buffalo, Univ. of, p. 91	★	★	-	-	-	-	-	-	-	-	-	-	-	-	-	-
Columbia Univ., p. 131	★	★	-	-	-	-	★	-	-	-	★	★	★	-	-	(1)
Cornell Univ., p. 137	★	★	★	-	-	-	-	-	-	-	-	-	★	-	-	(11)
Fordham Univ., p. 157	★	★	-	-	-	-	-	-	-	-	-	-	-	-	-	-
General Theol. Seminary	-	-	-	-	-	-	-	-	-	-	-	-	-	-	★	-
Jewish Theol. Seminary of America	-	-	-	-	-	-	-	-	★	-	-	-	-	-	-	(12)
New School for Social Research, p. 266	★	-	-	-	-	-	-	-	-	-	-	-	-	-	-	(13)
New York Law School	-	-	-	-	-	-	-	-	-	-	-	★	-	-	-	-
New York Medical Coll.	-	-	-	-	-	-	★	-	-	-	-	-	★	-	-	-
New York, State Univ. of, p. 267	★	★	-	-	-	-	-	-	-	-	-	-	★	-	-	-
New York Univ., p. 270	★	★	-	-	-	-	-	-	-	-	★	★	★	-	-	-
Rensselaer Polytech. Inst., p. 331	★	★	-	-	-	-	-	-	-	-	★	-	-	-	-	-
Rochester, Univ. of, p. 334	★	★	-	★	-	-	-	-	-	-	-	-	★	-	-	-
Rockefeller Inst., p. 338	★	-	-	-	-	-	-	-	-	-	-	-	★	-	-	-
St. Bonaventure Univ., p. 343	★	-	-	-	-	-	-	-	-	-	-	-	-	-	-	-
St. John's Univ., p. 344	★	★	-	-	-	-	-	-	-	-	-	-	-	-	-	-
Syracuse Univ., p. 365	★	★	★	-	-	★	-	-	-	-	-	-	-	-	-	(13)
Union Coll. and Univ., p. 386	★	-	-	-	-	-	-	-	-	-	-	-	-	-	-	-
Union Theol. Seminary, p. 387	★	★	-	-	-	-	-	-	-	-	-	-	-	-	★	(7)
Yeshiva Univ., p. 430	★	★	-	-	-	-	-	-	-	-	-	-	★	-	-	(14)
N. C. Duke Univ., p. 145	★	★	-	-	-	-	-	-	-	-	-	-	-	-	-	(15)
North Carolina Coll. at Durham, p. 274	★	-	-	-	-	-	-	-	-	-	-	-	-	-	-	-
North Carolina State Coll., p. 275	★	-	-	-	-	-	-	-	-	-	-	-	-	-	-	-
North Carolina, Univ. of, p. 277	★	★	-	-	-	-	★	-	-	-	-	-	-	-	-	-
N. D. North Dakota Agricultural Coll., p. 279	★	-	-	-	-	-	-	-	-	-	-	-	-	-	-	-
North Dakota, Univ. of, p. 280	★	★	-	-	-	-	-	-	-	-	-	-	-	-	-	-
Ohio Akron, Univ. of, p. 64	★	-	-	-	-	-	-	-	-	-	-	-	-	-	-	-
Case Inst. of Tech., p. 110	★	-	-	-	-	-	-	-	-	-	-	-	-	-	-	-
Cincinnati, Univ. of, p. 121	★	★	-	-	-	-	-	-	-	-	-	-	-	-	-	(16)
Hebrew Union Coll., p. 174	★	-	-	-	-	-	-	-	-	-	-	-	-	-	-	(14)
Ohio State Univ., p. 290	★	-	-	-	-	-	-	-	-	-	-	-	-	-	-	-
Ohio Univ., p. 296	★	-	-	-	-	-	-	-	-	-	-	-	-	-	-	-
Toledo, Univ. of, p. 380	★	★	-	-	-	-	-	-	-	-	-	-	-	-	-	-
Western Reserve Univ., p. 416	★	★	-	-	-	-	-	-	-	-	★	-	-	-	-	-
Okla. Oklahoma State Univ., p. 297	★	★	-	-	-	-	-	-	-	-	-	-	-	-	-	-
Oklahoma, Univ. of, p. 300	★	★	★	-	-	-	-	-	-	-	-	-	-	-	-	-
Tulsa, Univ. of	-	★	-	-	-	-	-	-	-	-	-	-	-	-	-	-
Ore. Oregon State Coll., p. 302	★	★	-	-	-	-	-	-	-	-	-	-	-	-	-	-
Oregon, Univ. of, p. 304	★	★	★	-	-	-	-	-	-	-	-	-	-	-	-	-
Portland, Univ. of, p. 323	★	★	-	-	-	-	-	-	-	-	-	-	-	-	-	-
Pa. Bryn Mawr Coll., p. 88	★	-	-	-	-	-	-	-	-	-	-	-	-	-	-	-
Carnegie Inst. of Tech., p. 107	★	-	-	-	-	-	-	-	-	-	-	-	-	-	-	-
Dropsie Coll., p. 144	★	★	-	-	-	-	-	-	-	-	-	-	-	-	-	-
Duquesne Univ., p. 148	★	-	-	-	-	-	-	-	-	-	-	-	-	-	-	-
Hahnemann Medical Coll., p. 167	★	-	-	-	-	-	-	-	-	-	-	-	-	-	-	-
Jefferson Medical Coll., p. 198	★	-	-	-	-	-	-	-	-	-	-	-	-	-	-	-
Lehigh Univ., p. 211	★	★	-	-	-	-	-	-	-	-	-	-	-	-	-	-
Pennsylvania State Univ., p. 307	★	★	-	-	-	-	-	-	-	-	-	-	-	-	-	-
Pennsylvania, Univ. of, p. 314	★	-	-	-	-	-	-	-	-	-	★	-	★	★	-	-
Philadelphia Coll. of Pharmacy, p. 319	★	-	-	-	-	-	-	-	-	-	-	-	-	-	-	-
Pittsburgh, Univ. of, p. 319	★	★	-	-	-	-	★	-	-	-	★	-	★	-	-	(8)
Temple Univ., p. 368	★	★	-	-	-	-	-	-	-	-	-	-	★	-	-	-
Women's Medical Coll.	-	-	-	-	-	-	-	-	-	-	-	-	★	-	-	-
R. I. Brown Univ., p. 86	★	-	-	-	-	-	-	-	-	-	-	-	-	-	-	-
Rhode Island, Univ. of, p. 332	★	-	-	-	-	-	-	-	-	-	-	-	-	-	-	-
S. C. Clemson Coll., p. 126	★	-	-	-	-	-	-	-	-	-	-	-	-	-	-	-
South Carolina, Medical Coll. of, p. 350	★	-	-	-	-	-	-	-	-	-	-	-	-	-	-	-
South Carolina, Univ. of, p. 351	★	-	-	-	-	-	-	-	-	-	-	-	-	-	-	-
S. D. South Dakota State Coll., p. 352	★	-	-	-	-	-	-	-	-	-	-	-	-	-	-	-
South Dakota, State Univ. of, p. 353	★	★	-	-	-	-	-	-	-	-	-	-	-	-	-	-
Tenn. George Peabody Coll. for Teachers, p. 159	★	★	-	★	-	-	-	★	-	-	-	-	-	-	-	-
Tennessee, Univ. of, p. 369	★	★	-	-	-	-	-	-	-	-	-	-	-	-	-	-
Vanderbilt Univ., p. 393	★	-	-	-	-	-	-	-	-	-	-	-	-	-	-	-

* Boldface type indicates institutions having exhibits in this volume; lightface type indicates the institutions which do not offer programs leading to the Ph.D., but which do award other doctoral degrees.

† For details on fields of study leading to the Ph.D., *see* the individual exhibits in this volume or the Index to Fields of Study for the Ph.D., p. 445.

‡ The Ph.D. is also awarded in many of the areas in which other doctoral degrees may be earned. Consult the Index to Fields of Study for the Ph.D., p. 445, for such information.

§ This category also includes the D.Sc. in any of the fields of engineering and such degrees as the Doctor of Civil Engineering, the Doctor of Mechanical Engineering, etc.

	Institution*	Ph.D.†	Ed.D.	D.B.A.	D.Mus. & A.Mus.D.	D.Mus.Ed.	D.P.A.	D.P.H.	D.Phys.Ed.	D.R.E. & Ed.R.D.	D.S.W.	Eng.D. & D.Sc.Eng.§	J.S.D.	Med.Sc.D.	S.T.D.	Th.D.	Named below
Texas	Baylor Univ., p. 75	★	★	–	–	–	–	–	–	–	–	–	–	–	–	–	–
	Houston, Univ. of, p. 175	★	★	–	–	–	–	–	–	–	–	–	–	–	–	–	–
	North Texas State Coll., p. 282	★	★	–	–	–	–	–	–	–	–	–	–	–	–	–	–
	Rice Univ., p. 333	★	–	–	–	–	–	–	–	–	–	–	–	–	–	–	–
	Southern Methodist Univ., p. 359	★	–	–	–	–	–	–	–	–	–	–	–	–	–	–	(17)
	Southwestern Baptist Theol. Seminary	–	–	–	–	–	–	–	–	★	–	–	–	–	–	★	–
	Texas, A&M Coll. of, p. 371	★	–	–	–	–	–	–	–	–	–	–	–	–	–	–	–
	Texas Tech. Coll., p. 374	★	★	–	–	–	–	–	–	–	–	–	–	–	–	–	–
	Texas, Univ. of, p. 375	★	★	–	–	–	–	–	–	–	–	–	–	–	–	–	–
	Texas Woman's Univ., p. 378	★	★	–	–	–	–	–	–	–	–	–	–	–	–	–	–
Utah	Brigham Young Univ., p. 83	★	★	–	–	–	–	–	–	–	–	–	–	–	–	–	–
	Utah State Univ., p. 388	★	★	–	–	–	–	–	–	–	–	–	–	–	–	–	–
	Utah, Univ. of, p. 390	★	★	–	–	–	–	–	–	–	–	–	–	–	–	–	–
Vt.	Middlebury Coll., p. 242	–	–	–	–	–	–	–	–	–	–	–	–	–	–	–	(18)
	Vermont, Univ. of, p. 396	★	–	–	–	–	–	–	–	–	–	–	–	–	–	–	–
Va.	Union Theol. Seminary	–	–	–	–	–	–	–	–	–	–	–	–	–	–	★	–
	Virginia, Medical Coll. of, p. 396	★	–	–	–	–	–	–	–	–	–	–	–	★	–	–	–
	Virginia Polytech. Inst., p. 397	★	–	–	–	–	–	–	–	–	–	–	–	–	–	–	–
	Virginia, Univ. of, p. 399	★	★	–	–	–	–	–	–	–	–	–	★	★	–	–	–
Wash.	Washington State Univ., p. 401	★	★	–	–	–	–	–	–	–	–	–	–	–	–	–	–
	Washington, Univ. of, p. 407	★	★	★	–	–	–	–	–	–	–	–	–	–	–	–	–
W. Va.	West Virginia Univ., p. 414	★	★	–	–	–	–	–	–	–	–	–	–	–	–	–	–
Wis.	Marquette Univ., p. 220	★	–	–	–	–	–	–	–	–	–	–	–	–	–	–	–
	Paper Chemistry, The Inst. of, p. 306	★	–	–	–	–	–	–	–	–	–	–	–	–	–	–	–
	Wisconsin, Univ. of, p. 417	★	–	–	–	–	–	–	–	–	–	–	–	–	–	–	–
Wyo.	Wyoming, Univ. of, p. 424	★	★	–	–	–	–	–	–	–	–	–	–	–	–	–	–

* Boldface type indicates institutions having exhibits in this volume; lightface type indicates the institutions which do not offer programs leading to the Ph.D., but which do award other doctoral degrees.

† For details on fields of study leading to the Ph.D., *see* the individual exhibits in this volume or the Index to Fields of Study for the Ph.D., p. 445.

‡ The Ph.D. is also awarded in many of the areas in which other doctoral degrees may be earned. Consult the Index to Fields of Study for the Ph.D., p. 445, for such information.

§ This category also includes the D.Sc. in any of the fields of engineering and such degrees as the Doctor of Civil Engineering, the Doctor of Mechanical Engineering, etc.

---

1. Doctor of Library Science
2. Doctor of Fine Arts and Doctor of Forestry
3. Doctor of Canon Law and Doctor of Architecture
4. Doctor of Comparative Law
5. Doctor of Health and Safety and Doctor of Recreation
6. Doctor of Medieval Studies
7. Doctor of Sacred Music
8. Doctor of Science in Hygiene
9. Doctor of Science in all of the fields in which the Ph.D. is also offered.
10. Doctor of Pharmacy
11. Doctor of Science in Veterinary Medicine
12. Doctor of Sacred Music and Doctor of Hebrew Literature
13. Doctor of Social Science
14. Doctor of Hebrew Literature
15. Doctor of Forestry
16. Doctor of Industrial Medicine; Doctor of Science in Industrial Health, in Surgery, and in certain other areas.
17. Doctor of Civil Law
18. Doctor of Modern Languages

Appendix II: Abbreviations Used in the Text

General

ACE   American Council on Education
ACS   American Chemical Society
AEC   Atomic Energy Commission
CAVD   Thorndike Test of General Ability (Completion, Arithmetic, Vocabulary, and Direction)
DCAT   Dental College Admissions Test
ETS   Educational Testing Service
FFA   Future Farmers of America
GED   General Educational Development Tests
GPA   Grade Point Average
GRE   Graduate Record Examinations
MAT   Miller Analogies Test
MCAT   Medical College Admissions Test
MMPI   Minnesota Multiphasic Personality Inventory
NSF   National Science Foundation
TEEP   Teacher Education Examination Program

Degrees

A.B.   Bachelor of Arts
A.M.   Master of Arts
A.Mus.D.   Doctor of Musical Arts
B.A.   Bachelor of Arts
B.B.A.   Bachelor of Business Administration
B.D.   Bachelor of Divinity
B.S.   Bachelor of Science
B.S.E.   Bachelor of Science in Engineering
D.Arch.   Doctor of Architecture
D.B.A.   Doctor of Business Administration
D.C.L.   Doctor of Civil Law
D.C.S.   Doctor of Commercial Science
D.Comp.L.   Doctor of Comparative Law
D.D.S.   Doctor of Dental Science or Doctor of Dental Surgery
D.Eng.   Doctor of Engineering
D.Eng.S.   Doctor of Engineering Science
D.F.   Doctor of Forestry
D.F.A.   Doctor of Fine Arts
D.H.L.   Doctor of Hebrew Literature or Doctor of Hebrew Letters
D.L.S.   Doctor of Library Science
D.M.A.   Doctor of Musical Arts
D.M.D.   Doctor of Dental Medicine

D.M.L.   Doctor of Modern Languages
D.M.S.   Doctor of Medieval Studies
D.Mus.   Doctor of Music
D.Mus.A.   Doctor of Musical Arts
D.Mus.Ed.   Doctor of Music Education
D.P.A.   Doctor of Public Administration
D.P.H.   Doctor of Public Health
D.Phys.Ed.   Doctor of Physical Education
D.R.E.   Doctor of Religious Education
D.S.M.   Doctor of Sacred Music or Doctor of Medieval Studies
D.S.S.   Doctor of Social Science
D.S.W.   Doctor of Social Welfare or Doctor of Social Work
D.Sc.   Doctor of Science
D.V.M.   Doctor of Veterinary Medicine
Ed.D.   Doctor of Education
Ed.R.D.   Doctor of Religious Education
Eng.D.   Doctor of Engineering
Eng.Sc.D.   Doctor of Science in Engineering
J.C.D.   Doctor of Canon Law
J.S.D.   Doctor of the Science of Law
L.H.D.   Doctor of Humane Letters
M.A.   Master of Arts
M.A.L.D.   Master of Arts in Law and Diplomacy
M.B.A.   Master of Business Administration
M.C.P.   Master of City Planning
M.D.   Doctor of Medicine
M.Ed.   Master of Education
M.Eng.   Master of Engineering
M.F.A.   Master of Fine Arts
M.P.A.   Master of Public Administration
M.P.H.   Master of Public Health
M.S.   Master of Science
M.S.E.   Master of Science in Engineering
M.S.W.   Master of Social Work
Med.Sc.D.   Doctor of Medical Science
Ph.D.   Doctor of Philosophy
Ph.L.   Licentiate in Philosophy
Pharm.D.   Doctor of Pharmacy
S.J.D.   Doctor of the Science of Law
S.M.D.   Doctor of Sacred Music
S.T.B.   Bachelor of Sacred Theology
S.T.D.   Doctor of Sacred Theology
Th.D.   Doctor of Theology

INDEXES

Institutional Index

Index to Fields of Study for the Ph.D.

(This index contains references to the programs offered by the institutions having exhibits in Part II. However, to avoid tedious repetition of institutional names, the programs which are offered by 50 or more institutions are reported in the Tabular Supplement beginning on p. 455, and this index is appropriately footnoted to indicate which programs are so treated. In using the index, the reader should also be aware that the programs are here classified by general area, rather than by the specific name (used in the body of the text) by which the program may be known in a particular institution. Furthermore, he should realize that areas which constitute "fields of study" in certain institutions may be treated as areas of concentration within broader designations at other institutions. Extensive cross references give additional guidance in this respect.)

Accounting. *See* Business and Commerce

Aeronautics. *See* Engineering, aeronautical

Agricultural

  biochemistry: Arizona, Minnesota, Ohio State, West Virginia

  botany: Minnesota

  chemistry: Arizona, U. California, Idaho, Louisiana State, Missouri, N. Dakota Ag. Coll., Pennsylvania State

  economics: U. California, Clemson, Connecticut, Cornell, U. Florida, U. Illinois, Kansas State, Kentucky, Louisiana State, Maryland, Michigan State, Minnesota, Mississippi State, Missouri, Montana State Coll., Nebraska, N. Carolina State, Ohio State, Oklahoma State, Oregon State, Pennsylvania State, Purdue, S. Dakota State, Texas A&M, Virginia Polytech., Washington State, Wisconsin

  education: Cornell, Louisiana State, Ohio State, Pennsylvania State, Wisconsin

  engineering. *See* Engineering, agricultural

  microbiology: Rutgers, West Virginia

Agronomy. *See also* Crops; Plant Sciences; Soil Science

  Arizona, Auburn, Cornell, U. Florida, U. Illinois, Iowa State U. Sc. and Tech., Kansas State, Louisiana State, Maryland, U. Massachusetts, Mississippi State, Nebraska, N. Dakota Ag. Coll., Ohio State, Pennsylvania State, Purdue, Rhode Island, S. Dakota State, Texas A&M, Virginia Polytech., Washington State, West Virginia, Wisconsin

American Language and Literature. *See* English

American Studies. *See* Area Studies, American

Analysis of Ideas and Study of Methods. *See also* Philosophy

  Chicago

Anatomy*

Animal and Poultry Sciences. *See also* Veterinary Sciences

  animal husbandry: Auburn, Cornell, U. Florida, Iowa State U. Sc. and Tech., Kentucky, Maryland, Michigan State, Minnesota, Missouri, N. Carolina State, Pennsylvania State, Oregon State, Rhode Island, S. Dakota State, Texas A&M, Utah State, Wisconsin

  biochemistry: Texas A&M, Utah State, Virginia Polytech.

  breeding: Cornell, Kansas State, N. Carolina State, N. Dakota Ag. Coll., Oklahoma State, Pennsylvania State, Texas A&M

  dairy: Cornell, U. Georgia, U. Illinois, Kentucky, Louisiana State, Maryland, U. Massachusetts, Michigan State, Minnesota, Missouri, Nebraska, N. Carolina State, Ohio State, Oregon State, Pennsylvania State, Purdue, Rutgers, S. Dakota State, Texas A&M, Wisconsin

  general: U. Illinois, Louisiana State, U. Massachusetts, Mississippi State, Ohio State, Purdue, Washington State, Wyoming

  genetics: Nebraska, Ohio State, Pennsylvania State

* For programs in this field, *see* Tabular Supplement to this index beginning on p. 455.

445

nutrition: Arizona, Auburn, U. California, Connecticut, Cornell, U. Georgia, Kansas State, N. Carolina State, N. Dakota Ag. Coll., Ohio State, Oklahoma State, Pennsylvania State, Texas A&M, Utah State, Virginia Polytech.

parasitology: Texas A&M

physiology of reproduction: Texas A&M

poultry: Auburn, Iowa State U. Sc. and Tech., Louisiana State, Maryland, U. Massachusetts, Michigan State, Minnesota, Missouri, Ohio State, Oregon State, Pennsylvania State, Purdue, Rhode Island, Rutgers, S. Dakota State, Texas A&M, Wisconsin

production: N. Dakota Ag. Coll.

Anthropology

Arizona, Boston U., Brandeis, Bryn Mawr, U. California, Catholic U., Chicago, U. Colorado, Columbia, Cornell, Harvard, U. Illinois, Indiana, Michigan State, U. Michigan, Minnesota, U. New Mexico, New York U., U. North Carolina, Northwestern, Ohio State, U. Oregon, U. Pennsylvania, Pittsburgh, Southern Illinois, Stanford, Syracuse, Tulane, U. Utah, Washington U. (Mo.), U. Washington, Wisconsin, Yale

Applied Arts. *See also* individual arts
Ohio State

Applied Sciences. *See also* individual sciences
Cincinnati, Delaware

Archaeology
Bryn Mawr, Columbia, U. Pennsylvania, Princeton, Washington U. (Mo.)

Architecture. *See also* Housing and Design
Columbia, Harvard, Mass. Inst. Tech., Princeton

Area Studies
American: Brown, Harvard, State U. Iowa, Maryland, Minnesota, Missouri, U. New Mexico, New York U., Notre Dame, U. Pennsylvania, Western Reserve, Yale
African: American U., Johns Hopkins, Yale
Asian: American U., U. California, Harvard, Johns Hopkins, St. John's, U. Pennsylvania
European: American U., Johns Hopkins, Notre Dame
Far Eastern: Cornell, Georgetown, U. Washington
general: Yale
Hispanic American: Stanford
Ibero-American: U. New Mexico
Indian: Harvard
Inter-American: U. Florida
Judaic: Brandeis
Latin-American: American U., U. Florida,

Georgetown, Indiana, U. Texas
Mediterranean: Brandeis
Middle Eastern: American U., Dropsie, Georgetown, Harvard, Johns Hopkins
Near Eastern: Brandeis, U. Michigan, Princeton
Russian: American U., Georgetown, U. Washington
Soviet Union: American U., Georgetown, Harvard, Notre Dame
world affairs: St. John's

Art. *See also* Fine Arts
Johns Hopkins, Michigan State, Minnesota, Northwestern, Princeton, Washington U. (Mo.), Western Reserve, Wisconsin

Art Education
Ohio State, Pennsylvania State, Wisconsin

Art History
U. California, Chicago, Columbia, State U. Iowa, Minnesota, U. Pennsylvania, Wisconsin, Yale

Astrogeophysics. *See* Geophysics

Astronautics. *See* Engineering, astronautical

Astronomy. *See also* Astrophysics
Cal. Inst. Tech., U. California, Case, Chicago, Cincinnati, Columbia, Cornell, Georgetown, Harvard, U. Illinois, Indiana, State U. Iowa, Michigan State, U. Michigan, Northwestern, Ohio State, U. Pennsylvania, Princeton, Rochester, U. Texas, Vanderbilt, U. Virginia, Wisconsin, Yale

Astrophysics. *See also* Astronomy
Chicago, Johns Hopkins

Audiology. *See* Speech

Bacteriology*

Biochemistry*

Biology*

Biophysics
Brandeis, Buffalo, Chicago, Columbia, Harvard, U. Illinois, Iowa State U. Sc. and Tech., Johns Hopkins, U. Michigan, Minnesota, U. Mississippi, State U. New York, U. Pennsylvania, Pittsburgh, Purdue, Rochester, Stanford, Tennessee, Vermont, Virginia Med. Coll., U. Washington, Wisconsin, Yale

Biostatistics. *See also* Statistics
U. California, Minnesota

Botany*

Business and Commerce
accounting: U. Illinois, State U. Iowa, Missouri, Ohio State
business administration: Alabama, American U., Arkansas, Buffalo, U. California, Carnegie, Cornell, U. Florida, Louisiana State, Michigan State, U. Michigan, Min-

---

* For programs in this field, *see* Tabular Supplement to this index beginning on p. 455.

nesota, New York U., U. North Carolina, Northwestern, Pennsylvania State, Pittsburgh, Rice, St. Louis, U. Texas, Vanderbilt, Washington U. (Mo.)

business economics: Illinois Inst. Tech., Indiana

business education: U. North Dakota

business organization: Nebraska, Ohio State

commerce: Wisconsin

finance: U. Illinois

general business: Chicago, Columbia, U. Illinois, State U. Iowa, Stanford, U. Utah

industrial management and labor relations: Cornell, State U. Iowa, Mass. Inst. Tech., U. North Carolina, Wisconsin

marketing: State U. Iowa

Cell Physiology
Miami

Celtic Languages
Catholic U., Harvard

Ceramics. See also Engineering, ceramic
Alfred, U. Illinois, Pennsylvania State, Rutgers

Chemistry*

Child or Human Development
Brigham Young, Chicago, Cornell, Delaware, Florida State, State U. Iowa, Minnesota, Oregon State, Pennsylvania State, Texas Woman's

Child Guidance, Somatology, Psychology, and Welfare
State U. Iowa

Chinese. See Far Eastern Languages

Chinese Art and Archaeology
Princeton

Church History
Boston U.

City and Regional Planning
Cornell, Illinois Inst. Tech., Mass. Inst. Tech., U. Pennsylvania

Classical Civilization
Minnesota

Classics. See also Greek; Latin; Sanskrit
Brown, U. California, Chicago, Cincinnati, Cornell, Fordham, Harvard, U. Illinois, Indiana, State U. Iowa, Johns Hopkins, U. Michigan, Minnesota, New York U., U. North Carolina, Northwestern, Ohio State, U. Pennsylvania, Pittsburgh, Princeton, Stanford, U. Virginia, Washington U. (Mo.), U. Washington, Wisconsin, Yale

Climatology
U. Washington

Clothing and Costume Design
Pennsylvania State, Texas Woman's

* For programs in this field, see Tabular Supplement to this index beginning on p. 455.

Communication Arts and Sciences. See also Journalism
U. Illinois, State U. Iowa, Michigan State, U. Michigan, Stanford, Syracuse, Wisconsin

Comparative Literature
Arkansas, Chicago, Columbia, Cornell, Harvard, Indiana, Johns Hopkins, Michigan State, U. Michigan, Minnesota, New York U., U. North Carolina, Occidental, Pennsylvania State, Redlands, U. So. California, Vanderbilt, Wisconsin, Yale

Conservation. See Resource Conservation and Management

Criminology and Corrections. See also Sociology
Florida State

Crops. See also Agronomy; Plant Sciences
farm: Michigan State, Rutgers
field: Missouri, N. Carolina State
fruit: Cornell, U. Florida
vegetable: Cornell, U. Florida

Crystallography. See also Chemistry; Geology; Physics
Johns Hopkins

Culture, History of
Chicago

Dairy Science. See Animal and Poultry Sciences, dairy

Dance
Texas Woman's

Dentistry
Northwestern, Pittsburgh

Diplomacy and International Economics
Kentucky

Dramatic Arts
Cornell, Denver, Florida State, U. Illinois, Indiana, State U. Iowa, U. Kansas, Minnesota, Missouri, U. Oregon, Stanford, Tulane, U. Utah, Western Reserve, Yale

Economics*

Economics History
American U., U. Pennsylvania

Education*

Educational Psychology. See also Education; Psychology
Brigham Young, Denver, Fordham, State U. Iowa, Kentucky, Minnesota, Nebraska, Pennsylvania State, U. Utah, Wayne

Egyptian. See Near and Middle East Languages

Engineering
aeronautical: Cal. Inst. Tech., U. Colorado, Cornell, U. Illinois, Maryland, Mass. Inst. Tech., U. Michigan, Minnesota, Ohio State, Pennsylvania State, Princeton, Purdue, Rensselaer, U. So. California, Stanford, Virginia Polytech., U. Washington
aerospace: Arizona, U. Texas

agricultural: Auburn, Cornell, Iowa State U.
Sci. and Tech., Michigan State, Missouri,
N. Carolina State, Oklahoma State

astronautical: Mass. Inst. Tech., U. Michigan

ceramic: U. Illinois, Iowa State U. Sc. and
Tech., Missouri, N. Carolina State, Ohio
State, U. Utah

chemical*

civil: Arizona, Cal. Inst. Tech., U. California,
Carnegie, Colorado State, U. Colorado,
Columbia, Cornell, Georgia Inst. Tech.,
Harvard, Illinois Inst. Tech., U. Illinois,
State U. Iowa, Iowa State U. Sc. and
Tech., Lehigh, Maryland, Mass. Inst.
Tech., Michigan State, U. Michigan, Min-
nesota, Missouri, N. Carolina State,
Northwestern, Ohio State, Oklahoma
State, Oregon State, Pennsylvania State,
U. Pennsylvania, Princeton, Purdue, Rens-
selaer, Rice, Rutgers, U. So. California,
Stanford, Texas A&M, U. Texas, U.
Utah, U. Washington, Wisconsin, Wyo-
ming, Yale

electrical*

electronic: Harvard

fuels: U. Utah

gas: Illinois Inst. Tech.

geological: Princeton, Texas A&M, U. Utah

hydraulic: State U. Iowa

industrial: Columbia, Georgia Inst. Tech.,
Illinois Inst. Tech., State U. Iowa, Iowa
State U. Sc. and Tech., Johns Hopkins,
U. Michigan, Northwestern, Ohio State,
Oklahoma State, Oregon State, Purdue,
U. So. California, Stanford

industrial arts: Oregon State

instrumentation: Case, U. Michigan

irrigation: U. California

marine: Mass. Inst. Tech., U. Michigan

materials: Cornell

mechanical: Arizona, Arkansas, Cal. Inst.
Tech., U. California, Carnegie, Case, U.
Colorado, Columbia, Cornell, Duke,
Georgia Inst. Tech., Harvard, Illinois Inst.
Tech., U. Illinois, State U. Iowa, Iowa
State U. Sc. and Tech., Kansas State,
Lehigh, Maryland, Mass. Inst. Tech.,
Michigan State, U. Michigan, Minnesota,
Missouri, N. Carolina State, Northwest-
ern, Notre Dame, Ohio State, Oklahoma
State, Oregon State, Pennsylvania State,
U. Pennsylvania, Pittsburgh, Princeton,
Purdue, Rensselaer, Rice, U. So. Cali-
fornia, Stanford, Syracuse, Texas A&M,

U. Texas, U. Utah, U. Washington, Wisconsin, Yale

mechanics: Arizona, Buffalo, Case, Colum-
bia, Cornell, U. Florida, Iowa State U.
Sc. and Tech., Johns Hopkins, Michigan
State, U. Michigan, Nebraska, Ohio State,
Pennsylvania State, Stanford, U. Texas,
Virginia Polytech., Wayne, Wisconsin

metallurgical: Carnegie, Cincinnati, Colum-
bia, Cornell, Illinois Inst. Tech., U. Illi-
nois, Iowa State U. Sc. and Tech.,
Lehigh, Maryland, Michigan State, U.
Michigan, Minnesota, Missouri, Notre
Dame, Ohio State, U. Pennsylvania, Pitts-
burgh, Purdue, Stanford, Tennessee,
Wayne, Wisconsin, Yale

mineral: Minnesota, Stanford

mining: U. California, Columbia, U. Illinois,
Missouri, Pennsylvania State, U. Utah,
Wisconsin

natural gas: Pennsylvania State

nuclear: Iowa State U. Sc. and Tech., Mary-
land, Mass. Inst. Tech., U. Michigan,
Northwestern, Purdue, Texas A&M, U.
Virginia

petroleum: U. California, Pennsylvania
State, U. So. California, Stanford, Texas
A&M, U. Texas

physics: Cornell, Missouri, U. Virginia

sanitary: U. California, Case, U. Florida,
Georgia Inst. Tech., Harvard, U. Illinois,
State U. Iowa, Johns Hopkins, Rutgers,
Virginia Polytech.

science (general): Arkansas, Brown, Cal.
Inst. Tech., U. California, Cincinnati,
Connecticut, Delaware, Mississippi State,
Notre Dame, Oklahoma State, U. Okla-
homa, Purdue, Tennessee

soils: Harvard

structural: Case, U. Florida

theoretical: Northwestern

English*

Entomology

Arizona, Auburn, U. California, Clemson,
Connecticut, Cornell, U. Florida, Hawaii,
Idaho, Iowa State U. Sc. and Tech., U. Illi-
nois, Kansas State, U. Kansas, Maryland,
U. Massachusetts, Michigan State, Minne-
sota, Missouri, Montana State Coll., Ne-
braska, N. Carolina State, N. Dakota Ag.
Coll., Ohio State, Oklahoma State, Oregon
State, Pennsylvania State, Purdue, Rutgers,
Tennessee, Texas A&M, Utah State, U.
Utah, Virginia Polytech., Washington State,
Wisconsin

Family Relationships

Brigham Young, Cornell, Florida State, State

---

* For programs in this field, *see* Tabular Supplement to this index beginning on p. 455.

U. Iowa, Oregon State, Pennsylvania State, Texas Woman's

Far Eastern Languages
U. California, Chicago, Columbia, Harvard, U. Michigan, U. Washington, Yale

Fine Arts. *See also* Art
Boston U., Bryn Mawr, Harvard, U. Michigan, New York U., Ohio State, Pittsburgh

Fisheries
Arizona, Auburn, Colorado State, Cornell, Idaho, Miami, Michigan State, U. Michigan, Minnesota, Montana State Coll., Oregon State, U. Washington

Floriculture. *See* Horticulture

Fluid Mechanics and Hydraulics
Utah State

Folklore
Indiana

Food Science and Technology. *See also* Home Economics
Cornell, Florida State, U. Georgia, U. Illinois, Iowa State U. Sc. and Tech., Kansas State, Mass. Inst. Tech., U. Massachusetts, Minnesota, Oregon State, Pennsylvania State, Rutgers, Stanford, Texas A&M, Texas Woman's, Virginia Polytech., Washington State, Wisconsin

Foreign Area Studies. *See* Area Studies

Forest Products. *See also* Forestry
Michigan State, U. Michigan, State U. New York, Paper Chem. Inst.

Forestry. *See also* Forest Products
Colorado State, Cornell, Idaho, Iowa State U. Sc. and Tech., Michigan State, U. Michigan, Minnesota, State U. New York, N. Carolina State, Ohio State, Oregon State, U. Washington, Wisconsin, Yale

French. *See also* Romance Languages
Alabama, Brown, Bryn Mawr, U. California, Catholic U., U. Colorado, Columbia, Connecticut, Fordham, U. Illinois, Indiana, U. Kansas, Louisiana State, Maryland, Middlebury, Minnesota, Missouri, U. North Carolina, U. Oklahoma, U. Pennsylvania, Pittsburgh, Rice, Rutgers, U. So. California, Stanford, Tulane, U. Utah, Wayne, Western Reserve, Wisconsin, Yale

Fuel Technology
Pennsylvania State

Game Management. *See* Wildlife Management

Genetics. *See also* individual biological sciences
U. California, Colorado State, Connecticut, Hawaii, Iowa State U. Sc. and Tech., Kansas State, Michigan State, U. Michigan, Missouri, Montana State Coll., N. Carolina State, Oregon State, Pennsylvania State, Southern Illinois, Texas A&M, Tulane, U. Utah, Virginia

Polytech., Washington State, U. Washington, Wisconsin, Yeshiva

Geochemistry
U. California, Pennsylvania State

Geography
Boston U., U. California, Chicago, Clark, Columbia, Cornell, U. Florida, George Washington, U. Illinois, Indiana, State U. Iowa, Johns Hopkins, U. Kansas, Louisiana State, Maryland, Michigan State, U. Michigan, Minnesota, Nebraska, U. North Carolina, Northwestern, Ohio State, U. Oregon, Pennsylvania State, Pittsburgh, Syracuse, Tennessee, U. Washington, Wisconsin

Geology*

Geophysics
Alaska, U. California, U. Colorado, Harvard, Mass. Inst. Tech., New Mex. Inst. Mining & Tech., Pennsylvania State, Rensselaer, St. Louis, Stanford, Texas A&M, U. Utah

Germanic Languages
German: Boston U., Brown, Bryn Mawr, U. California, Catholic U., Chicago, Cincinnati, U. Colorado, Columbia, Cornell, George Washington, Harvard, U. Illinois, Indiana, State U. Iowa, Johns Hopkins, U. Kansas, Louisiana State, Maryland, U. Michigan, Middlebury, Minnesota, New York U., U. North Carolina, Northwestern, Ohio State, Pennsylvania State, U. Pennsylvania, Princeton, Rutgers, U. So. California, Stanford, Syracuse, U. Texas, Tulane, U. Utah, Vanderbilt, Washington U. (Mo.), U. Washington, Wayne, Wisconsin, Yale

other: U. California, Chicago, Columbia, George Washington, Harvard, U. Michigan, Princeton, U. Texas

Government. *See* Political Science, government

Greek. *See also* Classics
Bryn Mawr, Catholic U., Columbia, Minnesota, St. Louis, U. Texas

Guidance and Counseling. *See also* Education; Psychology
Fordham, State U. Iowa, St. John's, Southern Illinois

Health, Physical Education, and Recreation
Florida State, U. Illinois, State U. Iowa, Louisiana State, Maryland, Ohio State, U. Oregon, Pennsylvania State, St. Louis, U. So. California, Southern Illinois, Texas Woman's, U. Utah, Washington State, Wisconsin

Hebrew Studies. *See* Jewish and Hebraic Studies

History*

History of ———. *See* most significant term

---

* For programs in this field, *see* Tabular Supplement to this index beginning on p. 455.

Home Economics. *See also* Nutrition
  Cornell, U. Illinois, Iowa State U. Sc. and Tech., U. Massachusetts, Michigan State, Minnesota, Missouri, Ohio State, Pennsylvania State, Purdue, Syracuse, Texas Woman's, Wisconsin
Home Economics Education. *See also* Education
  Cornell, Iowa State U. Sc. and Tech., Pennsylvania State, Texas Woman's
Horticulture
  Arizona, U. California, Cornell, U. Illinois, Iowa State U. Sc. and Tech., Kansas State, Louisiana State, Maryland, Michigan State, Minnesota, New Hampshire, Ohio State, Oregon State, Pennsylvania State, Purdue, Rhode Island, Rutgers, Texas A&M, Utah State, Virginia Polytech., Washington State, Wisconsin
Hospital Administration
  State U. Iowa, Minnesota
Hotel Administration
  Cornell
Housing and Design. *See also* Architecture
  Cornell
Human Development. *See* Child or Human Development
Humanities (General). *See also* individual humanities
  interdepartmental program: Florida State
  liberal arts seminars: Emory
  program for college teachers: Syracuse
Hygiene
  State U. Iowa, Minnesota, Oregon State
Indic Languages
  Yale
Industrial Arts Education
  Pennsylvania State
Industrial Management. *See* Business and Commerce, industrial management and labor relations
Institution Management
  Iowa State U. Sc. and Tech.
International Relations. *See* Political Science, international relations
Italian. *See also* Romance Languages
  Brown, Bryn Mawr, U. California, Catholic U., Columbia, U. Illinois, Middlebury, Wisconsin, Yale
Japanese. *See* Far Eastern Languages
Jewish and Hebraic Studies
  Brandeis, Dropsie, Hebrew Union, Yeshiva
Journalism. *See also* Communication Arts and Sciences
  Minnesota, Missouri, Northwestern, Wisconsin
Labor Relations. *See* Business and Commerce, industrial management and labor relations

Latin. *See also* Classics
  Bryn Mawr, Catholic U., Columbia, Minnesota, St. Louis, U. Texas
Library Science
  Chicago, U. Illinois, U. Michigan, Rutgers, Western Reserve
Limnology
  Cornell
Linguistics. *See also* Comparative Literature and individual languages
  Buffalo, U. California, Chicago, Columbia, Cornell, Harvard, Indiana, Louisiana State, U. Michigan, U. North Carolina, U. Pennsylvania, U. Texas, U. Washington, Wisconsin, Yale
Literature. *See* Comparative Literature and individual languages
Machine Design. *See also* Engineering, mechanical
  Case
Marine Biology. *See also* Biology
  U. California, Delaware, Miami, Stanford
Mass Communications. *See* Communication Arts and Sciences
Materials Science
  Northwestern
Mathematics*
Mathematics History
  Brown
Mechanics. *See also* Engineering, mechanics
  Brooklyn Polytech., Illinois Inst. Tech., U. Illinois, Indiana, Iowa State U. Sc. and Tech., Kansas State, Minnesota, Northwestern, Rensselaer, Virginia Polytech.
Medical Specialties
  administrative medicine: Columbia
  cancer biology: Minnesota
  chemistry of biological systems: Buffalo
  cytology: Baylor
  dermatology: Chicago, Minnesota
  endocrinology: U. California
  epidemiology: Baylor, U. Michigan, Minnesota
  gynecology: Minnesota, Nebraska
  histochemistry: Tulane
  history of medicine: Johns Hopkins, Yale
  immunology: Baylor, Buffalo, Marquette, State U. New York, U. North Carolina, U. Pennsylvania, Yeshiva
  infectious diseases: U. California
  internal medicine: Nebraska
  medical biochemistry: Northwestern
  medical microbiology: U. Kansas, State U. New York, Northwestern, U. Pennsylvania, Wisconsin

---

* For programs in this field, *see* Tabular Supplement to this index beginning on p. 455.

medical pharmacology: U. Kansas
medical physics: U. California
medical physiology: U. Pennsylvania
medicine: Chicago, Minnesota
neurology: Chicago, Minnesota, Nebraska
neurosurgery: Minnesota
obstetrics: Minnesota, Nebraska
oncology: Wisconsin
orthopedic surgery: Minnesota, Nebraska
otolaryngology: Minnesota
pediatrics: Minnesota, Nebraska
physical biochemistry: U. Pennsylvania
physical medicine and rehabilitation: Minnesota
physiological chemistry: U. California, Temple, Wayne
physiology of human diseases: Buffalo
preventive medicine: State U. Iowa, U. Mississippi, U. Oklahoma
psychiatry: George Washington, Minnesota, Nebraska
radiology: U. California, Minnesota, Nebraska, Rochester, Tennessee
surgery: Chicago, U. Illinois, Minnesota
urology: Minnesota
virology: Baylor, U. Michigan, U. Pennsylvania

Medieval Studies
Bryn Mawr, Notre Dame, Yale

Metallurgy. *See also* Engineering, metallurgical
Arizona, U. California, Case, Mass. Inst. Tech., Minnesota, Northwestern, Pennsylvania State, Rensselaer, U. Utah

Meteorology
Arizona, U. California, Chicago, Florida State, Johns Hopkins, Mass. Inst. Tech., U. Michigan, New York U., Pennsylvania State, Texas A&M, U. Washington, Wisconsin

Microbiology*

Middle East Languages. *See* Near and Middle East Languages

Milling Industry
Kansas State

Mineral Economics
Pennsylvania State

Mineral Preparation
Pennsylvania State

Mineralogy and Petrology
U. Michigan, Ohio State, Pennsylvania State, U. Utah

Music. *See also* Music Education; Music History
Boston U., Brandeis, Brigham Young, Bryn Mawr, U. California, Catholic U., Chicago, Columbia, Cornell, Florida State, George

Peabody, Harvard, U. Illinois, Indiana, State U. Iowa, Michigan State, U. Michigan, Minnesota, New York U., U. North Carolina, North Texas State, Northwestern, Ohio State, U. Pennsylvania, Pittsburgh, Princeton, Rochester, U. So. California, Stanford, U. Texas, U. Utah, Washington U. (Mo.), U. Washington, Wisconsin

Music Education. *See also* Education; Music
Boston U., Brigham Young, Florida State, George Peabody, U. Kansas, Michigan State, Rochester

Music History. *See also* Music
Yale

Naval Architecture
Mass. Inst. Tech., U. Michigan

Near and Middle East Languages
Egyptian: Brown, Catholic U., Chicago
Middle East: Columbia
Near East: Chicago, Columbia, Harvard, Hebrew Union, Yale
Semitic: Brandeis, Catholic U., Columbia, Dropsie, Hebrew Union, Yeshiva

Nursery Education
Texas Woman's

Nursing Education
Pittsburgh

Nutrition. *See also* Animal and Poultry Sciences, nutrition; Home Economics
Arizona, Cornell, Florida State, State U. Iowa, Iowa State U. Sc. and Tech., Kansas State, U. North Carolina, Rutgers, Tennessee, Texas Woman's

Oceanography
U. California, Cornell, Johns Hopkins, Miami, New York U., Rhode Island, Stanford, Texas A&M, U. Washington

Oil Seed Technology
Texas A&M

Operations Research
Case

Optical Sciences
opthalmology: Minnesota
optics: U. California, Indiana, Rochester
optometry: Ohio State
physiological optics: U. California, Ohio State

Oriental Languages. *See* Far Eastern Languages; Near and Middle East Languages

Oriental Studies. *See also* Area Studies, Asian and Far Eastern
Chicago, Johns Hopkins, U. Pennsylvania, Princeton

Paleontology
U. California

Paper and Pulp Products. *See* Forestry; Forest Products

---

* For programs in this field, *see* Tabular Supplement to this index beginning on p. 455.

Parasitology
  U. California, Columbia, Kansas State, Miami, U. Michigan, U. Pennsylvania, Tulane
Pastoral Counseling
  Boston U.
Pathology
  Baylor, Boston U., Chicago, Cincinnati, U. Colorado, Columbia, Georgetown, Hahnemann Medical, Harvard, U. Illinois, Jefferson Medical, Marquette, U. Michigan, Minnesota, Missouri, Nebraska, New York U., Ohio State, U. Oklahoma, U. Pennsylvania, Pittsburgh, Rochester, St. Louis, S. Carolina Med. Coll., Tennessee, Union Coll., Virginia Med. Coll., Washington U. (Mo.), Western Reserve, Wisconsin, Yeshiva
Pharmaceutical Science*
Philology. *See* individual languages and language groups
Philosophy*
Philosophy of Education. *See also* Education; Philosophy
  Boston U.
Physical Education. *See* Health, Physical Education, and Recreation
Physics*
Physiology*
Plant Sciences. *See also* Agronomy; Botany; Crops
  plant breeding: Arizona, Cornell, Oklahoma State, Texas A&M
  plant genetics: Minnesota, Oklahoma State, West Virginia
  plant nutrition: Connecticut
  plant pathology: Arizona, Auburn, U. California, Clemson, Cornell, U. Florida, U. Illinois, Iowa State U. Sc. and Tech., Louisiana State, U. Massachusetts, Michigan State, Minnesota, Nebraska, N. Carolina State, N. Dakota Ag. Coll., Ohio State, Pennsylvania State, Purdue, Rhode Island, Rutgers, Texas A&M, Washington State, West Virginia, Wisconsin
  plant physiology: U. California, Rutgers, Texas A&M, Utah State
  plant science (general): U. Georgia, U. Oklahoma, Purdue, S. Dakota State, Wyoming
Plastics
  Princeton
Political Science
  American government: Fordham
  foreign affairs: U. Virginia

general: Alabama, American U., Brown, Bryn Mawr, Chicago, Cincinnati, U. California, U. Colorado, Duke, Emory, Florida State, U. Florida, George Washington, Georgetown, Harvard, Idaho, U. Illinois, State U. Iowa, Johns Hopkins, U. Kansas, Kentucky, Michigan State, U. Michigan, Minnesota, Missouri, New School for Social Research, U. North Carolina, Northwestern, Notre Dame, Ohio State, U. Oregon, Pennsylvania State, U. Pennsylvania, Pittsburgh, Rutgers, St. John's, St. Louis, U. So. California, Southern Illinois, Stanford, Syracuse, Tennessee, Tulane, U. Utah, Vanderbilt, U. Virginia, Washington State, Washington U. (Mo.), U. Washington, West Virginia, Western Reserve, Wisconsin, Yale
government: American U., Boston U., Buffalo, Claremont, Columbia, Cornell, Harvard, Indiana, Maryland, New York U., U. Oklahoma, U. Texas
international affairs: Princeton
international economics: Kentucky
international relations: American U., Clark, Connecticut, Fordham, George Washington, Georgetown, Kentucky, Minnesota, Nebraska, U. Pennsylvania, Syracuse, Tufts, U. Virginia, Yale
political economy: Harvard, Johns Hopkins
politics: Catholic U., Maryland, Princeton
public administration: American U., Cornell, New York U.
public affairs: Princeton
public law: Columbia
Pomology. *See* Agronomy; Crops, fruit
Portuguese. *See also* Romance Languages
  Columbia, U. Illinois, Indiana, Wisconsin
Poultry. *See* Animal and Poultry Sciences, poultry
Psychodynamics
  Tulane
Psychology*
Public Administration. *See* Political Science, public administration
Public Health
  U. California, Michigan State, U. Michigan, U. North Carolina, U. Oklahoma, St. Louis, Yale
Range Management
  Arizona, N. Dakota Ag. Coll., Texas A&M, Utah State, Wyoming
Recreation. *See* Health, Physical Education, and Recreation
Regional Science
  U. Pennsylvania

---

* For programs in this field, *see* Tabular Supplement to this index beginning on p. 455.

Religion
  Boston U., Brigham Young, Brown, Chicago, Claremont, Columbia, Drew, Duke, Emory, Hartford Seminary, Harvard, Hebrew Union, State U. Iowa, Princeton, St. Mary's, U. So. California, Union Theological Seminary, Vanderbilt, Western Reserve, Yale
Religion, History of
  Chicago, Harvard
Religious Education. *See also* Education
  Boston U., Catholic U.
Resource Conservation and Management. *See also* individual resources
  Cornell, U. Michigan, State U. New York
Romance Languages. *See also* individual Romance languages
  Boston U., U. California, Chicago, Cincinnati, Cornell, Duke, George Washington, Harvard, State U. Iowa, Johns Hopkins, Louisiana State, U. Michigan, Nebraska, New York U., Northwestern, Ohio State, U. Oregon, Pennsylvania State, U. Pennsylvania, Pittsburgh, Princeton, Syracuse, U. Texas, U. Virginia, Washington U. (Mo.), U. Washington
Rural Education. *See* Agricultural Education; Education
Rural Sociology. *See also* Sociology
  Cornell, Kentucky, Missouri, N. Carolina State, Ohio State, Pennsylvania State, Wisconsin
Russian. *See* Slavic Languages
Sanitary Chemistry
  Wisconsin
Sanitation
  Minnesota, Rutgers
Sanskrit. *See also* Classics
  U. California, Harvard
Scandinavian Languages. *See also* Germanic Languages, other
  U. California
Science Education. *See also* Education and individual sciences
  State U. Iowa, Oregon State, Syracuse
Science, History of
  Harvard, Indiana, Pittsburgh, Wisconsin, Yale
Seed Technology
  Cornell
Semitic Languages. *See* Near and Middle East Languages, Semitic
Slavic Languages
  Russian: Brown, Bryn Mawr, U. California, Chicago, Columbia, Cornell, Harvard, Indiana, U. Michigan, Middlebury, New York U., U. Pennsylvania, U. Washington, Yale

other: Brown, U. California, Chicago, Columbia, Harvard, Indiana, U. Michigan, New York U., U. Pennsylvania, Yale
Social
  ethics: Boston U.
  institutions: U. California
  relations: Harvard, Johns Hopkins
  science: S. Dakota State
  studies education: State U. Iowa
  thought: Chicago
  welfare: Brandeis
  work: Bryn Mawr, Chicago, Minnesota, Ohio State
Sociology*
Soil Science. *See also* Agronomy
  Arizona, Auburn, U. California, Colorado State, Connecticut, U. Florida, Hawaii, Michigan State, Minnesota, Missouri, N. Carolina State, N. Dakota Ag. Coll., Oklahoma State, Oregon State, Rutgers, Texas A&M, Utah State, Wisconsin
Solid-State Science and Technology. *See also* Chemistry; Physics
  Syracuse
Spanish. *See also* Romance Languages
  Alabama, Arizona, Brown, U. California, Catholic U., U. Colorado, Columbia, Connecticut, Florida State, U. Florida, U. Illinois, Indiana, U. Kansas, Maryland, Middlebury, Minnesota, Missouri, U. New Mexico, U. North Carolina, U. Oklahoma, U. Pennsylvania, Pittsburgh, Rutgers, St. Louis, U. So. California, Stanford, Tulane, U. Utah, U. Virginia, Wayne, Western Reserve, Wisconsin, Yale
Speech
  U. California, Cornell, Denver, Florida State, U. Florida, U. Illinois, Indiana, State U. Iowa, U. Kansas, Louisiana State, Michigan State, U. Michigan, Minnesota, Missouri, Northwestern, Ohio State, Ohio U., U. Oklahoma, U. Oregon, Pennsylvania State, Pittsburgh, Purdue, U. So. California, Southern Illinois, Stanford, Syracuse, U. Utah, Washington U. (Mo.), U. Washington, Wayne, Western Reserve, Wisconsin
Statistics. *See also* Biostatistics; Mathematics
  American U., Chicago, Columbia, Cornell, George Washington, Harvard, U. Illinois, Iowa State U. Sc. and Tech., Michigan State, Minnesota, N. Carolina State, U. North Carolina, Rutgers, Stanford, Virginia Polytech., Western Reserve, Wisconsin
Tanning Research
  Cincinnati

---

* For programs in this field, *see* Tabular Supplement to this index beginning on p. 455.

Textiles
Pennsylvania State, Texas Woman's
Theater. *See* Dramatic Arts
Theater History
Yale
Toxicology
U. California, Indiana, Maryland, New York
U., Rochester
Ural-Altaic Languages
Columbia
Veterinary Sciences
U. California, Colorado State, Connecticut,
Cornell, U. Illinois, Iowa State U. Sc. and
Tech., Kansas State, Michigan State, Minne-
sota, Nebraska, Ohio State, Oklahoma State,

U. Pennsylvania, Purdue, Rhode Island,
Texas A&M, Washington State, Wisconsin
Vocational Education. *See also* Education
Iowa State U. Sc. and Tech., Pennsylvania
State
Wildlife Management
Arizona, Auburn, Colorado State, Cornell,
Idaho, Michigan State, U. Michigan, Minne-
sota, Montana State Coll., State U. New
York, Oklahoma State, Oregon State, Texas
A&M, Utah State, Virginia Polytech., Wis-
consin
Zoology*

* For programs in this field, *see* Tabular Supplement to this index beginning on p. 455.

Tabular Supplement to the Index to Fields of Study for the Ph.D.: Programs Offered by 50 or More Institutions

★ Indicates Ph.D. programs are offered.
– Indicates Ph.D. programs are not offered.

Institution	Anatomy	Bacteriology	Biochemistry	Biology	Botany	Chemistry	Economics	Education	English	Engineering: Chemical	Engineering: Electrical	Geology	History	Mathematics	Microbiology	Pharmaceutical Science	Philosophy	Physics	Physiology	Psychology	Sociology	Zoology
Adelphi Coll. (N.Y.)	–	–	–	–	–	★	–	–	–	–	–	–	–	★	–	–	–	–	–	★	–	–
Akron, Univ. of (Ohio)	–	–	–	–	–	★	–	–	–	–	–	–	–	–	–	–	–	–	–	–	–	–
Alabama, Univ. of	★	–	★	★	–	★	–	★	★	–	–	–	★	★	★	★	–	★	★	★	–	–
American Univ. (D.C.)	–	–	–	–	–	–	★	–	–	–	–	–	★	★	–	–	–	–	–	★	★	–
Arizona, Univ. of	–	★	–	–	★	★	★	★	–	–	★	★	★	★	–	–	★	–	★	–	★	★
Arkansas, Univ. of	★	★	★	–	★	★	★	–	★	–	★	–	–	★	–	★	★	★	–	★	–	★
Auburn Univ. (Alab.)	–	–	–	–	★	★	★	–	–	–	–	–	–	★	–	–	–	–	–	–	–	★
Baylor Univ. (Texas)	★	–	★	–	–	★	–	–	★	–	–	–	–	★	★	★	–	–	★	★	★	–
Boston Coll. (Mass.)	–	–	–	–	–	★	★	★	–	–	–	–	★	–	–	–	–	–	–	–	–	–
Boston Univ. (Mass.)	★	–	★	★	–	★	★	★	–	–	★	–	★	★	★	★	★	★	★	★	★	–
Brandeis Univ. (Mass.)	–	–	★	★	–	★	–	–	★	–	–	–	★	★	–	–	–	★	–	★	–	–
Brigham Young Univ. (Utah)	–	–	–	–	–	★	–	–	–	–	–	★	★	–	–	–	–	★	–	★	★	–
Brooklyn, Polytech. Inst. of (N.Y.)	–	–	–	–	–	★	–	–	–	–	–	–	★	–	–	–	–	★	–	–	–	–
Brown Univ. (R.I.)	–	–	★	★	★	★	★	–	★	–	–	★	★	★	–	–	★	★	–	★	★	–
Bryn Mawr Coll. (Pa.)	–	–	–	★	–	★	★	★	★	–	–	★	★	★	–	–	★	★	–	★	★	–
Buffalo, Univ. of (N.Y.)	★	★	★	★	–	★	★	–	★	–	–	★	★	★	★	★	★	★	★	★	★	★
California Inst. of Tech.	–	–	–	★	–	★	–	–	–	★	★	★	–	★	–	–	–	★	–	–	–	–
California, Univ. of	★	★	★	–	★	★	★	★	★	★	★	★	★	★	★	★	★	★	★	★	★	★
Carnegie Inst. of Tech. (Pa.)	–	–	–	–	–	★	★	–	–	★	★	–	–	★	–	–	–	★	–	★	–	–
Case Inst. of Tech. (Ohio)	–	–	–	–	–	★	★	–	–	★	–	–	–	★	–	–	–	★	–	–	–	–
Catholic Univ. of America (D.C.)	–	–	–	★	–	★	★	★	★	–	–	–	★	★	–	–	★	★	–	★	★	–
Chicago, Univ. of (Ill.)	★	–	★	★	★	★	★	★	★	–	★	★	★	★	★	★	★	★	★	★	★	★
Cincinnati, Univ. of (Ohio)	★	★	★	–	★	★	★	★	★	–	★	–	★	★	★	★	★	★	★	★	–	★
Claremont Coll. (Calif.)	–	–	–	–	★	–	★	★	★	–	–	–	★	–	–	–	–	★	–	★	–	–
Clark Univ. (Mass.)	–	–	–	–	–	★	★	–	–	–	–	–	★	–	–	–	–	–	–	★	–	–
Clemson Coll. (S.C.)	–	–	–	–	–	★	–	–	–	–	–	–	–	–	–	–	–	–	–	–	–	–
Colorado State Univ.	–	★	★	–	★	★	–	–	–	–	–	–	–	–	–	★	–	–	–	–	–	★
Colorado, Univ. of	★	–	★	★	★	★	★	★	★	–	–	★	★	★	★	★	★	★	★	★	★	★
Columbia Univ. (N.Y.)	★	–	★	–	★	★	★	★	★	★	★	★	★	★	★	★	★	★	★	★	★	★
Connecticut, Univ. of	–	★	★	–	★	★	–	★	★	–	–	★	–	★	–	★	–	★	–	★	★	★
Cornell Univ. (N.Y.)	–	★	★	–	★	★	★	★	★	★	★	★	★	★	–	★	★	★	★	★	★	★
Delaware Univ. of	–	★	–	–	★	★	–	–	–	★	–	–	★	–	–	–	–	–	★	★	★	★
Denver, Univ. of (Colo.)	–	–	–	–	–	–	–	–	–	★	★	–	★	–	–	–	–	–	★	★	–	–
Dropsie Coll. (Pa.)	–	–	–	–	–	–	★	–	–	–	–	–	–	–	–	–	–	–	–	–	–	–
Duke Univ. (N.C.)	★	–	★	–	★	★	★	–	★	–	★	–	★	★	★	–	★	★	★	★	★	★
Duquesne Univ. (Pa.)	–	–	–	–	–	★	–	–	–	–	–	–	★	–	–	★	★	–	–	★	★	–
Emory Univ. (Ga.)	★	★	★	★	–	★	–	–	–	–	–	★	–	–	★	–	★	★	★	★	–	–
Florida State Univ.	–	–	–	★	★	★	–	★	★	–	–	★	★	★	–	–	★	★	★	★	★	★
Florida, Univ. of	★	★	★	★	★	★	★	★	★	★	★	★	★	★	★	–	★	★	★	★	★	–
Fordham Univ. (N.Y.)	–	–	–	★	–	★	★	★	★	–	–	–	★	–	–	–	★	★	–	★	★	–
George Peabody Coll. (Tenn.)	–	–	–	–	–	–	–	★	★	–	–	–	★	–	–	–	–	–	–	★	–	–
George Washington Univ. (D.C.)	★	★	★	★	★	★	★	★	–	★	–	–	★	★	–	–	★	★	★	★	–	★
Georgetown Univ. (D.C.)	★	★	★	–	–	★	–	–	–	–	–	–	★	–	–	–	★	★	★	★	–	★
Georgia Inst. of Tech.	–	–	–	–	–	★	–	–	–	★	★	–	–	★	★	–	–	★	–	–	–	–
Georgia, Univ. of	–	★	–	–	–	★	–	★	–	–	–	★	★	–	–	–	★	–	★	–	–	★
Hahnemann Medical Coll. (Pa.)	★	★	★	–	–	–	–	–	–	–	–	–	–	–	–	★	–	–	★	–	–	–
Harvard Univ. (Mass.)	★	★	★	★	★	★	★	★	★	–	–	★	★	★	★	–	★	★	★	★	★	★
Hawaii, Univ. of	–	–	★	–	★	★	–	–	–	–	–	–	–	★	–	–	–	–	★	–	–	★
Houston, Univ. of (Texas)	–	–	–	★	–	★	★	–	–	★	–	–	★	–	–	–	–	★	–	★	–	–
Howard Univ. (D.C.)	–	–	–	–	–	★	–	–	–	–	–	–	★	–	–	–	–	–	★	★	–	★
Idaho, Univ. of	–	–	–	–	★	★	–	★	–	–	–	★	★	–	–	–	–	–	–	–	–	★
Illinois Inst. of Tech.	–	★	★	★	–	★	★	–	–	★	★	–	–	★	–	–	–	★	★	★	–	–
Illinois, Univ. of	★	–	★	–	★	★	★	★	★	★	★	★	★	★	★	★	★	★	★	★	★	★
Indiana Univ.	★	★	★	–	★	★	★	★	★	–	–	★	★	★	★	★	★	★	★	★	★	★
Iowa, State Univ. of	★	★	★	–	★	★	★	★	★	★	★	★	★	★	–	★	★	★	★	★	★	★
Iowa State Univ. of Sci. & Tech.	–	★	★	–	★	★	★	★	–	★	★	★	–	★	–	–	–	★	–	★	★	★

Institution	Anatomy	Bacteriology	Biochemistry	Biology	Botany	Chemistry	Economics	Education	English	Engineering: Chemical	Engineering: Electrical	Geology	History	Mathematics	Microbiology	Pharmaceutical Science	Philosophy	Physics	Physiology	Psychology	Sociology	Zoology
Jefferson Medical Coll. (Pa.)	★	–	★	–	–	–	–	–	–	–	–	–	–	–	★	★	–	–	★	–	–	–
Johns Hopkins Univ. (Md.)	★	–	★	★	–	★	★	★	–	★	★	★	★	★	★	–	★	★	★	★	–	–
Kansas City, Univ. of (Mo.)	–	–	–	–	–	–	–	★	–	–	–	–	–	–	★	–	–	–	–	–	–	–
Kansas State Univ.	–	★	–	–	★	★	–	–	–	★	★	–	–	–	–	–	–	★	–	★	–	★
Kansas, Univ. of	★	★	★	–	★	★	★	★	★	★	★	★	★	★	★	–	★	★	★	★	★	★
Kentucky, Univ. of	–	–	–	★	–	★	★	★	★	★	★	–	★	★	★	–	–	★	–	★	★	–
Lehigh Univ. (Pa.)	–	–	–	★	–	★	★	–	★	★	★	★	★	★	–	–	–	★	–	★	–	–
Louisiana State Univ.	★	★	★	–	★	★	★	★	★	★	★	★	★	★	–	★	★	★	★	★	★	★
Louisville, Univ. of (Ky.)	★	–	★	★	–	★	★	–	★	–	–	–	★	★	★	–	★	–	★	–	–	–
Lowell Tech. Inst. (Mass.)	–	–	–	–	–	★	–	–	–	★	–	–	–	★	–	–	–	–	–	–	–	–
Loyola Univ. (Ill.)	★	–	–	–	★	–	★	★	–	–	–	★	–	★	★	–	–	★	★	★	★	–
Maine, Univ. of	–	–	–	–	–	★	–	–	–	–	★	–	★	–	–	–	–	–	–	–	–	–
Marquette Univ. (Wis.)	★	–	★	★	–	–	–	–	–	–	–	★	★	★	★	–	★	–	★	–	–	–
Maryland, Univ. of	★	–	★	–	★	★	–	–	–	–	★	–	★	★	★	–	★	★	★	★	★	–
Massachusetts Coll. of Pharmacy	–	–	–	–	–	–	–	–	–	–	–	–	–	–	–	★	–	★	–	–	–	–
Massachusetts Inst. of Tech.	–	–	–	★	–	★	★	–	–	★	★	★	–	★	–	–	★	–	–	–	–	–
Massachusetts, Univ. of	–	★	–	–	★	★	★	–	–	–	–	–	–	–	–	–	–	–	★	–	–	★
Medical Evangelists, Coll. of (Calif.)	★	–	★	–	–	–	–	–	–	–	–	–	–	–	★	–	–	★	★	–	–	–
Miami, Univ. of (Fla.)	★	–	★	–	–	–	★	–	–	–	–	–	★	★	–	–	–	★	–	★	–	★
Michigan State Univ.	★	–	★	–	★	★	★	★	–	★	★	★	★	★	★	–	★	★	★	★	★	★
Michigan, Univ of.	★	★	★	–	★	★	★	★	★	★	★	★	★	★	★	★	★	★	★	★	★	★
Minnesota, Univ. of	★	★	★	–	★	★	★	★	★	★	★	★	★	★	★	★	★	★	★	★	★	★
Mississippi Southern Coll.	–	–	–	–	–	–	★	–	–	–	–	–	–	–	–	–	–	–	★	–	–	–
Mississippi State Univ.	–	–	–	–	–	–	–	–	–	–	–	★	–	★	–	–	–	–	–	★	–	–
Mississippi, Univ. of	★	–	★	–	–	★	★	–	–	–	–	★	–	★	★	–	–	★	–	★	–	–
Missouri, Univ. of	★	–	★	–	★	★	★	★	★	★	★	★	★	★	★	★	★	★	★	★	★	★
Montana State Coll.	–	★	–	–	★	★	–	–	–	★	★	–	★	–	–	–	–	–	–	–	–	★
Montana State Univ.	–	★	–	–	–	–	–	–	–	–	★	–	–	–	–	–	–	–	–	–	–	–
Nebraska, Univ. of	★	★	★	–	★	★	★	★	★	★	★	★	★	★	★	–	★	★	★	★	★	★
New Hampshire, Univ. of	–	–	★	–	★	★	–	–	–	–	–	–	–	★	–	–	–	–	–	–	–	★
New Mexico Highlands Univ.	–	–	★	–	–	–	–	–	–	–	–	–	–	–	–	–	–	–	–	–	–	–
New Mexico State Univ.	–	–	–	–	–	–	–	–	–	–	–	–	–	★	–	–	–	★	–	–	–	–
New Mexico, Univ. of	–	–	–	–	★	★	★	★	★	–	–	★	★	★	–	–	–	★	–	★	–	★
New School for Social Research (N.Y.)	–	–	–	–	–	–	★	–	–	–	–	–	–	–	–	–	★	–	–	★	★	–
New York, State Univ. of	★	★	★	–	–	–	–	–	–	–	–	–	–	★	★	★	–	–	★	–	–	–
New York Univ.	★	–	★	★	–	★	★	★	★	–	★	–	★	★	★	–	★	★	–	★	★	–
North Carolina Coll. at Durham	–	–	–	–	–	–	★	–	–	–	–	–	–	–	–	–	–	–	–	–	–	–
North Carolina State Coll.	–	★	–	–	★	–	–	–	★	★	★	–	–	–	–	–	–	★	–	–	–	★
North Carolina, Univ. of	–	★	★	–	★	★	★	★	★	–	–	–	★	★	–	–	★	★	★	★	★	★
North Dakota Agri. Coll.	–	–	★	–	★	★	–	★	–	–	–	–	★	★	–	–	–	–	–	★	–	★
North Dakota, Univ. of	★	–	★	★	–	★	★	–	★	–	–	★	★	★	–	–	–	★	★	★	–	★
Northwestern Univ. (Ill.)	–	★	★	★	★	★	★	★	★	★	★	★	★	★	–	★	★	★	★	★	★	★
Notre Dame, Univ. of (Ind.)	–	–	★	★	–	★	★	★	★	★	★	–	★	★	–	–	★	★	–	–	–	★
Ohio State Univ.	★	★	★	–	★	★	★	★	★	★	★	★	★	★	–	★	★	★	★	★	★	★
Ohio Univ.	–	–	–	–	–	★	–	★	–	★	–	–	–	–	–	–	–	★	–	★	–	–
Oklahoma State Univ.	–	–	–	–	★	★	★	–	–	★	★	–	–	★	★	–	–	★	★	★	–	★
Oklahoma, Univ. of	★	★	★	–	★	★	★	★	★	★	★	★	★	★	–	★	★	★	★	★	★	★
Oregon State Coll.	–	★	–	–	★	★	★	–	–	–	–	–	★	★	–	–	★	–	★	–	–	★
Oregon, Univ. of	★	★	★	–	★	★	★	★	★	–	–	★	★	★	–	–	★	★	★	★	★	★
Paper Chemistry, Inst. of (Wis.)	–	–	–	–	–	★	–	–	–	–	–	–	–	–	–	–	–	–	–	–	–	–
Pennsylvania State Univ.	–	★	★	–	★	★	★	★	★	★	★	★	★	★	–	–	★	★	★	★	★	★
Pennsylvania, Univ. of	★	–	★	–	★	★	★	★	★	★	★	★	★	★	★	★	★	★	★	★	★	★
Philadelphia Coll. of Pharm. (Pa.)	–	–	–	–	–	★	–	–	–	–	–	–	–	–	–	★	–	–	–	–	–	–
Pittsburgh, Univ. of (Pa.)	★	★	★	–	★	★	★	★	★	★	★	★	★	★	★	★	★	★	★	★	★	★
Portland, Univ. of (Ore.)	–	–	–	–	–	–	–	★	–	–	–	–	–	–	–	–	–	★	–	–	–	–
Princeton Univ. (N.J.)	–	–	–	★	–	★	★	★	–	★	★	★	★	★	–	–	★	★	–	–	★	–
Purdue Univ. (Ind.)	–	★	★	–	★	★	★	★	★	★	★	★	–	★	–	★	★	★	★	★	–	★
Radcliffe Coll. (Mass.)	★	★	★	★	–	★	★	★	★	–	–	★	★	★	★	–	★	★	★	★	★	★
Rensselaer Polytech. Inst. (N.Y.)	–	★	–	–	–	★	–	–	–	★	★	★	–	★	–	–	★	★	–	–	–	–
Rhode Island, Univ. of	–	★	–	–	★	★	–	–	–	–	–	–	–	★	–	–	–	★	–	–	–	★
Rice Univ. (Texas)	–	–	–	★	–	★	★	–	–	★	★	★	★	★	–	–	★	★	–	–	–	–
Rochester, Univ. of (N.Y.)	★	★	★	★	–	★	★	★	★	★	★	★	★	★	–	–	★	★	★	★	–	–
Rutgers Univ. (N.J.)	–	★	★	–	★	★	★	★	★	★	★	–	★	★	★	★	★	★	★	★	–	★
St. Bonaventure Univ. (N.Y.)	–	–	★	–	–	–	–	★	–	–	–	–	★	–	–	–	–	★	–	★	★	–
St. John's Univ. (N.Y.)	–	–	–	–	–	★	–	★	★	–	–	–	★	–	–	–	★	★	–	★	★	–
St. Louis Univ. (Mo.)	★	–	★	★	–	★	★	★	★	–	–	–	★	★	★	★	★	★	–	★	★	–
South Carolina, Medical Coll. of	★	–	★	–	–	★	–	–	–	–	–	–	★	★	★	–	★	–	★	–	–	–
South Carolina, Univ. of	–	–	–	★	–	★	★	★	★	–	–	–	★	★	–	–	★	–	–	–	–	–
South Dakota State Coll.	–	–	–	–	–	–	–	–	–	–	–	–	–	★	–	–	–	★	–	–	–	–
South Dakota, State Univ. of	★	★	★	–	–	–	–	–	–	–	–	–	–	★	–	–	–	★	–	–	–	–
Southern California, Univ. of	★	★	★	★	–	★	★	★	★	★	★	★	★	★	–	–	★	★	★	★	★	–
Southern Illinois Univ.	–	–	–	–	–	★	–	–	–	–	–	–	★	★	–	–	–	–	★	★	–	★
Southern Methodist Univ. (Texas)	–	–	–	–	–	★	★	–	★	–	–	–	★	★	–	–	★	★	–	–	★	–
Stanford Univ.	★	★	★	★	–	★	★	★	★	★	★	★	★	★	–	–	★	★	★	★	★	★
Stevens Inst. of Tech. (N.J.)	–	–	–	–	–	★	★	–	–	★	★	–	–	★	–	–	★	★	–	–	–	–
Syracuse Univ. (N.Y.)	–	★	★	–	★	★	★	★	★	★	★	–	★	★	–	–	★	★	–	★	★	★

Institution	Anatomy	Bacteriology	Biochemistry	Biology	Botany	Chemistry	Economics	Education	English	Engineering Chemical	Engineering Electrical	Geology	History	Mathematics	Microbiology	Pharmaceutical Science	Philosophy	Physics	Physiology	Psychology	Sociology	Zoology
Temple Univ. (Pa.)	★	–	–	–	–	★	–	–	★	–	–	–	–	–	★	★	–	★	★	★	–	–
Tennessee, Univ. of	★	★	★	★	★	★	–	–	★	★	–	★	★	★	–	★	–	★	★	★	★	★
Texas, A&M Coll. of	–	–	–	★	★	★	–	–	★	★	★	★	–	★	★	–	–	★	–	–	★	★
Texas Tech. Coll.	–	–	–	–	–	★	–	–	★	–	–	★	–	★	–	–	–	★	–	–	★	–
Texas, Univ. of	★	★	★	★	★	★	★	★	★	★	★	★	★	★	★	★	★	★	★	★	★	★
Toledo Univ. (Ohio)	–	–	–	–	–	–	–	★	–	–	–	–	–	–	–	–	–	–	–	–	–	–
Tufts Univ. (Mass.)	★	–	★	★	–	★	–	–	★	–	–	–	–	★	★	–	★	★	★	★	★	–
Tulane Univ. (La.)	★	–	★	–	–	★	★	–	★	–	–	★	★	★	★	–	★	★	★	★	★	★
Union Coll. and Univ. (N.Y.)	★	–	★	–	–	–	–	–	–	–	–	–	–	–	★	★	–	–	★	–	–	–
Utah State Univ.	–	–	–	–	–	★	–	–	–	–	★	–	–	★	–	–	–	–	★	–	★	★
Utah, Univ. of	★	★	★	★	★	★	★	–	★	★	★	★	★	★	–	★	★	★	★	★	★	★
Vanderbilt Univ. (Tenn.)	★	–	★	★	–	★	★	★	★	–	–	★	★	★	★	★	★	★	★	★	★	★
Vermont, Univ. of	–	–	★	–	–	–	–	–	–	–	–	–	–	–	★	–	★	–	★	–	–	★
Virginia, Medical Coll. of	★	–	★	★	–	–	–	–	–	–	–	–	–	★	–	★	–	★	–	–	–	–
Virginia Polytech. Inst.	–	★	–	–	★	★	–	–	–	★	–	★	–	★	–	–	–	★	–	★	–	★
Virginia, Univ. of	★	–	★	★	–	★	★	–	★	★	★	–	★	★	★	–	★	★	★	★	★	★
Washington State Univ.	–	★	–	–	★	★	★	★	–	–	★	★	★	–	★	–	★	–	★	★	★	★
Washington Univ. (Mo.)	★	–	★	–	★	★	★	★	–	★	★	★	★	–	★	–	★	★	★	★	★	★
Washington, Univ. of (Wash.)	★	–	★	–	★	★	★	★	★	★	★	★	★	★	★	★	★	★	★	★	★	★
Wayne State Univ. (Mich.)	★	–	–	★	–	★	★	★	★	★	–	–	★	★	★	★	–	★	★	★	★	–
West Virginia Univ.	–	★	★	–	★	★	–	–	–	★	–	★	★	–	–	★	–	★	★	★	–	★
Western Reserve Univ. (Ohio)	★	–	★	–	★	★	★	–	★	–	–	★	★	★	★	–	★	★	★	★	★	★
Wisconsin, Univ. of	★	★	★	–	★	★	★	★	★	★	★	★	★	★	–	★	★	★	★	★	★	★
Worcester Polytech. Inst. (Mass.)	–	–	–	–	★	–	–	–	★	–	–	–	–	–	★	–	–	★	–	–	–	–
Wyoming, Univ. of	–	–	–	–	–	★	–	–	–	–	★	–	–	–	–	–	–	★	–	★	–	★
Yale Univ. (Conn.)	★	–	★	–	★	★	★	–	★	★	★	★	★	★	★	★	★	★	★	★	★	★
Yeshiva Univ. (N.Y.)	★	–	★	–	–	–	–	–	–	–	–	–	–	★	★	★	–	★	★	–	–	–

AMERICAN COUNCIL ON EDUCATION

ARTHUR S. ADAMS, *President*

The American Council on Education is a *council* of national educational associations; organizations having related interests; approved universities, colleges, teachers colleges, junior colleges, technological schools, and selected private secondary schools; state departments of education; city school systems and private school systems; selected educational departments of business and industrial companies; voluntary associations of higher education in the states; and large public libraries. It is a center of cooperation and coordination whose influence has been apparent in the shaping of American educational policies and the formation of educational practices during the past forty-two years.